Joseph V. Smith

Feldspar Minerals

In Three Volumes

With Editorial Assistance of Brenda F. Smith

1 Crystal Structure and Physical Properties

With 252 Figures

Springer-Verlag Berlin Heidelberg New York 1974

Professor Dr. Joseph V. Smith
The University of Chicago
Department of the Geophysical Sciences
Chicago, IL 60637/USA

ISBN 3-540-06490-7 Springer-Verlag Berlin · Heidelberg · New York
ISBN 0-387-06490-7 Springer-Verlag New York · Heidelberg · Berlin

Dedicated to

Helen D. Megaw and W. H. Taylor
for thesis supervision

Wm. Scott MacKenzie
for collaboration and advice since 1952

Julian R. Goldsmith and Fritz Laves
whose brilliant research at the
University of Chicago
encouraged me to go there

Paul H. Ribbe and David B. Stewart
for collaboration and advice since 1965.

Preface

During the past two centuries, crystallography, mineralogy and petrology have evolved from simple compilations of data to powerful disciplines based on interlocking networks of laws, hypotheses and rules-of-thumb. While many data still consist of isolated facts which defy synthesis, a gratifying portion can be organized according to physical and chemical principles. Unfortunately the separation of physical sciences into sub-divisions, especially at the teaching level, makes it difficult to integrate the different approaches to minerals. This separation is worsened by the increasing technical demands of chemical and physical theories, by the number and complexity of experimental methods, by the sheer mass of facts in an observational discipline such as mineralogy or petrology, and by the explosion of papers. This book concentrates on those aspects of the genesis and properties of feldspar minerals which can be related to physical and chemical principles.

My main aim is frankly pedagogic: I wish to show how chemical and physical principles can be combined with geologic observation to produce an enhanced level of understanding of the genesis of minerals. The feldspars which demonstrate almost all of the general principles provide the most suitable example.

As I began to organize this book, it became obvious that a fundamental decision was necessary concerning the level of treatment. At one extreme, I could write to the feldspar specialists and assume a knowledge of the latest crystallographic, thermodynamic and petrologic techniques. At the other, I could attempt to develop the book on the assumption that the reader had only an elementary knowledge of the basic disciplines and would require a detailed explanation of the latest advances. Obviously I could not reproduce all the basic theoretical studies, but I have deliberately provided surveys of the basic ideas with listings of valuable text books and review articles. Furthermore I have deliberately emphasized uncertainties in theoretical understanding to reduce the danger of a reader accepting uncritically some of the claims in the literature. Probably most readers will find some sections too elementary because of their specialized knowledge in those areas, while other sections will appear somewhat obtuse without study of ancillary textbooks and articles. If so, I will have achieved my aim. Education in earth sciences should be a life-time process requiring continual expansion into new subjects.

The literature on feldspars is so massive and chaotic, and contains so many errors of fact and interpretation, that I have attempted to critically evaluate all important papers distilling from them material likely to have permanent value. Hopefully the treatment is sufficiently complete that even feldspar specialists will rarely need to consult the primary literature before 1973.

Controversial matter is especially emphasized in order to stimulate new research and to warn non-specialists. I have deliberately stated my opinions trying to separate them carefully from an objective evaluation of the available experimental data and theories.

It proved impossible to write this book without assuming knowledge of some aspect of feldspar behavior which it was not expedient to explain at that time. Thus in the section on crystal structure, some chemical properties and phase relations are assumed. Fortunately many readers will have a sufficient working knowledge of feldspar minerals to tide them over until a particular subject is treated in detail: many will have read the feldspar section in Vol. 4 of "Rock Forming Minerals" by W. A. DEER, R. A. HOWIE, and J. ZUSSMAN. To supplement this prior understanding, I have introduced the book with a summary of the important features of feldspar minerals plus a review of the nomenclature. Readers would also profit from the excellent introductions by F. LAVES in the McGraw Hill Encyclopedia of Science and Technology and by W. S. MACKENZIE in Encyclopedia Britannica.

The book "The feldspars-phase relations, optical properties, and geological distribution" by A. S. MARFUNIN (translated in 1966 from the original Russian version of 1962) provided a valuable summary of his own important work and of the work of many Russian mineralogists. Since I cannot read Russian fluently, I would have been severely handicapped without this book. Taking advantage of this monograph, I have not attempted to compile a definitive reference list to Russian and Ukrainian works.

The monograph "Feldspars" by the late T. F. W. BARTH, issued in 1969, provides an uneven treatment, some parts excellent, some parts incomplete, and some parts uncritically accepting factual errors and mistaken interpretation. Nevertheless many readers would profit by reading it.

The section "Feldspat-Familie" by H. U. BAMBAUER (1966, in „Optische Bestimmungen der gesteinsbildenden Minerale" by W. E. TRÖGER) offers an excellent review of the optical properties and occurrence of feldspars.

The present treatise aims to be more comprehensive and critical than the above volumes, but at the expense of greater length.

Unquestionably the hardest problem has been the nightmare of nomenclature. Even if all uncertainties had been resolved in the physical and chemical properties which should underlie any system of nomenclature, there would remain two problems: first, a system of nomenclature must take into account the different needs of field geologists and crystal physicists to mention only two types of specialist; second, historical usage often tied to personal preference (dare I say pride and prejudice?) provides overlapping auras around the existing terms. But we cannot begin anew: few would welcome a new set of terms completely free of historical association. The problem of nomenclature is especially bothersome for the novice who is unaware of the personal nuances: the old hand knows that when Dr. X uses the term T, he is following in the tradition of laboratory L which favors hypothesis H; in addition he knows that orthoclase to the field geologist implies a looser definition than orthoclase to the structural crystallographer, just as metamorphic to the crystallographer calls into mind a smaller range of associations than to the geologist. Accordingly I believe that a system of nomenclature should be sufficiently flexible to be used by all the specialists, that the level of usage should be implied by context (i.e. what was orthoclase to the field man using only a microscope might turn out to be low sanidine plus microcline to the X-ray specialist), and that a minimum of dislocation with historical usage be sought. In 1973, there was no agreed system of nomenclature of feldspars; I discussed the present system with many feldspar specialists and find that none will agree with all aspects. Since many objections are mutually conflicting it is necessary to put forward unilaterally the present system. Of course, I hope that criticism will not be too severe, but I have spent too many days arguing about nomenclature to have any illusions. Throughout the book I endeavor to point out alternative nomenclatures together with their historical provenances, and I apologize for the implied criticisms of other systems.

Many readers will wish to learn the appropriate techniques for the study of feldspars. Although the theoretical bases of the techniques are mentioned in this book, and the most important data are given in tables and graphs, no attempt was made to expound the mechanical details. Modern equipment is so complex that the day-to-day operation can be learnt only by actual use, preferably under the guidance of a skilled practitioner.

Initially I hoped to publish the treatise in a single volume, but the mass of material enforced publication in several volumes. Furthermore the labor has become so immense that a few years must elapse before publication of the last volume. Each section has been written to be intelligible in itself, but full comprehension may require turning to another section.

My wife and I have assembled as comprehensive a bibliography as was reasonably feasible, and we have profited by comparison with the handbook "A Bibliography of the Feldspars" issued by D. R. Waldbaum in 1969. Each chapter of the treatise has its own bibliography to permit independence between the different parts of the book.

The text of Chapters 1–20 was prepared for publication in June 1973, and additions were made in December 1973. I plan to review incoming material for future publication either as addenda or in a revised edition. To minimize the bibliographic work, I would be grateful if authors would send me a reprint or preprint of papers mentioning feldspars: in addition, I would be grateful for glossy prints of interesting photographs or diagrams. Of course, corrections to the present text would be gratefully received.

The treatise begins deliberately with the crystal structure, and proceeds to physical properties and experimental techniques. The chemical properties and experimental techniques form a third part. Growth, diffusion, defects and intergrowths are the subject of the fourth part, providing an introduction to the problems of understanding the genesis of feldspars. The fifth part deals with the thermodynamic properties and phase relations, both under idealized conditions of stable equilibrium and under realistic experimental conditions. All these five parts provide a prolonged introduction to the sixth part which deals with the petrology and occurrence of the feldspars. There is some overlap between the parts but the whole is conceived as a symphony on feldspars, rather more Mahleresque than Mozartian in texture.

Chicago, February 1974   JOSEPH V. SMITH

Contents

Summary. 1

Part 1   Crystal Structures 17

Chapter 1   Brief Review of Concepts and Experimental Techniques . . . 19
    1.1   Crystallographic Theory. 19
    1.2   Experimental Techniques Giving Information on the
        Crystal Structure 22
    1.3   Crystal Chemical Theory 23
    References 25

Chapter 2   Crystal Structure of Feldspar. Principal Features. Related
    Structures 26
    2.1   The Topology of the Aluminosilicate Framework 26
        2.1.1   Discovery 26
        2.1.2   Linkage of the Crankshaft Chain in Feldspar
            and Other Minerals 28
        2.1.3   Relation to Coesite. 31
        2.1.4   Projection Down c^* 33
    2.2   General Features of Feldspar Structures. 35
    2.3   Pseudo Close-packing of Atoms: Pseudo-symmetry . . . 39
    2.4   Structures of Related Minerals 43
        2.4.1   Minerals with Double Crankshafts 43
        2.4.2   Hollandite Structure Type. 44
        2.4.3   The Hexagonal Structures 46
        2.4.4   Orthorhombic $CaAl_2Si_2O_8$ 47
    References 47

Chapter 3   Order-disorder 50
    3.1   Mathematical and Crystallographic Bases of Ordering . . 50
    3.2   Experimental Techniques for Determination of Si, Al
        Order in Feldspars 56
    3.3   Mathematical Description of Si, Al Order in Feldspars . . 60
        3.3.1   Algebraic Description of Site Populations and
            Atomic Order 60
        3.3.2   Matrix Description of Ordered Phases 64
    3.4   Experimental Data on Si, Al Ordering in $AlSi_3$ Feldspars . 66
        3.4.1   Historical 66
        3.4.2   Detailed Interpretation 70
    3.5   Experimental Data on Si, Al Ordering in More Aluminous
        Feldspars 74
        3.5.1   Historical 74
        3.5.2   Detailed Interpretation 75

3.6   Crystal-chemical Explanation of Ordering   78
        3.6.1   Alternation in Al_2Si_2 Feldspar   78
        3.6.2   Choice of T_1 Site in $AlSi_3$ Feldspar   79
        3.6.3   Limitation of Al:Si Ratio between 1:3 and 2:2 .   80
References   81

Chapter 4   Detailed Geometry and Atomic Coordination   85
4.1   General Features   85
4.2   Geometry of the Framework   102
        4.2.1   T–O Distances and O–T–O Angles   102
        4.2.2   T–O–T Angles   106
4.3   Environment of M Atoms   107
        4.3.1   General Features of M–O Bonding   107
        4.3.2   M–O Bonding in Anorthite   109
        4.3.3   Angular Environment   113
        4.3.4   Conclusion   115
4.4   Atomic Displacements from Thermal Motion and Substitu-
        tional Disorder   115
        4.4.1   Isotropic Approximation   116
        4.4.2   Anisotropic Approximation   118
        4.4.3   Na Atoms in Albite   122
4.5   Temperature Variation of Atomic Positions and Dis-
        placements   124
References   124

Chapter 5   Complex Crystal Structures   127
5.1   Summary of Theoretical Concepts   127
5.2   Anorthite Structures in Calcic Plagioclase   137
        5.2.1   Order-disorder of T Atoms: b Diffractions . . .   137
        5.2.2   Domains of M Atoms: c and d Diffractions . . .   140
        5.2.3   Sub-solidus Phase Relations   145
5.3 e-plagioclase   150
        5.3.1   Diffraction Data   151
        5.3.2   Heat-treatment and Petrologic Occurrence   155
        5.3.3   Models and Ideas   157
        5.3.4   A Subjective Review   171
References   174

Part 2   **Physical Properties and Experimental Techniques**   177
References   178

Chapter 6   X-ray Diffraction Techniques   179
6.1   Single-crystal Techniques   179
        6.1.1   General   179
        6.1.2   Standard Photographs of Alkali Feldspar   181
        6.1.3   Standard Photographs of Plagioclase   197

6.2   Powder Techniques. 203
      6.2.1   General. 203
      6.2.2   Standard Patterns of Alkali Feldspars and Celsian 206
      6.2.3   Standard Patterns of Plagioclase and Reed-
              mergnerite   210
References 215

Chapter 7   Cell Dimensions and Macroscopic Thermal Expansion 217
7.1   General 217
7.2   End-member Feldspars 218
7.3   Alkali Feldspars 222
      7.3.1   General and Historical 222
      7.3.2   Homogeneous Alkali Feldspars 224
      7.3.3   Interpretation in Terms of Si, Al Order and K,
              Na Substitution 255
      7.3.4   Cell Dimensions of Perthites and Anomalous
              Specimens. 276
      7.3.5   Simple Determinative Methods 280
      7.3.6   Dimensional Changes Caused by Heating 289
7.4   Plagioclase Feldspars 306
      7.4.1   General and Historical 306
      7.4.2   Cell Dimensions of Natural and Synthetic Spe-
              cimens 307
      7.4.3   Interpretation in Terms of Crystal Structure . . . 319
      7.4.4   Simple Determinative Methods 322
      7.4.5   Dimensional Changes Caused by Heating 328
7.5   Ternary Feldspars and K-exchanged Plagioclase 340
      7.5.1   General. 340
      7.5.2   K-exchanged Plagioclase 340
      7.5.3   Structural Implication of Cell Dimensions. . . . 346
      7.5.4   Ternary Feldspars 346
7.6   K, Ba Feldspars 353
7.7   Synthetic Analogs 355
References 357

Chapter 8   Light Optics 365
8.1   General 365
      8.1.1   Historical Survey: Justification of Present Survey:
              Theory 365
      8.1.2   Accuracy of Optical Measurements 367
      8.1.3   Effect of Compositional and Morphological In-
              homogeneities 369
      8.1.4   Effect of Fine-scale Twinning 371
      8.1.5   Effect of Fine-scale Intergrowths 375
      8.1.6   Optical Scattering from Iridescent Feldspars . . . 377
8.2   Alkali Feldspars 379
      8.2.1   Introduction. 379

8.2.2   Optic Axial Angle: Relation to Order-disorder of
        T Atoms 379
8.2.3   Refractive Indices and Birefringence 385
8.2.4   Optic Orientation and Extinction Angle 387
8.2.5   Polymorphism and Determinative Methods . . . 389
8.3 Plagioclase Feldspars 391
8.3.1   Introduction 391
8.3.2   Optic Axial Angle 395
8.3.3   Refractive Indices 396
8.3.4   Optic Orientation and Twin Relations 400
8.3.5   Comparison of Determinative Methods 405
8.4 K, Ba Feldspars 406
8.5 Other Feldspars and Related Phases 408
References 408

Chapter 9   Nomenclature and General Properties of Feldspars 415
9.1 General 415
9.2 Alkali Feldspars 416
9.2.1   K-feldspars 416
9.2.2   Na-feldspars and Ternary Feldspars 436
9.2.3   General 449
9.3 Plagioclase Feldspars 450
9.4 Other Feldspars 455
References 457

Chapter 10   Electron-optical Techniques 461
10.1 General 461
10.2 Transmission Electron Microscopy 461
10.2.1   Experimental Details 461
10.2.2   Twinning, Dislocations, Deformation 464
10.2.3   Alkali Feldspars 468
10.2.4   Anorthite and Bytownite 477
10.2.5   Intermediate Plagioclase Compositions 488
10.2.6   Sodic Plagioclase 496
10.2.7   Chemical Alteration in Feldspar 501
10.3 Scanning Electron Microscopy 502
10.4 Photo-emission Electron Microscopy 505
References 508

Chapter 11   Infra-red Absorption; Nuclear Magnetic Resonance; Electron
             Spin Resonance; Mössbauer Resonance 511
11.1 General 511
11.2 Infra-red Absorption 511
11.2.1   Assignment of Absorption Bands 512
11.2.2   K-feldspar 519
11.2.3   Na-feldspar 521
11.2.4   Alkali Feldspar Solid Solutions 525
11.2.5   Plagioclase 525
11.2.6   Anorthite 528

11.3 Nuclear Magnetic and Electric Quadrupole Resonance . 530
   11.3.1 Alkali Feldspar 532
   11.3.2 Anorthite 539
   11.3.3 Electric Field Gradient and Oxygen Polarizability 541
11.4 Electron Paramagnetic Resonance 544
   11.4.1 Fe^{3+} in Alkali Feldspar 544
   11.4.2 Fe^{3+}, Ti^{3+} and Mn^{2+} in Plagioclase 546
   11.4.3 Other Ions and Electron Centers 547
11.5 Mössbauer (Gamma-ray) Resonance 548
   11.5.1 Iron Sanidine 548
   11.5.2 Plagioclase 549
References 553

Chapter 12 Miscellaneous Physical Properties 556
12.1 Color 556
12.2 Luminescence 558
   12.2.1 Electron- and Proton-excited Luminescence . . . 559
   12.2.2 Thermoluminescence 562
12.3 Electrical Phenomena 563
   12.3.1 Electrical Conductivity 564
   12.3.2 Dielectric Phenomena 566
12.4 Thermal Conductivity 566
12.5 Mechanical Properties 567
   12.5.1 Elastic Deformation, Photoelasticity, Grinding
           Hardness, Surface Energy, Cleavage 568
   12.5.2 Controlled Uniaxial Deformation of Plagioclase . 572
   12.5.3 Shock Deformation 578
12.6 Density 589
12.7 Thermogravimetry and Differential Thermal Analysis . . 591
12.8 Separation and Visual Identification Procedures . . . 591
   12.8.1 Separation of Feldspars 592
   12.8.2 Rapid Visual Identification 593
References 594

Subject Index 601

Name Index 613

Locality Index 620

Index of Rock Types 623

Location of Figures 624

List of Tables 626

Acknowledgements

While at Pennsylvania State University, I planned to write a critical treatise on Rock Forming Minerals, but the project seemed too large for one person. Fortunately the appearance of "Rock Forming Minerals" by DEER, HOWIE, and ZUSSMAN made readily available the basic data up to 1960 on the crystallography, mineralogy and petrology of the rock-forming minerals. I was thus able to concentrate on one mineral group using a more critical and comprehensive treatment. Professor Wm. SCOTT MACKENZIE and I had considered writing a book on feldspars back in 1954 but various academic shifts (translations not subterfuges) made collaboration too difficult. Professor T. F. W. BARTH and Dr. O. H. J. CHRISTIE discussed writing a book after their successful international conference at Oslo in 1962. The real impetus for the book came as the result of an invitation to spend a quarter at the California Institute of Technology in 1965: preparation of a course of lectures on feldspars re-kindled my interest, and further fuel was added by an invitation to organize a short course on feldspars for the Committee of Education of the American Geological Institute. Thanks to the unstinted cooperation of P. H. RIBBE, E. H. ROSEBOOM, and D. B. STEWART, and the welcoming response of the audience which included learned mineralogists and petrologists, it became clear that there was a strong demand for consolidation of the results obtained from laboratory and field studies.

Professor Wm. SCOTT MACKENZIE invited me to spend the summer of 1966 at the University of Manchester where I had the benefit of his advice and facilities. Professor JULIAN R. GOLDSMITH gave permission for me to be relieved of some duties from the University of Chicago for the year 1966-67. Professors W. A. DEER and JOSEPH NEEDHAM kindly provided facilities at the Department of Mineralogy and Petrology and at Gonville and Caius College, Cambridge for the summer of 1967, and Dr. and Mrs. M. G. BOWN were most helpful in many ways. Since then I am indebted to both Manchester and Cambridge Universities for allowing use of their libraries in the summers.

Almost every feldspar worker in the world has helped by providing material or answering queries. Illustrative material is acknowledged in the figure legends. Those who provided extensive ideas and printed material are acknowledged in the text. Many others unfortunately cannot be acknowledged in detail. Special thanks are reserved for those scientists who critically reviewed chapters in draft: Chapters 1–4, P. H. RIBBE and M. W. PHILLIPS; parts of Chapter 5, A. J. FRUEH, M. KOREKAWA, J. D. C. McCONNELL, and H. SCHULZ; Chapter 6, I. M. STEELE; Chapter 7, D. APPLEMAN, P. H. RIBBE and D. B. STEWART; Chapter 8, W. S. MACKENZIE; Chapter 10, A. H. HEUER, A. C. McLAREN, J. D. C. McCONNELL, and H.-U. NISSEN; Chapter 11, S. HAFNER and R. A. WEEKS; parts of Chapter 12, I. Y. BORG and K. E. SEIFERT;

Chapter 14, A. T. ANDERSON, J. R. GOLDSMITH, and K. HEIER; part of Chapter 14, M. J. DRAKE; Chapters 15 and 16, R. PETROVIĆ; Chapters 17 and 18, J. A. VANCE; Chapter 18, I. Y. BORG; Chapter 19, W. L. BROWN; Chapter 20, D. S. BARKER.

The source of quotations and figures may be obtained from the list of references. Most authors and publishers did not ask for specific acknowledgement.

Several publishers have kindly given permission to use certain figures and quotations on condition that they are specifically acknowledged as follows:

RIBBE, P. H.: Journal of Geophysical Research 77, No. 29, Fig. 1, p. 5792 (1972). Copyright by American Geophysical Union.

NORD, G. L. et al.: Transactions, American Geophysical Union 53, No. 4, Abstract Vol. 101, p. 549 (1972). Copyright by American Geophysical Union.

AKIZUKI, M.: The American Mineralogist 57, 797–808 (1972), author's abstract, 1972. Copyright of The American Mineralogist.

BURRI, C.: Die Optische Orientierung der Plagioclase. 334 pp. 108, 15–43, Plate VI, 1967. Copyright by Birkhauser Verlag, Basel.

WILLAIME, C., BROWN, W. L.: Comptes Rendus de L'Academie des Sciences, Ser. D. 275, 627–629, Figs. 1 and 2 (1972). Copyright by Central des Revues Dunod-Gautier-Villars, Paris.

WIDENFALK, L.: Lithos 5, 255–267, Fig. 4 (1972). Copyright Universitetsforlaget, Oslo.

RAMBERG, I. B.: Lithos 5, 281–306, Figs. 3b, 4, 6b, 7, 8, and 9 (1972). Copyright Universitetsforlaget, Oslo.

PHEMISTER, J.: Mineralogical Magazine 23, 541–555. Quotations from (1) "deposition of plagioclase" to "more sodic compositions". 83 words, and from "find an echo" to "more calcic than the core". 90 words; plus two figures (1934). Copyright by the Mineralogical Society, London.

HEUER, A. H. et al.: Philosophical Magazine 26, 465–482, Figs. 2 and 5 (1972). Copyright by Taylor and Francis, Ltd., London.

The cover is an electron micrograph of Spencer N perthite by courtesy of G. W. LORIMER and P. E. CHAMPNESS, University of Manchester. Taylor and Francis Ltd., publishers of Philos. Mag., kindly gave permission for reproduction from Vol. 28, p. 1397, Fig. 4(a).

Finally, the unstinting bibliographic and editorial work of BRENDA F. SMITH is gratefully acknowledged both here and on the title page. There is a popular theory that a wife is a hindrance to scholarly work: even if this theory were commonly true, BRENDA SMITH would provide a perfect refutation. Fortunately VIRGINIA and SUSAN SMITH had so much homework from the University of Chicago Laboratory School that they did not notice their father's absence as much as they might have otherwise. IRENE BALTUSKA conscientiously and cheerfully provided an excellent manuscript for the publisher and prepared the author index. ERIKA HOLLE and UTE BUJARD carefully supervised the press-work on the manuscript. To all of these women, many thanks indeed.

Chicago, 1974   J. V. SMITH

Bibliography

The bibliography was compiled from many sources, and almost all articles were read either in the original or in translation. A few articles in very early or obscure journals were not read but the source of the reference is believed to be reliable. Whenever available, an English translation is listed. For brevity, the titles of certain journals are replaced by an obvious acronym:

AC   Acta Crystallographica

AJS   American Journal of Science: the first vols. were arranged in series of 50

AM   American Mineralogist

ARDGL   Annual Report of the Director of the Geophysical Laboratory, Carnegie Institution, Washington, D. C., issued as year books

BCGF   Bulletin of the Geological Society of Finland

BMP   Beiträge z. Mineralogie u. Petrologie (Heidelberger)

BSFMC   Bulletin Societé Française de Minéralogie et Cristallographie Note: BSFM until 1948, when crystallography was added

CCILM   Cursillos y Conferencias del Instituto "Lucas Mallada", Paseo de la Castellana, 84 Madrid. Fasc. 8 is a special issue containing papers presented at a feldspar symposium organized by the Int. Mineral. Assoc. at Copenhagen, 1960

CM   Canadian Mineralogist

CMP   Contributions to Mineralogy and Petrology: replaced BMP in 1947

DAN   Doklady Akad Nauk SSSR, Earth Sci. Sect., reference is to English translation after 1959

EG   Economic Geology

EPSL   Earth and Planetary Science Letters

FMKP   Fortschritte der Mineralogie, Kristallographie u. Petrographie

GCA   Geochimica et Cosmochimica Acta

GM   Geological Magazine, London

JACS   Jour. American Ceramic Society

JCS   Jour. Chemical Society, London

JG   Jour. Geology

JGR   Jour. Geophysical Research

JSP   Jour. Sedimentary Petrology

MM   Mineralogical Magazine, London

N   Nature

NGT   Norsk Geologisk Tidskrifft: Vol. 42, No. 2 is the Proceedings of the NATO Study Institute on Feldspars, Oslo, 1962

NJMA   Neues Jahrbuch f. Mineralogie, Abteilungen

NJMM   Neues Jahrbuch f. Mineralogie, Monatshefte

PM	Periodico di Mineralogica, Roma
S	Science
SAWW	Sitzberichte Akademie Wiss. Wien Math., Naturwiss. Kl., Abteilungen I
SMPM	Schweizerische Mineralogische u. Petrographische Mitt.
ZK	Zeitschrift f. Kristallographie: before 1920, Zeit. Krist. Mineralogie
ZM	Zentralblatt f. Mineralogie: before 1935, Centralblatt f. Min

Units

The move for adoption of SI units began after I started writing the manuscript for this book. At the time of completion of the manuscript, few if any mineralogists were using SI units: nevertheless I concluded that since SI units were being accepted by physicists and chemists, they would also be accepted by earth scientists. Accordingly data are given here in SI units with an occasional reference to traditional units. Some of the important conversion factors are:

$$1 \text{Å} = 0.1 \text{ nanometer (nm)}$$
$$1 \text{ dyne} = 10^{-5} \text{ Newton (N)}$$
$$1 \text{ bar} = 10^5 \text{ Newton/meter}^2$$
$$1 \text{ cal} = 4.187 \text{ Joule (J)}$$
$$1 \text{ erg} = 10^{-7} \text{ Joule}$$
$$1 \text{ atmosphere} = 1.013 \text{ N/m}^2$$
$$1 \text{ dyne/cm}^2 = 10^{-1} \text{ Newton/meter}^2$$
$$1 \text{ eV} = 1.6021 \times 10^{-19} \text{ Joule}$$

The old term micron is replaced by micrometer (μm). The prefixes kilo, centi, milli, micro, nano and pico mean 10^3, 10^{-2}, 10^{-3}, 10^{-6}, 10^{-9}, and 10^{-12}.

Summary

a) The crystal structure of a feldspar is composed of an aluminosilicate framework whose interstices are occupied by alkali and alkali-earth atoms. The aluminosilicate framework consists of large oxygen atoms lying at the corners of tetrahedra. Each oxygen atom forms a vertex for two tetrahedra, and each tetrahedron is centered by a silicon or aluminum atom (collectively denoted T). Each quadruply-charged silicon atom balances electrostatically the four half-oxygens in its tetrahedron, but each aluminum-centered tetrahedron is unbalanced by one charge. Charge balance is maintained by entrance of large atoms (M) into the interstices; because there is one interstice for each four tetrahedra, and the interstices are fully occupied, the ideal formula of a feldspar is MT_4O_8. For monovalent M atoms (e.g. Na and K) one of the T atoms is Al while for divalent M (e.g. Ca and Ba) two are Al.

At low temperatures the truly stable structures have ordered T atoms. The ordering patterns are different for $AlSi_3$ and Al_2Si_2 frameworks, and the latter cannot be obtained from the former by mere replacement of 1 Si by 1 Al; a complete reorganization is necessary. At high temperatures, the T atoms in the $AlSi_3$ framework become strongly disordered while those in the Al_2Si_2 framework stay strongly ordered. This is consistent with a general rule that usually not more than one Al atom is attached to an oxygen atom of an aluminosilicate framework. The principal end-members are $KAlSi_3O_8$-sanidine (disordered), low microcline (ordered); $NaAlSi_3O_8$-high albite (disordered), low albite (ordered); $CaAl_2Si_2O_8$-anorthite; $BaAl_2Si_2O_8$-celsian.

The crystal symmetry is controlled by both the arrangement of T atoms and the tendency of the framework to distort to lower symmetry by collapse about the small cations Na and Ca. In high sanidine, the $AlSi_3$ atoms are disordered and the framework is held apart in a regular configuration by the large K atoms: the space group is C $2/m$ with a monoclinic unit cell a 0.84, b 1.30, c 0.72 nanometer, β 116°. Microcline has ordered $AlSi_3$ atoms resulting in a small distortion to a triclinic unit cell with space group C $\bar{1}$. Both high and low albite are triclinic because of twisting of the aluminosilicate framework to adjust to the small Na atoms. Celsian is monoclinic because the large Ba atoms hold apart the framework, but the regular alternation of Al and Si atoms results in a doubled c repeat with space group I $2/c$. Anorthite is similar, but structural collapse around the small Ca atoms results in a triclinic cell with space group P $\bar{1}$.

The key feature of the topology of the aluminosilicate framework is a chain of four-membered rings, alternately horizontal and vertical, extended along the a-axis. This chain is like a crankshaft, and can expand in response to substitution of larger M cations and to increased thermal vibration. In K-feldspars, the anisotropy of all bulk physical properties such as thermal expansion is explain-

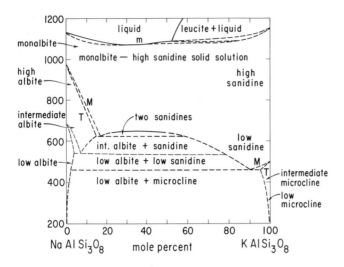

Fig. S-1. Schematic temperature-composition diagram for the $NaAlSi_3O_8$(Ab)–$KAlSi_3O_8$(Or) join at low pressure to illustrate possible relations for true equilibrium and to show the nomenclature of the phases. The melting relations show a minimum at m and incongruent melting to leucite plus siliceous liquid for potassic compositions. Crystallization from a liquid yields a single feldspar in the monoclinic series monalbite to high sanidine. At low temperature, low albite and low microcline show little solid solution. The top of the unmixing solvus bounds the field of two sanidines. The ordering inversions of the endmember compositions are assumed to be first-order. The solid lines show stable equilibria determined in the laboratory, while the dashed lines show phase boundaries whose nature or exact position is in doubt

able qualitatively in terms of the chain flexing in the overall framework subject to interaction with M atoms. All triclinic feldspars have a puckered chain distorted from the more regular geometry required for monoclinic symmetry. The puckering is greatest for anorthite and least for microcline.

At high temperatures, Na and K in all proportions can occupy the interstices at random. The same is true for Na and Ca, but only partial substitution occurs for K and Ca. Hence there are two principal series of feldspars, the alkali feldspars and the plagioclases, which meet at the composition of albite.

b) Most alkali feldspars crystallize with disordered Al and Si atoms. The sanidine-high albite series is stable at high temperatures, but at low temperatures the assemblage microcline plus low albite becomes thermodynamically stable (Fig. S-1). The ordering transformation is complex and sluggish, being governed by diffusion and catalytic processes. Many natural alkali feldspars do not achieve full order of Al and Si atoms. The ordering transformation is not unique, and depends on the temperature-time history of the individual feldspar.

c) At low temperatures, the thermodynamically stable assemblage for the composition (Na, K)$AlSi_3O_8$ is a mixture of albite and microcline. Direct growth at low temperatures ($100 - 400°$ C) produces relatively pure feldspars. Growth at high temperature (over $700°$ C) produces a member of the sanidine-high albite solid solution series with mixed Na and K atoms. Slow cooling from higher temperatures results in segregation of Na and K atoms to form intergrowths of remarkable complexity whose features are governed by kinetic factors. Such intergrowths are known as perthites, and display textures ranging from those visible to the naked eye (macroperthite), through those visible in an optical microscope (microperthite) to those detectable only by X-ray and electron microscope techniques (cryptoperthite). The nature of the perthite depends critically on the extent of Si, Al ordering achieved by the cooling feldspar. Because Na, K atoms diffuse more easily than Si, Al atoms, laboratory heating studies produce a wide range of artificial perthites and homogenized feldspars, each with its own arrangement of Si and Al atoms, and varying degrees of K, Na segregation. For each Si, Al pattern, the temperature distribution of the Na and K atoms can be related to an unmixing solvus.

A key feature of the unmixing of a homogeneous sanidine into a perthite is the mechanism for movement of the atoms. At one extreme is diffusion of Na and K atoms to form clusters or lamellar regions while the aluminosilicate framework remains unbroken and merely flexes to accommodate the different sizes of the Na and K atoms. The coherence of the framework results in strain and anomalous cell dimensions with anisotropic shape of the Na- and K-rich regions. Such exsolution takes place by a coherent spinodal governed by the diffusion coefficients. At the other extreme is nucleation at surfaces and defects in which the new framework crystallizes in a near-parallel orientation to the old framework without structural continuity.

d) The third type of transformation in an alkali feldspar consists of a rapid, non-quenchable change in Na-rich specimens occurring upon cooling through a critical temperature. Above this temperature, the feldspar is monoclinic (Fig. S-1). Below the critical temperature the feldspar is triclinic, and the framework is puckered around the sodium atoms whose thermal vibration is no longer sufficient to maintain the framework in an expanded configuration. The critical temperature falls rapidly with substitution of K for Na, and is increased by Al, Si ordering.

A key feature of a symmetry change from monoclinic to triclinic in alkali feldspar, either from Si, Al ordering or from thermal effects on M cations, is the formation of a domain texture. Loss of the mirror plane and two-fold rotor in the monoclinic symmetry results in accidental nucleation of domains in either a "left" or a "right" configuration. Unlike domains cannot merge, and they form a boundary which can disappear only by reversal of one of the domains. Such a reversal is hard to achieve, and the typical product of the symmetry change is an intimate domain texture, with domains related by Albite and Pericline twin laws.

e) Because of the complexity of the transformations in alkali feldspars, only some of the phase relations can be determined by direct synthesis. Roughly speaking, the relations above 600° C can be determined directly, but those below 500° can be inferred only from a combination of experimental data (e.g. by examination of natural feldspars by X-ray diffraction and thermochemical methods) and theoretical considerations. Furthermore, there is an infinity of metastable situations in addition to the truly stable equilibrium. Figure S-1 is a schematic diagram showing an estimate of the stable phase relations at low pressure. The unmixing solvus separates homogeneous feldspars from the field of two coexisting feldspars. Feldspar of composition $KAlSi_3O_8$ changes from high sanidine to low sanidine (both monoclinic) as the temperature falls and then transforms into microcline (triclinic). With falling temperature the Si, Al order increases, probably increasing sharply at the symmetry change. The feldspar of composition $NaAlSi_3O_8$ similarly changes from monalbite (monoclinic) to high albite (triclinic) at about $980°$ C with little difference in Si, Al order. Ultimately the high albite transforms into low albite perhaps with a rapid increase of Si, Al order between 500 and $700°$ C. For intermediate compositions, the ordering reaction and symmetry change are related in a complex way. For simplicity, the inversions between microcline and sanidine, and between high albite and monalbite, are shown as discontinuous, but they may be continuous.

f) Many natural alkali feldspars from igneous rocks are not represented by mixtures of nearly pure low albite and microcline. Those from volcanic rocks may consist of homogeneous sanidine or high albite solid solution, or as crypto-perthites. Those from more slowly cooled rocks often occur as complex perthites. Many of the K-rich feldspars occur as "orthoclase", a type of feldspar recognized from its monoclinic optics and range of optic axial angles. X-ray study of orthoclase specimens reveals a wide range of properties dependent on the texture of domains and the extent of Si, Al order. The nomenclature for K-feldspars is very controversial, but basically the problem results from the fact that only if certain complex measurements are made can most feldspars be given a satisfactory description. Broadly speaking, it seems that K-rich feldspars from most igneous rocks order by a two-step process, in which initial ordering obeys monoclinic symmetry and later ordering switches to triclinic symmetry. Laboratory heating of microcline does not reverse the process, and disordering proceeds by a one-step process directly to sanidine. Alkali feldspars grown directly at low temperature in veins have unusual morphology and structural properties. Adularia, the K-feldspar, crystallizes with considerable Si, Al disorder and follows idiosyncratic non-equilibrium ordering paths towards microcline. Microcline rarely crystallizes directly, and is formed typically by inversion of earlier sanidine or perhaps sometimes by ion-exchange and recrystallization of sodic plagioclase.

g) In plagioclase feldspars, the crystal structures and transformations are seriously complicated by the varying ratio of Al/Si from albite $NaAlSi_3O_8$ to anorthite $CaAl_2Si_2O_8$, and by the charge linkage of Ca + Al and of Na + Si. The activation energy for migration of Na and Ca atoms is considerably lower than that for Al and Si atoms. Because of the charge linkage, break-up of a disordered plagioclase into two plagioclases of different bulk composition is governed essentially by the activation energy of Si and Al atoms. Hence exsolution in plagioclase is much more difficult than for alkali feldspar. Possibly the assemblage stable at low temperature in the plagioclase system would consist of a mechanical mixture of low albite and primitive anorthite. However, most plagioclases from slowly-cooled rocks contain a complex superstructure with an anti-phase texture several unit cells across. The simplest, but possibly erroneous, interpretation is that the aluminosilicate framework is coherent, and that the superstructure consists of regions with compositions and atomic distributions similar to those of low albite and anorthite. This type of plagioclase shows non-integral dif-fractions of type *e*, and is denoted *e*-plagioclase. It is believed to result from random development of tiny regions resembling albite and anorthite in a solid solution of albite or anorthite type, the regions being unable to grow into macroscopic units because of energy barriers. Consequently it is necessary to consider plagioclase from a kinetic viewpoint. The phase diagram for true thermodynamic equilibrium is unknown, but Fig. S-2a is useful for pedagogic purposes. Figure S-2b summarizes the principal features of plagioclase determined by X-ray and electron-optical techniques.

At solidus temperature, plagioclase from An_0 to about An_{12} occurs as mon-albite solid solution, and then occurs as high albite solid solution for more calcic compositions. The symmetry change from monoclinic to triclinic symmetry is shown for convenience as a discontinuous change. Near the albite composition, disorder of the Na, Ca atoms and Al, Si atoms is almost complete, but incorporation of the anorthite component results in growing short-range order of the T atoms culminating in long-range order at the anorthite composition. The anorthite structure has a doubled c-dimension with respect to the high albite structure: both have type a diffractions, while anorthite has subsidiary type b diffractions giving body-centered symmetry. The nature of the transformation from high albite s.s. to anorthite s.s. is unknown, and the two-phase region is purely hypothetical.

The stable form of $CaAl_2Si_2O_8$ at low temperature has strict alternation of Si and Al atoms on the tetrahedral nodes. The Ca atoms occupy either a left or right position and the framework puckers resulting in primitive triclinic symmetry. At low temperature, primitive anorthite occurs either as a single crystal or with coarse domains, each having Ca atoms in one choice of position. With increasing temperature, thermal vibration causes the Ca atoms to jump between left and right positions. Above a few hundred degrees Celsius, the symmetry becomes body-centered as the Ca atoms occupy the left and right positions with similar factors. The Si, Al distribution remains essentially ordered during these changes of cation position and framework geometry, but some disorder probably occurs above $1100°$ C. Substitution of NaAl for CaSi, and disorder in the tetrahedral sites, causes increasing fineness and complexity of the domain texture.

The situation for intermediate compositions at medium to low temperatures is uncertain, and the phase relations in Fig. S-2a are quite speculative. In the laboratory, annealing of synthetic plagioclase under hydrothermal conditions at temperatures down to $500°$ C produces changes of cell dimensions that imply considerable atomic ordering. However no evidence of a two-phase assemblage has been obtained.

Specimens from igneous and metamorphic rocks show a bewildering array of phenomena governed by incomplete adjustment to equilibrium. Those from volcanic rocks are structurally homogeneous with various degrees of order. Those from plutonic rocks mostly show some evidence of an intergrowth or a domain texture as in Fig. S-2b. Most spectacular are three types of intergrowth (collectively described as micrometer intergrowths) which are either just visible optically or are below optical resolution. Some of these specimens show iridescence resulting from multiple diffraction between lamellae whose spacing is comparable to optical wavelengths. Less striking are specimens with subsidiary diffractions suggesting lamellar superstructures on the scale of a few unit cells (i.e. in the nanometer range).

The *peristerite intergrowth* is found for bulk compositions from An_2 to An_{16}, and gives X-ray patterns with two sets of spots whose positions suggest components of composition near pure albite and An_{25}. The calcic component has type *e* diffractions. Peristerite may form by decomposition of intermediate albite solid solution into a low albite s.s. and an intermediate albite s.s. of higher An-content as shown by the binary loop in Fig. S-2a. The dashed curve shows the effective region of dissociation because of the strain between the components of the intergrowth (i.e. it is related to a coherent spinodal). Alternatively there may be an asymmetric unmixing solvus with its crest close to pure albite.

The *Bøggild intergrowth* occurs in some specimens (typically from old, deep-seated rocks) of bulk composition from about An_{47} to An_{58}. The composition of the lamellae is uncertain, but inconclusive electron-optical data suggest a difference of about 10% An. Perhaps the most calcic component reaches An_{60} while the most sodic one reaches An_{45}. The Bøggild intergrowths give type *e* diffractions. The simplest explanation is that incomplete unmixing occurred

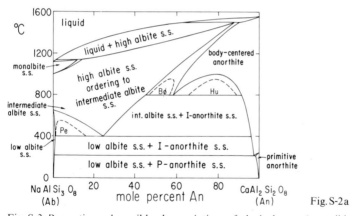

Fig. S-2a

Fig. S-2. Properties and possible phase relations of plagioclase. a A possible phase diagram in which all relations are idealized to first order. The dashed lines show metastable curves which govern the peristerite, Bøggild and Huttenlocher intergrowths. Note that all relations are uncertain except for the solidus, liquidus and the inversion from monalbite to high albite. b Schematic diagram showing chemical and diffraction properties of plagioclase structures. The upper section shows the situation at solidus temperatures. The second section is for solid solutions of anorthite examined at room temperature. The stippling and dashed lines indicate the diffuseness and intensity of the diffractions. The question marks indicate uncertainty in the range of bulk compositions. For the *e*-plagioclase, the *e* diffractions lie in irrational positions symmetrically about the position occupied by *b* diffractions in anorthite. The *f* diffractions lie symmetrically about the *a* diffractions with double the spacing of the *e* diffractions. Because of evidence for a discontinuity near An_{50}, the calcic and sodic ranges are distinguished as e_1 and e_2. The micrometer intergrowths occur on a scale of about 0.01 to 1 μm. The solid line shows the range of bulk compositions, and the circles show the probable compositions of the lamellae. Note that compositions of the lamellae probably correlate with the bulk composition and the coarseness of the lamellae. The symbols *e* and *b* show the types of diffractions associated with the lamellae. c A possible phase diagram given by J. D. C. McConnell (see Chapters 5 and 19 for detailed reference). Ordering in albite, e_2- and e_1-plagioclases and anorthite begins at the lines labelled with the characteristic diffractions *a*, e_2, e_1 and *b*. Spinodal decomposition may occur in the regions with the light hatching, and true exsolution in the regions with coarse hatching

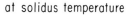

at solidus temperature

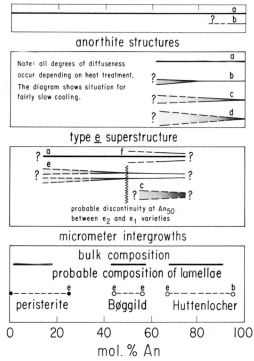

anorthite structures

type _e_ superstructure

micrometer intergrowths

Fig. S-2b. Legend see opposite page

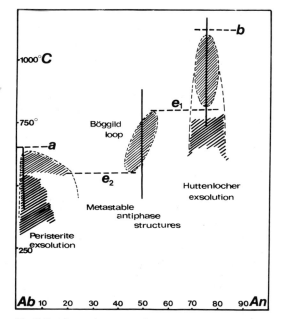

Fig. S-2c. Legend see opposite page

with strong coherence between two plagioclase components, each with e diffractions. A dashed curve lying inside the binary loop between albite and anorthite solid solutions is shown in Fig S-2a. The e-diffractions would develop metastably at a lower temperature.

The *Huttenlocher intergrowth* occurs in certain calcic plagioclases from igneous and metamorphic rocks with bulk composition from about An_{67} to An_{90}. X-ray and electron-optical data show that the lamellae consist of an e-plagioclase near An_{67} and a body-centered anorthite s.s. of uncertain composition, perhaps as calcic as An_{95}. A simple explanation is that of Fig. S-2a, in which there is a coherent spinodal lying inside the crest of a solvus between two solid solutions of anorthite type. At lower temperature the Na-rich component changes metastably into e-plagioclase.

Many plagioclases show no evidence of micrometer intergrowths, but show subsidiary diffractions indicating a fine-scale superstructure. Primitive anorthite shows four types of diffractions:

a $(h+k)$ even l even

b $(h+k)$ odd l odd

c $(h+k)$ even l odd

d $(h+k)$ odd l even .

The a diffractions are common to all feldspars. The b diffractions indicate the presence of Al_2Si_2 ordering of the anorthite type, and are absent in albite. The c diffractions indicate that the Ca atoms move to one side with associated deformation of the aluminosilicate framework. The d diffractions indicate the same thing, but are weaker. With increasing Ab-content, the b diffractions become diffuse and have not been reported in natural plagioclase for compositions more sodic than about 40 % Ab.

Many low plagioclases from oligoclase to about An_{75} yield e diffractions, sometimes called split-b diffractions because they occur in pairs about the position expected for b diffractions. The separation of the e diffractions, and the orientation of the vector joining them changes irrationally with Ab-content. Although no rigorous mathematical analysis has been made, it is likely that e-plagioclase contains lamellae of calcic plagioclase a few unit cells across whose Al, Si distributions are out of phase at the boundaries. This causes the b diffractions expected for calcic plagioclase to split into two. In addition, the sizes of the tetrahedra suggest that part of the intergrowth resembles low albite. Consequently e-plagioclase might be interpreted as a fine-scale coherent intergrowth of regions similar to anorthite and low-albite. Indeed if ordering occurs in high albite s.s. as the temperature falls, one can envisage nuclei of anorthite developing randomly. Because there are two choices for the alternating pattern of Al and Si atoms, domains would develop out-of-phase with each other. The albite component would also segregate, and contribute to the out-of-phase texture. Once an out-of-phase texture had developed, there would be little driving force for segregation into large regions of albite and anorthite. This explanation of e-plagioclase is consistent with low albite and primitive anorthite being the stable assemblage of plagioclase at low temperature as in Fig. S-2a.

In detail, e-plagioclase shows various complexities. The e diffractions become more diffuse as the Ab-content increases. The separation increases with increasing Ab-content showing that the out-of-phase texture becomes finer. Labradorites show f diffractions, sometimes known as split-a diffractions, whose spacing and angular orientation are related to the e diffractions. The composition range over which e diffractions occur is at least An_{15} to An_{75}, and may be even greater. There is evidence of discontinuities in the variation of e diffractions with An-content, especially near An_{50}. Diffuse c diffractions occur in some e-plagioclases with calcic composition.

The occurrence of plagioclase in deep-seated metamorphic rocks is complicated by breakdown under hydrous conditions into albite plus some type of calcium aluminum silicate hydroxide or hydrate. However some metamorphic plagioclases show composition gaps consistent with the 2-phase region for peristerite. One remarkable occurrence of plagioclase shows tree-like intergrowths of anorthite and sodic plagioclase consistent with unmixing of a plagioclase near An_{50}.

All natural plagioclase can be converted into high plagioclase by heating at temperatures near the solidus. The reactions follow a non-equilibrium path. Rapid heating and cooling produces reversible changes of a metastable nature.

It must be emphasized that the phase equilibria of Fig. S-2a are highly uncertain, and that the diagram is given mainly for pedagogic reasons. As an antidote to uncritical acceptance, a phase diagram given by McConnell is shown in Fig. S-2c. This diagram is based on the idea that dissociation is governed by a coherent spinodal in which there is complete structural continuity between the exsolving components. At low temperature, diffusion is very sluggish and e-plagioclase develops on a unit-cell scale. At higher temperature, spinodal decomposition occurs for favored compositions. McConnell postulated that major discontinuities of structure occur at An_3, An_{50} and An_{75} between albite (with a diffractions), e_2-plagioclase, e_1-plagioclase, and anorthite (with b diffractions). The temperature for the beginning of ordering in each composition range is shown by horizontal dashed lines. Regions with lighter shading show where spinodal behavior is likely, corresponding to the peristerite, Bøggild and Huttenlocher intergrowths. The heavy shading shows regions in which true exsolution is possible. Whatever the true equilibrium relations of plagioclase, it is certain that natural plagioclase develops principally under metastable conditions.

h) Fig. S-3 sketches the relation between the liquidus, the solidus and the unmixing surface in the Or–Ab–An–H_2O system for a water pressure near 5000 kg/cm^2.

On the Or–An face the melting relations are of eutectic type (ABCDE), while on the Ab–An face they show a tilted solid-solution loop (CFGH). On the Or–Ab face, the high water pressure has reduced the melting temperature so much that the minimum seen in Fig. S-1 is replaced by a eutectic at I. The melting intervals on the side faces are shown by stippling.

The liquidus surface is shown by contours every 50° C, from which it may be seen that there is a large field in which plagioclase is the first phase to crystallize

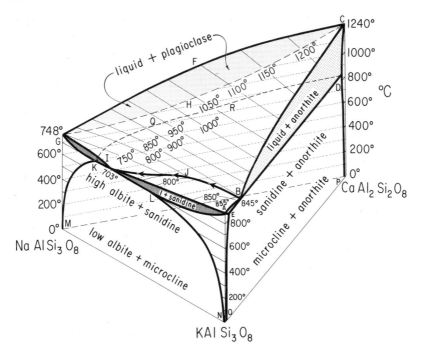

Fig. S-3. Schematic temperature-composition diagram for the Ab–Or–An system near 5000 kg/cm². Detailed explanation is given in the text. Readers should note that the sub-solidus region has been simplified deliberately, and that Figs. S-1 and 2 should be consulted

with falling temperature. This field is separated from the field for primary alkali feldspar by the boundary BJI joining the two binary eutectics at B and I.

The sub-solidus relations have been simplified deliberately but could be constructed with the aid of Figs. S-1 and S-2. The curves MK and LN represent the truncated solvus in the Ab–Or system, as do the curves OE and PD in the Or–An system. The ternary solvus incorporates these curves plus the line MP which represents the low-temperature limit of solid solution of K in plagioclase (this implicitly ignores all the exsolution phenomena in Fig. S-2a). With increasing temperature, solid solution increases and the ternary solvus folds inwards to form a curved surface for the plagioclase limit and a "leg" for K-feldspar. The solidus, which marks the beginning of melting, incorporates the straight line DE, a curved surface AEL (the line EL is not shown), the straight line LK, and the curved surface KQRDCHG. The line KQRD is asymptotic to the back plane of the diagram in accordance with the decreasing solid solution of K as the Ca content increases in plagioclase. At lower pressures, the phase relations are even more complex because a minimum on the Or–Ab face must be related in some complex way to the field boundary BJI.

Equilibrium crystallization would result in either a plagioclase or an alkali feldspar crystallizing from the liquid depending on the bulk composition. With falling temperature, the feldspar and liquid should change compositions, and ultimately the bulk composition would be represented by a mechanical mixture of two or three feldspars. For various reasons, including metastable persistence of the early-crystallized feldspar, crystallization of natural feldspars commonly occurs out of equilibrium. Generally speaking such non-equilibrium crystallization tends to yield residual liquids nearer the minimum or the eutectic temperature on the Ab–Or join, and complex chemical zoning of the feldspars.

The actual crystallization of feldspars in rocks is complicated by the presence of other constituents in the bulk rock composition which generally tend to lower the temperature for beginning and completion of melting. Pressure tends to raise the solvus temperatures a few degrees Celsius per thousand kg/cm^2 pressure, while water pressure reduces the melting temperatures by the order of a hundred degrees Celsius per thousand kg/cm^2.

Very high pressures cause inversion of feldspar into denser minerals such as jadeite plus quartz or coesite from albite and hollandite from K-feldspar. Most feldspars occur within a few tens of kilometers of the Earth's surface.

i) Because most feldspars are examined at ambient temperature instead of at the temperature of formation, and because the rate of attainment of equilibrium is so variable, it is important to examine the nomenclature of feldspars brought to different levels of metastable or stable equilibrium. Figure S-4 shows the products for rapid quenching, for slow cooling, and for supposed true or highly metastable equilibrium. The three sub-diagrams should be studied in conjunction with Figs. S-1 and S-2a which are intended to describe specimens in equilibrium at the temperature of observation.

The maximum range of compositions of natural feldspars from quenched rocks is shown in Fig. S-4a. An arbitrary boundary at An = Or is used to distinguish between plagioclase and alkali feldspar. Plagioclases are divided into six divisions by the boundaries at 10, 30, 50, 70 and 90 mol.-% An. Alkali feldspars quenched from high temperature are monoclinic at room temperature if they contain more than 40% Or. The boundary at 70% Or between Na- and K-sanidines has no structural meaning. Quenched alkali feldspars with less than 40% Or are triclinic and are described as solid solutions of high albite. Again the boundary at 10% Or between Na- and K-rich varieties is arbitrary. Most alkali feldspars in the high albite field become monoclinic before reaching the solidus temperature for dry conditions, whereas plagioclases are triclinic at all temperatures. Those alkali feldspars which become monoclinic above room temperature are then called monalbite. Whereas plagioclase shows twin relations consistent with primary triclinic symmetry (T-twinning), high albites inverted from monalbite show Albite-Pericline inversion twinning (M-twinning) developed at the monoclinic-triclinic symmetry change. The term anorthoclase roughly corresponds to inverted high albite, but some specimens show unmixing into a cryptoperthite. For rapid quenching from solidus temperature, all the feldspars except the calcic plagioclases have strong disorder of both the M and T atoms. Slower cooling as in volcanic rocks allows some ordering of the T atoms and fine-scale unmixing of alkali feldspars from about Or_{15} to Or_{60}.

Figure S-4b depicts relations typical of feldspars from small plutonic bodies. The region of two feldspars occupies most of the diagram, leaving a small field for K-feldspar and a thin strip for plagioclase. Ordering of the T-atoms has in-

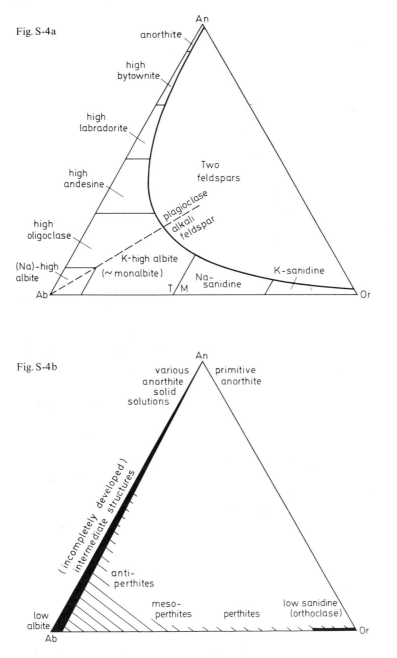

Fig. S-4a

Fig. S-4b

Fig. S-4. Schematic diagrams to illustrate the compositions and nomenclature of feldspars in the Or–Ab–An system examined at room temperature. a Feldspars quenched from high temperature. The maximum solid solution corresponds to crystallization under low pressure in the pure system. b Feldspars derived from some intermediate conditions of annealing such as might occur in small plutons. The solid areas show homogeneous feldspars while the hatched areas show ranges of composition for perthites, mesoperthites and antiperthites. c Feldspars subjected to prolonged annealing such as in deep-seated plutonic and metamorphic rocks

Fig. S-4c.
Legend see opposite page

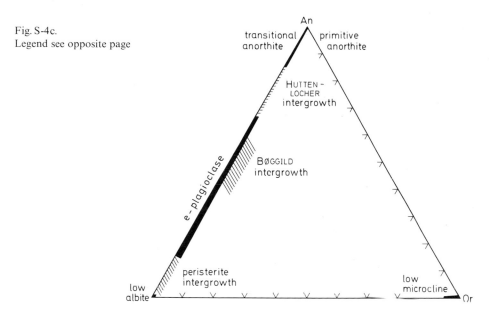

creased, being essentially complete for anorthite and albite and about half-way for K-feldspar. The plagioclases have developed a fine-scale domain structure on a unit-cell scale, probably consisting of tiny regions somewhat similar to anorthite and albite but with considerable disorder. Ordering in the K-feldspar produced low sanidine whose general properties are monoclinic but whose local atomic environment somewhat resembles that of microcline. The term orthoclase is commonly given to these K-feldspars, whose properties are rather variable. Most feldspars consist of a perthitic intergrowth of alkali feldspar and plagioclase resulting from segregation from an original homogeneous feldspar. Because of the lower temperature of crystallization for plutonic rocks than for volcanic rocks the extent of solid solution of the primary feldspar is less in Fig. S-4b than in Fig. S-4a. Perthites dominated by plagioclase are called antiperthites, while those with roughly equal amounts of plagioclase and alkali feldspar have a special texture and are described as mesoperthites.

   For true equilibrium at low temperature, the feldspar diagram probably would show mechanical mixtures of microcline, low albite and primitive anorthite for the entire composition range. Because of the difficulty of reaching equilibrium, plagioclases show a complex series of structures and intergrowths. The three hatched regions show the composition ranges of the peristerite, Bøggild and Huttenlocher intergrowths. All specimens with the Bøggild intergrowth contain more than about 1.5% Or, and some contain as much as 6% Or. Plagioclase with type e diffractions occurs from at least An_{15} to An_{75}. Solid solutions of anorthite type with diffuse c diffractions occur in the bytownite region.

   j) Perthites are feldspar intergrowths of which at least one component must be an alkali feldspar. There is controversy about the relative roles of exsolution and chemical replacement in the development of perthites, but the former mechanism is favored for many perthites. Iridescence is the term used to describe special optical scattering given by those feldspar intergrowths with fairly regular lamellae spaced about the wavelength of light. Iridescent perthites are called moonstones. The term labradorescence is reserved for the iridescence of the Bøggild intergrowth. Schiller is reserved for light scattering from visible as against invisible inclusions; thus it applies to aventurine in which light is scattered from visible hematite inclusions.

k) In rocks there is a tendency for a correlation of the feldspar properties with the bulk composition of the rock and with the temperature-pressure-time history deduced from geological observation. Thus sanidine and high plagioclase are not found in plutonic rocks. However the persistence of metastable forms such as xenocrysts of microcline caught up in volcanic rocks, the non-conversion of low sanidine to microcline even in some large plutonic bodies, and the lack of a strict correlation between the occurrence of low sanidine and microcline with the facies classification of metamorphic rocks renders impossible a simple summary of the occurrence of feldspars. The best guide is an estimate of the factors which encourage annealing — slow cooling, presence of catalysts, presence of shearing stress, etc. — and of the geological settings which make it likely that these factors are available.

l) The morphological habit of feldspars and the occurrence of the different twin laws depends on the structure and growth of the feldspar as well as on the subsequent tectonic history of the enclosing rock. Again it is impossible to present a simple summary, though three factors can be recognized. Higher temperatures provide increased atomic disorder and a greater chance of growth twinning. The frequency of mechanical twinning (restricted to Albite and Pericline laws) caused by rock stress depends on the ease of the necessary atomic movements. Thus twinning which requires movement of T atoms is much more difficult and less frequent than twinning which requires merely a puckering of the framework and small movements of M atoms. Symmetry changes produce inversion twinning such as the cross-hatched Albite and Pericline twinning in microcline and in high albite. The morphology is dependent on many factors too complex to describe here: however, it should be mentioned that the terms adularia, pericline and cleavelandite should be reserved for habits of feldspars and not for specific structural properties.

m) Most initial observations of feldspars are made by optical microscopy, supplemented to an increasing extent by X-ray powder diffraction. Such techniques cannot yield the detailed structural information obtainable from single-crystal diffraction and electron-optical methods and from various techniques depending on resonance. Nevertheless they are of primary value to most petrologists.

For alkali feldspars, determination of the cell dimension a provides a measure of the K/Na ratio while comparison of b with c evaluates the extent of Si, Al ordering. The optical axial angle also provides a measure of ordering if the composition is known.

For plagioclase, the refractive indices provide an accurate measure of the Na/Ca ratio while the optic axial angle and orientation of the optical indicatrix yield some information on the extent of ordering. A better estimate of ordering is obtainable from X-ray powder methods if the Na/Ca ratio is known. The composition can be determined best by electron microprobe methods.

n) Apart from the major substituents Na, Ca, K and rare Ba in the M sites and Al, Si in T sites, the extent of chemical substitution in natural feldspars is small. Many elements such as Rb, Sr, Fe, Ge occur as minor or trace constituents in natural feldspars providing valuable information on the source of the host rock and perhaps on the temperature of equilibration. Synthetic feldspars cover a much wider composition, embracing many low-valence cations in the M sites and high-valence cations in the T sites. Unstable isotopes yield information on the age of feldspars, whereas stable isotopes provide data on the equilibration temperature with coexisting minerals.

o) Shock deformation of feldspars yields complex lamellar structures and ultimately a dense phase, perhaps of hollandite structure.

p) Feldspars occur as intergrowths with many minerals. The myrmekite intergrowth of plagioclase and quartz probably results in large part from unmixing of neighboring K-feldspar of non-stoichiometric composition. The graphic intergrowth of K-feldspar or oligoclase with quartz probably results from simultaneous crystallization involving nucleation of quartz on a feldspar surface. Both external and internal surfaces of grains probably play a major role in governing diffusion and alteration processes in feldspars.

Part 1 Crystal Structures

Chapter 1 Brief Review of Concepts
and Experimental Techniques

1.1 Crystallographic Theory

In considering the structure of solid matter, crystallographers begin with the strict mathematical formulation of an atomic pattern repeating endlessly with exact regularity. The truly stable form for a chemical compound at a particular pressure and temperature has the lowest value for the Gibbs energy function $G = U - TS + PV$ (U internal energy, T absolute temperature, S entropy, P pressure, V volume). At the absolute zero of temperature only one atomic pattern at a given pressure could have minimum internal energy. Because attractive forces between atoms lead to a condensed state at lowered temperature, the stable form at the limit consists of a single edifice composed of regularly repeating units. At elevated temperatures, the entropy increases because of thermal motion and because of substitutional and positional disorder. A structural variant with disorder is favored over an ordered form if the entropy term outweighs the increase of internal energy caused by the disordered atoms. As the heat motion increases, the difference between the internal energies of ordered and disordered forms becomes less significant in relation to the entropy term, and certain types of disorder become favored, culminating in breakdown to the liquid or vapor state. Thus the *idealized* concept of a *strictly-regular* crystal structure becomes less applicable as the temperature rises, and it is the resultant disorder which provides a petrogenetic value to crystallographic studies of minerals. However mathematical analysis of the idealized regular structure is fundamental to all mineralogic analysis.

The basic reference to the symmetry of crystals is Vol. I of "International Tables for X-ray Crystallography" edited by Henry and Lonsdale (1952). Suitable textbooks are Azàroff (1968), Bloss (1971), Buerger (1965), and Phillips (1963).

The idealized structure of a feldspar is based on the *space group* C 2/m of *equivalent general positions* (which are potential sites for atoms) and of *equivalent symmetry elements* which relate them (Fig. 1-1). The total concept of a space group may be derived by considering first a *space lattice* in which the reference positions are related only by *rotation axes of symmetry* passing through the positions (e.g. solid dots in Fig. 1-1). The vectorial environment of all the positions must be identical for the positions to form a lattice.

It is customary to choose for the *unit cell* the smallest part of the lattice which could generate the whole lattice merely by translations (i.e. there must be no rotations), subject to selecting a unit cell which has the highest geometrical regularity consistent with the rotational symmetry. This unit cell may be chosen in different ways when the symmetry is low, and there are special conventions covering the labelling of the *reference axes a, b* and *c* which are taken parallel to the three edges of the unit cell.

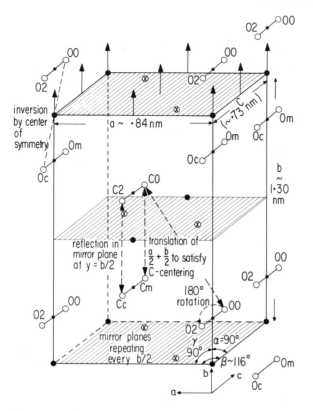

Fig. 1-1. Lattice, symmetry elements and geometry of idealized feldspar structure with space group symmetry C2/m. The unit cell of the crystal structure is shown with the b-axis vertical, a to the left, and c going to the right rear. The positions of the interaxial angles α, β and γ are shown. Mirror planes are shown by hatching repeated every $b/2$. The two-fold rotation axes are shown by arrows projecting from the upper face of the unit cell. To illustrate the symmetry operations, tetrahedral atoms of type T_1 are shown. The small circular symbol labelled 00 occur at fractional coordinates (x 0.01, y 0.18, z 0.22: see Table 2-1). The T_1 atom labelled 02 is obtained by a $180°$ rotation about a 2-fold axis. The T_1 atom labelled C0 is obtained from the T_1 atom at 00 by translation by the vector distance $\frac{a}{2} + \frac{b}{2}$ to satisfy the centering of the C-face. The T_1 atom at C2 is obtained from the T_1 atom at C0 by rotation, the one at Cm by reflection in the mirror plane at $y = b/2$, and the one at Cc by inversion in the center of symmetry lying at a large solid dot. Note that combination of two-fold rotation plus mirror reflection is equivalent to inversion of a center of symmetry. Other equivalent positions for T_1 atoms are shown. Readers are advised to examine closely a ball-and-spoke model of feldspars to follow through the symmetry operations in three dimensions. There are eight T_1 sites per unit cell. To illustrate a special position, the locations of the M cations on the mirror planes are shown by crossed circles. Only the C and 2 operations are possible, resulting in a total of only 4 M-type cations per cell. The starting coordinates for M cations are x 0.28, y 0, z 0.14 (Table 2-1)

Of the four ways in which points can be chosen to lie on rotation axes of unit cells showing the highest geometrical regularity, three are found in the unit cells used to describe feldspars. These are P (primitive, one point at each corner), I(body centered, an extra point at each body center), C (P plus a point at the center of each *ab* face). The idealized feldspar structure is based on a C lattice with a single two-fold axis (denoted 2) which relates equivalent positions by a rotation of 180°, and hence the structure belongs to the *monoclinic system*. The *b*-axis is chosen to be parallel to the 2-fold axis. Loss of the 2-fold rotation axis (and symmetry planes) in the "crumpled" structures of microcline and plagioclase results in *triclinic* symmetry. The monoclinic C-cell must have $\alpha = \gamma = 90°$ in order to obey the symmetry, but the triclinic cell has these angles not equal to 90° except by accident. There are no restrictions on *a*, *b* and *c*, the repeat distances along the axes, and on the angle β. For convenience of comparison with monoclinic feldspars, triclinic feldspars are referred to a C-centered unit cell with axes pseudo-parallel to those of monoclinic feldspars: because there is no symmetry control over the geometry, a smaller primitive unit cell with different axial directions could have been chosen.

The next step in building up a space group is to release the unnecessary restriction that the positions lie on the rotational symmetry elements. In addition the concepts of *mirror plane of symmetry*, *glide plane of symmetry* (mirror reflection followed by translation parallel to a principal lattice direction) and *screw axis of symmetry* (rotation followed by translation parallel to the axis) may be used. Figure 1-1 shows the positions of mirror planes and two-fold rotation axes in the unit cell of feldspar, plus the sites of the T_1 tetrahedral nodes of the aluminosilicate framework (open circles). The figure legend explains in detail the operations of the symmetry elements. Figure 1-2 shows positions and operations of screw diad axes (denoted 2_1) and *a* glide planes of symmetry in the space group C 2/m, together with the set of equivalent positions for the T_1 tetrahedral nodes.

The symmetry about a point is known as the *point symmetry*: if the point lies on a mirror plane, a rotation axis or a center of symmetry, the number of its equivalent positions per unit cell is reduced, and the position is described as a *special position*. The M cations of feldspars lie on mirror planes as shown in Fig. 1-1 by crossed circles.

In a real crystal structure, there is usually more than one type of chemical species and often there is more than one type of environment for atoms of the same species. Each type of environment is associated with a particular *xyz* position in the unit cell (usually specified in decimal fractions of the cell edge); once one position has been specified, all other positions with the same environment can be developed just from the symmetry properties of the space group and from the cell vectors. For space group C 2/m, the appropriate information is given on p. 95 of Vol. 1 of International Tables for X-ray Crystallography.

Some physical properties are governed by the local environment of a specific atom (e.g. nuclear magnetic resonance) and hence depend on the point symmetry. Others are bulk properties of the structure (crystal habit, thermal expansion, cell dimensions, etc.) and are governed by the *point-group* symmetry (to be distinguished from point symmetry of individual atoms). The point-group symmetry is obtained by removing all the translational elements from the space group symmetry leaving only symmetry elements passing through a single point (C 2/m goes to 2/m point-group symmetry). For example, the angular orientations of the external faces of a feldspar are governed by the point-group symmetry 2/m, and provide no direct information on the atomic arrangement which is governed by the space group symmetry C 2/m.

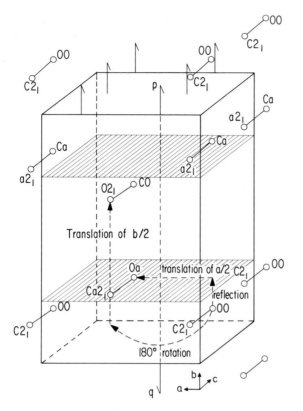

Fig. 1-2. Perspective drawing to illustrate the operations of *a* glide planes and 2_1 screw axes in the feldspar structure. The small circle labelled 00 shows the position of a T_1 tetrahedral node near decimal coordinates (0.01, 0.18, 0.22). The *a* glide planes lie spaced every $b/2$ at $y = {}^1\!/_4$ and $^3\!/_4$ (i.e. they lie midway between the mirror planes shown in Fig. 1-1). The T_1 node labelled 0a is obtained by the combined operations of reflection followed by translation of $a/2$. The screw axes (symbolized by 2_1 and shown by half-arrows) lie half-way between the rotation axes of Fig. 1-1. The T_1 node labelled 02_1 is obtained by 180° rotation about the 2_1 axis labelled pq followed by translation of $b/2$. All other nodes are labelled by symbols which show the operations required to obtain that node from the starting node at 00

1.2 Experimental Techniques Giving Information on the Crystal Structure

The atomic positions of feldspars were determined initially from the centers of electron-density concentrations deduced from X-ray diffraction methods, and were confirmed by neutron diffraction studies which reveal the positions of the atomic nuclei. Interpretation of these data for feldspars is complicated by chemical substitutions (such as occupancy of one set of tetrahedral sites by both Si and Al atoms), by anisotropic thermal vibration, and by domain textures. The theory of diffraction by disordered structures is covered thoroughly by the monograph "Theory of X-ray and thermal-neutron scattering by real crystals" by Krivoglaz (1969).

Complementing the diffraction techniques are those of nuclear magnetic and quadrupole resonance, gamma-ray resonance, electron spin resonance and of infra-red absorption which give information on the local environment of atoms (see Part 2 for details). Nuclear magnetic resonance depends on the interaction between a nuclear magnetic moment and an applied magnetic field, and on the interaction between the nuclear electric quadrupole moment and the second spatial derivative of the electrostatic potential at the atomic position. In an ordered structure only one set of sharp resonances is obtained for each set of equivalent positions: in a disordered structure, the electrostatic potential varies from atom to atom and the resonances become blurred. Infra-red absorption depends on the frequencies of atomic vibrations or rotations in the crystal structure. Specific vibrations and rotations can be identified from the wave lengths of the absorptions. Ordered crystals give sharp absorptions while disordered ones give blurred absorptions.

Taken together the various crystallographic techniques provide data on the atomic positions, atomic displacements, site populations and estimates of ordering for suitable feldspars.

1.3 Crystal Chemical Theory

Because it is quite impossible to relate structural features of complex substances like feldspar to the Schrödinger wave equation, interpretation of chemical bonding in crystal structures is based on simple, but usually effective, rules-of-thumb involving elementary concepts.

The simplest approach for multiple oxides including feldspars is to imagine that atoms transfer electrons to achieve the electronic structure of an inert-gas atom. Then the resulting ions arrange themselves to minimize the electrostatic potential (Pauling, 1960). Qualitatively one considers just the electrostatic attractive forces between the centers of near-spherical ions of opposite polarity, repulsive forces between centers of ions of the same polarity, and repulsive forces between the outer electrons of all ions in contact. To a first approximation, ions can be conceived as rigid balls each with its own characteristic radius, and many tables of ionic radii have been developed (e.g. Shannon and Prewitt, 1969). However the approximation is only of moderate accuracy (e.g. individual Si–O distances vary from about 0.155 to 0.170 nanometer while K–O distances range from about 0.25 to 0.30 nm). The mean distances of all the bonds from one atom are less variable (e.g. 0.161 to 0.164 nm for SiO_4 tetrahedra in the entire range of silicate structures). If ions are conceived as having the consistency of tennis balls, and the deformations of the ions to be similar to those produced by squeezing tennis balls in one's hand, a reasonable qualitative impression is gained. The larger, lower-valence ions are "softer" than the smaller higher-valence ions and their positions in the crystal structure are not so critical as those of the smaller cations. Thus the natural sequence of steps in studying the feldspar structure is to examine first the aluminosilicate framework and secondly the positions of the large cations and their relation to the framework.

The most quantitative application of the concept of ionic bonding involves the calculation of the electrostatic potential and the related electrostatic field gradient by summing the contributions from all the ions in the structure. Such calculations have been made for feldspars and compared with information obtained by resonance techniques (Chapter 11). The agreement is only moderate, showing that the simple ionic model is useful but not sufficient.

An alternative model utilizes covalent bonding in which electrons from neighboring atoms are regarded as held in common. Each orbital electron has a wave function whose spatial profile is governed by symmetry determined by quantum numbers. Covalent bonding should be highly sensitive to interatomic angles and to polymerization in contrast to the lower sensitivity of ionic bonding. Although σ-bonds must provide the largest contribution to covalent bonding, π-bonds may provide a significant addition. Cruickshank (1961) showed that the interatomic distances in phosphates and various other complex oxides could be interpreted nicely in terms of some contribution from π-bonds using $3d$ orbitals. In silicates the bond-length variation correlates less clearly with the interatomic angles and polymerization, and the importance of π-bonding is controversial.

Brown and Gibbs (1970) reviewed various ideas on the bonding of silicates, and studied the relations between bond lengths and angles in the tetrahedral portion of silicate structures. Gibbs and co-workers advocated covalent bonding and provided strong evidence based on good correlations between observed and calculated displacements of atoms from ideal positions in regular polyhedra. An opposing view is that of Baur (1971) who correlated observed bond lengths in silicates with the ionic forces from both first and second neighbors. Although Baur's calculations with the extended electrostatic valence rule fit quite well with the observed interatomic distances, I think that the calculations of Gibbs and co-workers are on the right track because they give good correlations with the distortions of polyhedra and the interatomic angles. The following abstract by Gibbs et al. (1972) at the Study Institute on Feldspars illustrates calculations involving molecular orbitals:

"Extended Hückel molecular orbital (EHMO) calculations have been completed for the TO_4 (T = Al, Si) tetrahedra in anorthite, low albite and maximum microcline, clamping all the Si–O distances at 1.61 Å and all the Al–O distances at 1.75 Å, and using the observed T–O–T and O–T–O angles and a valence basis set that consists of the $3s$, $3p$ and $3d$ atomic orbitals of T and the $2s$ and $2p$ orbitals of oxygen. Mulliken bond overlap populations, n(T–O), computed for all the T–O bonds in the three feldspars correlate with the observed T–O bond lengths. Shorter bonds are associated with the larger n(T–O) despite the assumption in the calculations that all Si–O and all Al–O bond lengths are constant. This indicates that at least part of the T–O bond length variations observed in the feldspars can be rationalized in terms of covalent bonding model.

Charges calculated for the oxygen atoms in the three feldspars also correlate with the observed T–O bond lengths, longer bonds being involved with oxygen atoms with larger charges, Moreover, the magnitudes of the charges (see averaged values below) computed for the framework atoms are significantly smaller than those implicit in an electrostatic model:

Atom	Anorthite	Low albite	Max. microcline
O(Si–O–Al linkage)	−1.07	−1.06	−1.05
O(Si–O–Si linkage)	—	−0.86	−0.86
Si	+1.37	+1.62	+1.62
Al	+2.03	+2.02	+1.98

Summations of the charges over all the atoms comprising the tetrahedral frameworks require charges of $+1.6$ on Ca in anorthite and $+0.8$ on Na and K in the two alkali feldspars. Despite the *total* neglect of the non-tetrahedral cations in the calculations, the charge distribution predicted by the EHMO theory correlates with the observed number of Ca–O linkages in anorthite:

No. of Ca neighbours	Average charge on oxygen
0	-1.04
1	-1.07
2	-1.09

However, a correlation between coordination number of oxygen and its calculated charge cannot be made for the two alkali feldspars".

Whatever the outcome of the controversy concerning the relative roles of ionic and covalent bonding, it is certain in 1973 that no chemical model is capable of yielding the topology and the overall scheme of bonding between the atoms in feldspars. All that can be achieved is to take the observed structure and correlate the details with predictions from the chemical models. Fortunately many of the features of the feldspar structure can be described without reference to a particular chemical model. The descriptions here utilize the simplest and most direct ideas whenever possible, building up from the geometrical ideas of topology and using the concept of bonding dominated by ionic and σ-covalent contributions from first neighbors. Only when necessary are π-bonding and the contributions from more distant neighbors considered.

References

Azaroff, L. V. (1968): Elements of X-ray crystallography. New York: McGraw Hill.

Baur, W. H. (1971): The prediction of bond length variations in silicon-oxygen bonds. AM **56**, 1573–1599.

Bloss, F. D. (1971): Crystallography and crystal chemistry. New York: Holt, Rinehard and Winston, Inc.

Brown, G. E., Gibbs, G. V. (1970): Stereochemistry and ordering in the tetrahedral portion of silicates. AM **55**, 1587–1607.

Buerger, M. J. (1965): Elementary crystallography. New York: John Wiley and Sons, Inc.

Cruickshank, D. W. J. (1961): The role of $3d$-orbitals in π-bonds between (a) silicon, phosphorous, sulphur, or chlorine and (b) oxygen or nitrogen, JCS 5485–5504.

Gibbs, G. V., Louisnathan, S. J., Phillips, M. W., Ribbe, P. H. (1972): A covalent model for bonding in feldspars. Abstr. 1.9 in program for Advanced Study Institute on Feldspars, July 1972, Manchester.

Henry, N. F. M., Lonsdale, K. (1952): Editors of International Tables for X-ray Crystallography. Vol. I. Symmetry Groups. Birmingham: Kynoch Press.

Krivoglaz, M. A. (1969): Theory of X-ray and thermal-neutron scattering by real crystals. English translation from Russian, New York: Plenum Press.

Pauling, L. (1960): The nature of the chemical bond, 3rd ed. New York: Cornell University Press.

Phillips, F. C. (1963): An introduction to crystallography. 3rd edition. London: Longmans, Green and Co.

Shannon, R. D., Prewitt, C. T. (1969): Effective ionic radii in oxides and fluorides. AC B**25**, 925–946.

Chapter 2 Crystal Structure of Feldspar.
Principal Features. Related Structures

2.1 The Topology of the Aluminosilicate Framework

2.1.1 Discovery

Machatschki (1928) correctly proposed that the feldspar structure is based on a framework of linked TO_4 tetrahedra, but Taylor (1933) took the crucial step when he envisaged the actual topology of the framework structure on Christmas Day, 1932, followed by a comprehensive survey of the structural variants (Taylor *et al.*, 1934). The pseudo-tetragonal structure proposed by Schiebold is wrong, but his X-ray measurements and some speculations were of temporary value (Schiebold, 1927; 1928; 1929a, b, c; 1930; 1931).

The oxygen atoms lie at the corners of nearly regular tetrahedra centered by Al or Si atoms: all oxygens are shared by two T atoms to yield a framework. The oxygen atoms of the framework form irregularly-shaped cavities occupied by the large M cations. This concept of a framework with occupied voids applies

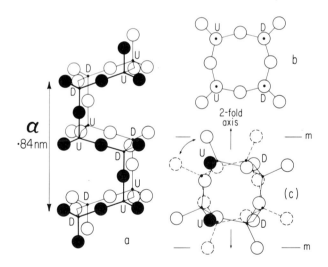

Fig. 2-1. The double-crankshaft chain in feldspar. a Perspective drawing showing a view perpendicular to the *a*-axis. b Projection down the *a*-axis of the idealized crankshaft. c Projection down the *a*-axis of the actual crankshaft as exemplified in sanidine. Oxygen atoms are shown with a radius about three-tenths of the formal ionic radius, while tetrahedral atoms are shown as solid dots. Tetrahedra pointing upwards or downwards along the *a*-axis are shown, respectively, by U and D. In (b) alternate 4-rings exactly superimpose thereby alternating U of one ring with D of the next ring. In (c), distortion of the crankshaft allows distinction between one ring (shown in solid line) and the next ring (shown in dashed line). The positions of mirror planes and a 2-fold rotation axis are shown. (After Taylor, 1933, Fig. 5 and Taylor *et al.*, 1934, Fig. 5)

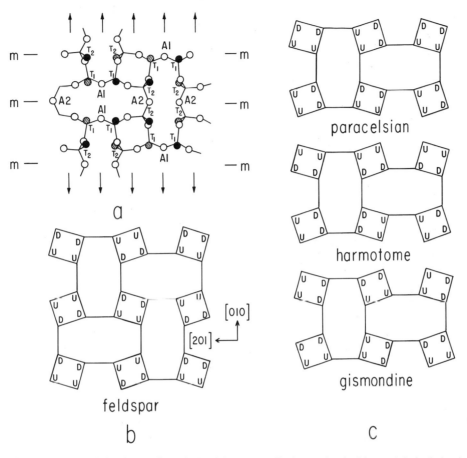

Fig. 2-2. Nature of the sheets of tetrahedra lying perpendicular to the double-crankshaft chains in feldspar and related structures. a The actual shape of a sheet in feldspar as given by Taylor (1933, Fig. 4) for sanidine. The projection was made onto the (20$\bar{1}$) plane defined by the [010] and [102] zone axes using the oblique axis a for projection. Each double crankshaft is represented by a four-membered ring composed of two tetrahedra of type T_1 and two of the type T_2 shown at the intersection of lines plus the associated oxygens shown as circles. The solid and hatched circles, respectively, show oxygen atoms of type B pointing upwards or downwards. The 4-membered rings of tetrahedra are joined by oxygen atoms of type A2 on mirror planes (m) and oxygens of type A1 on 2-fold axes (shown by the arrowed lines) to form eight-membered rings of elliptical cross-section. b Schematic representation of a tetrahedral sheet in the feldspar structure showing a skeleton composed of lines joining the tetrahedral nodes plus the symbol U and D to show an upward or a downward pointing tetrahedron. The area covered is somewhat larger than in (a). c Corresponding diagrams to (b) for paracelsian, harmotome and gismondine. (After Smith and Rinaldi, 1962, Fig. 3)

to many silicates and other complex oxides. The particular characteristic of feldspar is the occurrence in the framework of chains of tetrahedra shaped like double crankshafts (Fig. 2-1), cross-linked in a special way to form elliptical 8-membered rings of tetrahedra (Fig. 2-2).

The structure determination by Taylor (1933) was achieved in an elegant manner. Taylor assumed that feldspar contained an aluminosilicate framework.

He noted that, by use of pseudotetragonal axes [100], [010] and [102], the feldspar lattice could be divided into boxes separated by mirror planes and pairs of two-fold rotation axes. Each box should contain four tetrahedra. Taylor found only one way in which the four tetrahedra could fit into the box while obeying the symmetry and having reasonable bond lengths. The structure determination was completed by placing the K atoms on mirror planes at reasonable bond distances to oxygen atoms. Tedious trial-and-error adjustment of atomic coordinates yielded a satisfactory fit between observed and calculated X-ray diffraction amplitudes. Table 2-1 shows the atom nomenclature plus the atomic coordinates for a least-squares refinement of sanidinized orthoclase by Ribbe (1963).

Table 2-1. Atomic parameters of sanidinized orthoclase

Atom	x	y	z	Point symmetry
O_{A1}	0	0.1472(6)	0	2
O_{A2}	0.6343(10)	0	0.2858(12)	m
O_B	0.8273(10)	0.1469(6)	0.2253(12)	1
O_C	0.0347(10)	0.3100(6)	0.2579(12)	1
O_D	0.1793(10)	0.1269(6)	0.4024(12)	1
T_1	0.0097(3)	0.1850(2)	0.2233(4)	1
T_2	0.7089(3)	0.1178(2)	0.3444(4)	1
M	0.2840(3)	0	0.1352(4)	m

The labelling of the atoms is inherited from the work of Taylor (1933). The oxygen atoms are labelled with the letters A to D; subscripts 1 and 2 distinguish the two atoms labelled A, which have point symmetry higher than 1. T stands for tetrahedral, and refers to sites for which the Si and Al atoms are not distinguished. M stands for the site which is principally occupied by potassium, but with some substitution by Na and Ca. x, y and z are decimal fractions of the cell edges based on the conventional cell a 0.84 nm, b 1.30 nm, c 0.72 nm, β 116°, C 2/m. See text and Megaw (1956) for further comments on labelling of positions. Data from Ribbe (1963).

The feldspar specimen is labelled Spencer C with chemical composition near $(K_{0.922} Na_{0.068} Ca_{0.025})$ $(AlSi_3)O_8$. The accurate cell dimensions are a 0.85642(2), b 1.30300(4), c 0.71749(2), β 115.994(5), with error in brackets. See Cole et al. (1949) for further data.

2.1.2 Linkage of the Crankshaft Chain in Feldspar and Other Minerals

To some degree, selection of the double-crankshaft for special notice in the feldspar framework is misleading because the chains are not isolated as in amphibole: nevertheless the double-crankshaft is of key importance, first because it permits a simple explanation of the anisotropy of the physical properties and secondly because the principal structural change caused by substitution of larger M cations by smaller ones is a shortening of the double-crankshaft by crumpling.

Because of the complex twisting and crumpling of the aluminosilicate framework in feldspar, it is not easy to locate the double-crankshaft in an accurate ball-and-spoke model of a feldspar. The double-crankshaft lies along the a-axis, but is more easily visualized in the diagrams of Figs. 2-1 and 2-2 in which the feldspar framework has been idealized to produce a more regular geometry.

(All framework structures should be examined from the viewpoint of the most regular geometry, or of the highest symmetry; not only would there be an interesting topologic problem of defining the highest symmetry and most regular geometry, there should result a unique topologic characterization of the structure, and probably a way of classifying frameworks.)

The idealized double-crankshaft consists of four-membered rings alternately parallel and nearly perpendicular to the a-axis (Fig. 2-1a). Using a T–O distance of 0.16 nm, the repeat distance down the crankshaft is about 0.86 nm. In projection along the a-axis, the 4-membered rings appear to merge into a single 4-membered ring (Fig. 2-1b). Furthermore the topologic relations can be implied by an algebraic code developed by Smith and Rinaldi (1962) in which a tetrahedron pointing up is denoted U and one pointing down is denoted D. The double-crankshaft can be specified by the code UUDD with the understanding that each ring of type UUDD is bonded to rings DDUU by joining U of a lower ring to D of an upper ring.

Actually in a real feldspar, the rings do not superimpose in projection along a, and Fig. 2-1c shows the extent of misfit for sanidine. Furthermore, the UUDD rings are not perpendicular to the a-axis as implied by Fig. 2-1a. The alternate UUDD and DDUU rings are parallel because of the space group symmetry, but the a-axis is inclined at about 70° to the plane of the rings in a real feldspar. Figure 2-1c shows how the atomic positions are related by mirror planes lying perpendicular to the paper and by a 2-fold axis lying parallel to the paper.

Figure 2-2a shows how the structure of feldspar can be described as a series of sheets composed of 4- and 8-membered rings of tetrahedra. A detailed explanation of symbols is given in the figure legend. The 4-rings have the UUDD configuration, and can be composed into double-crankshafts as shown in Fig. 2-1. The 8-rings are elliptical, and each sheet of Fig. 2-2a is composed of two types of 8-rings viz. UUUUDDDD and DUUDUDDU. These two types of 8-rings are the fundamental feature of the feldspar framework, and distinguish feldspar from all other combinations of U's and D's that can be invented. Each sheet of tetrahedra lies parallel to the (20$\bar{1}$) plane defined by the [010] and [102] zone axes, and lies at an angle of about 100° to the a-axis, the direction of the double-crankshaft chains. In an actual feldspar, the sheets are crumpled as may be seen from Fig. 2-2a. The linkage of the 4- and 8-rings can be described in projection as a tessellation of squares and octagons.

Before describing the different ways in which double-crankshaft chains can be cross-linked (Fig. 2-2), it is advisable to describe first the two basic ways in which the chains can be linked to form frameworks (Fig. 2-3). Smith (1968) showed that the double-crankshaft could be linked in two ways to give the *flexible* and the *inflexible* types of structure. The actual structure of feldspar (Fig. 2-3b) differs only from the flexible analog of feldspar (Fig. 2-3a) by the way in which the four-rings of the double-crankshaft are linked together before cross-linking to form sheets of tetrahedra.

Both diagrams are projections down the double-crankshaft chains. Each horizontal 4-ring consists of a UUDD combination of tetrahedra, the two U tetrahedra linked to the two D tetrahedra of the 4-ring above, and the two D

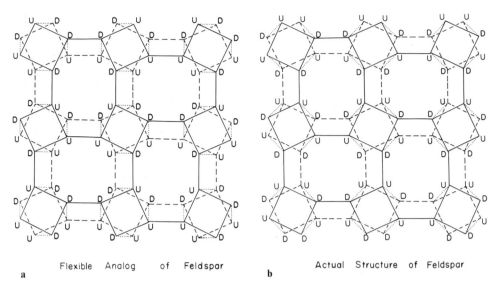

Fig. 2-3. Comparison of the flexible analog (a) of feldspar with the actual feldspar structure (b). Tetrahedral atoms lie at the intersections and oxygen atoms near the centers of the lines. The symbols U and D represent tetrahedra pointing upwards or downwards. Each diagram shows an upper layer (continuous lines) joined to a lower layer (dashed lines) by the dotted lines. (From Smith, 1968, Fig. 1)

tetrahedra linked to the two U tetrahedra of the 4-ring below. In these diagrams, the T atoms lie at the intersection of the lines, while the oxygen atoms lie near the mid-points of the lines. Cross-linking of double-crankshafts occurs by sharing of the projecting oxygens seen in Fig. 2-1. Although each 4-ring of a crankshaft must have a UUDD configuration, there is a two-fold choice for the linkage between pairs of adjacent crankshafts because the adjacent tetrahedron can point either U or D.

It may be seen from Fig. 2-3 that both the actual structure of feldspar and its flexible analog consist of UUUUDDDD and DUUDUDDU rings. The difference consists in the direction of the vertical links in the double-crankshaft, shown by dotted lines. In the feldspar structure, the links from the upper layer of tetrahedra (solid lines) turn clockwise to join the lower layer of tetrahedra (dashed lines) whereas in the flexible analog the links turn counter-clockwise. This has the consequence that in feldspar UUUUDDDD rings lie over DUUDUDDU rings whereas in the flexible analog UUUUDDDD rings lie over each other while DUUDUDDU rings form their own system of super-position.

Smith (1968) distinguished the two structures by the adjectives *flexible* and *inflexible* because the horizontal 4-rings of the inflexible type (as exemplified by feldspar) cannot rotate cooperatively whereas 4-rings of the flexible type can. Indeed in the flexible type, cooperative rotation would permit the ellipsoidal-shaped 8-rings of Fig. 2-3a to turn first into regular octagons and then into ellipsoids of opposite eccentricity. If the flexible analog did adopt the regular octagonal shape, it would occupy a greater volume than when it is in an ellipsoidal configuration.

Smith and Rinaldi (1962) had not recognized the distinction between the flexible and inflexible types of frameworks composed of double-crankshafts. However they showed that there were an infinite number of frameworks of the flexible type because it is possible to choose the rotational orientation of each UUDD chain without disturbing the rest of the framework (of course, the angular orientation must be restricted because of the cross-linking). Smith and Rinaldi worked out the seventeen structures that result when the repeat distance in the plane of the 8-membered rings is not over 1.5 nm. Corresponding to these seventeen structures of flexible type, Smith (1968) showed that there are only thirteen structures of inflexible type. Unfortunately Smith and Rinaldi implicitly described feldspar as a member of the flexible type of framework. They correctly predicted the framework of the then unknown structure of the zeolite gismondine.

Of the 17 flexible and 13 inflexible structures that are theoretically possible with the above restriction on repeat distance, four are known in natural minerals. Paracelsian, the polymorph of the celsian variety of feldspar, and the two zeolites, gismondine and harmotome, display three of the flexible types. There are other isostructural varieties: danburite is isostructural with paracclsian and phillipsite with harmotome. It is noteworthy that the zeolite minerals belong to the flexible group, thereby permitting the framework to adopt an expanded configuration capable of accommodating the water molecules. The paracelsian framework is collapsed because there is no water in the structure. The flexible analog of feldspar has not been found so far, but perhaps it may turn up in synthetic material belonging to the zeolite family.

2.1.3 Relation to Coesite

The aluminosilicate framework of feldspar is topologically related to the silicate framework of coesite, one of the high-pressure polymorphs of SiO_2. Zoltai and Buerger (1959) noticed a structural resemblance, but Megaw (1970) first quantified the relationship. The key feature is depicted in Fig. 2-4, but readers are referred to Megaw's paper for various crystallographic details and for a discussion of the factors governing the distortion of the structures.

Figure 2-4a is a projection down the b-axis of the contents of slightly more than one unit cell of sanidine using the coordinates of Table 2-1. The symbolism is described in the figure legend. The principal topologic feature is the double crankshaft extending parallel to the a-axis across the middle of the diagram. One of the four-membered rings lies at the center of the unit cell with two T_1 atoms at percentage height 32 and two T_2 atoms at height 38. This ring is approximately parallel to the plane of projection, and will be called a *horizontal* 4-ring. Adjacent to this ring are two 4-rings shown by hatching and composed of T_1 atoms at heights 18 and 32 and T_2 atoms at heights 12 and 38. These 4-rings would be described as chair-shaped by organic chemists. Roughly speaking these 4-rings lie perpendicular to the plane of projection of Fig. 2-4a. Study of the heights on the diagram will show that the horizontal 4-rings lie alternately at heights near 35 and 15, and hence can be described as being higher and lower.

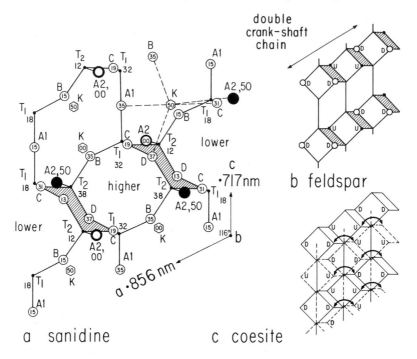

Fig. 2-4. Relation between structures of feldspar and coesite. a Projection on the ac plane of the structure of sanidine using symbols and coordinates of Table 2-1. The heights of the atoms are shown in percentages of the b repeat (1.3 nm). The tetrahedral nodes (solid dots) are connected to the oxygen atoms (circles) to show the linkage of the aluminosilicate framework. There are mirror planes at heights 00 and 50. Only atoms from 00 to 50 are shown because those from 50 to 100 exactly super-impose on those related by a mirror plane. The atoms of type A 2 are specially marked because they lie on the mirror planes. Slightly more than one unit cell is shown at the upper left in order to show the shape of a six-membered ring and to show the relative positions of nearby K atoms (hexagons). The nearest oxygen neighbors to a K atom are shown at the upper right by dashed lines. The unit cell is bounded by the extreme Al atoms. b Schematic drawing of the aluminosilicate framework in feldspar. Each double-crankshaft consists of 4-membered rings, alternately shown as squares and parallelograms (hatched). The crankshafts are connected in the plane of the paper to yield hexagons. The crankshafts are connected out of the plane of the paper by the linkages going upwards (U) or downwards (D). c Schematic drawing of the aluminosilicate framework in coesite. See text for explanation. (Diagrams slightly modified from Megaw, 1970, Figs. 1 and 2)

The stippled, chair-shaped 4-rings tilt alternately to the left and to the right. The whole assemblage produces a double crankshaft and this projection is merely another way of looking at Fig. 2-1a. An idealized, schematic drawing is given in Fig. 2-1b in which the 4-rings are shown by squares and parallelograms.

The linkage of the crankshafts is clearly displayed when the symmetry elements are considered. The operation of two-fold rotation axes is readily seen: for example, a two-fold axis at the center of Fig. 2-1a would relate pairs of atoms in the central 4-ring. The lattice repeat along c causes the crankshaft to repeat in a vertical direction every 0.72 nm, and the framework linkage in this direction is composed of A 1 oxygen atoms joining pairs of T_1 atoms. This linkage produces

6-rings, only one of which is shown in its entirety in Fig. 2-1a. At the upper left, a 6-ring is formed of T_1 18; T_2 12; T_1 32; T_1 32; T_2 38 and T_1 18 plus the oxygen atoms of type A 1, B and C. The schematic drawing in Fig. 2-4b shows the relationship between the 4- and 6-membered rings more clearly. In projection, this is a tessellation of hexagonal and quadrilateral tiles, but in three dimensions these units are not coplanar.

The framework linkage in the b direction can be envisaged by relating the atomic positions to mirror planes of symmetry at percentage heights of 00 and 50 along b. All the atoms in Fig. 2-4a lie between heights 00 and 50. Each has a superimposed mirror image between heights 50 and 100, e.g. a T_1 atom at height 32 is mirrored by one at 68. There is one exception: the A 2 atoms lie on a mirror plane either at height 50 or height 00, as distinguished by the solid circles and heavy open circles. The framework linkage along b can now be understood because the crankshafts lying at 00 and 50 are joined to those between 50 and 100 by linkages from A 2 to pairs of T_2 tetrahedral nodes. Thus an A 2 oxygen atom at height 50 bonds to T_2 tetrahedral atoms at heights 38 and 62. In Fig. 2-4b the linkages are shown schematically by dots and circles marked U and D.

The silicate framework of cocsite (Fig. 2-4c) also contains double-crankshaft chains with linkages pointing upwards and downwards. Whereas in feldspar, adjacent crankshafts are related by a mirror plane of symmetry perpendicular to b, in coesite the crankshafts are related by a glide plane. The glide plane lies parallel to the plane of the diagram and translates in a northerly direction. The mirror operation is shown by change from continuous lines to dashed lines with associated switch of the connections from U to D and vice versa. The glide translation is nearly equal to the diagonal of the square 4-rings. The result of the combined mirror-glide operation is to place the dashed-line material midway in projection between the continuous-line material. The D and U links do not lie above each other. However by completing the linkages shown by the curved arrows, the topology of coesite is achieved. By distorting the framework, the actual geometry of coesite is obtained as explained in detail by Megaw (1970).

2.1.4 Projection Down c^*

So far the feldspar framework has been described in terms of projections down the a and b axes. A projection down c^*, as used by Taylor (1933, Fig. 6) and by Laves (1960, Fig. 1), nicely displays how the double-crankshafts are distorted, and how they are linked by 10-membered rings as well as by the 8- and 6-membered rings already described.

Figure 2-5 shows a slight modification of the diagram by Laves. The unit cell is projected onto the ab plane down c^* such that the lower corners are marked by EFGH and the upper corners by ABCD. The tetrahedral framework can be envisaged as two sheets per unit cell joined by near-vertical links. One of the sheets is shown by the very thick lines, the other by the thin lines, and the joins by the tapered lines. Only the tetrahedral nodes are shown in the drawing. Each sheet of linked tetrahedral nodes is corrugated with a height variation of thirteen percent of the c^* repeat.

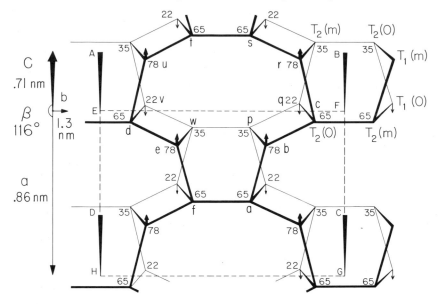

Fig. 2-5. Topology of the tetrahedral nodes of the feldspar framework. The projection is down the c^* axis onto the ab plane. The c-axis slopes upwards to the reader from bottom to top of the diagram as shown by the tapered line. The upper and lower corners of the unit cell are shown by ABCD and by EFGH. The arrows attached to some of the tetrahedral nodes show linkages into unit cells higher and lower than the one shown here: see text for explanation of the continuity of the framework in the vertical direction. The Megaw symbols for tetrahedral nodes are shown at the upper right. (After Taylor, 1933, Fig. 5; Laves, 1960, Fig. 1 and Smith, 1970, Fig. 1)

Two double crankshafts are shown lying parallel to the a-axis. Alternate 4-rings occur in this projection as near-rectangles and bow-ties. Mirror planes of symmetry lie in the middle of the diagram and at the left and right sides of the unit cell. The crankshafts are joined across the mirror planes.

The 6-rings described in Fig. 2-4 may be recognized at the centers and corners of Fig. 2-5. At the center the nodes at 35, 78, 65, 65, 78 and 35 form a 6-ring as do nodes at 35, 22, 65, 65, 22 and 35.

The 8-rings described in Fig. 2-2a are not fully outlined in Fig. 2-5 and it would be necessary to extend the framework into adjacent unit cells to show them. An 8-ring would be formed by nodes p q r′ s′ t′ u′ v w. The nodes p q v w are the ones marked in Fig. 2-5. The nodes r′ s′ t′ u′ lie in a unit cell below the one in Fig. 2-5, but are displaced from the nodes r s t u marked in the figure. Projection down c^* is rather confusing: in order to obtain the atomic positions for the next unit cell it is necessary to displace the atomic positions of the starting unit cell by $c \cos \beta$ along the projection of a. In Fig. 2-5, this displacement is roughly equal to that between the nodes q and r′ and between v and u′. The heights of r′ s′ t′ and u′ would be -22, -35, -35 and -22 percentage units of c^*.

The new feature shown in Fig. 2-5 is the 10-ring shaped like a letter T or the cross-section of a mushroom. The only complete mushroom is formed by the nodes a b c r s t u d e f, but extension of the structure to neighboring unit cells will show that each sheet of tetrahedra when seen in projection consists of a tessellation comprised entirely of mushrooms.

In conclusion to this section, it is perhaps desirable to point out the implicit danger of dissecting the aluminosilicate framework into chains and sheets. Although the feldspar structure is anisotropic, the most fundamental feature about it is the three-dimensional linkage. Comparison of feldspar with mica will clearly emphasize the difference between a framework and a sheet structure.

2.2 General Features of Feldspar Structures

The different distributions of the T atoms over the tetrahedral nodes, and the geometrical changes caused by interaction of the M cations with the alumino-silicate framework, makes it necessary to use a detailed nomenclature.

Taylor (1933) arbitrarily assigned the codes A 1 and A 2 to oxygen atoms lying in special positions on a two-fold rotation axis or a mirror plane, re-spectively. The three oxygens in general positions were arbitrarily labelled B, C and D as given in Table 2-1. Taylor labelled the tetrahedral nodes Si_1 and Si_2, but these are now labelled T_1 and T_2. I have labelled the large cation with M. Laves (1960) used the symbols A and B instead of the T_2 and T_1 used here, but this nomenclature should be dropped because most feldspar workers have adopted the T nomenclature.

Table 2-2 lists the chemical compositions, approximate cell dimensions, space group, topochemical symmetry, tetrahedral order and nature of M cation position for the principal structures of end-member compositions. In using Table 2-2, it must be remembered that the cell dimensions vary with chemical substitution in the end-member composition. Two of the structures, primitive-anorthite and celsian, have c-repeats of about 1.43 nm which is double that of other feldspars: this results from Al_2Si_2 ordering as described later.

The term *topologic symmetry* describes the symmetry of the aluminosilicate framework when idealized into its most regular shape by movements which leave intact the topologic relationships between nodes. Interatomic angles can change during the movements, but not contacts between first neighbors. The term *topochemical* symmetry is used to describe the symmetry of the idealized frame-work when the chemical occupancy of the nodes is considered. The topo-chemical and topologic symmetries must be identical for a fully-disordered chemical distribution, but for an ordered distribution the topochemical symmetry may be lower than or equal to the topologic symmetry. This distinction between topologic and topochemical symmetry was proposed by P. B. Moore in Smith and Ribbe (1969). Earlier Laves (1960, p. 271) had used topologic symmetry for the symmetry of a framework when angular distortions are removed, and his term corresponds to topochemical symmetry as used here. All feldspars have topologic symmetry C 2/m according to the new usage, but the topochemical symmetry is either C 2/m, C $\bar{1}$ or I 2/c for the various types of feldspars.

The doubling of the c-repeat in celsian and anorthite, and the changes in the space group symmetry, make it necessary to use a code to specify the relation of atoms in the complex structures to their corresponding prototypes in the simplest structure – that of sanidine. The prototype was arbitrarily chosen as in Table 2-1. The code devised by Megaw (1956) adds four symbols in brackets after the label of the prototype. The symbols are 0 for no operation, m for a mirror plane at

Table 2-2. General features of feldspar structures

(a) *The types of simple feldspar structures observed at room temperature*

Name	End-member composition	Nanometers			Degrees			Space group	Topochemical symmetry of framework	Tetrahedral order	M-cation positions
		a	b	c	α	β	γ				
Sanidine	$KAlSi_3O_8$	0.860	1.303	0.718	90	116.0	90	$C\,2/m$	$C\,2/m$	Disordered	One: near-spherical
Microcline	$KAlSi_3O_8$	0.859	1.297	0.722	90.6	115.9	87.7	$C\,\bar{1}$	$C\,\bar{1}$	Ordered	One: near-spherical
High albite	$NaAlSi_3O_8$	0.816	1.287	0.711	93.5	116.4	90.3	$C\,\bar{1}$	$C\,2/m$	Disordered	One: irregular
Low albite	$NaAlSi_3O_8$	0.814	1.279	0.716	94.3	116.6	87.7	$C\,\bar{1}$	$C\,\bar{1}$	Ordered	One: distorted
P-anorthite	$CaAl_2Si_2O_8$	0.818	1.288	1.417	93.2	115.8	91.2	$P\,\bar{1}$	$I\,2/c$	Ordered	Four: near-spherical
Celsian	$BaAl_2Si_2O_8$	0.864	1.305	1.440	90	115.1	90	$I\,2/c$	$I\,2/c$	Ordered	One: near-spherical
Reedmergnerite	$NaBSi_3O_8$	0.783	1.236	0.680	93.3	116.4	92.1	$C\,\bar{1}$	$C\,\bar{1}$	Ordered	One: spherical
Buddingtonite	$NH_4AlSi_3O_8\,1/2H_2O$	0.880	1.302	0.718	90	116.1	90	$P\,2_1/m$ or $P\,2_1$	$C\,2/m$	Disordered	One: distorted

(b) *Complex feldspar structures*

Orthoclase — a K-rich feldspar with properties similar to those for sanidine, except for partial tetrahedral order. The nature of the ordering and the true symmetry are controversial.

Adularia — K-feldspars with the adularia habit may exist in infinite ways between the extremes of sanidine and maximum microcline. Some show extra diffuse diffractions which violate C lattice symmetry.

Transitional anorthite — a Ca-rich feldspar whose sharp diffractions obey the space group $I\bar{1}$ but whose diffuse diffractions (type c) require the symmetry $P\bar{1}$ of P-anorthite.

I-anorthite — a Ca-rich feldspar for which the diffuse diffractions of transitional anorthite are not observed.

Intermediate Plagioclase — Ca, Na feldspars showing pairs of extra diffractions (type e) in non-integral positions symmetrically about the type b positions appropriate for I-anorthite. The positions change with composition.

$y=0$, c for a center of symmetry at $(0, 0, 0)$, i for either the C face-centering operation or the I body-centering operation depending on the lattice type of the feldspar, z to show for feldspars with a 1.4 nm c-repeat an atom displaced nearly 0.7 nm along the c-axis from the prototype atom. The symbols are arbitrarily placed in the order m z i c; any unused operation is denoted by the zero operator. Because prototype sites M, O_{A1} and O_{A2} lie in special positions on the mirror plane, the symbol m is redundant for them. For M the first symbol may be 0 or be omitted; for O_{A1} and O_{A2} the first symbol is taken as 1 or 2 to denote the type of oxygen atom. Sometimes the symbols may be shortened. Because there are two possible origins in a cell with a 1.4 nm c-repeat, the convention is to choose the origin such that $z_1 < 0.5$ and $z_1 > z_2$ for M cations at (x_1, y_1, z_1) and $(x_2, y_2, \frac{1}{2} + z_2)$. All unnecessary symbols are omitted here if no confusion ensues.

Note that use of a symbol such as m does not mean that there is a true symmetry element: in sanidine and celsian, the symbols do specify true symmetry, but in all other feldspars the symbols denote only pseudo-symmetry.

Also in Table 2-2 are brief descriptions of some complex feldspar structures.

The principal factors governing the feldspar structures are:

a) The Al and Si atoms may be ordered or disordered among the T sites. This important conclusion was not proved until completion of the careful X-ray studies at Cambridge under the direction of W. H. Taylor (Cole et al., 1949; Bailey and Taylor, 1955); however the suggestion by Barth (1934) that the polymorphism of potassium feldspars results from order-disorder of the Al and Si atoms was so compelling that it became accepted by many scientists before "direct" proof was obtained. Completely disordered feldspars have a topochemically monoclinic framework with c 0.7 nm. There are two distinct types of T ordering: in ordered Al_2Si_2 feldspars, the atoms alternate producing a pattern with a 1.4 nm c-repeat and monoclinic topochemical symmetry I 2/c; in ordered $AlSi_3$ feldspars, half of the T_1 sites are occupied by Al to yield a pattern with c 0.7 nm and triclinic topochemical symmetry C $\bar{1}$ (Fig. 2-6).

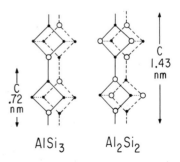

Fig. 2-6. Perspective drawings of the $AlSi_3$ and Al_2Si_2 types of perfect Al, Si order in a feldspar framework. The Al and Si atoms are shown respectively by open and filled circles on the tetrahedral nodes. The location of the nodes may be identified by comparison with Fig. 2-4b. The linkages shown by the continuous lines correspond to part of the tessellation in Fig. 2-4b. The linkages shown by the dashed lines correspond to reflection in a mirror plane parallel to (010). The dotted lines correspond to the D (or U) linkages. Note that the strict alternation in the Al_2Si_2 pattern enforces a c repeat twice that of the $AlSi_3$ pattern. (After Megaw, 1962, Fig. 1)

It is mathematically impossible to add Al atoms to the $AlSi_3$ pattern to obtain the Al_2Si_2 pattern. Hence there are many structural complexities for intermediate compositions in the plagioclase and K, Ba series with Al, Si ordering.

b) The coordination polyhedra of the M cations are highly irregular in regard to both bond distances and interatomic angles. Figure 2-4a shows in the upper right the nearest neighbors of a K atom in sanidinized orthoclase. The distances to the nearest oxygens are: O_{A2} 0.271; O_{A1} 0.291; O_D 0.295; O_B 0.302 and O_C 0.314 nanometer. Because K and O_{A2} lie on a mirror plane, there is only one $K-O_{A2}$ bond whereas there are two each for the other oxygen types. The $M-O_{A2}$ distance is shorter than the other M–O distances in all feldspars.

The large cations K and Ba have large coordination polyhedra, and the symmetry of the framework is monoclinic unless the Al, Si distribution (as in microcline) causes a distortion to triclinic symmetry. At room temperature, the Na and Ca cations are too small to "fill" the cavities in the aluminosilicate framework, and a puckering occurs with reduction of volume. For Ca, the cavities become near-spherical but are alternately displaced to left and right of positions corresponding to monoclinic symmetry, together with distortions of the framework. The symmetry becomes primitive triclinic though the topochemical symmetry remains monoclinic. Upon heating complex changes occur in geometry and symmetry (Chapter 5). The situation for Na is very complex and depends strongly on the temperature. At high temperature Na acts like the larger ion K. At low temperature, the ordered framework of low albite is already topochemically triclinic, but the additional distortion from the Na cation results in an even greater deviation from monoclinic symmetry than would result from the Al,Si atoms.

c) In addition to the framework distortions which are specific to the individual structure types, there are distortions which are common to all feldspars. These common distortions apparently derive ultimately from the manner in which the bonding is affected by the topology of the framework and the compromises between the spatial requirements of the framework and the M atoms.

Details are given in Chapter 4, but the following general rules are obeyed quite well. The M polyhedra are irregular both in regard to distances and angles. The T–O–T angles tend to depend mainly on the size and only weakly on the charge of the M cation; the O–T–O angles tend to depend more on the charge of the M cation than on other factors; and the T–O distances tend to depend on the Al, Si distribution over the tetrahedral nodes.

d) High temperature causes strong disorder of the T atoms, except for the Al_2Si_2 feldspars which probably remain strongly ordered at all temperatures; it increases the effective size of the M cation; and it tends to make the framework more regular geometrically. Applied pressure ultimately converts the feldspar structure to a denser polymorph, or to a combination of structures whose average packing is denser.

All feldspars have been assumed to be strictly centrosymmetric by crystallographers and by thermochemists. The most detailed evidence for this is afforded by statistical analysis of X-ray diffraction intensities by Bailey et al. (1951), and by Srinivasan and Ribbe (1965). The statistical procedures consist of comparing the observed distribution of diffraction intensities with a probability distribution calculated theoretically for random distributions of atoms obeying either a center of symmetry or lacking such a control. The basic theory is highly technical, especially for structures showing pseudosymmetry and other types of correlation between atomic positions. Readers are referred to Srinivasan and Ribbe (1965) for details. Here it is sufficient to report that all X-ray diffraction data for feldspars are consistent with a center of symmetry, but that local deviations from a center of symmetry (as in domain structures or disordered atomic distributions) could not be tested by the method.

All physical evidence in the literature is consistent with a center of symmetry, except for a single report of a pyro-electric effect in adularia (Hankel, 1877 quoted by Taylor, 1933). In spite of the overwhelming evidence for centro-symmetry, it is possible that small deviations such as those caused by the difference between Al and Si could be overlooked; a feldspar following a non-equilibrium path of ordering, such as is thought to occur in some adularias, is more likely to lack a center than those with equilibrium order. Further measurements of pyro-electricity (and piezo-electricity) are desirable, especially for adularia and plagioclase.

The crystal-structural studies of feldspar were carried out during a period of vigorous theoretical and technical development. Earlier studies were mostly made by two-dimensional methods using hand calculations or rudimentary machine computations: they suffer from uncertainties caused by peak overlap and by incomplete iteration of the Fourier series. Later studies have corrected the earlier deficiencies and provided new data for further structure types. As far as possible, I have ignored the earlier work and described only the later results: unfortunately it is necessary to discuss briefly some of the earlier less-accurate work because various models or hypotheses were developed therefrom. Future improvements of accuracy can be expected to improve bond lengths by a rather small amount (say 0.001 nm) but should yield much improvement in estimates of atomic displacements ascribed to thermal motion and to chemical substitutions.

2.3 Pseudo Close-packing of Atoms: Pseudo-symmetry

Interpretation of actual crystal structures in terms of models of close-packing is a fascinating exercise in pure mathematics that provides both a philosophic and a practical basis for the study of chemical bonding. Brunner (1971) reviewed the ideas of close packing that date back to the sixteenth century. He pointed out that there is an alternative view to the conventional use of hard spheres packed together with the largest coordination number. This unconventional view considers merely the centers of the objects irrespective of their size and shape. The concept of close-packing of such objects is therefore transformed into the more abstract concept of placing points in a limited volume such that repelling neighbors have the largest possible separations while the frequency distribution of the distances between the points tends towards a certain pattern. I have not seen a rigorous mathematical definition and analysis of the problem, but naively it seems that all close-packed patterns should tend to yield frequency distributions with narrow peaks related by special ratios (for example in the well-known hexa-gonal and cubic close-packing the peaks are infinitely narrow and related by simple values different from those of a body-centered pattern). An abstract concept of close-packing allows the NaCl structure to be described as the inter-penetration of cubic close-packed patterns of Na and Cl atoms. More complex patterns are possible, including interpenetrations of hexagonal close-packing with cubic close-packing. (Readers unfamiliar with conventional concepts of close-packing will find discussions in most books on crystal structure such as Wells (1962): see Bragg and Claringbull (1965) for detailed application to minerals.)

The conventional concepts of close-packing of spheres are of limited value in study of feldspars, but Brunner (1969) considered successfully the feldspar structure as a compromise between the interpenetration of T atoms in hexagonal close-packing (hcp) and oxygen atoms in cubic close-packing (ccp).

Earlier, Fedorow and Niggli had supposed that all crystals are essentially either cubic or hexagonal simply because symmetry is beautiful. Hence feldspars had been considered from the viewpoint of pseudo-cubic geometry by morpho-logical crystallographers (Fedorow, 1897a, b, 1902, 1903a, b; Beckenkamp, 1919; Niggli, 1926) as summarized by Burri et al. (1967). Such a pseudo-cubic description permits an elegant survey of the twin laws (Burri, 1962: see Chapter 18).

Figure $17-32$ shows the faces of a crystal of anorthite drawn by Burri to mimic a truncated rhombic dodecahedron. In the pseudo-cubic description, the a-axis of the feldspar becomes a tetrad rotation axis, and the c-axis a triad axis. To obtain the cubic axes a', b', c', the feldspar axes can be transformed by the vector equations:

$$a' = a - b + 2c ; \quad b' = a + b + 2c ; \quad c' = -2a .$$

Transformations of face and zone symbols are given by Burri et al. An albite (Krebs, 1921) with axial elements

$$a : b : c = 0.6352 : 1 : 0.5548 ; \quad \alpha\,94°15', \ \beta\,116°36', \ \gamma\,87°46'$$

yields the pseudocubic elements

$$a' : b' : c' = 1.0629 : 1 : 0.9218 ; \quad \alpha\,93°15', \ \beta\,93°46', \ \gamma\,89°33' .$$

Brunner (1969 and personal communication in 1971) considers just the T and O atoms of feldspars thereby yielding a structure of type AB_2. He finds that the T and O atoms can be related respectively to the familiar concepts of hexagonal and of cubic close-packing.

The first step of the mathematical analysis considers the possible ways in which the hcp lattice can be related to the ccp lattice by homogeneous deformation. Figure 2-7a shows the particular relationship pertinent to feldspars. Nine unit cells of cubic symmetry are shown enclosing the distorted hexagonal cell. The extent of the distortion can be seen from the stippled triangles which would be truly equilateral in the hexagonal cell but have sides $\sqrt{3} : \sqrt{3} : 2$ in the distorted cell. The vertical axis is perpendicular to the base plane even for the distorted cell, and the angular deformation is entirely in the base plane of the hexagonal

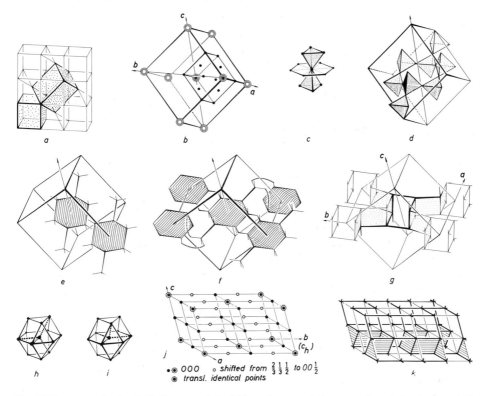

Fig. 2-7. Interpretation by G. O. Brunner of the feldspar framework in terms of an abstract concept of close-packing. a One of the possible relations between cubic and near-hexagonal unit cells. b—g Interpretation of feldspar framework in terms of oxygen atoms in pseudo cubic close-packing. h—k Interpretation of feldspar framework in terms of T atoms in pseudo hexagonal close-packing. From unpublished manuscript of talk by G. O. Brunner at 1968 meeting of Sektion F. Kristallkunde of the Deutsche Min. Ges. at Bern. (Figs. I-IX; 2-II, IV-VI, VIII-X; 3-II, III, V, VI)

cell. The axial ratio c/a would be 1.633 for the undistorted hexagonal cell using the body-diagonal of the cubic cell as the a-axis of the hexagonal cell. Furthermore, there are two points for the face-centered cubic unit cell of ccp per one point for the hexagonal unit cell of hcp. Therefore this geometrical relationship would be suitable for attempting to explain the O atoms of feldspars in terms of ccp and T atoms in terms of hcp.

The next step explains the configuration of the O atoms in feldspar as shown by the sequence of diagrams Fig. 2-7b–g. Diagram b shows a large cubic cell composed of eight smaller F-centered cells of which one is shown. The positions of the axes of the equivalent feldspar structure are shown: a is parallel to a cube edge, b to a face diagonal, and c to a body diagonal, hence this large cell is identical with the Fedorow pseudocubic cell. In ccp, each point is related to the twelve first neighbors as in diagram c. In framework silicates like feldspar, the oxygen atoms lie at the apices of tetrahedra whose corners are shared in pairs to form the framework. If preservation of tetrahedral shape and maximum conservation of symmetry are taken as the criteria, the best way to achieve such a linkage from ideal ccp is given in diagram c. The central point joins two sets of three points to form the dumb-bell group. The remaining six points are not joined. Consequently, they must be shifted to longer distances in one of the next steps and this is one of the reasons for the distortions to be described later on. Of course, to produce a framework the dumb-bell group must form further linkages. Reduction of the coordination number from 12 to 6 for all points of the distorted ccp yields two interpenetrating frameworks of linked tetrahedra (two diamond structures, if the tetrahedral centers are compared with C in diamond) that have no connection with each other. Each framework may be decomposed into building blocks of six tetrahedra in a ring plus two attached tetrahedra as shown in diagram d. Diagram e shows two building blocks of the framework, one at a corner and one at the body center of the cubic cell. For brevity, tetrahedral centers are shown now by the intersection of the lines, while diagram e shows the cell enlarged relative to the size of the building block. This increase in cell volume causes the six non-bonded points of diagram c to be moved away from the dumb-bell group. When comparing e to d, note the rotation of the cell to avoid overlap of the six-rings, which are shown by hatching.

Diagram f shows how the building blocks may be linked together after rotation and distortion of the 6-rings, either by relatively minor changes (linked lines) or major changes (dotted lines). Diagram g shows the completed framework linked together in the manner described earlier in this chapter. Two of the double crankshafts are shown by the stippling oriented along the a-axis. One of the linking 6-rings is shown by the heavy lines. Geometrically, very large distortions are required in the transformation from the nodes of the ccp structure first to the oxygens and then to the tetrahedral nodes of the feldspar structure, but topologically the transformation is quite simple.

The transformation in diagrams b–g was based on oxygens though the final description was given with tetrahedral nodes. The diagrams h–k account for the arrangement of the T-atoms and show how the tetrahedral nodes can be derived directly from the nodes of hcp. Diagrams h and i show the twelve first neighbors in hcp plus two ways in which four of these can be selected to provide a tetrahedral linkage. The feldspar framework cannot be derived from just one of these ways, and diagrams j and k show how it is derived from an equal mixture of the two ways. In hexagonal close-packing, the points lie at $0\,0\,0$ and $2/3\,1/3\,1/2$. Diagram j shows a hexagonal supercell with double a and c in which the points at $2/3\,1/3\,1/2$ have been shifted to $0\,0\,1/2$ (open circles) thereby giving the impression of a superstructure. Diagram k shows how the points in diagram j can be linked together (heavy lines) to give the tetrahedral linkage of the feldspar structure. The orientations of the feldspar axes equivalent to the hexagonal axes are given in diagram j. Double crankshafts parallel to feldspar a can be seen in diagram k.

To complete his analysis, Brunner compared the cell dimensions of feldspar with the two different sets to be expected from the geometrical analogy of the oxygens to ccp and of the T atoms to hcp. He found that the dimensions of natural feldspars tended to lie about half-way between the two calculated values.

Readers are cautioned that Brunner's elegant analysis is topologic in nature. Oxygen atoms in feldspar are not close-packed in the sense of the packing in spinel, and the chemical bonding is different. Indeed feldspar must be regarded as a structure with medium density of packing as is evinced by the transformation of feldspars to other structure types as the pressure increases. The detailed translational coordinates of the O and T atoms of feldspars deviate by around 0.1 nm from the ideal coordinates required by Brunner's topologic analysis. Such deviations are unavoidable because for chemical reasons the coordination number must be reduced from 12 to 4 and 6, respectively, for the T and O atoms. Nevertheless Brunner's analysis shows that the feldspar structure type is the "best solution" to deriving a tetrahedral framework from the simple patterns of ccp and hcp. The topologic analysis emphasizes the 6-rings which are a relict from ccp while permitting the occurrence of 4-rings which are "bad" from the viewpoint of close-packing. Thus one might regard the dominance of feldspar on the Earth's surface as the result of this successful development of its framework from the ideal concepts of close-packing. Certainly Brunner's study of feldspar shows that topologic analysis in terms of abstract concepts of close-packing has great potential for classification of structures, and even greater aesthetic and intellectual value as a branch of pure mathematics.

I am indebted to G. O. Brunner for providing a detailed description of his analysis plus figures.

2.4 Structures of Related Minerals

2.4.1 Minerals with Double Crankshafts

Section 2.1.2 shows how the double-crankshaft chain of the feldspar structure may be linked together in different ways (Fig. 2-2).

The structure of paracelsian, a polymorph of celsian $BaAl_2Si_2O_8$, was determined by Smith (1953) and improved by Bakakin and Belov (1961) who showed that there is a regular alternation of Al and Si on the tetrahedral nodes. Paracelsian is isostructural with danburite $CaB_2Si_2O_8$ (Dunbar and Machatschki, 1930; new refinement, Craig et al., 1973) and hurlbutite $CaBe_2P_2O_8$ (Bakakin and Belov, 1959; Bakakin et al., 1959). In hurlbutite, the Be and P atoms alternate on the tetrahedral nodes resulting in P 2_1/a symmetry as in paracelsian. In danburite, the B atoms occur in pairs alternating with Si atoms thereby resulting in true Pnam symmetry in contrast to the pseudo symmetry Pnam of the others.

Paracelsian has $a \sin \beta$ 0.9076, b 0.9583, $c \sin \beta$ 0.8578 nm, β 90 ± 0.5°, P 2_1/a, $Z = 4$; n_α 1.570, n_β 1.582, n_γ 1.587, $2V - 50°$ (Na light); G 3.29 − 3.31; {110} cleavage; simple {100} and lamellar {201} twins; colorless to white (Spencer, 1942; Smith, 1953).

The structural details of paracelsian are obscure because of the pseudo-symmetry. For the averaged structure with pseudo space group Pnam, the Ba atom has seven near oxygens at about 0.28 nm and two more at 0.33. Deviations up to 0.01 nm can be expected in the true structure as a result of the difference in Si–O and Al–O distances.

Chao (1958) in an unpublished Ph. D. thesis determined the crystal structure of the paracelsian form of $KAlGe_3O_8$ (a 0.9422, b 0.9832, c 0.8703 nm; G 3.34;

n_α 1.5835, n_β 1.5877, n_γ 1.5917, $2V - 88°$, $a = X$, $b = Z$, $c = Y$). No significant evidence was found for symmetry lower than Pnam, nor for ordering of the Al and Ge atoms. The atomic coordinates are:

K 0.100, 0.417, 0.250; Ge,Al(1) 0.225, 0.083, 0.065; Ge,Al(2) 0.435, 0.303, 0.565; O(1) 0.077, 0.192, 0.067; O(2) 0.313, 0.420, 0.492; O(3) 0.355, 0.142, 0.563; O(4) 0.290, 0.055, 0.250; O(5) 0.493, 0.343, 0.750. The tetrahedral distances are essentially regular with mean values of 0.1755 and 0.1752 nm from Ge,Al(1) and (2) to the oxygens. The intra-tetrahedral angles range from 102.7 to 113.4° with mean values of 109.1 and 109.2°. The intertetrahedral angles range from 126.9 to 134.6° with a mean of 130.2°. The K atom has oxygen neighbors at 0.274 (two), 0.293 (two), 0.278 (two) and 0.293 (one). No estimates of accuracy were given.

Long (1966) synthesized materials thought to have paracelsian structure type for compositions $KAlGe_3O_8$ and $KGaGe_3O_8$. No detailed structural data are available, but the cell dimensions are consistent with a paracelsian structure type modified for larger ions in the framework. Pentinghaus (1970) independently synthesized the same phases from glasses held at 550° C and 1 kbar for 6 days. From least squares refinement from Guinier powder patterns, he obtained more accurate cell dimensions: $KAlGe_3O_8$ (a 0.94401, b 0.98303, c 0.87088) and $KGaGe_3O_8$ (a 0.94916, b 0.98926, c 0.87205), all ± 5 to 7 parts in the fifth place. Pentinghaus (pers. comm. in 1971) also synthesized paracelsian structure types from $CaGa_2Si_2O_8$, $SrGa_2Si_2O_8$ and $SrGa_2Ge_2O_8$. These gave monoclinic, pseudo-orthorhombic geometry from X-ray powder data. For $SrGa_2Ge_2O_8$, the cell dimensions are: a 0.8587, b 0.9637, c 0.9217 nm, β 90.43°, V 0.7628 × 10^{-27} cubic meters.

The other naturally-occurring minerals with double-crankshaft chains are zeolites: gismondine $CaAl_2Si_2O_8 \cdot 4H_2O$ (Fischer, 1963); and the isostructural harmotome $BaAl_2Si_2O_{16} \cdot 6H_2O$ (Sadanaga et al., 1961) and phillipsite (Ca, Na, K)$_x$ $(Al, Si)_8O_{16} \cdot \sim 6H_2O$ (Steinfink, 1962).

The mineral banalsite, $BaNa_2Al_4Si_4O_{16}$ (Campbell Smith et al., 1944) has not been investigated structurally, but its cell dimensions and symmetry suggest that it may have some structural feature in common with either feldspar or the above minerals: see Deer et al. (1963, Vol. 4, p. 168). The body-centered ortho-rhombic cell (a 0.850, b 0.997, c 2 × 0.836 nm) has only weak diffractions showing the doubled c repeat and the I symmetry, possibly the result of Al, Si alternation and disorder of Ba and Na atoms. A pseudo-monoclinic cell with axes [100], [021] and [0$\bar{2}$1] has dimensions a' 0.850, b' 1.30, c' 1.30 nm, α 100°, β 90° which compare with a' 0.858, b' 1.32, c' 1.32, α 93.6°, β 90° for the pseudo-cell of para-celsian with axes [100], [011] and [0$\bar{1}$1] and with a 0.863, b 1.30, c 1.33, α 90°, β 99° for the pseudo-cell of celsian with axes [100], [010] and [102].

2.4.2 Hollandite Structure Type

Ringwood et al. (1967) converted synthetic sanidine $KAlSi_3O_8$ at 120 kbar and 900° C into a fibrous material whose X-ray powder pattern definitely indicated a hollandite structure type. The tetragonal unit cell, a 0.938, b 0.274 ± 0.001 nm, I 4/m, was assigned 2 K at 0 0 1/2; 8($Al_{0.25}Si_{0.75}$) at 0.167, 0.384, 0; 8 oxygens

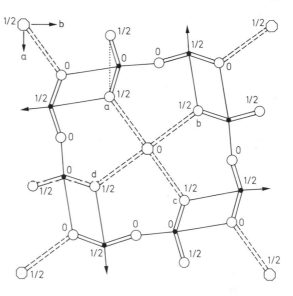

Fig. 2-8. The crystal structure of the hollandite form of KAlSi$_3$O$_8$ as given by Ringwood *et al.* (1967). The projection is down the tetragonal *c*-axis. The Si, Al atoms (solid dots) are each coordinated to two oxygens (open circle) at the same height (single line) and two pairs of oxygens at different heights (double line). Each K atom (octagon) is bonded to four pairs of oxygens (broken lines). One set of shared edges of the octahedra is shown by a dotted line: such sharing results in columns of octahedra. The coordination polyhedron around each K atom is a flattened cube. The polyhedra share square faces (e.g. from oxygens labelled abcd) to form columns. One unit cell is shown, and the heights are given in fractions

at 0.208, 0.152, 0; 8 oxygens at 0.152, 0.542, 0 (fractional coordinates). Basically the hollandite structure (Fig. 2-8) consists of an expanded rutile type of structure with small metal atoms each coordinated by six oxygens. The oxygen octahedra share edges to form columns lying along the *c*-axis; the columns are cross-linked by sharing of apices. The expansion in the *ab* plane provides tunnels along *c* occupied by the large metal atoms.

Unfortunately the crystal structure was not refined accurately, especially because of overlap between hkl and khl diffractions, and the metal-oxygen distances may be uncertain to 0.02 nm. The listed coordinates yield mean (Al,Si)-O distances of 0.18 nm, but it is not possible to judge whether the octahedron is really as distorted as implied by the coordinates of Ringwood *et al.* The K atom has eight oxygen neighbors in a distorted cube at 0.28 nm and four more at 0.33 nm. The powder X-ray data imply disorder of the Al and Si atoms, but single-crystal electron diffraction data should be taken to test for a possible superstructure.

Whatever the details of the hollandite structure of KAlSi$_3$O$_8$, the important feature is the enormous increase of specific gravity (3.84 from 2.55) produced by the inversion from the sanidine structure. Some of this increase results from change of coordination of the Al, Si atoms from 4 to 6, but some results from the more efficient packing of oxygens around the K atoms and some from the large number of shared edges of the octahedra, and from the shared faces of the distorted cubes.

Other chemical analogs of the hollandite structure are $KAlGe_3O_8$ (a 0.972, b 0.286; Kume et al., 1966); $RbAlGe_3O_8$ (0.978, 0.286) and $NaAlGe_3O_8$ (0.9648, 0.2856), both by Reid and Ringwood (1969). In addition, "defect" varieties with vacant sites in the tunnels were synthesized by Reid and Ringwood at high pressure: $Ba_xAl_{2x}Si_{4-2x}O_8$ (0.9415, 0.272) and the Sr-equivalent (0.932, 0.272). Refinement of the structures from the powder X-ray data was quite uncertain, but Reid and Ringwood found improved agreement for x between 0.7 and 0.75 for the Ba-form. The starting compositions for both the Ba and Sr varieties had $x = 1$, and disproportion to the hollandite structure plus a less siliceous phase was the interpretation. This experimental result is reasonable because the centers of the distorted cubes are only 0.28 nm apart: whereas monovalent cations like K should undergo only moderate repulsion, divalent cations such as Ba and Sr should be severely affected thus favoring vacant sites.

At high pressures, Na- and Ca-Al,Si feldspars have not been observed to form the hollandite structure. Instead they disproportion into other phases (Chapter 24). It is obvious that there is considerable scope for further studies on the stability and crystal structures of hollandite structures of feldspar composition, and of as yet unidentified phases made at high pressures (e.g. Reid and Ringwood).

2.4.3 The Hexagonal Structures

In addition to celsian and paracelsian, $BaAl_2Si_2O_8$ yields an hexagonal structure that is similar but not identical to the hexagonal variety of $CaAl_2Si_2O_8$.

The hexagonal form of $BaAl_2Si_2O_8$ inverts near $300°$ C from the high-temperature form with strict hexagonal symmetry to the low-temperature form with pseudo-hexagonal symmetry, perhaps orthorhombic. The basic structure was determined by Ito (1950) and thoroughly characterized by Takéuchi (1958). Tetrahedra share three corners to yield an hexagonal sheet with the remaining apices pointing in the same direction. Pairs of sheets share apices to yield a sandwich. The Ba atoms are bonded to oxygens from two sandwiches thereby providing structural continuity. Because the Ba–O bonds are weaker than the T–O bonds, the structure has a perfect basal cleavage.

Takéuchi found true hexagonal symmetry with a 0.531, c 0.781 nm at $450°$ C. At room temperature, the X-ray photographs were interpreted in terms of twinning of an orthorhombic cell with a 0.529, b 0.917, c 2×0.779. Structural analysis was made on the basis of the hexagonal pseudo-cell, yielding average coordinates in $P\,6/mmm$ of: Ba 0 0 0; Al,Si 1/3 2/3 0.288; O(1) 1/3 2/3 0.5; O(2) 0.450 0 0.209. The ellipticity of the electron density peaks indicated deformation of the hexagonal structure upon passing through the reversible transition. The diffractions with l odd were weak, and might result either from the deformation or from undetected Si,Al order. In the averaged structure, the Ba atom has 6 near oxygens at 0.289 nm and 6 further away at 0.334. It is convenient to use the terms high-and low-hexagonal $BaAl_2Si_2O_8$ to distinguish these structure types from celsian and paracelsian.

The hexagonal variety of $CaAl_2Si_2O_8$ has an even greater rotation of the sheets to permit adjustment to the smaller Ca atom (Takéuchi and Donnay, 1959). No inversion was found by Davis and Tuttle (1952) upon heating in a differential-thermal-apparatus up to 1200° C. The crinkling of the sheets can occur either clockwise or anticlockwise with respect to choice of a particular origin. Takéuchi and Donnay explained diffuseness of hk. l reflexions with l odd as the result of stacking errors between the sheets. Ideally the crinkling alternates …ABABA… in accord with the space group P 6_3/mcm producing a trigonal antiprism of oxygens around each calcium. A mistake in which two A's (or two B's) are adjacent produces a trigonal prism. Such a mistake cannot occur for high-hexagonal $BaAl_2Si_2O_8$ because there is no crinkling to distinguish A from B. Domains of perfect stacking in hexagonal $CaAl_2Si_2O_8$ and low-hexagonal $BaAl_2Si_2O_8$ linked by a mistake can be described as twins, analogous to Dauphiné twins in quartz. The crystallographic data are: a 0.5110, c 1.473 nm; n_o 1.585, n_e 1.590. The platy morphology and perfect {0001} cleavage result from the weak bonding between the aluminosilicate sheets. The atomic coordinates are: Ca 0 0 0; Si,Al 1/3 2/3 0.1375; O(1) 1/3 2/3 1/4; O(2) 0.370, 0, 0.100. Each calcium atom has six near oxygens at 0.239 nm forming a trigonal antiprism. No experimental evidence was given for order of the Si,Al atoms, but regular alternation would be expected.

Long (1966) synthesized at high pressures from compositions $KAlGe_3O_8$, $KGaGe_3O_8$ and $KFeGe_3O_8$ materials whose X-ray powder patterns indicated a common crystal structure. The d-spacings were consistent with hexagonal geometry with cell dimensions for the three compositions: a 0.790, c 0.691; 0.797, 0.696; 0.799, 0.699 nm. Such indexing of powder patterns in the absence of single crystal data is notoriously uncertain. However it seems reasonably certain that these materials do not have a structure like that of hollandite or of hexagonal $BaAl_2Si_2O_8$ and $CaAl_2Si_2O_8$.

2.4.4 Orthorhombic $CaAl_2Si_2O_8$

The orthorhombic form of $CaAl_2Si_2O_8$ (Davis and Tuttle, 1952) gave a powder pattern indexable on an orthorhombic cell with a 0.822, b 0.861, c 0.484 nm. Single crystal data showed that the space group is $P 2_1 2_1 2$ with a pseudo-absence for (h + k) odd in hkl. No structure analysis has appeared. The refractive indices are n_α 1.553, n_β 1.580 and n_γ 1.584. The morphology is equant and no cleavages were seen.

Pentinghaus (pers. comm., 1971) synthesized hydrothermally from $NaAlGe_3O_8$ a material whose cell dimensions (a 0.8428, b 0.8901, c 0.4955 nm) indicate isotypy with orthorhombic $CaAl_2Si_2O_8$.

References

Bailey, S. W., Ferguson, R. B., Taylor, W. H. (1951): X-ray determination of centrosymmetry in three felspars. MM **29**, 759–764.

Bailey, S. W., Taylor, W. H. (1955): The structure of a triclinic potassium felspar. AC **8**, 621–632.

Bakakin, V. V., Belov, N. V. (1959): Crystal structure of hurlbutite. DAN **125**, 383 385. In Russian.

Bakakin, V. V., Belov, N. V. (1961): Crystal structure of paracelsian. Kristallografiya **5**, 864–868. In Russian.

Bakakin, V. V., Kravchenko, V. B., Belov, N. V. (1959): Crystal structures of danburite, $CaB_2Si_2O_8$, and hurlbutite, $CaBe_2P_2O_8$. DAN **129**, 420–423. In Russian.

Barth, T. F. W. (1934): Polymorphic phenomena and crystal structure. AJS Ser. 5, **27**, 273–286.

Beckenkamp, J. (1919): Leitfaden der Kristallographie. Berlin: Bornträger.

Bragg, W. L., Claringbull, G. F. (1965): The crystalline state, Vol. IV. Crystal structures of minerals. Ithaca: Cornell University Press.

Brunner, G. O. (1969): Abstr. in ZK **128**, 435 of paper presented at the Tenth Diskussionstagung der Sektion F. Kristallkunde der Deutsche Min. Ges., Bern, Switzerland.

Brunner, G. O. (1971): An unconventional view of the "closest sphere packings". AC A **27**, 388–390.

Burri, C. (1962): A survey of feldspar twinning. NGT **42**, No. 2, 193–206.

Burri, C., Parker, R. L., Wenk, E. (1967): Die optische Orientierung der Plagioklase-Unterlagen und Diagramme zur Plagioklasbestimmung nach der Drehtisch-methode, 334 pp. Basel and Stuttgart: Birkhauser Verlag.

Campbell Smith, W., Bannister, F. A., Hey, M. H. (1944): Banalsite, a new barium-felspar from Wales. MM **27**, 33–46.

Chao, G. Y.-C. (1958): The crystal structure of orthorhombic $KAlGe_3O_8$. Ph. D. thesis, University of Chicago.

Cole, W. F., Sörum, H., Kennard, O. (1949): The crystal structures of orthoclase and sanidinized orthoclase. AC **2**, 280–287.

Craig, J. R., Louisnathan, S. J., Gibbs, G. V. (1973): Al/Si order in paracelsian. Trans. Amer. Geophys. Union **54**, 497 (Abs.).

Davis, G. L., Tuttle, O. F. (1952): Two new crystalline phases of the anorthite composition $CaO.Al_2O_3.-2SiO_2$. AJS, Bowen Vol., 107–114.

Deer, W. A., Howie, R. A., Zussman, J. (1963): Rock forming minerals. 4. Framework silicates, 435 pp. London: Longmans, Green and Co., Ltd.

Dunbar, C., Machatschki, F. (1930): Structure of danburite, $CaB_2Si_2O_8$. ZK **76**, 133–146.

Fedorow, E. von (1897a): Beitrag zur Syngonielehre. ZK **28**, 36–38.

Fedorow, E. von (1897b): Versuch einer Theorie der Thermodynamik der Krystalle. ZK **28**, 483–501.

Fedorow, E. von (1902): Beiträge zur zonalen Krystallographie. V. Complicationsgesetz und richtige Aufstellung der Krystalle. ZK **35**, 25–74.

Fedorow, E. von (1903a): Über die Anwendung des Dreispitzzirkels für Krystallographische Zwecke. ZK **37**, 138–142.

Fedorow, E. von (1903b): Zonale Kristallographie und Theorie der Krystallstruktur. ZK **37**, 22–49.

Fischer, K. (1963): The crystal structure determination of the zeolite gismondite, $CaAl_2Si_2O_8.4H_2O$. AM **48**, 664–672.

Ito, T. (1950): X-ray studies on polymorphism. Tokyo: Maruzen Co. Ltd.

Krebs, B. (1921): Der Albit von Rischuna in morphologischer Bedeutung. ZK **56**, 386–407.

Kume, S., Matsumoto, T., Koizumi, M. (1966): Dense form of germanate orthoclase ($KAlGe_3O_8$). JGR **71**, 4999–5000.

Laves, F. (1960): Al/Si-Verteilungen, Phasen-Transformationen und Namen der Alkalifeldspäte. ZK **113**, 265–296.

Long, R. S. (1966): The stability of feldspar structures containing Ga, Fe and Ge under conditions of high pressure. Ph. D. thesis, Univ. Chicago, 113 p.

Machatschki, F. (1928): The structure and constitution of feldspars. Centr. Min. Abt. A, 97–104.

Megaw, H. D. (1956): Notation for felspar structures. AC **9**, 56–60.

Megaw, H. D. (1962): Order and disorder in felspars. NGT **42**, No. 2, 104–137.

Megaw, H. D. (1970): Structural relationship between coesite and felspar. AC B **26**, 261–265.

Niggli, P. (1926): Lehrbuch der Mineralogie II (Spezielle Mineralogie). Berlin.

Pentinghaus, H. (1970): Der Einbau von Al (III), Ga (III), Fe (III) und Si (IV), Ge (IV) in synthetische Alkalifeldspäte. Inaug.-Diss. der Westfälischen Wilhelms-Universität in Münster.

Reid, A. F., Ringwood, A. E. (1969): Six-coordinate silicon: high pressure strontium and barium aluminosilicates with the hollandite structure. J. Solid State Chemistry **1**, 6–9.

Ribbe, P. H. (1963): A refinement of the crystal structure of sanidinized orthoclase. AC **16**, 426–427.

Ringwood, A. E., Reid, A. F., Wadsley, A. D. (1967): High pressure $KAlSi_3O_8$, an aluminosilicate with sixfold coordination. AC **23**, 1093–1095.

Sadanaga, R., Marumo, F., Takéuchi, Y. (1961): The crystal structure of harmotome, $Ba_2Al_4Si_{12}O_{32} \cdot 12H_2O$. AC **14**, 1153–1163.

Schiebold, E. (1927): Über den Feinbau der Feldspate. FMKP **12**, 78–82.

Schiebold, E. (1928): Über den Feinbau der Feldspate. ZK **66**, 488–493.

Schiebold, E. (1929a): Über den Feinbau der Feldspate. Trans. Faraday Soc. **25**, 316–320.

Schiebold, E. (1929b): Über den Feinbau der Feldspate. Centr. Min. Abt. A, 378–386.

Schiebold, E. (1929c): Kristallstruktur der Feldspate. FMKP **14**, 62–68.

Schiebold, E. (1930): Über den Feinbau der Feldspate. ZK **73**, 90–95.

Schiebold, E. (1931): Über die Isomorphie der Feldspatmineralien. NJMA **64**, 251–319.

Smith, J. V. (1953): The crystal structure of paracelsian, $BaAl_2Si_2O_8$. AC **6**, 613–620.

Smith, J. V. (1968): Further discussion of framework structures built from four- and eight-membered rings. MM **36**, 640–642.

Smith, J. V. (1970): Physical properties of order-disorder structures with especial reference to feldspar minerals. Lithos **3**, 145–160.

Smith, J. V., Ribbe, P. H. (1969): Atomic movements in plagioclase feldspars: kinetic interpretation. CMP **21**, 157–202.

Smith, J. V., Rinaldi, F. (1962): Framework structures formed from parallel four- and eight-membered rings. MM **33**, 202–212.

Spencer, L. J. (1942): Barium-felspars (celsian and paracelsian) from Wales. MM **26**, 231–245.

Srinivasan, R., Ribbe, P. H. (1965): Some statistical investigations of feldspar structures. ZK **121**, 21–35.

Steinfink, H. (1962): The crystal structure of the zeolite, phillipsite. AC **15**, 644–652.

Takéuchi, Y. (1958): A detailed investigation of the structure of hexagonal $BaAl_2Si_2O_8$ with reference to its α-β inversion. Mineral. J. (Japan) **2**, 311–332.

Takéuchi, Y., Donnay, G. (1959): The crystal structure of hexagonal $CaAl_2Si_2O_8$. AC **12**, 465–470.

Taylor, W. H. (1933): The structure of sanidine and other felspars. ZK **85**, 425–442.

Taylor, W. H., Darbyshire, J. A., Strunz, H. (1934): An X-ray investigation of the felspars. ZK **87**, 464–498.

Wells, A. F. (1962): Structural inorganic chemistry. 3rd edition. Oxford: University Press.

Zoltai, T., Buerger, M. J. (1959): The crystal structure of coesite, the dense high-pressure form of silica. ZK **111**, 129–141.

Chapter 3 Order-disorder

3.1 Mathematical and Crystallographic Bases of Ordering

The early scientific measurements of ordering, and the development of mathematical theory, were made on binary alloys. The simple crystal structures and the fairly rapid attainment of thermodynamic equilibrium permitted detailed understanding of order-disorder. The most comprehensive treatments of the phenomenon are in "The Theory of Transformations in Metals and Alloys" by Christian (1965) and "The Theory of Order-Disorder in Alloys" by Krivoglaz and Smirnov (1965).

Although some alloys show rather complex order-disorder reactions, feldspars present even more complicated and hence more interesting phenomena. The extra complications result from (a) the low symmetry of and multiplicity of atomic sites in the crystal structure (b) charge linkage between ions occupying different sites (c) sluggishness of atomic migration resulting in extensive development of metastable atomic configurations. In consequence, the theoretical description and the nomenclature must be more complex, though the essential ideas and terms developed for alloys can be adapted.

The present account draws heavily on ideas by Barth (1934, 1959, 1969 plus many other papers), Goldsmith and Laves (1954), Laves (1950, 1952, 1960), Megaw (1959, 1960, 1962), Smith and MacKenzie (1961), and Thompson (1969, 1970). However there are some differences in approach and in nomenclature that would make it advisable for a reader to consult the original papers if he wished to obtain a full understanding of the ideas of other workers. A general account of my recent views is given in Smith (1970). Particularly controversial in 1973 was the importance of short-range order in relation to physical properties of feldspars.

Megaw (1960, p. 59) distinguished between *unit-cell* and *lattice disorder*. In the former (Megaw, 1959), atoms may be slightly displaced from mathematically-regular positions (described as *positional disorder*), or atoms of more than one chemical species may occupy the same type of crystallographic site (described as *substitutional disorder*). In Fig. 3-1b, the crystallographic lattice is shown by the grid, and the atoms are displaced erratically from the lattice nodes. In Fig. 3-1a, there are three types of atoms: those represented by dots lie exactly on a lattice and are fully ordered. The second lattice has its nodes occupied by two types of atoms shown by large and small circles.

For lattice disorder, the structure is split up into regions; each region has the same atomic pattern and is related to each adjacent region by a fault which operates on the boundary. The simplest type of fault consists of a fractional translation of a lattice repeat unit (not necessarily a cell edge) relating the structure on the two sides of a planar boundary (Fig. 3-1c). The geometrical

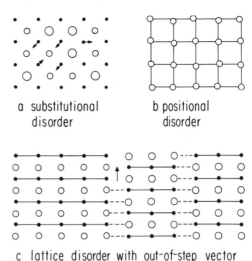

a substitutional
disorder

b positional
disorder

Fig. 3-1. Three types of disorder described by
Megaw (1959, 1960)

c lattice disorder with out-of-step vector

relation at the boundary between two blocks of structure may be expressed by
an *out-of-step vector*.

Three types of positional disorder can be envisaged: (a) atomic displacements
caused by thermal motion about a node which itself strictly obeys the lattice
symmetry, (b) atomic displacements caused by substitutional disorder (e.g. the
large circular atoms in Fig. 3-1a might be expected to displace the point atoms
in the directions of the arrows), (c) occupancy of two or more closely-spaced minima of potential energy either on a time or space basis (e.g. there might be two
energy minima, one to the left and one to the right, between which an atom
jumped). Thermal motion is always present, and need not be specifically
mentioned. Nor need the second type be mentioned specifically under the
category of positional disorder, because automatically the mention of substitutional disorder implies the existence of positional disorder. In consequence, the
term positional disorder can be used to imply just the third type unless the
wider sense is deliberately stated.

In feldspars there are several types of substitutional disorder. In alkali feldspars, there is only one crystallographically-distinct M site and this may be
occupied by Na or K (and by minor amounts of other atoms). In contrast
the T atoms may occupy two crystallographically-distinct sites in monoclinic
alkali feldspars (the T_1 and T_2 sites) and four sites in the triclinic varieties: therefore, complex relations may exist between the substitutional disorder among the
sites. In plagioclase feldspars, the situation is even more complex because there
is a charge-balance relation, $Si + Na \rightleftharpoons Al + Ca$, between atoms in M and T
sites.

With falling temperature, substitutional disorder becomes unstable, and a
solid solution proceeds either towards a single ordered structure with two or
more symmetry-equivalent sites each occupied by its own atom type, or
towards a mechanical mixture of two or more phases each with its own ordered
pattern. A key feature is whether dissimilar atoms tend to occur as neighbors.

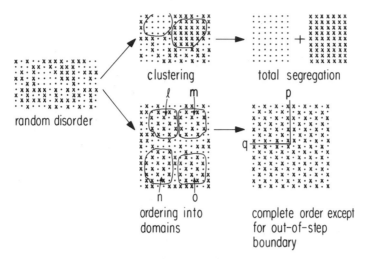

Fig. 3-2. The two paths for elimination of disorder from a structure with one type of site and two types of atoms (dots and crosses)

Consider for clarity a simple binary compound with two chemical species B and C. Ordering of an initially-disordered configuration can proceed in two ways (Fig. 3-2): (a) atoms of type B may prefer B atoms as neighbors, and similarly for C atoms, resulting first in *clustering* and ultimately in separation of phases B and C, (b) atoms of type B may prefer C atoms as neighbors resulting in maintenance of a single phase but with development of an ordered structure with a large unique unit. Non-stoichiometric bulk compositions would go to a mixture of two ordered structures.

The complications that can occur with clustering and segregation into two phases are described in Chapter 19. Here it is sufficient to state that the initial clusters are strongly influenced by each other, and that complex intergrowths can develop that may persist indefinitely without crystallization into separate phases. Such intergrowths may consist of alternating slabs of the two phases whose properties are governed by a *coherent spinodal curve* in a phase diagram.

Ordered structures are described by a complex jargon. In simple binary alloys of high symmetry, e.g. CuAu, it is easy to give mathematical meaning to the terms *short-range order* and *long-range order*.

Consider two sets of crystallographically-equivalent sites labelled p and q with fractional frequency N_A and N_B occupied only by A and B atoms in the fully ordered state. For complete disorder all the sites would be occupied statistically by N_A atoms of A type and N_B atoms of B type. Let r_p be the probability that p sites are occupied correctly by A atoms in a partly ordered structure. The *long-range order coefficient S* is defined as $\dfrac{r_p - N_A}{1 - N_A}$. For complete disorder, $r_p = N_A$ and $S = 0$. For complete order, $r_p = 1$ and $S = 1$. S is called the long-range order coefficient because of the deliberate assumption that the probability r_p is taken over all p sites. The definition automatically normalizes S from 0 to 1 between the extremes of disordered and ordered states, and this kind of normalization has been followed for all order coefficients by deliberate choice of the formulae.

The *short-range order coefficient* σ was developed by Bethe to express the correlation of occupancy of neighboring sites. Consider nearest neighbors in a simple pattern with alternation of sites. The short-range order coefficient for first neighbors can be defined as $(P_a - P_d)/(P_o - P_d)$ where P_a, P_o and P_d are the correlations between first neighbors actually observed (*a*) and calculated theoretically for full order (*o*) and full disorder (*d*). The correlations are taken over all pairs of atoms in the structure. Short-range order coefficients can be calculated for second, third and increasingly higher neighbors.

Megaw in a discussion to a paper by Smith and MacKenzie (1961) suggested that the terms long-range and short-range order should not be applied to feldspars because the details of Si, Al ordering were not known well enough. In this treatise the terms *local* and *distant order* are used in a general sense to emphasize the imprecision of our knowledge of feldspar ordering.

The concept of an *out-of-step domain boundary* is best seen by following the process of ordering in the lower half of Fig. 3-2. At an intermediate stage, four domains with perfect alternation of atoms have grown in a matrix which is still disordered. The domains labelled m, n and o can merge into one domain, whereas the domain labelled l cannot merge except by a complete switch of occupancy of all the A and B atoms on its sites. The sites can be envisaged as being numbered. Only when domains nucleate with A atoms on sites with like parity can they merge when they come into contact. Domains of unlike parity develop an *out-of-step domain boundary* with the other type of domain. The older name *anti-phase boundary* implies the same phenomenon, but the concept of out-of-step is more accurate than that of anti-phase for patterns more complex than the one shown here.

The examples of Fig. 3-2 are too simple in several ways. It is not necessary for domains to have perfect order. Strain occurs at out-of-step boundaries. Most natural materials do not have a composition ratio which is a simple fraction, thereby resulting in some residual disorder in the domains.

However there are more subtle complications. The concept of short-range order can be applied quite simply to both the ordered and disordered patterns of Fig. 3-2, but the concept of long-range order cannot because the site labelling changes parity over each out-of-step boundary. One solution is to calculate long-range order only inside each domain, to ignore the walls and to apply the necessary parity change when summing the contributions from all the domains. But suppose that the domains are so small and rudimentary that the boundaries cannot be delineated clearly: obviously, the long-range order must be calculated for the entire pattern and will tend to be zero unless the rudimentary domains tend to have the same parity. The short-range order coefficients could be large even when the long-range order coefficient is small.

The most subtle complication of all is the implicit assumption in Fig. 3-2 and in the above description that for random disorder there is only one type of symmetry-equivalent site. Actually there may be two or more lattice sites that are topologically different as in Fig. 3-3. At all temperatures there will be a site preference, and the parity problem does not occur. Ordering consists of increasingly effective segregation into the preferred sites, as explained in the figure

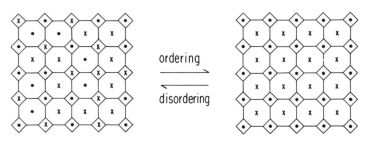

Fig. 3-3. Disordered and ordered configurations for a structure with two types of sites (centers of squares and octagons) and two types of atoms (dots and crosses). In the ordered pattern (right), crosses occupy only the octagons and the dots only the squares. In the disordered pattern, there is still a small tendency for crosses to prefer octagons and dots to prefer squares. Note by comparison with Fig. 3-2 that there is no parity problem leading to out-of-step boundaries

legend. In feldspar, there are two tetrahedral sites for the monoclinic sanidine and four for the triclinic high albite. The T_1 and T_2 sites in sanidine, and the T_10, T_1m, T_20 and T_2m sites of high albite, have different chemical environments and the sites therefore are labelled. As the Si, Al atoms rearrange themselves during the ordering of triclinic high albite, there is no stage at which domains of unlike parity can grow so long as the albite crystallized with triclinic symmetry; hence there is a distinction between the 0 and m sub-sites. In monoclinic sanidine, the T_1 and T_2 sites are labelled but not the 0 and m subsites. As soon as ordering occurs preferentially into the T_10 site of microcline, there is a four-fold choice of T_10 from the T_1 sites of sanidine: hence domains with out-of-step boundaries develop. When sufficiently coarse they can be recognized optically as the cross-hatched twinning of microcline.

The disordering process depends on whether the fully-disordered material has one or more topologically distinct sites for the disordered atoms. For multiple sites, one of the sites is favored for occupancy by one of the atomic species at all temperatures. Hence disorder never becomes completely random, though increasing temperature will favor disorder. For a single site, there should be some critical temperature at which long-range disorder becomes complete, although short-range order remains finite. A detailed discussion of the temperature variation is given in Chapter 21. Thompson (1969) used the terms *convergent* and *non-convergent* to distinguish the single-site from the multiple-site situation.

Even with all sites labelled, there are complexities. Consider for simplicity just two labelled sites p and q, and consider a specific lattice vector linking them. The short-range order coefficient for neighbors linked by that vector can be taken over the entire structure. There are four possible occupancies of each pair of sites

        (1) A in p and B in q

        (2) A in p and A in q

        (3) B in p and A in q

        (4) B in p and B in q .

Suppose case (1) is the correct occupancy for the fully ordered distribution. Case (3) could be called an *anti-ordered* configuration, while (2) and (4) could be called *neutral* configurations. For each distribution, the probability can be obtained over the entire structure viz. $P(1)$, $P(2)$, $P(3)$ and $P(4)$. For a completely random distribution $P(1) = x_A x_B$, $P(2) = x_A x_A$, $P(3) = x_A x_B$ and $P(4) = x_B x_B$ where x_A and x_B are mole fractions of atoms A and B. For a completely ordered distribution, $P(1) = 1$, $P(2) = P(3) = P(4) = 0$. For a partly ordered distribution with a particular value of $P(1)$, the distribution of the remaining probability between $P(2)$, $P(3)$ and $P(4)$ is not unique, though only one particular distribution can be thermodynamically stable.

Obviously in feldspars it is dangerous to talk blithely about a *coefficient of order*. If all feldspars were at thermodynamic equilibrium for some particular temperature, the coefficient of order would be unique. However many feldspars are not in equilibrium, and the Si, Al ordering is not a unique function of some measured physical property such as a cell dimension. Hence it is necessary to be absolutely clear about the degree of uncertainty implied in any statement in the literature about ordering. Such an understanding can come only from a thorough study of the theoretical and practical aspects of experimental techniques.

So far the discussion of order-disorder has implicitly assumed that the atomic sites do not change xyz coordinates as the occupants change. Actually both the xyz coordinates and the cell dimensions change during ordering transformations. This brings up the concepts of *cooperation* and *symmetry constraint*. The segregation of Al into the $T_1 0$ sites of microcline results in a change of symmetry from monoclinic for the sanidine precursor to triclinic for the microcline. Crudely speaking, when an Al atom occupies a $T_1 0$ site it tends to distort the neighboring crystal structure to favor the movement of Al atoms into the $T_1 0$ site of neighboring unit cells. This cooperative feature encourages the formation of domains which grow outwards from a nucleus with the "correct" ordering pattern. When there is a change of symmetry during the ordering process (as for the sanidine-microcline transition), domains can nucleate independently with different parity. When domains of unlike parity meet, there is a symmetry constraint on their further development, as described earlier in the section dealing with out-of-step domain boundaries. In addition, atoms in the boundary region are influenced by atoms in domains with opposite parities. In the middle of the boundary region, the influences cancel out leading to atomic coordinates similar to those for the high-symmetry disordered structure. Moving away from the boundary, the atoms increasingly approach the coordinates of the isolated low-symmetry structure.

McConnell (1970) in a Hallimond lecture to the Mineralogical Society of London reviewed the application of symmetry constraints to phase transformations with particular reference to feldspars. This lecture brings together nicely the theoretical basis of symmetry constraints and the interpretation of observations made by electron and X-ray techniques.

Finally the terms *superlattice* and *superstructure* must be explained. The lower right diagram of Fig. 3-2 has a unit cell twice as large in volume as the unit cell would have for a similar pattern with no distinction between dot and cross. In most literature, the structure is described as a superlattice. However many crystallographers claim that this is a misuse of the term lattice, and the word superstructure is used here. The superstructure in Fig. 3-2 is completely regular and is quite simple. The term superstructure will also be applied to more complex patterns, including ones in which the pattern is ordered only on a statistical basis.

Added in Proof. Anderson (1973) described infinitively adaptive structures which provide an alternative to a mixture of simple ordered phases for the ordering of a non-integral disordered material.

3.2 Experimental Techniques for Determination of Si, Al Order in Feldspars

This section largely follows the treatment of Smith (1970).

X-ray Diffraction. X-ray diffraction involves vector summation of the amplitude scattering of the incoming beam by the orbital electrons. In a perfect crystal structure, transformation of the observed intensity data into electron density maps is theoretically straightforward (see Lipson and Cochran, 1953; Buerger, 1960).

The most obvious way to distinguish Si and Al atoms is to count the number of electrons for each atom because the former apparently should have 14 and the latter 13. Actually the situation is complicated by chemical bonding because completely ionic bonding should result in Si^{4+} and Al^{3+} ions each with 10 orbital electrons: furthermore there is the problem of selecting the volume over which electrons are counted. In practice, the best procedure is to make least-squares adjustment of the atomic scattering factors using only the larger diffraction angles. This procedure reduces the complication of chemical bonding because it favors electron density close to the atomic center and tends to measure the effect of the nuclear charge on the inner orbital electrons. For details readers are referred to Fischer (1965) and Fischer and Zehme (1967). By 1973, the method had not been explored up to its limit: improvement in the accuracy of intensity measurements probably would lead to a 2-fold increase of precision in the electron density counts. In 1971, the best data perhaps might correspond to detection of 20 steps between Si and Al end-members.

The second way to distinguish Si and Al atoms by diffraction methods is from the mean T–O distance of the oxygen tetrahedron. Chao *et al.* (1940) applied the technique to orthoclase but the data were later shown to be inconclusive because of incomplete data. By 1973, experimental techniques had improved to permit experimental accuracy of about 0.0003 nm in an individual T–O distance. (All errors are estimated as a standard deviation in this Chapter: hence three times the error corresponds to about a 1% statistical probability.) Smith (1954) proposed that Si–O and Al–O distances were respectively near 0.160 and 0.178 nm. These values were refined (Smith and Bailey, 1963; Jones, 1968; Ribbe and Gibbs, 1969), apparently permitting detection of about 50 to 100 steps between Si and Al end-members.

However, there are four problems when attempts are made to quantify Si, Al contents in disordered structures. The first problem is theoretical. There is no basic theory relating interatomic distances of disordered structures to the ratio of chemical species. Of course, the simplest model assumes that the interatomic distance is linearly related to the chemical substitution. Thereby a coefficient of order can be derived from the mean T–O distances of the tetrahedra. Because X-ray diffraction involves vector summation of amplitudes from all related lattice sites, such a coefficient of order should measure the long-range order.

The second problem is both theoretical and practical. Crystals actually consist of a mosaic of blocks, each of which scatters coherently. When X-ray diffractions are sharp, the estimated coefficient of order is a scalar average of the long-range order for each coherent block. When X-ray diffractions are diffuse, it is necessary to consider both the experimental problem of measuring the intensity and the problem of interpreting the meaning of a derived electron density. A detailed theoretical analysis of the distribution of scattering intensity with diffraction angle would permit evaluation of the short-range order coefficients (e.g. Cowley, 1950; Moss, 1964), but there is an extra complication from diffuse scattering caused by thermal vibration. A thorough study of a disordered feldspar over a range of temperatures is badly needed to permit evaluation of the effects of substitutional and thermal disorder. This study should include selected-area electron diffraction analysis of the domain texture. By 1973, such measurements had not been made, and the interpretation of electron density distributions of disordered feldspars is uncertain to an unknown degree. The fundamental theory is covered thoroughly in Krivoglaz (1969).

The third problem involves chemical bonding. Atoms are not rigid spheres, and an interatomic distance depends on the chemical nature and position of atoms other than the two first neighbors. Smith and Bailey (1963), from a review of extensive measurements on many kinds of silicates, concluded that (1) individual T–O distances of the same tetrahedron may differ by up to 0.01 nm under the influence of other structural components, and (2) the mean T–O distance of a tetrahedron decreases as the tetrahedra are polymerized into larger units, the effect being about 0.003 nm from isolated tetrahedra to frameworks (3) additional factors in the mean T–O distance up to a total of about 0.001 to 0.002 might occur but be unrecognized. Subsequently Appleman and Clark (1965) found that the three largest tetrahedra in reedmergnerite had mean T–O distances of 0.1610, 0.1614 and 0.1622 nm, a variation several times larger than the random experimental error. Because these tetrahedra should contain only Si, they suggested that estimates of Al-content from the 0.161 to 0.175 linear relation might be in error by up to 8%.

Obviously the situation will remain unsatisfactory until an interatomic distance can be expressed to an accuracy of (say) 0.0001 nm in terms of quantified structural features such as the polymerization of the tetrahedral framework, the bond angles of the framework, the number and polarizing power of nearby cations and so on. Brown et al. (1969) examined the factors governing the nature and variation in length of the Si–O and Al–O bonds in framework silicates by (a) preparing scatter diagrams of Si–O and Al–O distances against T–O–T bond angles and cation-oxygen distance, and (b) discussing various models for bonding in the light of theoretical expectations and of measurement of X-ray emission spectra. Observed correlation coefficients were found to range from 0.4 to 0.7. Perhaps multiple regression analysis using selected factors will permit development of empirical relationships from which measured T–O distances may be "corrected" to a "standard" structural environment. In 1973, the chemical significance of a measured T–O distance can only be evaluated subjectively, and my own view is that a linear interpolation may be subject to errors of 5% in the Al content.

The fourth problem is of a technical nature. When atoms vibrate or oscillate, the mean interatomic distance between two atoms is actually greater than the distance between the centers of their electron distributions. (Consider one atom rotating about a second atom: for this extreme example, the distance between the centers of the electron distributions is zero.) By 1973, all plots of T–O distances in feldspars ignored this effect thereby assuming that the vibrations were essentially the same in all feldspars. Actually this is not true, but correction factors cannot be applied accurately without knowledge of the extent of coupling of the atomic vibrations. A rough estimate suggests that this effect should not amount to more than 0.0003 nm differential between T–O distances in K-feldspar (highest correction) and anorthite (lowest correction).

In order to use the linear model for chemical interpretation of T–O distances, it is necessary to estimate a reference curve. Because the polymerization factor is known to be important, a reference curve is best derived from data for framework structures especially those with a feldspar framework.

Smith and Bailey (1963) estimated Si–O and Al–O as 0.1606 and 0.1757 from examination of mean tetrahedral distances for about twenty framework structures, but cautioned that the likely error of Al contents deduced from a linear relation between the above distances might be as high as 5% for feldspars and even greater for other structural types.

Jones (1968) reviewed data for 32 structures, omitting reedmergnerite because of the large effect expected from the B atoms. For the feldspar structures, the plot of mean tetrahedral distance versus bulk Al content yielded a correlation coefficient of 0.997 for a linear relation between 0.1603 and 0.1761 nm. Non-feldspar framework structures yielded a weaker correlation coefficient of 0.987 and distances 0.1604 and 0.1759. Distances for individual tetrahedra in anorthite and microcline were consistent with the above values if incomplete ordering and some environmental factors were assumed to occur.

Ribbe and Gibbs (1969) made an extremely thorough statistical analysis, especially of feldspars plus reedmergnerite, concluding that a linear relation excluding reedmergnerite appeared best for estimation of Al–Si feldspars. Because the bulk composition of B-free feldspars ranges only from $Al/(Al + Si) = 0.25$ to 0.5, strictly speaking the values for Si–O and Al–O are extrapolations with increasing uncertainty as the end-members are approached. At the 95% confidence level (i.e. about 2.3 standard deviations), the predicted end-member distances are 0.1605 ± 0.0004 and 0.1757 ± 0.0007 nm assuming a random distribution of errors. Their Fig. 2 shows how an experimental error in measuring the mean T–O distance transforms into an error in estimating the Al-content. For a typical error in T–O of 0.0003 nm, the error in Al-content is about 2% for an intermediate Al/Si ratio to about 3% for a high Al content.

To many readers, this long discussion of the interpretation of Al-contents from T–O distances may seem like counting angels on a pin-head. Actually this is not true because estimates of the configurational entropy are extremely sensitive to errors in Al-content for nearly-ordered feldspars. Thus for low albite, Ribbe and Gibbs calculated that T–O distances indicated 0.8 and 1.8 entropy units for the configurational entropy depending whether the $0.1610 - 0.1749$ or $0.1605 - 0.1757$ relations were used.

Neutron Diffraction. Exploitation of this technique began only in 1971, and data on only three feldspars were available in 1973. Nevertheless it is clear that neutron diffraction should provide more accurate data than X-ray diffraction on Si, Al order. Prewitt (1972) reviewed the basic theory and experimental technique. The difference in scattering factor for Si and Al is constant at 17% for all diffraction angles in contrast to that for X-rays which changes from 4% at low angle to 14% at high angle. Efficient collection of data by neutron diffraction requires a crystal 1 mm^3, considerably bigger than crystals 0.1 mm^3 which can be used in X-ray diffraction. From the scattering amplitudes, it appears that neutron diffraction can yield estimates of Al-content with a standard error of 0.02. In addition the observed T–O distances yield an estimate of Al-content which has the same or slightly better precision than corresponding estimates from X-ray diffraction.

Nuclear Quadrupole Resonance: Infra-red Absorption. These techniques are described in detail in Chapter 11. The nuclear quadrupole resonance spectrum of Al^{27} nuclei permits examination of the electrostatic field gradient around the nucleus. The infra-red absorption spectrum depends on vibrations and oscillations. For both techniques the observed signal is a *scalar* average for all appropriate atoms in the entire specimen of the signal intensity which is a *vectorial* function of the environment of the atoms involved. By 1973, no quantitative attempt had been made to determine the degree of Al, Si order. Qualitatively the difference between ordered and disordered feldspars had been demonstrated very elegantly. A quantitative study would involve analysis of the half-width of the absorption peaks, resulting in problems as severe as those in the X-ray diffraction methods. Not only would Al, Si disorder broaden the signals, but so would substitutional disorder of M cations.

Electron spin resonance and Mössbauer techniques are not applicable to Al and Si atoms: however, they have potential for study of the distribution of transition metals on T sites.

Macroscopic Physical Parameters. All the above techniques are too complex for routine work and some can be applied only to especially favorable crystals. Most measurements of feldspars are optical parameters or cell dimensions. Such macroscopic physical parameters provide very useful implications on the state of Si, Al order in a feldspar, but care must be taken in correlating them with submicroscopic ordering parameters. Smith (1970) claimed that the cell dimensions and optical properties are governed principally by the local Si,Al ordering and that only if there is a unique correlation between local and distant order will there be a strict relation between Al occupancies deduced from electron-density maps and Al occupancies implied by cell dimensions. In particular, a fine-scale domain texture causes complications. For optical data there is an additional problem when a domain texture is finer than the resolution of the optical microscope. In many feldspars there will be a correlation between local and distant order such that cell dimensions and optical properties will correlate with Al-contents deduced from electron density maps, Detailed discussion of the macroscopic physical parameters (especially of the use of the *b* and *c* cell dimensions by Stewart and Ribbe, 1969) is given in Part 2.

3.3 Mathematical Description of Si, Al Order in Feldspars

3.3.1 Algebraic Description of Site Populations and Atomic Order

The mathematical description of Si, Al order in feldspars is complicated because (a) there is an infinite number of ways for a given bulk composition in which Al and Si can be distributed among the T sites, and (b) charge linkage between M and T atoms in plagioclase and K,Ba feldspars results in non-integral compositions.

Figure 3-4 illustrates simply the infinite number of ways in which Al and Si atoms can be distributed in a framework with $AlSi_3$ composition. The horizontal axis shows the Al-content of each tetrahedron, while the vertical axis shows the Al-content of the $T_1 0$ tetrahedron. In the right-hand diagram, the fully-ordered state (with all Al in $T_1 0$) is approached from the fully disordered state by Al moving at an equal rate from $T_1 m$, $T_2 0$ and $T_2 m$ into $T_1 0$. In the left-hand diagram, the Al atoms first segregate into T_1 from T_2 sites preserving monoclinic symmetry by equal occupancy of 0 and m sub-sites. Such an artificial restriction must be violated if all the Al is to end up in the $T_1 0$ site, and the second stage of ordering proceeds with triclinic symmetry as Al moves from $T_1 m$ to $T_1 0$. Obviously there is an infinite number of ordering paths between these extremes, which will be called the *one-step* and *two-step* paths for a feldspar framework with $AlSi_3$ composition. These correspond to the German terms, Direktweg and Umweg, used by Kroll (1971). Theoretically one can envisage the Al atoms ordering into T_2 sites, but natural feldspars do not show this alternative.

The possibility of multiple paths of ordering was first pointed out by Hafner and Laves (1957) and has been reiterated by many later workers (e.g.

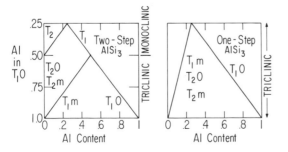

Fig. 3-4. The two-step and one-step ideal ordering trends for an $AlSi_3$ distribution on a feldspar framework. The horizontal axis shows the average fractional occupancy of Al atoms for the four types of sites, while the vertical axis shows the Al occupancy of the $T_1 0$ site. In the two-step trend the topochemical symmetry is monoclinic when there is no difference between the occupancy of 0 and m sub-sites: i.e. for less than 0.5 Al in $T_1 0$. See Fig. 2-5 for the location of tetrahedral nodes

Barth, 1959, 1965, 1969; Smith and MacKenzie, 1961). Barth (1969) presented a tetrahedral diagram with apices corresponding to complete occupancy by Al of $T_1 0$, $T_1 m$, $T_2 0$ or $T_2 m$. Although any point within the tetrahedron represents a possible Al, Si distribution, Barth thought that experimental data were consistent with all alkali feldspars plotting on a plane extending between the coordinates 0.25, 0.25, 0.25, 0.25; 0.50, 0.50, 0.0, 0.0 and 1.0, 0.0, 0.0, 0.0. For $KAlSi_3O_8$ composition, the former is *high sanidine*, the latter is *microcline* and the middle one was called *hypo-orthoclase*. (Hypo-orthoclase corresponds to the *ideal theoretical* concepts of *low sanidine* by Laves, and of *orthoclase* by Smith and Mac-Kenzie: the term *theoretical low sanidine* is used in this treatise as explained in Chapter 9).

Actually the situation is complicated by out-of-step domain textures and by deviation from symmetry C 2/m. Let us follow here, however, the mathematical treatment of Thompson (1969) which implicitly ignores complications from out-of-step textures and assumes C 2/m symmetry for monoclinic feldspars and C Ī symmetry for triclinic ones. The treatment ends with a tetrahedron for $AlSi_3$ order-disorder, which is strictly analogous to that of Barth (1965, 1969) but merely uses different axes. It is convenient here to give the complete formalism which involves the atoms on the M sites as well as those on the T sites.

Consider p unit cells of albite or microcline in C Ī with pairs of atomic sites labelled $T_1 0$, $T_1 m$, $T_2 0$, $T_2 m$, B_0, B_m, C_0, C_m, D_0, D_m and the sites M, A_1 and A_2 which would lie on special positions in a monoclinic cell. Assume that the M site is completely filled with Na, K and Ca atoms, while the T_1 and T_2 sites are filled with Si and Al atoms to give the formula MT_4O_8. Then the formal algebraic procedure of Thompson or simple inspection gives seven equations for p unit cells when the site occupancies and charge balance are considered:

$$n_K = n_{K(M)}$$
$$n_{Ca} = n_{Ca(M)}$$
$$n_{Al} = n_{Al(T10)} + n_{Al(T1m)} + n_{Al(T20)} + n_{Al(T2m)}$$
$$(n_K + n_{Na} + n_{Ca}) = 4p$$
$$(n_{Al} + n_{Si}) - 4(n_K + n_{Na} + n_{Ca}) = 0$$
$$n_O - 8(n_K + n_{Na} + n_{Ca}) = 0$$
$$n_{Al} - (n_K + n_{Na}) - 2n_{Ca} = 0.$$

For monoclinic crystals with no divalent calcium, the equations reduce to five equations, again for p unit cells:

$$n_{Na} = n_{Na(M)}$$
$$n_{Al} = n_{Al(T1)} + n_{Al(T2)}$$
$$(n_{Na} + n_K) = 4p$$
$$(n_{Al} + n_{Si}) - 4(n_{Na} + n_K) = 0$$
$$n_O - 8(n_{Na} + n_K) = 0$$
$$n_{Al} - (n_{Na} + n_K) = 0.$$

In these equations the subscripted quantities n refer to the number of atoms of a chemical species (e.g. n_{Al}) or the number of atoms in a particular site (e.g. $n_{Al(T1)}$). Readers are referred to Thompson's treatment for the development of the algebraic formalism designed to facilitate treatment of chemical reactions within crystals.

For each type of site (e.g. T_2), a site occupancy fraction (N) can be expressed with a double suffix. Because Al atoms in monoclinic (Na, K) feldspar occupy only one-quarter of the T_1 and T_2 sites,

$$1 = 2N_{Al(T1)} + 2N_{Al(T2)}.$$

By defining Z, a long-range ordering parameter as

$$Z \equiv 2(N_{Al(T1)} - N_{Al(T2)}),$$

the following equations were derived by algebraic manipulation:

$$N_{Al(T1)} = \frac{1+Z}{4}; \quad N_{Al(T2)} = \frac{1-Z}{4};$$

$$N_{Si(T1)} = \frac{3-Z}{4}; \quad N_{Si(T2)} = \frac{3+Z}{4}.$$

The validity of these equations is seen graphically from the upper part of the left-hand diagram in Fig. 3-4. When Z is zero, the feldspar is completely disordered with $N_{Al} = 1/4$ for both T_1 and T_2 sites. The maximum value of Z is 1 corresponding to no Al in T_2 and $N_{Al} = 1/2$ in T_1 (i.e. theoretical low sanidine).

For triclinic ternary feldspar, the corresponding equations and definitions are:

$$1 + N_{An} = N_{Al(T10)} + N_{Al(T1m)} + N_{Al(T20)} + N_{Al(T2m)},$$

$$X \equiv N_{Al(T20)} - N_{Al(T2m)},$$

$$Y \equiv N_{Al(T10)} - N_{Al(T1m)},$$

$$Z \equiv N_{Al(T10)} + N_{Al(T1m)} - (N_{Al(T20)} + N_{Al(T2m)}),$$

$$N_{Al(T10)} = \frac{1 + N_{An} + Z + 2Y}{4}; \quad N_{Al(T1m)} = \frac{1 + N_{An} + Z - 2Y}{4};$$

$$N_{Al(T20)} = \frac{1 + N_{An} - Z + 2X}{4}; \quad N_{Al(T2m)} = \frac{1 + N_{An} - Z - 2X}{4};$$

$$N_{Si(T10)} = \frac{3 - N_{An} - Z - 2Y}{4}; \quad N_{Si(T1m)} = \frac{3 - N_{An} - Z + 2Y}{4};$$

$$N_{Si(T20)} = \frac{3 - N_{An} + Z - 2X}{4}; \quad N_{Si(T2m)} = \frac{3 - N_{An} + Z + 2X}{4}.$$

Here $\dfrac{n_{Ca}}{n_K + n_{Na} + n_{Ca}} = N_{Ca(M)} \equiv N_{An}$ is needed because of the charge linkage of Ca with Al as given formally in the first equation. The three ordering parameters X, Y and Z, respectively show the deviation in the Al content of the T_2

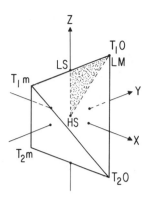

Fig. 3-5. Physically accessible region for $AlSi_3$ feldspars in terms of the Thompson ordering parameters X, Y and Z plotted as coordinates with reference to the three axes. The limiting tetrahedron has apices corresponding to Al completely occupying the labelled site. For alkali feldspars, all experimental data are consistent with the indicated triangle, marked by HS, LS and LM to correspond for K-feldspar to the theoretical extremes for high sanidine, low sanidine and low microcline. (Slightly modified from Thompson, 1969, Fig. 5)

site from monoclinic symmetry, the deviation from monoclinic symmetry of the T_1 site, and finally the amount of Al transferred from the T_2 sites into the T_1 sites. For a completely disordered pattern, all three ordering parameters are zero. For ideal microcline and low albite, Y and Z are both 1 but X is zero.

Figure 3-5 illustrates the theoretical limits on the X, Y and Z ordering parameters for an $AlSi_3$ feldspar with four possible sites T_10, T_1m, T_20 and T_2m. All ordering patterns must lie inside the tetrahedral volume, and all those with monoclinic symmetry must have $X - Y - 0$. The actual situation is much simpler. All experimental data for natural alkali feldspars are consistent with $X = 0$ and with ordering trending to $Y = Z = 1$ from the disordered state with $Y = Z = 0$. Hence in practice it seems necessary to consider only the triangle between 0, 0, 0; 0, 0, 1 and 0, 1, 1. For K-feldspar, these points would correspond to the theoretical end-members for high sanidine, low sanidine and low microcline.

For feldspars with Al/Si greater than 1/3, the accessible region changes shape (Thompson, 1969). The tetrahedron expands because X, Y and Z each have a maximum value of $1 + N_{An}$ (assuming a plagioclase feldspar). However the expanded tetrahedron is truncated at the corners resulting for Al_2Si_2 feldspars in an octahedron bounded by the planes $2 \pm Z \pm 2X = 0$ and $2 \pm Z \pm 2Y = 0$ and limited by vertices at $0, 0, \pm 2$ and $\pm 1, \pm 1, 0$. Actually the ordering pattern in the Al_2Si_2 feldspars, anorthite and celsian, does not correspond to any point in this octahedron because the tetrahedral sites split into a new set based on a unit cell with a double c-repeat (Fig. 2-6). To cover disorder in the anorthite and celsian structures, a different set of ordering parameters would be needed: unfortunately sixteen tetrahedra are involved in primitive anorthite requiring a description in 15-dimensional space.

If the Al-contents of T_20 and T_2m sites in alkali feldspars were always equal, and if the local order correlated exactly with the distant order, two ordering parameters (e.g. the Thompson Y and Z parameters) would be sufficient. At thermodynamic equilibrium, there must be a unique ordering trend for each bulk composition, and a single ordering function suffices so long as comparison is not made between ordering of two or more bulk compositions. Ribbe and Gibbs (1967) and Stewart and Ribbe (1967) used a coefficient of order equal to $(p-0.25)/0.75$ where p is the fractional occupancy of Al in the $T_1 0$ site. This coefficient changes theoretically from 0 for high sanidine to 0.33 for low sanidine to 1 for low microcline. It is important to remember that it does not distinguish between a one-step and a two-step trend with equal occupancy of $T_1 0$ sites and different distributions for the other three sites. The ordering function $S = \sum_{i=1}^{i=4} \dfrac{0.25 - Al_i}{1.50}$ where Al_i is the fractional Al content of the ith tetrahedral site, as defined by Smith and MacKenzie (1961), is ambiguous for that part of the theoretical two-step ordering trend between Al contents of 0.5 and 0.75 in $T_1 0$ sites, and should be abandoned.

3.3.2 Matrix Description of Ordered Phases

Niggli (1967) developed an elegant geometrical and algebraic method to delineate possible ordered patterns for stoichiometric formulae between $AlSi_3$ and Al_2Si_2. Figure 3-6a shows Niggli's description of the topochemistry of the feldspar framework for a unit cell with $c \sim 0.7$ nm. Solid and dashed lines link those tetrahedral nodes of the same unit cell that share oxygen atoms. To complete the framework it would be necessary to use links that pass into adjacent unit cells.

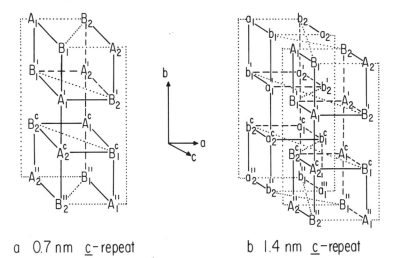

a 0.7 nm c-repeat   b 1.4 nm c-repeat

Fig. 3-6. Schematic diagram showing the linkage of the tetrahedral nodes in the feldspar structure when the c-axis is either 0.7 nm or 1.4 nm long. The continuous and dashed lines show linkages occurring in the same unit cell. The dotted lines show linkages into the next unit cell, but drawn for convenience to a tetrahedral node of the appropriate type in the same unit cell. Table 3-1 shows how the notation transforms into Megaw's scheme for the pattern of (a). In (b), the notation uses small letters for the second half of the unit cell whereas Megaw would use an operator z. (Combined from Niggli, 1967, Figs. 1b and 2)

Table 3-1. Matrix of adjacent tetrahedral nodes for a cell with $c \sim 0.7$ nm

Megaw Code	Niggli Code	A_1	A_2	B_1	B_2	A'_1	A'_2	B'_1	B'_2	A_1^c	A_2^c	B_1^c	B_2^c	A''_1	A''_2	B''_1	B''_2
$T_2(000)$	A_1	○		×	×			×							×		
$T_2(m0c)$	A_2		○	×	×				×					×			
$T_1(m0c)$	B_1	×	×	○	×	×											
$T_1(000)$	B_2	×	×	×	○		×										
$T_2(0ic)$	A'_1			×		○		×	×		×						
$T_2(mi0)$	A'_2				×		○	×	×	×							
$T_1(mi0)$	B'_1	×				×	×	○	×								
$T_1(0ic)$	B'_2		×			×	×	×	○								
$T_2(0i0)$	A_1^c						×			○		×	×			×	
$T_2(mic)$	A_2^c					×					○	×	×				×
$T_1(mic)$	B_1^c									×	×	○	×	×			
$T_1(0i0)$	B_2^c									×	×	×	○		×		
$T_2(00c)$	A''_1		×									×		○		×	×
$T_2(m00)$	A''_2	×											×		○	×	×
$T_1(m00)$	B''_1									×				×	×	○	×
$T_1(00c)$	B''_2										×			×	×	×	○

× denotes adjacent nodes sharing the same oxygen. ○ denotes identical nodes. From Niggli (1967, Table 1).

Niggli's elegant gimmick is to complete such links to the appropriate atom of the same unit cell by means of a loop (shown by dotted lines), thereby reducing the framework topology from an infinite to a finite pattern.

From a crystal-chemical viewpoint, occupancy of adjacent tetrahedral nodes by Al atoms is unfavorable. Hence Niggli drew up a matrix of "forbidden" Al–O–Al contacts (Table 3-1). This table does not provide a unique solution to the topochemistry of a feldspar framework with $AlSi_3$ ratio, but it does provide a mathematical way of determining all possible distributions which have non-adjacent Al atoms for $c \sim 0.7$ nm.

Niggli also prepared a diagram for feldspars with the doubled c-axis that is characteristic of anorthite and celsian (Fig. 3-6b). The notation used by Niggli differs from that proposed by Megaw.

Niggli applied his system to inventing possible ordering schemes for plagioclase, but the system also applied to any solid-solution series between $AlSi_3$ and Al_2Si_2 feldspars. Arbitrarily Niggli considered only the 0.7 nm cell for compositions from $AlSi_3$ to Al_3Si_5 and the 1.4 nm cell for compositions then onwards up to Al_2Si_2.

For albite ($AlSi_3$) there are many possible distributions in the 0.7 nm cell of which two have topochemical symmetry $C\bar{1}$ as had been recognized by DeVore (1955). The observed one, of course, has Al in T_10, while the other one would have Al in T_20. Assignment of Al to T_1m or to T_2m does not provide new ordering schemes because 0 and m can be chosen arbitrarily in the first instance: once the cell axes have been chosen, then 0 and m sites are different.

Ordered distributions can occur only for integral numbers of Al and Si atoms. The first ordered distributions encountered as Al is added in the 0.7 nm cell have compositions An_{25} (Al_5Si_{11}) and An_{50} (Al_6Si_{10}). If 1.4 nm cells were considered, ordered distributions at $An_{12.5}$ (Al_9Si_{23}) and $An_{37.5}$ ($Al_{11}Si_{21}$) would be possible. At An_{25} use of the matrix shows that there are various ordering possibilities, all of which have topochemical symmetry P1 because of the odd number of atoms. None of the possibilities for An_{25} can be derived by adding an Al atom to the pattern for albite: indeed it is not possible to add any Al atoms to the albite pattern without sharing an oxygen atom by two Al atoms. This mathematical conclusion has crucial significance for the phase diagram and the crystal structures of plagioclase.

For An_{50} (Al_6Si_{10}) there are four possible patterns in the 0.7 nm cell with Al occupying the following sites in Megaw notation:

$T_2(000)$, $T_2(0ic)$, $T_2(m0c)$, $T_2(mi0)$, $T_1(mic)$, $T_1(m00)$,

$T_2(000)$, $T_2(0ic)$, $T_2(m0c)$, $T_2(mi0)$, $T_1(0i0)$, $T_1(00c)$,

$T_2(0i0)$, $T_2(00c)$, $T_2(mic)$, $T_2(m00)$, $T_1(m0c)$, $T_1(mi0)$,

$T_2(0i0)$, $T_2(00c)$, $T_2(mic)$, $T_2(m00)$, $T_1(000)$, $T_1(0ic)$.

All four patterns have symmetry P$\bar{1}$ and contain alternating chains of albite and anorthite type, corresponding to a proposal by DeVore (1956).

Ordered structures with additional Al must have a 1.4 nm c-axis. Hence Niggli's implicit assumption in his choice of axial lengths is that the c-axis should have the smallest value that will permit an ordered Al, Si distribution irrespective of the topochemical symmetry. For $An_{62.5}$ and $An_{87.5}$ all the possible configurations have symmetry P1, but for An_{75} and An_{100} the symmetry can be centrosymmetric. For anorthite (Al_2Si_2) there is only one ordering scheme with strict alternation of Al and Si, and Niggli's two complementary patterns are topochemically identical. Incidentally Niggli gives the symmetry as P$\bar{1}$, but it should be I2/c as actually observed for celsian.

Readers are warned that experimental data for plagioclase indicate that these theoretical ordering patterns for intermediate compositions do not appear to occur naturally in plagioclase, and that complex out-of-step structures actually occur (Chapter 5).

3.4 Experimental Data on Si, Al Ordering in $AlSi_3$ Feldspars

3.4.1 Historical

The first attempt to measure Al-content from T–O distances was by Chao et al. (1940) on a non-perthitic "orthoclase" described as specimen C by Spencer (1930, 1937). Optically it was monoclinic with $2V - 44°$. The two-dimensional Fourier analysis was found by Cole et al. (1949) to suffer from enough uncertainties that no valid conclusion could be obtained from the T–O distances. A three-dimensional Fourier refinement of sanidinized Spencer C by Cole et al. showed that the T_1 and T_2 tetrahedra had essentially the same size, consistent with Al,Si disorder. A least-squares refinement of the same intensities by Ribbe (1963a) changed the mean T–O distances by only 0.0003 nm. The conversion to high sanidine was made by heating to 1075° C for 300 hours, followed by cooling to room temperature.

Bailey and Taylor (1955) made a detailed 3D Fourier analysis of Spencer U, a microperthitic specimen with triclinic optics. The specimen is rather variable, but small untwinned cubes were cut from a cross-hatched area with a razor blade. A total of 3875 diffractions were measured from two of the crystals, and the structure was refined by difference Fourier methods. A later least-squares refinement by Bailey (1969) produced small changes. Bailey and Taylor found differences in the mean T–O distances of the four tetrahedra that were large enough to yield definite proof that the polymorphism of sanidine and microcline results from an order-disorder relationship between Si and Al.

Brown (1962) and Brown and Bailey (1964) refined the structure of a microcline with $2V - 82.5°$ from a plutonic rock at Pellotsalo, Finland. The 2341 observed diffractions were refined by 3D least-squares methods yielding evidence of a strong concentration of Al in the $T_1 0$ site. An authigenic microcline with similar optics ($2V - 77°$) taken from the Pontiskalk limestone, Switzerland was refined similarly using only 797 observed diffractions (Finney and Bailey, 1964). The analyzed crystal was cut with a razor blade from a four-ling twin. The T–O distances for the Pontiskalk specimen were consistent within experimental error with those from the Pellotsalo specimen, indicating that cooling from high temperature and direct growth at low temperature yield essentially the same type of order in K-feldspar. Both the T–O distances and the optic axial angles suggest slightly greater order in the Pellotsalo microcline.

Fischer and Zehme (1967) refined the atomic scattering factors of the T sites in the Pellotsalo microcline using the data of Brown and Bailey. Anisotropic refinement using intensities with the lowest residuals yielded Al-contents 1.00, 0.02, -0.02, 0.00 (± 0.03) to be compared with 0.89, 0.06, 0.04 and 0.05 estimated from T–O distances measured by Brown and Bailey. Although the data agreed qualitatively in demonstrating strong segregation of Al into the $T_1 0$ site, the quantitative comparison was disturbing. The T–O distances indicate considerable residual disorder whereas the atomic scattering factors indicate complete order within one standard deviation. Surprisingly, there has been no application of Fischer's technique to other feldspars.

Returning to unheated Spencer C orthoclase from a Burma ruby deposit, Jones and Taylor (1961a, b) found indications of partial order between the monoclinic T_1 and T_2 sites using data from four two-dimensional projections on [100], [010], [001] and [$\bar{1}$10]. The intensity data were later subjected to 3D least-squares analysis by Colville and Ribbe (1968) who reached a similar conclusion.

Colville and Ribbe subjected an adularia from St. Gotthard, Switzerland to a least-squares refinement using 750 diffractions measured in a counter diffractometer. The adularia (Spencer B) shows strong diffuse streaks resulting from formation of out-of-step domains (Figs. 6-7 and 18-18; Section 18.3.2). The diffuse streaks show secondary maxima indicating loss of C face-centering and formation of domains with symmetry P 2_1/a. Because the X-ray refinement by Colville and Ribbe ignored the intensities of the streaks and assumed C 2/m symmetry, only the combined occupancy of 0 and m sub-sites could be obtained for each of the T_1 and T_2 nodes. Certainly the T–O distances provide an underestimate of the degree of order in the centers of the domains, but no quantitative estimate can be given. The Spencer C orthoclase also has diffuse streaks, but they are much weaker than those in the Spencer B adularia. The simplest explanation of the streaks again involves the formation of rudimentary domains in a structure that maintains a statistical monoclinic symmetry.

Phillips and Ribbe (1971, 1973) prepared a thorough X-ray analysis of an adularia from Switzerland, obtaining similar results to those obtained by Colville and Ribbe for Spencer B adularia.

Brown et al. (1973) prepared the first neutron diffraction study of a feldspar, using 805 intensities for a low sanidine from Laacher See, Eifel. The positional coordinates were fully consistent with those obtained by Phillips and Ribbe (1971) by X-ray analysis of another crystal from the same sample. The site occupancy from the neutron diffraction study (0.32 Al in T_1 and 0.18 Si in T_2) is consistent within the standard error 0.02 with the values predicted from the T–O distances (0.29 and 0.18). X-ray study by Weitz (1972) of a natural sanidine before and after heating for 3 weeks at $1000°$ C confirmed earlier studies.

Prince et al. (1972) reported a neutron diffraction study of a K-feldspar described by them as "ordered orthoclase". The specimen has composition determined by an electron microprobe $(K_{0.863}Na_{0.105}Rb_{0.014}) (Al_{0.982}Si_{3.018})O_8$. It occurs as a gem-quality overgrowth on perthite crystals from the hanging wall of a pegmatite dyke at the Himalaya mine in the Mesa Grande district, California. From a crystal $19 mm^3$, 764 independent diffractions were measured assuming space group C 2/m. In thin section, the extinction is uneven; refinement of cell dimensions in the neutron diffractometer gave indications of triclinic geometry; single-crystal X-ray patterns show diffuseness of diffractions which would be split in twinned low microcline. From these data, it seems quite certain that the Himalaya orthoclase is actually a domain-twinned microcline with such strong coherence that the physical properties are pseudo-monoclinic. Refinement of the neutron scattering factors yielded 0.50 Al $(+0.00, -0.02)$ in T_1 and 0 Al in T_2. The mean T–O distances for the T_1 and T_2 sites, 0.1667(1) and 0.1616(1) nm indicate 0.41 and 0.09 Al, respectively, from the $0.1605 - 0.1757$ linear relation. Prince et al. suggested that the reference value for Si–O should actually be 0.1616(1) nm rather than 0.1605, thereby removing the discrepancy between Al-contents estimated from T–O distances and those from neutron scattering factors. This suggestion is consistent with the work of Fischer and Zehme on X-ray scattering factors. Prince et al. claim that the Himalaya specimen is "the first example of an ordered orthoclase, a theoretical end-member not previously thought to occur in nature", and they claim that "This occurrence strongly suggests that ordered orthoclase does have a field of thermo-dynamic stability, close to the pegmatite solidus …". However, their neutron-diffraction analysis automatically gives a monoclinic Al-distribution, and ignores the evidence for triclinic symmetry. Based on the arguments given in Chapter 9 on the polymorphism of K-feldspar, I conclude that the Himalaya specimen is not the same as theoretical low sanidine, and that it is a domain-twinned microcline. Further study of this interesting material is needed, especially by electron-optical methods.

For albite, two-dimensional Fourier analyses by Ferguson et al. (1958) showed T–O distances indicating strong, but not complete, order in a low albite from the Ramona pegmatite and strong disorder in a high albite produced by heating a low albite from the Amelia pegmatite. In order to test the effect of temperature on the environment and position of the Na atom, Williams and Megaw (1964) obtained 2D data for low and high albite at $-180°$ C. Ribbe *et al.* (1969) reported a 3D least-squares refinement using 1994 and 1797 diffractions, respectively, for low and high albite. The resulting T–O distances are considerably more accurate than the earlier data. All these data were obtained by eye-estimation of blackness on a photographic film. New data were obtained with X-ray counter techniques by Wainwright and Starkey (1968) for a metamorphic low albite from Tiburon, California, and for a high albite produced by laboratory heating. Unfortunately these data have not been published in detail, and I am indebted to J. E. Wainwright for data and figures. Both sets of 3D data for low albite indicate strong but not complete ordering of Al into the $T_1 0$ site, when the T–O distances are interpreted from the Ribbe-Gibbs equation.

Harlow *et al.* (1973), from a neutron diffraction study of an Amelia albite, found from the scattering factors that essentially all the Al is in $T_1 0$ whereas the T–O distances indicated some Al in the T_2 sites if the $0.1605 - 0.1757$ linear relation is used. They suggested that there is a non-linear relation between T–O distance and Al content ranging from about 0.1615 nm for Si–O to 0.1745 for Al–O.

An unpublished X-ray analysis of an anorthoclase by S. Quareni and R. De Pieri gave T–O distances consistent with strong disorder.

Appleman and Clark (1965) determined the structure of reedmergnerite, $NaBSi_3O_8$, by least-squares analysis of 4399 intensities measured photometrically from films. Both the crystal-structure data and the absence of any structural change up to the melting point indicate that reedmergnerite has complete order on the T sites. The mean Si–O distances of 0.1610, 0.1614, 0.1622 ± 0.0002 nm were found to be larger than the value of 0.1605 expected for Si–O distances in Al, Si feldspars. This caused Appleman and Clark to question the reliability of an estimate of Al content from a T–O distance.

Gasperin (1971) refined the crystal structure of synthetic $RbAlSi_3O_8$ by X-ray methods obtaining mean T–O distances of 0.1635(3) and 0.1632(4) nm. The indistinguishability of these distances implies Si, Al disorder. Interpretation of the T–O distances on the Ribbe-Gibbs plot suggests 0.19(2) and 0.18(2) Al in the T_1 and T_2 sites, yielding a combined Al-content of 0.75(8) per eight oxygens. This value of 0.75 is about three standard errors from the expected value of unity, thereby casting further doubt on the interpretation of T–O distances in terms of Al-content.

Brunton *et al.* (pers. comm., 1971), from an X-ray analysis of synthetic $RbFeSi_3O_8$, estimated the following contents of Fe atoms assuming Si–O 0.1614 and Fe–O 0.1850 nm: $T_1 0$ 0.49, $T_1 m$ 0.39, $T_2 0$ 0.11 and $T_2 m$ 0.10.

Turning to other techniques, details are given in Chapter 11 of the application of infra-red absorption techniques to alkali feldspars by Laves and Hafner (1956), Hafner and Laves (1957) and Laves and Hafner (1962). The data are consistent with the X-ray diffraction results in showing that low albite and microcline are strongly ordered and that high albite and sanidine are strongly disordered. In addition, the data confirmed the ideas of Laves (1950, 1952) about domain structure in orthoclase and adularia. Similar conclusions were obtained by study of nuclear magnetic resonance by Brun et al. (1960), Hafner et al. (1962), Hafner and Laves (1963) and Hafner and Hartmann (1964).

Chapter 10 describes the electron-optical results of McConnell (1965) and Nissen (1967) who showed that specimens of adularia and orthoclase contain a fine-scale domain intergrowth with strong coherence across boundaries.

The implications of cell dimensions on the Si, Al order in $AlSi_3$ feldspars are described in Chapter 7, and those of the optical parameters in Chapter 8. Although these macroscopic data do not provide direct information on the location of Al and Si atoms, they do provide an almost continuous coverage of all stages of ordering. Particularly important is the interpretation by Stewart and Ribbe (1969) of the cell dimensions in terms of expansion of the $T_1 0$ tetrahedron as ordering proceeds. It is likely that measurements of the b and c cell dimensions provide equally good estimates of changes in Si, Al order as measurements of T–O distances. Of course, their accuracy depends on knowledge of the true Al distribution in the end-members. Interpretation of optical data is less direct, but the observations reported in Chapter 8 suggest that the optic axial angle provides a good estimate of changes of Si, Al order, based on many data, especially those of Spencer (1937).

3.4.2 Detailed Interpretation

Table 3-2 summarizes the better data on the mean T–O distances in $AlSi_3$ feldspars, together with estimates of Al-content obtained from neutron and X-ray scattering factors. Until 1972, Al-contents were estimated from the T–O distances using the Gibbs-Ribbe relation. It is now certain that such estimates indicate erroneous values for the ordered alkali feldspars. After attempting to prepare a new conversion curve, it became obvious that whatever shape was chosen serious problems arise with one or more of the feldspars. Almost certainly there are idiosyncratic features in each feldspar structure which affect the interpretation: thus in low albite it seems likely that some structural factor causes the $T_1 m$ tetrahedron to be smaller than the $T_2 0$ and $T_2 m$ tetrahedra. In desperation, I decided to convert all T–O distances for all feldspars with a single relationship, even though I was aware of the errors thereby introduced. The alternative is to prepare a separate curve for each feldspar, but this is not justifiable until neutron-diffraction data are obtained for each feldspar; then, of course, the need to convert distances to Al-contents would disappear! The chosen universal relation consists of a straight line from 0.1612 for 0.0 Al to 0.1676 nm for 0.5 Al, and a second straight line therefrom to 0.1745 at 1.0 Al. Estimates of Al-content in Table 3-2 are rounded to 0.005. Thompson order coefficients are given in the last three columns.

Figure 3-7a shows Al-contents for K-feldspars plotted horizontally against the Al-content of $T_1 0$, while Fig. 3-7b shows a plot of the Thompson coefficients Y and Z. In Fig. 3-7b, the ideal one-step and two-step trends are shown. The accuracy (as distinct from the precision) is hard to judge for Al-contents deduced from the T–O distances. Probably systematic bias is low for the disordered feldspars, but there may be a bonding effect which is different for T_1 and T_2.

Table 3-2. Mean T–O distances, indicated Al-distributions, and Thompson coefficients in AlSi$_3$ feldspars

Feldspar	Reference	dis-ances (nanometer)				Al-contents				Total Al	Coefficients		
		T_1O	T_1m	T_2O	T_2m	t_1O	t_1m	t_2O	t_2m		X	Y	Z
high sanidine (Spencer C)	Ribbe (1963)	.1645	.1645	.1640	.1640	.26	.26	.22	.22	.96	.00	.00	.08
heated sanidine (Eifel)	Weitz (1972)	.1645	.1645	.1641	.1641	.26	.26	.225	.225	.97	.00	.00	.07
natural sanidine (as above)	do.	.1653	.1653	.1635	.1635	.32	.32	.18	.18	1.00	.00	.00	.28
low sanidine (Eifel 7002)	Brown et al. (1971)	.1650	.1650	.1635	.1635	.295	.295	.18	.18	.95	.00	.00	.23
do.	do.	neutron scattering				.32	.32	.18	.18	1.00	.00	.00	.28
do.	Phillips and Ribbe (1971)	.1649	.1649	.1637	.1637	.29	.29	.195	.195	.97	.00	.00	.19
low sanidine (Spencer C)	Colville and Ribbe (1968)	.1556	.1556	.1628	.1628	.345	.345	.125	.125	.94	.00	.00	.44
adularia (Spencer B)	do.	.1564	.1564	.1622	.1622	.405	.405	.08	.08	.97	.00	.00	.65
adularia (7007)	Phillips and Ribbe (1971)	.1565	.1565	.1621	.1621	.395	.395	.07	.07	.93	.00	.00	.65
domain-twinned microcline	Prince et al. (1972)	.1567	.1567	.1616	.1616	.43	.43	.03	.03	.92	.00	.00	.80
microcline (Himalaya)	do.	neutron scattering				.50	.50	.00	.00	1.00	.00	.00	1.00
int. microcline (Spencer U)	Bailey (1969)	.1694	.1642	.1618	.1616	.63	.235	.045	.03	.94	.015	.395	.79
low microcline (Pellotsalo)	Brown and Bailey (1964)	.1711	.1614	.1611	.1612	.97	.015	-.01	.00	.975	-.01	.955	.975
do.	Fischer and Zehme (1967)	X-ray scattering				1.00	.02	-.02	.00	1.00	-.02	.98	1.04
low microcline (Pontiskalk)	Finney and Bailey (1964)	.1735	.1613	.1619	.1609	.93	.01	.055	-.025	.97	.08	.92	.91
high albite (Amelia)	Ribbe et al. (1969)	.1648	.1644	.1639	.1643	.28	.25	.21	.24	.98	-.03	.03	.08
high albite	Wainwright and Starkey (unpublished)	.1650	.1640	.1641	.1643	.30	.22	.225	.24	.985	-.015	.08	.055
low albite (Ramona)	do.	.1746	.1610	.1615	.1612	1.005	-.015	.025	.00	1.015	.025	1.02	.995
low albite (Tiburon)	Wainwright and Starkey (1968)	.1740	.1609	.1614	.1615	.965	-.025	.015	.025	.98	-.01	.99	.95
low albite (Amelia)	Harlow et al. (1973)	.1743	.1608	.1614	.1615	.985	-.03	.015	.025	.995	-.01	1.015	.915
		neutron scattering				.97	.03	.00	.00	1.00	.00	.94	1.00
reedmergnerite	Appleman and Clark (1965)	.1465	.1610	.1614	.1622	(B)	-.015	+.015	.075	.075	–	–	–
RbAlSi$_3$O$_8$	Gasperin (1971)	.1635	.1635	.1632	.1632	.18	.18	.155	.155	.67	.00	.00	.05

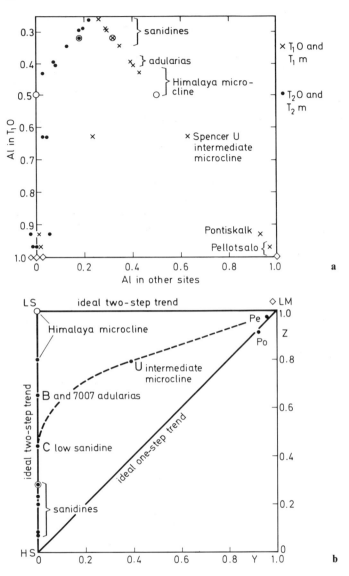

Fig. 3-7. Plots of estimated Al-contents and Thompson ordering coefficients for K-rich feldspars. a Al-contents. The dots and crosses show estimates from the T–O distances while the circles and diamonds show estimates from neutron and X-ray scattering factors, respectively. See Fig. 3-4 for ideal ordering trends. b Thompson coefficients Y and Z. The dots show data estimated from the T–O distances, and the circles and diamonds show estimates from the scattering factors. The three corners marked HS, LS and LM show the extreme positions for high sanidine, low sanidine and low microcline. See Table 3-2 for data

Systematic bias is probably greatest for the ordered feldspars and may be as high as 0.05.

Whatever the uncertainties it is quite clear that in all alkali feldspars Al concentrates into the T_1 sites during ordering, ending up in the T_1O site for both microcline and low albite. In high sanidine and high albite, there is almost complete disorder but the data are consistent with a small residual preference for $T_1 0$.

For K-feldspar, all the evidence apparently indicates that ordering in the measured specimens does not follow the ideal one-step trend, but the details are controversial. At first sight, the data for the Himalaya microcline suggest that it lies on the ideal two-step trend: however this results merely from the way in which the neutron diffraction data were collected. Actually the Himalaya microcline shows distinct evidence of a triclinic domain texture, and the real value of the Y coefficient cannot be zero. Similarly the Spencer B and 7007 adularias show evidence of a domain texture. Optically and by X-rays, the crystal of Spencer U microcline was reported to consist of a single triclinic unit. If this evidence is accepted, at least this specimen lies between the ideal one- and two-step trends. The dashed line in Fig. 3-7b is drawn on the assumption that the adularias really have non-zero Y coefficients, and the line shows one possible ordering trend. Of course, other trends could occur.

Alternatively it might be argued that K-feldspar under equilibrium conditions would follow a one-step trend and that coherency between domains is responsible for the monoclinic symmetry at the early stages of ordering. The diffraction peaks would obey monoclinic symmetry and automatically lead to no distinction between 0 and m sub-sites. On the basis of present experimental data it is impossible to refute this argument for many specimens, but it cannot explain the observations on the Spencer U microcline.

Proponents of a strict, two-step trend might argue that local fluctuations of ordering must occur in any partly-ordered system, and that some of the fluctuations must have imbalance between Al-occupancy of 0 and m sub-sites thereby yielding domains with incipient triclinic symmetry. Such proponents could argue that weak diffuse streaks in sanidine and some orthoclase specimens are consistent with an overall statistical tendency to an initial monoclinic ordering trend. For example, Smith and MacKenzie (1959) suggested that the longer and less intense streaks of orthoclase and low sanidine had a different character than the shorter, stronger streaks of domain-twinned microcline. However, until detailed measurements are made of the diffuse streaks in X-ray patterns, together with electron-optical studies of the domain texture and n.m.r. and infra-red studies of the local environment of the atoms, it is futile to pursue the arguments.

My own current view, based on electron-optical evidence as well as X-ray data, is that a domain texture is so common for K-feldspars from igneous rocks that it either represents a trend of quenched equilibrium or a highly metastable situation. Natural K-feldspars from igneous rocks seem to follow a two-stage trend of ordering, the first stage consisting of Si, Al ordering in a statistically monoclinic framework, and the second consisting of the development of a domain texture coarse enough to reveal triclinic geometry to X-ray and other techniques. In the second stage, the scale of the domain texture, and the degree of coherence, vary greatly leading to a broad range of physical properties. Detailed discussion is given in Chapter 9 on the polymorphism of K-feldspar and the difficulty of developing a reliable nomenclature.

Heating of microcline above 1000° C produces direct conversion to high sanidine without passage through a two-step sequence. Natural K-feldspars grown directly at low temperature (e.g. adularia) have erratic X-ray and optical properties suggesting strong deviations from the two-step igneous trend — see summary by Smith and MacKenzie (1961).

Turning to Na-feldspars, there are no structure analyses for intermediate states of order. However, the interpretation by Stewart and Ribbe (1969) of the cell dimensions of synthetic albites (Chapter 7) shows that they lie on or very close to the ideal one-step trend. Below 980° C, these albites crystallized directly with triclinic symmetry, and migration of Al into the $T_1 0$ site took place directly without development of a domain texture as in K-feldspars. Almost certainly, future structure analyses will confirm the Stewart-Ribbe interpretation.

To conclude this discussion of ordering in $AlSi_3$ feldspars, it should be emphasized that diagrams such as those in Fig. 3-7 provide absolutely no information on the way in which ordering varies with temperature. Such diagrams merely describe the correlation between the Al-contents at the tetrahedral nodes. The data on the temperature variation of Al, Si ordering, and the thermodynamic nature of the ordering and disordering transformations are described in Chapters 24 and 25.

3.5 Experimental Data on Si, Al Ordering in More Aluminous Feldspars

3.5.1 Historical

Taylor et al. (1934) discovered that anorthite yields extra weak X-ray diffractions indicating that the true c-repeat is 1.42 nm, twice that of the alkali feldspars. However, they incorrectly suggested that the doubling results from modification of the oxygen framework by the calcium atoms. Chao and Taylor (1940) correctly outlined the complexities of the X-ray diffraction patterns of the intermediate plagioclases, and many later workers filled in the experimental details (see summary by Gay, 1962). The interpretation is so complex that a special treatment is given in Chapter 5.

Goldsmith and Laves at a meeting in 1951 (but not published till 1955) proposed that for feldspars with an Al_2Si_2 framework the best electrostatic charge distribution resulted from alternation of Al and Si on the tetrahedral nodes (as in Fig. 2-6). Qualitative examination of X-ray intensities for synthetic Ga- and Ge-substituted synthetic anorthites supported this structural proposal.

Simultaneously, Sörum (1951, 1953) was carrying out crystal structure analyses of calcic plagioclases, but the first complete determination of the anorthite structure was obtained much later by Kempster et al. (1962) and Megaw et al. (1962). This tour de force showed that T–O distances were indeed consistent with alternating Al and Si atoms, and that the topochemical symmetry of the framework was I 2/c when distortions caused by framework crumpling were removed. In the meantime, Newnham and Megaw (1960) had shown that celsian, $BaAl_2Si_2O_8$, had the same pattern of Al_2Si_2 atoms in an uncrumpled framework with actual symmetry I 2/c. Brinkmann and Stähli (1968) found that the nuclear magnetic resonance pattern of Al^{27} nuclei in anorthite was consistent with the ordered structure derived by the X-ray structure analysis.

The early X-ray studies were made by tedious collection of film intensities followed by difference Fourier refinement. These data are being supplemented by automatic collection of counter intensities processed by least-squares and Fourier series. The results of the earlier work are essentially confirmed, while the accuracy in distances has improved by a factor of 2 or so.

For anorthite, Megaw *et al.* (1962) used a crystal from the volcanic environment at Vesuvius, Italy; the chemical composition was not measured but should be between 95 and 100 % An. This crystal showed primitive symmetry characteristic of the stable form at low temperature. Ribbe (1963b) found similar data for the T–O distances in a transitional anorthite with diffuse *c* diffractions, examined at room temperature. The above film data have been supplanted by counter data of Wainwright and Starkey (1971) for a primitive anorthite, An_{100}, from a metamorphic rock at Val Pesmeda, Austria. Foit (1971), in an abstract, reported a structure analysis of an anorthite, An_{99}, from Miyake, Japan taken directly at 410° C. In 1973, Schulz, Czank and Laves were completing refinement of counter data for an anorthite from Vesuvius ($Or_{0.13}Ab_{1.7}An_{97.6}$; Fe 0.076, Ba 0.017; all wt. %) taken at room temperature, 240 and 1430° C by counter methods. All these data are consistent with essentially regular alternation of Al and Si atoms on the tetrahedral nodes. However, the variation of the cell angle β^* of anorthites may indicate weak Si, Al disorder at high temperature (Chapter 7). The measured T–O distances are not reliable enough to test for this possible weak disorder, and probably it will be necessary to wait for very careful neutron diffraction studies of unheated and heated anorthites to obtain a reliable check.

The counter determination by Wainwright (1969) of a bytownite, An_{76}, from Crystal Bay, Minnesota confirmed the film determination by Fleet *et al.* (1966) of a bytownite, near An_{80}, from St. Louis Co., Minnesota that the excess Si atoms over the anorthite composition enter tetrahedral sites of all types.

All other refinements of plagioclases with intermediate composition are based on type (a) diffractions of the pseudocell, thereby averaging out the complexities of the out-of-step domain structure. The film refinement by Hall *et al.* (pers. comm. in 1967) of an andesine, An_{48}, from Essex County, N. Y., showed that Al atoms preferentially entered T_10 sites, as in low albite, with roughly equal amounts in the other three sites. The counter refinements of two oligoclases, An_{16} and An_{28}, from pegmatites at Camedo, Switzerland and Mitchell Co., N. C., by Phillips *et al.* (1971) show the same phenomenon. These specimens illustrate the nature of the low structural state. There are no direct X-ray data on the structures of high plagioclases, and speculations are based on analogy of cell dimensions with those of high albite and anorthite, plus implications from thermochemical measurements.

3.5.2 Detailed Interpretation

Table 3-3 shows the T–O distances for feldspars more aluminous than $AlSi_3$ together with estimates of the Al-contents and the Thompson XYZ coefficients for the pseudo-structure.

For celsian, the doubling of the *c*-axis increases the number of independent tetrahedra from 2 in sanidine to 4. In a simplified Megaw notation these are labelled T_10, T_1z, T_20 and T_2z, where z is the translation operator of $c/2$.

For anorthite, the crumpling of the framework into primitive triclinic symmetry plus the doubling of the *c*-axis increases the number of independent

Table 3-3. Mean T–O distances, indicated Al-distributions, and Thompson coefficients in Al-rich feldspars

Feldspar	Reference	Extra code	T_1O	T_1m	T_2O	T_2m distances (nanometer)	t_1O	t_1m	t_2O	t_2m Al contents	Total Al	Or	Ab	An mol.%	X	Y	Z Coefficients
oligoclase (Camedo)	Phillips et al.(1971)	–	.1718	.1622	.1629	.1630	.805	.08	.135	.14	1.16	2	82	16	–.005	.725	.61
oligoclase (Mitchell Co.)	do.	–	.1700	.1637	.1638	.1639	.675	.195	.205	.21	1.285	2	70	28	–.005	.48	.455
andesine (Essex Co.)	Hall et al.(1967)	–	.1676	.1653	.1656	.1656	.50	.32	.345	.345	1.51	4	49	47	.00	.18	.13
bytownite (Crystal Bay)	Wainwright (1969)	00	.1630	.1716	.1703	.1628	.14	.79	.695	.125	1.76			76	not applicable to anorthite and celsian structure types.		
		zo	.1726	.1617	.1623	.1715	.86	.04	.085	.785							
bytownite (St. Louis Co., Minnesota)	Fleet et al.(1966) refinement in I1̄	00	.1620	.1728	.1749	.1608	.06	.875	1.03	.03	1.88	optical 80±2% An					
		10	.1622	.1724	.1728	.1628	.08	.85	.875	.125							
		zo	.1742	.1618	.1621	.1729	.98	.045	.07	.885							
		z1	.1710	.1610	.1611	.1732	.745	–.015	–.01	.905							
P-anorthite (Vesuvius)	Megaw et al.(1962)	00	.1613	.1752	.1746	.1602	.01	1.05	1.005	–.08	2.09	~95–100 % An					
		10	.1616	.1741	.1753	.1628	.03	.98	1.055	.125							
		zo	.1758	.1608	.1613	.1744	1.095	–.03	.01	.995							
		z1	.1746	.1626	.1610	.1752	1.005	–.11	–.015	1.05							
transitional anorthite (Vesuvius)	Ribbe (1963b)	00	.1619	.1738	.1752	.1601	–.055	.95	1.05	–.085	2.095	~95–100 % An					
		10	.1606	.1747	.1752	.1625	–.045	1.015	1.05	.10							
		zo	.1740	.1628	.1620	.1744	.965	.125	.06	.995							
		z1	.1755	.1601	.1629	.1749	1.07	–.085	.135	1.03							
P-anorthite (Val Pesmeda)	Wainwright and Starkey (1971)	00	.1616	.1750	.1742	.1615	.03	1.035	.98	.025	2.06	0	0	100			
		10	.1613	.1745	.1750	.1614	.01	1.00	1.035	.015							
		zo	.1747	.1613	.1617	.1744	1.015	.01	.04	.995							
		z1	.1755	.1613	.1608	.1745	1.07	.01	–.03	1.00							
celsian (Broken Hill)	Newnham and Megaw (1960) replace m by z	.1639	.1717	.1712	.1635	.21	.795	.76	.180	1.945	Ba	.84	K.18			

Note: until a proper calibration is obtained, it is recommended that 0.02 be subtracted from the above estimates of Al content for the anorthites and celsian. The total Al content then drops by 0.08.

tetrahedra to 16, four times as many as in microcline. The extra Megaw codes are listed in Table 3-3.

Interpretation of T–O distances in plagioclase is uncertain because of (1) danger of residual correlation between related site occupancies of structures with pseudo-symmetry, and (2) lack of neutron diffraction data to check estimates of Al-content. The mean T–O distances for the Si-rich and Al-rich tetrahedra cluster near 0.1614 and 0.1747 nm, which values are close to the assumed reference values of 0.1612 and 0.1745 used for pure Si and Al in alkali feldspars. Table 3-3 gives Al-contents based on the same conversion procedure as for the alkali feldspars, and it may be seen that the total Al-contents for the three anorthites are too high by an average of 0.08. Arbitrarily it is suggested that an adjustment of − 0.02 be applied to each individual Al-content of anorthites and celsian. With this adjustment the ranges of Al-contents for the Val Pesmeda anorthite are − 0.04 to + 0.03 and 0.97 to 1.025. Because the standard deviation of each mean T–O distance is 0.0001 nm, corresponding to about 0.01 Al, and because the Val Pesmeda anorthite is probably fully ordered, it is probable that there is a significant effect from details of the chemical bonding. Obviously a careful neutron-diffraction refinement of the Val Pesmeda anorthite is needed.

The data for the celsian indicate considerable Si, Al disorder, but Newnham and Megaw (1960) cautioned about the problems of refinement of pseudostructures.

Figure 3-8 compares the estimated Al-contents for the plagioclases of intermediate composition with those for albite and anorthite. To do this, the concept

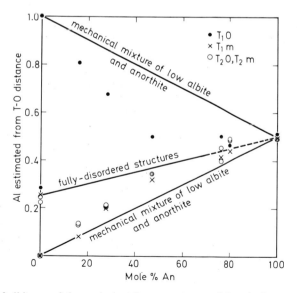

Fig 3-8. Al-content of the four T sites of albite or of the equivalent "average-structure" for plagioclases as estimated from T–O distances. The center line represents either (1) complete disorder of Al, Si atoms, or (2) mechanical mixtures of disordered high albite and anorthite, or (3) solid solution of anorthite type. Data from Table 3-3. (Modified from Smith and Ribbe, 1969, Fig. 3)

of "average structure" was developed by Smith and Ribbe (1969) to permit comparison between the feldspars. For each tetrahedral node in an alkali feldspar, there are four positions in primitive anorthite. Electron density maps of plagioclase using only the type (*a*) diffractions with (h + k) even and *l* even automatically average each set of four positions. For anorthite, the data for individual tetrahedra can be averaged. The two outer lines join the data points for low albite and anorthite and represent a mechanical mixture of the two feldspars. The inner line joins high albite and anorthite. All completely disordered plagioclases should lie on this line, as also would plagioclases composed of a mathematical mixture of disordered high albite and ordered anorthite. Furthermore an ordered anorthite with extra Si atoms substituting equally in all sites would lie on this line as shown by the dashed portion. Readers are cautioned that interpretation of this diagram may be ambiguous.

For albite composition, the ordered and disordered forms are clearly distinguished in Fig. 3-8. The data for anorthite and An_{80} indicate essentially complete disorder: this, however, is merely a mathematical effect because averaging over the four sites automatically combines tetrahedra with 0 and 1 Al.

The data for An_{15}, An_{28} and An_{48} lie between the theoretical line for complete disorder and the straight lines joining the data points for low-albite and anorthite. Smith and Ribbe (1969) utilized these data to indicate that models of intermediate plagioclase must show a preference for occupancy of T_1 sites (see Chapter 5). The An_{15} and An_{28} specimens were derived from pegmatites and are in a low-entropy state. The An_{48} specimen is from an anorthosite at Essex County, New York and was heated for 3 days at 1250° C: its X-ray powder pattern is consistent with a state of intermediate order.

Within experimental error, the indicated Al-contents of the T_1m, T_20 and T_2m sites of the averaged structure are equal for each of the plagioclase specimens. Hence for an averaged plagioclase, a single coefficient of order appears to be sufficient. Probably however there are subtle variations for both natural and synthetic plagioclases that cannot be described by a single coefficient of order.

3.6 Crystal-chemical Explanation of Ordering

Strictly speaking, a crystal-chemical explanation of Si, Al ordering should go back to Schrödinger's wave equation. Because this cannot be solved, various simple ideas have been proposed to explain Si, Al ordering in feldspars. These ideas must obey the thermodynamic control that for equilibrium the atomic pattern be ordered at the absolute zero of temperature.

There are three essential questions: (1) why do Al and Si atoms alternate in the Al_2Si_2 feldspar framework, (2) why do Al atoms segregate into T_1 sites in the $AlSi_3$ feldspar framework, and (3) why is the Al:Si ratio limited between 1:3 and 2:2?

3.6.1 Alternation in Al_2Si_2 Feldspar

Goldsmith and Laves (1955) stated "An ordered Al–Si array where the Al:Si ratio is 1:1 should be expected to follow Pauling's electrostatic valence principle best if each Al tetrahedron is surrounded by Si tetrahedra and vice versa". This statement implicitly assumes that the valence bonds from the Ca cations are approximately evenly distributed to the oxygen atoms of the framework. One might indeed try to envisage a structure in which the Ca cations bond preferentially to certain oxygens thereby favoring adjacent Al atoms bonded to these oxygens.

Actually, the bonding of Ca cations in anorthite to the framework oxygens is rather uneven (Chapter 4), indicating only approximate adherence to Pauling's second rule. Detailed study of the feldspar structure shows that, except perhaps for really fantastic geometrical distortions, it is not possible to place a Ca cation such that it gives a perfect balance of electrostatic valence-bonds even for alternating Al and Si cations.

Loewenstein (1954) stated that the electrostatic valence rule does not explain why an oxygen bridge between aluminum tetrahedra should be excluded because cations could balance the charge. He invoked Pauling's third rule that polyhedra around cations with small coordination number tend not to share elements with each other. Hence he argued that a higher coordination number should be favored when Al atoms share an oxygen (i.e. Al should go into 6-coordination). However it is not clear to me why it is all right that tetrahedral Al and Si should be able to share an oxygen when two tetrahedral Al atoms should not. Loewenstein correctly predicted the alternation of Al and Si in anorthite, but his underlying arguments are not convincing.

Since Loewenstein's paper appeared, there has been uncritical acceptance of the so-called aluminum avoidance rule. Actually there is excellent X-ray diffraction evidence that tetrahedral Al atoms do share the same oxygen atoms in nepheline (Dollase, 1970; Foreman and Peacor, 1970). In addition, tetrahedral Al atoms definitely share all the oxygen atoms in the framework structure of BaAl$_2$O$_4$ (Perrotta and Smith, 1968) while some of the oxygen atoms of the sheet silicate gehlenite are shared by two tetrahedral Al atoms (Louisnathan, 1971). Furthermore in danburite, CaB$_2$Si$_2$O$_8$, the B atoms occur in pairs, whereas in paracelsian, BaAl$_2$Si$_2$O$_8$, with the same framework topology the Al atoms alternate with Si atoms.

It seems clear that one should not be dogmatic in attempting a simple explanation for Si, Al alternation in Al$_2$Si$_2$ feldspars.

3.6.2 Choice of T$_1$ Site in AlSi$_3$ Feldspar

At first sight, one should ask why Al concentrates in T$_1$0 rather than T$_1$m, T$_2$0 and T$_2$m. However it is obvious that the designations 0 and m are arbitrary, and that the real question is why Al concentrates into T$_1$ rather than T$_2$. There are only half as many Al atoms as T$_1$ sites, and the simplest solution is to use half of them with C$\bar{1}$ topochemical symmetry.

Two basic suggestions have been made, one involving charge balance, and one involving π-bonding.

Ferguson et al. (1958, p. 346) proposed that, in albite, oxygen atoms of tetrahedron T$_1$ receive more bond strength from the Na atoms than oxygen atoms of other tetrahedra. Gait et al. (1970), confirmed this conclusion from detailed calculations assuming fully ionic bonding with charges distributed in proportion to the inverse square of the bond lengths. The conclusion is independent of uncertainties in assigning coordination to the large irregular polyhedron around the Na atom (see Chapter 4). Furthermore in K-feldspar, Chao et al. (1940) and Taylor (1962, p. 9) stated that atom O_{A1} is the only oxygen atom to contact two K atoms. Because it links two tetrahedra of type T_1, a favorable charge balance is obtained by placing Al atoms in T_1.

Brown and Gibbs (1970) examined ordering in tetrahedral sites from the viewpoint of Cruickshank's (1961) proposal that π-bonding is a significant factor. The observed statistical trends of T–O bond length with T–O–T angle and electronegativity of non-tetrahedral cations in many structures were interpreted to be consistent with a contribution from π-bonding. Because T–O bonds to oxygen bridges at wide T–O–T angles tend to have higher bond order than those at narrow angles, and because the π-bonding order for tetrahedral coordination decreases from Si–O (0.32) via Al–O (0.18) and Mg–O (0.08) to B–O (0.00) and Be–O (0.00), Brown and Gibbs proposed that "in framework silicates .... Si should prefer those tetrahedral sites involved in the widest average T–O–T angles and Al, B, Be and Mg those involved in the narrowest average T–O–T angles."

This proposal fits nicely with the crystal structure of low albite because the mean T_1O–O–T angle is 136.0° compared to the value of 141.7° for the other three tetrahedra which contain the Si atoms. The proposal also fits for reedmergnerite because the B-tetrahedron has mean angle 136.0 compared to 140.2 for the Si-tetrahedra. For maximum microcline (Finney and Bailey, 1964), the proposal is satisfied, but only just: 141.6 for T_1O vs. 141.9 for the other three tetrahedra. Because the individual distances vary from 131 to 151°, this is a very close margin. For anorthite, the regular alternation of Al and Si automatically results in equal values for mean T–O–T angles at Al and Si tetrahedra.

I suspect that there is merit in both kinds of ideas, and that the two factors may indeed complement each other. Both interpretations involve knowledge of the actual detailed geometry of the feldspar structures: a really fundamental interpretation would consider all possible geometries and show that the observed ones are the best according to the proposed criteria. For example, Brown and Gibbs should ask whether it is possible to invent a feldspar framework in which the widest average T–O–T angles occur for T_2 sites. A really fundamental interpretation is too difficult at this time, but must be placed on the agenda.

3.6.3 Limitation of Al:Si Ratio between 1:3 and 2:2

The limitation of the Al:Si ratio in natural feldspars can be explained by the following ideas:

(a) an Al, Si ratio below 1:3 would require vacancies in the M sites because the minimum valency of M atoms is one. Actually some alkali feldspars may contain a small excess of Si and a small deficiency of M atoms (Chapter 14) but the effect is certainly small (up to a few percent) if it does occur.

(b) an Al, Si ratio above 2:2 would require M atoms with valency greater than two because there is no room in the feldspar cavities for extra M atoms.

The common trivalent cations are too small and too highly polarizing to occupy the M sites. The rare-earth cations enter the M sites in such low concentrations in natural feldspars that it is not possible to test whether there are extra Al atoms in the framework. An attempt to synthesize the composition $(RE)_1Al_3SiO_8$ would provide a crucial test whether the feldspar structure can tolerate a significant amount of trivalent rare-earth ion in the M site.

References

Anderson,J.R. (1973): On infinitely adaptive structures. JCS, Dalton Trans., No. 2, 1107–1115.

Appleman, D. E., Clark,J.R. (1965): Crystal structure of reedmergnerite, a boron albite, and its relation to feldspar crystal chemistry. AM **50**, 1827–1850.

Bailey,S. W. (1969): Refinement of an intermediate microcline structure. AM **54**, 1540–1545.

Bailey,S. W., Taylor,W. H. (1955): The structure of a triclinic potassium felspar. AC **8**, 621–632.

Barth,T. F. W. (1934): Polymorphic phenomena and crystal structure. AJS Ser. 5, **27**, 273–286.

Barth,T. F. W. (1959): The interrelations of the structural variants of the potash feldspars. ZK **112**, 263–274.

Barth,T. F. W. (1965): On the constitution of the alkali feldspars. TMPM **10** (Machatschki Vol.), 14–33.

Barth,T. F. W. (1969): Feldspars, 261 pp. New York and London: Wiley Interscience.

Brinkmann, D., Stähli,J.L. (1968): Magnetische Kernresonanz von ^{27}Al im Anorthit, $CaAl_2Si_2O_8$. Helvetica Phys. Acta **41**, 274–281.

Brown, B.E. (1962): Aluminium distribution in an igneous maximum microcline and the sanidine microcline series. NGT **42**, No. 2, 25–36.

Brown, B.E., Bailey,S.W. (1964): The structure of maximum microcline. AC **17**, 1391–1400.

Brown, G.E., Gibbs,G.V. (1970): Stereochemistry and ordering in the tetrahedral portion of silicates. AM **55**, 1587–1607.

Brown, G.E., Gibbs,G.V., Ribbe,P.H. (1969): The nature and variation in length of the Si–O and Al–O bonds in framework silicates. AM **54**, 1044–1061.

Brown,G.E., Hamilton,W.C., Prewitt,C.T., Sueno,S. (1973): Neutron diffraction study of Al/Si ordering in sanidine. Preprint NATO Study Institute.

Brun,E., Hartmann,P., Staub,H.H., Hafner,S., Laves,F. (1960): Magnetische Kernresonanz zur Beobachtung des Al, Si-Ordnungs/Unordnungsgrades in einigen Feldspäten. ZK **113**, 65–76.

Buerger,M.J. (1960): Crystal-structure analysis. New York: John Wiley.

Chao,S.H., Hargreaves,A., Taylor,W.H. (1940): The structure of orthoclase. MM **25**, 498–512.

Chao,S.H., Taylor,W.H. (1940): Isomorphous replacement and superlattice structures in the plagioclase felspars. Proc. Roy. Soc. (Lond.) 176 A, 76—87.

Christian,J.W. (1965): The theory of transformations in metals and alloys, 973 pp. Oxford: Pergamon Press.

Cole,W.F., Sörum,H., Kennard,O. (1949): The crystal structures of orthoclase and sanidinized orthoclase. AC **2**, 280–287.

Colville,A.A., Ribbe,P.H. (1968): The crystal structure of an adularia and a refinement of the structure of orthoclase. AM **53**, 25–37.

Cowley,J.M. (1950): X-ray measurements of order in single crystals of Cu_3Au. J. Appl. Phys. **21**, 24–30.

Cruickshank,D.W.J. (1961): The role of 3d-orbitals in π-bonds between (a) silicon, phosphorous, sulphur, or chlorine and (b) oxygen or nitrogen. JCS 5485–5504.

Devore,G.W. (1955): Note on the Al and Si positions in ordered Na and K feldspars. S **121**, 707–708.

Devore,G.W. (1956): Al-Si positions in ordered plagioclase feldspars. ZK **107**, 247–264.

Dollase,W.A. (1970): Least-squares refinement of the structure of a plutonic nepheline. ZK **132**, 27–44.

Ferguson,R.B., Traill,R.J., Taylor,W.H. (1958): The crystal structures of low-temperature and high-temperature albites. AC **11**, 331–348.

Finney, J. J., Bailey, S. W. (1964): Crystal structure of an authigenic maximum microcline. ZK **119**, 413–436.

Fischer, K. (1965): Röntgenographische Unterscheidung von Silizium- und Aluminium-Punktlagen durch Verfeinerung des atomaren Streuvermögens. TMPM **10** (Machatschki Vol.), 203–208.

Fischer, K., Zehme, H. (1967): Röntgenographische Untersuchung der Si-Al-Verteilung in einem Mikroklin durch Verfeinerung des atomaren Streuvermögens. SMPM **47**, 163–167.

Fleet, S. G., Chandrasekhar, S., Megaw, H. D. (1966): The structure of bytownite ("body-centred anorthite"). AC **21**, 782–801.

Foit, F. F. (1971): The crystal structure of anorthite at 410° C. Prog. Geol. Soc. Amer. Mtg., Southeastern section, p. 311 (abstract). See AM, **58**, 665 – 675 (1973).

Foreman, N., Peacor, D. R. (1970): Refinement of the nepheline structure at several temperatures. ZK **132**, 45–70.

Gait, R. I., Ferguson, R. B., Coish, H. R. (1970): Electrostatic charge distributions in the structure of low albite, $NaAlSi_3O_8$. AC B **26**, 68–76.

Gasperin, M. (1971): Structure cristalline de $RbAlSi_3O_8$. AC B **27**, 854–855.

Gay, P. (1962): Sub-solidus relations in the plagioclase feldspars. NGT **42**, No. 2, 37–56.

Goldsmith, J. R., Laves, F. (1954): Potassium feldspars structurally intermediate between microcline and sanidine. GCA **6**, 100–118.

Goldsmith, J. R., Laves, F. (1955): Cation order in anorthite ($CaAl_2Si_2O_8$) as revealed by gallium and germanium substitutions. ZK **106**, 213–226.

Hafner, S., Hartmann, P. (1964): Elektrische Feldgradienten und Sauerstoff-Polarisierbarkeit in Alkali-Feldspäten ($NaAlSi_3O_8$ und $KAlSi_3O_8$). Helvetica Phys. Acta **37**, 348–360.

Hafner, S., Hartmann, P., Laves, F. (1962): Magnetische Kernresonanz von Al^{27} in Adular. Zur Deutung der Adularstruktur. SMPM **42**, 277–294.

Hafner, S., Laves, F. (1957): Ordnung/Unordnung und Ultrarotabsorption. II. Variation der Lage und Intensität einiger Absorptionen von Feldspäten. Zur Struktur von Orthoklas und Adular. ZK **109**, 204–225.

Hafner, S., Laves, F. (1963): Magnetische Kernresonanz von Al^{27} in einigen Orthoklasen. SMPM **43**, 65–69.

Hall, K. M. et al. (1967): Personal communication.

Harlow, G. E., Brown, G. E., Hamilton, W. C. (1973): Neutron diffraction study of Amelia low albite. Trans. Amer. Geophys. Union **54**, 497 (abstr.).

Jones, J. B. (1968): Al–O and Si–O tetrahedral distances in aluminosilicate framework structures. AC B **24**, 355–358.

Jones, J. B., Taylor, W. H. (1961a): The structure of orthoclase. CCILM **8**, 33–36.

Jones, J. B., Taylor, W. H. (1961b): The structure of orthoclase. AC **14**, 443–456.

Kempster, C. J. E., Megaw, H. D., Radoslovich, F. W. (1962): The structure of anorthite, $CaAl_2Si_2O_8$. I. Structure analysis. AC **15**, 1005–1017.

Köhler, A. (1949): Recent results of investigations on the feldspars. JG **57**, 592–599.

Krivoglaz, M. A. (1969): Theory of X-ray and thermal-neutron scattering by real crystals. English translation from Russian. New York: Plenum Press.

Krivoglaz, M. A., Smirnov, A. A. (1965): The theory of order-disorder in alloys. Translation from Russian. American Elsevier Publishing Company, Inc. British version by MacDonald and Co. Ltd. 1964.

Kroll, H. (1971): Feldspäte im System $K[AlSi_3O_8]$-$Na[AlSi_3O_8]$-$Ca[Al_2Si_2O_8]$: Al, Si-Verteilung und Gitterparameter, Phasen-Transformationen und Chemismus. Inaug.-Diss. der Westfälischen Wilhelms-Universität in Münster.

Laves, F. (1950): The lattice and twinning of microcline and other potash feldspars. JG **58**, 548–571.

Laves, F. (1952): Phase relations of the alkali feldspars. I. Introductory remarks. II. The stable and pseudo-stable phase relations in the alkali feldspar system. JG **60**, 436–450, 549–574.

Laves, F. (1960): Al/Si-Verteilungen, Phasen-Transformationen und Namen der Alkalifeldspäte. ZK **113**, 265–296.

Laves, F., Hafner, S. (1956): Ordnung/Unordnung und Ultrarotabsorption I. (Al, Si)-Verteilung in Feldspäten. ZK **108**, 52–63.

Laves, F., Hafner, S. (1962): Infrared absorption effects, nuclear magnetic resonance and structure of feldspars. NGT **42**, No. 2, 57–71.

Lipson, H., Cochran, W. (1953): The crystalline state – Vol. III. The determination of crystal structures. London: Bell and Sons Ltd.

Loewenstein, W. (1954): The distribution of aluminum in the tetrahedra of silicates and aluminates. AM **39**, 92–96.

Louisnathan, S. J. (1971): Refinement of the crystal structure of a natural gehlenite, $Ca_2Al(Al, Si)_2O_7$. Canadian Mineral. **10**, 822–837.

McConnell, J. D. C. (1965): Electron optical study of effects associated with partial inversion in a silicate phase. Philos. Mag. **11**, 1289–1301.

McConnell, J. D. C. (1970): Electron-optical study of phase transformations. MM **38**, 1–20.

Megaw, H. D. (1959): Order and disorder in the felspars, I. MM **32**, 226–241.

Megaw, H. D. (1960): Order and disorder. I. Theory of stacking faults and diffraction maxima. II. Theory of diffraction effects in the intermediate plagioclase felspars. III. The structure of the intermediate plagioclase felspars. Proc. Roy. Soc. (Lond.) **259** A, 59–78, 159–183, 184–202.

Megaw, H. D. (1962): Order and disorder in felspars. NGT **42**, No. **2**, 104–137.

Megaw, H. D., Kempster, C. J. E., Radoslovich, E. W. (1962): The structure of anorthite, $CaAl_2Si_2O_8$. II. Description and discussion. AC **15**, 1017–1035.

Moss, S. C. (1964): X-ray measurement of short-range order in Cu_3Au. J. Appl. Phys. **35**, 3547–3553.

Newnham, R. E., Megaw, H. D. (1960): The crystal structure of celsian (barium felspar). AC **13**, 303–313.

Niggli, A. (1967): Die Ordnungsmöglichkeiten der Si-Al-Verteilung in Plagioklasen. SMPM **47**, 279–287.

Nissen, H.-U. (1967): Direct electron-microscopic proof of domain texture in orthoclase ($KAlSi_3O_8$). CMP **16**, 354–360.

Perrotta, A. J., Smith, J. V. (1968): The crystal structure of $BaAl_2O_4$. BSFMC **91**, 85–87.

Phillips, M. W., Colville, A. A., Ribbe, P. H. (1971): The crystal structures of two oligoclases: A comparison with low and high albite. ZK **133**, Fritz-Laves-Festband, 43–65.

Phillips, M. W., Ribbe, P. H. (1971): Personal communication reporting X-ray structure analyses of sanidine 7002 and adularia 7007.

Phillips, M. W., Ribbe, P. H. (1973): The structures of monoclinic potassium-rich feldspars. AM **58**, 263–270.

Prewitt, C. T. (1972): Use of neutron diffraction for determining Al/Si distributions in feldspars. Abstr. 1.5 in program for Advanced Study Institute on Feldspars, July 1972, Manchester.

Prince, E., Donnay, G., Martin, R. F. (1972): Neutron structure refinement of an ordered orthoclase. Abstr. 1.6 in program for Advanced Study Institute on Feldspars, July 1972, Manchester. In press, AM, **58**, 500–507 (1973).

Ribbe, P. H. (1963a): A refinement of the crystal structure of sanidinized orthoclase. AC **16**, 426–427.

Ribbe, P. H. (1963b): Structural studies of plagioclase feldspars. Dissertation, University of Cambridge.

Ribbe, P. H., Gibbs, G. V. (1967): Statistical analysis of Al/Si distribution in feldspars. Trans. Amer. Geophys. Union Mtg. XI, 229–230 (abstr.).

Ribbe, P. H., Gibbs, G. V. (1969): Statistical analysis and discussion of mean Al/Si–O bond distances and the aluminum content of tetrahedra in feldspars. AM **54**, 85–94.

Ribbe, P. H., Megaw, H. D., Taylor, W. H., Ferguson, R. B., Traill, R. J. (1969): The albite structures. AC **25** B, 1503–1518.

Smith, J. V. (1954): A review of the Al–O and Si–O distances. AC **7**, 479–483.

Smith, J. V. (1970): Physical properties of order-disorder structures with especial reference to feldspar minerals. Lithos **3**, 145–160.

Smith, J. V., Bailey, S. W. (1963): Second review of Al–O and Si–O tetrahedral distances. AC **16**, 801–810.

Smith, J. V., Mackenzie, W. S. (1959): The alkali feldspars. V. The nature of orthoclase and microcline perthites, and observations concerning the polymorphism of potassium feldspar. AM **44**, 1169–1186.

Smith, J. V., Mackenzie, W. S. (1961): Atomic, chemical and physical factors that control the stability of alkali feldspars. CCILM **8**, 39–52.

Smith, J. V., Ribbe, P. H. (1969): Atomic movements in plagioclase feldspars: kinetic interpretation. CMP **21**, 157–202.

Sörum, H. (1951): Studies in the structures of plagioclase felspars. Norsk Vidensk.-Akad. Oslo, Mat.-Nat. Kl., Skr. No. 3, 1–160.

Sörum, H. (1953): The structures of the plagioclase felspars II. AC **6**, 413–416.

Spencer, E. (1930): A contribution to the study of moonstone from Ceylon and other areas and of the stability-relations of the alkali-felspars. MM **22**, 291–367.

Spencer, E. (1937): The potash-soda-felspars. I. Thermal stability. MM **24**, 453–494.

Stewart, D. B., Ribbe, P. H. (1967): Al/Si ordering, lattice parameters, and composition in alkali feldspars. Trans. Amer. Geophys. Union 48, 230 (abstr.).

Stewart, D. B., Ribbe, P. H. (1969): Structural explanation for variations in cell parameters of alkali feldspar with Al/Si ordering. AJS, Schairer Vol. **267**-A, 144 – 462.

Taylor, W. H. (1962): The structures of the principal felspars. NGT **42**, No. 2, 1 – 24.

Taylor, W. H., Darbyshire, J. A., Strunz, H. (1934): An X-ray investigation of the felspars. ZK **87**, 464–498.

Thompson, J. B., Jr. (1969): Chemical reactions in crystals. AM **54**, 341–375.

Thompson, J. B. (1970): Chemical reactions in crystals: corrections and clarification. AM **55**, 528–532.

Wainwright, J. E. (1969): A refined structure for bytownite. Progr. Eighth Inter. Congr. Crystallography, abstr. XII-48.

Wainwright, J. E., Starkey, J. (1968): Crystal structure of a metamorphic low albite. Progr. Geol. Soc. America Mtg. Mexico City, p. 310.

Wainwright, J. E., Starkey, J. (1971): A refinement of the structure of anorthite. ZK **133**, Fritz-Laves-Festband, 75–84.

Weitz, G. (1972): Die Struktur des Sanidins bei verschiedenen Ordnungsgraden. ZK **136**, 418–426.

Williams, P. P., Megaw, H. D. (1964): The crystal structures of high and low albites at −180° C. AC **17**, 882–890.

Chapter 4 Detailed Geometry and Atomic Coordination

The details of the feldspar structure cannot be comprehended in one grand sweep of imagination and it is necessary to consider them separately, while attempting to retain a sense of their interrelationships.

Section 4.1 describes the major features common to all the structural variants, and relates them to ideas involving the topology of the framework and the electrostatic interaction between the framework and the cations. Section 4.2 discusses the fine details of the framework, beginning with the shape of the tetrahedra and ending with the T–O–T angles. Section 4.3 describes the geometrical relations between the M cations and the nearby oxygen atoms. Section 4.4 interprets the data on atomic displacements in terms of thermal motion and substitutional disorder, while Section 4.5 describes the fragmentary data on the temperature variation of the crystal structures.

The reviews by Taylor (1962, 1965a, b) are a valuable summary of the principal features, but require some augmentation to cover later ideas and improved data.

Table 4-1 lists recent positional coordinates for low microcline, orthoclase (low sanidine), low albite, quenched high albite, primitive anorthite, celsian, reedmergnerite and Rb-feldspar. Data for quenched sanidine are given in Table 2-1. These structural data delineate the range of the feldspar type of structure, and are sufficient for the general discussions in this chapter. The bulk of this chapter was prepared in 1971, and Figs. 4-6a, b, d and e use the atomic coordinates for low albite, high albite and P-anorthite measured by Ribbe et al. (1969) and Kempster et al. (1962) instead of the ones listed in Table 4-1.

The following papers are not referred to in the text because their data and ideas have been superseded: Brown (1962), Chandrasekhar (1957), Chandrasekhar et al. (1961), Chao et al. (1940), Clark and Appleman (1960), Cole et al. (1949), Colville and Ribbe (1968), Finney and Bailey (1964), Jones and Taylor (1961), Onorato et al. (1963), Ribbe and Megaw (1962), Ribbe et al. (1962), Sörum (1951, 1953), and Waring (1961).

4.1 General Features

Naively one might envisage the actual geometry of the feldspar framework to be governed by three factors: its own inherent tendency to adopt a particular shape; the perturbation caused by the distribution of the T atoms; and the perturbation caused by interaction with M atoms.

Hopefully it will be possible to synthesize a feldspar of formula T_4O_8 without any M atoms and containing just tetravalent T atoms. Perhaps a metastable feldspar form of SiO_2 may be synthesized by fortunate choice of starting

Table 4-1. Atomic parameters in feldspars

	Microcline			Low albite			High albite			Reedmergnerite		
	x	y	z	x	y	z	x	y	z	x	y	z
Na or K	.2827	.9928	.1365	.2683	.9890	.1463	.2727	.0070	.1339	.2586	.0075	.1332
$T_1(0)$	.0104	.1875	.2169	.0089	.1682	.2080	.0091	.1650	.2146	.0127	.1617	.2217
$T_1(m)$	.0097	.8198	.2327	.0037	.8205	.2374	.0049	.8149	.2294	.0059	.8100	.2097
$T_2(0)$	.7110	.1202	.3399	.6917	.1102	.3147	.6904	.1080	.3200	.7029	.1015	.3204
$T_2(m)$	.7059	.8856	.3507	.6815	.8818	.3607	.6846	.8779	.3539	.6847	.8644	.3547
$O_A(1)$	.0007	.1448	.9831	.0048	.1312	.9662	.0054	.1345	.9835	.0076	.1364	.0040
$O_A(2)$	.6366	.0058	.2853	.5922	.9973	.2809	.5918	.9908	.2782	.5929	.9812	.2758
$O_B(0)$	.8202	.1476	.2205	.8125	.1099	.1902	.8195	.1091	.1962	.8455	.0995	.2126
$O_B(m)$	.8316	.8570	.2416	.8196	.8512	.2583	.8179	.8474	.2449	.8163	.8347	.2335
$O_C(0)$	.0352	.3203	.2514	.0128	.3021	.2708	.0159*	.2908	.2772	.0064	.2762	.2725
$O_C(m)$	.0366	.6953	.2689	.0239	.6939	.2291	.0211	.6875	.2187	.0289	.6799	.2070
$O_D(0)$	.1911	.1229	.4053	.2073	.1089	.3891	.1963	.1119*	.3862	.1900	.1200	.3815
$O_D(m)$	.1753	.8742	.4127	.1840	.8681	.4368	.1878	.8674	.4272	.1922	.8682	.4172

Primitive anorthite

	x	y	z		x	y	z
Ca(000)	.2651	.9864	.0867	$O_B(0000)$	.8154	.1018	.0806
Ca(z00)	.2692	.0312	.5435	$O_B(0z00)$	.8124	.0968	.6057
Ca(0i0)	.7737	.5359	.5412	$O_B(00i0)$	.3325	.5957	.6047
Ca(zi0)	.7634	.5052	.0747	$O_B(0zi0)$	.2854	.6034	.0798
$T_1(0000)$	.0092	.1592	.1044	$O_B(m000)$	.8175	.8554	.1443
$T_1(0z00)$	.0066	.1610	.6112	$O_B(mz00)$	.8113	.8518	.6034
$T_1(00i0)$	.5062	.6560	.6042	$O_B(m0i0)$	.2987	.3559	.6115
$T_1(0zi0)$	.4984	.6658	.1128	$O_B(mzi0)$	.3419	.3587	.1333
$T_1(m000)$	.9912	.8152	.1176	$O_C(0000)$	.0141	.2796	.1351
$T_1(mz00)$	.0061	.8154	.6135	$O_C(0z00)$	.0205	.2909	.6474
$T_1(m0i0)$	.5073	.3145	.6212	$O_C(00i0)$	.5094	.7769	.6344
$T_1(mzi0)$	.5041	.3204	.1099	$O_C(0zi0)$	.5092	.7965	.1510
$T_2(0000)$	.6845*	.1130	.1519	$O_C(m000)$	.0008	.6806	.1044
$T_2(0z00)$	.6814	.1034	.6646	$O_C(mz00)$	.0089	.6899	.6013
$T_2(00i0)$	.1907	.6110	.6674	$O_C(m0i0)$	.5165	.1788	.6101
$T_2(0zi0)$	.1713	.6067	.1495	$O_C(mzi0)$	.5071	.1963	.0975
$T_2(m000)$	.6742	.8829	.1876	$O_D(0000)$	.1826	.1059	.1917
$T_2(mz00)$	.6809	.8719	.6725	$O_D(0z00)$	.2155	.1025	.6847
$T_2(m0i0)$	.1762	.3789	.6734	$O_D(00i0)$	.6989	.6079	.6790
$T_2(mzi0)$	.1852	.3775	.1816	$O_D(0zi0)$	.6908	.6043	.2019
$O_A(1000)$	.0269	.1242	.9960	$O_D(m000)$	.2038	.8740	.2107
$O_A(1z00)$	.9812	.1257	.4835	$O_D(mz00)$	.1709	.8564	.7197
$O_A(10i0)$	.4875	.6241	.4868	$O_D(m0i0)$	.6884	.3628	.7332
$O_A(1zi0)$	.5169	.6247	.9966	$O_D(mzi0)$	.7006	.3697	.1970
$O_A(2000)$	.5744	.9913	.1434				
$O_A(2z00)$	.5720	.9897	.6379				
$O_A(20i0)$	.0731	.4875	.6354				
$O_A(2zi0)$	.0734	.4932	.1386				

Celsian

	x	y	z
Ba(0000)	.2826	.0000	.0653
$T_1(0000)$	.0091	.1828	.1096
$T_1(0z00)$	.0073	.1832	.6142
$T_2(0000)$	.7058	.1205	.1733
$T_2(0z00)$	.7004	.1165	.6735
$O_{A1}(0000)$	.9996	.1382	.0003
$O_{A2}(0000)$	.6238	.0001	.1429
$O_B(0000)$	.8323	.1388	.1111
$O_B(0z00)$	.8221	.1368	.6133
$O_C(0000)$	.0224	.3072	.1233
$O_C(0z00)$	.0300	.3130	.6321
$O_D(0000)$	.1826	.1298	.1947
$O_D(0z00)$	.1904	.1232	.7019

Orthoclase

	x	y	z
K	.2838	0	.1373
T_1	.0095	.1844	.2239
T_2	.7089	.1178	.3443
O_{A1}	0	.1459	0
O_{A2}	.6346	0	.2851
O_B	.8280	.1470	.2282
O_C	.0349	.3106	.2607
O_D	.1815	.1258	.4065

Rb-feldspar

	x	y	z
Rb	.2958	0	.1468
T_1	.0104	.1904	.2227
T_2	.7227	.1195	.3440
O_{A1}	0	.1525	0
O_{A2}	.664	0	.283
O_B	.832	.1596	.226
O_C	.0464	.3145	.263
O_D	.1682	.1283	.403

Microcline, Brown and Bailey (1964); Low albite, Wainwright
(1968 and pers. comm.); High albite, Wainwright (pers. comm.);
Reedmergnerite, Appleman and Clark (1965); Primitive anorthite,
Wainwright and Starkey (1971); Celsian, Newnham and Megaw (1960);
Orthoclase, Ribbe (1963); Rb-feldspar, Gasperin (1971).

*Corrected from original data.

material and synthesis conditions. Alternatively it may be possible to remove M and Al atoms from an existing feldspar, resulting in recrystallization to Si_4O_8 composition and retention of the feldspar topology. This type of process has been achieved by several methods for the molecular sieve zeolites, Linde types X and Y, with the faujasite structure (e.g. see Proceedings of the Second International Conference of Zeolite Molecular Sieves; Gould, 1971).

Of actual feldspar structures, those of high sanidine and of Rb-feldspar should come closest to revealing the geometry of a T_4O_8 ideal framework free of M cations. They have the highest Si content, a disordered Al, Si distribution, and relatively weak M–O bonds.

In the absence of a T_4O_8 feldspar, an idea of its framework geometry can be obtained by building a model with tetrahedral stars made from metal rods linked together by tubes of plastic spaghetti. Such a skeletal model automatically adopts a configuration of least strain under the conditions that (a) the O–T–O bond angles are rigidly fixed at the ideal tetrahedral angle, (b) the T–O distances are rigidly held equal, and (c) the T–O–T angles are flexible. When the model is carefully made for a block of about 20 unit cells, it is remarkable how uniform is the framework.

I have not explored fully the features of this type of model, but even a casual examination shows that several features of feldspars can be "explained":

(a) The symmetry is monoclinic.

(b) The model is more compressible along the double crankshafts than along other directions (this is obvious merely by pulling on the model with one's fingers).

(c) The 8-membered rings of tetrahedra are non-circular and elongated as in Fig. 2-2.

(d) The twisting of the 4-rings from the ideal configuration of Fig. 2-1a is partly mimicked by the model, but not completely.

Obviously such a crude model could not be expected to closely represent a framework dependent on complex chemical bonding. Nevertheless it does show that there is an overall tendency in the feldspar framework to adopt a particular geometry that is dependent only on its particular topology. Even with stereoscopic photographs it is difficult to convey the features of a spaghetti-metal-rod model of the feldspar framework, and readers are urged to build an actual model.

The T–O–T angles of the spaghetti-metal rod model are not equal, showing that there are variations in the amount of strain at the oxygen sites. This implicitly invokes the idea of an aluminosilicate framework as an engineering structure. Such an approach was used explicitly by Megaw et al. (1962) to explain the geometrical features in anorthite and other feldspars. Indeed they found that in all feldspars there is a strong correlation between the observed strain irrespective of the type of M atom and irrespective of the distribution of T atoms. There are subtle variations from one feldspar to another, but here we shall consider the general nature of the interaction of the framework with the M atoms. In this discussion it is easiest to use just the idea of electrostatic interaction between ions, but it must be remembered that this is only one way of looking at the complex bonding.

Table 4-2. Size of tetrahedra in feldspars (nanometer and degree)

		T-O_A	T-O_B	T-O_C	T-O_D	mean	O_A-O_B	O_A-O_C	O_A-O_D	O_B-O_C	O_B-O_D	O_C-O_D	mean	ATB	ATC	ATD	BTC	BTD	CTD
Rb-Feldspar	T_1	.1633	.1629	.1644	.1634	.1635	.263	.273	.262	.269	.269	.266	.267	107.6	112.9	106.5	110.6	110.9	108.3
	T_2	.1633	.1627	.1634	.1635	.1632	.268	.260	.266	.267	.269	.270	.267	110.7	105.4	109.0	109.7	110.0	111.0
high sanidine	T_1	.1643	.1645	.1647	.1643	.1645	.2626	.2744	.2623	.2713	.2723	.2679	.2685	106.0	113.0	105.9	111.0	111.8	109.0
	T_2	.1645	.1631	.1645	.1638	.1640	.2686	.2598	.2675	.2676	.2709	.2717	.2717	110.1	104.6	108.8	109.9	111.5	111.7
low sanidine	T_1	.1654	.1641	.1661	.1666	.1656	.2642	.2774	.2655	.2712	.2735	.2700	.2703	106.6	113.6	106.2	110.4	111.5	108.5
	T_2	.1641	.1620	.1631	.1621	.1628	.2674	.2586	.2648	.2677	.2678	.2685	.2658	110.2	104.4	108.5	110.8	111.4	111.3
low microcline	T_1O	.1738	.1739	.1745	.1741	.1741	.2761	.2910	.2770	.2900	.2863	.2839	.2841	105.2	113.3	105.5	112.7	110.7	109.1
	T_1m	.1592	.1608	.1629	.1627	.1614	.2591	.2689	.2598	.2632	.2667	.2638	.2636	108.1	113.2	107.6	108.8	111.0	108.2
	T_2O	.1614	.1574	.1633	.1621	.1611	.2638	.2556	.2613	.2648	.2648	.2665	.2628	111.7	103.8	107.8	111.3	111.9	110.0
	T_2m	.1644	.1617	.1593	.1592	.1612	.2606	.2562	.2638	.2631	.2647	.2684	.2628	106.1	104.7	109.3	110.1	111.2	114.9
high albite	T_1O	.1652	.1651	.1645	.1653	.1650	.2606	.2778	.2615	.2711	.2749	.2697	.2693	104.2	114.9	104.6	110.7	112.6	109.8
	T_1m	.1653	.1630	.1643	.1632	.1640	.2626	.2736	.2626	.2692	.2704	.2675	.2677	106.2	112.3	106.2	110.6	112.0	109.5
	T_2O	.1653	.1646	.1637	.1629	.1641	.2676	.2614	.2664	.2701	.2702	.2715	.2679	108.5	105.2	108.5	110.7	111.2	112.5
	T_2m	.1646	.1628	.1641	.1656	.1643	.2683	.2643	.2674	.2676	.2695	.2721	.2682	110.1	107.0	108.1	109.9	110.3	111.3
low albite	T_1O	.1745	.1738	.1735	.1742	.1740	.2726	.2950	.2752	.2879	.2871	.2849	.2838	103.0	115.9	104.3	112.0	111.2	110.1
	T_1m	.1596	.1601	.1619	.1620	.1609	.2609	.2671	.2590	.2613	.2661	.2620	.2627	109.4	112.3	107.3	108.5	111.4	108.4
	T_2O	.1632	.1594	.1617	.1612	.1614	.2663	.2571	.2606	.2661	.2650	.2652	.2634	111.2	104.6	106.9	111.9	111.5	110.4
	T_2m	.1643	.1616	.1599	.1601	.1615	.2623	.2588	.2632	.2638	.2640	.2688	.2635	107.2	106.0	108.5	110.3	110.3	114.3
reedmerg- nerite	T_1O	.1478	.1470	.1443	.1467	.1465	.2338	.2444	.2345	.2402	.2415	.2401	.2391	104.9	113.4	105.6	110.9	110.6	111.0
	T_1m	.1595	.1602	.1624	.1618	.1610	.2579	.2712	.2580	.2631	.2644	.2622	.2628	107.6	114.8	106.8	109.3	110.4	107.9
	T_2O	.1634	.1585	.1625	.1613	.1614	.2619	.2552	.2620	.2690	.2672	.2640	.2632	108.9	103.1	107.6	113.9	113.4	109.3
	T_2m	.1646	.1620	.1606	.1614	.1622	.2653	.2595	.2619	.2637	.2669	.2703	.2646	108.6	105.9	106.9	109.7	111.3	114.2
celsian	T_1O	.1651	.1640	.1633	.1630	.1639	.2575	.2786	.2568	.2702	.2737	.2666	.2672	103.0	116.2	103.0	111.3	113.7	109.6
	T_1z	.1722	.1703	.1711	.1733	.1717	.2674	.2911	.2669	.2856	.2880	.2805	.2799	102.6	115.9	101.1	113.6	113.8	109.0
	T_2O	.1702	.1698	.1714	.1733	.1712	.2725	.2638	.2794	.2842	.2858	.2888	.2791	106.5	101.1	108.9	112.8	112.8	113.8
	T_2z	.1640	.1645	.1617	.1637	.1635	.2630	.2554	.2665	.2727	.2718	.2705	.2667	106.4	103.3	108.9	113.5	111.8	112.4

primitive anorthite																		
T_1O	.1645	.1619	.1582	.1616	.1616	.2517	.2767	.2524	.2650	.2710	.2627	.2632	100.9	118.1	101.4	111.7	113.8	110.4
T_1^1	.1632	.1606	.1588	.1626	.1613	.2536	.2736	.2533	.2664	.27C4	.2641	.2636	103.1	116.4	102.0	11C.9	113.6	110.5
T_1mc	.1777	.1705	.1738	.1779	.1750	.2810	.2917	.2706	.2893	.2874	.2905	.2851	107.6	112.2	99.1	114.3	111.1	111.4
T_1mic	.1777	.1747	.1752	.1702	.1745	.2685	.2944	.2824	.2928	.2860	.2809	.2845	99.3	113.1	108.5	113.6	113.3	108.8
T_1z	.1760	.1743	.1709	.1776	.1747	.2679	.2966	.2688	.2875	.2978	.2877	.2844	99.7	117.5	99.0	112.8	115.6	111.2
T_1zi	.1772	.1755	.1727	.1767	.1755	.2647	.3046	.2654	.2907	.2994	.2874	.2854	97.2	121.0	97.2	113.2	116.4	110.7
T_1mzc	.1647	.1617	.1617	.1571	.1613	.2515	.2733	.2618	.2671	.2665	.2589	.2632	100.8	113.7	108.8	111.4	113.4	108.6
T_1mzic	.1644	.1583	.1599	.1626	.1613	.2580	.2693	.2543	.2656	.2661	.2650	.2630	106.1	112.3	102.1	113.1	112.1	110.5
T_2O	.1760	.1769	.1740	.1698	.1742	.2871	.2760	.2795	.2920	.2807	.2900	.2842	108.9	104.1	107.8	112.6	108.1	115.0
T_2^1	.1769	.1751	.1754	.1727	.1750	.2715	.2698	.2822	.2916	.2949	.2964	.2844	101.0	99.9	107.6	112.7	115.9	116.7
T_2mc	.1644	.1581	.1607	.1629	.1615	.2572	.2569	.2664	.2658	.2585	.2672	.2637	111.9	104.4	108.9	113.0	107.3	111.3
T_2mic	.1641	.1618	.1586	.1616	.1615	.2550	.2584	.2633	.2666	.2629	.2659	.2637	108.8	106.4	107.9	112.6	108.7	112.3
T_2z	.1635	.1620	.1606	.1605	.1617	.2588	.2505	.2657	.2682	.2670	.2706	.2635	105.3	101.2	110.2	112.5	111.8	144.8
T_2zi	.1617	.1628	.1614	.1574	.1608	.2645	.2520	.2630	.2701	.2576	.2675	.2624	109.2	102.5	111.0	112.9	107.1	114.1
T_2mzc	.1755	.1748	.1716	.1757	.1744	.2844	.2767	.2751	.2845	.2905	.2934	.2841	108.6	105.7	103.1	110.4	111.9	116.3
T_2mzic	.1759	.1713	.1735	.1774	.1745	.2850	.2776	.2846	.2858	.2834	.2928	.2849	110.3	105.2	107.3	112.0	108.7	113.1

See Table 4-1 for sources of data.

Table 4-3. Intertetrahedral angles (in degrees) at specified oxygen

	A_1	A_2	B_0	B_m	C_0	C_m	D_0	D_m
Rb-feldspar	144.9	143.8	152.2		130.9		142.1	
High sanidine	145.1	137.9	152.3		131.4		141.7	
Low sanidine	144.8	137.8	153.3		131.1		141.6	
Low microcline	144.7	138.5	151.2	155.9	130.7	130.7	140.0	143.2
High albite	143.1	129.7	140.7	158.3	130.5	134.3	134.9	149.8
Low albite	141.6	130.2	139.7	160.9	129.6	136.0	134.1	152.0
Reedmergnerite	143.1	128.7	140.5	158.1	124.9	135.9	135.4	146.3
Celsian 0	139.4	135.2	150.2		127.0		139.4	
z			149.6		130.2		138.1	
Anorthite 0	136.2	125.3	129.4	170.8	132.8	130.5	137.8	140.3
i	140.0	122.5	135.9	145.3	130.8	130.9	124.6	166.9
z	135.3	124.0	139.6	143.5	131.2	127.5	125.2	161.4
iz	136.1	125.9	128.3	163.6	130.8	130.5	132.6	138.5

See Table 4-1 for sources of numbers. Because Starkey and Wainwright did not list T–O–T angles for anorthite those given by Megaw et al. (1962) are quoted instead; probably the maximum difference is about 1°.

The basic data on feldspar structures are given in Table 4-2 (T–O and O–O distances and O–T–O angles), Table 4-3 (T–O–T angles) and Table 4-4 (M–O distances). The O–T–O and T–O–T angles are plotted on Figs. 4-1 and 4-2: see Smith and Ribbe (1969) for detailed explanation of averaging of tetrahedra for the low-symmetry structures. From these figures, it is obvious that the distortions of the framework in all feldspars have common features modified to a greater or lesser extent depending on the type of M atom and the type of Al, Si order or disorder.

Entrance of large M atoms into the interstices involves only moderate deformation of the aluminosilicate framework, but entrance of small M atoms involves considerable distortion. The details of such distortions are given later; here it is convenient to look at the situation for large K atoms in high sanidine. Figure 4-3 is a projection down the c-axis onto the $a^* b^*$ plane, rotated 26° with respect to Fig. 2-5 which is projected down c^*. Whereas Fig. 2-5 shows the linkage between the tetrahedral nodes for a full unit cell, Fig. 4-3 selects only that part of the atomic structure sufficient to illustrate the bonding between the K and O atoms. The tetrahedral nodes labelled t u d e f are common to both figures: the nodes a b c r s of Fig. 2-5 are also present in Fig. 4-3, but are unlabelled. These nodes outline a T-shaped 10-membered ring of tetrahedra as described in Chapter 2. The heights of the oxygen atoms of the 10-membered ring vary only from 71 to 78 hundredths of the c-axis, showing that they are almost coplanar.

The K atom at 86 hundredths has nine nearest neighbors (at distances given in Table 4-4), five of which (A_2; A_1, twice; C, twice) belong to the same 10-membered ring. The coordination polyhedron is completed by two O_D at height 60 and two O_B at height 122 (i.e. at height 22 hundredths in the overlying unit cell). From the heights it is possible to envisage the shape of the coordination polyhedron. The K atom at height 114 is related to the one at height 86 by a two-

Table 4-4. Cation-oxygen distances (nanometer)

	Cation	A_{10}	A_{1c}	A_2	B_0	B_m	C_0	C_m	D_0	D_m
Rb-feldspar	Rb	0.307		0.295		0.317		0.312		0.304
High sanidine	K, Na	0.2910		0.2707		0.3017		0.3140		0.2953
Low sanidine	K, Na	0.2893		0.2711		0.3045		0.3129		0.2945
Low microcline	K, Na	0.2877	0.2881	0.2750	0.2961	0.3136	0.2907	0.3335	0.2892	0.2993
High albite	Na	0.2596	0.2693	0.2348	0.2507	0.3188	0.3358	0.2927	0.2474	(0.313)
Low albite	Na	0.2669	0.2535	0.2369	0.2454	0.3460	0.2978	0.3260	0.2435	0.3003
Oligoclase, An_{28}	Na, Ca	0.2561	0.2635	0.2338	0.2455	0.3215	0.3275	0.3012	0.2443	0.3133
Reedmergnerite	Na	0.2455	0.2489	0.2397	0.2410	0.3117	0.3452	0.2808	0.2380	0.2860
Celsian	Ba, K		0.2850	0.2667	0.2927	0.2939	0.3112	0.3135	0.2909	0.2902
Anorthite (0)	Ca	0.2608	0.2515	0.2292	0.2378	(0.384)	0.3098	(0.328)	0.2390	0.2538
(zi)	Ca	0.2454	0.2658*	0.2300	0.2405	(0.325)	(0.354)	0.2834	0.2440	0.2717
(z)	Ca	0.2496	0.2733	0.2333	0.2443	0.2494	(0.382)	0.2559	0.2372	(0.372)
(i)	Ca	0.2448	0.2817	0.2336	0.2494	0.2494	(0.380)	0.2563	0.2434	(0.388)

See Table 4-1 for sources of data: oligoclase, Phillips et al. (1971). Note that one or two extra atoms of type A_2 lie at distances of 0.32 nm upwards, but have been ignored. The bracketed numbers were calculated by Ribbe et al. (1969) and Megaw et al. (1962). The asterisked number was calculated by M. W. Phillips; Wainwright and Starkey gave 0.2616.

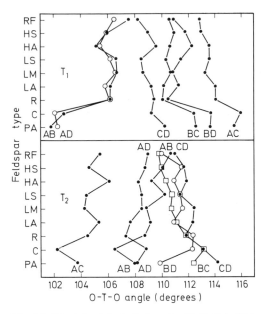

Fig. 4-1. The intra-tetrahedral angles O–T–O in feldspars. The abbreviations for the feldspar types represent Rb-feldspar, high sanidine, high albite, low sanidine, low microcline, low albite, reedmergnerite, celsian and primitive anorthite. The lines are labelled by the codes of the two oxygens involved in the angle. Averaged data are used when there is more than one type of T_1 (or of T_2) tetrahedra. See Table 4-2 for numerical data

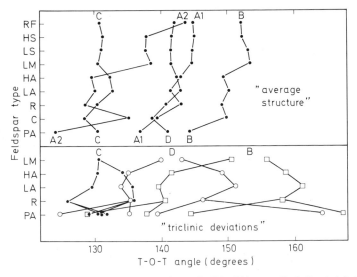

Fig. 4-2. The inter-tetrahedral angles T–O–T in feldspars. Each line is labelled with the code of the oxygen. The upper half shows the angles for the "average structure" as explained in the text. The lower half shows the individual angles for the triclinic feldspars, thereby revealing the "triclinic deviations". The abbreviations for the feldspar types represent Rb-feldspar, high sanidine, high albite, low sanidine, low microcline, low albite, reedmergnerite, celsian and primitive anorthite. See Table 4-3 for numerical data

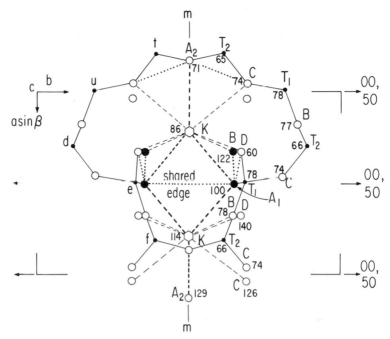

Fig. 4-3. The environment and bonding of K atoms in high sanidine, as seen in a projection down the c-axis. The heights of atoms are given in percentage of c. A 10-membered ring of tetrahedra is outlined. Potassium-oxygen bonds are shown by dashes, the heavy ones showing the short distances to A_2 and A_1 oxygens. Oxygen edges shared between polyhedra are shown by dotted lines. The positions of some rotation diad axes are shown. The labelling of some of the tetrahedral nodes is like that in Fig. 2-5

fold rotation axis at height 100 halfway along the edge $a \sin \beta$. The related 10-membered ring is not outlined to avoid confusion. Figure 2-4 shows the coordination viewed down the b-axis.

A crucial factor in the cation-oxygen bonding is the shared edge of the oxygen polyhedra of the two K ions, joining the pair of A_1 oxygens in the middle of Fig. 4-3. This feature was particularly emphasized by Megaw et al. (1962). Sharing of this edge results in a closer approach of these two K atoms than of any other pair of K atoms.

Each coordination polyhedron around a K atom has three other types of shared edges: the A_2C edge shared with a T_2 tetrahedron, and the A_1B and A_1D edges shared with two different T_1 tetrahedra. Each of these shared edges occurs twice per coordination polyhedron to satisfy the mirror plane (see dotted lines in Fig. 4-3). The simple electrostatic model of Pauling yielded his second rule that a shared edge results in cation repulsion plus shortening of the edge in order to maintain the usual cation-oxygen distance. The distances and angles of tetrahedra in Table 4-2 show good agreement with this rule when account is taken of the difficulties of satisfying all the geometrical features of a feldspar structure. In high sanidine, the A_2C edge of T_2 and the A_1B and A_1D edges of T_1 have lengths 0.260, 0.263 and 0.262 nm which are shorter than all the other tetrahedral edges which range from 0.268 to 0.274 nm. A similar pattern is seen in celsian. For the triclinic feldspars, there is a general tendency for the distances to obey the same pattern, but the distortions cause detailed changes too complex to pursue here. Such a study would be seriously complicated by the problem of deciding which oxygens are to be selected as being bonded to an M atom. The shortening of shared edges is shown clearly in Fig. 4-1: the average A_2T_2C, A_1T_1B and A_1T_1D angles for each feldspar are less than all other angles.

The effect of edge sharing on the oxygen polyhedron around each M atom is especially dramatic because edges shared with oxygen tetrahedra are about 0.1 nm shorter than unshared edges. However, this effect cannot be ascribed completely to Pauling's second rule because the major factor is the mismatch between the size of the polyhedral edges of the T and M cations. A complete tabulation of edges for the M polyhedra in reedmergnerite and low albite is given by Appleman and Clark (1965, Table 8). The $O_A(1000) - O_A(100c)$ edge shared between two M polyhedra is shorter than most of the shared edges, but is slightly longer than the unshared edge $O_D(0) - O_D(m)$.

Certainly the common features of the feldspar variants cannot be explained completely just in terms of shared edges. An alternative approach by Megaw et al. ignored the shared edges between the M and T polyhedra, and concentrated on the shared edge between adjacent M polyhedra (Fig. 4-3) and especially the short $M - O_{A2}$ distance (Table 4-4). The treatment especially concerned anorthite, for which the $Ca - O_{A2}$ distances are particularly short.

Megaw et al. stated that the "shielding shell of Ca comprises ten O's (two each of $O_A(1)$, $O_A(2)$, O_B, O_C, O_D). The only serious gap in it is at the edge $O_A(1) - O_A(1)$ across which there is another Ca at a distance of about 4 Å" (i.e. 0.4 nm). Repulsion of the pair of Ca cations causes the cations to recede, and the $O_A(1)$ atoms to approach. However shortening of the $O_A(1) - O_A(1)$ distance is resisted by the aluminosilicate framework. Megaw et al. went on to develop an engineering model of feldspar depicted here in projections down the b and c axes in Fig. 4-4.

The b-axis projection (Fig. 4-4a) is bounded approximately by $y = \pm 0.3$ and includes all atoms except O_C. In this idealized model, the slab obeys symmetry mmm with M, O_{A1} and O_{A2} each lying at the intersection of two mirror planes, while atoms O_B and O_D are equivalent lying on a single mirror plane. The c-axis projection (Fig. 4-4c) shows how the slabs are cross-linked by bonds to O_{A2} atoms, and by bonds from the Ca atom.

Returning to the b-axis projection (Fig. 4-4b), the linkage is displayed between the upper rings of the slab centered at $y = 0$ in Fig. 4-4a and the lower rings of a slab centered at $y = 1/2$ but not shown in Fig. 4-4a. This linkage destroys the orthorhombic symmetry and provides a topologic distinction between O_B and O_D.

Megaw et al. pointed out that the repeat distance in the a^* direction is determined by the links EF and EF' in Fig. 4-4a and GH in Fig. 4-4b shown as heavy lines. In anorthite, the $Ca - O_{A2}$ bonds are short (0.229 to 0.234 nm; Table 4-4) compared to a typical $Ca - O$ distance of 0.24 nm. Hence the links EFF' should be under compression to be balanced by a tension in the links joining G to H. Megaw *et al.* assumed that the tension would affect bond angles rather than bond lengths. Making the *implicit* assumption that T–O–T angles stayed constant, and that only O–T–O angles varied, they deduced that there should be increases in the angles marked in Fig. 4-4d and decreases in BT_2D and AT_2C. The latter decrease causes T_2-O_C to rotate downwards into the plane of the diagram. In Fig. 4-4a, the stress on EFF′ should cause BT_1D to decrease and BT_2D to increase. Because change in BT_1D affects the length GH more than the lengths EF, EF′, Megaw *et al.* deduced that the angle BT_1D should increase. For BT_2D, they estimated that the strains should roughly compensate. Hence for the twelve O–T–O angles, they predicted that BT_1C, BT_1D, BT_2C and CT_2D should be greater than the ideal tetrahedral angle while AT_2C should be less. Examination of Fig. 4-1 shows that the prediction is obeyed by all feldspars.

I think that there is considerable merit in the model of Megaw *et al.*, but that it needs further examination in the light of possible changes of T–O–T angles and of the effect of edge sharing between T and M polyhedra.

The K–O distances in high sanidine vary from 0.271 for A_2 to 0.314 nm for the C oxygens (Table 4-4), and it is possible to find further oxygens at distances below 0.4 nm. For such an irregular polyhedron, it is difficult to interpret the bonding even on a simple electrostatic model. However taking into account the effect of shielding by closer oxygens, at least the nine oxygens shown in Fig. 4-3 should be considered as bonded to each K atom on an electrostatic model. Ideally for an electrostatic model, there is a local charge balance. If the bond strength were taken to be equal for each bond emanating from a cation, there would be a local charge imbalance for sanidine and all other feldspars. Indeed one can show that no matter how the Al and Si atoms are distributed in $AlSi_3$ feldspars there would be some charge imbalance except for very extreme distortions of the framework. Just consider the A_1 and A_2 oxygen atoms: at least one of these must be bonded to two silicons giving complete electrostatic neutralization on a simple ionic model. It is impossible to move the K cation into a position in which it is not within bonding distance to two A_1 and one A_2 oxygen atoms (see heavy bonds in Fig. 4-3). Hence at least one of these oxygens must be oversatisfied electrostatically. On an ionic model, such a lack of local charge balance can be compensated by variations of T–O distances (as was used by Smith (1953) for interpretation of the melilite structure). It is futile to attempt to understand the bonding of the M cations separately from that of the aluminosilicate framework.

For M atoms smaller than K, the aluminosilicate framework contracts. It is impossible for all nine oxygens coordinated to a K atom to approach the M site simultaneously while maintaining the proper T–O distances. Bonding of M atoms to the A_2 and two A_1 oxygens is retained in all feldspars (Table 4-4). As these three oxygen atoms approach a small atom in the M site, at least two or three of the B, C and D oxygens are forced away to greater distances while several approach to shorter distances. This reciprocal movement results in loss of the plane of symmetry, as for example in albite (Taylor *et al.*, 1934). All feldspars with small atoms in the M site are triclinic, but the details of the distortion are very complex (Table 4-4 and Fig. 4-5). Of course, a feldspar may become tri-

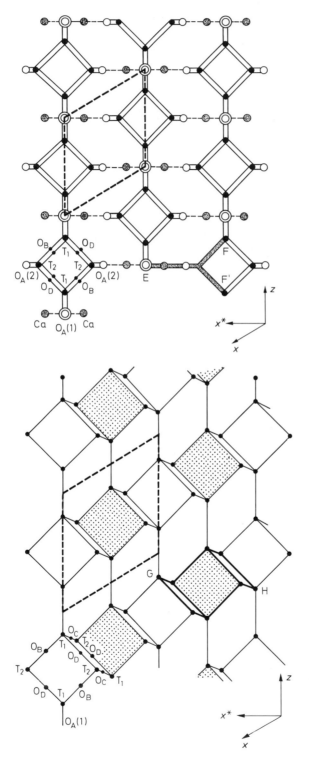

Fig. 4-4a. Legend see opposite page

Fig. 4-4b. Legend see opposite page

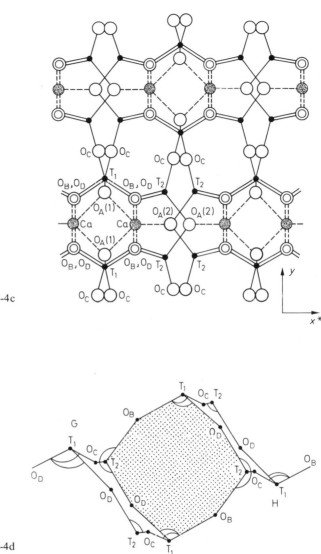

Fig. 4-4c

Fig. 4-4d

Fig. 4-4. The engineering model of feldspar by Megaw, Kempster, and Radoslovich. a Projection down *b* of a slab bounded by $y = \pm 0.3$. The T, O and Ca atoms are shown respectively by large dots, open circle and speckled circles. The O_{A1} atoms, however, are shown by the concentric circles. Light dashes show Ca–O_{A2} bonds. Heavy dashes outline a unit cell of the ideal feldspar structure. The heavy lines joining EFF' are interpreted to be under compression to compensate for the short Ca–O_{A2} bonds. Double lines show overlap. b Skeletal version of (a) showing T and O atoms as small dots, and showing how the slabs from (a) are linked to form the framework. Note the region GH interpreted to be under tension. c Projection down *c* using the same symbols as in (a). d Details of linkage between GH of (b). The marked angles are interpreted to increase to compensate for the short Ca–O_{A2} bonds. (From Megaw *et al.*, 1962, Figs. 5a, 5b, 5c and 6)

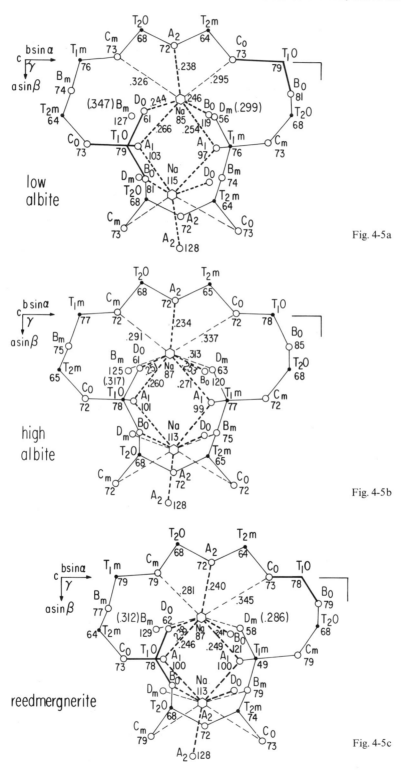

Fig. 4-5a

Fig. 4-5b

Fig. 4-5c

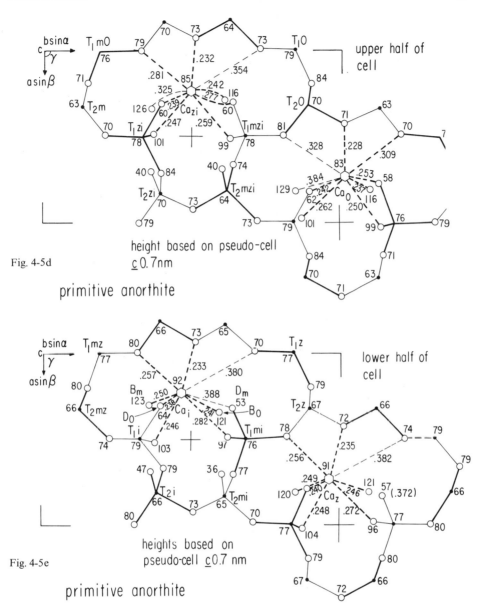

Fig. 4-5d

height based on pseudo-cell
$\underline{c}\,0.7\,nm$

primitive anorthite

Fig. 4-5e

heights based on
pseudo-cell $\underline{c}\,0.7\,nm$

primitive anorthite

Fig. 4-5. The environment of Na atoms in (a) low albite (b) high albite (c) reedmergnerite (d, e) primitive anorthite as viewed down the c-axis. The symbolism follows Fig. 4-3. a The long bonds to the $T_1 0$ nodes occupied by Al atoms are emphasized by heavy lines. The five short Na–O bonds are shown by heavy dashes. The long bonds to C_0 and C_m oxygens are shown by light dashes; those to B_m and D_m are not shown to avoid overlap, but the distances are given in brackets. Heights are given as percentage of c. One unit cell is outlined, but only about half of the atoms are shown. b As for (a), except that tetrahedral nodes are equally occupied by Al, Si atoms on a statistical basis. c as for (a), except that the heavy lines show the short distances to tetrahedral nodes occupied by boron atoms. d and e. The upper and lower halves of the 1.4 nm unit cell are shown separately, as explained in the text. The Al–O bonds are shown by heavy lines. Abbreviated Megaw codes are used for the Ca and T atoms: note that the operator c for a center of symmetry has been omitted. Slightly more than one unit cell is shown to permit comparison of Ca atoms related by the pseudo C-face-centering

clinic anyway because of the topochemistry of the Al, Si distribution (Chapter 2), but this is a relatively small effect when the M atom is large (cf. sanidine and microcline; Table 4-4).

Apparently there is an upper size limit on M atoms, because Cs does not substitute fully for K unless a larger atom is simultaneously substituting for Al or Si in T sites. The crystal-chemical control of chemical substitutions is explored in detail in Chapter 14.

The role played by local charge neutralization has been controversial since Ferguson et al. (1958) proposed that maximum stability of a feldspar at room temperature corresponded to the best approach to local balance of charge on a formal ionic model. For their calculations for both ordered and disordered $AlSi_3$ feldspars, they concluded that the most stable feldspar might be partly disordered. MacKenzie and Smith (1959) criticized the proposal on several grounds: (a) it took no account of the variation of stability of feldspars with temperature (b) its prediction of the stability of orthoclase (i.e. low sanidine) rather than microcline at room temperature was inconsistent with many geological observations (c) the method of calculation of charge balance for disordered patterns implicitly assumed that the electric charges operated over large distances because an average Al content was used for every T site.

MacKenzie and Smith thought that the charge balance should be calculated for near neighbors because atoms act as partial electrostatic screens subject to an overall electrostatic neutrality of the whole crystal. For high sanidine and low sanidine, MacKenzie and Smith estimated the charge balance by averaging the results for individual Al, Si distributions which added up to the disordered Al, Si pattern. Such mean charge balances were unfavorable with respect to that for microcline, a conclusion opposite to that using the Ferguson et al. procedure. Ferguson et al. (1959) replied to the criticism, but by 1973, it seems safe to say that qualitative use of ideas based on local charge balance as modified by MacKenzie and Smith is consistent with experimental and geologic evidence on the stability of feldspars at low temperature (see supporting arguments by Laves and Goldsmith, 1961).

Crystal-chemical criticisms of the ideas of Ferguson et al. also were made by Brown and Bailey (1964) and Appleman and Clark (1965). Nevertheless Gait et al. (1970) went on to provide a very thorough analysis of low albite.

First, they considered the effective coordination of oxygen atoms around Na on the basis of shielding by oxygens lying closer to the Na atom using exactly the same method as for an astronomical eclipse. The shielding of the nearest five oxygens is zero, and for the next four is less than 7%. Because they obtained the lowest electrostatic charge unbalance for a coordination number of 6, they accepted this value rather than a larger value. Secondly, they assumed that the charge from a cation is distributed to the oxygens in the ratio of the inverse square of the bond length (supposedly, but not actually a consequence of Coulomb's law). Finally, they changed mathematically the distribution of Al and Si atoms among the four tetrahedral sites by varying the assumed distances of Al–O and Si–O for complete order and interpolating linearly with the observed T–O distances. Using a computer program and a coordination number of six, they found that the smallest unbalance of charge at the oxygen atoms occurred for Al–O 0.1777 and Si–O 0.1602 nm.

Gait *et al.* concluded that low albite "can reasonably be interpreted as conforming exactly to Pauling's second rule governing ionic crystals" with the formal charge of the ions distributed according to the inverse square of the bond lengths. They concluded that the error in the reference T–O distances in the light of charge unbalance could be considered as ± 0.0003 for Al–O and ± 0.0002 nm for Si–O. Finally they concluded that the best charge distribution occurs for 82% Al in $T_1 0$, rather than for a fully ordered pattern.

My own view is that the ionic model is valuable, and gives a semiquantitative interpretation of some features of albite and other feldspars. Nevertheless I do not accept these detailed conclusions about the T–O distances, because the arguments are not based firmly on physical laws.

The problem of interpretation of disordered structures comes up in another guise. All the data in Tables 4-1 and 4-4 are for an average of the contents of all unit cells. In quenched high albite it is quite clear that the Al, Si disorder results in displacements of atoms from one unit cell to another of up to 0.05 nm, in round figures (e.g. Ribbe *et al.*, 1969).

In addition to this type of disorder, there is thermal vibration. Chapter 11 contains a detailed analysis of the infra-red spectrum of feldspars in terms of vibrations and rotations of adjacent atoms, together with estimates of force constants. These force constants provide a quantitative justification for the qualitative analysis of the bonding in feldspars by Megaw. Badly needed is a study of the thermal diffuse scattering of X-rays by feldspars in order to measure the coupling between clusters of atoms: the study of Na_2BeFa_4 with monochromatized radiation by S. Deganello (1971, Ph. D. thesis at the University of Chicago) is a suitable guide. Measurements of "temperature factors" by routine X-ray structure analysis give some information on the vibrations of atoms, but do not reveal coupled vibrations.

Megaw *et al.* (1962) proposed that because the T–O bonds of anorthite are stiffer than the Ca–O bonds, the tetrahedral framework should vibrate as a whole unit in "lattice" modes, while the Ca ions should vibrate more independently in Einstein modes. The sparse structural data suggest that with increasing temperature to a first approximation the feldspar framework tends to adopt a more symmetric geometry and the M atoms tend to act as though they are larger. Apart from these effects, there is no need to modify any of the general remarks made in this section.

Megaw *et al.* (1962) found that in anorthite the T atoms were displaced less from the mean positions for the pseudo-structure than were the oxygen atoms. They interpreted this as the result of easier flexing of T–O–T than of O–T–O angles, and related this observation to speculations on thermal vibration.

In conclusion, the general features of the feldspar structures can be envisaged in terms of a framework of fairly rigid tetrahedra which adopts a configuration of least strain by flexing of T–O–T and O–T–O angles in response to interaction with M atoms. The electrostatic model provides considerable help for interpretation of the interaction of the atoms, but the chemical bonding must be more complex requiring consideration of a covalent contribution.

The detailed analyses in the succeeding sections will reveal the following general rules for comparing the geometry of the various feldspar structures. For the coordination polyhedra, the Si tetrahedra tend to be more regular than the

Al tetrahedra, while the T_1 tetrahedra tend to be more distorted than the T_2 tetrahedra. The M polyhedra are extremely irregular both as regards distances and angles. For the framework (averaged to the pseudo-monoclinic 0.7 nm cell for the low-symmetry types): the T–O–T angles tend to depend mostly on the size and considerably less on the charge of the M cation; the O–T–O angles tend to depend more on the charge of the M cation than on other factors; and the perturbations of T–O distances in a tetrahedron tend to depend on the Al, Si distribution over the tetrahedral nodes.

4.2 Geometry of the Framework

4.2.1 T–O Distances and O–T–O Angles

Table 4-2 yields abundant evidence for variations of T–O distances in the same tetrahedron much greater than the experimental error. The effect is especially evident for the ordered structures, but is still significant for high sanidine and high albite. In anorthite and celsian the alternation of Si and Al atoms means that the variation has nothing to do with the occupancy of neighboring tetrahedra nodes, but in the ordered $AlSi_3$ structures such an effect must be considered.

Detailed interpretation began with the study of anorthite by Megaw et al. (1962). Initially attention was focused on single features such as the correlation between T–O distance and the number of M atoms bonded to the oxygen. Such correlations were found to be only moderate, partly because the T–O distances actually correlate with several factors, and partly because of experimental error. Recently, Phillips and Ribbe (1972) and Phillips et al. (1972a, b) used multiple linear regression analysis to evaluate simultaneously the correlations between T–O distances and other structural features. In addition new structural analyses reduce the obscuring effect of experimental error. The present treatment utilizes the review by Ribbe et al. (1972).

For anorthite, Megaw et al. (1962) found a nice correlation between the T–O distance and the number of Ca atoms bonded to the oxygen when mean values were taken for each group. For Si–O tetrahedra, the mean T–O distances were 0.1632, 0.1622 and 0.1588 nm and for Al–O, 0.1780, 0.1755 and 0.1719 nm, respectively, for 2, 1 and 0 Ca neighbors. Not only are the differences statistically significant with respect to experimental error, they are also in the expected direction for a strengthening (and hence shortening) of the T–O distance as the bonding from the Ca atoms is reduced. Revised values for the Wainwright and Starkey data are: 0.1641, 0.1620, 0.1583; 0.1773, 0.1755 and 0.1714. Fleet et al. (1966) showed that in primitive anorthite and in bytownite, An_{80}, with the body-centered anorthite structure, the mean of the two T–O distances to a framework oxygen tends to fall about 0.008 nm as the distance to the adjacent (Ca, Na) cation increases from 0.23 to 0.38 nm. These correlations are also consistent with a compensation of stronger bonding from M atoms by weaker bonding from T atoms.

In $AlSi_3$ feldspars the situation is more complex. In high albite, the mean T–O distance decreases with decreasing number of M atoms bonded to the oxygen: 0.1652, 0.1648, 0.1638 nm, respectively, for 2, 1 and 0 Na neighbors. However in microcline (Brown and Bailey, 1964) the trend is opposite: for Si–O the trend is 0.1592, 0.1609, 0.1622 or 0.1592, 0.1610 and 0.1631 depending whether the K atom is taken as bonded to seven or eight oxygens. In reedmergnerite and low albite, the data are inconclusive (Appleman and Clark, 1965). More recent analysis by Ribbe et $al.$ (1972) shows that the situation is complicated by the ordering of the $AlSi_3$ atoms. Thus in low albite the mean Si–O distance to oxygens bonded to 1 Si and 1 Al is 0.1596 compared to 0.1621 for oxygens bonded to 2 Si. The multiple regression analysis by Phillips and Ribbe (1972) shows that the T–O distances in monoclinic K-rich feldspars correlate with the Al-content of the T site, the T–O–T angle, the sum of K–O distances and the Al-content of the adjacent T site. Complete regression analyses have been completed for only a few feldspars, but it is obvious that the situation is complex. Now to details.

Jones and Taylor (1968) reported an inverse relation between the T–O–T angle and the constituent T–O distances. Independently Brown et $al.$ (1969) studied the possible factors influencing T–O distances using regression analysis of T–O distances with other structural features in 14 accurate framework structures including 7 feldspars. In all the structures, there was a good correlation coefficient between Si–O or Al–O bond length and T–O–T bond angle which was used as evidence for $d-p\pi$ bonding. All data were consistent with a regression line in which the T–O distance dropped by about 0.004–0.007 nm as the T–O–T angle increased from 120 to 180°. The correlation coefficients were around 0.4 to 0.7.

For anorthite, they found that on average the Ca–O distance correlated inversely with distances from the oxygen to each of the adjacent Si and Al atoms, consistent with the earlier data of Fleet et $al.$ (1966) for the sum of Al–O and Si O distances in bytownite and anorthite. The Ca–O distance correlated positively with the T–O–T angle, but the scatter of the data points is rather large. The new data by Wainwright and Starkey (1971) give considerably less scatter, and enhance the conclusions of Brown et $al.$

Multiple regression analysis of the Wainwright-Starkey data was used by Phillips et $al.$ (1972a, b) to determine the factors most highly correlated with individual Si–O and Al–O bond lengths. All 4 calciums were assumed to be bonded to 7 oxygens (the unbracketed ones in Table 4-4). Because every oxygen is bonded to 1 Al and 1 Si, the only possible bonding effects from first neighbors involve the Al–O–Si angle and the sum of the Ca–O bonds. The parameter $\Sigma(Ca-O)^{-2}$ and several other functions which measure the strength of bonding from the Ca atoms gave strong correlation coefficients with both Si–O and Al–O distances (e.g. 0.82 and 0.70 for Si–O and Al–O, respectively, vs. the above parameter). There was a weak correlation with $-1/\cos(T-O-T')$: 0.30 and 0.28 for Si–O and Al–O respectively.

Phillips and Ribbe (1972) analyzed the more difficult problem of K-feldspars in which ordering of Al, Si atoms between the T sites provides an additional complexity. They utilized the T–O data for five K-feldspars refined with monoclinic symmetry and chose the following parameters as independent variables (a) Al-content of the T site estimated from the Ribbe-Gibbs relation, (b)

$-1/\cos(T–O–T)$, (c) $\Sigma(K–O)^{-2}$, and (d) the Al-content of the other T site linked to the oxygen. The K atom was arbitrarily assumed to bond to 7 oxygens because addition of 2 more (type C in Table 4-4) gave poorer regressions. After t-tests indicated that all four independent variables were statistically significant, the following data were obtained:

Variable	Regression coefficient	Computed t	Partial correlation coefficient
Al-content	0.137(12)	11.6	0.89
$-1/\cos(T–O–T)$	0.067(16)	4.1	0.57
$\Sigma(K–O)^{-2}$	0.070(25)	2.8	0.43
Al-content of other T site	−0.031(12)	− 2.6	−0.40

Added in Proof. Phillips and Ribbe (1973) made a similar study of sodic plagioclase, and found the following regression coefficients corresponding to column 2 of the above text-table: 0.122, 0.029, 0.063 and −0.037.

Phillips and Ribbe attributed the smaller effect of K–O in alkali feldspars compared to Ca–O in anorthite to result in part from the divalent nature of the Ca ion. They stated that the linkage factor (i.e. the Al-content of the other T site) was least for disordered alkali feldspars, and that it increased with ordering in alkali feldspars, and decreased with substitution of Ca. Finally they calculated equations relating individual T–O distances to the cell dimensions c and b which depend on the degree of ordering (Chapter 7): the standard deviation between observed and predicted distances is 0.0005 nm.

In summary, the individual T–O distances of feldspars correlate rather well (mostly within 0.001 nm) with factors involving the local atoms of the aluminosilicate framework and the nearby M atoms. Qualitatively it seems reasonable to interpret the data by combining concepts of local charge balance for an ionic model with the effects of σ- and π-bonding in a covalent model.

Fleet *et al.* (1966) compared the distortions of T–O distances in tetrahedra of type $T_1 0$, $T_1 m$, $T_2 0$ and $T_2 m$ for anorthite, bytownite, high and low albite, maximum microcline and reedmergnerite ("averaged structures" were used for the first two). The correlation coefficients were high between low albite, maximum microcline and reedmergnerite; and between anorthite, bytownite and to a lesser degree high albite. Similar conclusions were reached by Srinivasan and Ribbe (1965). Obviously the distortions strongly depend on the distribution of Al and Si in ordered feldspars, being similar for $AlSi_3$ and BSi_3 feldspars and different from the distortions in Al_2Si_2 feldspars. In the disordered $AlSi_3$ feldspar, high albite, the even distribution over the nodes tends to cause distortions similar to those for the strictly alternating pattern of anorthite and celsian.

In the preceding section, the persistence of structural features from one feldspar to another was discussed in terms of shared polyhedral edges and the Megaw engineering model involving tension at the short $Ca–O_{A2}$ bonds. Readers are referred to Megaw *et al.* (1962, Table 10) and Appleman and Clark (1965, Table 11) for pertinent tables on distortions. Fig. 4-1 shows that the O–T–O angles for the averaged structure of $AlSi_3$ and BSi_3 feldspars are mostly consistent within $2°$. The close resemblance between the angles for high albite and low albite and for the three K-feldspars shows that disordering the Al and Si atoms has little effect on distortion of the tetrahedra. The angular distortions for anorthite and celsian are quite different from those of the $AlSi_3$ feldspars, and tend to be about 50% larger. This would be consistent with at least some of the distortion resulting from the M atom. On the whole, the difference between anorthite and celsian is similar to that between albite and K-feldspar, indicating the effect of going from a small to a large M atom. For the low-symmetry feldspars, the individual deviations are larger than the averaged ones shown in Fig. 4-1. By 1973, there had been no attempt to interpret the subtle differences in O–T–O angles from one feldspar to another. Perhaps correlation with the ionic potential of and distance to the M cation would permit a detailed analysis.

Ribbe *et al.* (1972) quantified the distortion of tetrahedra by the parameter σ where

$$\sigma^2 = \sum_6 [(O–T–O) – 109.5°]^2/5 .$$

Table 4-5 shows values of σ calculated from data in Table 4-2. Rb-feldspar has the lowest distortion of all feldspars. Distortion is greatest in the ordered feldspars, and tends to be greater for Al- than Si-bearing tetrahedra. It also tends to be

Table 4-5. Distortion (σ) of tetrahedra (degrees)

| | Monoclinic $AlSi_3$ | | |
	Rb-feldspar	High sanidine	Low sanidine
T_1	2.40	3.01	2.90
T_2	2.05	2.60	2.68

| | Triclinic $AlSi_3$ and BSi_3 | | |
	Low microcline	High albite	Low albite	Reedmergnerite
$T_1 0$	3.48	4.27	4.28	3.38
$T_1 m$	2.18 (Si)	2.72	1.92 (Si)	2.91 (Si)
$T_2 0$	3.15 (Si)	2.60	2.97 (Si)	3.98 (Si)
$T_2 m$	3.66 (Si)	1.58	3.11 (Si)	3.03 (Si)

Celsian		Anorthite			
$T_1 0$	5.48 (Si)	$T_1 0$	6.89 (Si)	$T_2 0$	3.58
$T_1 z$	6.24	$T_1 i$	5.74 (Si)	$T_2 i$	7.11
$T_2 0$	4.90	$T_1 m$	5.51	$T_2 m$	3.24 (Si)
$T_2 z$	3.95 (Si)	$T_1 mi$	5.47	$T_2 mi$	2.61 (Si)
		$T_1 z$	8.01	$T_2 z$	5.09 (Si)
		$T_1 zi$	6.50	$T_2 zi$	4.24 (Si)
Calculated from		$T_1 mz$	2.81 (Si)	$T_2 mz$	4.67
data in Table 4-2		$T_1 mzi$	4.32 (Si)	$T_2 mzi$	1.61

greater for T_1 than for T_2 tetrahedra. These tendencies are well obeyed for the disordered $AlSi_3$ feldspars and the ordered Al_2Si_2 feldspars, but microcline is unusual. In detail, the data are complex, and the distortion correlates with the number of shared polyhedral elements.

4.2.2 T–O–T Angles

The intertetrahedral angles (Fig. 4-2 and Table 4-3) have not been interpreted in detail. The upper half of Fig. 4-2 shows that, for the "average structure", there is a fair tendency for the angles to show a similar pattern. As would be expected, the feldspars with large M atoms have larger T–O–T angles, on average, than those with small atoms. The effect of Al, Si order-disorder is trivial with a maximum variation of about 1° between comparable angles in high sanidine and microcline. The biggest variation of angle is at the A_2 oxygen whose T–O–T angle increases with the size of the M atom and decreases with the formal charge on the M cation: Rb-feldspar has the largest angle of 144° and anorthite the smallest angle of 124°; celsian has a smaller angle than K-feldspar, and anorthite a smaller angle than Na-feldspar. The angles at C and D oxygens are fairly constant whereas those at A_1 and B oxygens change considerably. For the tri-clinic feldspars, the angular deviations of the actual as distinct from the "averaged" structure are very large. Each of the oxygen atoms B, C and D has two angles for the O and m sub-sites in the C-centered feldspars, and four angles in primitive anorthite. Microcline has the smallest deviations, and anorthite the largest.

Qualitatively the variation in T–O–T angles from one feldspar to another can be interpreted in terms of change in bonding of framework oxygens to M atoms (Fig. 4-3). Maintenance of bonding to the A_2 and two A_1 oxygens must result in crumpling of the T-shaped 10-membered ring when a smaller atom enters the M site (as shown in Fig. 4-5). The effect on the T_1–A_1–T_1 and T_2–A_2–T_2 angles is particularly severe because all the atoms involved in each angle are nearly coplanar (the latter in the plane of the drawing, and the former perpendicular to the drawing). Inward movement of A_1 and A_2 atoms tends to occur by rotation of T_1 and T_2 tetrahedra about D and C atoms which tend to move relatively little. The distances from the M atom to C and D atoms are relatively long, and the bonds seem to be rather uncritical in determining the shape of the framework. The bond from the M atom to the B oxygen also tends to be rather long, and projects upwards at a steep angle from the plane of Fig. 4-3. Movement of the B oxygen is closely dependent on that of the A_1 oxygen because they share a T_1 atom, and the B and A_1 oxygens must move approximately "in step" if the normal T–O distances are preserved; this is consistent with the trends of Fig. 4-2. It is impossible for O_C to come close enough to the M atom to permit bonding unless the T–O_C–T angle is small. The high value of the T–O_B–T angle results from the O_B atom approaching the M atom as closely as possible, subject to constraints from nearby atoms.

Loss of monoclinic symmetry permits additional movements of oxygen atoms (Fig. 4-6). Casual study shows that the changes in T–O–T angles are interpretable in terms of changes of bonding at M atoms, but no thorough study has been made.

Anorthite is intriguing because the geometry of the framework tends to approach the body-centered symmetry of the idealized alternating arrangement of the Al and Si atoms, whereas the bonding between the Ca atoms and framework oxygens tends toward C face-centered symmetry: conflict between these tendencies results in primitive symmetry. Details of the geometry are given in the next section, and the structural conflict is used as a basis for understanding the complex polymorphism of anorthite (Chapter 5).

4.3 Environment of M Atoms

Preceding sections have emphasized the nature of the framework and the dependence on bonding to the M atoms. Here emphasis is placed on the M atoms, but the preceding arguments must be borne in mind because no structural feature exists in isolation. Modern X-ray structural analysis yields centroids of electron-density peaks accurate to at least 0.0005 nm without serious systematic bias. This accuracy is considerably better than predictions made from theories of chemical bonding, and it is unnecessary to pay detailed attention to the individual accuracies for the various structural determinations.

4.3.1 General Features of M–O Bonding

Table 4-4 lists the distances from the M atom to the nine oxygen atoms shown in Fig. 4-3 for high sanidine. For the low-symmetry feldspars, certain distances lose their degeneracy requiring use of an abbreviated Megaw code for the oxygens. The situation is especially complex for anorthite with four independent calcium atoms, each with nine independent distances.

For clarity, the symmetry control on the M atoms is shown in Fig. 4-6. Sub-figure (a) shows schematically the four different Ca atoms of primitive anorthite lying in the unit cell of symmetry $P\bar{1}$ and c repeat 1.4 nm. The centers of symmetry shown by small circles produce two Ca atoms for each symmetry-related position, as shown respectively by open and closed symbols. The Ca atom at arbitrary position 0 is related to the other three types by the operators z (displacement of $c/2$), i (body-centering), c (center of symmetry). Combination of i and z yields the face-centering operator C. The other four sub-diagrams show the possible types of M atoms and permitted displacements for the $I\bar{1}$ and $I\,2/c$ variants with 1.4 nm repeat, and for the $C\bar{1}$ and $C\,2/m$ variants with 0.7 nm repeat. These correspond respectively to I-anorthite, celsian, albite and sanidine.

The analysis of electrostatic shielding in low albite by Gait $et\ al.$ (1970) showed that for a hard-sphere model, the five nearest oxygens (A_{1o}, A_{1c}, A_2, B_0 and D_0) are unshielded, while the next four are only slightly shielded. Most discussions of feldspar structures have assumed that only oxygens up to 0.03 nm more distant than the nearest oxygen are bonded to the M cation. Probably this assumption needs reexamination, and certainly one should not speak blithely of a coordination number when discussing an ionic model. If covalent bonding is assumed to make a contribution, the degree of bonding should fall off more rapidly with

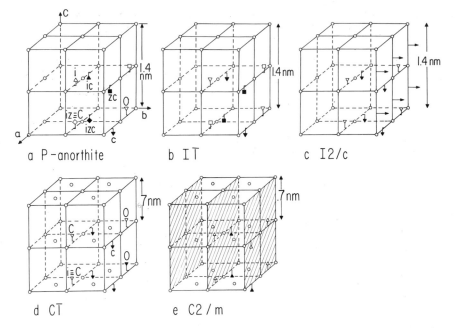

Fig. 4-6. Symmetry restraints on positions of M cations. Each diagram shows the M cations for a unit cell with c 1.4 nm, or for two unit cells with c 0.7 nm. a The actual positions of the four types of Ca atoms in primitive-anorthite, P $\bar{1}$. The symmetry centers are shown by small circles, and relate the Ca atoms in pairs. Each pair of Ca atoms is shown by a differently-shaped symbol: the absence or presence of filling merely shows the effect of the symmetry centers. The Megaw operators are used to distinguish the Ca atoms: 0 prototype; i body-centering; z 0.7 nm translation along c; c center of symmetry. The capital C denotes the C face-centering operation. b for I $\bar{1}$, there are two types of M atoms. c For I 2/c, there is only one type of M atom, whose position is restricted by the 2-fold rotation axes shown as arrows. The c glide plane is not depicted. Note that the y-coordinate may be non-zero. d For C $\bar{1}$, there is only one type of M atom when c is 0.7 nm. Note that the Megaw operator i is now identical to the C operator because z has become a superfluous operator. Note new centers of symmetry. e For C2/m, there is only one type of M atom with y-coordinate of zero to obey the mirror operation (hatched planes)

bond distance, and selection of the nearest oxygens to form a coordination poly-hedron is more reasonable. Particularly long distances in anorthite are shown by brackets in Table 4-4. Even after eliminating these distances from considera-tion, a wide range of distances remains.

There is a definite distinction between the distances from the small as con-trasted with the large M atoms. The small atoms select a few of the oxygens as nearest neighbors, whereas the large atoms show little discrimination.

In all feldspars, the A_2 oxygen is closer than all other oxygens, as has been described earlier. This can reasonably be interpreted as the result of repulsion between M cations (Megaw et al., 1962) as described earlier, but other factors are probably involved.

The monoclinic K-feldspars have almost identical environments around the K, Na atom. In celsian, the reduction of symmetry caused by alternation of Al and Si atoms permits the Ba atom to occupy a general position: nevertheless the

Ba atom has a y-coordinate of zero, corresponding to a special position on a mirror plane. Newnham and Megaw (1960) suggested that, in pseudo-symmetric structures, heavy atoms are stable only in positions of higher symmetry. This may be true, but in celsian the special position of the Ba atom is not surprising because all its first neighbors are bonded to 1 Al and 1 Si thus producing a close approximation to a symmetrical electrostatic field.

The environments of the Na atoms in low albite and reedmergnerite (Fig. 4-5) are quite similar except for the distances to B_m and especially to C_0 and C_m oxygens (Table 4-4). In low albite, the Na atom is further from C_m(0.326) than the C_0 oxygen (0.298), whereas in reedmergnerite, the distances have switched around (0.281 and 0.345). This reversal can be ascribed to replacement of the larger Al atom by the smaller boron atom in $T_1 0$ sites, resulting in movement of the C oxygens with respect to the Na atom together with compensating movement of other atoms, especially the B oxygens.

The separate effects of (a) ordering of Al atoms into $T_1 0$ sites, and (b) change of size of M atoms, can be seen by comparing the data for albites and K-feldspars. Entrance of Al into $T_1 0$ causes the distance from the M atom to be greater to B_m, C_m and D_m oxygens than to B_0, C_0 and D_0. This means that the aluminosilicate framework has sheared in the same direction for microcline and low albite to accommodate the larger Al atom in $T_1 0$. The substitution of Na for K produces dramatic changes as described in the preceding section.

Phillips *et al.* (1971) stated that the Na, Ca–O coordination polyhedra of two oligoclases are remarkably similar to those of high albite (see Table 4-4). "Those oxygen atoms in the oligoclases bonded to $T_1 0$ show remarkable similarities to those in low albite, whereas $O_A(2)$ (bonded to $T_2 0$ and $T_2 m$) is like those in high albite".

4.3.2 M–O Bonding in Anorthite

The bonding of Ca atoms in primitive anorthite is extremely complex, but can be interpreted qualitatively in terms of a strong tendency for the Ca atoms to form a small coordination polyhedron using oxygens from an ordered framework. Because the high content of Al atoms causes an increase in the mean T–O distance with respect to albite, and the Ca–O and Na–O distances are similar, the crumpling of the framework in anorthite is more severe than in albite.

Figures 4-5d, e show the environment of Ca atoms in primitive anorthite as viewed down the c-axis. The alternation of Al and Si atoms in the framework requires that c is 1.4 nm rather than 0.7 nm for the $AlSi_3$ feldspars. Hence it is necessary to show two slabs of the structure, one for the upper half (d) and one for the lower half (e). The alternation of Al and Si atoms would allow body-centered symmetry such that Ca_0 in the upper half could have the same environment as Ca_i in the lower half (and similarly for Ca_{zi} and Ca_z). (Readers should note that the unit cell has centers of symmetry, and that most of the positions in Fig. 4-5d, e are related by a center of symmetry to the Megaw prototypes). However, the Ca atoms adopt environments with primitive symmetry such that there are four individual types. The framework, of course, must also have primitive symmetry. Figure 4-7 shows a projection down b^* given by Wainwright and Starkey (1971).

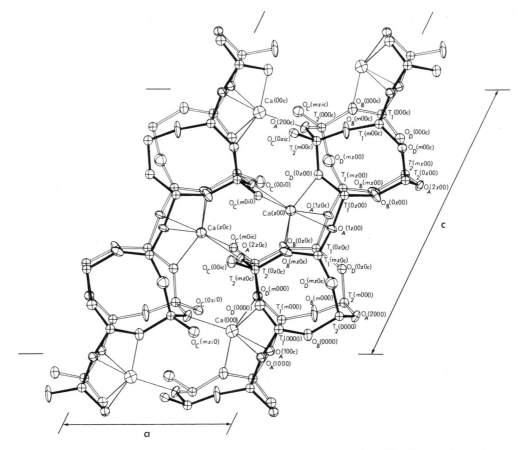

Fig. 4-7. Projection of the structure of primitive anorthite onto the ac plane. The diagram shows the slab from $y = -0.3$ to $+0.3$. Atoms lie at the centers of the vibration ellipsoids. The aluminosilicate framework is outlined by the heavy and doubled lines whose taper indicates height. The Ca–O bonds are shown by single lines. (From Wainwright and Starkey, 1971, Fig. 1)

The key feature of the primitive anorthite structure is that the Ca atoms tend to occur in two pairs, each pair obeying approximately C face-centered symmetry. In Fig. 4-5e, the positions of the Ca_i and Ca_z atoms nearly obey C-symmetry, *and the nearby oxygens lie at similar distances and angles.* The resulting coordination polyhedra are quite similar, with corresponding distances mostly agreeing within 0.01 nm. A similar correspondence occurs for Ca_0 and Ca_{zi} (Fig. 4-5d), but here the deviations are much greater. The shorter distances agree within 0.02 nm, but the longer distances differ by up to 0.06 nm.

The two pairs differ considerably from each other. The z-coordinates of Ca_i and Ca_z are 0.92 and 0.91 with reference to the 0.7 nm pseudo-cell compared to 0.85 and 0.83 for Ca_{zi} and Ca_0. The y-coordinates of the first two Ca atoms are about 0.03 smaller than for the latter two. This change in the z and y coordinates results in major differences in bonding to oxygens of type B, C and D, but relatively small changes to oxygens of type A_1 and A_2. Some of the changes in bond distances result from the differences of position of corresponding oxygen atoms rather than from displacement of the Ca atom.

It is quite obvious that the coordination of the Ca atoms is affected little by the distribution of Al and Si atoms. In Fig. 4-5e, note that the Ca–O distances show no clear correlation with the placement of the Al and Si atoms, even though the Al–O distances tend to be about 0.015 nm longer than the Si–O distances. It appears that the O–Ca–O angles tend to compensate for this change rather than the Ca–O distances. This is not surprising because the bonding of highly-coordinated atoms, whether of an ionic or covalent nature, should be relatively insensitive to angle. In celsian, the coordination of the Ba atom obeys monoclinic symmetry and is essentially the same as that of the K atom in sanidine when account is taken of the minor perturbations caused by the Al, Si alternation. The conclusion is inescapable that the primitive symmetry of anorthite results principally from crumpling of the framework to yield a small coordination polyhedron around the Ca atoms. Such a crumpling also occurs in albite, and a key question is how the crumpling differs between P-anorthite and albite. A second question involves the structural change as primitive anorthite transforms with increasing temperature to body-centered anorthite (see Chapter 5).

In albite and reedmergnerite the c-repeat is 0.7 nm, and the symmetry is $C\bar{1}$. Let us ignore for the present the difference between Ca_0 and Ca_{zi}, and between Ca_i and Ca_z in primitive anorthite. Each averaged pair could then be compared with the single Na atom in albite. Table 4-4 shows that the Ca_0Ca_{zi} pair of P-anorthite has distances to oxygens fairly similar to those of the albites and reedmergnerite. For the Ca_zCa_i pair, the fit is considerably worse. None of the Na-bearing feldspars shows the very long distance to the D_m oxygen found for Ca_zCa_i, while the distance to the C_0 oxygen of the Ca atoms is considerably longer than for the Na-feldspars. All the structures have short distances to A_1 and A_2 atoms, with a mixture of distances to B, C and D atoms.

Three factors will now be considered: the effect of the mean T–O distance; the divalent character of Ca; and the distribution of Al and Si atoms.

In going from reedmergnerite to albite to anorthite the mean T–O distance increases from 0.1578 to 0.1643 to 0.168 nm. In order to permit bonding to the Na and Ca atoms, which have essentially the same ionic radius, the framework must crumple increasingly in going from reedmergnerite to anorthite unless the coordination number decreases. The crumpling could occur in several ways resulting in different kinds of pseudo-symmetry. The actual structure of P-anorthite has either six or seven oxygen atoms at distances of 0.23 to 0.28 nm for each of the four Ca atoms. Supposing the symmetry were truly body-centered would it be possible to obtain satisfactory distances? It is impossible to investigate this *ab initio*, but an answer may be indicated by averaging the distances for Ca_0 and Ca_i, and for Ca_z and Ca_{zi}. The 36 distances in Table 4-4 yield the following 9 for Ca_0 and Ca_i: 0.253, 0.267, 0.231, 0.243, 0.317, 0.345, 0.292, 0.241, 0.322; and for Ca_z and Ca_{zi}: 0.247, 0.266, 0.232, 0.242, 0.287, 0.368, 0.270, 0.239, 0.327. These distances are not unreasonable at first sight when compared with Ca–O distances for a wide range of silicates. The averaging has resulted in an increase of the shorter distances and a decrease of the longer distances. For each Ca atom there is one less distance in the range 0.23 to 0.28. Perhaps one can argue that the Ca atoms in anorthite must distort the framework such that oxygen atoms form relatively distinct coordination groups, and cannot stop at a half-way house with a wide spectrum of distances. From the viewpoint of ionic bonding, this argument might seem rather weak at first sight; however when account is taken of repulsive as well as attractive forces it may be plausible.

Does the divalent character of Ca have any effect on the bonding, except of course for the indirect effect via charge linkage to Al? Celsian with divalent Ba atoms has monoclinic symmetry, and a coordination rather similar to that in sanidine. Hence it seems that if the M atom is large enough, the divalency is unimportant. Nevertheless, the divalency may be important when the M atom is small. A univalent atom probably can "tolerate" a wider range of distances to oxygen atoms than can a divalent atom. Probably one can speak loosely of the Ca atoms of anorthite pushing or pulling oxygen atoms of the framework more strongly than the Na atoms of Na-feldspars.

The third possible factor involves the Al and Si atoms. Of course, their topochemical distribution enforces a doubling of the c-repeat in anorthite. However, the difference in the Al–O and Si–O distances causes the oxygen atoms to be alternately displaced about 0.015 nm with respect to the tetrahedral nodes. Detailed study of Figs. 4-5d, e shows how individual Ca–O distances correlate with the Al, Si distribution. Nevertheless the effects are rather subtle, and certainly not as obvious as the effect of the smallness of the Ca atom.

Megaw *et al.* (1962) specifically considered the distortions resulting from the small Ca atom. They emphasized that the Ca atoms are tightly bonded between one A_2 and two A_1 atoms, thus ruling out significant movement along the a^* axis (this is clear from Fig. 4-5 and various other figures). In the $a\,b$ plane, the M atom has four oxygen neighbors at roughly equal distances when the symmetry is monoclinic and the framework expanded (cf. high sanidine: two O_B at 0.302 and two O_D at 0.295 nm). The Ca atom moves off the symmetry plane, and the three oxygen atoms readjust themselves so that three are close to it and "one is pushed right out". These four oxygens can be seen in Fig. 4-6e around Ca_i. The three oxygens B_0, B_m and D_0 at heights 121, 123 and 64 lie at distances 0.241, 0.250 and 0.238 while the fourth oxygen D_m at height 53 lies at 0.388 nm. Actually the four oxygens and the Ca atom do not quite lie in the (001) plane, but the general idea is correct. Similar patterns can be seen for the other three Ca atoms in Figs. 4-6d, e.

Megaw *et al.* went on to suggest that the "detailed pattern of Ca displacement in anorthite can be predicted qualitatively with the help of two general principles: (1) that when strong internal stresses are related by symmetry or pseudo symmetry in the ideal structure, this symmetry will be retained, at least locally, in the distorted structure, (2) that all periodicities will remain as small as is compatible with (1)". "There is nothing in the sideways linkage to forbid the original C-face-centred arrangement (of the ideal structure), which is therefore retained. A body-centred arrangement would have the disadvantage, because of the centre of symmetry at (1/4, 1/4, 1/2), of introducing two 170° angles into the same vertical 4-membered ring, which looks unlikely". "The argument thus predicts a 14 Å C-face-centred structure". "The Si/Al alternation, however, does not satisfy the C-face-centring condition, and the consequent atomic displacements result in small differences between members of each of the above pairs". "The argument would apply equally to albite, except that the electrostatic forces and their resultant strains are smaller, and mistakes of sequence therefore more likely". The final phrase refers to the possibility that Ca atoms can move either to left or to right of the potential mirror plane of symmetry, and to the formation of out-of-step domains (see Chapter 5).

In conclusion, I think that the detailed environment of the Ca atoms in anorthite has not been explained thoroughly at the present time, but that the various general ideas provide a good starting point.

4.3.3 Angular Environment

The preceding discussion concentrated on M–O distances, but the angular distribution of oxygens around the M atoms must also have some importance even if the bonding is essentially ionic. Figure 4-8 shows the published stereographic projections for anorthite and albite. No stereographic diagrams have been published for K-feldspars, celsian and reedmergnerite. Megaw *et al.* plotted the poles for the directions of the vectors from the four Ca atoms of P-anorthite to the nearest oxygens. They interpreted the directions to correspond generally to oxygens lying at the vertices of a distorted cube with one corner missing (or two corners for Ca_o, if taken to have 6 rather than 7 near oxygens). Figure 4-8a shows projections on the a^*c plane. A regular cube would be represented by poles falling at the intersections of the two great circles shown by dashed straight lines and by overlapping small circles at 54°44′ to the central pole (i.e. by the poles for octahedral [111] directions). It may be seen that the four bonds to two O_{A1} and to either two O_B or two O_D atoms fit well with octahedral directions, while the bond to O_{A2} deviates greatly, falling approximately along the bisector of the directions to the two O_{A1}. The triangular relation of the two A1 and one A2 oxygens is well displayed in Fig. 4-6. Megaw *et al.* suggested that the steric necessity to fit in the A2 oxygen at a short distance upsets the angular arrangement of the neighboring oxygens.

Figure 4-8b shows the angular position of the nearest eleven oxygens to the Na atoms of low albite. To orient in the same way as Fig. 4-8a rotate by 26° about the center and invert about the a^* axis. The five nearest atoms lie at the apices of a distorted trigonal bipyramid, whose triangular cross-section is formed from two A1 and one A2 oxygens. As in anorthite, there is some resemblance to a pseudo-cubic environment.

Although stereographic projections have not been given for other feldspars, it is obvious that for reedmergnerite the nearest oxygens tend to lie at the apices of a distorted trigonal bipyramid with a tendency to a pseudo-cubic environment. For the monoclinic feldspars, the nine nearest oxygens tend to lie near the corners of a distorted cube, together with a ninth (oxygen A2) projecting outwards between the two C oxygens.

Unquestionably, the angular environment of the M atom is strongly influenced by the topology of the aluminosilicate framework with its steric hindrance towards formation of a regular coordination polyhedron about the M atom. Nevertheless there is some weak tendency for the framework oxygens to occupy regular positions consistent with Brunner's model of close packing (Chapter 2).

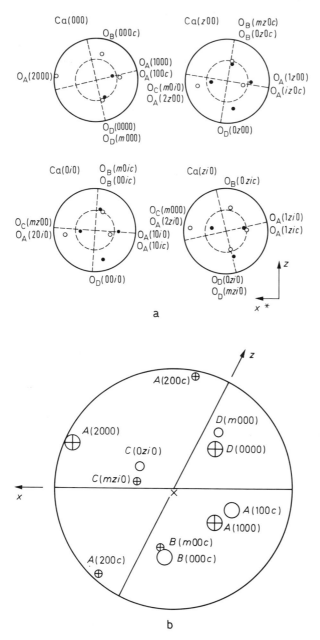

Fig. 4-8. Stereographic projections of the environment of (a) the four Ca atoms in primitive anorthite and (b) the Na atom of low albite. In (a), upwards and downward directions are shown by solid dots and circles respectively. The upper Megaw code for paired atoms refers to the solid dot. In (b), the projection is on (010), slightly different from the a^*c projection in (a). The cross shows the upward pole of the $+b$ axis. Oxygen atoms closer than 0.27 nm are shown by large circles, between 0.29 and 0.30 by medium ones, and between 0.32 and 0.4 nm by small circles. Upwards and downwards direction are shown by crossed and open symbols. See text for angular relation to (a). (From Megaw et al., 1962, Fig. 2 and Ribbe, et al., 1969, Fig. 2)

4.3.4 Conclusion

Looking at the whole group of feldspar structures, it seems clear that there are common features depending on the topology plus idiosyncratic features depending on the size and valency of the M atom, and on the type and distribution of the T atoms. No single factor can be studied in isolation because of the interaction between the bonding of M and T atoms as revealed by correlations between (say) T–O distances and O–T–O angles. Perhaps the most useful experimental approach would be structural analysis of feldspar analogs containing atoms of different sizes and valencies: for example, comparison of Ga- and Ge-substituted feldspars with their Al- and Si-equivalents would permit a test of ideas on the effect of the size of the T atom. It is relatively easy to produce plausible "explanations" of structural features when the atomic parameters have been measured. Particularly valuable would be predictions of the essential structural features prior to experimental measurements.

4.4 Atomic Displacements from Thermal Motion and Substitutional Disorder

Atoms in feldspars are displaced from the lattice-related sites by thermal disorder and by the various types of substitutional disorder. By 1973, there had been no comprehensive study of atomic displacements in feldspars and the available data must be treated cautiously. Ideally the atomic displacements should be studied at a series of temperatures in order to separate effects of thermal motion from effects of substitutional disorder. In 1973, only data from X-ray and neutron structural analysis were available, but hopefully data from X-ray thermal diffuse scattering will be forthcoming.

It is necessary to state the problems involved in measuring and interpreting atomic displacements. The diffraction data are usually fitted with a model that assumes a Gaussian distribution of displacements from the centroid. Initially the displacements were interpreted solely on the basis of thermal vibration. The resulting *temperature factor* B is equal to $8\pi^2\bar{u}^2$ where $\bar{u}$ is the root-mean-square displacement of a Gaussian model with isotropic angular distribution. For nonspherical distribution of vibrations, the simplest model assumes an ellipsoidal distribution governed by a second-order tensor. Each of the principal axes X, Y, Z has its own value of B (or $\bar{u}$) along with a set of angles relating it to the crystallographic axes a, b and c. Thermal vibrations need not obey a second-order tensor, but present X-ray data on ordered feldspars are not sufficiently accurate to reveal perturbations.

Atomic displacements resulting from substitutional disorder are automatically lumped together with thermal displacements. Such substitutional effects are not ellipsoidal as shown by the data for high albite (Ribbe *et al.*, 1969). However, the standard technique of least squares analysis with an *artificial temperature factor* $\exp(-B\sin^2\theta/\lambda^2)$ automatically assumes an ellipsoidal model. The differential Fourier technique used by the Cambridge workers (e.g. Ribbe *et al.*, 1969, Fig. 3) provides a direct measure of the perturbation. In some structural studies, the M cation was approximated by two half-atoms displaced by 0.0x nanometer. This is merely a mathematical convenience that cannot be distinguished experimentally from an ellipsoidal model (e.g. appendix in Ribbe *et al.*, 1969).

Good X-ray structural analyses can yield values of $\bar{u}$ accurate to a standard deviation near 0.001 nm, and orientation angles accurate to about $3°$. However, unknown systematic errors can arise from various faults in the experimental technique. For framework structures, the T atoms appear to provide a useful check because their displacements seem to be consistent with $\bar{u}$ nearly isotropic near 0.008 nm. A serious systematic error results from use of an incorrect atomic form factor. Thus if Al is incorrectly assigned to a site occupied by Si the B-value will be too high by about 50%.

4.4.1 Isotropic Approximation

Table 4-6 compares data on the artificial temperature factors obtained by least-squares analysis for an isotropic approximation. The quality of the data is uneven, tending to be better for the counter data given after 1970.

Because of the problems caused by disorder, attention is focused initially on the ordered structures: low microcline, low albite, reedmergnerite, anorthite and celsian. All five of the 3D refinements show larger displacements for the oxygens than for the T atoms, but only by a small amount: indeed for anorthite, the ranges for O and T atoms overlap. Among the oxygens, O_{A2} tends to have the smallest B, and O_{Bm} the largest. The B-values for the M atoms range between 0.8 for one of the Ca atoms of anorthite and 2.4 for low albite. Presumably the smaller B for the Na atom in reedmergnerite than in low albite results from the smaller size of the cavity in the former caused by substitution of B in the framework. Crudely speaking the higher B for Na in low albite than for K in low microcline suggests that the former atom cannot "fill" the cavity as effectively as the latter: this is a vexed question which is considered separately.

Megaw *et al.* (1962) suggested that qualitatively the framework of anorthite (and by implication of all feldspars) will vibrate as a whole in "lattice modes" while the M atom will vibrate more nearly independently in Einstein modes. Also they suggested that the T atoms would act as nodes for standing waves because of the greater mass of Si, Al than O atoms and because T–O–T angles are more compliant than O–T–O angles. The data in this chapter are incapable of testing this idea, but are not inconsistent with it. Measurements of thermal diffuse scattering are needed to provide the crucial test.

For the M atom, the thermal motion at a given temperature can be considered in terms of a crude model in which the atom vibrates inside a cavity formed by framework oxygens. Therefrom the thermal displacement should be reduced by three factors: greater mass of the M atom; smaller size of the coordination polyhedron; stronger bonding. The latter two factors tend to work together because an atom of higher valency should "pull in" the oxygens to form a smaller, more regular coordination polyhedron as in anorthite. The data of Table 4-6 are insufficient to test this model rigorously, but are consistent with it.

Table 4-6. Artificial temperature factors (spherical approximation B)

	Reference	M	T_1O	T_1m	T_2O	T_2m	O_{A1}	O_{A2}	O_{BC}	O_{Bm}	O_{CO}	O_{Cm}	O_{DO}	O_{Dm}
Rb-feldspar	Gasperin (1971)	1.88(3)	0.76(4)	0.76(4)	0.75(4)	0.75(4)	1.6(2)	1.7(2)	1.5(1)	1.5(1)		1.4(1)	1.5(1)	1.5(1)
sanidine 7002	Brown et al. (1971)*	2.58(4)	0.74(2)	0.74(2)	0.75(2)	0.75(2)	1.54(2)	1.51(2)	1.88(2)	1.88(2)		1.43(2)	1.45(2)	1.45(2)
sanidine 7002	Phillips and Ribbe (1971)	2.10(2)	0.70(2)	0.70(2)	0.63(2)	0.63(2)	1.53(5)	1.36(5)	1.91(5)	1.91(5)		1.34(4)	1.34(4)	1.46(4)
low sanidine C	Ribbe (1963)	2.25(6)	0.84(3)	0.84(3)	0.65(3)	0.65(3)	1.7(1)	1.3(1)	2.2(1)	2.2(1)		1.6(1)	1.3(1)	1.3(1)
int. microcline U	Bailey (1969)	1.48(2)	0.41(2)	0.43(2)	0.40(2)	0.41(2)	1.15(7)	0.90(6)	1.36(7)	1.30(7)	0.86(6)	1.01(7)	1.03(7)	1.01(7)
low microcline Pe	Brown and Bailey (1964)	1.41(3)	0.29(3)	0.38(2)	0.38(2)	0.35(2)	0.76(7)	0.67(7)	1.03(7)	1.02(7)	0.77(7)	0.74(6)	0.97(7)	0.93(7)
high albite Ra	Ribbe et al. (1969)	5.7	1.00	1.06	1.03	1.00	1.90	1.63	1.86	2.34	1.81	1.75	1.75	1.83
high albite Ti	Wainwright (pers. comm.)	5.2	0.72	0.71	0.75	0.69	1.56	1.20	1.54	1.55	1.45	1.41	1.24	1.50
low albite Am	Ribbe et al. (1969)	2.4	0.62	0.60	0.65	0.61	1.01	0.78	1.15	1.38	1.02	1.07	1.17	1.37
low albite Ti.	Wainwright (pers. comm.)	2.33+	0.54(1)	0.55(1)	0.51(1)	0.52(1)	0.99(1)	0.73(1)	1.02(1)	1.29(1)	0.97(1)	0.93(1)	1.01(1)	1.14(1)
reedmergnerite	Appleman and Clark (1965)	1.22	0.38	0.28	0.31	0.31	0.56	0.55	0.70	0.71	0.66	0.74	0.66	0.63
oligoclase Ca	Phillips et al. (1971)	4.8(1)	1.13(5)	0.85(5)	0.92(5)	0.87(5)	-	1.4(1)	1.6(1)	2.1(1)	1.6(1)	1.6(1)	1.5(1)	1.6(1)
oligoclase MC	do.	5.4(2)	0.92(4)	0.85(4)	0.81(4)	0.82(4)	2.0(1)	1.0(1)	1.6(1)	2.3(1)	1.7(1)	1.5(1)	1.3(1)	1.7(1)
anorthite VP	Wainwright and Starkey (1971)	1.20(1)	0.66(1)	0.60(1)	0.64(1)	0.62(1)	0.73(1)	0.61(1)	0.65(1)	1.19(1)	1.03(1)	0.66(1)	0.75(1)	0.69(1)
		0.80(1)	0.61(1)	0.56(1)	0.60(1)	0.57(1)	0.71(1)	0.66(1)	0.75(1)	0.86(1)	0.84(1)	0.54(1)	0.65(1)	1.10(1)
		0.86(1)	0.63(1)	0.62(1)	0.66(1)	0.67(1)	0.66(1)	0.63(1)	0.81(1)	0.80(1)	0.82(1)	0.57(1)	0.89(1)	1.12(1)
		1.43(1)	0.61(1)	0.61(1)	0.67(1)	0.66(1)	0.75(1)	0.80(1)	0.81(1)	1.4(1)	0.71(1)	0.90(1)	0.70(1)	1.06(1)
celsian	Newnham and Megaw (1960)	0.95	-	-	-	-	-	-	-	-	-	-	-	-

Note: B is given in $Å^{-2}$. To convert to nanometer, divide by 100. *neutron diffraction. +incorrectly given as 0.51.

The Ba atom of celsian has a smaller displacement than the K atom of microcline consistent with the heavier mass and greater valency of Ba, and the similar size and shape of the framework. The displacement of Na in reedmergnerite (reported to be spherical by Appleman and Clark, 1965) is smaller than for low albite consistent with contraction of the framework and the shorter Na–O distances.

The disordered feldspars have larger atomic displacements than their ordered counterparts, the excess being attributable semi-quantitatively to positional displacements caused largely by the difference in Si–O and Al–O bond lengths and necessary adjustment of positions of M atoms. Probably the thermal vibrations about the displaced atomic nodes are quite similar in size to those for atoms in the ordered counterpart.

4.4.2 Anisotropic Approximation

For the ordered feldspars, anisotropic approximations are available only for low microcline, low albite and anorthite. Tables 4-7 and 4-8, respectively, contain data measured for Spencer U microcline (Bailey, 1969), which is not completely ordered, and low albite (Wainwright, pers. comm.) which is fully ordered. These data are expressed by an ellipsoid with axes X, Y and Z assuming a Gaussian distribution of displacements. Data for anorthite are too voluminous to give here, but are listed by Wainwright and Starkey (1971).

Figure 4-9 shows a stereoscopic view of the displacement ellipsoids in low albite, together with the chemical bonds and a key to the nomenclature. Figure 4-10 is another view of low albite showing especially the displacements of the framework atoms, and the distortion of the double crankshaft. Figure 4-11 shows the coordination polyhedron of Na together with the displacement ellipsoids of Na and the oxygens. Figure 4-7 shows the bonding and displacement ellipsoids of anorthite, unfortunately not in stereoscopic view. The following description concentrates on albite, but the general ideas are applicable to anorthite and microcline, and probably to all feldspars.

Wainwright used isotropic refinement for the T atoms, and it is not known if these atoms are significantly anisotropic in low albite and anorthite. For Spencer U microcline, Bailey found a distinct anisotropy for all four T atoms (Table 7): because the principal axes are not parallel within experimental error, the anisotropy cannot be attributed merely to some spurious experimental error such as differential absorption of X-rays. It is interesting that the largest displacements lie at 16, 17, 41 and 45° to the a-axis, which is the direction of the double crankshaft: perhaps there is a tendency for the T-atoms, and perhaps the whole crankshaft, to vibrate in this direction because the crankshafts flex easily along this direction.

For the oxygens of all three ordered structures, the largest displacement tends to lie nearly normal to the pair of T–O bonds with the shortest axis nearly perpendicular to the plane of the T–O bonds. In addition, there is a tendency for the displacement to be lower in the direction of a bond to an M atom. Although no detailed analysis has been made, qualitative study of the data suggests that the displacement of the oxygens is controlled principally by the forces from the adjacent T and M atoms with the former being dominant. This

Table 4-7. Anisotropic displacement ellipsoids for Spencer U intermediate microcline

Atom	r.m.s. displacement picometer			Angle between XYZ and abc axes								
	X	Y	Z	aX	bX	cX	aY	bY	cY	aZ	bZ	cZ
K, Na	12.0(2)	14.3(3)	14.9(2)	45(4)	88(3)	71(4)	133(6)	72(19)	27(14)	102(14)	162(19)	72(18)
T_{1O}	3.5(9)	7.0(5)	9.7(3)	113(5)	88(7)	4(7)	122(5)	146(5)	86(7)	41(5)	124(5)	91(3)
T_{1m}	3.8(8)	7.5(4)	9.5(3)	109(4)	100(5)	12(6)	128(6)	40(6)	78(6)	135(7)	128(7)	91(4)
T_{2O}	3.5(9)	6.7(4)	9.5(3)	106(3)	133(7)	43(7)	89(5)	135(7)	130(6)	16(3)	99(5)	104(4)
T_{2m}	5.5(5)	6.6(4)	8.8(3)	106(5)	100(20)	13(14)	93(7)	169(20)	99(19)	17(5)	95(8)	100(5)
O_{A1}	9.8(11)	12.0(8)	14.4(6)	115(7)	100(19)	10(19)	86(11)	170(18)	100(19)	25(7)	89(12)	91(7)
O_{A2}	6.7(9)	10.6(8)	14.4(9)	81(5)	76(9)	38(5)	88(10)	166(10)	78(8)	9(5)	89(10)	125(5)
O_{BO}	7.9(17)	14.94	15.1(5)	38(5)	71(5)	145(5)	53(21)	103(75)	65(58)	83(83)	157(75)	113(62)
O_{Bm}	8.4(15)	13.9(7)	15.1(5)	31(5)	93(3)	146(5)	73(11)	29(18)	77(12)	65(8)	118(18)	59(7)
O_{CO}	7.6(8)	11.2(11)	12.4(7)	109(10)	118(7)	127(11)	36(29)	70(26)	143(11)	60(29)	144(18)	88(26)
O_{Cm}	7.5(11)	11.9(7)	13.1(9)	50(7)	129(5)	85(8)	92(21)	58(20)	39(27)	140(70)	125(19)	52(27)
O_{DO}	6.7(12)	11.5(7)	14.8(8)	93(5)	124(7)	40(60)	100(10)	145(8)	115(7)	10(10)	99(9)	119(6)
O_{Dm}	8.4(8)	9.6(9)	14.9(8)	89(6)	102(33)	29(12)	93(7)	168(34)	100(29)	3(7)	92(7)	117(5)

Standard error in brackets to same significance level. From Bailey (1969, Table 2).

Table 4-8. Anisotropic displacement ellipsoids of low albite

Atom	r.m.s. displacement picometer			Angle between ellipsoid axes XYZ and crystallographic axes abc								
	X	Y	Z	aX	bX	cX	aY	bY	cY	aZ	bZ	cZ
Na	11.9(2)	17.3(2)	24.8(3)	36.6	83.1	80.7	122.3	58.3	38.4	74.6	32.6	126.9
O_{A1}	9.3(4)	11.1(4)	14.5(4)	91.4	88.4	25.8	89.6	2.5	94.9	1.4	88.1	115.2
O_{A2}	7.3(4)	9.3(2)	12.8(4)	87.4	4.4	90.5	43.9	93.3	72.7	133.8	93.0	17.2
O_{BO}	10.6(3)	12.3(2)	13.6(4)	45.3	59.5	82.8	122.1	34.6	82.2	118.2	104.8	10.7
O_{Bm}	12.0(3)	13.9(3)	15.3(4)	34.8	116.4	93.5	76.4	37.7	68.6	121.4	114.8	21.7
O_{CO}	9.0(4)	10.9(1)	14.4(5)	81.9	17.2	82.5	49.6	105.9	69.5	41.6	83.6	158.0
O_{Cm}	8.8(4)	10.6(3)	14.6(4)	100.1	13.0	92.2	49.0	79.8	69.3	42.7	83.5	159.2
O_{DO}	8.9(3)	11.5(4)	13.7(4)	72.5	97.0	132.1	100.1	16.7	78.8	20.3	74.9	44.3
O_{Dm}	9.0(3)	11.6(4)	15.0(4)	69.2	80.8	48.9	96.1	84.6	138.2	21.7	10.7	96.4

Note: T atoms refined as isotropic with r.m.s. displacements 8.4(2), 8.1(2), 8.1(2) and 8.1(2) for T_{1O}, T_{1m}, T_{2O} and T_{2m}. No errors given for angles, but values would range from 2° up to 90° depending on degree of anisotropy.

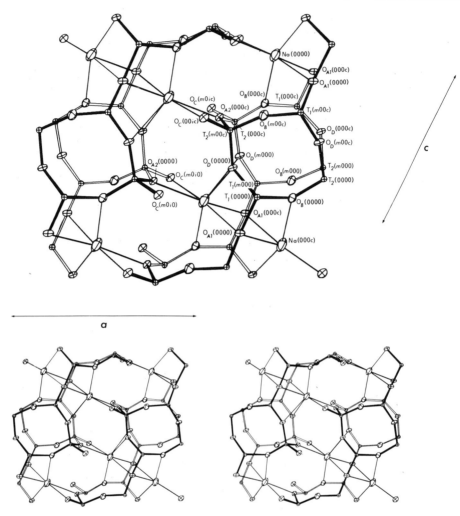

Fig. 4-9. Displacement ellipsoids and bonding in low albite. a Projection down b^* showing the nomenclature for atoms between $y = \pm 0.3$. b Stereoscopic pair. (From Wainwright, pers. comm., Figs. 2a, b)

is consistent with the force constants deduced from infra-red absorption studies (Chapter 11).

The displacement of the Na atom in albite correlates nicely with the bonding to the nearest neighbors (Fig. 4-11). The smallest displacement is nearly along the shortest bond, that to the O_{A2} oxygen, and the longest displacement lies in the general direction of the longest bonds.

For anorthite, Wainwright and Starkey did not attempt to correlate the displacement ellipsoids of the Ca atoms with the bonding to the adjacent atoms. Such a study should be made because of the role of vibration of the Ca atoms in the polymorphism of anorthite (Chapter 5).

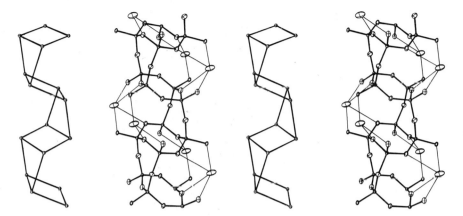

Fig. 4-10. Stereoscopic pair illustrating the feldspar crankshafts and atomic displacements in low albite. The *a* axis is N–S in the plane of the diagram, and *b* lies at 15° to the plane. (From Wainwright, pers. comm., Fig. 5)

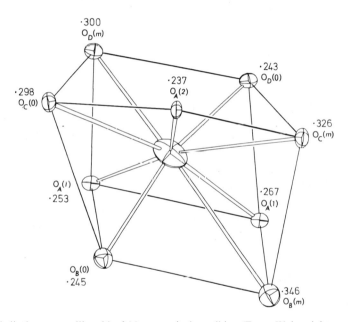

Fig. 4-11. Coordination and displacement ellipsoid of Na atom in low albite. (From Wainwright, pers. comm., Fig. 6)

Turning now to the K-feldspars, solid solution of Ab causes a complication which is probably trivial for the X-ray analyses of microcline but is quite significant for the sanidines carrying 10 to 15% Ab. The problem is particularly severe for neutron diffraction in which the scattering factor for Na is almost equal to that for K. In Pellotsalo microcline (Brown and Bailey, 1964) the displacement ellipsoid for K is disc-shaped with its minor axis almost parallel to a^* with the other two axes lying in (100) symmetrically disposed about c. The position of the minor axis is readily explained by the presence of the short distances to the triangular group of two A_1 and one A_2 oxygen atoms (cf. Fig. 4-3), and by repulsion from the nearby K atom. The major axis of the ellipsoid is oriented at $41°$ to c, and points between three oxygens of type O_{A2c}, O_{Cm} and O_{Bm} on one side and towards O_{Dm} on the other side. These four oxygens are more distant than the other oxygen neighbors; 0.05, 0.04, 0.02 and 0.01 nm greater than for the average of 0.289 for the seven nearest oxygens.

In the monoclinic K-feldspars, the ellipsoid is restricted in orientation with the minor displacement almost exactly along a^*. There is a major discrepancy between the X-ray and neutron analyses of the displacements in the 7002 sanidine, both as regards magnitude (Table 4-6) and anisotropy.

The data for high albite and the sodic plagioclases cannot be expressed accurately in terms of a displacement ellipsoid. Ferguson et al. (1958), Ribbe et al. (1969) and Phillips et al. (1971) found electron density distributions which deviate significantly from an ellipsoidal distribution: undoubtedly, this results from atoms adopting different centers-of-motion in different unit cells in response to different local patterns of Si and Al atoms. It is debatable whether rudimentary domains occur.

4.4.3 Na Atoms in Albite

The literature on the displacement of Na atoms in albite is complex and confusing, partly because the earlier data were relatively inaccurate and partly because of suggestions of a domain structure or superstructure with Na atoms occupying two different positions. For clarity, let us emphasize that in 1973 there is no need to postulate anything other than anisotropic thermal vibration of Na atoms about a single node, as stated by Ribbe et al. (1969).

For the albites, the anisotropy of the displacement of the Na atom is large especially for high albite. Extensive discussion was given by Ferguson et al. (1958), Williams and Megaw (1964) and Ribbe et al. (1969) of whether the displacement results from (1) just anisotropic thermal vibration about one set of lattice-related sites (2) the sum of thermal vibrations about more than one set of lattice-related sites. If (2) were true, there was the further question whether the sites were selected cooperatively to form an out-of-step domain texture.

Distinction between thermal motion about one node and thermal motion about two or more nearby nodes is not easy. Megaw, in an appendix to Ribbe et al. (1969), showed that from X-ray structural analysis it was experimentally impossible to distinguish a single node with ellipsoidal thermal motion from two nodes with spherical motion when the nodes were closer than 0.02 nm. Essentially this derives from the close approximation of an ellipsoid to the sum of two displaced spheres. For high albite, the displacement is large enough, and indeed Fig. 4 of Ribbe et al. shows that at least four nodes are necessary to obtain a reasonable approximation to the experimental data. However for low albite the anisotropy is too small to permit a distinction.

The second approach to distinguishing the two types of displacement utilizes X-ray structural analysis at more than one temperature. Williams and Megaw (1964) investigated the structures of low albite (Ramona) and high albite (hydrothermal synthesis at 700° C) at −180° C using two-dimensional Weissenberg intensity data. Quareni and Taylor (1971) extended the data for low albite to 300 and 600° C. Within the accuracy of these two-dimensional refinements, there is little difference from the data obtained at room temperature. The displacements of the T atoms at lowered temperature were essentially zero. Some changes of the framework geometry were apparent but need confirmation by 3D methods. Particularly important was the retention at low temperature of the large anisotropy for the Na atoms, amounting to 0.027 and 0.062 nm, respectively, for low and high albite using a model for spherical motion about two nodes.

At first sight, the essential similarity of the anisotropy of the Na atoms at −180° C and room temperature suggests that it does not arise from thermal motion. Williams and Megaw, however, emphasized that the Debye model of thermal motion with its linear dependence between Kelvin temperature and $\bar{u}^2$ can be expected theoretically to apply only to structures all of whose bonds have similar strengths. In feldspars, the M–O bonds are much weaker than the T–O bonds, and it would not be surprising if the temperature variation were non-linear. Indeed one might envisage the M atom vibrating in a well of potential energy that is a shallow bowl with steep walls. With increasing temperature the vibration rapidly fills the shallow bottom, while further temperature increase merely causes a slow increase of displacement at the steep walls. The data of Williams and Megaw could be explained if the shallow bottom were filled by the vibration of the Na atom in low albite at some temperature below −180° C. Obviously data taken at liquid helium temperature would be valuable.

The third approach utilizes the nuclear quadrupole resonance data for Na and Al atoms in low albite (see Chapter 11). The resonance frequency depends critically on the electrostatic field at the atomic site. Two nodes should yield two sets of resonance. At the feldspar conference in 1962, I suggested that calculations of the electrostatic field be made for single node and double node models for low albite. Unfortunately this has not been done, but the observation of sharp peaks in the n.q.r. patterns for low albite (Laves and Hafner, 1962) favors the single node. However, it may not be possible to resolve experimentally a pair of overlapping resonances.

Although the experimental data for low albite are consistent with anisotropic thermal motion about a single node, the multinode model should be considered theoretically. Megaw (1962) examined the possible types of domains and faults that might occur, especially by analogy with the domains that definitely occur in Ca-rich feldspars.

Of prime importance for understanding the distribution of T atoms in disordered feldspars is the degree of local order and the scale of out-of-step domain textures. The greater the degree of local order and the greater the regularity of domain texture, the greater will be the splitting of the displacement of the M atom into vibrations about multiple nodes. At one extreme, the Al/Si disorder could be so random that the contours of electron density for M atoms would be indistinguishable from an ellipsoid. At the other extreme, the contours would show distinct peaks and shoulders. Unfortunately it is impossible to estimate the relation between "lumpiness" of the electron density peaks in disordered feldspars and the Al/Si distribution until sophisticated calculations have been made of the crystal field for a range of assumed Al/Si distributions. Unquestionably, the data for high albite and sodic plagioclases contain information bearing on the nature of disorder, and deserve analysis in relation to the infra-red and n.q.r. data.

4.5 Temperature Variation of Atomic Positions and Displacements

By 1972, there were no published data on the variation of the crystal structure of feldspars determined directly at high temperature, except for anorthite whose problems are extremely severe (see Chapter 5).

Added in proof. Sueno *et al.* (1973) compared the crystal structures of high albite at 24 and 1080° C. The mean $T - O$ distance decreased from 0.1642 to 0.638 nm with increasing temperature while the mean $Na - O$ distance increased from 0.280 to 0.288 nm. Several structure analyses of silicates in the July-August 1973 issue of Amer. Mineral. show that with increasing temperature the TO_4 tetrahedra stay constant or contract slightly, whereas the large $M - O$ polyhedra expand considerably.

References

Appleman, D. E., Clark, J. R. (1965): Crystal structure of reedmergnerite, a boron albite, and its relation to feldspar crystal chemistry. AM **50**, 1827–1850.

Bailey, S. W. (1969): Refinement of an intermediate microcline structure. AM **54**, 1540–1545.

Brown, B. E. (1962): Aluminium distribution in an igneous maximum microcline and the sanidine microcline series. NGT **42**, No. 2, 25–36.

Brown, B. E., Bailey, S. W. (1964): The structure of maximum microcline. AC **17**, 1391–1400.

Brown, G. E., Gibbs, G. V., Ribbe, P. H. (1969): The nature and variation in length of the Si–O and Al–O bonds in framework silicates. AM **54**, 1044–1061.

Brown, G. E., Hamilton, W. C., Prewitt, C. T., Sueno, S. (1971): Neutron diffraction study of Al/Si ordering in sanidine. Progr. Geol. Soc. Am. Mtg. Washington, D. C., p. 514.

Chandrasekhar, S. (1957): The structure of body-centred anorthite and some observations on extinction in crystals. Ph. D. thesis University of Cambridge.

Chandrasekhar, S., Fleet, S. G., Megaw, H. D. (1961): Structure of "body-centred anorthite". CCILM **8**, 141.

Chao, S. H., Hargreaves, A., Taylor, W. H. (1940): The structure of orthoclase. MM **25**, 498–512.

Clark, J. R., Appleman, D. E. (1960): Crystal structure refinement of reedmergnerite, the boron analog of albite. S **132**, 1837–1838.

Cole, W. F., Sörum, H., Kennard, O. (1949): The crystal structures of orthoclase and sanidinized orthoclase. AC **2**, 280–287.

Colville, A. A., Ribbe, P. H. (1968): The crystal structure of an adularia and a refinement of the structure of orthoclase. AM **53**, 25–37.

Ferguson, R. B., Traill, R. J., Taylor, W. H. (1958): The crystal structures of low-temperature and high-temperature albites. AC **11**, 331–348.

Ferguson, R. B., Traill, R. J., Taylor, W. H. (1959): Charge balance and the stability of alkali felspars: a discussion. AC **12**, 716–718.

Finney, J. J., Bailey, S. W. (1964): Crystal structure of an authigenic maximum microcline. ZK **119**, 413–436.

Fleet, S. G., Chandrasekhar, S., Megaw, H. D. (1966): The structure of bytownite ("body-centred anorthite"). AC **21**, 782–801.

Foit, F. F. (1971): The crystal structure of anorthite at 410° C. Prog. Geol. Soc. Amer. Mtg., South-eastern section, p. 311 (abstract).

Gait, R. I., Ferguson, R. B., Coish, H. R. (1970): Electrostatic charge distributions in the structure of low albite NaAlSi₃O₈. AC B **26**, 68–76.

Gasperin, M. (1971): Structure cristalline de RbAlSi₃O₈. AC B **27**, 854–855.

Gould, R. F. (1971): Editor of Molecular Sieve Zeolites – I., Advances in Chemistry Series **101**. American Chemical Society, Washington.

Jones, J. B., Taylor, W. H. (1961): The structure of orthoclase. CCILM **8**, 33–36.

Jones, J. B., Taylor, W. H. (1968): Bond lengths in alkali feldspars. AC B **24**, 1387–1392.

Kempster, C. J. E., Megaw, H. D., Radoslovich, E. W. (1962): The structure of anorthite, CaAl₂Si₂O₈. I. Structure analysis. AC **15**, 1005–1017.

Laves, F., Goldsmith, J. R. (1961): Polymorphism, order, disorder, diffusion and confusion in the feldspars. CCILM **8**, 71–80.

Laves, F., Hafner, S. (1962): Infrared absorption effects, nuclear magnetic resonance and structure of feldspars. NGT **42**, No. 2, 57–71.

Mackenzie, W. S., Smith, J. V. (1959): Charge balance and the stability of alkali feldspars. AC **12**, 73–74.

Megaw, H. D. (1962): Order and disorder in felspars. NGT **42**, No. 2, 104–137.

Megaw, H. D., Kempster, C. J. E., Radoslovich, E. W. (1962): The structure of anorthite, CaAl₂Si₂O₈. II. Description and discussion. AC **15**, 1017–1035.

Newnham, R. E., Megaw, H. D. (1960): The crystal structure of celsian (barium felspar). AC **13**, 303–313.

Onorato, E., Penta, M., Sgarlata, F. (1963): Struttura del sanidino. PM **32**, 1–34.

Phillips, M. W., Colville, A. A., Ribbe, P. H (1971): The crystal structures of two oligoclases: A comparison with low and high albite. ZK **133**, Fritz-Laves-Festband, 43–65.

Phillips, M. W., Ribbe, P. H. (1971): Personal communication reporting X-ray structure analyses of sanidine 7002 and adularia 7007.

Phillips, M. W., Ribbe, P. H. (1972): Bond length variations in monoclinic potassium-rich feldspars. Preprint and abstr. 2.9 for Advanced Study Institute in Feldspars, July 1972, Manchester.

Phillips, M. W., Ribbe, P. H. (1973): The variation of tetrahedral bond lengths in sodic plagioclase feldspars. CMP **39**, 327–339.

Phillips, M. W., Ribbe, P. H., Gibbs, G. V. (1972a): Analysis of parameters related to Si-O and Al-O bond lengths in anorthite. Revised abstr. V 102 in Program for Am. Geophys. Union Mtg., Washington, D. C.

Phillips, M. W., Ribbe, P. H., Gibbs, G. V. (1972b): Tetrahedral bond length variations in anorthite. Preprint. In press. AM, 1973, **58**, 495–499.

Quareni, S., Taylor, W. H. (1971): Anisotropy of the sodium atom in low albite. AC B **27**, 281–285.

Ribbe, P. H. (1963): A refinement of the crystal structure of sanidinized orthoclase. AC **16**, 426–427.

Ribbe, P. H. (1968): An explanation of the discontinuities at An₃₃ and An₅₀ in the low plagioclase lattice parameters, γ* and (2θ₁₃₁–2θ₁₃̄₁). Progr. Geol. Soc. America Mtg., Mexico City, p. 247.

Ribbe, P. H., Ferguson, R. B., Taylor, W. H. (1962): A three-dimensional refinement of the structure of low albite. NGT **42**, No. 2, 152–157.

Ribbe, P. H., Megaw, H. D. (1962): The structure of transitional anorthite: A comparison with primitive anorthite. NGT **42**, No. 2, 158–167.

Ribbe, P. H., Megaw, H. D., Taylor, W. H., Ferguson, R. B., Traill, R. J. (1969): The albite structures. AC **25** B, 1503–1518.

Ribbe, P. H., Phillips, M. W., Gibbs, G. V. (1972): Bonding in feldspars: A review. Abstr. 1.2 in program for Advanced Study Institute on Feldspars, July 1972, Manchester.

Smith, J. V. (1953): Reexamination of the crystal structure of melilite. AM **38**, 643–661.

Smith, J. V., Ribbe, P. H. (1969): Atomic movements in plagioclase feldspars: kinetic interpretation: CMP **21**, 157–202.

Sörum, H. (1951): Studies in the structures of plagioclase feldspars. Norsk Vidensk.-Akad. Oslo, Mat.-Nat. Kl., Skr., No. 3, 1–160.

Sörum, H. (1953): The structure of the plagioclase felspars II. AC **6**, 413–416.

Srinivasan, R., Ribbe, P. H. (1965): Some statistical investigations of feldspar structures. ZK **121**, 21–35.

Sueno, S., Prewitt, C. T., Papike, J. J. (1973): High temperature crystal chemistry of albite. Trans. Am. Geophys. Union **54**, 1230 (Abs. V 89).

Taylor, W. H. (1962): The structures of the principal felspars. NGT **42**, No. 2, 1–24.

Taylor, W. H. (1965a): The felspar structures. TMPM **10** (Machatschki Vol.), 5–13.

Taylor, W. H. (1965b): Framework silicates. The felspars. In Bragg, W. L., and Claringbull, G. F., Crystal structures of minerals, p. 293–339. London: G. Bell and Sons.

Taylor, W. H., Darbyshire, J. A., Strunz, H. (1934): An X-ray investigation of the felspars. ZK **87**, 464–498.

Wainwright, J. E., Starkey, J. (1971): A refinement of the structure of anorthite. ZK **133**, Fritz-Laves-Festband, 75–84.

Waring, J. R. S. (1961): The crystal structure of oligoclase. Dissertation, University of Cambridge.

Williams, P. P., Megaw, H. D. (1964): The crystal structures of high and low albites at −180° C. AC **17**, 882–890.

Chapter 5 Complex Crystal Structures

5.1 Summary of Theoretical Concepts

This section reviews structural complexities and their diffraction patterns in preparation for evaluation of the data on feldspar intergrowths. Many of these intergrowths result from development of order with falling temperature, as illustrated briefly in Figs. 3-1 and 3-2.

Figure 5-1 shows complexities in chemically *homogeneous* intergrowths. For each type of intergrowth, the left-hand diagram shows schematically the crystal lattice, and the right-hand diagram the reciprocal lattice. The latter shows the geometrical evidence available from a diffraction pattern: actually the intensity of the spots changes greatly from one node to the other depending on the detailed atomic distribution in the direct lattice. In (a) there is no complexity, and a single set of spots occurs in the diffraction pattern. In (b), the direct lattice is oblique, and a single twin boundary occurs: the resulting reciprocal lattice shows two sets of spots which overlap completely in the direction normal to the twin boundary. In (c), the twin boundaries occur every three unit cells resulting in a superstructure based on a rectangular unit cell (not depicted) with 6 times the repeat of the small pseudo-cell. The distribution of intensity strongly resembles that for the simple twin: i.e. the closer a diffraction node of the periodic twin to one for the simple twin the stronger is its intensity. A periodic twin is a *transverse modulation* as described in Fig. 5-3b. Irregular periodic twinning yields streaks which replace the strings of spots in (c). Regular periodic twinning with a long spacing between the twin boundaries (e) results in closely-spaced strings of spots whose intensity varies systematically such that the spots form clusters around the positions occupied by single spots in simple twinning. For clarity, the reciprocal lattice of (e) is enlarged four times over that in (b). In a real crystal, insertion of a twin boundary must cause displacement of atoms as shown schematically by (f). At each boundary, the compensating effect of the neighboring structure results in rectangular geometry. Such strain tends to reduce the separation of spots in the diffraction pattern and must affect the intensities. Examples of the above complexities are given in Chapter 18.

Figure 5-2 summarizes complexities in chemically heterogeneous intergrowths. In (a), the two components have different lattice repeats and the lattices are incoherent. The diffraction phenomenon occurs quite independently in the two individuals, even though the lattices are parallel, and the reciprocal lattice contains two sets of spots. For clarity, a grid is drawn for each set of spots, but no lines would be visible in a diffraction pattern. In (b), the two components cohere along the boundary thereby enforcing equality of the cell repeat along the boundary. Diffraction occurs as a single phenomenon because of the regularity of

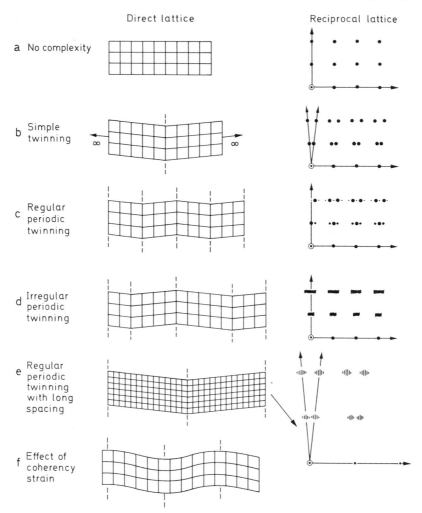

Fig. 5-1. Complexities in chemically-homogeneous material. In the left-hand diagrams, dashed lines show twin boundaries. In the right-hand diagrams, the arrows show the axes and the circle the origin. For (e), the height of the lines shows schematically the intensity in a diffraction pattern: actually spots of different density would be seen on a photographic film

the phases of the scattered waves. If there is a single boundary, and the two components extend for many hundreds or more of unit cells away from the boundary, two sets of sharp diffraction spots occur. If the boundaries repeat every few unit cells and the spacing is quite regular, a superstructure is obtained. For the simple rectangular lattices of (b), the modulation is longitudinal, and strings of spots would occur along the vertical axis (see Fig. 5-3). Diagram (b) is idealized because it assumes that all unit cells have the same horizontal edge length. In practice, the two components would have different cell edges in both

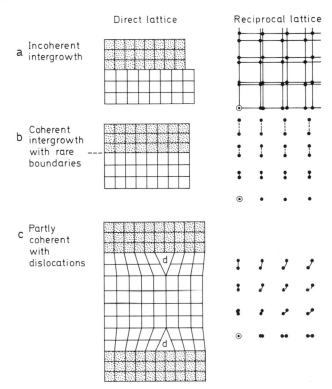

Fig. 5-2. Complexities in chemically-heterogeneous material

directions, and distortion would occur at the interfaces. Diagram (c) shows schematically an example in which the mis-fit at the interface is accommodated by both geometrical distortion and dislocations. The corresponding diffraction pattern shows pairs of spots, each pair being connected by a curved streak. The larger the size of the domains, the closer do the spots approach those for an incoherent intergrowth. Unfortunately the mathematics of diffraction from distorted and partly coherent intergrowths is extremely complex, and it is quite impossible here to describe all the details. Jagodzinski and Korekawa (1972) gave an introduction to a mathematical theory, and emphasized the problems of a complete interpretation. Unfortunately it is not possible to determine the degree of coherency and the frequency of dislocations from just a casual examination of diffuse streaks. Of course, if the streaks are strong the components cohere strongly, and the interfaces are close together. However, if the streaks are weak, it is possible for the coherency to be strong if the interfaces are far apart. The best way to determine the texture of the intergrowth is by phase-contrast electron microscopy (Chapter 10).

The crystal structure of feldspars is strongly anisotropic. For convenience, the lattices in Fig. 5-2 are shown as rectangular, but oblique lattices are needed for feldspars. In addition, the bonding is strongly anisotropic, and the boundary occurs in one or more specific directions. It is quite certain that minimization of some energy function determines the position of the boundary. The introduction to Chapter 19 describes two successful approaches for explaining the orientation of interfaces in perthites and plagioclase intergrowths.

Periodic intergrowths give complex diffraction phenomena. Korekawa (1967) devoted a Habilitationsschrift to a systematic mathematical classification of such intergrowths and their diffraction phenomena, and McConnell (1971) gave an analysis set in the context of non-equilibrium phase transformations and experimental techniques. The following treatment utilizes diagrams and mathematical expressions from Korekawa (1967).

Figure 5-3 summarizes the major effects. Three simple types are possible: those with *density*-, *transverse*- and *longitudinal*-modulation. For density modula-

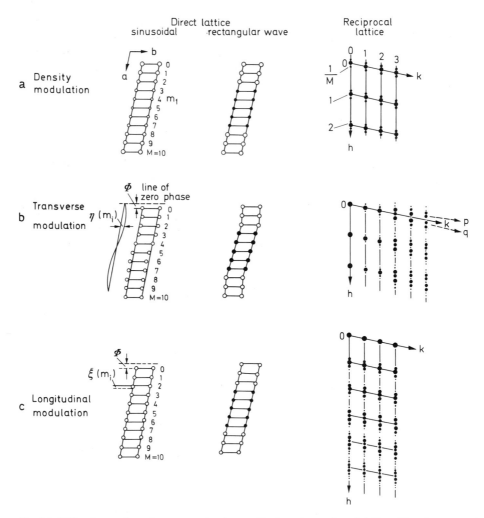

Fig. 5-3. Diffraction patterns from superstructures with three types of modulation. (Based on several figures in Korekawa, 1967)

tion, the atoms occupy positions related exactly by the lattice translation, but have a periodic variation of scattering power. In Fig. 5-3a, the period M is 10 pseudo-unit cells along the a-axis. In the upper left-hand drawing, the scattering power is assumed to vary sinusoidally with m_i, where m_i is the ith node, whereas in the upper middle drawing, the scattering power changes abruptly from that for one type of atom to that for the other. Both the sinusoidal and rectangular models yield a diffraction pattern with strong nodes for the pseudo-lattice and weak nodes for the modulation. A simple sine wave in which the scattering factor $f(m_i) = 1 + D \cos 2\pi \left(\dfrac{m_i + \Phi}{M} \right)$ yields intensity only for the first subsidiary nodes with $h = H \pm 1/M$: D is the modulation in the scattering factor, Φ is merely a phase angle dependent on the choice of origin, and H is an integer. All the subsidiary nodes have the same intensity no matter what the value of H. The ratio of intensity of the subsidiary to the principal nodes is $D^2/4$. For the rectangular wave, it is necessary to express the box-shaped scattering power by an infinite Fourier series: consequently the diffraction pattern has intensity associated with all possible subsidiary nodes.

The box function can be expressed as

$$f(m_i) = \bar{f} + \frac{2\Delta}{\pi} \sum_{n=1}^{\infty} \frac{1}{n} \sin \pi nQ \cos 2\pi \left(\frac{nm_i + \Phi_n}{M} \right)$$

where the mean scattering factor $\bar{f} = Qf_A + (1-Q) f_B$, $\Delta = f_A - f_B$, n is an integer running from 1 to ∞, and Φ_n is a phase angle. Figure 5-4a shows a box function in which the scattering powers of atoms A and B are f_A and f_B, and the relative lengths occupied by A and B are Q and $1-Q$. This model assumes a continuous density, rather than a discontinuous density for occupancy just of lattice nodes, but the general relations for the latter are similar if M is large.

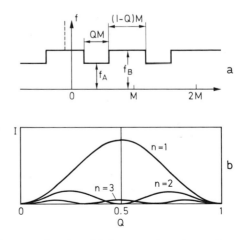

Fig. 5-4. Diffraction intensities I for subsidiary nodes n as a function of Q the proportion of scattering matter for a rectangular density modulation. The true cell repeat consists of M pseudo-cells. f is the scattering factor, changing abruptly from f_A to f_B. (Based on Korekawa, 1967, Fig. 7)

Figure 5-4b shows how the intensities on the subsidiary nodes vary with Q:

$$I(H \pm 1/M) = \left(\frac{\varDelta}{\pi} \sin \pi Q\right)^2$$

$$I(H \pm 2/M) = \frac{1}{4}\left(\frac{\varDelta}{\pi} \sin \pi 2Q\right)^2$$

$$I(H \pm 3/M) = \frac{1}{9}\left(\frac{\varDelta}{\pi} \sin \pi 3Q\right)^2 \text{ etc.}$$

For the first node, the intensity is greatest for equal amounts of A and B, falling to zero, of course, for all A or all B. The second node has zero intensity for all A, all B, or equal amounts of A and B, with maxima at 0.25 and 0.75. The third and higher nodes have increasingly complex forms which correspond to the harmonics of a plucked string. The intensities decrease rapidly with increasing n. The phase angle $\varPhi$ has no effect on the intensities.

Transverse modulation (b) is represented by a sinusoidal transverse displacement in the left middle diagram of Fig. 5-3, and is expressed by the amplitude $\eta(m_i)$ and the phase angle $\varPhi$. The corresponding "rectangular" wave consists of two types of nodes whose unit cells have different angles: the scattering power of the two types of atoms is assumed to be equal. If all the atoms are the same, the pattern is that of a periodic twin (Fig. 5-1c). A characteristic diffraction pattern results from transverse modulation. When $k = 0$, only the principal nodes occur. For increasing k, the principal nodes lose intensity which is transferred into the subsidiary nodes, with the intensity concentrating near the lines Op and Oq and their parallels. The angle pOq increases as η increases. Korekawa developed fully the mathematical equations for the relation of diffraction intensity to M, η and $\varPhi$, but they are not given here because transverse modulation in feldspar has been studied only qualitatively so far.

Longitudinal modulation (c) is represented by a sinusoidal variation in which $\xi(m_i)$ is the longitudinal displacement of the m_i node from the ideal lattice. The rectangular modulation for two types of atoms has unit cells with the same b and interaxial angle but different a. A characteristic diffraction pattern results again, but now it is the k axis for which only the principal nodes occur. With increasing h, the principal nodes lose intensity which is transferred into the subsidiary nodes. Whereas in the transverse modulation, the intensity maxima fall near lines Op and Oq, here the intensity maxima lie in pairs whose separation increases as h increases: this separation is proportional to ξ. Mathematically the two situations are quite similar.

In a real crystal, a more likely situation would be combination of two or three of the modulations. In Chapter 19, superstructure in peristerite was ascribed by Korekawa et al. to a transverse modulation of two components near An_0 and An_{25} in composition.

Finally in this section, it is necessary to consider diffraction effects from complex patterns in which atoms are ordered in a single coherent lattice. Figure 5-5 shows schematically how the nature of the ordering can be determined from the diffraction intensities. In (a), there are two types of atoms whose scattering power

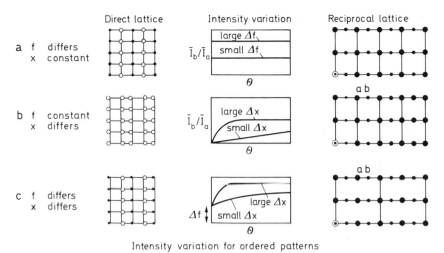

Intensity variation for ordered patterns

Fig. 5-5. Variation of diffraction intensity for ordered patterns. The scattering factor is denoted f and the positional displacement x. See text for significance of the mean intensity $\bar{I}$ for the diffractions a and b from the pseudostructure and superstructure, respectively

differs, but whose positions fall exactly on lattice nodes. The diffraction pattern consists of principal nodes (type a) for the pseudo-structure and the subsidiary nodes (type b) for the superstructure. The intensity ratio I_b/I_a is proportional to $(f_A - f_B)^2/(f_A + f_B)^2$, and is independent of the diffraction angle θ. The greater the difference between f_A and f_B, the scattering factors for the two types of atoms, the stronger are the b subsidiary diffractions. In (b), there is only one type of atom, and ordering involves displacements of x. Here the ratio I_b/I_a increases with θ. If Δx is small, the increase is near-linear, but if Δx is large the intensity ratio reaches a limiting value at a low angle. In X-ray diffraction, the qualifier large means that Δx is about 0.02 nm which is a significant fraction of the atomic radius. In a real crystal, combination of both a difference in f and in x is more likely: here the intensity variation is more complex with an intercept at $\theta = 0$ dependent on Δf, and an increase with θ dependent on Δx.

Figure 5-5 is deliberately simplified, as were the earlier figures, to use just one or two types of atomic positions. In a feldspar, there are many atomic positions whose scattering causes complex interference with a resultant change of intensity between the diffraction nodes. Indeed, the variation of intensity is so complex that it appears random to the eye (e.g. diffraction patterns in Chapter 6). Consequently all the diffraction patterns shown schematically in Figs. 5-1, 2, 3 and 5 must be modified by the diffraction effect from the total assemblage of atoms. Instead of the systematic trend of intensities there is an erratic trend which only obeys the simple theoretical models in a *statistical* manner. Therefore any attempt to analyze a diffraction pattern for its type of modulation or ordering should be made by statistical averaging. Such an analysis by Toman and Frueh (1971) is given later in this chapter.

Figure 5-6 summarizes some complex features of ordered patterns. For convenience, all these patterns are given with two types of atoms strictly oc-

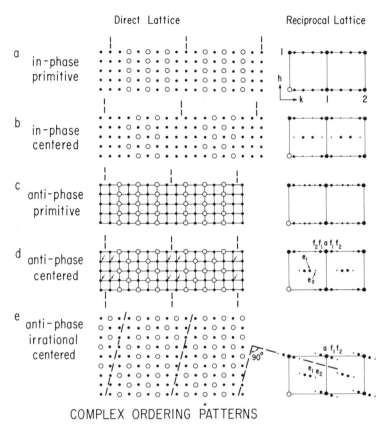

COMPLEX ORDERING PATTERNS

Fig. 5-6. Diffraction patterns for ordered structures with different symmetries and phase characteristics

cupying the same set of lattice nodes: obviously positional displacement would cause extra complications, and would be expected in a real crystal. The intensities of the diffraction nodes are schematic only. Diagrams (a) and (b) contrast with (c) and (d) by the in-phase versus the anti-phase distribution of ordered atoms. In (a) and (b), addition of circles on the appropriate nodes would give a simple regular pattern like that in Fig. 5-5a. However, in (c) and (d), no matter how the extra circles are added, there is a barrier to obtaining a simple ordered pattern at the dashed lines which are described as *anti-phase boundaries*. The patterns (a) and (c) are based on primitive symmetry whereas those in (b) and (d) are centered. Characteristic diffraction patterns occur: (a) and (c) have the subsidiary nodes entirely on lines with integral values of h whereas (b) and (d) have nodes for both integral and half-integral values (h is specified in terms of the pseudo-structure).

Ordering pattern (d) is particularly important for understanding e-plagioclase, and the nomenclature of the diffraction nodes is deliberately chosen to correspond to that for e-plagioclase. The principal nodes a for the pseudostructure are flanked by pairs of nodes of type f_1 and f_2. At the center of the reciprocal unit cell are pairs of nodes e_1 and e_2. Usually the nodes f_2 and e_2 are so weak that they

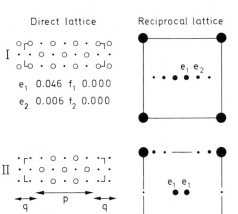

Direct lattice   Reciprocal lattice

I

e_1 0.046 f_1 0.000

e_2 0.006 f_2 0.000

II

e_1 0.031 f_1 0.006

e_2 0.000 f_2 0.003

III

e_1 0.013 f_1 0.008

e_2 0.004 f_2 0.001

Fig. 5-7. Diffraction patterns for ordered structures in which there are regular anti-phase boundaries in an intergrowth of regions with primitive symmetry (q) and centered symmetry (p). The right-hand side shows the diffraction intensities on an arbitrary visual scale, and the left-hand side shows the intensity of the subsidiary nodes normalized to unity for the pseudo-structure nodes. The scattering power of the dotted atoms was assumed to be twice that of the circled atoms. In the direct lattice, the unit cell is shown by the four corners

are unobservable in diffraction patterns. Diagram (e) shows the final degree of complexity with anti-phase boundaries in an irrational direction. In the left-hand diagram the boundaries are shown by dashed lines: obviously they represent a statistical averaging of the regions occupied by the dots. In the diffraction pattern, the subsidiary diffractions lie perpendicular to the anti-phase boundaries in the ordered atomic pattern. One can imagine the boundaries and clusters of subsidiary diffractions of model (d) rotating together to give the positions in model (e). Such a rotation actually occurs in e-plagioclase as the An-content changes.

Returning to model (d), some of the nodes are marked by arrows. If the dots are replaced by circles at these nodes, the positions of the e and f diffractions will not change but their intensities will. Figure 5-7 shows calculations of the diffraction patterns for ordered atomic arrangements in which the ratio changes of the strips with centered pattern (p) and those with primitive pattern (q). The nodes of the reciprocal lattice show the intensity (qualitatively), and the numbers give the intensities of the subsidiary nodes normalized to unity for the pseudo-structure nodes. The scattering factor for the dots was assumed to be twice that of the circles. For model I, the entire pattern is of type p, and the f nodes have zero intensity. The e_1 nodes have a normalized intensity of 0.046 and the e_2 nodes of

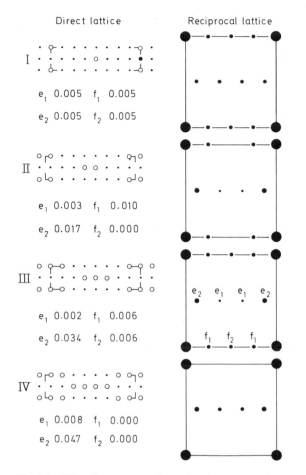

Fig. 5-8. Diffraction patterns for ordered structures in which the two types of atoms occur as clusters in a centered pattern. See legend to Fig. 5-7 for explanation

0.006. As the amount of centered pattern decreases in models II and III, the f_1 node gains intensity and the e_1 node loses intensity.

Figure 5-8 shows a different type of model in which both types of atoms occur in strings related by the centering vector, and whose proportions change from model I to model IV. The first obvious feature is that the diffraction patterns have a distribution of intensity on the nodes which is quite different from those in Fig. 5-7. The subsidiary diffraction nodes are spaced twice as far apart in reciprocal space compared to the spacing of the nodes for the pseudo-structure in the horizontal direction (note that the spacing in Fig. 5-7 is eight unit cells compared to seven for Fig. 5-6). If the nodes are labelled as shown, the e_2 node has greater intensity than the e_1 node, except for model I in which all subsidiary nodes have the same intensity. The intensity of the e_2 node increases steadily from model I to IV, being largest when the number of dots and circles is equal. On the other hand, the intensity of the f_1 node is largest for models II and III.

If a box-function of scattering power were used instead of a delta function for individual atoms, the intensity of the e_2 and f_1 nodes would vary in the same way as the $n = 1$ and $n = 2$ nodes in Fig. 5-4.

From this brief, semi-quantitative survey of diffraction phenomena from complex intergrowths, it should be clear that study of the distribution of intensity between the nodes can permit a characterization of the type of ordering or modulation. Unfortunately, all the above models are too simple, and actual intergrowths of feldspars involve subtle atomic displacements caused by perturbation of chemical bonding. In 1973, there was no complete analysis of any complex feldspar intergrowth.

5.2 Anorthite Structures in Calcic Plagioclase

The present treatment utilizes the review by Smith and Ribbe (1969). Readers should be familiar with the general description of plagioclase in the Summary, and the properties of the crystal structures in Chapters 3 and 4.

Important new structure data were kindly supplied prior to publication as follows: (1) preliminary X-ray structure analyses of a Vesuvius anorthite (An_{97}) by M. Czank, F. Laves and H. Schulz. Data were taken at room temperature, 240 and 1430° C using counter methods. Because the crystal was mounted in a hole in the thermocouple, absorption errors result in somewhat lower accuracy than that obtained by Wainwright and Starkey (Table 4-1). The Vesuvius anorthite is primitive at room temperature, but at 240 and 1430° C the weakness of the *c* diffractions resulted in collection of only *a* and *b* diffractions. Table 5-1 shows the atomic coordinates at 240 and 1430° C for body-centered symmetry. It was necessary to approximate each Ca atom by two part atoms, whose coordinates are quite similar to those of the whole atoms of P-anorthite at room temperature. Table 5-1 also shows that the framework atoms at 240 and 1430° C have similar positions to those of the room-temperature structure when the latter are averaged to the body-centered pseudo-symmetry. A thesis by M. Czank was completed in 1973, and a full publication is expected in Z. Krist. during 1974. A refinement of a Miyake anorthite (An_{99}) at 410° C was described by Foit (1971), but full data were not available. From this abstract, it seems that the data agree essentially with those of Czank *et al.* A paper by Foit and Peacor (1973) is scheduled for publication.

(2) Electron microscopy and diffraction by several groups (Chapter 10). These revealed the domain texture associated with *b* and *c* diffractions, and the Huttenlocher intergrowth in many specimens from about An_{67} to An_{90}. Exploratory heating studies showed how the domain texture changed in anorthite, and how the bytownites changed structural state.

5.2.1 Order-disorder of T Atoms: *b* Diffractions

The data on T–O distances (Chapter 3) and on the sharpness of peaks in the nuclear quadrupole resonance spectrum (Chapter 11) demonstrate strong Al, Si ordering in anorthite. A major question is the extent of the ordering and whether

Table 5-1. Atomic coordinates of anorthites at 240 and 1430° C (Czank *et al.*, 1974) compared with the pseudostructure of P-anorthite

Atom	240° C			1430° C			RT (pseudo-I)		
	x	y	z	x	y	z	x	y	z
Ca(0)	0.2684	0.9881	0.0847	0.2730	0.9846	0.0839	0.2655	0.9859	0.0869*
Ca(z)	0.2682	0.0307	0.5467	0.2818	0.0284	0.5526	0.2683	0.0313	0.5433*
Ca(i)	0.7749	0.5336	0.5454	0.7714	0.5273	0.5469	0.7741	0.5353	0.5416*
Ca(zi)	0.7671	0.5097	0.0691	0.7630	0.4996	0.0714	0.7640	0.5072	0.0729*
$T_1(0)$	0.0071	0.1584	0.1042	0.0079	0.1631	0.1049	0.0076	0.1578	0.1041
(z)	0.0028	0.1639	0.6126	0.0040	0.1680	0.6127	0.0038	0.1635	0.6124
(m)	0.0005	0.8146	0.1201	0.0007	0.8158	0.1198	0.9995	0.8150	0.1195
(mz)	0.0039	0.8171	0.6115	0.0038	0.8187	0.6113	0.0053	0.8177	0.6118
$T_2(0)$	0.6887	0.1136	0.1607	0.6935	0.1154	0.1631	0.6881	0.1124	0.1596
(z)	0.6760	0.1058	0.6574	0.6802	0.1074	0.6609	0.6765	0.1052	0.6570
(m)	0.6768	0.8822	0.1807	0.6796	0.8829	0.1795	0.6756	0.8812	0.1805
(mz)	0.6845	0.8751	0.6780	0.6911	0.8744	0.6765	0.6835	0.8747	0.6772
$O_A(1)$	0.0057	0.1265	0.9913	0.0043	0.1287	0.9952	0.0076	0.1254	0.9917
(1z)	0.0010	0.1268	0.4903	0.9995	0.1277	0.4901	0.9986	0.1253	0.4898
(2)	0.5752	0.9897	0.1392	0.5815	0.9916	0.1407	0.5749	0.9890	0.1396
(2z)	0.5734	0.9917	0.6378	0.5813	0.9954	0.6383	0.5737	0.9889	0.6371
$O_B(0)$	0.8228	0.0998	0.0931	0.8278	0.1075	0.0954	0.8244	0.0989	0.0922
(z)	0.7978	0.1025	0.5928	0.8058	0.1104	0.6007	0.7986	0.1007	0.5929
(m)	0.8057	0.8580	0.1241	0.8143	0.8587	0.1229	0.8086	0.8553	0.1284
(mz)	0.8218	0.8557	0.6152	0.8277	0.8592	0.6114	0.8265	0.8553	0.6177
$O_C(0)$	0.0135	0.2788	0.1371	0.0081	0.2830	0.1293	0.0116	0.2784	0.1346
(z)	0.0187	0.2938	0.6508	0.0257	0.2989	0.6485	0.0153	0.2936	0.6491
(m)	0.0068	0.6796	0.1082	0.0116	0.6817	0.1140	0.0090	0.6798	0.1077
(mz)	0.0042	0.6908	0.6005	0.0107	0.6927	0.6074	0.0075	0.6927	0.5999
$O_D(0)$	0.1903	0.1059	0.1850	0.1856	0.1082	0.1866	0.1905	0.1063	0.1848
(z)	0.2008	0.1019	0.6927	0.1952	0.1049	0.6969	0.2047	0.1038	0.6928
(m)	0.1971	0.8676	0.2216	0.1997	0.8728	0.2185	0.1960	0.8683	0.2212
(mz)	0.1870	0.8602	0.7083	0.1839	0.8623	0.7062	0.1853	0.8671	0.7085

The data for P-anorthite at room temperature (Table 4-1) are averaged for the body-centered pseudo-structure, except for the Ca atoms (asterisks) whose coordinates obey primitive symmetry. See text for population factors of Ca atoms.

it depends on temperature. Of course, solid solution of Ab must result in structural disorder, and the relation of this disorder to the dissociation into the Huttenlocher intergrowth is very important.

The presence of b diffractions is a certain qualitative indicator of ordering of Al and Si atoms in calcic plagioclase. Laves *et al.* (1970) found that b diffractions occur in Vesuvius anorthite right up to the melting point, and measured the intensity of the $01\bar{5}$ and $05\bar{3}$ diffractions with respect to the $06\bar{4}$ and 0, 2, $\bar{1}0$ diffractions of type a. Both the a and b diffractions changed intensity sharply near 230° C, at which temperature the c diffraction $06\bar{5}$ became very diffuse and weak. Above this temperature the $01\bar{5}$ and $05\bar{3}$ diffractions changed only a little, implying strong Al, Si ordering even at the melting point.

Using a counter diffractometer, Foit and Peacor (1967) found that a diffractions broadened with increasing temperature, but less than b diffractions. Major changes for both occurred at $0-200$ and $600-1000°$ C. The former correlates with the inversion from primitive to body-centered symmetry, but there is no explanation of the latter effect.

For pure $CaAl_2Si_2O_8$, there is indirect evidence that some order-disorder of Al, Si atoms occurs in material crystallized at elevated temperature (Smith, 1972). The angle β^* (Fig. 7-44) is about $0.15°$ smaller for anorthites annealed at low temperature in metamorphic rocks than for those crystallized at the melting point and quenched. The relaxation time for changes of cell dimensions appears to be some hours near $1400°$ C which is too long for effects associated with thermal vibration or chemical bonding of Ca atoms, but reasonable for migration of Al and Si atoms. Laves and Goldsmith (1955a, b) and Goldsmith and Laves (1956) found that synthetic anorthites examined by X-rays at room temperature shortly after crystallization had either no b diffractions or diffuse ones. Annealing for 15 minutes at $1500°$ C or 7 days at $1150°$ C increased the peak intensity and sharpened the b diffractions. I shall now assume that some Al, Si disorder occurs even in pure anorthite.

Unfortunately the influence of chemical bonding on T–O distances precludes detailed interpretation in terms of Al, Si distribution. Table 5-2 compares the mean T–O distances obtained by Czank $et\ al.$ for a Vesuvius anorthite with those obtained by Wainwright and Starkey (1971) for a Pesmeda anorthite (An_{100}). At room temperature, the distances for both anorthites cluster near 0.161 and 0.175 nm, consistent with complete or nearly complete order. The maximum difference between the two sets of data for any tetrahedron is 0.0009 nm and the mean difference is 0.0003 nm, showing that the two structure determinations are highly consistent. At $240°$ C, the Vesuvius anorthite yielded two groups of mean distances, each group being consistent within experimental error with complete order. However, at $1430°$ C, each group showed a much greater variation, consistent with some disorder, but not proving it. A critical experiment would be structure analysis by neutron diffraction of a pure anorthite before and after heat-

Table 5-2. Mean T–O distances (nm) in anorthite

	Vesuvius anorthite (Czank $et.\ al.$, 1974)			Val Pesmeda anorthite Wainwright and
	RT	$240°$ C	$1430°$ C	Starkey (1971)
$T_1 0$	0.1615, 0.1607[a]	0.1611	0.1594	0.1616, 0.1613[a]
$T_1 mz$	0.1615, 0.1607	0.1611	0.1597	0.1613, 0.1613
$T_2 z$	0.1615, 0.1611	0.1607	0.1599	0.1617, 0.1608
$T_2 m$	0.1614, 0.1614	0.1614	0.1612	0.1615, 0.1615
$T_2 0$	0.1742, 0.1751	0.1736	0.1741	0.1742, 0.1750
$T_2 mz$	0.1749, 0.1744	0.1739	0.1772	0.1744, 0.1745
$T_1 z$	0.1747, 0.1751	0.1743	0.1747	0.1747, 0.1755
$T_1 m$	0.1741, 0.1743	0.1736	0.1739	0.1750, 0.1745

[a] The second column gives the distance for the tetrahedron related by the pseudo body-centering vector i.

ing to about 1530° C followed by quenching. The cell angle β^* should be checked to see if heating increased it from about 63.96° to 64.1° or greater.

Several workers found no out-of-step boundaries in dark-field electron micrographs with b diffractions when the anorthite was more calcic than An_{95} (Chapter 10). Specimens from about An_{70} to An_{95} showed boundaries, but the situation is complicated by the occurrence of the Huttenlocher intergrowth in some specimens. The obvious explanation of the boundaries is that the plagioclase inverted from a solid solution of albite structure to one of anorthite structure, consistent with the hypothetical phase diagram of Fig. S-2a. The absence of boundaries in anorthites more calcic than An_{95} implies that these plagioclases grew directly with the anorthite type of Al, Si order. Any disorder in these calcic anorthites must be random over the entire crystal.

Type b diffractions were observed in specimens as sodic as An_{63} (e.g. Gay, 1954, 1956; Gay and Bown, 1956; Stewart et al., 1966). The most sodic specimens, An_{63} and An_{65}, had very diffuse b diffractions, but another specimen, An_{71}, had sharp b diffractions plus diffuse c diffractions (Gay, 1956). From the sparse data, it seems that diffuseness depends strongly on the rate of cooling and only slightly on the Ab content: however, detailed measurements are needed.

5.2.2 Domains of M Atoms: c and d Diffractions

Pure anorthite at low temperature has the primitive structure in which the Ca atoms occupy four distinct crystallographic sites. The aluminosilicate framework is strongly distorted to permit the oxygen atoms to bond to the Ca atoms. At high temperature, the c (and d) diffractions which characterize the primitive structure become diffuse and lose peak intensity, and anorthite can be loosely described as body-centered. The data and the structural interpretation are controversial, but I shall assume initially that the Ca atoms at high temperature occupy equally pairs of positions 0.05 to 0.10 nm apart, thereby giving an averaged body-centering symmetry. In 1973, there was no agreement about (1) the details of the diffraction pattern, (2) the presence of and change of domain texture with heating and Ab-substitution, (3) the relation between the positions of Ca and T atoms, and (4) the nature of movements of Ca atoms between the pairs of possible positions. The literature is complex and it is impossible to avoid my personal bias. Unfortunately there are few quantitative data, and the distinction between peak intensity and integrated intensity has not always been clearly stated. Electron-diffraction studies (Chapter 10) revealed the domain texture hidden to X-ray studies, but it is not certain how much structural damage was caused by the electron beam. Many studies suffered from uncertainty in the chemical composition of the specimen. Some lunar specimens are strongly zoned, and some of the bulk chemical analyses are probably in error by several percent An. Because the body-centered to primitive inversion in anorthite is non-quenchable, the early X-ray data taken at room temperature on quenched specimens were misleading, and must be reinterpreted in terms of the discovery by Brown et al. (1963) of the rapid inversion between 25 and 350° C.

When P-anorthite is heated, the c (and d) diffractions become progressively diffuse and invisible or nearly invisible by about 300° C (Brown et al., 1963;

Bruno and Gazzoni, 1967; Czank et al., 1970; Laves et al., 1970). The observed temperature certainly depends on the sensitivity of the apparatus, and probably on the chemical composition, and perhaps the pretreatment of the specimen. Foit and Peacor reported that the changes are promptly and instantaneously reversible. Using a Weissenberg counter diffractometer, Foit and Peacor could not detect the 025 and 0$\overline{2}$7 diffractions of a Miyake anorthite (98 ± 1 % An) above 285° C, and extrapolated the observed intensities to zero at 342 and 320° C. Integrated intensities were independent of the width of collimation slits and changes of diffraction coordinates, and Foit and Peacor believed that "there is indeed a true loss of intensity of the c maxima". Laves et al., for a Vesuvius anorthite, $An_{97.5}$, observed a continuous drop of peak intensity of the 06$\overline{5}$ diffraction to a near-zero value at 230° C. From then on up to 1500° C, the intensity stayed constant at about 3 % of the value for room temperature. There is considerable unpublished discussion whether c diffractions retain intensity above about 230° C, but the question is unresolved. I now assume that the aluminosilicate framework of anorthite is *statistically* body-centered above about 300° C for experiments taking longer than about a microsecond, but that the Ca atoms show a rudimentary domain structure. Chapter 11 reports the nuclear quadrupole resonance data which are consistent with inversion near $220 - 250°$ C for a Vesuvius anorthite. The n.q.r. spectrum above the inversion shows only one set of peaks for the Al isotopes indicating body-centered symmetry on a microsecond time-scale. Bloss (1964) saw a reversible change of optical extinction near 340° C for a natural anorthite near An_{97}. Chapter 7 records data on morphological elements and cell dimensions which are consistent with an inversion between 200 and 300° C.

The X-ray structural analyses of I-anorthite at elevated temperature show doubled peaks for the two independent Ca atoms. Czank et al. approximated the peaks by two part-atoms whose coordinates are given in Table 5-1. The coordinates differ little with temperature, and are quite similar to those of the four independent atoms of P-anorthite. Table 5-3 shows that the distances between each pair of part-atoms are only slightly smaller than those between the whole atoms of P-anorthite when displaced by the body-centering vector. The simplest interpretation of the X-ray data is that Ca atoms of I-anorthite jump rapidly between two positions related to those in P-anorthite. Presumably the aluminosilicate framework would flex in response to the movement of Ca atoms in order to maintain reasonable Ca-O distances. The displacements of about 0.08 nm for $Ca(0, i)$ and 0.05 nm for $Ca(z, zi)$ are large compared to the ionic radius of 0.10 nm. Smith and Ribbe (1969) stated that the jumping model could explain the X-ray and n.q.r. data if the Ca atoms of I-anorthite jump faster than 10^{-7} second

Table 5-3. Distances (nm) between Ca part-atoms (Czank et al., 1974)

Atoms	RT^a	240° C	1430° C
$Ca(0) - Ca(i)$	0.095	0.084	0.078
$Ca(z) - Ca(zi)$	0.055	0.043	0.053

[a] For P-anorthite, distance calculated after applying body-centered translation to one atom of pair.

Table 5-4. Root-mean-square atomic displacements (picometer) in anorthite (Czank *et al.*, 1974)

	RT	240° C	1430° C	Wainwright and Starkey
T	5.8 to 7.5	7.8 to 8.7	15.3 to 16.2	8.4 to 9.2
Ca(0)	9.8	14.7	24.3	12.9
Ca(i)	10.9	12.4	23.0	10.4
Ca(z)	9.0	9.5	20.3	10.1
Ca(zi)	11.7	11.3	23.8	13.4
O	7.3 to 13.7	10.9 to 15.7	18.7 to 26.2	8.3 to 12.3

and slower than 10^{-11} to 10^{-15} second. Such a frequency would yield an averaged electrostatic field gradient for the radio wave, but double peaks for the electron density distribution from X-ray diffraction. Simple thermal vibration has an infra-red frequency near 10^{13} cycles per second, thereby placing an upper limit on the jumping frequency of the Ca atoms.

If this simple model were correct, the jumping frequency should increase with temperature. At low temperature, the thermal vibration of the Ca atoms would be so low that they do not jump. Ideally all atoms would occupy one set of sites, giving a single crystal of P-anorthite. With rising temperature, jumping would begin. Domains would occur because of cooperation between neighbors, but with increasing temperature the Ca atoms would jump essentially independently from their neighbors.

Unfortunately the situation must be even more complex. The aluminosilicate framework cannot be regarded as a passive matrix (Megaw, 1961). It will undergo thermal vibration. Table 5-4 shows the root-mean-square atomic displacements estimated from the B-values obtained by Czank *et al.* The displacements for all atoms in anorthite increase strongly with temperature but it is impossible to distinguish any effects caused by jumping of Ca atoms. Detailed studies of thermal diffuse X-ray diffractions are needed to evaluate the extent of correlation between movements of neighboring atoms.

Unfortunately the simple model of jumping Ca atoms seems inadequate to explain all the experimental data. Czank *et al.* (1974) found that the occupation frequency of the Ca part-atoms is not one-half. At 240° C, the least-squares refinement yielded the following frequencies: Ca(0) 32% Ca(i) 67% Ca(z) 57% and Ca(zi) 44%, all with a standard error of 1%. Furthermore dark-field electron micrographs using *c* diffractions above 230° C showed a fine-scale pattern with bright spots apparently set in a black matrix (Fig. 10–18 f). With increasing temperature, the bright spots became smaller and smaller and the contrast with the matrix lessened until the whole micrograph became featureless and gray. The entire process was reversible. These data suggest that the low-temperature structure of coarse antiphase domains of P-anorthite changes to a high-temperature structure of tiny domains of primitive symmetry set in a matrix of body-centered symmetry. The domains must persist long enough to allow the electron micrographs to be taken. As the temperature increases, the domains either disappear completely or change position too rapidly to be observed giving statistical body-centered symmetry.

Czank *et al.* (1972) summarized their model as follows: "The Si–Al–O framework of the anorthite structure can be considered as being topologically body centered but in fact primitive at room temperature. With rising temperature the framework becomes more and more body centered and at the critical temperature (i.e. 230° C in Vesuvius anorthite) it is very nearly so, except for the Ca-ions which now occupy so-called split positions in large interstices of the framework. At room temperature all Ca-atoms are fixed in one or other of the two split positions, presumably the most favorable one from an energetic point of view. With rising temperatures the Ca-ions have an increasing probability of occupying the less favorable site of the split positions. However, correlation will be maintained between the occupied Ca-sites in neighboring unit cells, i.e. even in the high temperature body centered framework, the Ca-ions will tend to choose equivalent sites in neighboring unit cells leading to microdomains which have either a truly body centered structure, or microdomains which have a primitive structure, depending on which of the split positions are actually occupied. Using a *c*-reflection for imaging as in [Fig. 10–18 f] the primitive domains will show up bright since they contribute to these reflections. On the contrary, body centered microdomains will appear dark".

For this model, it seems likely that the position and size of the domains will depend in part on local structural features, probably including the degree of Al, Si disorder and the nature of Na, Ca substitution. Perhaps trivial factors such as mechanical defects also play a role. The following data appear pertinent.

The early X-ray studies on quenched anorthites and bytownites (Gay, 1953, 1954, 1962; Gay and Taylor, 1953; Laves and Goldsmith, abstracts in 1951; Goldsmith and Laves, 1956; Laves and Goldsmith, 1954a, b, c, 1955a, b, 1961a, b) are now summarized:

(1) Diffuse *c* diffractions occur for pure anorthites quenched from above 1100° C, being sharp after quenching from 1100° C and very diffuse for quenching from 1550° C. The diffuseness was unaffected qualitatively by quenching times up to 15 seconds, and was characteristic of the annealing temperature (Fig. 5-9).

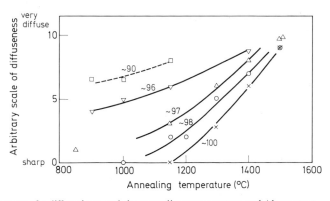

Fig. 5-9. Relation between diffuseness of *c* diffractions and the annealing temperature and Ab-content of five anorthites. Measurements of diffuseness were made qualitatively on X-ray patterns of quenched specimens. The specimens are: 100% An, synthetic; ~98, granulite, Greenland; ~97, recrystallized from melt of Miyakejima crystal lapilli; ~96, norite, Grass Valley, Calif.; ~90, Juvinas meteorite. The An-contents of the natural specimens were estimated optically. (From Laves and Goldsmith, 1954b, Fig. 6)

(2) Substitution of Ab caused increasing diffuseness, and sharp c diffractions were not obtained for natural specimens more sodic than 5% Ab (Fig. 5-9). Extrapolation to An_{100} revealed no obvious difference between synthetic and natural specimens.

(3) "Equilibrium" was attained rapidly at the annealing temperature, and there was no evidence that the Ab-content affected the reaction rate. One day at 900° C eliminated diffuseness produced by quenching anorthite, An_{100}, from temperatures above 1100° C, though a weak diffuse ring occurred around sharp c diffractions after heating for one hour. At 1500 to 1540° C, equilibrium was attained within 15 min. For an anorthite, An_{95}, equilibrium was approached but not attained in 5 days at 750° C. See also Chapter 7.

(4) The cell dimensions changed with the diffuseness of the c diffractions (see also Bruno and Gazzoni, 1967).

(5) Type c diffractions were never observed if b diffractions were absent or very diffuse. Furthermore b diffractions were sharp in all anorthites which had reached "equilibrium" with respect to c diffractions.

The simplest explanation of these observations is that Si, Al disorder, either independent of or dependent on Ab-substitution, strongly affects the domain texture responsible for the c diffractions (Megaw, 1962).

Chapter 10 records the electron-optical observations of domain texture. When account is taken of various experimental details, it seems certain that the coarseness of the domain texture and the diffraction contrast across the domain boundaries in dark-field micrographs both correlate with the sharpness of the c-diffractions. Unfortunately the observations of the different groups of investigators disagree in detail, and it is not certain whether the differences are genuine or whether they result merely from some trivial factors such as radiation damage. The results of Heuer et al. on 15415 anorthite suggest that domains of P-anorthite disappear completely at the inversion leaving I-anorthite, and that the domains reappear upon cooling at exactly the same positions. The results of Czank et al. on Vesuvius anorthite indicate that the inversion produces a fine-scale intergrowth of P- and I-anorthite. Undoubtedly many further studies will be made on this problem.

The diffuseness of the c diffractions is anisotropic. Ribbe and Colville (1968) took precession X-ray photographs on the a, b, c and [101] axes for a T-anorthite from Miyaké, Japan. It was not possible to obtain high accuracy in measuring the elongation of the diffuse c diffractions, but the closest rational direction in the [111] zone was the normal to $(2\bar{3}\bar{1})$. Choice of this plane rather than $(3\bar{4}\bar{1})$ permitted explanation of the diffuseness by stacking faults $(a + b + c)/2$ across domain walls. Electron diffraction data (Chapter 10) showed that domains tend to be elongated in the $(2\bar{3}\bar{1})$ plane, but detailed measurements of the texture and the out-of-step vector between domains have now been made. The possible role of Al, Si stacking faults should be considered in addition to the obvious role of the Ca atoms which can choose either a "left" or "right" displacement.

The discussions between Megaw (1961, 1962) and Laves and Goldsmith (1961a, b) are fascinating but obsolete. Several terms have been applied to the P–I transition in anorthite as authors tried to distinguish the transition from a simple displacive type (see Chapter 21). Laves and Goldsmith (1961) called it a "district" transformation, and Laves *et al.* (1970) used the term "Ferro-displacivity" because of a resemblance to ferromagnetic and ferroelectric transitions.

All calcic plagioclases with sharp or only slightly diffuse *b* diffractions show *c* diffractions as well. It is certain that the anorthite type of Al, Si ordering is a pre-requisite for development of *c* diffractions. The available data *measured at room temperature* suggest that the *c* diffractions become more diffuse the greater the Ab content and the higher the temperature from which quenching took place. However, there are no direct measurements at high temperature, and it is quite uncertain how the P to I transition in calcic anorthite changes as Ab enters in solid solution. Gay (1956) did not report *c* diffractions in two volcanic labradorites, An_{63} and An_{65}, which showed very diffuse *b* diffractions. Many labradorites with sharp *e* diffractions show very diffuse *c* diffractions. Again there are no data on whether these diffuse *c* diffractions undergo a non-quenchable change upon heating.

5.2.3 Sub-solidus Phase Relations

Because understanding of the phase relations depends on crystallographic interpretation, it is convenient to consider sub-solidus phase relations here. Many of the earlier ideas, such as those in Megaw (1961, 1962), are obsolete, but were important in stimulating further studies.

Table 5-5 summarizes the results of dry heat-treatment of calcic plagioclase by Gay (1954) and Gay and Bown (1956). All products were examined at room temperature by single-crystal X-ray diffraction. Figure 5-9 shows the key data of Laves and Goldsmith (1954b) on the heating of anorthites, but many more details are given in their tables. Laves and Goldsmith reported the following data for bytownites: (1) An_{77-78} from a troctolite at Merrill, Wis. had sharp *b*

Table 5-5. Dry heat-treatment of calcic plagioclase (Gay, 1954) and Gay and Bown (1956)

Specimen	mol.-% An	Unheated structure	Diffractions observed after heating for 3 days at given temperature (°C)		
Synthetic	100	*b*(s) *c*(vd)	1100: *b*(s) *c*(s)	1300: *b*(s) *c*(d)	
Pesmeda	100[a]	*b*(s) *c*(s)	1100: *b*(s) *c*(s)	1300: *b*(s) *c*(d)	1100: *b*(s) *c*(s)
Miyake	94[a]	*b*(s) *c*(d)	1100: *b*(s) *c*(d)		
Grass Valley	93	*b*(s) *c*(sd)	1100: *b*(s) *c*(sd)		
Rhum	88–91[a]	*b*(s) *c*(d)	1350: *b*(s) *c*(vd)	1400: *b*(vw)	
Rhum	88–91[a]	*b*(s) *c*(d)	1100: *b*(s) *c*(d)		
Rhum	88–91[a]	*b*(s) *c*(d)	900: *b*(s) *c*(d)		
Rhum	88–91[a]	*b*(s) *c*(d)	800: *b*(s) *c*(d)		
Stillwater	86	*b*(s) *c*(d)	1300: *b*(s) *c*(d)		
St. Louis Co.	80[a]	*b*(s)	900: *b*(s)	1250: *b*(w)	1350: *b*(vw)
Crystal Bay	70	*b*(s)	1350: none		

Abbreviations: *b* and *c*, diffraction types; s sharp, d diffuse, sd slightly diffuse, vd very diffuse, w weak, vw very weak.
[a] Means optical estimate.

and very diffuse c diffractions; after dry heating for 5 h at $1150°$ C the c diffractions were still observable (2) An_{75} (optical) from an anorthosite from India had e and f diffractions (δ_c 167°) connected by diffuse lines plus c diffractions of moderate diffuseness (3) An_{73} from an anorthosite at Split Point, Minn. had sharp b and very weak diffuse c diffractions (4) another crystal from the Minn. specimen showed only b diffractions.

Nord *et al.* (1972) heated a bytownite, An_{82}, from the Stillwater complex. Chapter 10 gives details of the electron-optical data which revealed a Huttenlocher intergrowth on the scale of 20 nm. Sharp b plus curved e and f diffractions were seen as well as diffuse elongated c diffractions. The Huttenlocher intergrowth was easily visible after dry heating at $1175°$ C for 4 days, but was not easily imaged after 7 days at 1215 or $1225°$ C. No intergrowth was seen after heating for 7 days at 1240 or 3 days at $1300°$ C, but sharp b diffractions were present.

Table 5-6 summarizes the hydrothermal experiments of McConnell (1972a, b). The products were examined by X-ray and electron-optical techniques.

Table 5-6. Hydrothermal heat-treatment of plagioclase (McConnell, 1972a, b)

(1) Bytownite, Stillwater Complex, $Or_{0.6}Ab_{22.9}An_{75.9}$.
   Untreated: Huttenlocher intergrowth of e-plagioclase and I-anorthite on 20 nm scale; $e(d) + b(vw)$
   Treated: Below 960° C; possibly slight weakening of e
   963° C, 28 days,   400 atm ⎫
   1020° C,   4 days,   400 atm ⎬ I-anorthite with no evidence of intergrowth.
   1101° C,   6 days, 1000 atm ⎭

(2) Bytownite, Stillwater Complex, $Or_{1.4}Ab_{22.7}An_{74.7}$.
   Untreated: Huttenlocher intergrowth with coarser texture than above; $e + b$
   No heat treatment.

(3) Labradorite, Duluth anorthosite, $Or_{2.6}Ab_{33.1}An_{65.4}$
   Untreated: sharp e
   Treated: 1011° C, 10 days,   420 atm ⎫
   1013° C,   4 days,   400 atm ⎬ I-anorthite with sharp b surrounded by diffuse halo.
   1019° C, 10 days,   420 atm ⎭

(4) Labradorite, red iridescence, $Or_{2.1}Ab_{43.0}An_{53.4}$
   Untreated: Bøggild intergrowth with sharp e
   Treated: 800° C, 28 days, 1000 atm   no change
   820° C, 28 days, 1000 atm   no change
   835° C, 28 days, 1000 atm e diffuse, weaker
   850° C,   7 days, 1000 atm e just detectable
   995° C,   4 days,   400 atm   Bø texture present
   1004° C,   4 days,   400 atm   Bø texture present

(5) Andesine, Yosemite monzonite, An_{37} (optical)
   Untreated: slightly diffuse e
   Treated: no change of cell dimension after 20 days at 601° C and 1000 atm; one to two weeks at 650° C to 730° C produced change of cell dimension with probable disappearance of e diffractions on X-ray patterns.

Table 5-7. Unheated and heated plagioclases (Gay, 1956; Gay and Bown, 1956)

Locality	Rock type	mol.% An	δ_a	δ_b	δ_c	Nature of e or b diffractions after heating 3 days at listed temperature (°C)	Notes on unheated material.
Lincoln Co., Wis.	anorthosite	73	–	37(2)	165(1)		c(d)
Duluth, Minn.	gabbro	71	–	–	180		b(s)
Wichita Mt., Okla.	do.	70	–	43(2)	163(1)		*
Chester Co., Pa.	diabase	67	9(3)	35(2)	157(1)	900(u); 1200(m); 700(m).	c(d)
Clear Lake, Ut.	volcanic	65	–	–	180	950(u); 800, 15 dys(u); 700, 36 dys(u)	b(vd)
Stillwater, Mt.	gabbro	64	8(2)	33(1)	159(.5)	950(u); 1000(ow); 1050(w); 1100(vw); 1150(sd); 1200(vd)	
S. J. P., Ireland	basalt	63	–	–	150	950(u); 1100(w); 1250(m); 800, 101 dys(m)	b(vd)
Shelby, N. C.	gabbro	60	14(2)	28(1)	146(1)		
Nain, Labr.	anorthosite	58	12(2)	–	151(1)	950(ow); 1000(w); 1050(vw); 1150(m)	
do.	do.	56	23(1)	17(2)	141(1)	900(u); 1200(m)	*
New Amalfi, S. A.	dolerite	55	16(2)	18(2)	148(1)		*
Skaergaard	gabbro	~53	18(2)	21(2)	145(1)		*
St. Paul, Labr.	?	53	25(1)	20(2)	137(1)	900(u); 1200(m); 800, 76 dys(m)	δ_c corr.*
New Amalfi	dolerite	51	20(1)	17(2)	138(2)		e(w)
Skaergaard	gabbro	~50	25(2)	21(2)	141(1)		*
Essex Co., N. Y.	anorthosite	50	24(2)	19(2)	139(1)	1000(ow); 1050(w); 1100(vw); 1150(m)	*
Sipoo, Finland	?	~47	28(1)	13(1)	132(2)		*
Linosa	volcanic	~46	–	–	132		e(vvw)*
Skaergaard	gabbro	~45	23(2)	19(2)	136(1)		e(m)*
do.	do.	45	23(3)	15(2)	136(1)	800, 66 dys(u); 1000(m); 900(m)	e(m)*
Beaver Bay, Minn.	diabase	44	27(4)	14(2)	132(2)	1000(m); 900(w)	e(w)
Skaergaard	gabbro	~41	–	–		900(w); 1200(m)	e(m)
Esterel	andesite	~40	31(3)	9(2)	125(2)	1000(w); 1150(vw); 1200(m)	e(wd)
Skaergaard	gabbro	~40					
Crestmore, Ca.	granodiorite	38	31(3)	–	128(3)		e(od)
Sierra Nevada	do.	~38	33(4)	8	125(4)		e(d)
Skaergaard	gabbro	37					e(m)*
Yosemite, Ca.	monzonite	37	32(3)	9(3)	121(4)	900(u); 1000(ow); 1100(vw); 1200(m)	e(od)
Skaergaard	gabbro	~37	–	–	–		e(m)*
San Luis Obispo	dacite	36	–	–	–		e(m)*
Spanish Peak	granodiorite	35	30(5)	7(3)	128(4)		e(vd)*
Knoydart, Scot.	schist	35	–	–	–		e(vvd)
Macon Co., N. C.	vein	30	~38	–	118(7)		e(vd)
Mitchell Co., N. C.	pegmatite	30	42(5)	~4	120(6)	500(u); 700(u); 800, 12 dys(u); 1200(m)	e(vd)
Bakersville, N. C.	do.	23	–	–	~121		e(vd)
Hawk Mine, N. C.	do.	22	~43	–	~12C		e(vvd)
S. C.	do.	17	–	–	~10C		e(vvd)*

Notes: column 3;   means optical estimate: columns 4,5,6;   error in brackets: column 7;   number of days given if more than 3, column 8; *means more than one crystal studied.

Abbreviations: u unchanged, m missing, s sharp, d diffuse, w weakened, v very, o only slightly.

Table 5-7 combines the data of Gay (1956) and Gay and Bown (1956) on plagioclases of intermediate compositions. Most of the data refer to *e*-plagioclase but three specimens of composition 71, 65 and 63% An show *b* diffractions characteristic of anorthite. Particularly pertinent to this section is the disappearance of *b* diffractions of the An_{63} specimen upon heating for 3 days at 1250° C, but not at 1100° C.

Figure 5-10 summarizes what I regard as the most important features of the structural data with respect to the phase relations. It must be emphasized that none of the laboratory studies have demonstrated reversible equilibria, and that there have been no rate studies. Probably the hydrothermal experiments of McConnell provide a better approach to equilibrium than the dry experiments, judging by experience with alkali feldspars.

One of the most important features is the overlap of the composition ranges of *e*-plagioclase and body-centered anorthite. The St. Johns Point specimen (An_{63}) in Table 5-7 is the most sodic specimen so far recorded with *b* diffractions. It occurs as phenocrysts in a basalt, and its *b* diffractions are very diffuse. The occurrence of the Huttenlocher intergrowth from about An_{67} to An_{90} causes difficulty in deciding what is the most calcic of observed *e*-plagioclase. Certainly *e*-plagioclase without *b* diffractions occurs up to An_{70} and perhaps up to An_{75} or even An_{80}.

Figure 5-10 contains the hypothetical phase boundaries taken from Fig. S-2a. Albite solid solution transforms into anorthite solid solution by means of a two-phase loop which intersects the dry solidus near An_{90}. The field of body-centered anorthite passes over the top of the solvus which encloses the field of two

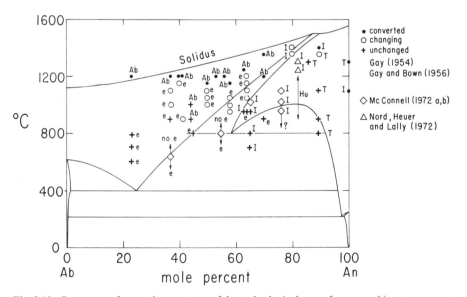

Fig. 5-10. Summary of crystal structures of heated plagioclases after quenching to room temperature. Each symbol is plotted at the heating temperature, and is labelled with the observed structure type: Ab albite; *e* *e*-plagioclase; I body-centered anorthite; T transitional anorthite; Hu Huttenlocher intergrowth. See Tables 5-5, 6 and 7 for details. The boundaries are from Fig. S-2a

coexisting anorthites. Below 800° C, albite solid solution coexists with body-centered anorthite, while below 250° C inversion occurs to primitive anorthite. It is obvious that some of the data shown on Fig. 5-10 are inconsistent with the proposed phase diagram, but I believe that the inconsistencies might be resolved if account is taken of metastability. In addition, the phase boundaries may require adjustment by considerable amounts consistent with the present topology.

The crest of the solvus is placed near 1000° C largely on the basis of McConnell's hydrothermal study of the Stillwater specimen, An_{76}. Heating at 963° C for 28 days produced I-anorthite with no electron-optical evidence of the Huttenlocher intergrowth. If e-plagioclase consists of a superstructure of regions similar to anorthite and albite (see next section), the e diffractions should disappear at 800° C according to the proposed phase diagram. McConnell thought that slight weakening of e diffractions occurred upon hydrothermal treatment below 960° C, but detailed kinetic studies are needed.

Nord et $al.$ homogenized the Huttenlocher intergrowth in a Stillwater specimen, An_{82}, by dry heating above 1225° C for one week. However, it is probable that the solvus is below this temperature. Detailed study using both dry and hydrothermal methods is desirable.

Because the Huttenlocher intergrowth is almost certainly coherent at the time of formation, dissociation of I-anorthite would not be governed by a classical binodal but by a coherent spinodal as shown by a dashed line in Fig. S-2a. If this diagram is correct, the Huttenlocher intergrowth should develop in rocks below 950° C and above 800° C, though it is possible that the coherent spinodal has a metastable extension below 800° C. Although there is no published study of the range of rock types in which the Huttenlocher intergrowth occurs, it is certain that it occurs in many high-grade metamorphic rocks and in igneous complexes large enough to give metamorphic conditions upon cooling. According to the proposed diagram, the Huttenlocher intergrowth should develop first as a coherent assemblage of two I-anorthites, the more sodic of which should invert into e-plagioclase. Perhaps detailed crystallographic studies will permit tests of whether this sequence occurred: electron microscopists should look for intergrowths of two I-anorthites in rocks cooled at an intermediate rate.

The dry heating studies of Gay (1954) and Gay and Bown (1956) are consistent with the proposed diagram if equilibrium was not attained. An I-anorthite (An_{64}) heated at 950° C for 3 days was unchanged, but heating at 1000 to 1200° C caused increasing diffuseness of the b diffractions consistent with transformation towards an albite type of structure. McConnell converted hydrothermally a specimen of similar composition, An_{65}, from e-plagioclase to I-anorthite by heating for about one week at 1011 to 1019° C. These data are consistent with I-anorthite solid solution being stable in sodic labradorites near 1000° C.

In anorthites, the data are consistent with P-anorthite being stable below about 250° C, though it is certain that the inversion to I-anorthite is not of the first-order. The diffuseness of the c diffractions of I-anorthite appears to increase with both the Ab-content and the annealing temperature prior to quenching. A systematic study of the diffraction pattern $directly$ at temperature is needed to clarify the phase relations at high temperature for anorthites and bytownites. I suspect that in bytownites *c* diffractions are extremely diffuse or unobservable above 300° C and that *b* diffractions become increasingly diffuse as the solidus temperature is approached.

The controversy between Laves and Goldsmith on the one hand and Gay and Taylor on the other hand about the interpretation of crystallographic properties of calcic plagioclases in terms of cooling rate requires amendment in view of the later data. For pure anorthite only the most rapidly quenched natural specimens such as crystal lapilli have very diffuse *c* diffractions: slow cooling under plutonic or metamorphic conditions is required to achieve complete change of the cell dimension β^*. With increasing Ab content, it is certain that a solid solution of body-centered anorthite occurs in specimens of volcanic and hypabyssal origin, but it is not clear under what conditions the transition occurs to the Huttenlocher intergrowth. The occurrence of out-of-step boundaries in specimens more sodic than 5% Ab implies inversion from the albite structure type. Metastable crystallization of the albite structure in the stability field of the anorthite structure is likely, and detailed studies are needed to define the inversion curves. In 1973, it seems certain that great care is needed in the interpretation of the diffraction patterns of calcic plagioclases, and that it is unwise to make detailed estimates of the crystallization conditions and cooling rate of the host rock therefrom.

Finally, there are some data which suggest the existence of a structural change in anorthite near 800° C. Bloss (1964) observed an inflexion near 800° C in a curve of optical extinction angle vs. temperature for an anorthite near An_{97}. Köhler and Weiden (1954) observed an endothermal d.t.a. peak near 800° C for two anorthites. Foit and Peacor (1967) observed changes of diffuseness of both *a* and *b* diffractions of a Miyaké anorthite between 600 and 1003° C. Smith and Ribbe (1969) suggested that these effects resulted from a change of vibrational modes of the aluminosilicate framework, but this is pure speculation.

5.3 *e*-plagioclase

There is no definitive structure analysis of a plagioclase with *e* diffractions, and the following treatment attempts to coordinate the experimental data and theoretical ideas while trying to avoid serious bias. However, it must be clearly stated that I favor a model (Smith and Ribbe, 1969) in which *e*-plagioclase consists of a coherent superstructure composed of regions resembling albite and anorthite separated by out-of-step boundaries. Furthermore, I believe that *e*-plagioclase develops because the truly stable assemblage of albite plus P-anorthite is thermodynamically inaccessible. Consequently I am prejudiced against any ideas involving the formation of ordered structures at stoichiometric ratios such as those developed theoretically by DeVore and by Niggli (see Chapter 3). I believe that the micrometer intergrowths form at a higher temperature than *e*-plagioclase (perhaps as in Fig. S-2a), and that *e*-plagioclase develops when the diffusion range is only a few unit cells.

5.3.1 Diffraction Data

The definitive review by Bown and Gay (1958) of the X-ray data has been essentially confirmed by all later workers, and the electron-optical data (Chapter 10) have demonstrated fringes consistent with an out-of-step texture. The early X-ray data were obtained by Chao and Taylor (1940), Cole *et al.* (1951), Sörum (1951), Gay (1956) and Gay and Bown (1956). The *e* diffractions occur as pairs of unequal intensity symmetrically about the positions which would be occupied by *b* diffractions of anorthite (Fig. 6-14). Mathematically the coordinates in reciprocal space can be referred to the anorthite cell as $(h+\delta h, k+\delta k, l-\delta l)$ and $(h-\delta h, k-\delta k, l+\delta l)$ where $(h+k)$ and l are both odd, and δh, δk and δl are positive and non-integral. Gay (1956) showed that δh, δk and δl vary from 0.12, 0.01 and 0.34 at An_{30} to 0.02, 0.10, 0.10, respectively, at An_{70}, the variation apparently being a continuous and near-linear function of An-content (Fig. 5-11). Gay, following Cole *et al.*, actually measured layer-line coordinates δa, δb and δc in degrees where δh, δk and δl respectively equal $\delta a/360°$, $\delta b/360°$ and $(180-\delta c)/180°$. Table 5-7 lists the measurements of Gay (1956), which extend and correct earlier data of Cole *et al.*

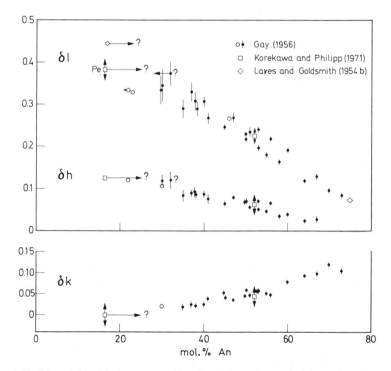

Fig. 5-11. Variation of δh, δk and δl with An-content. For Gay's data, the vertical bars give his stated error. The open circles show data of lower reliability because of extreme diffuseness of the *e* diffractions. The horizontal arrows for Gay's data relate the bulk chemical composition (tail) to the An-content estimated from refractive indices (head). The datum of Korekawa and Philipp (1971) was obtained for a peristerite, $An_{16.5}$, and the arrow-head shows the composition An_{25} which might represent the calcic component

All e-plagioclases more calcic than An_{55} show f diffractions as well. These were overlooked or poorly described in early papers, but occur in pairs symmetrically about a diffractions. In reciprocal space, their coordinates are $(h + 2\delta h, k + 2\delta k, l - 2\delta l)$ and $(h - 2\delta h, k - 2\delta k, l + 2\delta l)$ where $(h + k)$ and l are both even. Thus the vector joining f diffractions is parallel to and twice as long as that between e diffractions. Of great importance is the observation that f diffractions do not occur in e-plagioclases more sodic than An_{50} (perhaps even An_{55}), and this plus other evidence suggests a discontinuity near An_{50}. McConnell (1972a) distinguished the calcic from the sodic members by using e_1 versus e_2, and this nomenclature is adopted here (see Fig. S-2c).

Added in proof. McLaren reports very weak and diffuse f diffractions in electron-diffraction patterns of an andesine (see Chapter 10), but none have been reported so far in X-ray patterns which are less sensitive to subsidiary diffractions.

Figure 5-6e illustrates the *geometrical* relation between e and f diffractions as described earlier. Note that pairs of nodes labelled e_2 and f_2 are shown at double distance of the e_1 and f_1 nodes. Such extra nodes have not been recorded in X-ray patterns because of their low intensity, but Nissen (1973) detected them in long-exposure electron diffraction patterns.

It is quite certain that the e and f nodes belong to a single diffraction pattern. Any structural model must account for simultaneous occurrence of e and f diffractions in the e_1 type of e-plagioclase.

As explained in Chapter 10, the reciprocal vector $t = 2(\delta h \cdot a^* + \delta k \cdot b^* - \delta l \cdot c^*)$ obtained from either the X-ray or electron-diffraction pattern is related to the spacing T of fringes in dark-field electron micrographs using either paired e or a plus f diffractions by $T = 1/|t|$. The simplest explanation of these observations is that e-plagioclase is based on an anti-phase modulation of the anorthite structure as proposed by McConnell and Fleet (1963), and reiterated by McConnell (1972a, b).

Cinnamon and Bailey (1971) treated the measurements of δa, δb and δc as though they came from entirely different diffractions viewed along each axis, but in 1972 they confirmed that there was only one pair of e diffractions.

Bown and Gay (1958) used a vector s rather than t to give the orientation of the e and f diffractions. Although s is parallel to t, it is only half its length. Smith and Ribbe (1969) incorrectly used s rather than t to calculate the wavelength of the structural modulation. Figure 5-12 shows the wavelength T as a function of An-content. The data of Gay (1956) and Korekawa and Philipp (1971) were calculated from the values of δh, δk and δl given in Fig. 5-11: the arrow shows the uncertainty of composition for a peristerite. Actual fringe spacings from electron micrographs are shown by the open symbols, and the three for labradorites are consistent with the predictions from the X-ray data. The bytownite, An_{75}, has a complex structure, probably resulting from a superstructure of Huttenlocher type (Chapter 10), and it is likely that the datum should be plotted at a more sodic composition. In general, the wavelength varies from about 2 nm for oligoclases to about 5 nm for An_{70}: however, it is possible that subtle effects are obscured by the experimental error.

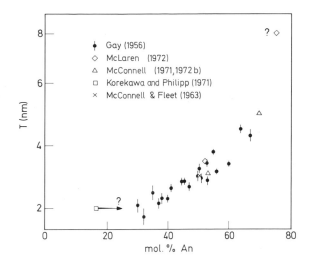

Fig. 5-12. Variation of T in nanometers with An-content of e-plagioclase

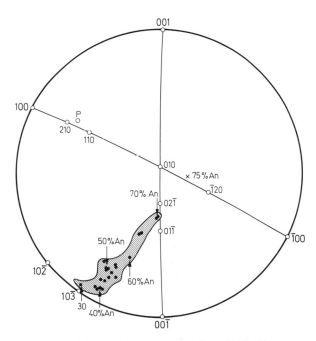

Fig. 5-13. Orientation of t in e-plagioclase. The dots are from Bown and Gay (1958). The cross shows the datum of McLaren (1972, Fig. 3-5) for An_{75} from the Bushveldt Complex. P is the pole of the great circle which approximates the trend of the data. Contrary to convention, the circles represent upward or horizontal directions of the face-normals. (After Bown and Gay, 1958, Fig. 1)

Figure 5-13 shows the orientation of t with An-content. The stereographic projection is plotted for An_{50} with b at the center and a^* and c^* at the circumference. The normals to faces in prominent zones are plotted. Bown and Gay's data show that t lies parallel to the $(10\bar{3})$ normal for An_{30} and moves near

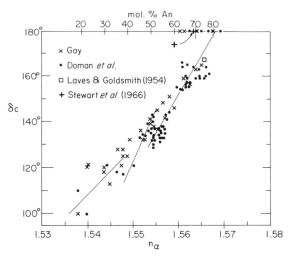

Fig. 5-14. Variation of δc with An-content for e-plagioclase. The data of Gay (1953) and Stewart *et al.* (1966) are plotted with respect to the An-content. The data of Doman *et al.* (1965) are plotted with respect to the refractive index n_α, which is converted to An-content by their determinative curve. Laves and Goldsmith estimated the An-content optically. (From Smith and Ribbe, 1969, Fig. 4)

(02$\bar{1}$) for An_{70}. The cross shows the datum given for An_{75} by McLaren (1972). If this datum is confirmed it implies that one or more of δh, δk and δl changes sign: referring to Fig. 5-11, it is likely that δk and δl remain positive while δh becomes negative.

So far, all the data on e-plagioclase can be interpreted in terms of a continuous variation of all properties with respect to An-content. However, Doman *et al.* (1965) made detailed measurements of the refractive indices, cell angle γ^*, and δc of many single crystals of plagioclase, and obtained evidence of discontinuities. Figure 5-14 shows the relation between δc and n_α for 75 single crystals of e-plagioclase. The three lines show the trends suggested by Doman *et al.* in which there are breaks near An_{50} and An_{35}. In addition, there is a compositional overlap between e-plagioclase and anorthite. Also plotted in Fig. 5-14 are data obtained by other workers, for most of which the An-content was measured for the bulk specimens. The data of Gay (1956) show a wide scatter of δc (or δl), probably because of error in both δc and An. Because δc correlates better with δb and δa than with An-content (see Figs. 1 and 2 of Gay, 1956), it seems likely that there are errors of perhaps 2–5% An in the An-contents plotted by Gay. Even so, there is a suggestion in Fig. 5-11 of a flexure in the trends of δh, δk and δl near An_{50}. Figure 5-15 shows the relation between the β and γ refractive indices and the γ^* angle for the specimens of Doman *et al.* This graph plus the one for the α refractive index (see their Fig. 2) again suggest discontinuities. It is extremely important that the chemical compositions of the actual crystals measured by Gay and by Doman *et al.* be analyzed accurately by an electron microprobe. Until then, the existence of discontinuities is not absolutely proven. However, I shall assume from now on that there is some kind of discontinuity near An_{50}, and perhaps another one near An_{35}. This is consistent with data on cell dimensions of

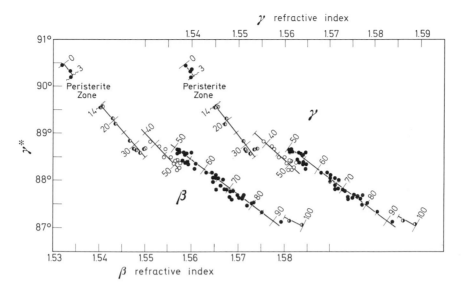

Fig. 5-15. Variation of refractive indices n_β and n_γ with cell angle γ^* for single crystals of plagioclase. (From Doman *et al.*, 1965, Fig. 3)

low plagioclase given in Chapter 7. Doman *et al.* (1965, p. 738) reported other evidence from physical properties of plagioclase.

Detailed intensity measurements of *e* diffractions of a labradorite were made by K. Toman and A. J. Frueh, as reported in a later section. Apart from these data, there are no systematic measurements of the intensity and diffuseness of subsidiary diffractions in *e* plagioclase. Bown and Gay (1958) stated that *e* diffractions do not change intensity very much in the labradorite region. However, the *f* diffractions increase strongly with An-content, being unobservable below An_{55}, and comparable with *e*-diffractions near An_{70-75}. Indeed Laves and Goldsmith (1954b) observed a specimen in which the *f* diffractions on average were ten times as strong as the *e* diffractions. This specimen has the highest value yet recorded of δc. Comprehensive measurements of both peak and integrated intensity are needed. In some e_1-plagioclases, very weak and diffuse *c* diffractions were seen by Bown and Gay (1958), but were never identified with certainty in e_2-plagioclase.

There are no published comprehensive data on the individual intensities of *e*, *f* and *c* diffractions in *e*-plagioclase. Bown and Gay (1958) stated that the intensities of the two spots forming a pair of *e* diffractions usually differ from each other in an unsystematic manner, but that the combined intensity is comparable to that of the corresponding *b* diffraction of anorthite. The *c* diffractions are weaker than, but otherwise similar to, those in transitional anorthites.

5.3.2 Heat-treatment and Petrologic Occurrence

Rapid heating and cooling up to about 1100° C produces no permanent effect on *e*-plagioclase, but causes major reversible changes in the sharpness but not the position of the *e* diffractions.

Foit and Peacor (1967) heated a crystal of andesine, An_{47}, from North Creek, N. Y., and measured the diffractions with a counter Weissenberg directly at temperature. The integrated intensities of 042, 024 and 026 increased linearly with temperature whereas that of 0, 4, $\overline{10}$ decreased. Of these four a diffractions, 042 and 024 sharpened with increasing temperature while 0, 4, $\overline{10}$ broadened. All three pairs of e diffractions (071, 07$\overline{1}$ and 09$\overline{3}$) showed decreasing integrated intensity and increasing diffuseness as the temperature increased. The intensities had dropped several-fold at 1070° C, and the trends would extrapolate to zero at 1400° C. Although the positions of the e diffractions did not change, the intensities of the two satellites approached each other as the temperature increased. All effects were independent of the heat treatment which involved heating at 7° C per minute and cooling at 45° C per minute. Forty-one hrs. at 930° C followed by 47 h at 1000° C caused no permanent change in 07$\overline{1}$. The integrated intensity was measured by scanning along phi using Weissenberg geometry, and the diffuseness was measured from the ratio of width at half-intensity to the peak height.

Bown and Gay (1969) used photographic methods to confirm that reversible changes accurred in the diffraction patterns of e-plagioclase upon heating to 1000° C. They used specimens of composition 56 and 64% An.

Prolonged heating at high temperature causes permanent reduction or loss of intensity of e diffractions (Gay and Bown, 1956). Table 5-7 summarizes the data obtained by X-ray methods after cooling to room temperature. Figure 5-10 shows the results with respect to a proposed phase diagram (Fig. S-2a). Dry heating near the solidus resulted in complete loss of the e diffractions, producing an albite solid solution. Heating for 3 days between about 1000 and 1100° C caused weakening of the e diffractions, and prolonged heating probably would cause complete elimination.

Table 5-6 summarizes the hydrothermal experiments of McConnell (1972a, b) which show loss of e diffractions near 800° C for a labradorite, An_{53}, and near 600° C for an andesine, An_{37}. A more calcic labradorite, An_{65}, lost its e diffractions near 1000° C and gained sharp b diffractions.

Bown and Gay (1958) stated that the transformation of e-plagioclase to a high albite solid solution at a constant temperature proceeded initially by rapid intensity changes which slowed up with longer periods of heating. The transformation is more rapid at higher temperature but proceeds at $\sim 950°$ C under dry conditions if heating is prolonged. They noted that the diffuse c diffractions are relatively unchanged as the e and f spots disappear. Near the end of the transformation, the weakened e spots become surrounded by a diffuse halo into which they merge, thereby producing a single diffuse region. All these observations were obtained at room temperature after heating.

There are no data on c diffractions studied directly at temperature. It is possible that they undergo a reversible loss of intensity at low temperature as in anorthite.

The laboratory heating data are supplemented by correlating the diffraction properties of e-plagioclase with the petrologic occurrence. Gay (1956) showed that specimens from slowly-cooled rocks tend to have sharper and stronger e diffractions than those from volcanic rocks, though more data are needed to confirm this tendency. It seems that this effect is more pronounced for e_2-than for

e_1-plagioclase. For andesines, even the specimens from gabbros show weak or absent e diffractions, whereas for labradorites, the e diffractions are fairly strong and sharp even when obtained from hypabyssal rocks. Smith and Gay (1958) suggested that low-plagioclase attains equilibrium much less easily as the Ab-content increases, and proposed that the kink in plots of cell dimensions vs. An-content in the andesine and oligoclase range (see Chapter 7) results from metastability.

Particularly important is the observation of b instead of e diffractions in three calcic specimens from igneous rocks (Table 5-7). These specimens have 71, 65 and 63% An. Type b diffractions were not observed in more sodic specimens from volcanic rocks. These data suggest that body-centered anorthite has a stability field at high temperature at least as sodic as An_{63}: however, the possibility of metastable formation must be considered. The hydrothermal conversion by Mc-Connell of an e-plagioclase (An_{65}) into a body-centered anorthite at 1011–1019° C (Table 5-6) strengthens greatly the evidence for a stability field for I-anorthite in the labradorite region, and is consistent with the phase relations in Fig. S-2a.

5.3.3 Models and Ideas

This section is strictly historical, and all ideas are given whether I think they are good or bad. After trying to give an unbiased description of each idea, I have attempted to give an evaluation. Unfortunately space restrictions prevent reproduction of all the mathematical derivations, and only the key results can be given. Many of the present ideas were given by Smith and Ribbe (1969).

Chao and Taylor (1940). These authors proposed a simple model in which sheets of (low) albite and anorthite structure alternate approximately on (001). A one-dimensional model with sinusoidal modulation of scattering intensity and constant lattice repeat yielded pairs of satellite diffractions.

Megaw (1960). This model is the most detailed so far, and although wrong in some features, provided ideas which must be incorporated in better models.

In paper I, Megaw developed the mathematical description of a superstructure in terms of sub-cells, domains, and slip-vectors. For brevity, the details are omitted here. Particularly important is the conclusion that sharp diffractions can occur even when the stacking faults are random: Megaw actually used a binomial distribution. Irrational boundaries were considered as the addition of independent, intersecting stacking faults.

Megaw (paper II) extrapolated the observations of δa, δb and δc to An_{78}, at which δa should be near zero. New axes a_0, b_0 and c_0 were defined in terms of a_{Ab}, b_{Ab} and c_{Ab} of the conventional albite cell as follows:

$$a_0 = a_{Ab}$$
$$b_0 = \tfrac{1}{2}(a_{Ab} + b_{Ab}) \qquad \text{(Note: Fig. 3 is incorrect).}$$
$$c_0 = \tfrac{3}{2} a_{Ab} + \tfrac{1}{2} b_{Ab} + c_{Ab}.$$

The axis b_0 is related to the C face-centering, and c_0 to the body-centering of the anorthite cell. A super-cell with edges a_0, $9b_0$ and $2c_0$ was developed in which

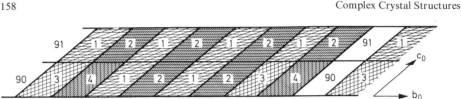

Fig. 5-16. Model of "ideal" e-plagioclase proposed by Megaw. The b_0 and c_0 axes, respectively, are related to the C face-centering and I body-centering vectors of the anorthite cell (see text). The model applies strictly to the composition An_{78} for which the shaded sub-cells contain Al_2Si_2 while the bridging sub-cells 90 and 91 contain only Si. For this composition, the splitting vector t is along b_0, corresponding to a repeat of 9 unit cells. The two choices of origin for ordered Al_2Si_2 distributions are distinguished by hatching sloping to left and right, while the two choices of framework puckering in P-anorthite are distinguished by the horizontal and vertical hatching. (From Megaw 1960, III, Fig. 1)

16 of the 18 sub-cells resemble one or other of the four sub-cells of P-anorthite. These sub-cells are juxtaposed to give sheets of anorthite-like structure separated by boundary regions of transitional material. Figure 5-16 shows the $b_0 c_0$ section of this *ideal* structure. The model applies to the *ideal* composition An_{78}. There are four sub-cells of anorthite type, labelled 1, 2, 3 and 4, whose topologic choice of Al_2Si_2 is shown by the hatching sloping to left and right, while the direction of framework puckering is distinguished by vertical and horizontal hatching. A block of 1234 corresponds to P-anorthite, and one of 1212 to I-anorthite as far as *symmetry* is concerned. The bridging sub-cells contain only Si.

Megaw clearly based her model on sub-cells of anorthite type. The 16 sub-cells composed of types 1, 2, 3 and 4 consist of two outer blocks with the 1234 configuration of P-anorthite, and an inner block of 12121212 with the configuration of I-anorthite. Smith and Ribbe suggested that the opposite is more likely because the 90, 91 sub-cells should disrupt the P pattern of their neighbors whereas the central block would have a better opportunity to adopt a configuration closer to P-anorthite.

Using an a diffraction in reciprocal space as the reference point, the e diffractions are specified by

$$(\delta a)_0 = \delta a$$
$$(\delta b)_0 = 180^\circ + \tfrac{1}{2}(\delta a + \delta b)$$
$$(\delta c)_0 = -180^\circ + \tfrac{1}{2}(3\delta a + \delta b + 2\delta c).$$

Gay's results show that $(\delta a)_0$ increases from about zero near An_{70} to about 40° near An_{30}. The parameter $(\delta b)_0$ varies randomly with composition from 197 to 203°; the deviations from the average value of 200° C might arise merely from experimental error. $(\delta c)_0$ is near zero but appears to change with composition from values near $+10^\circ$ for An_{70} to -7° for An_{30}. Megaw's ideal model assumes that δa, δb and δc, respectively, are 0, 200 and 0°. The deviation of 200° from 180° gives the 9 times repeat down the b_0 axis, which is the C face-centering vector of the albite cell. The c_0 repeat was doubled to explain the occurrence of the diffuse c diffractions.

Continuing to work only in the $b_0 c_0$ plane, Megaw modified the ideal plagioclase lattice by introducing stacking faults on $(010)_0$ and $(001)_0$ with respective slip vectors parallel to c_0 and b_0. From the variation of $(\delta c)_0$ with composition, Megaw deduced that there were essentially no stacking faults on $(001)_0$ near An_{50}, because $(\delta c)_0$ was essentially zero. Going from An_{50} to An_{70}, stacking faults of $-2b_0$ rising up to a maximum probability of $\frac{1}{2}$ were deduced (this value of $\frac{1}{2}$ corresponds to $(\delta c)_0 = 10°$). From the sharpness of the diffractions, Megaw deduced that the faults occurred regularly. Going the other way from An_{50} to An_{30}, the stacking faults change direction and magnitude to $+b_0$ and the probability rises to a maximum of 0.2. Because the diffractions are diffuse in this composition range, Megaw deduced that these stacking faults are random.

The variation of $(\delta a)_0$ from $\sim 0°$ to $\sim 40°$ as An goes from $\sim 70\%$ to $\sim 30\%$ is well-defined experimentally. Megaw (p. 169) deduced from the geometrical relations that faults of $2b_0$ were occurring on a $(100)_0$ fault plane with a probability ranging from 0 at $(\delta a)_0 = 0°$ to 1 at $40°$. Because $(\delta a)_0$ is a near-linear function of fault probability, she deduced that the fault probability varies approximately linearly with composition.

If $(\delta b)_0$ were exactly $200°$, there would be no need for stacking faults on $(010)_0$ when the *ideal plagioclase lattice* with $b = 9b_0$ is used to describe the diffraction geometry. However, Megaw wanted to explain the occurrence of c diffractions by faulting on $(010)_0$. She assumed that the observed values of $(\delta b)_0$ might differ from $200°$ by an amount undetectable within the error of $2°$; from this small value she calculated the effects of various probabilities of stacking faults. To me the introduction of these faults on $(010)_0$ is unconvincing because the calculated breadth ε and intensities of the c diffractions resulting therefrom seem hard to reconcile with the experimental values. Megaw stated that there is insufficient evidence from the qualitative experimental data to decide whether Ca, Na ordering occurs, though she suggested that, if it occurs, it distinguishes between odd- and even-numbered sub-cells. Megaw emphasized that the two principal slip vectors preserve the continuity of the Al_2Si_2 ordering pattern of anorthite type, and that blocks of 13 sub-cells slide against blocks of 34 sub-cells to increase the number of 1234 blocks characteristic of the puckered framework of P-anorthite. Only the third fault breaks the continuity of the Al_2Si_2 distribution, which is not unreasonable because it is used only for compositions more sodic than An_{50}.

The culmination of Megaw's scheme is given in the following quotation from p. 195, which is slightly changed in nomenclature (x is the mol. fraction Ab):

"Starting from pure anorthite, the substitution of Si for Al occurs at random on a specified selection of T_2 sites, the first-class T_2 sites [by first-class, Megaw is referring to preferential replacement by Si with respect to other Al-containing sites]. This is a cause of faulting with slip vector c_0, which affects the puckering differences between sub-cells but does not break up the existing Si–Al sequences. At this stage there is probably no (Ca, Na) ordering. At the composition $x = \frac{2}{9}$ (An_{78}) a rearrangement becomes possible in which the excess Si is relegated, in a perfectly regular way, to one sub-cell out of nine, occupying all the T_1 as well as the T_2 sites in this sub-cell; in the remaining eight-ninths of the sub-cells the original (Si, Al) sequence of anorthite is restored. There is probably some kind of (Ca, Na) ordering in this structure, though not complete; the evidence is rather uncertain. This is the ideal plagioclase structure. As x increases, excess Si again enters into the same first-class T_2 sites, causing faults with slip-vector c_0 as before, and also a new kind of fault on $(100)_0$ which is responsible for the conspicuous change of position of (e) maxima with composition. There is also faulting on $(001)_0$ due to (Na, Ca) distribution, present at $x = \frac{2}{9}$ but decreasing as x increases, but this is a minor feature.

At a composition $x = \frac{6}{9}$ (An$_{33}$), the first-class T_2 sites are fully occupied by Si. Entry of Si into the remaining T_2 sites, the second-class sites, now begins (indeed, it may probably have begun before the filling of the first-class sites is quite complete) and gives rise to a new kind of faulting on $(001)_0$ which breaks up the original Si, Al sequences in the c_0 direction. If completely random this fault would destroy the regularity of repeat between the T_1 sites occupied by Si and Al, giving in effect one kind of site occupied by $(Al_\frac{1}{2}Si_\frac{1}{2})$ — a situation resembling that in ideal orthoclase. However, before the occupation of second-class T_2 sites by Si has proceeded very far, at a composition of roughly $x = \frac{7}{9}$, An$_{22}$, (i.e. about one-third of the way to completion), the faulted structure becomes unstable and is superseded by the two unmixed structures of the peristerite. About these transitional states there is no detailed evidence, but the final product is of course low albite, where it is at least approximately true that one set of T_1 sites, $T_1(0)$, is wholly occupied by Al, and the other, $T_1(m)$, wholly by Si".

Megaw (III Fig. 3) gave a possible model for the bridging sub-cells 90 and 91, in which they act as a change-of-step between the anorthite sub-cells. Figure 5-17 is a simplified diagram by Smith and Ribbe (1969) which shows the same idea. In this a-axis projection, the tetrahedral nodes of the boundary region are populated only by Si. A change-of-step results between the two regions with anorthite structure. Such a change-of-step can also occur if the boundary region is populated with the AlSi$_3$ ordering pattern of albite.

During annealing of plagioclase, Megaw proposed that local strain encourages the formation of nuclei which coalesce if the structures are in phase, but which form a faulted boundary if out of phase. The fault boundaries tend to become

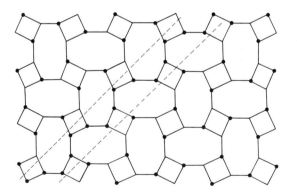

Fig. 5-17. Change-of-step in ordering patterns. In this diagram, which is based on that of Megaw (1960c, Fig. 3), regions with anorthite ordering of Al$_2$Si$_2$ are separated by a boundary (broken lines) populated only by Si atoms (black dots). The aluminosilicate framework is projected down the a-axis and the tetrahedral nodes are formed at the intersection of 4- and 8-rings (see Fig. 2-2). (From Smith and Ribbe, 1969, Fig. 7)

planar in order to minimize the strain, thereby producing blocks of nearly regular structure contacting at bridging layers.

Smith and Ribbe (1969) found that the Al-contents of the Megaw model did not agree with the estimates obtained from the T–O distances of crystal structure analyses (compare the Table in Smith and Ribbe, p. 182, with Fig. 3-8). For example, the Mcgaw model predicts 0.445 Al and 0.555 Si in both $T_1 0$ and $T_1 m$ at An_{25}, whereas crystal structure analyses of two oligoclases give 0.7 Al in $T_1 0$ and 0.3 Al in $T_1 m$. This discrepancy is far too big to explain by experimental error.

In conclusion, it is certain that the Megaw model is inadequate, but some of the geometrical features plus ideas involving bridging sub-cells and out-of-step Al, Si distributions appear to have permanent value.

Korekawa and Jagodzinski (1967). This model is incomplete but is being developed further. I am indebted to M. Korekawa for clarifying the model and for supplying a copy of his 1967 thesis which extends the data in the above paper.

Figure 5-18 shows the essential features of the model. Concentrations of electron density occur as shown by the heavy lines. The vectors *a* and *c* show the axes of anorthite, and the plane $(11\bar{4})$ is almost perpendicular to the *t* vector of the particular labradorite studied by Korekawa and Jagodzinski. In section, the density concentrations are face-centered. Korekawa expressed the modulations by two box functions $\varrho(m_1, m_2, m_3)$ and $\varrho(m_1, m_2, m_3 + \frac{1}{2})$ where m_1, m_2 and m_3 are integers associated with the *a*, *b* and *c* axes. The cell dimensions of the pseudo-cell of anorthite type are shown by a_0 and c_0. Anti-phase boundaries are shown by dotted lines. The repeat of each density modulation is given by $M_1 a_0$, and M_1 is taken as 16. The two box functions $\varrho(m_1, m_2, m_3)$ and

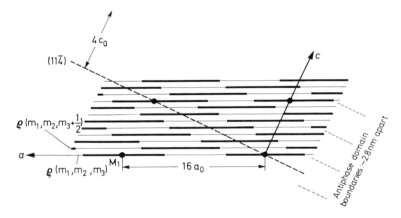

Fig. 5-18. The Korekawa-Jagodzinski model of *e*-plagioclase. Heavy lines show the position of Ca atoms, and light lines those of Na. Fig. 5-4a shows the rectangular density modulation. The axes *a* and *c* refer to the anorthite structure. The model is drawn for a labradorite with the *t* vector near $(11\bar{4})$ which is denoted the "plane-of-equal-phases". The two density modulations alternate down the *c*-axis giving antiphase domain boundaries about 5.6 nanometers apart. For convenience, the model is based on an integral superstructure with edges $16a_0$ and $4c_0$. See text for two other density modulations not shown here. (After Korekawa, 1967, Fig. 35 with additions from Korekawa, pers. comm.)

$\varrho(m_1, m_2, m_3 + \frac{1}{2})$ are anti-phase with respect to the "plane-of-equal-phases"; i.e. the plane almost perpendicular to t. Actually there are two other modulations $\varrho(m_1 + \frac{1}{2}, m_2 + \frac{1}{2}, m_3 + \frac{1}{2})$ and $\varrho(m_1 + \frac{1}{2}, m_2 + \frac{1}{2}, m_3)$ which are not shown in Fig. 5-18: these are respectively co-phase to $\varrho(m_1, m_2, m_3)$ and $\varrho(m_1, m_2, m_3 + \frac{1}{2})$.

Korekawa and Jagodzinski ascribed the density variation to Ca and Na atoms. No specific assignment of the Si and Al atoms was made although they suggested that Si and Al might unmix slightly because of charge linkage to Na and Ca. Smyth and Smith (1969) showed that clusters of M cations, $5 \times 5 \times 5$ unit cells across, in a neutral matrix would generate an electrostatic energy of 80 kJ/mole. Hence they argued that clustering of M cations must be accompanied by corresponding clustering of T cations (e.g. Al_2Si_2 with Ca, and $AlSi_3$ with Na). Such simultaneous clustering would result in domains similar in structure to anorthite and albite, which recalls the simple model of Chao and Taylor!

The orientation of the t vector was explained by the relative displacement of the chains of Na and Ca atoms, but no explanation was given why t varies with An-content.

Korekawa and Jagodzinski stated that one can distinguish between a density and a positional variation between corresponding atoms of the sub-cells by measuring the variation of diffraction intensity with scattering angle (as in Fig. 5-5). Because the variation for a labradorite was found to be small, K and J emphasized density variation, especially between Ca and Na. However, Smith and Ribbe pointed out that the equivalent atomic positions of sub-cells of anorthite differ from each other and from those in albite by several hundredths of a nanometer, and that models based on such sub-cells also would yield an intensity distribution which is nearly independent of angle (cf. the upper curves of the central diagrams of Fig. 5-5).

The intensities of the e and f satellites were explained by the rectangular density model of Fig. 5-4. The nodes $n = 1$ and 2 were equated, respectively, with the e and f diffractions of e-plagioclase. K and J stated that the variation of intensity of e and f diffractions with An-content agreed with the theoretical model, but S and R stated that this was true only for the range An_{50} to An_{75}. The model does not account for absence of both e and f diffractions above An_{80}, nor for the absence of f diffractions below An_{50} (however, Korekawa and Philipp (1971) reported streaks about the a diffractions of an oligoclase). The model does not explain the occurrence of diffuse c diffractions in labradorite.

Toman and Frueh pointed out that both the Megaw and KJ models were inadequate to explain the variation of satellite intensity throughout reciprocal space. In particular, the KJ model gives exactly the same intensity at all e nodes whereas the experimental data show large variations. Of course, the KJ model could be modified using positional displacements of the atoms from the ideal positions implied by Fig. 5-18.

Korekawa (pers. comm., 1972) stated that he was attempting to explain the strong inequality between the intensity of satellite pairs. In particular, removal of the center of symmetry apparently provided a possible avenue.

Although the KJ model does not provide a complete answer, the geometrical features have permanent value and can be used as the basis for further refinement.

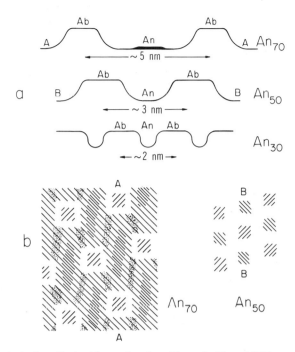

Fig. 5-19. The Smith-Ribbe model of *e*-plagioclase. See text for explanation. (From Smith and Ribbe, 1969, Fig. 10)

Smith and Ribbe (1969). This model is qualitative only, and is based on albite- and anorthite-like "domains" separated by hybrid boundary regions.

Figure 5-19 summarizes the features. The scale has been halved to correct for the use of *s* instead of *t*. In (a), cross-sections across the out-of-step texture are shown. At An_{70}, the domains of anorthite are thick enough to permit the atoms to approach the configuration of P-anorthite at the center (heavy line). At the boundaries, the configuration is more similar to that of I-anorthite. S and R suggested that, when atoms approached the positions of P-anorthite, weak diffuse *c*-diffractions were produced. At An_{50} and An_{30}, the domains become smaller, and indeed the regions ascribed to Ab and An are so small that description in terms of albite and anorthite might be misleading (but see later). In (b), a planar section through the out-of-step texture is shown, analogous to the section shown by Korekawa and Jagodzinski. Regions of albite- and anorthite-like structure are distinguished by the hatching. Dotted regions show where the Al_2Si_2 patterns of anorthite are out-of-step, and double-hatched areas show where the atomic positions may approach those of P-anorthite. Clear regions are transitional between those of albite and anorthite.

Toman and Frueh (1971, 1973a, b, c). Whereas all the preceding authors relied only on the geometry of the satellite diffractions and a few qualitative observations of intensities, Toman and Frueh actually made detailed measurements of the intensities of the satellites. Their important studies are only partly completed, but the results so far definitely place limits on models of *e*-plagioclase. I am greatly indebted to them for supplying preprints.

TF (1971) measured the intensities of a and b diffractions of a bytownite which also yielded a few diffuse c diffractions. Similar measurements were made for a labradorite crystal with sharp, strong e and weaker, slightly diffuse f diffractions. The values of 0.0625, 0.051 and 0.219 for δh, δk and δl suggest a composition near An_{53} on Fig. 5-11. An ω-scan with a graphite monochromator was used to measure the integrated intensity. About 2000 e and f diffractions plus 500 a diffractions were measured for the labradorite.

The data were interpreted in terms of a theory for the average variation of satellite intensity with the reciprocal lattice vector B, which is related to the diffraction angle. T and F calculated the intensity for a superstructure with four types of subcells as in P-anorthite. Each subcell was assumed to have the same number of atoms in approximately the same positions, but the X-ray scattering factors and positional coordinates were not the same. For position number j the deviation of positional coordinate in the four sub-cells is $\varDelta_{1j}$, $\varDelta_{2j}$, $\varDelta_{3j}$ and $\varDelta_{4j}$. The atomic scattering factor was approximated by $Z_j f$ where Z_j is the number of electrons in atom j and f is a function common to all atoms. The parameter $\varDelta Z_{1j}$ specifies the deviation of the scattering factor for position j in the first subcell, and similarly for subscripts 2, 3 and 4.

For b diffractions in anorthite, the following approximate equation was obtained

$$
\frac{|\bar{F}|_b^2}{|\bar{F}|_a^2} = \frac{1}{16}\left(\sum_j Z_j^2\right)^{-1}\left[\sum_j (\varDelta Z_{1j}+\varDelta Z_{2j})-(\varDelta Z_{3j}+\varDelta Z_{4j})\right]^2
$$

$$
+ \frac{8\pi^2|\boldsymbol{B}|^2}{3!}\sum_j Z_j^2\,[\,|\varDelta_{1j}-\varDelta_{2j}|^2+|\varDelta_{3j}-\varDelta_{4j}|^2-|\varDelta_{1j}-\varDelta_{3j}|^2
$$

$$
-|\varDelta_{1j}-\varDelta_{4j}|^2-|\varDelta_{2j}-\varDelta_{3j}|^2-|\varDelta_{2j}-\varDelta_{4j}|^2\,]
$$

$$
- \frac{32\pi^4|\boldsymbol{B}|^4}{5!}\sum_j Z_j^2\,[\,|\varDelta_{1j}-\varDelta_{2j}|^4+|\varDelta_{3j}-\varDelta_{4j}|^4-|\varDelta_{1j}-\varDelta_{3j}|^4
$$

$$
-|\varDelta_{1j}-\varDelta_{4j}|^4-|\varDelta_{2j}-\varDelta_{3j}|^4-|\varDelta_{2j}-\varDelta_{4j}|^4\,]\,.
$$

The mean intensity of the b diffractions normalized to the a diffractions has a positive intercept at zero diffraction angle given by the first term which depends only on the scattering factors. The second and third terms are proportional to $|B|^2$ and $|B|^4$: both depend on the deviation of positional coordinates. Here 1 and 2 refer to subcells related by the body centering vector, and 3 and 4 to the other two subcells. For c diffractions, it is necessary only to interchange the indices 2 and 3 in the above equation.

Figure 5-20 shows the experimental data for the bytownite and labradorite. The available data were separated into groups based on $|B|^2$, and averages were calculated. The intensities for the a diffractions fall off smoothly except for the group at 0.55 which gives anomalously high values for both bytownite and labradorite, presumably because of some special feature of the feldspar structure. The b diffractions of bytownite, normalized to the a diffractions, vary in accordance with the above equation. The intercept is trivial, and not statistically significant, in agreement with the detailed structure analysis of Fleet et al. (1966) for a body-centered bytownite which showed no significant segregation of Na and Ca atoms.

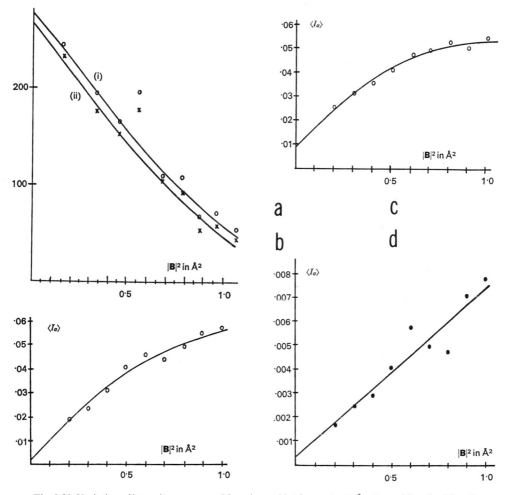

Fig. 5-20. Variation of intensity averages with reciprocal lattice vector $|\boldsymbol{B}|^2$. a Intensities of a diffractions in (1) bytownite and (2) labradorite. b Intensities of b diffractions of labradorite normalized to the a diffractions. c and d Intensities of e and f diffractions of labradorite normalized to the a diffractions. The curves in (b, c, d) were fitted by least squares. Note that there are few data for low values of $|\boldsymbol{B}|$. (From Toman and Frueh, 1971, Figs. 1—4)

The slope and curvature agree fairly well with those predicted from the atomic positions using a two-subcell model. For the labradorite, the e satellites show a positive intercept interpreted as the result of segregation of Na and Ca atoms, while the slope and curvature are similar to those in labradorite indicating positional displacements. For the f satellites, the slope is only about one-tenth that of the e satellites, and the intercept is trivial. Perhaps it should be emphasized that segregation of Al and Si atoms would not be detectable by this technique because the atomic scattering factors are so similar.

    TF (1972) extended their 1971 analysis by considering the directionality of the statistical variation. Instead of taking spherical shells in reciprocal space,

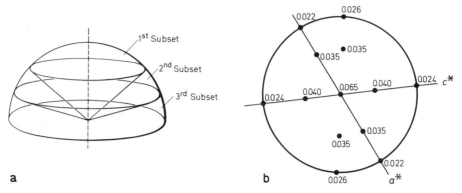

Fig. 5-21. Directionality of sub-structure responsible for satellites in *e*-labradorite. a Co-axial cones in reciprocal space used to give subsets of averaged intensities about a chosen axis. b Averaged intensities of *e* diffractions of labradorite. This stereographic projection shows the chosen axes and the intensity for the first subset. Note that the largest value is along *b* which is at the center. (From Toman and Frueh, 1972, Figs. 2 and 3)

they divided the Ewald sphere of reciprocal space into three cones co-axial with a chosen axis (Fig. 5-21a). The mean intensity for *e* and for *f* satellites, normalized to *a* diffractions, was calculated for each of the three cones of the chosen axis. The procedure was repeated for the following axes: [100], [010], [001], [110], [011], [10$\bar{1}$], [11$\bar{1}$] and [$\bar{1}$11]. Figure 5-21b is a stereographic projection for the first subset of *e* diffractions, and shows a strong preference for the *b*-axis. Figure 3 of TF (1972) compares data for the three sub-sets calculated for [010] and [100], again clearly demonstrating the preference for the *b*-axis. The situation was less clear for the *f* diffractions, probably the result of random experimental errors in the weak intensities. However, there was a definite preference down [01$\bar{1}$].

Quantitative interpretation depends on detailed mathematical calculations which although straightforward in principle are very complex in practice and cannot be given here. Let it suffice that for *e* diffractions, the mean displacement of Na and Ca atoms has an amplitude near 0.025 nm. This value is consistent with the broadening of electron-density peaks for M atoms in structure analyses of plagioclases using only *a* diffractions (see Chapter 4). For the *f* satellites, T and F concluded that the M atoms probably contributed only weakly.

TF (1973a) covers the theory of Fourier transforms and Patterson functions for the satellite diffractions of modulated structures. For those readers without an advanced training in crystallography, it should be stated that normal X-ray methods yield only the intensity and not the phase of the diffracted beam. If the phase were known, it would be possible to derive the electron density distribution directly from a Fourier synthesis of the diffraction pattern. Lacking knowledge of the phase, crystallographers prepare a Fourier synthesis using the intensities rather than the phased amplitudes. This Patterson function gives a superposition of all the interatomic vectors. The problem then devolves on devising a set of atomic positions which can explain the vectors. Unfortunately the problem is severely complicated by overlap of peaks.

TF (1973b) calculated the Patterson functions for e and f satellites of labradorite. Whereas the Patterson function for the a diffractions showed complex regions of high vector density caused by the superpositions of vectors between all the atoms, the Patterson function for the e diffractions was fairly simple, showing a number of well-separated peaks which could be assigned to M–M, M–T and M–O vectors on the basis of their positional coordinates and the general data on the atomic coordinates of plagioclase structures (Chapter 4). The vector peaks were associated with convolutions of Fourier transforms of the generalized atomic scattering factors which depend both on the positional displacements and chemical substitutions between corresponding scatterers in the different subcells. For the Patterson diagram based on e diffractions, all the convolutions consisted of sets of three peaks in a straight line with the peak heights of the two satellites of opposite sign to the central peak. Remarkably, all satellite pairs were connected by a vector which had roughly the same direction, no matter which central peak was chosen. This means that all atoms in e-plagioclase are displaced from their average positions in approximately the same direction. The length of the vector varies from one satellite pair to another. Four M–M triplets were seen in Patterson space ($0 \leq x \leq 1$, $0.1 \leq y \leq 0.6$, $0 \leq z \leq 0.5$), all with the satellite vector near $\lfloor 07\bar{2} \rfloor$ of the anorthite cell, which lies at about $20°$ to the b-axis. Forty-eight vectors were identified as M–T and M–O interactions.

In order to extract quantitative data, it was necessary to use some sophisticated ideas based on TF (1973a). The Patterson function was defined as

$$U(\eta)^s = \frac{1}{V} \sum_H^s I_H^s \exp(-2\pi i \eta \cdot B_H^s)$$

where the summation is taken over only one type of satellite, and B_H^s is the reciprocal vector. For the e diffractions, B_H is the vector for the b diffractions of body-centered anorthite, and $B_H^s = B_H - \dfrac{t}{2} = 0.062 a^* + 0.051 b^* - 0.219 c^*$. Because the intensities in a satellite pair are unequal, the Patterson function is complex with a real and imaginary part.

T and F supposed that there were two modulation waves for each atomic position, one governing the positional displacement, and one the scattering factor. They assumed that all modulation waves were normal to t, and that the wave profile is similar. However, the amplitude and phase of the wave were allowed to differ for each atomic position. Finally they accepted the geometrical model of K and J in which the phase of the modulation waves differs by π for atomic sites related by $\frac{1}{2}c$ or by $\frac{1}{2}(a + b)$, and the phase is equal for sites related by $\frac{1}{4}(a + b + c)$.

The phase difference ($\Delta\alpha$) between two modulation waves involved in a Patterson interaction can be estimated from the ratio of the peak heights of the central peaks in the real and imaginary parts of the Patterson function by

$$\tan(\Delta\alpha) = \frac{m_i}{m_r}$$

The amplitude of the modulation waves can be determined accurately only if the wave profile is known, but fortunately the answer is essentially the same

Table 5-8. Amplitude and phase of modulation waves for *e* satellites in a labradorite (Toman and Frueh, 1973b)

Atom	Megaw code	Amplitude (nm)	Phase (π)	Atom	Megaw code	Amplitude (nm)	Phase (π)
M	0	0.06	0	O_B	0	0.01	0.46
	c	0.06	0.28		c	0.01	0.82
T_1	0	0.04	0.08	O_B	m	0.01	1.39
	c	0.04	0.20		mc	0.02	0.95
T_1	m	0.05	0.11	O_C	0	0.04	0.00
	mc	0.05	0.19		c	0.05	0.28
T_2	0	0.03	0.91	O_C	m	0.05	1.96
	c	0.03	1.37		mc	0.05	0.28
T_2	m	0.03	1.12	O_D	0	0.02	0.14
	mc	0.03	1.16		c	0.02	0.16
O_{A1}	0	0.05	1.43	O_D	m	0.02	0.20
	c	0.05	0.92		mc	0.02	0.07
O_{A2}	0	0.02	0.97				
	c	0.02	1.14				

whatever profile is assumed. T and F estimated the amplitudes both from the position of the satellite peaks and from the height of the central peak.

Table 5-8 shows the amplitude and phase of the modulation waves associated with the various atoms. The phase is given in units of π, and is referred to zero phase for M atoms at the Megaw position (0).

Turning now to the Patterson diagram based on *f* satellites, the density lies mostly in three regions, consisting of systems of parallel streaks perpendicular to the [02$\bar{5}$] directions. Streaks in the imaginary part of the Patterson diagram lie between positive and negative streaks of the real part. The density does not correspond to vectors involving M atoms, but corresponds to interatomic vectors involving some T and some O atoms. A complete analysis was not achieved, but T and F believed that the streaks correspond to overlapping convolutions of Fourier transforms related to atoms displaced slightly (probably around 0.01 nm or less) in the [02$\bar{5}$] direction.

In the discussion, T and F pointed out that the detailed data on the modulation waves were roughly consistent with the results of the statistical analysis by TF (1972). They could not yet attempt a complete model because of lack of evidence on how the M atoms were ordered, and a lack of mean atomic coordinates for the pseudostructure. However, they deduced the following distortion of the aluminosilicate framework along [07$\bar{2}$] to explain the *e* satellites: rings near-parallel to the *b*-axis (i.e. dewv in Fig. 2-5), are alternately raised and lowered along [07$\bar{2}$] whereas rings nearly perpendicular to *b* (i.e. ewfz in Fig. 2-5) are twisted approximately around an axis going through O_B(i) and O_B(mzic). Figure 5-22 illustrates the displacements. Diagram (a) is the idealized drawing given by TF (1973b, Fig. 2). The 4-ring at the left is displaced along positive *b* while the 4-ring at the right is displaced along negative *b*. Table 5-9 gives the amounts of these displacements for the subcell in which the M(0) atom has the largest displacement. In comparing Table 5-8 and 5-9, readers should note that

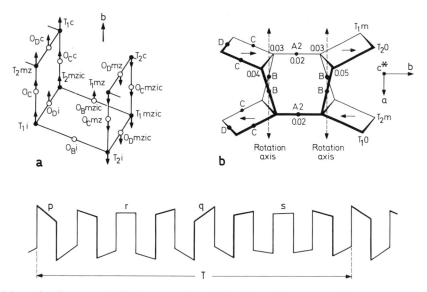

Fig. 5-22. Schematic diagrams of displacements in aluminosilicate framework of *e*-plagioclase.
a Diagram of TF (1973b, Fig. 2). b Interpretation of (a) in terms of Fig. 2-5. c Drawing of
modulation wave in aluminosilicate framework. From TF (1973b, Fig. 3). See Table 5-8 for
magnitude of displacements

the modulation waves have different phases, and that the maximum amplitude
is achieved in different subcells for the various types of atomic positions. Diagram
(b) is my interpretation of the TF diagram using the schematic drawing of
Fig. 2-5. The arrows show the direction and maximum displacement of the
4-rings, and the dashed lines join the O_B atoms which have only small displacements, and about which the rings tend to rotate. Diagram (c) from TF (1973b,
Fig. 3) shows schematically how a modulation wave distorts the aluminosilicate
framework across the out-of-step texture of *e*-plagioclase. The wavelength is
given by *T*, and the tilt is greatest in subcells at p and q, and least at r and s.

T and F had not proceeded further at the time of writing (Dec. 1972). They
rightly pointed out that the displacement of the M atoms with respect to the frame-

Table 5-9. Displacement of the aluminosilicate chain in the *e* modulation of a labradorite (Toman and
Frueh, 1973b)

Atom	Displacement (nm)	Atom	Displacement
T_1i	0.03	$O_B$mzic	0.02
T_1c	0.02	O_C	0.04
T_1mzic	−0.05	O_Cc	0.04
T_1mz	−0.05	$O_C$mz	−0.05
T_2i	−0.03	$O_C$mzic	−0.04
T_2c	0.01	O_Di	0.01
T_2mz	0.03	O_Dc	0.02
T_2mzic	0.03	$O_D$mzic	−0.01
O_Bi	0.00	$O_D$mz	−0.02

work must be considered (indeed I was able to produce a plausible model while preparing Fig. 5-22b). Furthermore, small displacements of some of the T and O atoms, but not of M atoms, must occur along $[02\bar{5}]$ to explain the f diffractions.

Finally TF (1973b) emphasized two subtle details which probably have fundamental significance. The pairs of satellite peaks in the Patterson function were not quite symmetric about the central peak, and the central peaks from the real and imaginary parts of the Patterson function lay at slightly different positions. These features may result from ordering of Na and Ca atoms on M sites, and of Al and Si atoms on T sites.

TF (1973c) refined the pseudo-structure of the labradorite using 720 diffractions. Refinement in $C\bar{1}$ with isotropic temperature factors was poor ($R = 0.18$). The M atoms were then allowed to refine in $C1$ while the framework was held in $C\bar{1}$ ($R = 0.13$). Refinement of all atoms in $C1$ resulted in little change ($R = 0.12$). Final refinement with anisotropic displacement factors of the M atoms gave $R = 0.10$. This evidence for absence of a center of symmetry is consistent with the observation by TF (1973b) of M–M peaks in both the real and imaginary part of the Patterson function for e satellites. Unfortunately the use of only 720 diffractions results in a relatively large standard error in the atomic positions. The mean T–O distances have a standard error near 0.001 nm, and the values imply preference of Al atoms for T_1 sites ($T_1 0\ 0.170$, $T_1 m\ 0.170$, $T_2 0\ 0.166$, $T_2 m\ 0.163$ nm). A refinement using more diffraction data should be carried out. See Fig. 3-8 for other data on T–O distances in plagioclase.

In summary, the TF papers give by far the best understanding of e-plagioclase, though there is still a long way to go. The nature of distortion of the aluminosilicate framework has been established in broad outline, though the fine details are still unresolved. The M sites are displaced in the same direction as the major displacement of the aluminosilicate framework, but the correlation between the displacements has not been established. The M atoms do not obey a center of symmetry, and there is some kind of ordering of Na and Ca atoms on the M sites but its nature is unknown. No information was obtained on the distribution of Al and Si atoms on T sites.

Cinnamon and Bailey (1971). This treatment of e-plagioclase is based on analogy with metal alloys for which there is an extensive literature concerning the relation of ordering to physical properties such as the hardness. Cinnamon and Bailey interpreted e-plagioclase to consist of domains whose length in the a, b and c directions is given by $180/\delta a$, $180/\delta b$ and $180/(180 - \delta c)$ subcells, respectively. Their Fig. 4 shows that the domain sizes vary from $3a$, $65b$ and $2c$ at An_{20} to $75a$, $2b$ and $13c$ at An_{80}. This approach assumes that the domains can be considered independently along the three axes, and is different from the approach of all other authors who consider that there is a single, out-of-step, modulation in an irrational direction t which varies with composition and whose wavelength T changes from 2 to 8 nm as the An-content changes from An_{20} to An_{70}.

Cinnamon and Bailey stated that domain walls are regions of high energy resulting from stacking mistakes. The closer the spacing of the walls, the greater is the energy per unit volume. Hence in their model, the wall energy is proportional to δa, δb and $180 - \delta c$. Consequently for the a and c domains, the wall energy increases from An_{80} to An_{20} whereas for the b domains it goes the opposite way. Indeed Cinnamon and Bailey proposed that δb increased asymptotically to $180°$ near An_{85}, while δa and $(180 - \delta c)$ did the same near An_{15}, thereby requiring infinite wall energies at these compositions. Hence e-plagioclase is replaced by transitional-anorthite and peristerite.

Cinnamon and Bailey interpreted measurements of Vicker's microhardness in terms of the force needed to cause plastic deformation. They estimated an average domain size from the cube root of the product of the domain sizes along the a, b and c axes, and plotted it against the Vickers microhardness.

McConnell (1972a, b). The present treatment utilizes preprints of two papers given at the 1972 Study Institute on Feldspars.

McConnell bases his analysis on hydrothermal experiments of the stability of e-plagioclase (Table 5-6 and Fig. 5-10), and the relation of e-plagioclase to the peristerite, Bøggild and Huttenlocher intergrowths. The structure of e-plagioclase is envisaged as a metastable antiphase state of ordering produced at relatively low temperature under conditions of high supersaturation. Figure S-2c shows four types of plagioclase solid solutions: albite with only a diffractions; e_2-plagioclase in the oligoclase-andesine region; e_1-plagioclase in the labradorite-bytownite region; and I-anorthite in the bytownite range. The temperature appropriate to the onset of ordering in each region is shown by the horizontal dashed lines lying respectively at 650, 500, 800 and 1150° C. Spinodal decomposition is likely to occur in the regions with the lighter shading, and true exsolution is possible at lower temperatures in the region of heavier shading. Closed spinodal loops are shown for the Bøggild and Huttenlocher regions. In some composition ranges, either e-plagioclase or spinodal decomposition occurs depending on the opportunity for atomic diffusion. No proposal was made by McConnell about the atomic nature of e-plagioclase except for the concept of an anti-phase nature based on body-centered anorthite.

5.3.4 A Subjective Review

This review attempts to distinguish between those features of e-plagioclase which are proven and those which are uncertain.

(1) *The Types of e-plagioclase.* The absence of f and c diffractions in e-plagioclase more sodic than An_{50}, plus the greater diffuseness of the e diffractions, suggests that there are at least two types of e-plagioclase. The data of Doman *et al.* imply that there is a discontinuity near An_{50}, and perhaps another one near An_{35}. I think that one must work on the assumption that there are at least two *structural* types of e plagioclase, and that the data of Toman and Frueh for a labradorite should not be taken to apply to andesine until appropriate measurements have been made. The Ca-rich specimen with f diffractions ten times as strong as e diffractions (Goldsmith and Laves) deserves detailed study to check whether it has the same structural features as labradorites with f diffractions weaker than e diffractions.

The possibility should be considered that e_1-plagioclase derives from anorthite solid solutions and e_2-plagioclase from albite solid solutions, as implied by the proposed phase diagram in Fig. S-2a. Perhaps the discontinuity near An_{50} is related to the occurrence of the Bøggild intergrowth whose lamellae may have compositions near An_{45} and An_{55}.

(2) *The Out-of-step Feature.* The experimental observation that the *e*-diffractions occur in pairs about the positions for *b*-diffractions of anorthite definitely means that the out-of-step feature involves the body-centered anorthite superstructure. This results from an argument similar to that used in deriving Fig. 5-6d. This does not mean that the superstructure is composed entirely of domains of I-anorthite. Figure 5-7 shows that *geometrically* the superstructure might be composed of alternating slabs of albite and I-anorthite structure. So long as the I-anorthite units are out of phase with each other, and so long as their spacing remains the same, the *e* diffractions will remain in the same positions. Of course, the intensity of the *e* diffractions must change as the ratio of volumes of albite and anorthite units is altered. One can regard the albite as a *neutral* matrix in which the anorthite resides. It is not necessary that a neutral matrix have the albite structure.

(3) *The Orientation and Length of* *t*. The vector *t* has nothing whatsoever to do with the out-of-step feature, as illustrated by Figs. 5-6d and e. The out-of-step feature determines the center-point between the pairs of *e* satellites, while the orientation and spacing of the boundaries determines the orientation and length of *t*, the splitting vector. I accept that there is a single set of domains whose irrational boundary and spacing result from statistical averaging of domains quantized to contain integral numbers of subcells. Although *t* may be approximately a single-valued function of An-content, it is possible that some deviation occurs as implied by the data of Doman *et al.*

There is no satisfactory explanation of the variation of *t* with An-content. Smith and Ribbe (p. 187) suggested that the scale of the superstructure is governed by growth of Al_2Si_2 regions before growth of $AlSi_3$ ordered regions. They pointed out that anorthite is ordered at all temperatures, and that in albite ordering becomes strong only below 700° C. Hence high-albite solid solution of intermediate composition might develop $CaAl_2Si_2$ nuclei, the initial stage consisting merely of local ordering. The nuclei would grow and sweep the excess Si and Na atoms into the boundaries between the $CaAl_2Si_2$ nuclei. Subsequently the boundary regions would organize into $NaAlSi_3$ regions flanked by out-of-step boundaries with the $CaAl_2Si_2$ nuclei. The boundaries would become fairly regular to minimize strain. Smith and Ribbe supposed that the boundary produced by prior nucleation of Al_2Si_2 has nearly constant thickness irrespective of the size of the Al_2Si_2 domains, perhaps because of need for a certain minimum thickness to permit out-of-step Al_2Si_2 distributions to join without forming Al–O–Al neighbors. Constancy of width of a boundary rich in Na and Si would produce an increase of T with An-content. Smith and Ribbe suggested that *t* changes direction to maximize the spacing of Al atoms in the hybrid regions, but this suggestion is completely *ad hoc* until a definite model is supplied. At first sight, the model of Megaw gives a complete explanation of the variation of *t*, but detailed study shows that all the parameters are *ad hoc*.

It is worth emphasizing that T is only a few unit cells across, especially for sodic compositions. It might be argued that one should not use the term domain. However, I think that this term can be used so long as it is realized that *e*-plagioclase is composed of a coherent superstructure on such a fine-scale that no region is free of the influence of another region. Atoms in the *topochemical* positions of I-anorthite would not have the exact *positional* coordinates of atoms in a single crystal of I-anorthite when the former atoms are adjacent in a superstructure to atoms with the topochemical positions of albite.

(4) *Positional Displacements.* The data of Toman and Frueh go a long way towards characterizing the positional displacements of an *e*-labradorite. The model of cooperative displacements of the aluminosilicate framework is internally consistent to about 0.001 nm, which is the uncertainty caused by lack of knowledge of the positions of Al and Si atoms. A model for the positions of the M atoms should soon be forthcoming from analysis of the amplitude and phase of the modulation waves. Such a model can be checked by comparing the M–O polyhedra with the limits expected for chemical bonding. Data should be collected on *e*-plagioclase of compositions near An_{25}, An_{45} and An_{70} to check whether the Patterson diagrams are similar. Particularly important is an analysis of a calcic specimen with strong *f* diffractions.

(5) *Ordering of M Atoms.* In 1973, the only reliable data are those of Toman and Frueh (1971) based on a statistical analysis. I believe that ordering of T atoms (next section) must be accompanied by ordering of M atoms, but detailed experimental proof is needed.

(6) *Ordering of T Atoms.* Unfortunately the scattering factors of Al and Si are too similar to show up in the analyses of Toman and Frueh. The Si–O and Al–O distances differ by about 0.015 nm, and analysis of positional displacements of T and O atoms may yield the Si, Al distribution. For example, in Table 5-7, the modulation amplitude for O_{A2} is less than that for the T_2 atoms between which it is bonded, whereas the amplitude for O_{A1} is about the same as that for the T_1 atoms between which it is bonded. The accuracy of the data is not certain in view of the uncertainty of the symmetry: however, one might propose that the T_2 sites are occupied preferentially by Si to give the lower modulation for the bridging O_{A2} atoms.

Smith and Ribbe pointed out that the data on the T–O distances of the "averaged" structures of *e*-plagioclase indicate preferential occupancy of the T_10 site as in low albite (Fig. 3-8). This is the only evidence in support of their suggestion that regions similar to low albite occur in the *e*-superstructure. The boundaries between domains of anorthite structure might have preferential occupancy of Al in T_10, without being similar to low albite. However, if there is ordering of Na on the M sites, the simplest idea is that when Al enters a T_10 site, Na tends to occupy a nearby M site.

Perhaps the best evidence for ordering of T atoms comes from the dry heating experiments. The relaxation time for conversion of *e*-plagioclase into either high albite or anorthite solid solutions is much too long for the process to be ascribed to framework puckering or displacement of M atoms. Furthermore the process has not been reversed in the laboratory.

(7) *Structural Changes During Heating.* Smith and Ribbe discussed the changes during heating in terms of their model, but the ideas would apply to any modulated superstructure with ordering of M and T atoms.

Rapid heating and cooling causes no permanent change because the Si and Al atoms remain in place and serve as a "memory" for the modulation. The weakening of the *e* diffractions during rapid heating must result from reduction of the amplitude of the modulation. Presumably increasing thermal vibration causes the subcells to become similar. Smith and Ribbe suggested that if any Na and Ca atoms diffused they would tend to return to their original positions because of charge linkage to the T cations. They also suggested that the greater the wavelength of the modulation, the less effective should be thermal vibration and ionic diffusion. Consequently a calcic specimen should lose intensity of the *e* diffractions more slowly than a sodic one: this agreed with the sparse experimental data.

Prolonged heating at high temperature causes diffusion of Al and Si atoms with permanent loss of the anti-phase modulation. Boundary regions should be more prone to diffusion than central regions while anorthite-like regions should be more resistant than albite-like ones. The modulation should lose amplitude but the wavelength should stay the same, thereby explaining why the *e* diffractions become weaker but stay in place. If there is a range of modulation wavelengths, the larger ones might be preserved longer, thereby implying a reduction of *t* in the later stages of heating.

(8) *Thermodynamical Description.* The present data on heating are far too sparse to permit a complete analysis of the thermal properties of *e*-plagioclase. Unfortunately the long relaxation time for movement of T atoms will hinder collection of experimental data. The existing thermal data on *e*-plagioclase are consistent with thermodynamic metastability. It is quite certain that *e*-plagioclase is based on an out-of-step structural modulation, and that it is not an ordered material appropriate for true thermodynamic equilibrium at low temperature. The properties are consistent with its formation as a metastable material under conditions of high supersaturation and low rate of atomic diffusion. Smith and Ribbe stated that it is futile to describe low-entropy plagioclase in terms of classical thermodynamics, and that only a kinetic interpretation based on atomic and sub-microscopical textural factors can be viable: nevertheless the attempt by Smith to consider *e*-plagioclase as a superstructure stranded in the stability field of low albite plus anorthite (Fig. S-2a) may deserve some consideration. Unquestionably the present understanding of *e*-plagioclase is insufficient to permit a definitive understanding of its structure, and of the relation of *e*-plagioclase to the coarse intergrowths.

An almost unending series of speculations might be made about the atomic nature and thermodynamic character of *e*-plagioclase. However, what is really needed is a comprehensive set of experimental data. I hope that the present review has correctly emphasized the missing information, and that crystallographers will tackle the remaining challenges.

References

Bloss, F. D. (1964): Optical extinction of anorthite at high temperatures. AM **49**, 1125–1131.

Bown, M. G., Gay, P. (1958): The reciprocal lattice geometry of the plagioclase feldspar structures: ZK **111**, 1–14.

Bown, M. G., Gay, P. (1969): The effect of heat treatment on the diffraction patterns of intermediate plagioclase: ZK **129**, 451–457.

Brown, W. L., Hoffmann, W., Laves, F. (1963): Über kontinuierliche und reversible Transformationen des Anorthits (CaAl$_2$Si$_2$O$_8$) zwischen 25 und 350° C. Naturwiss. **50**, 221.

Bruno, E., Gazzoni, G. (1967): Ricerche roentgenografiche su plagioclasi bytownitico-anortitici tra 15° C e 1300° C. PM **36**, 683–698.

Chao, S. H., Taylor, W. H. (1940): Isomorphous replacement and superlattice structures in the plagioclase felspars. Proc. Roy. Soc. (Lond.) **176** A, 76–87.

Cinnamon, C. G., Bailey, S. W. (1971): Antiphase domain structure of the intermediate composition plagioclase feldspars. AM **56**, 1180 – 1198.

Cinnamon, C. G., Bailey, S. W. (1972): Antiphase domain structure of the intermediate composition plagioclase feldspars. AM **57**, 1309–1310.

Cole, W. F., Sörum, H., Taylor, W. H. (1951): The structure of the plagioclase felspars I. AC **4**, 20–29.

Czank, M. (1973): Strukturen des Anorthits bei höheren Temperaturen. Thesis, E. T. H., Zürich.

Czank, M., Laves, F., Schulz, H. (1970): On the domains of anorthite: Naturwiss. **57**, No. 3, 128.

Czank, M., Laves, F., Schulz, H. (1974): Structure of anorthite at different temperatures between room temperature and 1430° C. Expected publication in ZK.

Czank, M., Landuyt, J. Van, Schulz, H., Laves, F., Amelinckx, S. (1972): Temperature dependence of domains in anorthite. Naturwiss. **59**, 646.

Doman, R. C., Cinnamon, C. G., Bailey, S. W. (1965): Structural discontinuities in the plagioclase feldspar series. AM **50**, 724–740.

Fleet, S. G., Chandrasekhar, S., Megaw, H. D. (1966): The structure of bytownite ("body-centered anorthite"). AC **21**, 782–801.

Foit, F. F. (1971): The crystal structure of anorthite at 410° C. Prog. Geol. Soc. Amer. Mtg., Southeastern section, p. 311 (abstract).

Foit, F. F., Peacor, D. R. (1967): High temperature diffraction data on selected reflections of an andesine and anorthite. ZK **1**, 1–6.

Foit, F. F., Peacor, D. R. (1973): The anorthite crystal structure at 410 and 830° C. AM **58**, 665 – 675.

Gay, P. (1953): The structures of the plagioclase felspars: III. An X-ray study of anorthites and bytownites. MM **30**, 169–177.

Gay, P. (1954): The structure of the plagioclase felspars. V. The heat-treatment of lime-rich plagioclases. MM **30**, 428–438.

Gay, P. (1956): The structures of the plagioclase felspars: VI. Natural intermediate plagioclases. MM **31**, 21–40.

Gay, P. (1962): Sub-solidus relations in the plagioclase feldspars: NGT **42**, No. 2, 37–56.

Gay, P., Bown, M. G. (1956): The structures of the plagioclase felspars. VII. The heat treatment of intermediate plagioclases. MM **31**, 306–313.

Gay, P., Taylor, W. H. (1953): The structures of the plagioclase felspars. IV. Variations in the anorthite structure. AC **6**, 647–650.

Goldsmith, J. R., Laves, F. (1956): Crystallization of metastable disordered anorthite at "low temperatures". ZK **107**, 396–405.

Jagodzinski, H., Korekawa, M. (1972): X-ray investigation of lunar plagioclase and pyroxenes. Proc. Third Lunar Sci. Conf. **1**, 555–568. M.I.T. Press.

Köhler, A., Wieden, P. (1954): Vorläufige Versuche in der Feldspatgruppe mittels der DTA. NJMM **12**, 249–252.

Korekawa, M. (1967): Theorie der Satellitenreflexe. Habilitationsschrift der Ludwigs-Maximilians-Universität zu München. 140 pp.

Korekawa, M., Jagodzinski, H. (1967): Die Satellitenreflexe des Labradorits. SMPM **47**, 269–278.

Korekawa, M., Philipp, D. (1971): Über zwei verschiedene Arten von Satellitenreflexen beobachtet an einem Tieftemperature-Plagioklas An$_{16.5}$. ZK **134**, 145–147.

Laves, F., Czank, M., Schulz, H. (1970): The temperature dependence of the reflection intensities of anorthite (CaAl$_2$Si$_2$O$_8$) and the corresponding formation of domains. SMPM **50**, 519–525.

Laves, F., Goldsmith, J. R. (1954a): Discussion of the anorthite superstructure. AC **7**, 131 – 132.

Laves, F., Goldsmith, J. R. (1954b): Long-range-short-range order in calcic plagioclases as a continuous and reversible function of temperature. AC **7**, 465–472.

Laves, F., Goldsmith, J. R. (1954c): On the use of calcic plagioclases in geologic thermometry. JG **62**, 405–408.

Laves, F., Goldsmith, J. R. (1955a): Cation order in anorthite (CaAl$_2$Si$_2$O$_8$) as revealed by gallium and germanium substitution. ZK **106**, 213–226.

Laves, F., Goldsmith, J. R. (1955b): The effect of temperature and composition on the Al–Si distribution in anorthite. ZK **106**, 227–235.

Laves, F., Goldsmith, J. R. (1961a): Polymorphism, order, disorder, diffusion and confusion in the feldspars. CCILM **8**, 71–80.

Laves, F., Goldsmith, J. R. (1961b): Comments on the anorthite papers by Megaw and co-workers presented at this symposium. CCILM **8**, 155–157.

McConnell, J. D. C. (1971): Electron-optical study of phase transformation. MM **38**, 1–20.

McConnell, J. D. C. (1972a): Analysis of the time-temperature-transformation behaviour of the plagioclase feldspars. Preprint for abstr. 5.1 in program for Advanced Study Institute on Feldspars, July 1972, Manchester.

McConnell, J. D. C. (1972b): Electron-optical study of the fine structure of a schiller labradorite. Preprint for abstr. 4.4 in program for Advanced Study Institute on Feldspars, July 1972, Manchester.

McConnell, J. D. C., Fleet, S. G. (1963): Direct electron-optical resolution of anti-phase domains in a silicate. N **199**, 586.

McLaren, A. C. (1972): Transmission electron microscopy of the feldspars. Preprint of abstr. 4.1 in program for Advanced Study Institute on Feldspars, July 1972, Manchester.

Megaw, H. D. (1960): Order and disorder. I. Theory of stacking faults and diffraction maxima. II. Theory of diffraction effects in the intermediate plagioclase felspars. III. The structure of the intermediate plagioclase felspars. Proc. Roy. Soc. (Lond.) **259** A, 59–78, 159–183, 184–202.

Megaw, H. D. (1961): Effects of temperature and composition in the plagioclases and other felspars. CCILM **8**, 149–153.

Megaw, H. D. (1962): Order and disorder in feldspars. NGT **42**, No. 2, 104–137.

Nissen, H.-U. (1972): Electron microscopy of low plagioclases. Abstr. 4.2 in program for Advanced Study Institute on Feldspars, July 1972, Manchester.

Nord, G. L., Heuer, A. H., Lally, J. S. (1972): Transmission electron microscopy of substructures in Stillwater bytownites. Proc. NATO Study Inst., Manchester.

Ribbe, P. H., Colville, A. A. (1968): Orientation of the boundaries of out-of-step domains in anorthite. MM **36**, 814–819.

Smith, J. V. (1972): Critical review of synthesis and occurrence of plagioclase feldspars and a possible phase diagram. JG **80**, 505–525.

Smith, J. V., Gay, P. (1958): The powder patterns and lattice parameters of plagioclase felspars. II. MM **31**, 744–762.

Smith, J. V., Ribbe, P. H. (1969): Atomic movements in plagioclase feldspars: kinetic interpretation: CMP **21**, 157–202.

Smyth, J. R., Smith, J. V. (1969): Electrostatic energy for ion clustering in intermediate plagioclase feldspar. MM **37**, 181–184.

Sörum, H. (1951): Studies in the structures of plagioclase feldspars. Norsk Vidensk. — Akad. Oslo, Mat. — Nat. Kl., Skr. No. 3, 1–160.

Stewart, D. B., Walker, G. W., Wright, T. L., Fahey, J. J. (1966): Physical properties of calcic labradorite from Lake County, Oregon. AM **51**, 177–197.

Toman, K., Frueh, A. J. (1971): On the origin of plagioclase satellite reflections. AC B **27**, 2182–2186.

Toman, K., Frueh, A. J. (1972): Intensity averages of plagioclase satellites: distribution in reciprocal space. AC B **28**, 1657–1662.

Toman, K., Frueh, A. J. (1973a): The intensities and Fourier transforms of difference reflections. Acta Cryst. A **29**, 121–127.

Toman, K., Frueh, A. J. (1973b): Patterson function of plagioclase satellites. Acta Cryst. A **29**, 127–133.

Toman, K., Frueh, A. J. (1973c): On the centrosymmetry of intermediate plagioclase. ZK **138**, 337–342.

Wainwright, J. E., Starkey, J. (1971): A refinement of the structure of anorthite. ZK **133**, Fritz-Laves-Festband, 75–84.

Part 2 Physical Properties
and Experimental Techniques

The value of a particular technique to a scientist studying feldspars depends on his aim: whereas the research mineralogist desires the most informative techniques almost irrespective of the time involved, the field petrologist wants the most rapid technique that will give sufficient characterization. After the research mineralogist has obtained a definitive description of a particular phenomenon by the use of complex techniques, he can often show that a rapid technique gives the same implication. Hence in the following chapters, detailed accounts of techniques and results are followed by descriptions of the simplest possible methods. Experimental details are mentioned when important for avoidance of fundamental errors, and guidance is given in choice between competing techniques.

The problems of nomenclature are conveniently covered here in Chapter 9 because most feldspars in practice are described from their X-ray and optical properties as outlined in Chapters 6–8.

The relation of a bulk physical property to the sub-microscopic chemical and physical features is not clear. Smith (1970) discussed the general problems of order-disorder structures with especial reference to feldspar minerals, collating and extending ideas going back to the nineteenth century. "Experimental data on physical properties are always based on two fundamental factors: the interaction of an atom (especially its constituent electron clouds) with other atoms (especially its nearest neighbors), *and* the texture of the minimum volume resolved by the observing instrument. Thus optical properties are determined by the resolving power of the microscope as well as by the interaction of the electric vector of the electromagnetic wave with the electron cloud". "The effect of instrument resolution on measurement of a physical property was recognized by Mallard (1876), who proposed that an optically monoclinic material might actually be a sub-microscopically twinned triclinic material". The basic concepts of order-disorder are given in Chapter 3. Smith proposed that "physical properties depend more on local than on distant atoms and that only if local and distant ordering are correlated will there be a true relation between physical properties and electron density distribution".

There is a further problem for techniques involving an interaction time that is comparable with atomic motion. Thus Smith and Ribbe (1969) in discussing the structural features of the polymorphism of anorthite as determined by X-ray and resonance methods made the following comparison of techniques. The nuclear quadrupole spectrum is "determined by the *scalar* summation over the entire crystal of the spectral intensity from each ^{27}Al atom: the individual spectrum for each atom is determined by the local electrostatic field which is primarily determined by the nearer neighbors, and which is only slightly affected by atoms more than 20 Å (i.e. 2 nanometers) away. Since the frequency is about 10 megacycles, atomic movements more rapid than about 10^{-7} second will be averaged out. A sharp spectrum implies that all the contributing atoms lie in equal electrostatic fields when averaged over 10^{-7} sec. A broadened spectrum implies that the atoms lie in unequal fields when averaged over 10^{-7} sec. Simple thermal vibration (infra-red frequency) is too rapid ($\sim 10^{-13}$ sec) to cause broadening of n.q.r. spectra. Domain structure should cause observable broadening only if the domains persist longer than 10^{-7} sec, and if the domain boundaries are closer than (say) 100 Å". " The coherent X-ray diffraction spectrum is determined by the *vector* summation over each *mosaic* unit of the spectral *amplitude* from all electrons". "Simple uncorrelated thermal vibration about lattice-related centers-of-motion merely causes a reduction of intensity of the principal peaks. Correlated thermal motion of atomic groups (e.g. silicate chains) produces extra diffuse reflections in the background region. Domains produced by *correlated* displacement of lattice-related atoms cause new reflections whose diffuseness decreases as the domains become larger". "If the domains grow, disappear and regrow extremely rapidly, the X-ray pattern ultimately becomes like that for uncorrelated thermal vibration".

Consequently for feldspars which show complex chemical and physical variations it is imperative to exercise the utmost caution in the interpretation of experimental data, and in the choice of nomenclature.

References

Mallard, F. (1876): Explications des phénomènes optiques anomaux qui présentent un grand nombre de substances cristallisées. Annales des mines **10**, 187–240. Alternatively, see ZK **1**, 201–237 (1877).

Smith, J. V. (1970): Physical properties of order-disorder structures with especial reference to feldspar minerals. Lithos **3**, 145–160.

Smith, J. V., Ribbe, P. H. (1969): Atomic movements in plagioclase feldspars: kinetic interpretation. CMP **21**, 157–202.

Chapter 6 X-ray Diffraction Techniques

Perhaps the greatest advances in determining the atomic structure and texture of feldspars have resulted from single-crystal X-ray diffraction techniques. Structure analysis using the intensity of the Bragg diffractions yields the electron distribution in the average unit cell as described in Part 1. Single-crystal techniques are particularly valuable for determining the nature of and the angular relations between the components of feldspar intergrowths, and in characterizing the geometry and symmetry of the unit cell. Powder X-ray techniques lose the three-dimensional information inherent in single-crystal techniques and have insufficient sensitivity to permit detection of subsidiary diffractions and to allow full characterization of complex intergrowths. However, they are particularly valuable for determination of cell dimensions and symmetry because of the greater speed than in single crystal methods. Routine identification is normally carried out by powder methods if optical methods are insufficient.

For convenience the data on cell dimensions and thermal expansion are given in Chapter 7. Electron-optical techniques tend to be complementary to single-crystal X-ray methods because they are particularly valuable for study of fine intergrowths, but are too tedious for routine studies (Chapter 10). Neutron-diffraction techniques are too costly for routine work but are very valuable for determination of atomic coordinates and site distributions (Part 1).

6.1 Single-crystal Techniques

6.1.1 General

The available techniques are described in elementary terms by Azaroff (1968), Nuffield (1966) and Henry et al. (1960).

The most elegant technique utilizes a precession camera with a crystal aligned such that a zone-axis precesses about the X-ray beam. After suitable orientation to within 0.1°, one layer of the reciprocal lattice is projected without distortion onto the flat photographic film after selection with a screen. For feldspars, precession about a and then about the c axis with b^* parallel to the spindle axis is most convenient. Precession about a allows measurement of b^*, c^* and α^*, while precession about c yields b^*, a^* and γ^*. The angle β can be estimated from the rotation on the spindle axis, but is of little value in feldspar studies. The angles α^* and γ^* can be measured to about 0.05° by averaging data for several lattice rows to minimize film distortion and setting errors. However, the reciprocal cell edges can be measured only to about 1 part in 400 even with a calibrated film, though somewhat greater accuracy is obtainable by coating the single crystal with a powder of a calibrating material: unfortunately this accuracy is insufficient for detailed characterization of alkali feldspars from the b^*c^* plot.

A Weissenberg photograph also yields a layer of the reciprocal lattice on each film, but the layer undergoes a complex one-to-one geometrical distortion on the cylindrical film that hinders easy interpretation. On a normal front-diffraction instrument, an inter-axial angle can be measured only to an accuracy of $\frac{1}{2}^\circ$ but with a back-diffraction instrument both reciprocal edges and angles can be measured to high accuracy (edges to 0.01% and angles to 0.01°). To obtain a Weissenberg photograph, one of the zone axes should be set parallel to the rotation axis. A crystal set with b^* parallel to the spindle axis of a precession camera could be transferred to a Weissenberg camera and set with b parallel to the rotation axis. Thereby the a^*, c^* and β^* parameters could be measured.

In Chapter 7, it is shown that for alkali feldspars, the plots of b^*c^* and $\alpha^*\gamma^*$ are very useful for characterizing the structural state. In addition, the simultaneous measurement of a^* allows estimation of the Na/K ratio. In order to obtain these measurements from a back-reflection Weissenberg, it would be necessary to set the crystal on both the a and c axes. So far no systematic measurements have been made by this approach, but it is the obvious way to obtain accurate data for perthites.

For plagioclases, the cell dimensions b^*, c^*, α^* and γ^* tend to vary together while β^* is independent: the edge a^* may depend on Or-content, but no real test has been made. Perhaps the most suitable axis for routine study with a back-reflection Weissenberg is the b-axis. This would permit accurate measurement of a^*, c^* and β^*, of which the latter two should provide an estimate of An-content and structural state (see Chapter 7). In addition, the subsidiary diffractions can be clearly observed from oscillation and Weissenberg photographs about this axis. The most common twin laws in plagioclase are the Albite and Pericline laws: for these, the doubled layer lines can be clearly recognized in a b-axis oscillation pattern.

By removing the screen and keeping the film stationary in a Weissenberg camera, or by using a special oscillation/rotation camera, information about all the layers can be gathered simultaneously but at the price of losing the angular information associated with a moving film. For many purposes, this oscillation method is preferable because of its high speed and cheapness. Smith and MacKenzie (1955) adopted a simple technique for alkali feldspars using oscillation about the morphological b-axis. This revealed at a glance the qualitative features of perthites. Bown and Gay (unpublished) developed a similar technique for characterization of plagioclase using oscillation about c.

These photographic techniques are more valuable than counter methods for most studies of feldspars because of their simultaneous recording of a large volume of reciprocal space with easy examination by the human eye and brain. Counter techniques are particularly valuable for (a) measurement of intensities for determination of electron-density distribution and (b) monitoring a single diffraction during a phase transformation (e.g. Foit and Peacor, 1967).

The X-ray diffraction pattern of feldspars is so complex that the X-ray beam should be filtered except for reconnaissance and alignment. Monochromatized radiation is not needed for most studies, but is highly desirable for those feldspars with weak, diffuse diffractions. Diffuse haloes around strong diffractions are readily seen in monochromatized radiation, and care must be taken not to ascribe thermal diffuse scattering to domain texture.

Various technical developments permit X-ray studies at high temperature. Feldspar crystals can be attached firmly to a platinum-rhodium thermocouple by preliminary heating to an elevated temperature. The thermocouple can be heated by an a.c. current and its temperature measured by a d.c. method. Alternatively the crystal can be heated by a gas flame. It may be mounted in a silica-glass capillary.

Domain structure in the range of 100 nm can be studied by special low-angle methods (Korekawa and Jagodzinski, 1967).

Very high accuracy can be obtained in the cell dimensions using the tedious theta-method of Weisz et al. (1948). Such high accuracy (0.002% in cell dimensions, 0.002° in cell angles) is not needed in normal work on feldspars because minor chemical substitutions cause greater effects than the errors. The ten-fold poorer accuracy of the best powder methods is sufficient for routine work.

Complications arise from accidental aggregation of two feldspars at a small angle, and especially from strained feldspar. Both of these give spots lying strictly on curves of constant Bragg angle about the center of the photograph, thereby permitting a distinction from twinning. Strained feldspars may give either circumferential streaks, or a string of sharp spots, the latter perhaps the result of polygonization during recrystallization.

6.1.2 Standard Photographs of Alkali Feldspar

Preliminary optical study can take advantage of the dominant {010} and {001} cleavages together with the {100} or Murchisonite partings. If the sample is abundant, crushing to a grain size of 0.1–0.5 mm is desirable. Examination of many grains in alcohol or oil should reveal a few with low birefringence and a rectangular cross-section. These should be lying on the {100} or Murchisonite parting. The {010} and {001} cleavages can then be identified either by conoscopic determination of the optic axial plane, or by moving the grain onto a side face and measuring the optical extinction angle. Grains with cross-hatched twinning or with macro- or micro-perthite can be oriented rapidly. Rare grains are dominated by {110} cleavages. It is important to identify twinning. Simple twins such as Carlsbad, Manebach and Baveno types give two sets of diffraction spots whose lattices lie at large angles: one set of spots may be correctly oriented but care must be taken not to assign the other set to a superstructure. Albite twinning in albite is useful for orientation. It is impossible to orient correctly all components of specimens with Albite and Pericline twinning (e.g. cross-hatched microcline), and the usual procedure is to orient the twin axes which correspond approximately to the morphological axes. Optical study with a spindle stage is easy and rapid. Alternatively, the crystal may be mounted on a U-stage.

Precession Photography. At first sight, precession photography is the most obvious technique for reconnaissance of alkali feldspars because it can yield an undistorted picture of the reciprocal lattice if the crystal is exactly aligned with a

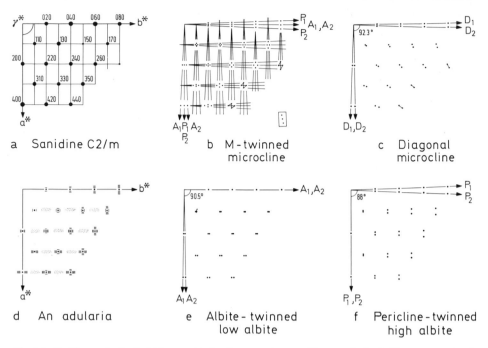

Fig. 6-1. Lattices of alkali feldspars. Each diagram shows either a single lattice or a set of intersecting lattices. The c-axis zero-layer of each lattice is shown. In b, c, d, e and f, the lattices are not coplanar, and projection is made onto the plane of an average lattice. In a, the lattice nodes are indexed, and the intensity of diffraction for a sanidine is shown by the size of the circles. In b, there are 4 lattices for the Albite and Pericline twins, whose orientations obey the M twin relation that b^* (Albite) is parallel to b (Pericline). Many M-twinned microclines show precession photographs with streaks connecting the spots, as shown for the 440, 350 and 280 clusters. In c, there are two lattices for the diagonal association. Here an orientation with D_1 midway between P_1 and A_1 of diagram b is chosen. In d, the complex situation is shown for an adularia. The hatching and stippling show intense and weak streaks, respectively. Diagrams e and f show the lattices for twinned albites. See Chapter 7 for cell dimensions

zone axis along the precession axis. Figures 6-1 and 6-2 are drawings of the reciprocal lattices for the 0-layers of the c and a axes, respectively.

Sanidine is monoclinic with space group C 2/m, and its lattice nodes fall on a rectangular grid in both Figs. 6-1a and 6-2a. The size of the circle indicates the intensity of the associated diffraction, but of course on a precession photograph the spots would be approximately the same size and the intensity would vary. In all other diagrams, spots of the same size are used, but the intensities may be obtained from Table 6-1.

Microcline and albite are triclinic with cell dimensions given in Chapter 7. Most microclines and albites are twinned on either or both of the Albite and Pericline laws. Figures 6-1e and 6-2c show the lattices for Albite-twinned low albite with α^* 86.4° and γ^* 90.5°. The twin components A_1 and A_2 have a common b^* axis resulting in superposition of spots of type 0k0. The a^* and c^* axes each occur in pairs symmetrically about the trace of the (010) plane. Consequently there are two sets of lattice nodes. Figures 6-1f and 6-2d show the corresponding

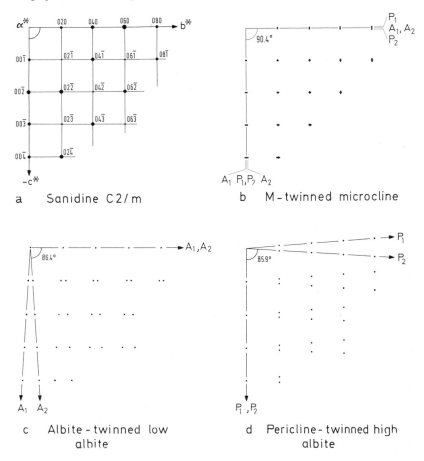

Fig. 6-2. Lattices of alkali feldspars. The diagrams show the 0-layer of the a-axis, but otherwise are constructed in the same way as those in Fig. 6-1. In a, the marked angle is actually $-\alpha^*$, whereas in b, c, d it is α^* for the twin

situation for Pericline twins of high albite in which the b axis is common to the twin units. Here the lattices superimpose at the a^* and c^* axes.

Ideally, inversion of a monoclinic feldspar to a triclinic feldspar yields both Albite and Pericline twinning, with the b^* axis of the former being parallel to the b axis of the latter, and both being parallel to the b symmetry axis of the monoclinic cell (Chapter 18). Figures 6-1b and 6-2b show the resultant lattices. Low microcline has α^* 90.4° and γ^* 92.3°. The directions of the reciprocal lattices are shown by the labels A_1, A_2, P_1, and P_2. The lattice nodes form clusters of four in a cross whose geometry changes such that two nodes merge at the axial directions leaving only three spots. In some triclinic alkali feldspars, there are two lattices which do not obey Albite or Pericline twin relations: instead two lattices occur in a diagonal association with axes lying at some irrational position part-way between the extremes for Albite and Pericline twinning. Figure 6-1c shows a position exactly half-way between those for the ideal twins.

There are many possible complications, all of which occur! Twin relations are not always obeyed exactly, probably because of the effect of stress, either between different components or perhaps from outside the crystal. Periodic twinning gives superstructures (Fig. 5-1). The cell dimensions vary with composition: e.g. the cell angles α^* and γ^* of high albite change to $90°$ as 40% Or enters in solid solution; the cell angles of microcline vary from $90°$ to the values used in Figs. 6-1 and 6-2. The lattices may have unusual cell dimensions because of strain between the components: such strain is usually revealed by streaks connecting diffraction spots. Thus in M-twinned microcline, the clusters of 4 spots are usually joined by streaks as shown by the patterns for the 350, 440 and 280 diffractions. Figure 6-1d shows a type of pattern found in adularia. Each spot in a position like that for sanidine is crossed by short streaks in the directions of spots for M-twinning of microcline. In addition, very weak diffuse bands occur elongated along b^*, and centered on positions for $(h+k)$ odd. Many of the complications are described by Laves (1950, 1952), Laves and Goldsmith (1961), Laves and Soldatos (1962, 1963), and Soldatos (1962).

Figure 6-3 is a 0-layer c-axis precession photograph of a microcline perthite described by Laves and Soldatos (1962). Approximately it consists of the addition of dominant spots from M-twinned microcline (Fig. 6-1b) and very weak spots for Albite-twinned low albite. Close examination shows that the Pericline spots

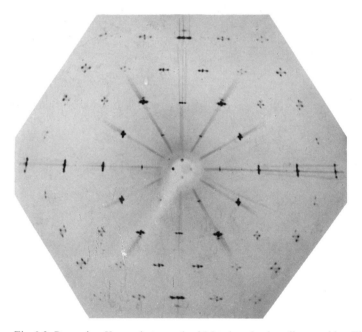

Fig. 6-3. Precession X-ray photograph of M-twinned microcline perthite. This 0-layer c-axis photograph shows spots from M-twinned microcline (see Fig. 6-1b) and weak Albite-twinned low albite (see Fig. 6-1e). It shows a full circle whose four quadrants are similar to those in Fig. 6-1 when account is taken of the pseudo-symmetry. See text for explanation of tilting of spots and distortion of the twin relation. The four black spots and the white shadow result from the beam-catcher of the precession camera. Filtered CuK radiation. Similar to Laves and Soldatos (1962, Fig. 1)

of the microcline are not centered about the Albite spots (e.g. the three spots for 400). Because the intensities do not obey monoclinic symmetry, it is not possible to estimate the relative concentrations of the four twin components just by looking at one cluster of four spots. However by taking an average over the whole photograph, one can determine that one Albite component and one Pericline component are stronger than the other two components. Furthermore the spots from the two stronger components are closer than those for the weaker components. Hence Laves and Soldatos (1962) proposed that the distortion of the M-twinning results from strain between the twin components, with the stronger components tending to coalesce.

Figure 6-3 shows a feature which makes it difficult to give an exact interpretation of precession photographs of a multi-component crystal. The $0k0$ spots are tilted with respect to the nodes of the lattice in Fig. 6-1b (see inset diagram for tilt of the 080 diffractions). A correctly-oriented 0-layer precession photograph should have a center of symmetry, but the tilts of the $0k0$ and $0\bar{k}0$ diffractions in Fig. 6-3 violate this condition. The simple reason is that the lattices in Fig. 6-1b are not strictly in the plane of the X-ray film: e.g. if the b^* axes of A_1 and A_2 are in the plane of the paper, those of P_1 and P_2 are tilted up and down respectively by about 0.4°. Diffraction occurs either earlier or later than for nodes exactly in the plane of Fig. 6-1b resulting in a horizontal displacement, and tilting of the set of three spots in Fig. 6-3. This feature of precession photography has not been analyzed for feldspar perthites, but a systematic calculation should be made: for example, the tilt of the $0k0$ spots in Fig. 6-3 could yield a measure of α^*.

Unfortunately the tilting of spots for a-axis photographs of microcline causes severe problems. Figure 6-2b shows that the ideal lattices of M-twinned microcline almost superimpose in projection. Actually the b^* axes of P_1 and P_2 and the a^* axes of A_1 and A_2 are about 2° out of the plane of the drawing. Severe tilting occurs as shown in Fig. 6-4b. The corresponding c-axis precession photograph (Fig. 6-4a) shows a strictly M-twinned microcline with its characteristic cluster

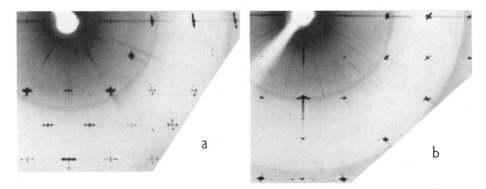

Fig. 6-4. Precession X-ray photographs of M-twinned microcline perthite. a The 0-layer c-axis photograph reveals M-twinned microcline strictly obeying the M-relation of Fig. 6-1b (but note the tilting of the $0k0$ diffractions). Weak monoclinic K-feldspar gives a spot near the center of each cluster. Weak Albite-twinned low albite is also visible. b The corresponding 0-layer a-axis photograph clearly reveals the low albite (see especially 400), but the spots for the K-feldspars are confusing because of the tilting. Filtered CuK radiation. (From Laves and Soldatos, 1963, Figs. 4 and 5)

of four spots. In addition there is a fifth spot approximately at the center of the four spots: this results from a weak monoclinic component. The spots for Albite-twinned low albite are weak and almost superimposed. However in the a-axis precession photograph the spots for the albite are wide apart and easily recognizable, especially those for the 400 diffraction. Identification of albite by precession photography should be made by using both the a and c axes. Several photographs of both high and low albite were given by Laves and Chaisson (1950). The a-axis photograph gives a measure of α^* and the c-axis photograph a measure of γ^*: when these angles approach 90°, as for low albite in Fig. 6-3, the pairs of spots for twins nearly merge. However, simultaneous study of both a and c axis photographs, as in Fig. 6-4, allows reliable identification.

Figure 6-5 shows how periodic twinning of Na-rich feldspar causes complications. The K-feldspar of this cryptoperthite (Spencer R) is monoclinic. The Na-feldspar gives complex clusters of spots which tend to give two maxima near the positions for Albite twinning of low albite (see the 062 diffraction, for example). Streaks join the spots for the Na- and K-rich feldspars indicating structural continuity. Many complex intermediates occur between the extremes for simple twinning and for regular periodic twinning, and each must be identified on its own merits: particularly troublesome are photographs in which streaks occur rather than distinct spots.

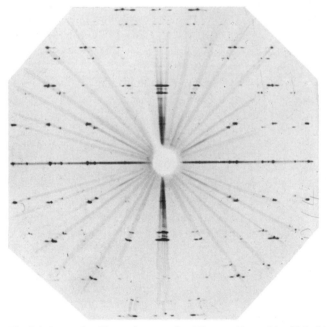

Fig. 6-5. Precession X-ray photograph of Spencer R perthite. This 0-layer a-axis photograph shows monoclinic K-feldspar and periodically-twinned low albite. Slight doubling of the spots for the K-feldspar occurs, but this arises merely from lack of parallelism of the a-axis and the X-ray beam. The spots for the albite occur as two clusters at the approximate positions of Albite-twinned low albite. Beta spots and strong radiation streaks result from the unfiltered Cu radiation. (From Laves and Soldatos, 1962, Fig. 4)

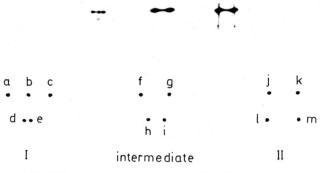

Fig. 6-6. Relation between K- and Na-feldspars as revealed by the 400 diffractions in *c*-axis precession photographs. See text for explanation. (From Laves and Soldatos, 1962, Fig. 1 and Laves and Soldatos, 1963, Figs. 6 and 7)

The radial streaks in Fig. 6-3 and the other photographs result merely from the continuous X-ray spectrum. However, the streaks joining spots of each cluster represent structural continuity between the components in the composite crystals (as shown especially for the 350 cluster in Fig. 6-3). Figure 6-5 was taken with unfiltered radiation and β spots at one-ninth of the distance to the center are seen on the radiation streaks through the dominant α spots.

The relative orientation between the lattices of the Na-rich and K-rich feldspars is important for understanding the sequence of the ordering and unmixing. Figure 6-6 shows two extremes and an intermediate. The 400 diffractions are shown in *c*-axis 0-level precession photography. In the Type I orientation of Laves and Soldatos, the albite is oriented to the pseudo-monoclinic orientation of the microcline. Spots a and c are for Albite-twins of the microcline, and spot b is for the Pericline twins. Spots d and e are for Albite twinning of the albite. The b^* axis of the albite is parallel to the b^* axis of the Albite-twinned microcline and the b axis of the Pericline-twinned microcline. (Actually there is a slight distortion as shown in Fig. 6-3). In the Type II orientation of Laves and Soldatos, both the albite (spots *l* and *m*) and microcline (spots *j* and *k*) are apparently Albite-twinned with the same γ^* angle. However only the microcline is truly twinned. The albite adopted the orientation of the microcline such that the a^* axes are parallel: it is not twinned on the Albite law. An intermediate case is also shown in Fig. 6-6. Care must be taken with untwinned alkali feldspars. The inter-axial angle should be carefully measured, and the intensities compared across the axes. For albite, the deviation from monoclinic symmetry is so large that no problem should arise. Untwinned K-feldspars occur rarely, but could be overlooked by a careless examination.

Laves and Sáenz (1973) showed how the precession method can be used to determine the orientation of submicroscopic twins.

In conclusion, it is wise to take both *a* and *c* axis photographs if precession photography is being used. Care must be taken not to confuse doubling of spots from misorientation with a genuine structural effect.

Weissenberg Photography. This has been used rarely for study of alkali feldspars, but should be used for the reasons given in the introduction. Figure 3 in

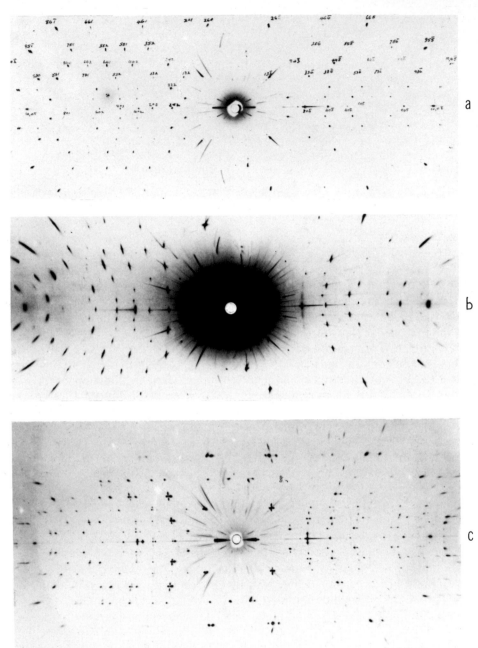

Fig. 6-7. Single-crystal X-ray oscillation photographs of alkali feldspars. Standard orientation of Smith and MacKenzie (1955) 3 cm camera. Filtered CuK$_\alpha$ radiation. a Sanidine from Kokomo, Colorado. Some diffractions are indexed. See Smith and MacKenzie (1955, Fig. 3) for complete indexing. b Adularia from St. Gotthard; Spencer B. c Microperthite from Burma, Spencer O. Item (b) is given in Smith and MacKenzie (1959, Fig. 10). Item (c) is published in Smith and MacKenzie (1955, Fig. 1 with a key)

MacKenzie (1954) is a front-reflection Weissenberg photograph of the c-axis 0-layer of a cross-hatched microcline. It shows clusters of five spots, four in the relation for M-twinning and one in the monoclinic orientation. Unlike the precession technique, there is no problem of doubling of spots because of misorientation: in the Weissenberg technique, misorientation causes merely a distortion of the festoons. Of course, for accurate measurement of cell dimensions the rotation axis must be carefully oriented, and high-angle spots must be used.

Oscillation Photography. Oscillation photographs taken in the special orientation of Smith and MacKenzie (1955) are easy to interpret. A series of photographs is given in Figs. 6-7 and 6-9 to 6-13. For these photographs, the feldspar crystal is mounted with the morphological b-axis parallel to the cylindrical film, and is oscillated about the b-axis with the X-ray beam normal to b and parallel to the (001) plane in the center of the 15° oscillation. Such a photograph can be taken with a Weissenberg camera or with a special oscillation camera. The initial trial orientation can be made optically using the {010} and {001} cleavages. Final orientation of b is made by angular adjustments of the goniometer arcs based on curvature of layer lines, and of (001) by rotation of the goniometer head based on examination of the continuous radiation streaks.

A monoclinic feldspar yields spots lying on straight layer lines for the flattened X-ray film, with k increasing from 0 at the center to 6 for the extreme layer lines when CuK_α radiation is used (Fig. 6-7a). Indices are given for the spots on the upper half. Note that $(h+k)$ is even to obey the C face-centering. The strong radiation streak at the center is from 001 and 00$\bar{1}$, and is symmetrical when the (001) cleavage lies in the middle of the 15° oscillation. The $\alpha_1\alpha_2$ doublet becomes resolved at high Bragg angles. Because the spots for the 10, 0, $\bar{6}$ and 10, 4, $\bar{5}$ diffractions are very sharp, the sanidine is essentially homogeneous chemically. Variation of a few percent in the Or content gives detectable broadening in such high-angle diffractions. At the left-hand side each of the α_1 and α_2 spots shows two spots some of which are just resolved. Each pair of spots has the same Bragg angle showing that the spots result merely from two crystals lying at an angle of about 1°. By chance the disorientation is not visible on the right-hand side. A plane of symmetry passes through the equatorial layer: actually the intensities are rather stronger on the upper half of the photograph but this results from trivial experimental factors. An untwinned microcline would give slight tilting of the row lines and detectable intensity variations between pairs of spots above and below the equator.

A Pericline-twinned feldspar oscillated about b has common layer lines and tilted row lines which cross at the zero layer line (Fig. 6-8a). Hence there is only one spot for each diffraction on the zero layer line (e.g. for 20$\bar{4}$) whereas there are two spots for each diffraction on higher layer lines. Spots on the 4th and 6th layer lines are shown together with tilted row lines for the 26$\bar{2}$ and 66$\bar{5}$ diffractions. The twinned diffraction is shown by underlining.

An Albite-twinned feldspar oscillated about b^* has common row lines but tilted layer lines (Fig. 6-8b). There are two spots for each diffraction as shown by the indices in the figure. The zero layer lines are shown, but the 4th and 6th layer lines are not given to avoid confusion: the dashed lines show the positions for a monoclinic feldspar.

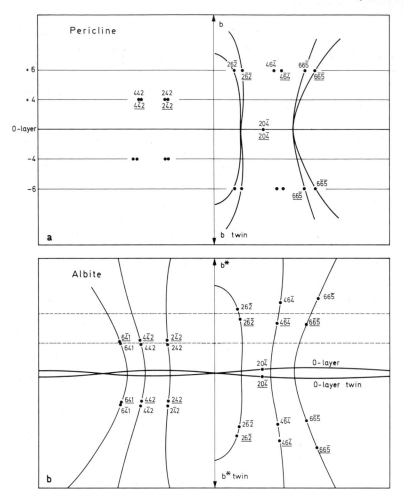

Fig. 6-8. Interpretation of X-ray oscillation photographs of Pericline- and Albite-twinned feldspars

An M-twinned feldspar yields clusters of 4 spots arranged in a distorted cross which changes shape with the diffraction indices, becoming a set of 3 spots for zero k. Figure 6-7c shows the combination of a monoclinic K-feldspar and an M-twinned low albite. Figure 6-9a shows an Albite-twinned microcline plus an Albite-twinned low albite.

MacKenzie and Smith (1955) showed that the α^* and γ^* angles could be readily determined from the separation of the pairs of spots for Albite- or of Pericline-twinned feldspars using the equations:

$$4\,kb^*[l c^* \cos\alpha^* + h a^* \cos\gamma^*] = \zeta^2_{hkl} - \zeta^2_{\bar{h}k\bar{l}} \ \ (\text{Albite})$$

$$= \xi^2_{hkl} - \xi^2_{\bar{h}k\bar{l}} \ \ (\text{Pericline})$$

where ζ and ξ are the coordinates of the reciprocal lattice referred to the oscillation axis. They showed how α^* and γ^* could be determined by measurement of the linear separations of several pairs of spots to a precision of about $0.05°$ for sharp spots and rather less for smeared spots. The technique depends critically on the twin relation being accurately obeyed. This assumption is correct for many alkali feldspars, but not for all components of perthites. Strain between components with continuity of structure across boundaries leads to distortions. Caution must be used in evaluating the significance of $\alpha^* \gamma^*$ values deduced from such distorted associations.

A systematic description is now given of the figures. Figure 6-7b shows the Spencer B adularia from St. Gotthard, another crystal of which was used for X-ray structure determination (Chapters 2 and 3). Instead of the sharp spots in the Kokomo sanidine, each diffraction is represented by a central spot crossed by two short streaks along row lines and layer lines, the former streak being more visible. Electron diffraction data (Chapter 10) showed that the streaks result from a coherent lattice locally distorting towards the geometry of M-twinned microcline. Above and below the $20\bar{4}$ diffraction are streaks centered on the positions for $21\bar{4}$ and $2\bar{1}\bar{4}$ which are forbidden in a C-centered lattice. These streaks were interpreted by Laves and Goldsmith (1961) as the result of formation of boundary regions with local symmetry $P\,2_1/a$ between out-of-step domains with microcline-type ordering (see Chapter 18).

Figure 6-7c shows the Spencer O microperthite from Burma. Each diffraction is represented by five spots, except where overlap occurs. The clearest groups are for the 442 and $26\bar{2}$ diffractions. The K-feldspar yields a single spot which obeys monoclinic symmetry: however each spot is drawn out in a direction diagonal to the row and layer lines (see especially 641). Presumably it is actually a microcline with only a small deviation from monoclinic geometry, and consisting of two units in the diagonal association (Fig. 6-1c). The Na-feldspar consists of a low sodic plagioclase twinned on both the Albite and Pericline laws. This M-twinning is the result of exsolution occurring in a monoclinic environment. The clusters of spots on the zero layer line are almost symmetrical, but close examination shows that the b-axis of the K-feldspar is not quite parallel to be b^* axis of the Pericline twins. Smith and MacKenzie (1955) used this photograph as an example of the calculation of the cell angles α^* and γ^* from the separation of pairs of diffractions for the twinned albite. The 001 streaks at the center project an unequal amount: this results from lack of parallelism of the c^* axes of the component feldspars.

Figure 6-9a shows a microperthite from Tugtutôq (MacKenzie and Smith, 1962) whose albite and K-feldspar are both Albite-twinned. Two pairs of spots occur for each diffraction, except when accidental overlap occurs. More detailed examination shows that the spots for the K-feldspar do not lie exactly on row lines parallel to b^* (e.g. the 242 diffraction), and strictly speaking the K-feldspar has a diagonal association. Measurement of α^* and γ^*, by the method of Smith and MacKenzie assuming Albite twinning, indicates a microcline with angles half-way to those for maximum microcline. However X-ray powder data indicate a maximum microcline, and the discrepancy results merely from the incorrect assumption about the twin law.

Figure 6-9b shows an orthoclase microperthite from Slieve Gullion (Emeleus and Smith, 1959) which contains a monoclinic K-feldspar and an almost perfectly-

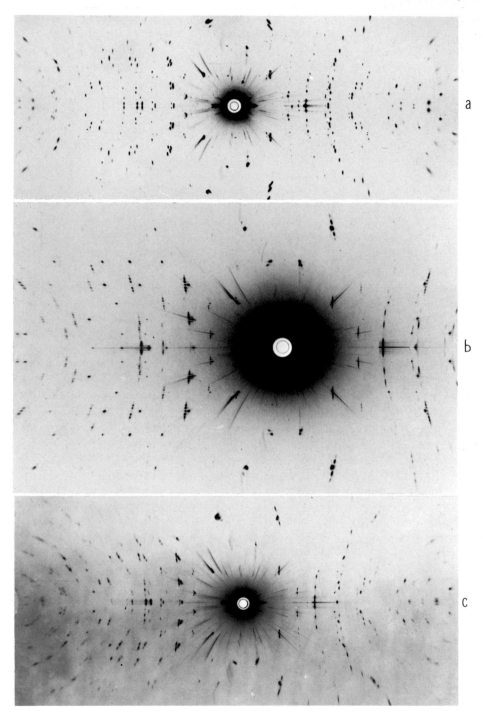

Fig. 6-9. Single-crystal X-ray oscillation photographs of alkali feldspars. a Microperthite from Tugtutôq, Greenland. b Microperthite with periodic Albite twinning from Slieve Gullion, N. Ireland. c Microperthite from Mogok, Burma; Spencer N. Item (b) is from Emeleus and Smith (1959, Fig. 10). Item (c) is published in Smith and MacKenzie (1955, Fig. 2 with a key)

regular periodic twin on the Albite law. The periodic twin definitely consists of an Na-rich feldspar, but its chemical and structural nature will remain uncertain until a full structure analysis is made. The K-rich and Na-rich regions have structural continuity as shown by the streak between the spot for the K-rich feldspar and the central spot for the Na-feldspar (see 242 and 222, especially): furthermore, weak streaks extend from the other spots for the Na-feldspar producing satellites to the spot for the K-feldspar. The spots for the Na-feldspar are not quite regularly spaced but correspond to an average spacing of about $7b$. Laves (1952) first explained a specimen of this type. See Chapter 5 for explanation of diffraction from periodic structures.

Figure 6-9c shows a Spencer N microperthite from Burma. The sodic component is an Albite-twinned albite. There are two K-rich components — a monoclinic one and a microcline whose two components have the diagonal association. The spots for the monoclinic K-rich feldspar are slightly further away from the center than the average for the spots of the diagonal association: this indicates a smaller cell dimension and a higher Ab-content of the monoclinic feldspar. Note that the axes of the microcline components are not symmetrical about those for the monoclinic feldspar.

MacKenzie and Smith (1955, Fig. 3) showed small sections of X-ray photographs of 14 orthoclase microperthites displaying a variety of phenomena. Smith and MacKenzie (1959) showed further photographs.

Figure 6-10 shows X-ray photographs of three anorthoclases described by Smith and MacKenzie (1958). The specimen from Grande Caldeira (a) shows seven spots, those from 641 being outlined. The Na-rich feldspar is M-twinned giving the cluster of spots most distant from the center of the photograph. The K-rich feldspar apparently consists of a monoclinic feldspar plus an Albite-twinned triclinic feldspar. However, this triclinic feldspar is not microcline. Actually the Na- and K-rich feldspars occur as domains in a single aluminosilicate framework which merely distorts to accommodate the different sizes of the Na and K atoms. The Na-rich domains dominate the K-rich domains and force them to distort in a similar way. Consequently the triclinic geometry of the K-feldspar is merely adopted from the Na-feldspar. Whenever strong streaks occur, there must be structural continuity and strain between the components.

Figure 6-10b shows a specimen from Mt. Franklin. Three spots plus a weak streak occur for each diffracting plane. The three spots result from an Na-rich phase which is both Albite and Pericline twinned, but not in the M-relation. Spot q is related to spot p by Albite twinning and to spot r by Pericline twinning to give the L-pattern characteristic of twinning occurring when the symmetry is triclinic. The weak streaks (see 641 and other diffractions at the left) result from incipient exsolution of K-feldspar.

Figure 6-10c shows the anorthoclase cryptoperthite from Victoria, Australia. Both the Na-rich and K-rich regions are represented by a pair of spots which are in positions for Albite twinning. Streaks join the spots to give a trapezium. This pattern is interpreted as the result of a coherent aluminosilicate framework in which the dominant Albite-twinned sodic regions constrain the K-rich regions to adopt a similar orientation. All the sodic regions in Fig. 6-10 are solid solutions of high albite.

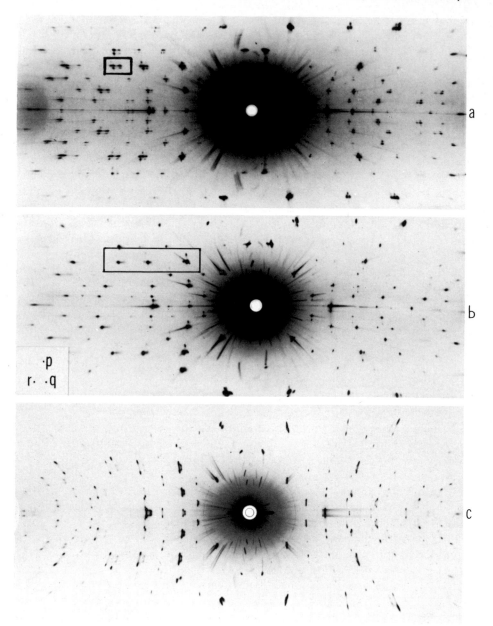

Fig. 6-10. Single-crystal X-ray oscillation photographs of cryptoperthites. a Anorthoclase crypto-perthite from Grande Caldeira. b Anorthoclase cryptoperthite from Mt. Franklin, c Anorthoclase cryptoperthite from Victoria. (From Smith and MacKenzie, 1958, Figs. 6, 7 and 8)

Figure 6-11 shows the 641, 442 and 242 diffractions of cryptoperthites of (a) two sanidines (b) sanidine and high-albite solid solution with Pericline twinning, and (c) sanidine plus Pericline-twinned high-albite solid solution and weak Albite-

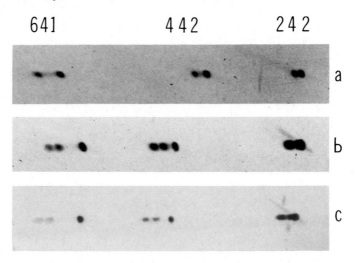

Fig. 6-11. Single-crystal X-ray oscillation photographs of cryptoperthites. Each photograph shows an enlargement of the 641, 442 and 242 diffractions. a Spencer P cryptoperthite heated to 560° C. b Spencer P cryptoperthite heated to 425° C. c Cryptoperthite from Slieve Gullion. See Smith and MacKenzie (1958) and Emeleus and Smith (1959) for background information

twinned low albite solid solution. A streak connects each pair of spots in (a) and each set of three spots in (b). The spots for Pericline twinning in (c) are actually fine doublets resulting from periodic twinning.

Figure 6-12 illustrates the difficulty of interpreting X-ray photographs of some perthites. Sub-figures a and b show the 641, 442, 242, 262, 46$\bar{4}$ and 66$\bar{5}$ diffractions for a microperthite from the Arran granite. At a casual glance, the spots result from a monoclinic K-feldspar and a periodic Albite twin similar to that in Fig. 6-9b, but less regular. For this interpretation, the first node would be sharp and the second node would be smeared out into a diffuse streak. The intensity distribution of the first nodes over the entire pattern suggests that the Na-rich phase is a high albite solid solution, rather than the low albite solid solution indicated by Fig. 6-9b. It is quite possible that the diffuse streaks near the expected second nodes actually mask a weak Albite twin of low sodic plagioclase. Two weak spots for 2$\bar{6}$2 (see arrows) indicate low sodic plagioclase almost Pericline twinned but actually in the diagonal association.

Figure 6-12c, d shows similar enlargements for a microperthite from the Beinn an Dubhaich granite. The 641, 442 and 242 spots can be interpreted as the result of a monoclinic K-feldspar coexisting with an M-twinned solid solution of high albite. However there are two extra weak spots for 46$\bar{4}$ and 66$\bar{5}$ (see arrows) which result from a low plagioclase with Albite twinning. These spots are hidden by the stronger spots for the other diffractions.

It is obvious that great care must be taken with such perthites. Electron diffraction and microscopy (Chapter 10) will be required to fully resolve the phenomena.

Figure 6-13 shows enlargements of two areas of an X-ray oscillation photograph of Spencer U microperthite. The 641 and 442 diffractions show two spots

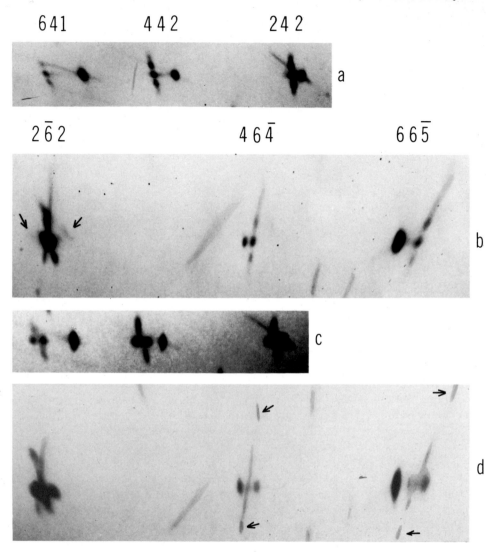

Fig. 6-12. Complications in two perthites. Enlargements of X-ray oscillation photographs. a, b Microperthite from Arran granite. c, d Microperthite from Beinn an Dubhaich granite. Slightly retouched to augment weak diffractions. See MacKenzie and Smith (1962) for background information

of identical shape for the coexisting Na- and K-rich feldspars. Each spot has a more intense center corresponding to monoclinic geometry, associated with diffuse streaks like those in Spencer B (Fig. 6-7b). The streak from $20\overline{4}$ shows maxima near $21\overline{4}$ and $2\overline{1}\overline{4}$. Indeed this specimen is like the Spencer B adularia except for the presence of an Na-rich phase. The latter has the same geometry as the dominant K-feldspar, and presumably is "clamped" to it because of structural continuity of the aluminosilicate framework. Note that the crystal structure

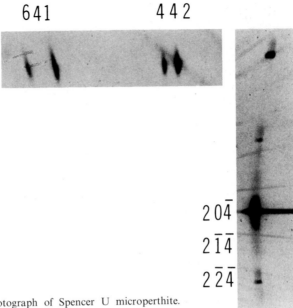

641 442

$20\bar{4}$

$2\bar{1}\bar{4}$

$2\bar{2}\bar{4}$

Fig. 6-13. Single-crystal X-ray photograph of Spencer U microperthite. Enlargements are given of two sections

determination of Spencer U (Chapters 2 and 3) was carried out with a single crystal cut from another part of the material supplied by E. Spencer. The strong difference between the two crystals cautions against assuming that one crystal is representative of a perthitic sample.

6.1.3 Standard Photographs of Plagioclase

General. By 1972, all single-crystal X-ray studies of plagioclase had been made by skilled crystallographers: other workers had confined themselves to X-ray powder methods. However, single-crystal study of plagioclase is amenable to a mineralogist or petrologist with a moderate training in crystallography.

Probably the simplest technique for a novice utilizes the precession method. The most informative photograph for most plagioclases is the 0-layer of the *a*-axis. Laves and Goldsmith (1954, Figs. 1-5) showed such photographs for synthetic anorthite heated at various temperatures, and Müller *et al.* (1972) gave photographs for natural anorthites. No systematic set of photographs has been published for the whole plagioclase series, but the relationships are clear from the summary of the reciprocal lattices of plagioclases by Bown and Gay (1958, Fig. 3). Usually the investigator will know the An-content of the plagioclase from preliminary optical or electron microprobe study: by consulting Fig. S-2b he will know what categories of subsidiary diffractions might occur. The 0-layer of a *b*-axis precession photograph also contains information on all categories of subsidiary diffractions, but the 0-layer of a *c*-axis precession photograph lacks information on the *b, c,* and *e* diffractions.

Highly skilled crystallographers may wish to use the oscillation technique developed by Drs. M. G. Bown and P. Gay of Cambridge University, England. A 15° oscillation photograph about the *c*-axis allows ready identification of all the important diffraction phenomena of plagioclases. However, the preliminary identification of the *c*-axis and alignment of the crystal in the X-ray camera requires considerable skill.

Whatever technique is used, preliminary optical study is mandatory. Plentiful samples should be checked under a binocular for either natural faces or well-defined cleavages which should be either {001} {010} or more rarely {110} and {100}. Coarse twinning can be recognized sometimes. Selected crystals should be examined in oil under a petrographic microscope to check for twinning, multigrain nature and excessive chemical zoning. Inclusions such as antiperthite, mica and opaque oxides may be recognized. Sometimes the faces or cleavages can be identified from the optical orientation, especially if the An-content is known: measurements of extinction angles on a spindle stage may be useful. Fine-scale twinning is usually on the Albite or Pericline law. Usually twins should be avoided because of confusion caused by the two reciprocal lattices: however in some plagioclases, twinning is ubiquitous. For Pericline twinning, either a 0-layer *b*-axis precession photograph or a *b*-axis oscillation photograph gives the simplest result. For Albite twinning, the 0-layer *a*-axis precession photograph has doubling of the lattice grid. A *b*-axis oscillation photograph would show doubled layer lines as for the albite component of perthites (preceding section). Coarse twinning may occur on any of the numerous twin laws (see Chapter 18), and each crystal must be treated on its merits. Hopefully untwinned crystals with two cleavages will be seen: if so, they may turn out to be the {010} and {001} cleavages whose intersection gives the *a*-axis. For the Bown-Gay method it is necessary to locate the *c*-axis which lies at 26° to the (001) normal in the (010) plane. Serious confusion can arise from the pseudo-symmetry of plagioclase (and indeed for all feldspars). For example, for a C-centered feldspar, the [110] axis has a repeat distance quite close to that for the *c*-axis. Measurement of the lattice dimensions provides a reliable identification.

Many plagioclases give subsidiary diffractions which are so weak and diffuse that they can be overlooked in a routine examination. It is advisable to expose the photograph long enough so that the background is visible to the naked eye. A graphite monochromator permits detection of much weaker diffractions than in beta-filtered radiation: however alignment is difficult with monochromatized radiation, and preliminary alignment with unfiltered radiation is advisable.

Figure 6-14 shows portions of the 0-layer *a*-axis section of the reciprocal lattice. Primitive anorthite is indexed with the doubled *c*-axis. All four types of diffractions are sharp with the *a* type stronger than *b* than *c* than *d* on average: however there are very large changes of intensity from one diffraction to another as listed in Table 6-2. The *a* diffractions with $(h + k)$ even and *l* even occur in all plagioclases, but for plagioclases indexed on the albite cell they obey the rule $(h + k)$ even and *l* any integer. The *b* diffractions with $(h + k)$ odd and *l* odd occur in all solid solutions of anorthite and can be found in some specimens with bulk compositions at least to An_{65}. The *c* diffractions with $(h + k)$ odd and *l* even are sharp for P-anorthite but become weaker and diffuse in

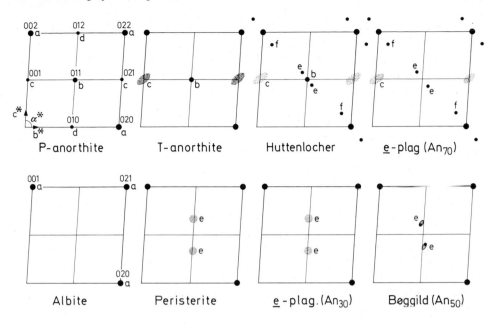

Fig. 6-14. Portions of the reciprocal lattice for various types of plagioclase. Each diagram shows a part of the zero layer of the a-axis with symbols depicting the diffraction types

anorthites transitional to the ideal concept of body-centered anorthite: there is some doubt whether any anorthites lack c diffractions, but in some specimens with b diffractions it is not possible to detect c diffractions in routine studies. The c diffractions tend to be elongated along the normal to $(\bar{2}3\bar{1})$.

Type e diffractions can be found in certain plagioclases with bulk composition from below An_{10} to about An_{85}. Those up to An_{16} are peristerites which are unmixed into albite and oligoclase: in these, the e diffractions come from the oligoclase which has a composition near An_{25}. Only e-diffractions are seen easily in plagioclases more sodic than An_{50}, but more calcic specimens show f diffractions as well. The e diffractions occur in pairs about the positions for b diffractions, and their positions change continuously and irrationally with composition, becoming stronger and sharper as the An-content increases. For andesines and oligoclases, the e diffractions can be overlooked in routine studies. The f diffractions occur in pairs about the a diffractions and have double the separation of the e diffractions. They become stronger and sharper as the An-content increases, being comparable in strength to the e diffractions for An_{70}. Most pairs of e and f diffractions show major intensity differences, but roughly speaking the combined intensity of the e diffractions varies in the same way as that of the b diffractions of anorthite. Weak, diffuse c diffractions are sometimes seen in specimens showing f diffractions.

Plagioclases with the Huttenlocher intergrowth show b, e, f and c diffractions, consistent with a mixture of transitional anorthite and a labradorite with e and f diffractions: however routine studies show no splitting of the a diffractions.

The diffraction phenomena of plagioclases with the Bøggild intergrowth are somewhat controversial. Again only one set of a diffractions is seen in routine work. There are no reports of two distinct sets of e diffractions, but the latest studies suggest that e diffractions may consist of partially-overlapping pairs as shown in Fig. 6-14 (see Chapters 10 and 19).

The peristerites show two sets of a diffractions consistent with near-parallelism of the b^* and c^* axes and about $1°$ between the a^* axes. Each pair of a diffractions is linked by a streak indicating some continuity of the aluminosilicate framework. Unfortunately in 0-layer a-axis precession photographs, the two sets of spots essentially overlap. Consequently for albites and oligoclases it is necessary to use another precession axis or a different technique.

When the peristerite intergrowth is on a scale of about ten unit cells across, the diffraction patterns are complex. Instead of two spots for a coarse peristerite, a cluster of spots occurs for the superstructure (Fig. 19-59). Korekawa et al. (1970) describe such a superstructure in an oligoclase, An_{16}. The cluster of spots could be misinterpreted as the effect of three or more coexisting plagioclases, and high-angle Weissenberg photographs are desirable if there is any uncertainty for precession or oscillation photographs. Probably complexities will occur for fine-scale Huttenlocher intergrowths, and the subsidiary diffractions should be carefully examined.

The drawings in Fig. 6-14 are given for plagioclases in a low structural state. Those in a high structural state should have the albite structure type over most of the composition range, giving an anorthite type only in the anorthite and perhaps bytownite range.

No systematic description has been given of the complexities caused by twinning. Bhatty et al. (1970) described complex diffraction patterns of anorthite caused by fine-scale Albite and Carlsbad twinning.

There have been few single-crystal X-ray studies of the inclusions in plagioclase. The K-feldspar of antiperthite is readily recognized because it occurs in near-parallel orientation with the plagioclase and yields spots in similar positions to those in perthites (Fig. 6-16d). However the angular relations are somewhat different because the K-feldspar of antiperthite forms in a triclinic host rather than growing as a monoclinic host in perthite.

Identification of mica, epidote, opaque oxides, etc. is a special problem, but could be tackled by similar techniques to those used by Bown and Gay (1959) for inclusions in pyroxene.

Bown-Gay Method. Figure 6-15 shows the orientation of the plagioclase at the center of a $15°$ oscillation about the c-axis. The indices of the diffractions are shown with respect to the albite cell. Three principal layers occur above and below the zero layer. Each pair of numbers gives the h and k indices. Because the cell dimensions change across the plagioclase series, not all the diffractions occur on any chosen photograph.

Figure 6-16 shows six selected photographs very kindly taken by M. G. Bown. In (a), an albite, An_0, from Amelia shows only type a diffractions. The doubling of spots at high angles results merely from the $\alpha_1\alpha_2$ doublet. Spots marked by arrows lie on the continuous radiation streaks and can be identified as type a spots from CuK_β and tungsten radiation.

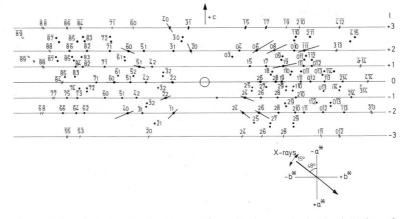

Fig. 6-15. Orientation of the plagioclase in the Bown-Gay oscillation method, plus indexing of diffractions for a labradorite showing a and e diffractions. The e diffractions are indexed with the h and k indices of the corresponding b diffraction of anorthite. Each pair of numbers gives the h and k indices: the l index is given at the right for each layer line. (From M. G. Bown and P. Gay, pers. comm.)

In (b), a peristerite, An_{12}, from Peekskill, N. Y. shows curved layer lines because the c-axis was not quite oriented along the oscillation axis. High-angle diffractions show a doubling (e.g. those marked by arrows) which results from non-parallel sub-crystals. Pairs of e diffractions are visible at center right. The separation of the spots is greater than that in (c) for an andesine An_{37}: this is consistent with the calcic component of the peristerite having a composition near An_{25}. The e spots are remarkably sharp, and much more diffuseness is found in some sodic plagioclases.

In (c), an andesine, An_{37}, from Yosemite Valley, California shows no splitting of the a diffractions, and occurrence of well-defined e diffractions. The spots are slightly diffuse and appear to have a weak halo on one side: this may result from chemical zoning or perhaps from some structural effect. Two spots marked by arrows do not fit the geometry of the other spots, and must result from a very tiny crystal in a different orientation: actually they have the same Bragg angles as the $\bar{4}03$ and $\bar{6}02$ diffractions, suggesting that the second crystal is a plagioclase.

In (d), a labradorite, An_{50}, from Essex County, N. Y. shows strong sharp e diffractions whose spacing is less than for the andesine. No f diffractions are visible either in (c) or (d). The arrows show diffractions from a weak K-feldspar occurring as antiperthite.

In (e), a labradorite, An_{64}, from the Stillwater Igneous Complex, Montana shows both e and f diffractions. The latter are best seen about the $\bar{4}03, \bar{6}02$ and $\bar{6}00$ diffractions. No c diffractions are visible on the photograph, but have been seen as very-weak, diffuse blobs in some labradorites.

In (f), a pure anorthite synthesized at $1520°$ C by J. F. Schairer shows the transitional type of structure. The sharp spots half-way between the main layer lines are type b diffractions, and the diffuse blobs are c diffractions with a tendency to be elongated. The type d diffractions are too weak to be visible.

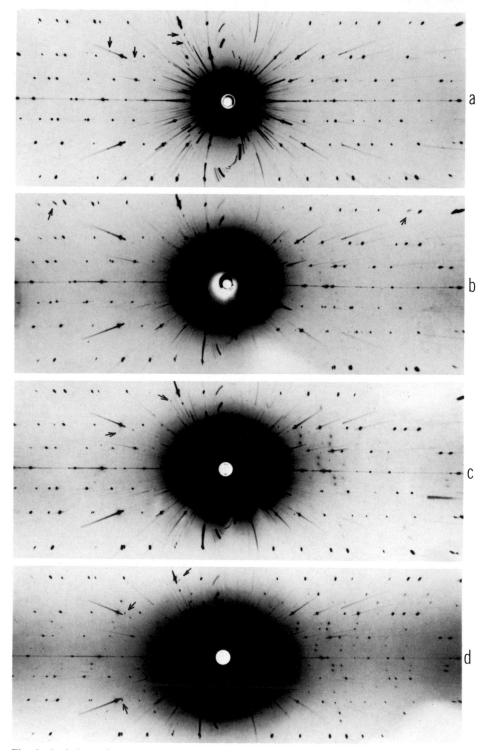

Fig. 6-16a-d. Legend see opposite page

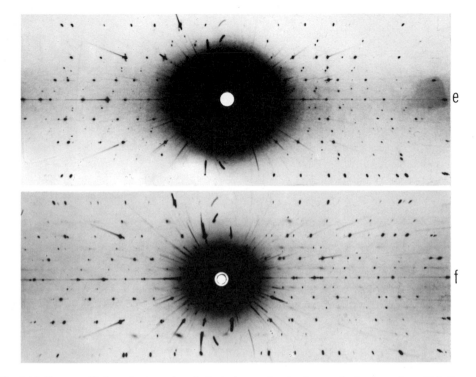

Fig. 6-16. X-ray oscillation photographs of plagioclases taken in the standard orientation of M. G. Bown and P. Gay. Approximately half of each photograph is shown. 3 cm oscillation camera. Filtered CuK radiation. a Albite, An_0 from Amelia, Va. b Peristerite, An_{12}, from Peekskill, N. Y. c Andesine, An_{37}, from Yosemite Valley, Cal. d Labradorite, An_{50}, from Essex Co., N. Y. e Labradorite, An_{64}, from Stillwater, Mont. f Synthetic anorthite. (From M. G. Bown and P. Gay, pers. comm.)

6.2 Powder Techniques

6.2.1 General

X-ray powder techniques are used for three major purposes: rapid identification, accurate measurement of cell dimensions, and detection of non-quenchable phase inversions.

Identification of homogeneous specimens is quite satisfactory by powder methods, thereby avoiding the complex orientation procedures for single crystals. However, weak subsidiary diffractions are not detectable by powder methods, and evidence on twinning is completely absent.

Multi-phase specimens cause problems. The powder pattern of a simple perthite with no structural continuity between the K- and Na-feldspars is the simple addition of patterns for the individual feldspars. With great care, all cell dimensions can be measured for the two feldspars. Perthites with 3 components (e.g. sanidine + microcline + albite) yield so many overlapping peaks that measurement of cell dimensions is a severe and perhaps impossible problem. Perthites with structural coherence between the K- and Na-feldspars cause problems because of the distortion of cell dimensions (Chapter 7). The powder patterns are not the simple addition of those for isolated K- and Na-feldspars and many peaks overlap completely. Furthermore such coherent perthites commonly show periodic twinning or diffuseness of diffractions (see Section 6.1), which are not recognizable in powder patterns. It is imperative that all lines be identified for powder patterns of perthites: casual examination of just a few lines may lead to serious misinterpretation. Whenever possible, at least one or two feldspars from a suite of rocks should be examined by single-crystal methods. There is a suspicion that grinding may cause changes in the cell dimensions of feldspars in some perthites: unfortunately no careful studies had been made by 1973.

Mineral impurities should be checked carefully in powder patterns because of the possibility of inaccurate indexing. Quartz is easy to detect from the first two low-angle lines. Lines from clay minerals mostly overlap with feldspar lines but the first line is characteristic. Lines from hematite and other ore minerals will escape notice except in patterns of very high resolution and sensitivity. However the major products of alteration of plagioclase, such as epidote, calcite and prehnite, can be detected fairly easily in good powder patterns. The Powder Diffraction File is continuously up-dated with the best available reference patterns.

Powder diffraction patterns can be obtained by four main methods: Guinier semi-focusing film; counter diffractometer with strip-chart or numerical recording; Debye-Scherrer non-focusing film; and Gandolfi film using an undestroyed single crystal.

Except for routine identification, the Debye-Scherrer technique is obsolete for feldspars because of the broadness and systematic displacement of low-angle lines.

Most feldspar studies utilize the diffractometer or Guinier techniques, each of which has advantages, and each of which tends to arouse somewhat uncritical enthusiasm in some advocates. The diffractometer offers the advantage of a rapid visual output on a strip chart plus digital output and automatic operation for wealthy mineralogists. A small section of the pattern can be chosen for study (e.g. the $\bar{2}01$ peak for estimating the composition of a homogeneous alkali feldspar). With careful calibration, cell edges may be measured to around 1 part in 4000 and cell angles to $0.01°$. Unquestionably the diffractometer is a prime instrument for studying feldspars, and the main aim here is to point out the subtle features requisite for high sensitivity and accuracy.

The main advantages of the Guinier camera are (1) the greater resolution at the angular range where the dispersion of the monochromator compensates for the opposite dispersion of the specimen (normally chosen for 2θ $30°$ in commercial instruments) and (2) the ease of picking up very weak diffractions because of the low background from the monochromator, and the integrating effect of the eye and brain in looking along a line.

In the diffractometer, the α_1, α_2 doublet is unresolved at $2\theta \sim 20°$, becomes partly resolved near $2\theta \sim 30°$, and well resolved at $2\theta \sim 50°$: consequently the line width is greater than for a Guinier pattern. Because the diffractometer gives only a single cross-section of each diffraction line, there is no integrating effect:

however, prolonged counting at a low scan rate provides high sensitivity for a diffractometer.

For the best work, a diffractometer should be fitted with a proportional detector and pulse discrimination. Furthermore, addition of a graphite monochromator reduces the background with little loss of sensitivity. For accurate measurements, the instrument must be accurately aligned: in addition to checking for resolution of the $\alpha_1 \alpha_2$ doublets, the low-angle lines should be checked for the least possible asymmetry. An attempt should be made to measure the centroid of unresolved $\alpha_1 \alpha_2$ doublets.

In addition to making a very careful alignment of a Guinier camera, it is important to use the best quality of X-ray film stored in a refrigerator to reduce fogging. Each film should be warmed to room temperature before insertion in the cassette. After development and fixing, the film must be dried slowly and evenly under slight tension to hold it straight. A travelling microscope of low magnification is desirable for measurement.

Specimen preparation is very important for both Guinier and diffractometer techniques. For the diffractometer, the specimen surface must be as flat as possible, but the thickness is unimportant. For the normal Guinier camera, the X-rays penetrate the specimen, which must be both thin and planar. A thin coating of powder on a stretched plastic film is suitable. For both techniques the specimen must be ground to a fine powder: grinding in a liquid results in a more uniform powder than dry grinding. Rotation or reciprocation of the sample holder gives a better approximation to an ideal powder.

Plas, van der (1966) provided a detailed comparison of the Guinier and diffractometer techniques as applied to the identification of detrital feldspar. Because angular resolution is of such importance in study of these samples which may contain several types of feldspar brought together by the accidental processes of sedimentation, his enthusiasm for the Guinier method is understandable. However a general laboratory should find that both methods are valuable.

The cleavages {010} and {001} of feldspars produce preferred orientation with distortion of intensities unless special methods are used for preparing the sample.

In both the Guinier and diffractometer techniques, X-rays of long wavelength produce improved resolution. The latest X-ray tubes provide high intensity even for Fe and Cr radiation. Air scattering is serious for long wavelengths but can be reduced with a vacuum chamber.

The accuracy of cell dimensions depends critically on the calibration of the diffractometer record or Guinier film. The only known method of high accuracy for feldspars is to grind into the sample an appropriate amount of some material with a few lines resolvable from the feldspar lines, and whose line positions are accurately known. Usually spec-pure silicon is used, but other standards are used in various laboratories [e.g. pure spinel, CaF_2, $KBrO_3$, $Pb(NO_3)_2$]. It is imperative that all workers check their standards against spec-pure silicon to avoid unnecessary systematic error.

Of course, accurate cell dimensions can be obtained only if lines are correctly indexed. Except for obvious patterns that check exactly with a standard reference pattern, it is important to identify every line of the pattern both with regard to position and intensity. Automatic indexing programs, in which indices are assigned by multiple iterations on the basis of agreement of observed and calculated angles, are very valuable when correctly used. However serious errors have resulted from uncritical acceptance of indexed lines. Fortunately, it is fairly easy to detect an incorrect indexing of the lines of a pattern. When some low-angle lines are unindexed while high-angle lines are indexed, it is certain that something is wrong. Thorough inspection of the computer output with check of the intensity of all lines with those for standard patterns of feldspars is mandatory. Least-squares fitting of the cell dimensions is routinely carried out by a standard computer program.

X-ray powder data can be obtained at high-temperature by a variety of techniques applied to the diffractometer and Guinier camera. In most techniques, there is a temperature variation over the sample of $10°$ C or more thus inhibiting precise evaluation of symmetry inversions. In addition, differential thermal expansion of some of the sample holders gives small systematic errors in the cell edges (but not cell angles) thereby affecting coefficients of thermal expansion.

When very little sample is available, the Guinier and diffractometer techniques may be unsuitable. The Debye-Scherrer technique allows use of very tiny samples. A useful trick for a single grain or a tiny amount of powder is to add a drop of solution containing rubber cement. The specimen is either ground in a small mortar or crushed during rolling between two glass slides. The rubber forms a small ball with the feldspar powder randomly oriented.

Particularly valuable for single crystals is the Gandolfi modification of the Debye-Scherrer technique in which the single crystal is rotated and oscillated over a large angular range to simulate a powder. The crystal may be as small as 0.05 mm, and very sharp lines can be obtained. Note that only half the pattern is produced for non-orthogonal crystals, and that it is necessary to remount the crystal at $180°$ half-way through the exposure to obtain all the lines.

X-ray powder patterns can be calculated from the cell dimensions and atomic positional coordinates using complex formulae which take into account the experimental parameters. Borg and D. K. Smith (1968, 1969a, b) published simulated patterns for feldspars based on the best extant structure determinations. Probably the intensities of most of these simulated patterns are accurate to about 10% on average: the absolute error tends to be the same no matter what the intensity, and the proportional error becomes more severe as the intensity falls. Ideally the intensity should be measured from a single-crystal X-ray pattern, but in practice the best calculated patterns of Borg and Smith provide a good starting point for checking the indexing of a feldspar pattern.

6.2.2 Standard Patterns of Alkali Feldspars and Celsian

Figure 6-17 shows Guinier patterns of a low microcline, a sanidine, and a microcline-low albite perthite kindly provided by K. Viswanathan. Figure 6-18 compares a diffractometer pattern of a low microcline with a pattern calculated by Borg and Smith (1969a). When account is taken of preferred orientation and of noise in the experimental pattern, the calculated pattern fits very well

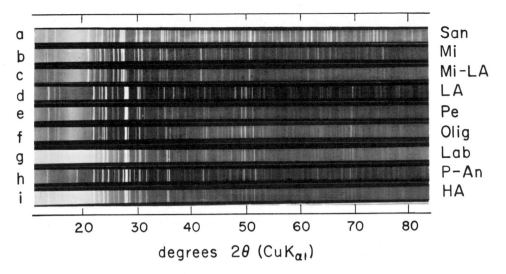

Fig. 6-17. Guinier powder patterns of feldspars. a Sanidine; Laacher See, W. Germany; b micro-cline; actually a K-exchanged albite from Dorfgastein, Austria; c microcline - low albite perthite; Ticino, Switzerland; d low albite; Graubünden, Switzerland; e peristerite; $An_{12.5}$, Verona, Ontario, Canada; f oligoclase; An_{25}, Kragerö, Norway; g labradorite; An_{50}, Madagascar; h anorthite; An_{95}, Monzoni, Italy; i high albite; synthetic. $CuK\alpha_1$ radiation. The weak line at 21.4° 2θ in all samples belongs to Apiezone T grease used for mounting. Other impurity lines are 23.0(a), 23.7(b), 14.5(f), 8.8(g) and 9.5(i). (From K. Viswanathan, pers. comm.)

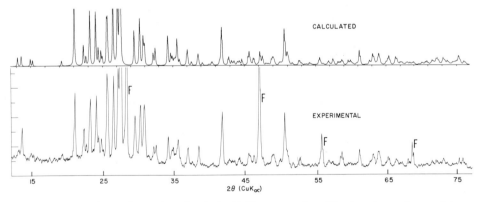

Fig. 6-18. Comparison of actual and calculated X-ray powder diffractometer patterns of low microcline. F denotes lines from fluorite intermixed for calibration. (From Borg and Smith, 1969a, Fig. 1)

with the observed diffractometer pattern. The Guinier pattern of the low micro-cline has rather sharper lines than the diffractometer pattern, but otherwise fits rather closely. Figure 6-19 compares simulated diffractometer patterns for a low microcline, an intermediate microcline, a low sanidine (orthoclase), a high sani-dine and a celsian (Borg and Smith, 1969a, b). Borg and Smith also showed real diffractometer patterns obtained by D. B. Stewart, all of which compare very well with the calculated equivalents. Other diffractometer patterns were

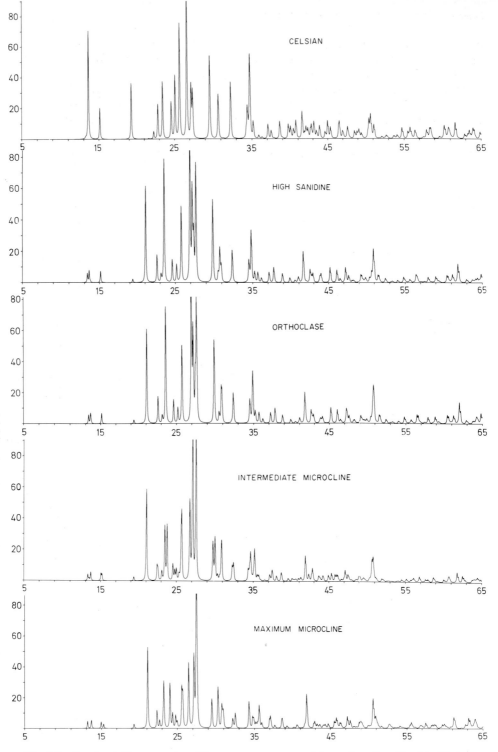

Fig. 6-19. Simulated X-ray powder diffractometer patterns of low microcline (Pontiskalk), intermediate microcline (Spencer U), low sanidine (Spencer C orthoclase), high sanidine (heated Spencer C), and celsian. See Chapter 2 for data on the crystal structure of these feldspars. (From Borg and D. K. Smith, 1969 a, b)

given by MacKenzie (1954). Plas, van der (1966, Figs. 54 and 55) gave Guinier patterns of microcline and both unheated and heated perthites. Other patterns are illustrated in many papers too numerous to list here.

Table 6-1 contains calculated spacings and intensities for low microcline, low sanidine and celsian taken from Borg and Smith (1969b). Each set of data lists the *hkl* indices, the integrated intensity and the spacing for all diffractions up

Table 6-1. Calculated X-ray powder diffractometer patterns of K- and Ba-feldspars. (Borg and D. K. Smith, 1969b)

Low microcline

Peak 2θ	d nm	hkl	I int	I peak
13.14	.6736	1 10	6	5
13.66	.6506	-1 10	1	5
	.6494	0 01	3	
	.6477	0 20	4	
14.96	.5923	-1 11	6	4
15.28	.5800	-1 11	4	3
19.28	.4603	0 21	4	3
21.08	.4213	-2 01	76	53
22.30	.3984	1 11	17	12
22.64	.3924	1-11	8	6
23.20	.3831	1 30	44	31
24.02	.3704	-1 30	46	30
24.36	.3652	-1-31	15	11
24.76	.3595	-2-21	13	9
24.94	.3566	1-31	6	5
25.56	.3484	-1-12	40	29
	.3471	-2 21	2	
25.68*	.3466	-1 12	29	26
26.44	.3368	2 20	67	43
27.12	.3286	-2 02	73	49
27.46	.3253	-2 20	61	100
	.3247	0 02	100	
	.3238	0 40	4	
29.44	.3033	1 31	33	20
30.22	.2691	-2-22	6	27
	.2954	1-31	42	
30.74	.2912	0 22	8	17
	.2907	0 41	19	
	.2900	-2 22	3	
30.92	.2889	0-41	13	13
32.16	.2782	-1-32	11	7
32.48	.2758	-3 11	1	10
	.2755	-1 32	16	
34.24	.2616	-3-12	9	18
	.2616	-3-12	21	
	.2614	2 21	1	
34.72	.2581	-3 12	13	8
34.86*	.2570	1 12	8	7
35.14	.2553	2-21	3	4
	.2551	1-12	3	
35.36	.2536	3 10	5	4
35.58	.2528	2 40	2	15
	.2521	-2 41	26	
35.92	.2499	-3 10	6	4
36.94	.2432	-1-51	7	6
	.2431	-2 40	3	
37.06*	.2423	-3-31	11	8
37.62	.2389	-1 51	4	2
38.60	.2334	-3 31	6	7

Low microcline (cont.)

Peak 2θ	d nm	hkl	I int	I peak
	.2333	-1-13	4	
	.2330	-1 13	6	
39.20	.2296	-3-32	3	2
40.12	.2247	-2-23	1	1
	.2245	3 30	1	
40.52	.2226	-3 32	2	2
	.2224	1 51	2	
	.2224	-2 23	1	
41.80	.2165	0 03	1	22
	.2160	2 41	12	
	.2159	0 60	31	
42.76	.2113	-4 01	5	3
42.88*	.2106	-4 02	6	5
43.20	.2092	2-41	5	3
43.58	.2079	3 11	2	3
	.2076	2 02	3	
	.2074	-1 33	1	
44.06	.2057	3-11	2	2
	.2053	0 61	3	
44.28	.2044	0-61	5	
44.70	.2026	-4-22	6	3
45.50	.19920	2 22	9	5
45.76	.19810	-4 22	13	7
45.88*	.19742	-3-33	3	5
46.24	.19619	2-22	7	4
46.36*	.19562	-3-51	3	4
47.18	.19246	4 00	16	8
47.58	.19110	3 31	1	5
	.19096	-4 03	9	
48.04	.18922	2 61	2	1
48.18*	.18862	-3-52	1	1
48.40	.18790	-3 51	1	1
48.78	.18660	1 13	4	
	.18651	4 20	1	
48.92*	.18602	3 50	3	5
	.18596	3-31	1	
49.00*	.18576	1 52	2	5
	.18573	1-13	4	
49.14*	.18520	-2 60	3	4
49.26*	.18480	-4-23	1	2
49.92	.18261	-2-62	2	2
	.18253	-4 20	2	
50.04	.18216	1-52	2	
50.20*	.18158	-4 23	1	2
	.18156	1 70	1	
50.56	.18060	0 43	5	20
	.18042	0 62	5	
	.18037	-4-41	4	
	.18034	-2 04	29	

Low sanidine

Peak 2θ	d nm	hkl	I int	I peak
13.38	.6621	110	5	6
13.62	.6498	020	5	7
	.6464	001	2	
15.12	.5861	-111	6	7
19.36	.4583	021	2	2
21.06	.4217	-201	57	61
22.54	.3941	111	17	18
23.10	.3847	200	5	6
23.56	.3775	130	74	75
24.60	.3616	-131	15	16
25.16	.3537	-221	10	11
25.70	.3465	-112	52	51
26.92	.3310	220	100	100
27.14	.3283	-202	59	66
27.44	.3249	040	29	40
27.58	.3232	002	78	82
29.84	.2991	131	59	54
30.48	.2930	-222	7	8
30.78	.2903	041	25	25
30.86*	.2894	022	10	24
32.34	.2767	-132	22	20
34.46	.2600	-312	18	16
34.84	.2578	221	4	34
	.2574	-241	37	
35.16	.2550	112	8	9
35.66	.2516	310	8	8
36.16	.2482	240	3	3
37.18	.2417	-151	8	7
37.74	.2381	-331	12	10
38.74	.2323	-113	7	6
39.80	.2263	-332	3	3
40.40	.2231	-223	1	1
	.2229	132	1	
40.98	.2201	151	4	4
41.66	.2166	060	25	20
42.52	.2125	241	11	9
42.72*	.2114	-401	4	5
42.84*	.2108	-402	5	6
43.84	.2068	202	5	4
	.2064	311	3	
44.06	.2054	061	5	5
45.18	.2006	-422	13	10
46.02	.19705	222	12	9
46.44	.19536	-333	3	3
47.22	.19267	-261	1	10
	.19235	400	11	
	.19207	-351	3	
47.56	.19101	-403	6	5
48.18	.18874	260	4	3
48.30*	.18825	331	2	3
49.12	.18533	113	7	6
49.36	.18444	420	2	3
49.54*	.18383	152	2	3
49.70*	.18326	-423	1	2
49.92*	.18256	350	3	3
50.44	.18080	-262	4	5
50.74	.17993	062	9	25
	.17976	-204	23	
	.17956	043	10	
51.52	.17722	-441	7	6
51.64	.17687	-442	3	5
52.40	.17445	242	4	3
52.98	.17271	-114	1	1

Celsian

Peak 2θ	d nm	hkl	I int	I peak
13.24	.6698	110	1	2
13.58	.6522	020	39	71
	.6517	002	20	
15.10	.5864	-112	17	20
19.24	.4610	022	32	36
22.22	.3997	112	5	5
22.78	.3902	200	21	23
23.40	.3799	130	35	37
24.54	.3625	-132	23	24
25.04	.3553	-222	40	42
25.64	.3472	-114	74	76
26.60	.3349	220	100	100
27.16	.3282	-204	35	37
27.34	.3259	004	30	33
29.56	.3021	132	58	54
30.64	.2916	042	29	29
	.2915	024	3	
32.24	.2774	-134	41	37
34.38	.2606	-314	21	22
34.70	.2584	-242	43	55
	.2582	114	22	
35.14	.2551	310	12	12
35.86	.2502	240	3	3
36.28	.2474	150	1	1
37.04	.2425	-152	11	10
37.48	.2398	-332	6	6
38.02	.2377	-206	1	1
38.58	.2332	-116	14	12
38.88	.2313	-244	1	1
39.70	.2118	-404	1	10
39.98	.2253	134	9	8
40.36	.2233	-226	3	7
	.2233	330	3	
40.68	.2216	152	14	12
41.50	.2174	060	21	18
	.2172	006	1	
41.82	.2158	-316	4	5
42.02	.2148	242	9	8
42.28	.2136	-402	8	8
42.64	.2118	-404	7	7
42.76*	.2113	-154	7	10
43.10	.2100	204	3	12
	.2097	312	12	
43.46	.2081	-136	6	6
43.86	.2062	062	8	9
44.60	.2030	-422	3	5
44.96	.2015	-245	15	12
45.34	.19986	224	9	8
46.50*	.19546	-336	9	12
	.19512	400	10	
46.94	.19344	-262	6	5
	.19319	-352	2	
47.28	.19207	-246	1	1
47.60	.19121	-406	3	8
	.19089	332	9	
48.52	.18751	116	7	5
48.86	.18624	-354	5	5
49.10	.18538	154	7	6
49.44	.18422	350	4	4
50.42	.18086	064	4	14
	.18080	046	11	
50.64	.18009	-208	19	16

Notes: 2θ for CuKα₁ radiation

*denotes strong contribution from α₂ of preceding peak.

Rows without a peak intensity contribute to first peak with higher d.

Calculated for half-width of 0.11° 2θ

Intensity cut-off at 1.

to the $\bar{2}04$ diffraction, which is the last strong diffraction that is readily recognizable. In addition, the 2θ angle and intensity are given for the peaks on a simulated diffractometer pattern with CuK_α radiation assuming a half-width of $0.11°$ at $40°$ 2θ. The intensities are normalized to 100 for the strongest peak. Diffractions weaker than 0.5 are omitted.

A preliminary indexing for all homogeneous feldspars rich in K and/or Ba can be obtained by interpolation in Table 6-1. All microclines have patterns between those of low microcline and low sanidine. The major change in the angles α and γ is easily recognized from the splitting of the diffractions 130 and 131 (see for example, MacKenzie, 1954). Substitution of Ab is usually less than 15%, showing up principally as a reduction of the a dimension: the positions of the $\bar{2}01$ and 400 diffractions indicate the degree of substitution so long as the cell dimensions are not anomalous (Chapter 7). High sanidine differs from low sanidine principally by small changes in b and c (and in a if the Ab-content is different): however, preliminary indexing can be readily obtained by comparison with the pattern for low sanidine.

Alkali feldspars rich in sodium have diffraction patterns which are intermediate between those of K-feldspar and the extremes of high and low albite whose data are given in the next section. The variation of cell dimensions with composition is non-linear, especially for the cell angles (Chapter 7) but indexing of any particular pattern can be accomplished by visual comparison with standard patterns to permit identification of certain lines (such as $\bar{2}01$ and $\bar{2}04$), followed by detailed calculations to identify the other lines. An automatic indexing program on a computer is helpful.

The major problem involves perthites as mentioned earlier. Fortunately the $\bar{2}01$ peaks of K- and Na-feldspars are resolved from all other lines permitting an easy test of the presence of a perthitic intergrowth. However, great care must be taken not to overlook a weak peak. In microcline perthites, the strong peak of low albite near $d = 0.319$ nm is usually recognizable. For a diffractometer it is advisable to step-scan the appropriate angular region to obtain high sensitivity. The $\bar{2}01$ peak for K-feldspar may actually result from a low sanidine plus a microcline. If the entire pattern can be explained by the addition of sharp peaks for two feldspars (e.g. low microcline plus albite), the powder identification is usually satisfactory though a third minor phase may be overlooked. If difficulty is experienced in identifying all the peaks, a single-crystal X-ray pattern should be obtained. If the peaks of the powder pattern are broad, single-crystal X-ray study is always desirable. A study of the single-crystal patterns in Section 6-1 should convince anyone of the fool-hardiness of relying on powder patterns for identification of perthites except in favorable circumstances.

6.2.3 Standard Patterns of Plagioclase and Reedmergnerite

Figure 6-17 shows Guinier patterns of a low albite, a peristerite $An_{12.5}$, an oligoclase An_{25}, a labradorite An_{50}, an anorthite An_{95} and a high albite. These patterns were kindly provided by K. Viswanathan.

Figure 6-20 shows simulated powder diffractometer patterns with CuK_α for low albite, high albite, anorthite and reedmergnerite taken from Borg and

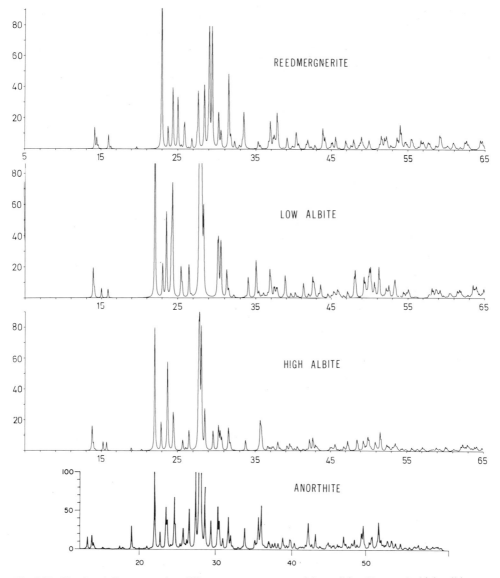

Fig. 6-20. Simulated X-ray powder diffractometer patterns of low albite (Ramona), high albite (heated Amelia), anorthite (Vesuvius) and reedmergnerite. See Chapter 3 for data on the crystal structure of these feldspars. (From Borg and D. K. Smith, 1968, 1969 b)

Smith (1969b). These are based on crystal structure analyses given in Chapter 3. Borg and Smith (1968) found excellent agreement between their simulated patterns and actual patterns of plagioclases taken by W. Parrish and D. B. Stewart. Figure 1 of Borg and Smith (1968) compares simulated and actual patterns of low albite taken with CrK_α. The increased resolution for the complex of peaks near 0.319 nm is noticeable, but even with chromium radiation the resolution in

Table 6-2. Calculated X-ray powder diffractometer patterns of plagioclase and reedmergnerite. (Borg and D. K. Smith, 1969b)

Low albite

Peak 2θ	d (nm)	h k l	I int	I peak
13.88	.6387	0 01	7	10
	.6376	0 20	7	
14.04	.6343	-1 10	3	4
14.98	.6299	1 10	3	3
	.5912	-1 11	4	
15.88	.5581	-1 11	93	
22.06	.5427	2 01	67	
23.06	.3854	-2 01	15	11
23.54	.3777	-1 11	39	28
24.32	.3668	-1 31	16	37
25.40	.3558	-1 30	41	10
25.54*	.3505	-1 12	15	
26.42	.3483	-2 11	12	11
26.74	.3370	-1 12	16	
	.3332	-2 21	1	
27.74	.3214	-1 02	72	55
27.96	.3194	0 02	100	100
28.32	.3188	0 40	66	
30.12	.3150	-2 20	39	30
	.2965	1-31	25	19
30.20*	.2956	-2 22	16	20
30.50	.2931	0-41	12	19
31.24	.2928	-1 31	18	
31.46	.2840	-2 21	15	9
32.14	.2782	0 41	1	1
33.62	.2664	-3 11	11	1
33.98	.2637	-2 41	11	7
35.00	.2562	-2 41	21	12
35.34	.2537	-3 12	3	2
35.72	.2512	1-21	1	1
35.96	.2496	2 40	3	2
36.20	.2479	-3 12	1	1
36.52	.2459	2 21	1	2
36.78	.2442	-2 41	9	9
36.86*	.2431	-1 51	6	7
37.32	.2408	-1 32	5	4
37.42*	.2401	-1 50	4	4
37.64	.2388	-2 40	4	3
	.2387	3 10	2	

High albite

Peak 2θ	d (nm)	h k l	I int	I peak
13.76	.6445	-1 10	9	16
	.6425	0 20	10	
13.92	.6356	0 01	4	6
14.14	.6255	1 10	6	6
15.22	.5822	-1-11	6	
15.68	.5648	-1 11	6	6
18.96	.4681	0-21	2	2
20.30	.4372	0 21	1	1
22.04	.4032	-2 01	100	100
22.88	.3884	2 01	23	80
23.70	.3752	-1 30	45	58
	.3749	1 11	30	
24.44	.3639	1 30	30	25
25.64	.3472	-1-12	9	7
26.02	.3422	-2-21	2	2
26.44	.3368	-1 02	17	17
27.76	.3212	0 40	68	85
27.82*	.3203	-2 02	83	100
28.06*	.3178	0 02	81	81
28.52	.3127	2 20	35	28
29.60	.3016	1-31	18	13
30.28	.2949	0-41	16	17
30.50	.2929	0-22	16	16
30.68	.2911	-2-22	10	9
31.54	.2835	1 31	21	15
31.76	.2815	-1-32	6	6
33.72	.2656	-1 32	4	7
35.64	.2518	-2-41	24	20
	.2516	-3-12	3	
	.2515	1-12	3	
36.60	.2455	2 40	3	3
36.88	.2435	2 21	3	3
37.16	.2417	-1-51	3	3
37.32	.2407	-3 10	3	
37.92	.2376	3 10	9	6
38.20	.2371	2 40	7	
38.80	.2354	-1 51	2	2
	.2319	-1-13	1	1
39.12	.2300	-3 31	5	3

P-anorthite

Peak 2θ	d (nm)	h k l	I int	I peak
6.94	1.2718	0 01	c 1	1
9.42	.9379	0-11	b 1	1
13.00	.6807	-1-11	c 9	9
13.58	.6522	1-11	c 1	10
13.78	.6420	0 20	4	5
15.00	.5904	0-21	c 1	1
	.5896	0 21	c 1	
15.90	.5573	0 21	c 3	1
17.32	.5118	-1-11	b 2	3
17.72	.5002	-1-21	b 2	2
18.92	.4690	0-22	17	16
19.30	.4594	-1-22	d 1	1
19.94	.4448	-1 22	c 1	1
20.56	.4316	-1-13	c 1	1
20.72	.4286	-1 21	b 1	1
20.94	.4439	0 03	c 2	2
22.00	.4039	-2 02	58	52
22.70	.3916	-1-12	13	12
23.04	.3859	-1-23	b 1	1
23.50	.3783	-1 30	30	29
23.66*	.3756	1 12	17	21
24.10	.3690	-1-23	b 1	3
24.30	.3689	-2 03	c 2	
24.58	.3620	0-23	c 1	
25.18	.3535	-2 13	b 1	
25.36	.3510	-1 32	c 1	
25.92	.3434	-2 22	c 1	
	.3426	0 23	c 1	
26.16	.3403	-2-22	6	7
26.56	.3362	-1 14	31	26
27.32	.3261	-1-31	64	53
	.3253	1 31	c 1	
27.78	.3215	-2-23	58	58
27.92*	.3210	0 40	53	100
28.04**	.3194	-2 04	93	100
28.58	.3180	0-04	49	41
29.34	.3042	1-32	23	19

P-anorthite (cont.)

Peak 2θ	d (nm)	h k l	I int	I peak
38.96	.2322	-3-15	c 1	
39.22	.2309	0 25	c 1	3
	.2297	-2-44	c 1	
39.50	.2295	-1-53	c 3	3
	.2280	-3 31	c 1	2
39.68	.2270	-3-32	c 1	
39.78*	.2269	-3 32	c 1	6
	.2264	-1 16	c 1	5
40.24	.2260	-1-34	c 3	7
	.2239	1-52	c 1	4
40.36*	.2233	-2 44	3	5
41.00	.2202	-3-31	c 1	2
	.2199	-2-41	c 1	
41.18	.2192	0-24	c 1	2
	.2190	-3 34	c 1	
41.32	.2182	-1-12	1	2
41.50	.2174	-3 30	c 1	4
41.82	.2158	-1-22	b 1	
42.14	.2143	-2-42	19	16
	.2140	0 60	c 1	10
42.66	.2118	-2-45	c 3	4
	.2116	-1-34	b 1	
43.14	.2095	1 52	14	10
43.24*	.2091	-3 16	c 1	7
43.76	.2067	0-45	c 3	3
43.88*	.2061	-1-53	b 1	2
44.22	.2047	-3 35	c 1	1
44.72	.2025	-1-54	c 3	3
44.92	.2019	-4 04	c 3	5
45.18	.2016	-4 02	c 1	3
45.46	.2005	-1 14	c 1	
45.60*	.1991	-1 36	c 1	3
	.1985	0 26	c 1	4
46.10	.1971	0 26	c 1	4
46.34	.1968	1-35	c 1	
	.1966	0-63	c 1	
46.44*	.1957	3 12	c 1	3
	.1953	-2-27	c 1	

Reedmergnerite

Peak 2θ	d (nm)	h k l	I int	I peak
14.12	.6275	-1 10	12	14
14.38	.6155	0 20	16	8
14.58	.6076	0 01	8	3
15.96	.5550	-1-11	1	9
16.26	.5449	1-11	1	2
19.66	.4513	-1 21	1	1
22.94	.3874	0-21	100	100
23.74	.3745	-1-11	14	15
24.36	.3651	1 30	35	34
25.00	.3550	-1 11	11	
25.42	.3501	2 00	2	3
25.88	.3449	-1-31	12	17
26.38	.3377	-1 31	10	1
26.80	.3324	-1-12	7	7
27.64	.3225	-1 12	39	38
28.42	.3137	-2 20	45	41
29.04	.3078	0 40	41	79
29.38	.3038	0 02	53	79
30.20	.2957	2 20	25	24
30.48	.2930	-1 31	21	12
31.46	.2841	0-41	55	48
31.72	.2818	-1 31	58	10
32.24	.2775	-2-22	6	5
32.84	.2725	-2 22	3	3
33.24	.2695	-1 32	5	5
33.64	.2680	-1-11	27	24
35.26	.2544	-1 32	6	5
35.52	.2526	-3-11	3	3
36.84	.2452	2 21	25	18
36.84	.2438	-1-12	21	18
37.20*	.2406	-3 12	8	7
37.52*	.2394	-2 40	9	6
37.72	.2383	-2-41	28	23
37.82	.2374	-1 50	4	17
38.52	.2335	-1 12	1	1
39.06	.2307	2 21	3	3
	.2304	-1-51	7	7

See Table 6-1 for notes.

For anorthite, the subsidiary diffractions are marked with b,c or d under I (int).

the diffractometer pattern is not as good as that in the Guinier pattern of Fig. 6-17d which shows four definite peaks.

Table 6-2 contains calculated spacings and intensities for low albite, high albite, anorthite and reedmergnerite taken from Borg and Smith (1969b). See Table 6-1 for comments.

Bambauer, Corlett, Eberhard, and Viswanathan (1967) and Bambauer, Eberhard and Viswanathan (1967) gave diffractometer patterns of five plagioclases plus a chart for indexing low plagioclases. In general the chart agrees well with the calculations of Borg and D. K. Smith, but there are a few minor differences. These data replace those of earlier workers which are now obsolete (Claisse, 1950; Goodyear and Duffin, 1954, 1955; Smith, J. V., 1956; Smith, J. V. and Gay, 1958; Smith, J. R. and Yoder, 1956).

To a first approximation, the powder pattern of any plagioclase can be obtained by appropriate interpolation between the patterns for low albite and anorthite using γ^* to determine the degree of interpolation. Consequently the data in Table 6-2 are sufficient to allow a preliminary indexing. Of course, final indexing should be based on an accurate adjustment of the cell dimensions, together with consideration of the expected intensity of each diffraction.

All subsidiary diffractions of plagioclase are too weak to detect by normal powder methods except for the relatively strong b and c diffractions in almost pure anorthite. The most intense b and c diffractions are shown in Table 6-2. Because of overlap of diffractions, it is difficult to obtain reliable identification of b and c diffractions for spacings below 0.25 nm. Bruno and Gazzoni (1967) identified the $\bar{1}\bar{1}1$ and $1\bar{1}1$ diffractions in Guinier patterns of anorthite. Stewart (1967) observed the $\bar{1}11$, $11\bar{1}$, $0\bar{2}1$, 021, $1\bar{1}1$, $\bar{1}\bar{2}1$, 003, $\bar{2}05$ and $1\bar{3}3$ peaks in diffractometer patterns, but the $2\bar{2}1$ and $\bar{3}\bar{2}1$ diffractions reported by him may actually be confused with α_2 lines from type a diffractions. Of the observed subsidiary diffractions, all are of type c except for $\bar{1}\bar{2}1$ at 0.500 nm, which is at the limit of detection. Stewart (1967) gave a detailed indexing of an anorthite pattern which agrees mostly with that calculated by Borg and D. K. Smith.

There are no reports of doubled lines for plagioclases with the Bøggild and Huttenlocher intergrowths, but they might occur in coarser specimens of the latter type. The situation for peristerite is highly confused. Although it seems certain that peristerite consists of an intergrowth of albite and oligoclase, it is not clear how the powder pattern varies with the structural coherence and coarseness of the intergrowth. Figure 6-17e for a peristerite, $An_{12.5}$, shows only one set of powder lines lying between those for low albite and oligoclase (Figs. 6-17d, f). Although single-crystal X-ray patterns show more than one set of spots, the powder pattern can be interpreted with just one set of cell dimensions (Viswanathan, pers. comm.). Viswanathan and Eberhard (1968) interpreted X-ray patterns of peristerites with bulk composition from 8 – 16% An in terms of three components, but the possibility of a superstructure must be considered. Until this problem is clarified, great caution should be used with powder patterns of low sodic plagioclases from An_0 to An_{20}.

Chemical zoning causes broadening of lines if the zoning is continuous, but may give doubled lines if the zoning is discontinuous. For example, I found doubled lines corresponding to andesine and bytownite in a plagioclase from the S. California batholith. Fortunately I had noted discontinuous zoning during optical study, and did not claim incorrectly that the plagioclase was the product of exsolution! Reedmergnerite poses no problems because it has little compositional and structural variation.

References

Azaroff, L. V. (1968): Elements of X-ray crystallography. New York: McGraw Hill.

Bambauer, H. U., Eberhard, E., Viswanathan, K. (1967): The lattice constants and related parameters of "plagioclases (low)". (Part IV of laboratory investigations on plagioclases.) SMPM **47**, 351–364.

Bambauer, H. U., Corlett, M., Eberhard, E., Viswanathan, K. (1967): Diagrams for the determination of plagioclases using X-ray powder methods. (Part III of laboratory investigations on plagioclases.) SMPM **47**, 333–350.

Bhatty, M. S. Y., Gard, J. A., Glasser, F. P. (1970): Crystallization of anorthite from $CaO–Al_2O_3–SiO_2$ glasses. MM **37**, 780–789.

Borg, I. Y., Smith, D. K. (1968): Calculated powder patterns: I. Five plagioclases. AM **53**, 1709 – 1723.

Borg, I. Y., Smith, D. K. (1969a): Calculated powder patterns. Part II. Six potassium feldspars and barium feldspar. AM **54**, 163–181.

Borg, I. Y., Smith, D. K. (1969b): Calculated X-ray powder patterns for silicate minerals. Geol. Soc. America, memoir 122.

Bown, M. G., Gay, P. (1958): The reciprocal lattice geometry of the plagioclase feldspar structures: ZK **111**, 1–14.

Bown, M. G., Gay, P. (1959): The identification of oriented inclusions in pyroxene crystals. AM **44**, 592–602.

Bruno, E., Gazzoni, G. (1967): Ricerche roentgenografiche su plagioclasi bytownitico-anortitici tra 15° C e 1300° C. PM **36**, 683–698.

Claisse, F. (1950): A roentgenographic method for determining plagioclases. AM **35**, 412–420.

Emeleus, C. H., Smith, J. V. (1959): The alkali feldspars, VI. Sanidine and orthoclase perthites from the Slieve Gullion Area, N. Ireland. AM **44**, 1187–1209. — Errata **48**, 208 (1963).

Foit, F. F., Peacor, D. R. (1967): High temperature diffraction data on selected reflections of an andesine and anorthite. ZK **125**, 1–6.

Goodyear, J., Duffin, W. J. (1954): The identification and determination of plagioclase feldspars by the X-ray powder method. MM **30**, 306–326.

Goodyear, J., Duffin, W. J. (1955): The determination of composition and thermal history of plagioclase by the X-ray powder method. MM **30**, 648–656.

Henry, N. F. M., Lipson, H., Wooster, W. A. (1960): The interpretation of X-ray diffraction photographs, second Ed. London: Macmillan.

Korekawa, M., Jagodzinski, H. (1967): Die Satellitenreflexe des Labradorits. SMPM **47**, 269–278.

Korekawa, M., Nissen, H.-U., Philipp, D. (1970): X-ray and electron-microscopic studies of a sodium-rich low plagioclase. ZK **131**, 418–436.

Laves, F. (1950): The lattice and twinning of microcline and other potash feldspars. JG **58**, 548–571.

Laves, F. (1952): Phase relations of the alkali feldspars. I. Introductory remarks. II. The stable and pseudo-stable phase relations in the alkali feldspar system. JG **60**, 436–450 and 549–574.

Laves, F., Chaisson, U. (1950): An X-ray investigation of the "high"-"low" albite relations. JG **58**, 584–592.

Laves, F., Goldsmith, J. R. (1954): Long-range-short-range order in calcic plagioclases as a continuous and reversible function of temperature. AC **7**, 465–472.

Laves, F., Goldsmith, J. R. (1961): Polymorphism, order, disorder, diffusion and confusion in the feldspars. CCILM **8**, 71–80.

Laves, F., Sáenz, I. M. de (1973): On the determination of submicroscopical twin orientations with Buerger's precession method, demonstrated by the rhombic section in K feldspars. ZK **138**, 449 – 456.

Laves, F., Soldatos, K. (1962): Über „verzerrte" Mikroklin-Verzwillingung und über unsymmetrische Albitausscheidung in Kryptoperthit. ZK **117**, 209–217.

Laves, F., Soldatos, K. (1963): Die Albit/Mikroklin-Orientierungs-Beziehungen in Mikroklinperthiten und deren genetische Deutung. ZK **118**, 69–102.

MacKenzie, W. S. (1954): The orthoclase-microcline inversion. MM **30**, 354–366.

MacKenzie, W. S., Smith, J. V. (1955): The alkali feldspars: I. Orthoclase microperthites. AM **40**, 707–732.

MacKenzie, W. S., Smith, J. V. (1962): Single crystal X-ray studies of crypto- and micro-perthites. NGT **42**, No. 2, 72–103.

Mallard, F. (1876): Explications des phénomènes optiques anomaux qui présentent un grand nombre de substances cristallisées. Annales des mines **10**, 187–240. Alternatively, see ZK **1**, 201–237 (1877).

Müller, W. F., Wenk, H. R., Thomas, G. (1972): Structural variations in anorthites. CMP **34**, 304–314.

Nuffied, E. W. (1966): X-ray diffraction methods. New York: John Wiley.

Plas, L. van der (1966): The identification of detrital feldspars, 305 pp. Amsterdam: Elsevier.

Smith, J. R., Yoder, H. S. (1956): Variations in X-ray powder diffraction patterns of plagioclase feldspars. AM **41**, 632–647.

Smith, J. V. (1956): The powder patterns and lattice parameters of plagioclase felspars. I. The soda-rich plagioclases. MM **31**, 47–68.

Smith, J. V. (1970): Physical properties of order-disorder structures with especial reference to feldspar minerals. Lithos **3**, 145–160.

Smith, J. V., Gay, P. (1958): The powder patterns and lattice parameters of plagioclase felspars. II. MM **31**, 744–762.

Smith, J. V., MacKenzie, W. S. (1955): The alkali feldspars: II, A simple X-ray technique for the study of alkali feldspars. AM **40**, 733–747.

Smith, J. V., MacKenzie, W. S. (1958): The alkali feldspars. IV. The cooling history of high-temperature sodium-rich feldspars. AM **43**, 872–889.

Smith, J. V., MacKenzie, W. S. (1959): The alkali feldspars. V. The nature of orthoclase and microcline perthites, and observations concerning the polymorphism of potassium feldspar. AM **44**, 1169–1186.

Smith, J. V., Ribbe, P. H. (1969): Atomic movements in plagioclase feldspars: kinetic interpretation. CMP **21**, 157–202.

Soldatos, K. (1962): Über die kryptoperthitische Albit-Ausscheidung in Mikroklinperthiten. NGT **42**, No. 2, 180–192.

Stewart, D. B. (1967): Four phase curve in the system $CaAl_2Si_2O_8$–SiO_2–H_2O between 1 and 10 kilobars. SMPM **47**, 35–59.

Viswanathan, K., Eberhard, E. (1968): The peristerite problem. SMPM **48**, 803–814.

Weisz, O., Cochran, W., Cole, W. F. (1948): The accurate determination of cell dimensions from single-crystal X-ray photographs. AC **1**, 83–88.

Chapter 7 Cell Dimensions
and Macroscopic Thermal Expansion

7.1 General

Cell dimensions of feldspars are affected principally by the bulk chemical composition and the distribution of T and M atoms among the lattice sites.

The chemical composition of synthetic feldspars can be controlled accurately, and attainment of the highest possible accuracy in measurement of cell dimensions is desirable for delineating structural details. The chemical composition of natural feldspars commonly involves several oxides at the 0.n wt.% level as well as the principal oxides. Such minor substituents cause changes in the cell dimensions of the order of 1 part per thousand such that interpretation of cell dimensions of natural feldspars in terms of just the principal constituents Or, Ab and An is limited unless corrections are made.

The distribution of T atoms affects the cell dimensions sufficiently to permit estimation of occupancy factors for the various sites: however, the effect of domain texture is imprecisely known.

Most of the data in this chapter result from powder X-ray methods with standard errors of about 1 in 4000 for cell edges and $0.02°$ for cell angles. A few data result from single-crystal X-ray methods with standard errors as large as 1 in 200 for some film techniques and as low as 1 in 50000 for the special theta-method: see Chapter 6.

The chapter begins with a compilation of data for the numerous end-member compositions that have been synthesized, plus an interpretation in terms of substitution by ions of different size (Section 7.2).

Sections 7.3 and 7.4 consider the data for synthetic and natural alkali and plagioclase feldspars. Most of these specimens tend towards a binary solid-solution series. Section 7.5 considers synthetic K-exchanged plagioclase plus natural ternary feldspars. Section 7.6 deals with K, Ba feldspars while Section 7.7 covers other synthetic binary feldspars.

Each of the sections is primarily concerned with measurements at room temperature, but the relatively sparse data on temperature variation of cell dimensions are thoroughly analyzed in relation to macroscopic data on thermal expansion derived from dilatometry and optical goniometry. The macroscopic data were reviewed by Saucier and Saplevitch (1962).

Cell dimensions can be given either for the direct or the reciprocal cell. The former are desirable for interpretation in terms of atomic substitution, while the latter are more useful for experimental work since diffraction angles are simply related to the reciprocal lattice elements but not to those of the direct lattice. The literature contains both direct and reciprocal elements, and I have taken whatever was most appropriate.

Published figures for cell dimensions have been plotted in several different orientations. I have deliberately decided to plot cell dimensions on diagrams that fit as closely as possible to conventional phase diagrams. For example, the bc plot for alkali feldspars has been reoriented so that low albite is near the bottom left and high sanidine near the top right, thereby mimicking the temperature-composition section. Several drawings from the literature have been copied in their original orientation to avoid tedious redrafting.

In alkali feldspars, the difference between *high* and *low* structural states is known to result principally from Si, Al order-disorder, but the situation in plagioclase is obscure. However, even when the structural details are unknown, it is possible to characterize the structural state from the physical properties. Thus the structural state of a plagioclase can be estimated from the lattice angle γ when the An content is known. It is customary to measure the structural state by some indicator using a linear variation between the smallest and largest observed values of that property. Thus Goldsmith and Laves (1954b) characterized triclinic K-feldspars from the splitting of hkl and h$\bar{k}$l peaks in an X-ray powder pattern using an index of unity for maximum microcline and zero for monoclinic K-feldspars. For precision, I shall always specify data on the structural state by the actual physical measurement since there is not necessarily a one-to-one relation between different indicators. A specific term such as 131 *triclinic indicator* is used rather than the general term *triclinicity*. The symbol Δ is used for all indicators of structural state, normalized between 1 and 0 for the states of extreme order and disorder, respectively.

Historically, the first data on cell dimensions were derived from optical goniometry of the external morphology. Measurements of five or more interfacial angles yield the axial ratios $a:b:c$ and the inter-axial angles α, β and γ. I have checked many of these data against recent X-ray data for the cell edges and angles. The quality of the optical data is highly variable. Most feldspar crystals have non-planar faces as the result of lack of equilibrium during growth and because of later inversion or deformation. The morphological crystallographers selected the faces with the sharpest optical signals, but this apparently did not guarantee correct data. A further problem was simple arithmetic error during the tedious hand calculations. In general, it appears that some data are in error by up to $0.4°$ in the interaxial angles and up to 1 in 200 in axial ratios while other data are remarkably consistent with X-ray estimates. Indeed for anorthite crystals from Vesuvius, it is possible that the optical estimates of Beckenkamp (1881) and Schnaase (1936) are more accurate than present X-ray data.

The optical goniometric data for K-rich feldspars have no permanent value, but the following papers appear to have the best data (Beckenkamp, 1881; Kokscharow, 1884; Strüver, 1877). Selected data for plagioclase feldspars are listed in Table 7-9, and plotted in several figures. Other data on the optical morphology may be found in Goldschmidt (1916), Schmidt (1915), Dana (1920) and Hintze (1897).

7.2 End-member Feldspars

Chapter 14 describes the chemical range of end-member feldspars. Table 7-1 lists the cell dimensions of those end-members for which accurate cell dimensions were available in 1972. Deliberate synthesis of end-members was begun by

Table 7-1. Cell dimensions of end-member feldspars

Formula	Type	Source	a	b	c	α	β	γ	V
				nanometer			degrees		nm³
$BaAl_2Si_2O_8$	Cn	1(13)	.8640(2)	1.3046(2)	1.4404(3)	90	115.11(2)	90	1.470
$PbAl_2Si_2O_8$	D-Cn	19(2,16)	.8412(3)	1.3053(3)	.7172(2)	90	115.24(4)	90	.7127
	Cn	do.	.8398(1)	1.3055(2)	1.4326(2)	90	115.24(3)	90	1.4208
$SrAl_2Si_2O_8$	Cn	3(2)	.8389(2)	1.2972(2)	1.4262(3)	90	115.43(1)	90	1.404
$CaAl_2Si_2O_8$	H-An	4(3,15)	.8183(1)	1.2873(2)	1.4173(2)	93.19(2)	115.79(1)	91.24(1)	1.3404(4)
	P-An	17	.8173(1)	1.2869(1)	1.4165(1)	93.116(6)	115.913(6)	91.261(6)	1.3363
$RbFeGe_3O_8$	HS	5	.91980(14)	1.37037(15)	.75597(12)	90	116.670(10)	90	.8515(3)
$RbGaGe_3O_8$	HS	5	.91989(8)	1.36277(8)	.75107(8)	90	117.147(5)	90	.83783(17)
$RbAlGe_3O_8$	HS	5	.91297(10)	1.35705(14)	.74654(10)	90	116.740(7)	90	.82600(22)
$RbGaSi_3O_8$	HS	5	.89168(8)	1.3102(6)	.72493(7)	90	116.43(4)	90	.7584(14)
$RbAlSi_3O_8$	HS	5(12)	.88386(8)	1.30338(9)	.71824(7)	90	116.293(5)	90	.74182(15)
$RbAlSi_3O_8$	LM	6	.8844(2)	1.2964(2)	.7250(2)	90.51(5)	116.14(5)	88.05(5)	.7458(5)
$KFeGe_3O_8$	HS	5	.88914(22)	1.37031(14)	.75416(21)	90	115.859(23)	90	.8269(6)
$KGaGe_3O_8$	HS	5(7)	.8872(5)	1.3631(4)	.7491(4)	90	115.99(3)	90	.8143(9)
$KAlGe_3O_8$	HS	5	.88193(14)	1.35594(12)	.74532(11)	90	115.955(10)	90	.80139(28)
$KFeSi_3O_8$	HS	8	.869	1.312	.732	90	116.10	90	.7493(20)
$KFeSi_3O_8$	LM	8	.868	1.310	.734	90.75	116.05	86.23	.7477
$KGaSi_3O_8$	HS	5	.86693(32)	1.30991(22)	.72144(27)	90	116.132(20)	90	.7355(6)
$KGaSi_3O_8$	LM	5	.86601(11)	1.30457(11)	.72735(10)	91.116(9)	116.020(8)	87.199(8)	.73757(23)
$KAlSi_3O_8$	HS	9	.8604	1.3029	.7176	90	116.03	90	.7229
$KAlSi_3O_8$	LM	9	.8590	1.2966	.72232	90.65	115.96	87.65	.7226
$KbSi_3O_8$		14							
$NH_4AlSi_3O_8 \cdot \frac{1}{2}H_2O$	HS	10,18	.8804(3)	1.3024(3)	.7183(1)	90	116.11(2)	90	.7396
$NaGaGe_3O_8$	HA	5	.84506(16)	1.33723(13)	.73708(15)	94.448(11)	116.200(10)	90.788(11)	.74403(33)
$NaAlGe_3O_8$	HA	5	.84176(24)	1.32902(20)	.73429(17)	94.350(17)	116.241(16)	90.933(17)	.73353(39)
$NaGaSi_3O_8$	HA	5	.82087(21)	1.29653(14)	.71424(9)	93.553(12)	116.330(9)	90.187(11)	.67958(25)
$NaGaSi_3O_8$	LA	5	.81661(18)	1.28565(15)	.72026(15)	94.366(11)	116.539(12)	87.181(11)	.67445(32)
$NaAlSi_3O_8$	HA	9	.8160	1.2873	.7110	93.52	116.43	90.27	.66711
$NaAlSi_3O_8$	LA	9	.8138	1.2785	.7158	94.26	116.60	87.68	.66406
$NaBSi_3O_8$	LA	11	.7833(1)	1.2360(2)	.6803(1)	93.31(1)	116.35(1)	92.05(1)	.5878(2)

CN celsian; D-Cn disordered celsian; H- and P-An high-temperature and primitive anorthite; HS high sanidine; LM low microcline; HA high albite; LA low albite.

Notes on sources: 1, mean of data by Roy (1965) and Bruno and Gazzoni (1970b); 2, Bruno and Gazzoni (1970b); 2, Bruno and Gazzoni (1970a); 3, Nager, Hoffmann and Nissen (1969); 4, Kroll (1971b); 5, Pentinghaus (1970), Pentinghaus and Bambauer (1971a,b); 6, Viswanathan (1971b); 7, see also Long (1966); 8, Wones and Appleman (1961, 1963); 9, see section 7.3; 10, Erd et al. (1964); 11, Appleman and Clark (1965); 12, Ghélis and Gasperin (1970); .8843(4), 1.3042(5), .7195(3), 116.42(3), .743(2); 13, Rudert (1970) obtained .8631(8), 1.3025(10), 1.4383(10), 115.27(10) for pure synthetic material; 14, Eugster and McIver (1959) report synthesis but no cell dimensions; Martin (1971) reports for synthetic $K(Al_{.819}B_{.181})Si_3O_8$, .85908(9), 1.29827(13), .71486(11), 116.09(13), .71655(14); 15, Stewart (1967), see Table 7-6; 16, Scheel (1971); .8415(5), 1.3063(6), .7162(4), 115.13(3), .7128(10); 17, Wainwright and Starkey (1971); 18, correction by Appleman (pers. comm.); 19, Bruno and Facchinelli (1972), see paper for 6 sets of data.

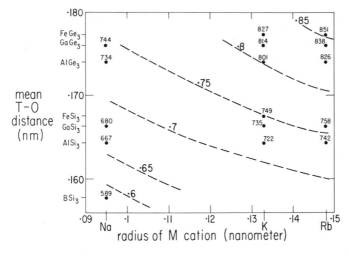

Fig. 7-1. Cell volumes of end-member feldspars shown at points specified by coordinates for the Pauling radius of the M cation and the mean T–O distance using Shannon-Prewitt reference values. The contours were estimated by eye, and are in units of 10^{-27} cubic meters. The individual values have been multiplied by 1000 and may be read directly as cubic Angstrom units. Data from Table 7-1

Goldsmith (1950), but accurate cell dimensions were not obtained because of the difficulty of refining powder data at that time. Half of the data in Table 7-1 result from the Inaugural-Dissertation of Pentinghaus (1970), upon which much of this discussion is based. An unpublished dissertation by Long (1966) provided cell dimensions of moderate accuracy for feldspars of composition $KAlGe_3O_8$, $KGaGe_3O_8$ and $KFeGe_3O_8$. All other data are for papers in regular journals as listed in Table 7-1.

Pentinghaus showed that the cell volume of the end-member alkali feldspars increases approximately linearly with the change in radius of the M cation and the change in mean T–O distance. Figure 7-1 shows the cell volumes plotted at the appropriate position with respect to the Pauling radius of the M cation and the mean T–O distance for the Shannon and Prewitt (1969) radii. For reed-mergnerite the actual mean T–O distance was used from the crystal structure analysis of Appleman and Clark. The datum for buddingtonite could not be plotted because of ignorance about the role of H_2O. All the plotted data, except for reedmergnerite, are for disordered feldspars. The volumes for ordered forms are quite close to those of the disordered forms.

The range of volumes is rather large (0.59–0.85 nm^3). For each M cation, the volume increases linearly with the mean T–O distance as shown directly by Pentinghaus (1970, Fig. 17). For the range $AlSi_3$ to $FeGe_3$, Pentinghaus derived for his own data the equations:

$$Rb: V = -0.6363 + 8.391 \, (T-O)$$
$$K: \quad -0.5878 + 7.974$$
$$Na: \quad -0.4254 + 6.651$$

where V is in cubic nanometers and the mean distance $T-O$ is in nanometers. Similarly for each composition of T atoms, the volume increases linearly with the radius of the M cation (Pentinghaus, Fig. 16). For the cations Na, K and Rb, Pentinghaus derived for his own data the equations:

$$GaGe_3: V = 0.5753 + 1.779\, r$$

$$AlGe_3: \quad 0.5672 + 1.753$$

$$GaSi_3: \quad 0.5362 + 1.500$$

$$AlSi_3: \quad 0.5332 + 1.415$$

where the Pauling radius r is in nanometers. The contours of Fig. 7-1 slope from top left to bottom right in accordance with these trends.

The individual cell edges show similar trends with the sizes of the M and T ions as may be seen directly from Table 7-1. The angle β shows a complex variation with composition. For Rb and K cations, the β-angle first increases and then decreases as the mean T–O distance increases in disordered varieties: e.g. for Rb-feldspars, β increases from $116.29°$ for $AlSi_3$ to $117.15°$ for $GaGe_3$ dropping to $116.67°$ for $FeGe_3$. In ordered feldspars, there is an additional perturbation. The Na-feldspars show a complex variation of angles that depends both on collapse about the small Na atom and on effects for the T atoms.

It seems likely that the cell dimensions of alkali feldspars can be predicted rather accurately by linear interpolation between the data of Table 7-1 taking into account the effects of order of T atoms as well as the mean size of the M and of the T atoms. Such predictions would be improved if cell dimensions were obtained for further ion-exchanged varieties of the ordered alkali varieties.

Turning now to the ordered Al_2Si_2 feldspars, the effects of substituting a larger M atom are obvious in the trend from Ca via Sr and Pb to Ba. Buckling of the monoclinic to the triclinic structure occurs between Sr and Ca. Determination of cell dimensions for varieties containing B, Ga, Fe and Ge is desirable to test the effect of substitution in the T sites. Goldsmith and Laves (1955) determined cell dimensions with a precession camera for substituted anorthites with 3/8 Ga, 3/8 Ge and 3/8 Ge 3/8 Ga substitution for Al and Si. The three substituted anorthites had α^*, β and γ^* angles indistinguishable from those of anorthite within the experimental error of 7′. The cell edges of the first two increased about $\frac{1}{2}\%$ and of the doubly-substituted one about 1%, but the detailed values are not quoted here because the experimental error was $\pm 0.2\%$.

Added in proof. Gazzoni (1973) determined the following cell dimensions

	a (nm)	b (nm)	c (nm)	β (deg.)
$SrGa_2Si_2O_8$	0.8481 (9)	1.3133 (10)	1.4480 (11)	115.39 (14)
$BaGa_2Si_2O_8$	0.8727 (5)	1.3240 (6)	1.4608 (6)	115.00 (6)
$BaAl_2Ge_2O_8$	0.8799 (5)	1.3371 (6)	1.4727 (6)	114.93 (7)
$BaGa_2Ge_2O_8$	0.8898 (6)	1.3528 (6)	1.4906 (6)	114.87 (6)

The data in this section are valuable for estimating the effect of minor elements on the cell dimensions of natural feldspars by a linear approximation (using mol. rather than mass ratios of the atoms). For example, substitution of

1 mol.-% of Fe for Al in sanidine should change the *a*-dimension by 0.0009 nm to be compared with the change of 0.045 nm for complete substitution of Na by K. Hence 1 mol.-% Fe acts like 2 mol.-% K on the *a* dimension of alkali feld-spars.

7.3 Alkali Feldspars

7.3.1 General and Historical

Cell dimensions of natural alkali feldspars depend on three main factors: the K/Na ratio; the Si, Al order; and in perthitic intergrowths, on the degree of coherence between the K- and Na-rich regions. Furthermore, the Si, Al order cannot be specified merely by a single ordering parameter since the cell dimensions are affected by domain texture as well as by the details of the site distribution.

Although there are four cell dimensions for the monoclinic varieties, and six for the triclinic ones, there are only three useful items of information. The *a* repeat (or better still the cell volume *V*) provides a measure of K/Na sub-stitution, subject to minor perturbations from the T atoms. For a fixed K, Na ratio, *b* correlates inversely with *c* within experimental error, while α correlates with γ. The variation in *b* and *c* provides a measure of transfer of Al atoms into the T_10 site of low albite and microcline, and provides a check on the K, Na ratio estimated from *a* or V. The variation in α and γ provides a measure of the

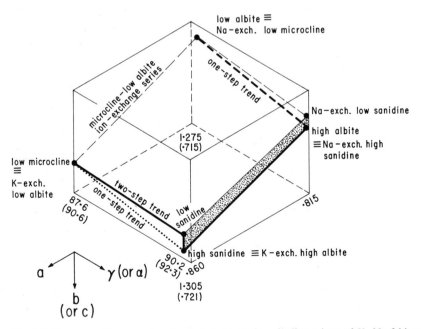

Fig. 7-2. Summary diagram of major variations of the cell dimensions of K, Na feldspars, plotted on a parallelepiped defined by *a*, *b* and γ. All known K, Na feldspars are represented by points inside the triangular prism. Heavy lines represent feldspars thought to be at thermodynamic equilibrium at some temperature. Feldspars that are topochemically monoclinic lie in the stippled plane

unbalance of Al atoms between the 0 and m sub-sites of the tetrahedral nodes, but is complicated by fine domain texture in K-feldspars. The change in β is trivial and has no determinative value.

Figure 7-2 displays the variation of cell dimensions for alkali feldspars. The limiting parallelepiped displays the ranges in a (0.815–0.860 nm), in b (1.275 to 1.305) and in γ (87.6–90.2°). The cell dimensions of all K, Na feldspars lie in the triangular prism bounded by low microcline, low sanidine and high sanidine for $KAlSi_3O_8$ and low albite, high albite and Na-exchanged low sanidine for $NaAlSi_3O_8$. Microcline and low albite have essentially the same Al, Si distribution and are connected by a *metastable* ion-exchange series. High sanidine and high albite have the same Al, Si distribution, but are connected by an ion-exchange series that is *stable* near the melting temperature. All synthetic albites annealed at a constant temperature, plus heated low albites, fall on the near-linear *one-step* trend between low and high albites. This trend is believed to represent thermodynamic equilibrium. Heated microclines fall on a near-linear one-step trend towards high sanidine, and can be transferred by ion-exchange to the one-step trend for albite. Those natural K-feldspars believed to represent the best approach to thermodynamic equilibrium fall close to the *two-step* trend between high sanidine, low sanidine and microcline. Other K-feldspars lie between the one- and two-step trends. Sodium-rich equivalents of the two-step trend can be prepared by ion-exchange, but have not been synthesized directly.

A similar diagram is produced by replacing b and γ with c and α as shown. Reciprocal cell parameters give the same implications.

Coherency between out-of-step domains of K-feldspar, and particularly between the K-rich and Na-rich parts of fine-scale (but not coarse) perthites, causes mutual distortion of the cell dimensions. Interpretation of such cell dimensions in terms of K/Na content and Si, Al distribution is difficult.

Historically, the contraction of the cell dimensions from K- to Na-feldspar was discussed first by Taylor et al. (1934) who explained it in terms of buckling of the framework around the smaller Na atom. Chao et al. (1939) used the a cell dimension to characterize the K/Na content of the components of natural and heated perthites. Bowen and Tuttle (1950) used the spacing of the $\bar{2}01$ diffraction to measure the K/Na content of synthetic alkali feldspars. Laves (1952), Coombs (1954) and others noted that the $\bar{2}01$ spacing yielded impossible values for the components of some perthites, and Smith (1961) interpreted this as the result of coherency at the boundary.

Cole et al. (1949) were the first to obtain really accurate cell dimensions of feldspar. They interpreted the constancy of a, the increase of b and the decrease of c during sanidinization of orthoclase as the result of transfer of Al from T_1 into T_2 sites. The development of accurate powder diffraction techniques permitted this effect to be used for rapid determination of the structural state of alkali feldspars (Wright, 1964; Orville, 1967; Jones, 1966; Wright and Stewart, 1968). Furthermore, quantitative interpretation of the Al-distribution from the cell dimensions, especially by Stewart and Ribbe (1969), permitted major advances in the understanding of ordering reactions, especially for albite.

Early X-ray studies of natural K-feldspars failed to detect the triclinic geometry of microcline, but the single-crystal studies by Laves (1950) clearly revealed the difference between low microcline and sanidine. Later studies, especially by Goldsmith and Laves (1954a, b) and MacKenzie (1954), outlined the complex continuous variation of cell dimensions between sanidine and microcline. The combination of X-ray and optical data on both natural and heated K-feldspars showed that there is an infinity of ordering paths between high sanidine and low microcline (see Chapter 3). The data on the cell dimensions of K-feldspar are interpreted in terms of variation between the extremes of a one-step and two-step trend of ordering; see for example the reviews by Laves (1960) and by Smith and MacKenzie (1961) of ideas by many workers including Barth and Hafner.

The ordering of Na-feldspar was studied rigorously by the experimental syntheses of MacKenzie (1957), Martin (1969, 1970) and Raase and Kern (1969) using cell dimensions to follow the changes. These and more recent studies show that the cell dimensions of equilibrium forms of albite follow a one-step trend of ordering.

Laves (1951) demonstrated ion-exchange of an alkali feldspar crystal by changes of cell dimension. Wyart and Sabatier (1956a, b), and especially Orville (1960, 1962, 1963, 1967), developed ion-exchange with alkali halide melts into a practical tool for systematic production of a feldspar of desired composition and structural state. Wright and Stewart (1968) emphasized the value of cell dimensions for a series of ion-exchanged feldspars whose Al, Si distribution stayed constant, and proposed a system of nomenclature based on measurement of cell dimensions.

Donnay and Donnay (1952) were the first to systematically measure cell dimensions for a series of synthetic alkali feldspars using X-ray powder methods. They demonstrated the symmetry change between monoclinic sanidine and triclinic high albite, which was shown by X-ray methods (Laves, 1952; MacKenzie, 1952) to be non-quenchable and to move to Na-rich compositions with elevation of temperature.

Laves (1952), MacKenzie (1952) and Goldsmith and Laves (1954a, b) began the interpretation of cell dimensions from a combined structural and petrologic viewpoint. The first index of order (based on deviation from monoclinic geometry of microcline) was called the *triclinicity*, and many thousands of measurements have been made. Smith and MacKenzie (1955) developed a simple method for estimating α^* and γ^* for twinned triclinic feldspars, especially those in perthites. These early methods have been supplemented by the X-ray powder techniques developed in the nineteen-sixties. Application of such techniques is mandatory for alkali feldspars in rocks, following initial reconnaissance study by optical methods. Particularly valuable is the 3-peak method of Wright (1968).

7.3.2 Homogeneous Alkali Feldspars

This section summarizes the data for alkali feldspars unaffected by lattice strain. It begins with essentially pure end-members, moves on to synthetic ion-exchange series, and ends with natural feldspars of intermediate composition.

Albite: Sources of Data. Cell dimensions of synthetic albite were measured as follows: (a) Grundy and Brown (1969): 8 specimens from MacKenzie (1957) believed to represent equilibrium under hydrothermal conditions for temperatures from 1000° C to 500° C; a high albite synthesized at 600° C for 3 hours; diffractometer with Ni specimen holder calibrated against MgO,

(b) Martin (1969, 1970): 26 specimens believed to represent near-equilibrium in the presence of persodic aqueous fluids for temperatures down to several hundreds of degrees Celsius, plus two "highly metastable" specimens; Guinier camera adjusted to eliminate α_2 radiation,

(c) Raase (1971); 10 specimens synthesized at 370–700° C hydrothermally from iron-bearing glass; diffractometer.

(d) Kroll (1971a, b): 7 specimens synthesized at 750–1000° C; Guinier camera,

(e) Donnay and Donnay (1952): 1 specimen, hydrothermal, 800 C, 5 days; diffractometer; recalculated by Orville (1967) for assumed systematic error in calibration; separate data by Smith (1956) for similar specimen,

(f) Orville (1967): 1 specimen, hydrothermal, 800° C; diffractometer,

(g) Stewart and von Limbach (1967): 1 specimen, hydrothermal, 925° C; diffractometer,

(h) Wright and Stewart (1968): 3 specimens synthesized hydrothermally at 925, 700 and 500° C; diffractometer,

(i) Rudert (1970): 1 specimen, hydrothermal, 930° C; Guinier camera,

Cell dimensions of natural albites were measured as follows:

(a) Cole, Sörum and Taylor (1951): Kodarma; $\sim An_0$; single-crystal θ-method,

(b) Smith (1956): Amelia; $An_0Or_{1.8}$; diffractometer,

(c) Ferguson, Traill and Taylor (1958): Ramona; $An_{0.5}Or_{1.0}$; single-crystal θ-method; used for 3D structure analysis,

(d) Waldbaum (1966) and Waldbaum and Robie (1971): Amelia and Na-exchanged Amelia; diffractometer,

(e) Orville (1967): Hugo; $An_{0.2}Or_{1.7}$; diffractometer,

(f) Bambauer, Eberhard and Viswanathan (1967): four albites; Brazil $An_{0.0}Or_{0.3}$; Amelia $An_{0.5}Or_{1.2}$; Piz Miez $An_{0.7}Or_{0.2}$; Eganville $An_{1.7}Or_{0.6}$; Guinier camera,

(g) Stewart and von Limbach (1967): Amelia; $An_{1.3}Or_{0.7}$; diffractometer,

(h) Wainwright and Starkey (1968): Tiburon; $An_{0.0}Or_{0.1}$; diffractometer; used for 3D structure analysis,

(i) Kastner and Waldbaum (1968): 3 authigenic albites from Crete and Rhodes; unanalyzed but probably pure; diffractometer,

(j) Grundy and Brown (1969): Amelia $An_0Or_{1.8}$ and Schyn-Schluct $An_{0.1}Or_{0.5}$; diffractometer,

(k) Müller (1969): Itatiaia; $An_{0.4}Or_{1.0}$; Guinier camera; also partial data for other albites,

(l) Kastner (1971): 9 authigenic albites from carbonate rocks, diffractometer,

(m) various single-crystal film data of moderate accuracy by Laves (1952) and other workers have been superseded by the above data; data by Baskin (1956) on authigenic albites are of doubtful significance because of errors in cell edges perhaps as large as 1%; data by Callegari and Pieri (1967) on chessboard albites have estimated errors of 5′ in cell angles and $\pm 0.07\%$ in cell edges.

Cell dimensions of heated natural albites were measured as follows:

(a) Smith (1956): Amelia; 23 days 1060° C dry; diffractometer; new refinement by Stewart and von Limbach (1967),

(b) Ferguson et al. (1958): Amelia; 16 days 1065° C dry; $An_{0.7}Or_{1.6}$; single-crystal θ-method; used for 3D structure analysis,

(c) Waldbaum (1966) and Waldbaum and Robie (1971): natural and Na-exchanged Amelia; diffractometer,

(d) Müller (1969, 1970): 52 specimens produced by heating Na-exchanged Itatiaia albite for various times up to 33 days at 1040° C and 33 h at 1130° C, Guinier camera; also partial data for other albites,

(e) various low-accuracy film data.

Cell dimensions of Na-exchanged K-feldspars were measured as follows:

(a) Orville (1967): NaCl-exchanged Hugo microcline; $An_{0.2}Or_{1.0}$; diffracto-meter,

(b) Wright and Stewart (1968): NaCl-exchanged forms of Syn San Shaw, Puye, P 50–90, Benson, SH 1070, Spencer B and Spencer U specimens; see next section for details of the original K-feldspars; diffractometer,

(c) Müller (1969, 1970); NaCl-exchanged forms of K-exchanged Itatiaia albite heated to 1040, 1070, 1100 and 1130° C after the first exchange; Guinier camera.

Most of the above data are plotted in Fig. 7-3 which shows the correlations of the cell dimensions a, b, c, α and β with the angle γ. The angle γ was selected because it shows the greatest variation with respect to experimental error. The cell dimensions are affected significantly by substitution of K and Ca. Most of the above-listed data are for essentially pure albites that can be plotted directly on Fig. 7-3. However NaCl-exchange was incomplete for several of the specimens of Wright and Stewart (1968), and incorporation of the data on Fig. 7-3 would be misleading. Such data are shown on Figs. 7-5 et seq., which were specially drawn to show the cell dimensions for the entire group of alkali feldspars. Selected data are given in Table 7-2.

Albite: Discussion of Natural and Synthetic Specimens. Within two standard errors, the data points of Fig. 7-3 mostly fall on a single linear trend between the two extremes of high and low albite. This single trend encompasses nearly all natural albites, most synthetic albites and all heated natural albites. Martin (1970) plotted some of the above data against the *triclinic indicator* 2θ (131) $-2\theta(1\bar{3}1)$, called the *obliquity* by him. Since α and γ tend to be linearly related and since this indicator depends on α and γ, his plot is similar to the present one.

Some synthetic albites deviate from the linear trend. Martin (1970) described two specimens with γ near 89.8° as "highly anomalous". In Fig. 7-3, they are shown as rectangles which encompass one standard error in each direction. It may be seen that a, b and α are lower and c higher than for other synthetic specimens. Hamilton and Edgar (1969) measured carefully on a diffractometer, using a $KBrO_3$ standard, the positions of the $\bar{2}01$, 131 and $1\bar{3}1$ diffractions of 25 albites synthesized hydrothermally at 500 to 1000° C for times from 12 to 2680

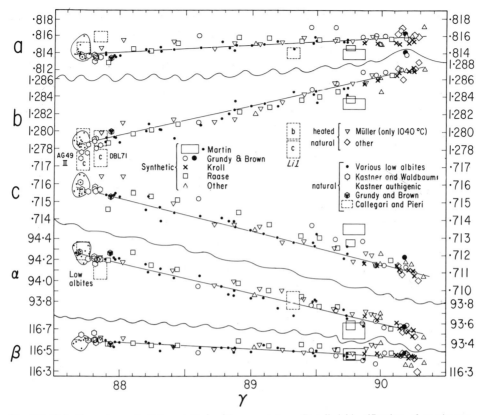

Fig. 7-3. Cell dimensions of albites plotted with respect to γ. Detailed identification of specimens may be obtained from the papers listed in the text together with the key to the symbols given in the center of the diagram. Some of the Callegari-Pieri data have been marked with the specimen number. Selected data are given in Table 7-2. The straight lines join the chosen values for extreme high and low albite given in Table 7-1. The rectangles show the standard errors for some of the data. Other errors are not related to the size of the symbols. Typical errors for the powder data are 0.0003 in a, 0.0004 in b, 0.0002 in c, and 0.03° in the angles, with a range over a factor of about 5 for most of the data. To these random errors, there may be systematic errors in the cell edges. Only one-quarter of Kroll's data for heated albites are shown, but the remainder are consistent with the linear relation (see Fig. 7-5). Data for natural low albites are enclosed in rings

hours. MacKenzie (1957) showed that synthetic albites held hydrothermally at a constant temperature changed towards a structural state characteristic of that temperature. The final product is believed to be at thermodynamic equilibrium, and is known as an *equilibrium albite*. Figure 7-4a shows that there is a monotonic relation between the $\overline{2}01$ angular position (which depends largely on a) and the angular difference Δ between the 131 and $1\overline{3}1$ diffractions (which depends largely on α and γ) for those albites that reached equilibrium. However, the other specimens, especially those near high albite, show a spread of 0.05° in $\overline{2}01$ for a chosen value of $\Delta(131)$. Similar variations were encountered with synthetic plagioclase. The anomalous specimens of Martin would lie to the right of the curve in Fig. 7-4a. One might expect that the deviations from the "equilibrium curve"

Table 7-2. Selected cell dimensions of alkali feldspars

(a) Specimens used in structure determinations: see Table 7-6 for albites.

Reference	Locality	mol.%	a	b (nanometer)	c	α	β (degrees)	γ	V 10^{-27} m³
Cole et al. (1949)	Spencer C, Burma unheated	An 0.7 Ab 8.4	.85616(2)	1.29962(4)	.71934(2)	90	116.015(5)	90	.71929
do.	do. sanidinized	do.	.85642(2)	1.30300(4)	.71749(2)	90	115.994(5)	90	.71965
Wright and Stewart (1968)	Spencer C, Burma unheated	do.	.85607(11)	1.29924(15)	.71921(7)	90	116.018(10)	90	.71886(11)
Bailey and Taylor (1955)	Spencer U, Kodarma	<0.4 <12	.85784	1.29600	.72112	90.30	115.97	89.12	.72067
Brown and Bailey (1964)	Pellotsalo	- -	.8560 (4)	1.2964(7)	.7215 (3)	90.65(8)	115.83(8)	87.70(8)	.7200
Finney and Bailey (1964)	Pontiskalk	~0 <2	.8573	1.2962	.7218	90.57	115.92	87.75	.7207
Wright and Stewart (1968)	Spencer B, Gothard	0.3 9.7	.8554(2)	1.2970(2)	.7207(2)	90	116.007(10)	90	.71865(13)
do.	Spencer U, Kodarma	as above	.8578(4)	1.2957(3)	.7213(1)	90.25(2)	116.03(2)	89.22(2)	.7203 (3)
Phillips and Ribbe (1971)	7002, Eifel	0.0 14.3	.8539(4)	1.3015(5)	>.7179(3)	90	115.99(2)	90	.7172
do.	7007, Switzerland	0.2 11.6	.8545(2)	1.2967(5)	.7201(3)	90	116.00(2)	90	.7171
Weitz (1972)	Eifel, unheated	Ab~13; Ca 0.02, Ba 0.86 wt.%	.8549(5)	1.3028(5)	.7188(5)	90	116.02(5)	90	.71943
do.	do., heated		.8546(5)	1.3037(5)	.7178(5)	90	115.97(5)	90	.71898
Prince et al. (1972)	Himalaya, Cal.	Ab 10.5; Rb-F 1.4	.85632(11)	1.29633(14)	.72099(11)	90	116.073(9)	90	.71890

(b) Ion-exchanged products of specimens used in structure determinations.

Reference	Locality		a	b	c	α	β	γ	V
Wright and Stewart (1968)	Spencer B, NaCl	wt.% Or 11	.8172(5)	1.2857(5)	.7156(3)	92.81(8)	116.38(6)	90.14(4)	.6725(4)
	Spencer U, KCl	estimated 94	.8574(3)	1.2963(4)	.7207(2)	90.29(4)	115.91(5)	89.27(4)	.7204(4)
	Spencer U, NaCl	from a	.8134(4)	1.2797(4)	.7152(2)	93.51(4)	116.51(3)	89.49(4)	.6647(3)

(c) Synthetic albites

°C days Kbar	a	b	c	α	β	γ	V
Martin (1971)							
700 1 -	.8157(3)	1.2855(4)	.7116(2)	93.57(5)	116.42(3)	89.85(3)	.6667(3)
600 1 -	.8158(4)	1.2846(5)	.7125(2)	93.82(5)	116.46(3)	89.49(4)	.6669(3)
503 1 -	.8145(3)	1.2845(7)	.7127(2)	93.61(5)	116.49(3)	89.32(4)	.6659(3)
550 1 -	.8154(2)	1.2829(3)	.7130(1)	93.74(3)	116.53(2)	89.20(3)	.6658(2)
452 1 -	.8143(5)	1.2825(13)	.7139(2)	93.86(8)	116.48(3)	88.87(7)	.6657(1)
415 1 -	.8142(4)	1.2802(8)	.7139(3)	94.12(7)	116.50(3)	88.31(4)	.6643(4)
352 1 -	.8142(3)	1.2808(5)	.7153(2)	94.08(4)	116.57(2)	88.22(5)	.6655(3)

T (°C)									
700	–	–	.8153(2)	1.2849(3)	.7118(2)	93.73(3)	116.45(2)	89.71(2)	.6660(2)
550	–	–	.8151(1)	1.2842(4)	.7127(1)	93.80(2)	116.48(1)	89.47(2)	.6661(2)
300	–	–	.8154(3)	1.2833(6)	.7132(2)	93.89(4)	116.50(3)	89.18(5)	.6663(4)
300	–	–	.8149(3)	1.2835(3)	.7136(2)	93.95(3)	116.53(2)	88.88(4)	.6661(3)
300	–	–	.8153(3)	1.2815(3)	.7141(2)	93.91(3)	116.58(2)	88.77(3)	.6659(2)
600	10	–	.8144(1)	1.2801(3)	.7151(1)	94.16(3)	116.58(2)	88.20(2)	.6650(2)
500	10	–	.8149(3)	1.2809(3)	.7134(2)	93.84(3)	116.49(2)	89.00(3)	.6660(2)
400	–	–	.8144(3)	1.2802(3)	.7144(2)	94.02(3)	116.53(3)	88.41(3)	.6648(3)
300	–	9.5	.8137(3)	1.2787(7)	.7153(2)	94.21(3)	116.58(1)	88.00(3)	.6638(3)
600	10	–	.8136(1)	1.2793(3)	.7155(1)	94.20(2)	116.52(2)	87.97(1)	.6642(3)
200	10	–	.8146(2)	1.2820(6)	.7139(2)	93.89(4)	116.53(2)	88.81(5)	.6655(3)
500	10	–	.8150(1)	1.2807(3)	.7132(2)	93.84(3)	116.47(1)	88.09(2)	.6650(1)
400	10	–	.8146(2)	1.2794(1)	.7142(1)	94.05(3)	116.53(1)	88.61(2)	.6650(2)
300	10	–	.8137(1)	1.2802(4)	.7154(1)	94.22(2)	116.53(1)	87.96(1)	.6646(1)
200	10	–	.8147(2)	1.2802(4)	.7147(2)	94.14(4)	116.44(2)	88.31(3)	.6650(2)
300	–	9.5	.8153(2)	1.2850(4)	.7125(2)	93.67(3)	116.47(2)	89.74(4)	.6663(2)
350	10	–	.8156(2)	1.2788(2)	.7121(2)	94.21(1)	116.59(1)	87.90(1)	.6665(3)
250	–	–	.8138(1)	1.2832(6)	.7154(1)	93.65(1)	116.60(2)	87.89(2)	.6641(2)
300	–	9.5	.8140(2)	1.2788(3)	.7154(1)	94.21(1)	116.59(2)	87.90(2)	.6657(6)
350	10	–	.8139(6)	1.2832(6)	.7135(3)	93.52(8)	116.47(5)	89.79(9)	.6657(6)
250	–	–	.8146(3)	1.2837(4)	.7127(2)	93.58(4)	116.44(3)	89.76(4)	.6658(3)
Raase (1971)									
700	21	1	.8155(4)	1.2846(3)	.7124(3)	93.75(3)	116.51(3)	89.66(3)	.6662(7)
550	4	1	.8151(3)	1.2840(2)	.7130(2)	93.76(2)	116.55(2)	89.52(2)	.6660(5)
600	42	1	.8154(3)	1.2837(2)	.7131(3)	93.35(2)	116.56(2)	89.38(3)	.6663(5)
550	25	1	.8157(4)	1.2828(2)	.7137(3)	93.91(3)	116.55(2)	89.13(3)	.6663(5)
550	62	1	.8158(6)	1.2822(3)	.7144(4)	93.98(3)	116.59(3)	88.44(5)	.6661(9)
500	83	1	.8151(6)	1.2808(4)	.7151(4)	94.11(4)	116.48(3)	88.24(5)	.6651(6)
500	26	1	.8142(4)	1.2801(3)	.7153(3)	94.15(3)	116.55(2)	88.10(2)	.6675(6)
340	3	1	.8145(3)	1.2801(3)	.7155(2)	94.15(3)	116.56(2)	88.10(2)	.6675(6)
370	167	1	.8129(4)	1.2787(3)	.7146(2)	94.20(2)	116.56(2)	87.91(3)	.6626(6)
Grundy and Brown (1969)									
500	112	–	.8160	1.2810	.7152	93.95	116.48	88.60	.6676
600	73	–	.8170	1.2848	.7137	93.77	116.51	89.46	.6688
700	50	–	.8170	1.2855	.7129	93.72	116.45	89.65	.6687
750	59	–	.8160	1.2868	.7125	93.62	116.37	89.85	.6687
800	60	–	.8160	1.2865	.7114	93.61	116.38	89.96	.6674
850	60	–	.8158	1.2869	.7118	93.58	116.48	90.01	.6672
900	1.7	.5	.8166	1.2871	.7113	93.57	116.48	90.15	.6675
1000	2.7	.16	.8157	1.2888	.7113		116.48	90.19	.6676
610	.1	1	.8163	1.2892	.7119		116.48	90.18	.6689
Kroll (1971b)									
1060	45	.005	.8156	1.2872	.7111	93.48	116.44	90.24	.6669
1000	4	.05	.8154	1.2869	.7108	93.54	116.44	90.25	.6662
950	5	.2	.8152	1.2867	.7111	93.53	116.43	90.21	.6664
900	11	.4	.8151	1.2867	.7112	93.55	116.45	90.14	.6662
850	21	.7	.8152	1.2864	.7114	93.60	116.46	90.05	.6658
800	3	1	.8151	1.2859	.7114	93.64	116.47	89.97	.6657
750	70	1	.8152	1.2854	.7115	93.67		89.87	
Wright and Stewart (1968)									
925	.1	.25 (S63-30)	.8160(5)	1.2870(6)	.7106(5)	93.54(3)	116.33(6)	90.19(1)	.6670(4)
700	44	2 (S62-34)	.8151(2)	1.2846(3)	.7121(1)	93.69(3)	116.57(2)	89.62(3)	.6653(2)
500	56	2 (Ab III)	.8151(2)	1.2820(3)	.7134(1)	93.86(2)	116.53(2)	89.02(2)	.6654(2)

Table 7-2. (continued)

(d) Synthetic K-feldspars

°C	days	Kbar	a	b	c	α	β	γ	V
Kroll (1971b)									
950	11	.2	.8606	1.3031	.7175	90	116.03	90	.7231
900	21	.4	.8605	1.3029	.7176	90	116.04	90	.7230
850	37	.7	.8605	1.3028	.7179	90	116.02	90	.7232
800	35	1	.8605	1.3026	.7180	90	116.02	90	.7231
700	78	1	.8604	1.3024	.7181	90	116.03	90	.7231
650	78	1	.8604	1.3025	.7182	90	116.02	90	.7233
Wright and Stewart (1968)									
700	14	2	.8606(2)	1.3018(2)	.7172(1)	90	116.04(1)	90	.7219(2)
Orville (1967)									
800	6	1	.86027(8)	1.3021(1)	.71777(5)	90	116.010(7)	90	.72257(8)
Martin (1968)									
325	98	4	.8606(1)	1.2995(2)	.7191(1)	90	116.06(1)	90	.7224(1)
600	2	2	.8603(1)	1.3018(2)	.7186(1)	90	116.06(1)	90	.7230(1)
250	14	5	.8608(1)	1.3023(1)	.7183(1)	90	116.02(1)	90	.7236(1)
250	28	5	.8605(2)	1.3014(2)	.7182(1)	90	116.06(2)	90	.7226(2)
325	28	4	.8605(3)	1.3004(6)	.7183(3)	90	116.06(2)	90	.7221(4)
250	14	2	.8604(1)	1.3023(2)	.7183(1)	90	116.02(1)	90	.7232(1)
250	126	2	.8606(1)	1.3020(1)	.7184(1)	90	116.02(1)	90	.7233(1)
250	126	2	.8605(2)	1.3018(3)	.7178(2)	90	116.03(2)	90	.7225(2)
325	98	2	.8607(1)	1.3003(2)	.7190(1)	90	116.05(1)	90	.7228(1)
325	28	4	.8612(3)	1.3012(3)	.7193(2)	90	116.00(3)	90	.7237(3)
250	14	5	.8604(3)	1.3025(3)	.7182(2)	90	116.02(2)	90	.7234(3)
250	126	5	.8607(2)	1.3024(2)	.7183(1)	90	116.02(2)	90	.7235(2)
500	7	10	.8604(1)	1.3008(2)	.7190(1)	90	116.04(1)	90	.7231(1)
250	7	10	.8606(4)	1.3009(5)	.7189(3)	90	116.07(3)	90	.7229(4)
Martin (1971)									
700	3.5	1	.86034(10)	1.30234(13)	.71812(7)	90	116.01(1)	90	.72314(9)

(e) Synthetic K,Na-feldspars

	mol.% Or	a	b	c	α	β	γ	V
Orville (1967)	0.0	.81506(24)	1.28616(20)	.71151(10)	93.650(19)	116.451(20)	89.985(16)	.66611(18)
	4.72	.81665(27)	1.28738(20)	.71175(9)	93.375(16)	116.460(19)	90.122(16)	.66842(19)
5 or 7 days,	9.47	.81988(28)	1.2883(27)	.71234(13)	92.990(23)	116.444(27)	90.235(25)	.67273(22)
	14.26	.82129(33)	1.29096(31)	.7-320(14)	92.710(28)	116.411(30)	90.193(38)	.67627(27)
800°C,	19.06	.82347(32)	1.29245(20)	.71368(10)	92.288(21)	116.395(21)	90.212(21)	.67965(23)
	23.90	.82526(28)	1.29351(19)	.71431(8)	91.927(17)	116.339(17)	90.141(23)	.68284(21)
1 Kbar.	28.76	.82820(45)	1.29541(32)	.71489(14)	91.425(27)	116.322(29)	90.145(32)	.68716(35)
	33.66	.82893(36)	1.29593(41)	.71537(20)	90.755(36)	116.287(35)	89.952(43)	.68894(34)
	38.58	.83205(12)	1.29771(17)	.71585(9)	90	116.196(15)	90	.69956(15)
	43.51	.83479(15)	1.29849(16)	.71637(9)	90	116.159(19)	90	.69699(17)
	48.51	.83752(13)	1.29895(17)	.71646(9)	90	116.144(19)	90	.69969(16)
	53.52	.84017(24)	1.29936(21)	.71643(10)	90	116.124(24)	90	.70222(21)
	58.56	.84250(20)	1.29988(17)	.71568(9)	90	116.094(21)	90	.70487(18)
	63.63	.84487(10)	1.30128(13)	.71701(6)	90	116.039(9)	90	.70828(9)
	68.73	.84705(7)	1.30111(17)	.71714(5)	90	116.031(7)	90	.71015(7)
	73.87	.84970(8)	1.30148(11)	.71759(7)	90	116.012(8)	90	.71273(8)
	84.22	.85447(11)	1.30206(13)	.71759(6)	90	116.021(9)	90	.71745(10)
	89.45	.85582(8)	1.30196(10)	.71788(7)	90	116.000(7)	90	.71876(8)
	94.71	.85851(9)	1.30273(12)	.71788(7)	90	116.014(8)	90	.72154(9)
	100.0	.86027(8)	1.30209(10)	.71777(5)	90	116.010(7)	90	.72257(8)
Kroll (1971b)								
950°C 5 days	10.0	.8194	1.2901	.7124	93.05	116.41	90.23	6732
900 .4 11	10.0	.8197	1.2902	.7126	93.02	116.40	90.22	6737
850 .7 21	10.0	.8196	1.2900	.7128	92.99	1-6.40	90.21	6738
800 1.0 28	10.0	.8198	1.2900	.7129	92.98	1-6.42	90.22	6739
750 1.0 70	10.0	.8197	1.2896	.7130	92.98	1-6.41	90.14	6739
950 .2 5	20.0	.8240	1.2931	.7135	92.34	116.34	90.18	6806
900 .4 11	20.0	.8239	1.2929	.7137	92.30	116.35	90.19	6805
850 .7 21	20.0	.8242	1.2931	.7-39	92.26	116.32	90.17	6813
800 1.0 28	20.0	.8243	1.2930	.7145	92.24	116.35	90.16	6818
750 1.0 70	20.0	.8245	1.2930	.7144	92.24	116.35	90.17	6818
950 .2 5	30.0	.8283	1.2965	.7152	91.44	116.20	90.17	6884
900 .4 11	30.0	.8286	1.2968	.7151	91.30	115.27	90.12	6888
850 .7 21	30.0	.8286	1.2972	.7153	91.27	115.27	90.11	6892
350 .7 28	30.0	.8288	1.2953	.7155	91.26	115.28	90.10	6885
800 1.0 28	30.0	.8286	1.2960	.7157	91.20	116.31	90.10	6888
750 1.0 70							90.13	

Table 7-2. (continued)

(f)   Ion-exchange series of natural specimens

	mol.-% Or	a	b	c	α	β	γ	V
Orville (1967)	.94	.81421(32)	1.27807(43)	.71554(18)	94.083(45)	116.674(35)	87.847(45)	.66367(31)
Hugo	10.27	.81808(36)	1.27967(103)	.71622(19)	93.814(65)	116.544(41)	87.772(70)	.66923(53)
microcline	19.71	.82319(33)	1.28442(24)	.71749(11)	93.175(35)	116.362(18)	87.772(26)	.67860(25)
with	29.27	.82848(20)	1.28848(14)	.71894(6)	92.663(25)	116.423(41)	87.807(21)	.68638(30)
0.2% An	38.96	.83374(30)	1.29071(36)	.71971(15)	91.946(62)	116.103(64)	87.631(27)	.69480(35)
	48.76	.83808(40)	1.29231(43)	.72019(19)	91.567(49)	116.020(32)	87.612(31)	.70030(31)
	58.68	.84197(16)	1.29345(30)	.72060(14)	91.180(29)	115.970(19)	87.659(24)	.70493(20)
	68.71	.84715(16)	1.29501(29)	.72124(14)	90.988(34)	115.921(20)	87.614(25)	.71104(21)
	78.86	.85091(20)	1.29545(26)	.72141(13)	90.745(27)	115.868(18)	87.741(22)	.71498(19)
	89.11	.85466(20)	1.29552(21)	.72160(9)	90.669(22)	115.921(18)	87.751(20)	.71803(16)
	99.48	.85891(34)	1.29628(38)	.72230(14)	90.617(46)	115.952(33)	87.740(37)	.72252(29)
K-exch. Hugo Ab	100?	.85823(24)	1.29644(28)	.72219(14)	90.630(24)	115.925(18)	87.681(23)	.72207(21)
Wright and Stewart (1968)	94.3, -	.86023(17)	1.29982(21)	.71970(11)	90	115.990(13)	90	.72336(16)
P50-56F	87.1, 85.3	.85694(15)	1.29989(19)	.71929(10)	90	116.007(12)	90	.72011(14)
orthoclase:	85.3, -	.85601(17)	1.29951(25)	.71941(14)	90	115.993(15)	90	.71939(17)
wet chemical	75.0, 76.3	.85206(17)	1.29987(25)	.71922(12)	90	115.985(15)	90	.71606(17)
An 0.4, Cn 1.2 wt.%;	66.2, 67.3	.84774(43)	1.29907(30)	.71881(15)	90	115.978(37)	90	.71162(34)
flame photometer	59.4, 58.6	.84451(41)	1.29992(34)	.71879(18)	90	116.097(28)	90	.70809(32)
Or + Ab, 95.9%	50.2, 50.0	.83952(33)	1.29775(27)	.71851(14)	90	116.092(25)	90	.70302(26)
	41.2, 41.5	.83434(25)	1.29682(21)	.71798(12)	90	116.180(20)	90	.69715(20)
	32.6, 33.0	.8298	1.2949	.7176				refinement incomplete
	25.6, 24.6	.82690(14)	1.29203(20)	.71656(10)	91.510(32)	116.353(15)	90.015(28)	.68601(14)
	15.8, 16.3	.82288(19)	1.28975(23)	.71495(11)	92.237(33)	116.438(17)	90.200(32)	.67872(18)
	8.0, -	.81859(38)	1.28856(25)	.71387(11)	92.887(22)	116.490(18)	90.242(28)	.67174(29)
Waldbaum and Robie (1971)	.16	.81413(52)	1.27743(72)	.71551(35)	94.105(53)	116.606(33)	87.741(48)	.66360
Amelia	1.94	.81336(58)	1.27790(99)	.71561(41)	94.152(93)	116.640(37)	87.732(100)	.66307
amazonite	1.48	.81418(40)	1.27759(88)	.71552(30)	93.983(57)	116.602(27)	87.912(59)	.66387
Or 82	1.50	.81515(40)	1.27842(65)	.71575(25)	94.133(38)	116.633(25)	87.729(37)	.66499
Ab 16	10.78	.81964(59)	1.27982(65)	.71719(38)	93.737(51)	116.493(35)	87.813(51)	.67186
Rb-f 2	19.77	.82346(58)	1.28314(66)	.71838(40)	93.003(42)	116.279(34)	87.925(45)	.67960
*Data by	30.14	.82908(36)	1.28515(37)	.71876(27)	92.049(37)	116.010(22)	87.708(28)	.68740
D. B. Stewart	39.58	.83350(36)	1.28775(30)	.72017(23)	91.534(42)	115.922(33)	87.862(67)	.69353
using fluorite	47.41	.83680(50)	1.29055(51)	.72043(41)	91.535(55)	115.954(38)	87.831(39)	.69919
as internal	49.98	.83893(62)	1.29204(62)	.72071(43)	91.068(29)	115.910(15)	87.684(46)	.70180
standard	62.40*	.84380(24)	1.29493(24)	.72123(17)	91.071(52)	115.946(38)	87.709(25)	.70684
	68.68*	.84316(38)	1.29478(46)	.72080(18)	90.863(62)	115.881(29)	87.640(39)	.71140
	68.68*	.84608(22)	1.29651(17)	.72078(18)	90.774(34)	115.957(14)	87.777(25)	.71199
	79.53*	.84937(74)	1.29514(55)	.72032(29)	90.790(33)	115.952(16)	87.791(60)	.71541
	89.86*	.85138(31)	1.29653(30)	.72119(19)	90.629(18)	115.911(29)	87.708(28)	.71787
	99.54	.85351(45)	1.29676(43)	.72157(18)	90.656(29)		87.718(35)	.71952
		.85553(22)	1.29674(13)	.72191(15)	90.671(43)		87.751(18)	.71925
		.85576(21)	1.29600(33)	.72183(14)			87.732(28)	.71925
		.85999(45)	1.29952(27)	.72246(35)			87.699(40)	.72396

Note: first analysis from flame photometry; second analysis calculated from assumed compositions.

(g) Natural K-rich feldspars

Reference	An	Mol.% chemical Ab	Cn	a	b	c	α	β	γ	V
Kastner (1971)	0.1	0.9	0	.85737(57)	1.29669(21)	.72230(30)	90.630(25)	115.921(25)	87.670(27)	.72162(73)
authigenic	–	0.9	0	.85852(26)	1.29610(14)	.72212(17)	90.537(16)	115.956(14)	87.984(15)	.72201(36)
microcline	–	–	–	.85656(72)	1.29632(24)	.72240(41)	90.682(33)	116.041(34)	87.804(31)	.72017(104)
Wright and Stewart (1968)										
Puye	1.2	58.2	–	.8333(2)	1.2974(1)	.7163(1)	90	116.257(12)	90	.69452(12)
P50-90KF	2.4	25	8	.8444(2)	1.3012(2)	.7176(1)	90	115.988(17)	90	.7050(20)
Benson	–	–	?	.8595(2)	1.2997(3)	.7200(2)	90	115.988(18)	90	.7206(24)
SH1070	–	–	–	.8559(3)	1.2983(3)	.7198(1)	90	116.003(15)	90	.71897(22)
Orville (1967)										
Hugo	0.2	11.6	0	.85774(25)	1.29610(27)	.72199(15)	90.637(30)	115.947(18)	87.746(20)	.72117(2)
Blue Mtn.	0.3	7.5	0	.8578	1.2961	.7221	90.67	115.98	87.63	.7211
Müller (1969)										
Hagendorf	–	2.0	–	.85985	1.29978	.72009	90.015	116.052	89.802	.72309
Bachinski and Müller (1971)										
Amaz A.	–	2.0	–	.85884	1.29675	.72254	90.73	115.96	87.60	.72284
Crosby (1971)										
electron	0.1	15.6	–	.85819(24)	1.29849(27)	.72008(16)	90	116.039(21)	90	.7206(22)
microprobe	0.8	12.7	–	.85823(28)	1.2972(25)	.71955(15)	90	115.997(18)	90	.7019(22)
analyses:	0.1	11.0	–	.85834(25)	1.29804(23)	.71947(13)	90	116.016(17)	90	.7140(21)
most K-rich	0.4	9.5	–	.85864(23)	1.29830(32)	.72054(17)	90	116.012(25)	90	.72187(25)
composition	–	–	–	.85963(24)	1.29972(24)	.72026(12)	90	116.073(15)	90	.7173(17)
of	0.1	10.3	–	.85799(17)	1.29760(24)	.72004(12)	90	116.036(15)	90	.7028(18)
mesoperthite	–	–	–	.85857(37)	1.29681(39)	.72077(16)	90	115.988(29)	90	.72136(32)
	0.2	8.6	–	.85784(25)	1.29617(45)	.72194(17)	90	116.036(29)	90	.7169(31)
	0.1	11.3	–	.85793(21)	1.29617(35)	.72218(16)	90	116.145(20)	90	.7201(25)
	0.0	10.4	–	.85791(18)	1.29645(34)	.72089(15)	90	116.006(17)	90	.7063(23)
Scott et al. (1971)	–	–	–	.85038(26)	1.30090(15)	.71772(14)	90	116.060(14)	90	.71327(37)
	–	–	–	.85146(52)	1.30075(45)	.71825(45)	90	116.116(42)	90	.71428(94)
	–	–	–	.84949(36)	1.30064(34)	.71757(28)	90	116.031(27)	90	.71249(63)
	–	–	–	.84977(20)	1.30042(12)	.71747(14)	90	116.037(12)	90	.71233(44)
	–	–	–	.84956(23)	1.30084(25)	.71774(20)	90	116.064(19)	90	.71253(44)
	–	–	–	.84834(22)	1.30101(19)	.71730(12)	90	116.029(12)	90	.71137(30)

(h) Natural Na-rich feldspars (see also Table 7-6)

Reference	Source	An	Mol.% chemical Ab	Or	a	b	c	α	β	γ	V
Müller (1969)	C1A	0.4	98.6	1.0	.81594	1.27983	.71645	94.163	116.605	87.690	.66716
Kastner (1971)	Glen Falls, N.Y.	0.1	99.9	0.1	.81301(36)	1.27851(30)	.71571(29)	94.216(44)	116.658(27)	87.805(50)	.66311(51)
	Rhodes	0.1	99.9	0.1	.81380(14)	1.27881(13)	.71571(8)	94.229(13)	116.605(9)	87.807(13)	.66414(20)
	Rhodes	–	–	–	.81367(21)	1.27865(18)	.71583(13)	94.170(25)	116.605(14)	87.813(25)	.66443(32)
	Ravdouka, Crete	–	–	–	.81345(26)	1.27850(18)	.71550(12)	94.227(18)	115.597(14)	87.789(26)	.66381(31)
	Liopedro, Crete	–	–	–	.81345(19)	1.27809(15)	.71561(8)	94.206(14)	116.581(12)	87.818(16)	.66355(26)
	Modane, France	0.1	–	–	.8378(17)	1.27752(20)	.71607(14)	94.256(16)	116.704(17)	87.704(17)	.66341(29)
	do.	–	–	–	.8379(17)	1.27759(17)	.71609(10)	94.218(17)	116.613(9)	87.758(17)	.66331(23)
	Pleasant Gap, Pa.	–	–	–	.81353(19)	1.27761(49)	.71572(20)	94.263(26)	116.635(10)	87.709(28)	.66310(29)
	Provo, Utah	–	99.9	0.1	.81350(89)	1.27836(33)	.71569(57)	94.211(73)	116.592(56)	87.849(66)	.66379(99)
Waldbaum & Robie (1971)	Amelia, Va.	0.5	99.9	1.0	.81414(16)	1.27836(16)	.71571(11)	94.233(16)	116.592(12)	87.680(15)	.66425(25)
	do.	–	–	–	.81425(16)	1.27912(22)	.71617(11)	94.221(19)	116.639(13)	87.749(18)	.66490(27)

Table 7-2. (continued)

(i) K-exchanged Na- and K-feldspars

Reference	Source	An	Ab	Or	a	b	c	α	β	γ	V
Müller (1969)	C1B	0.4	0.5	99.1	.85878	1.29726	.72276	90.625	115.957	87.618	.72328
Wright and	S63-30	0		98.*	.8595(3)	1.3032(2)	.7178(1)	90	115.888(28)	90	.72329(25)
Stewart (1968)	S62-34	0		100*	.86015	1.3015(2)	.7192(2)	90.150(43)	115.968(37)	89.537(42)	.72444(41)
	Ab III	0		100*	.8618(7)	1.2981(5)	.7204(2)	90.285(90)	115.850(53)	89.082(87)	.72511(55)
	Puye	1.2		95*	.8593(1)	1.3018(2)	.7183(1)	90	116.038(12)	90	.72198(14)
	P50-90	2.4		98*	.8596(2)	1.3022(2)	.7188(1)	90	115.943(13)	90	.72289(15)
	Benson			97*	.8606(2)	1.3000(4)	.7200(2)	90	116.033(22)	90	.72379(27)
	SH1070			96*	.8599(2)	1.2987(3)	.7201(1)	90	116.020(13)	90	.72272(18)
Waldbaum and	Amelia albite (a)	-	-	-	.85840(17)	1.29714(20)	.72234(10)	90.635(14)	115.919(12)	87.618(16)	.72275(26)
Robie (1971)	do. (b)	0.5	1.2	99	.85836(16)	1.29723(15)	.72238(9)	90.619(13)	115.924(10)	87.650(12)	.72279(26)
	do. (c)	0.5		99	.85801(21)	1.29646(11)	.72218(26)	90.611(14)	115.938(10)	87.642(14)	.72178(28)
	do. (d)	0.5	1.2	99	.85830(10)	1.29647(11)	.72226(9)	90.617(10)	115.920(10)	87.658(10)	.72223(9)
	do. (e)	0.5		-	.85764(26)	1.29621(17)	.72221(19)	90.612(23)	115.918(15)	87.686(20)	.72150(42)

*estimated from a

Notes: a, 860°C, 24 hrs., KCl; b, 910°C, 25 hrs., KCl; both a and b with Si standard; c, as b, measured by D. B. Stewart; d, as b, measured with spinel standard; e, 816°C, 2Q hrs., KCl, measured by M. Kastner.

Reference	Source	a	b	c	α	β	γ	V
Müller (1969)	IV33	.85953	1.29742	.72184	90.526	115.954	87.942	.72320
synthetic albites from	V 2	.86009	1.30247	.71837	90.000	115.967	90.000	.72330
Raase (1971)	V 3	.86016	1.29860	.72076	90.422	115.998	88.693	.72337
	V 4	.86019	1.29946	.72045	90.347	116.022	88.859	.72339
	V 8	.85903	1.29715	.72196	90.621	115.960	87.812	.72257
	V13	.85953	1.29755	.72128	90.495	115.979	88.262	.72280
	V24	.85970	1.29814	.72108	90.389	115.956	88.587	.72292
	V30	.85940	1.29709	.72157	90.546	115.961	88.035	.72282
	V32	.86086	1.30139	.71951	90.158	116.010	89.389	.72422
	V33	.86014	1.30035	.71972	90.183	116.010	89.249	.72348
	V34	.86019	1.29932	.72098	90.364	116.000	88.765	.72382
	V36	.86010	1.29920	.71979	90.277	115.995	88.960	.72298
	V39	.85942	1.29802	.72200	90.528	115.927	88.088	.72366

(j) Na-exchanged K- and Na-feldspars

Reference	Source	wt.% Or*	a	b	c	α	β	γ	V
Wright & Stewart (1968)	SSS synthetic	1	.8152(3)	1.2871(3)	.7116(1)	93.74(5)	116.55(3)	90.03(4)	.6661(3)
	Puye sanidine	2	.8161(3)	1.2858(3)	.7115(1)	93.33(4)	116.47(2)	90.32(4)	.6677(3)
	P50-90 orthoclase	12	.8203(2)	1.2895(2)	.7130(1)	92.75(2)	116.37(3)	90.27(2)	.6747(2)
	Benson orthoclase	8	.8178(3)	1.2857(4)	.7141(2)	93.18(3)	116.57(3)	90.13(3)	.6703(3)
	SH1070 orthoclase	6	.8165(2)	1.2848(3)	.7140(1)	93.19(3)	116.51(2)	90.12(3)	.6690(2)
Müller (1969)	C1B, 6 hrs. 1130°C	-	.81525	1.28067	.71534	94.123	116.585	88.326	.66566
*estimated from a	17	-	.81498	1.28108	.71451	94.090	116.594	88.547	.66472
	25	-	.81577	1.28314	.71308	93.931	116.576	89.185	.66618
	29	-	.81591	1.28666	.71202	93.665	116.454	89.816	.66952
	33	-	.81564	1.28616	.71175	93.683	116.498	89.892	.66828
			.81632	1.28661	.71185	93.648	116.542	89.959	.66832
Waldbaum & Robie (1971)	Amelia albite	-	.81359(31)	1.27844(49)	.71573(14)	94.245(22)	116.568(14)	87.689(27)	.66399(39)

(k)   Data on a*, b*, c* by Gubser and Laves (1967).

Adularia "homogenized" 5 hours 1050°C

wt.% Na₂O	a* (10⁹ meter⁻¹)	b* (10⁹ meter⁻¹)	c*
1.65	1.3032	.77076	1.5450
1.38	1.3011	.77113	1.5435
1.15	1.3000	.77040	1.5443
1.28	1.3006	.77065	1.5443
1.17	1.3004	.77099	1.5443
1.10	1.3005	.77119	1.5427
1.01	1.2993	.77071	1.5445
.98	1.2988	.77013	1.5450
.80	1.2980	.77076	1.5444
.56	1.2966	.76887	1.5473
.41	1.2958	.76978	1.5458
.34	1.2954	.77013	1.5461
.31	1.2962	.77071	1.5429
.58	1.2984	.77168	1.5416
.66	1.2973	.77021	1.5455
.20	1.3005	.77046	1.5451
.40	1.2956	.76794	1.5488
.15	1.3001	.77083	1.5449
.39	1.3015	.77065	1.5450
.15	1.3001	.77051	1.5447
.96	1.2991	.77021	1.5449
1.07	1.2997	.77023	1.5450
1.14	1.2996	.76985	1.5454
.44	1.2960	.77123	1.5428
1.32	1.3013	.77123	1.5428
1.24	1.3008	.77036	1.5451
1.21	1.2998	.76999	1.5453
.61	1.2971	.76970	1.5463
.61	1.2983	.77177	1.5405
1.60	1.3026	.77097	1.5435
1.41	1.3011	.77062	1.5448
1.16	1.3000	.77028	1.5446
1.08	1.2996	.77068	1.5446
1.06	1.2998	.77077	1.5443
1.05	1.2996	.77078	1.5446

Adularia after K-exchange

wt.% Na₂O	a* (10⁹ meter⁻¹)	b*	c*
—	1.2937	.76957	1.5462
—	1.2947	.77123	1.5424
—	1.2947	.77123	1.5418
—	1.2953	.77168	1.5405
—	1.2935	.76988	1.5454
—	1.2943	.77093	1.5425

Adularia "sanidinized" 200 hrs. 1100°C

wt.% Na₂O	a*	b*	c*
1.95	1.3016	.76818	1.5493
1.65	1.3012	.76731	1.5497
1.24	1.2996	.76735	1.5501
1.21	1.2987	.76712	1.5496
.80	1.2975	.76710	1.5505
.56	1.2957	.76718	1.5503
.61	1.2950	.76722	1.5501
.34	1.2950	.76718	1.5509
1.65*	1.3012	.76752	1.5503

*sanidine from Laacher See

Microcline "homogenized" 5 hrs. 1050°C

wt.% Na₂O	a*	b*	c*
2.02	1.3045	.77210	1.5406
1.89	1.3039	.77213	1.5407
1.02	1.3002	.77233	1.5402
.28*	1.2969	.77213	1.5407

*Pontiskalk authigenic

Microcline after K-exchange

wt.% Na₂O	a*	b*	c*
—	1.2959	.77202	1.5402
—	1.2958	.77214	1.5403

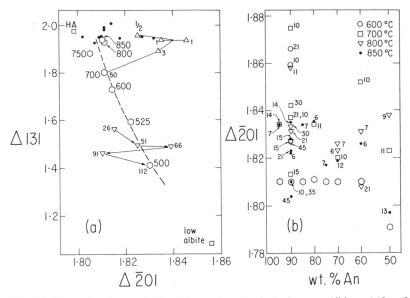

Fig. 7-4. X-ray data for synthetic albites and sodic plagioclases. a Albites. $\varDelta 131 = 2\theta_{131} - 2\theta_{1\bar{3}1}$.
$\cdot \varDelta \bar{2}01 = 2\theta_{\bar{2}01} - 2\theta_{101\,\mathrm{KBrO_3}}$. The hexagons show specimens thought to have equilibrated at the
temperature (°C) shown nearby. The squares show data for Amelia albite before and after prolonged
heating at 1065° C. The dashed line was estimated by eye for the equilibrium data. The triangles
show data for hydrothermal runs made at either 700° C (normal orientation) or 500° C (inverted)
for the times marked in days. The dots represent samples made at 750—1000° C. Note that the $\bar{2}01$
angle of Amelia albite may be displaced 0.01° because of substitution of Or. b Sodic plagioclases.
Selected data for hydrothermally-synthesized material. The numbers show the run time in days.
Hexagons show samples thought to be strongly disordered. Slightly modified from Hamilton and
Edgar (1969, Figs. 1 and 2)

would decrease with the heating time at a constant temperature. However, the
data for synthetic albites made at 700 and 500° C show erratic changes with time.
Hamilton and Edgar found that the $\bar{2}01$ peak was reproducible to 0.005° 2θ for
well-crystallized albites, but less reproducible for samples yielding smaller,
broader peaks.

It might be argued that the anomalies found by Hamilton and Edgar, and by
Martin, result merely from the difficulty of measuring poorly-defined X-ray
patterns and perhaps from the effect of surface energy on small crystals. However,
the anomalies may result from a genuine structural effect involving disorder of
the Al and Si atoms. From now on, it will be assumed that for synthetic albites
there is (1) an equilibrium trend for which there is a near-linear trend between
the cell dimensions, and (2) a non-equilibrium band with deviation from a linear
relation.

Natural albites are mostly in the low structural state. The ringed areas of
Fig. 7-3 enclose data points for 12 specimens with only 1 or 2% of other feldspar molecules. Some of the spread results from this chemical substitution, some
from experimental error, and some probably from small differences in structural
state. Several lines of evidence (optical data, X-ray structural analysis) are consistent with the Tiburon albite of Wainwright and Starkey having a slightly

higher structural state than the Ramona albite of Ferguson *et al.* The three authigenic albites of Kastner and Waldbaum were not analyzed chemically, but their cell dimensions are consistent with a structural state higher than for the 12 albites in the ringed areas. The Schyn-Schluct albite of Grundy and Brown is rather pure ($An_{0.1}Or_{0.5}$), and appears to have a higher structural state than the other albites. All these natural albites have cell dimensions consistent with a linear trend between low and high albites when account is taken of experimental error and chemical substitution.

The cell dimensions of the chessboard albites described by Callegari and de Pieri (1967) do not fall on the linear trend, even though the chemical compositions are quite pure (average $An_{0.4}Or_{0.3}$). The measurements were made from precession photographs and stated to have errors of $\pm 5'$ for the angles and $\pm 0.07\%$ for the edges. The angle β^* was assumed to be $63° 30'$. The spots were so diffuse and streaked for five specimens that γ^* was estimated to be $90°$, probably the result of overlapping of spots from disoriented domains. The cell dimensions for the remaining three specimens with relatively sharp spots are shown in Fig. 7-3 as rectangles defined by the listed errors. AG 49 II is a specimen with normal Albite twinning, while DBL 71 and LiI have chessboard twinning (see Chapter 18). The specimen with normal twinning has cell dimensions consistent with those for the other data for low albite, except for c which is high by twice the error. The DBL 71 specimen has a slightly higher value of γ while the c dimension is high by four times the error. The LiI specimen has anomalous cell dimensions. Whereas α is consistent with the linear relation, a is low by twice the error, b low by four times and c high by ten times. The five albites with diffuse spots have c varying from 0.7173–0.718, all higher than the linear trend whatever the γ value. The b values of 0.12766–0.12823 plot erratically with respect to the listed γ values of $88° 12'$ to $88° 19'$. The data for LiI are consistent with the trend for the anomalous specimens synthesized by Martin. Baskin's (1956) data for authigenic albites were obtained by single-crystal precession methods. They also are inconsistent with the linear trend, but the experimental error is too large for the deviations to be statistically significant. The data of Callegari and de Pieri, and of Baskin, are plotted in Figs. 1 and 2 of Martin (1970).

It is difficult to evaluate the cell dimensions of the chessboard albites and of Baskin's authigenic albites. I think that Callegari and de Pieri may have claimed too high an accuracy for their measurements of cell edges: in particular, I suspect that their measurements of c are systematically high as judged by the positions of AG 49 II and DBL 71. The data should be checked by techniques of proven accuracy, such as Guinier powder methods. In the meantime, I shall assume that the cell dimensions of those chessboard albites with high γ angles are anomalous. Since there is textural evidence from optical study of thin sections that some chessboard albites result from Na-metasomatism of K-feldspar, unusual cell dimensions would not be surprising.

The third group of specimens in Fig. 7-3 consists of heated natural specimens. The great bulk of data result from Müller (1969, 1970) who systematically back-exchanged with NaCl the heating products of K-exchanged Itatiaia albite. The K-exchanged material, of course, was essentially identical with natural microcline.

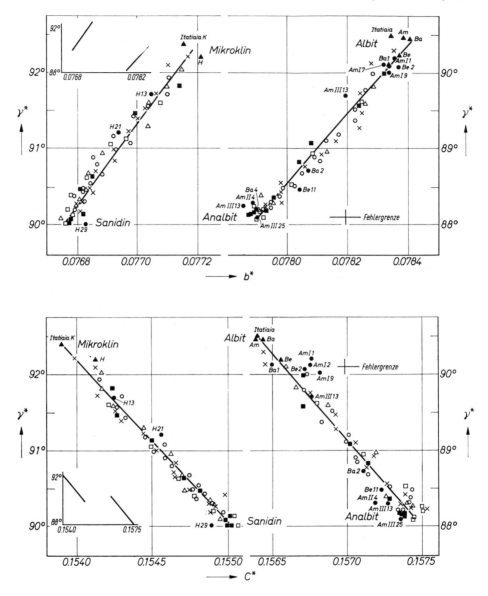

Fig. 7-5. Relation between b^* and γ^*, and c^* and γ^*, for heated K- and Na-feldspars. Albite from Itatiaia was K-exchanged and heated to yield the unlabelled points between microcline and sanidine. The samples were then back-exchanged to yield the points between low albite (Albit) and high albite (Analbit). The symbols show the heating temperature (cross, 1040°; circle, 1070°; open and filled squares, two different samples at 1100°; triangle, 1130°). The dots show the effect of heating Amelia albite at 1060° C (I and II) and at 1045° C (III) for the number of days shown by the dot. Similar data are given for albites from Bamle and Beverin. Solid triangles show the cell dimensions for unheated specimens including K-exchanged Itatiaia albite and K-exchanged Hugo microcline. Note that each pair of diagrams is related as shown by the inset diagram. The error bars (Fehlergrenze) were drawn to include composition deviation as well as errors in determination of cell dimensions. (From Müller 1970, Figs. 2 and 3)

These data actually show the effect of heating K-feldspar and not the effect of heating Na-feldspar. All 52 sets of cell dimensions for heating at temperatures from 1040° C to 1130° C are consistent with a linear trend from low albite to extreme high albite. All other data are for albites heated for a long period at one chosen temperature. Particularly important are the data for Amelia albite heated for 16 days at 1065° C, and used by Ferguson et al. (1958) for a crystal-structure analysis. Müller (1969, 1970) reported values of b^*, c^* and γ^* for three albites heated at various temperatures. Within experimental error all these data are consistent with a linear trend between high and low albites (Fig. 7-5).

From the combined sets of data, reference values for the extreme structural states of low and high albite can be estimated. The values listed in Table 7-1 are subject to personal choice dependent on evaluation of experimental errors, but are consistent with estimates of other feldspar workers within 0.0005 nm in the cell edges and 0.05° in the angles.

A detailed examination of the data with respect to a linear trend between these extreme values (Fig. 7-3) suggests the following comments. The spread of data for β is rather small and evenly distributed with most values closer than 0.1°. The spread for α is rather greater, perhaps partly the result of higher experimental error (e.g. Martin, 1970), and partly from a genuine structural effect. Nevertheless the deviation is so small that for practical purposes the angles α and γ can be assumed to be uniquely related. This means that to a high level of approximation, all diagrams plotted with respect to α or γ or any triclinic indicator based on these angles have the same structural implication.

The spread for a is difficult to evaluate because substitution by K tends to increase the cell edge slightly. I suggest that there is a tendency for some diffractometer data to have yielded high values of a because of inaccurate measurement of the asymmetric low-angle peaks, especially of the $\bar{2}01$ diffraction. The Guinier data tend to be dominated by high-angle peaks such as that for the 400 diffraction and hence to be accurately calibrated with respect to an internal standard. Bearing these factors in mind, the data are consistent with a linear relation, except for the anomalous specimens.

For b, the data are mostly consistent with a near-linear trend with γ except for the anomalous specimens. The high values obtained by Grundy and Brown are puzzling because any systematic error caused by their samples lying on top of the calibrated specimen holder should tend to reduce the cell dimension.

For c, the data tend to lie above the linear trend, especially the ones identified as anomalous. A least-square fit of a polynomial would yield a parabolic rather than a linear curve. The data for b also tend to fit a parabola rather than a straight line. Most of the deviations, however, result from random experimental error as shown by Fig. 1 of Martin (1970) in which rectangles were used to show the standard deviations.

In summary then, the data for natural and synthetic albites are mostly consistent with a single, near-linear trend between the cell dimensions. Synthesis data suggest that this trend is a monotonic function of temperature for thermodynamic equilibrium, though not a linear function. Under conditions that favor lack of thermodynamic equilibrium, albites apparently grow with anomalous cell dimensions.

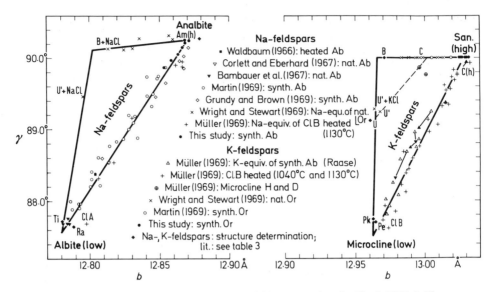

Fig. 7-6. Relation between b and γ for Na- and K-feldspars as given by Kroll (1971a). The sources of all the data are described in the text. This work refers to Kroll (1971a). Tables 7-2a and 7-6e contain data referred to under structure determination. Note that the data-points for Na-exchanged K-feldspar were obtained by extrapolation to take account of residual K. One correction is necessary: the open triangle refers to a specimen of Corlett and Eberhard (1967) — no. 206 from Wilberforce. Because of a printing error its composition is actually $An_{12.1}$ not $An_{2.1}$, and the intermediate position between high and low albite results from the An-content not from structural disorder. (From Kroll, 1971b, Fig. 8)

Albite: Na-exchanged K-feldspars. Wright and Stewart (1968) and Orville (1967) gave several diagrams that show the effect of Na-exchange on cell dimensions of K-feldspars, but the plot of b vs. γ used by Kroll (1971b) gives a particularly graphic description (Fig. 7-6). This figure is directly copied from Kroll's dissertation, and includes many of the specimens shown in Fig. 7-3. Comparison with Fig. 7-2 will show that this $b\gamma$ plot for Na-feldspars corresponds to the left-front face of the parallelepiped, but with change of orientation.

The Na-exchanged K-feldspars lie on a two-step trend that is clearly distinguished from the one-step trend for all the Na-feldspars so far described. All seven feldspars (whose cell dimensions are given in Table 7-2) are triclinic, though six have monoclinic geometry when in the K-form. The cell dimensions α and c show a similar two-step variation.

Figure 7-14a shows the effect of ion-exchange on the b and c cell dimensions for three series: low albite-maximum microcline (Orville, 1967); P 50–56 orthoclase (Wright and Stewart, 1968) and high albite-high sanidine (Donnay and Donnay, 1952; Orville, 1967). Figure 7-14b shows the Na-exchanged equivalents of the K-feldspars studied by Wright and Stewart. The bc plot yields a parallelogram bordered by the extreme feldspars. Ion-exchange of a particular feldspar results in a path nearly parallel to one edge of the parallelogram. Crossing these ion-exchange paths in Fig. 7-14b are contours of the a dimension which measures the extent of K, Na substitution. The bc plot is particularly useful because it permits evaluation of the effect of residual K on the cell dimensions of the Na-exchanged K-feldspars. Indeed the data plotted in Kroll's diagram (Fig. 7-6) were extrapolated to take account of the effect of residual K. From Fig. 7-14b it may be seen that for the Spencer B, SH 1070 and Benson specimens, extrapolation to Ab_{100} decreases b by 0.002–0.004 nm. This is equal to the difference between the one- and two-step trends. Hence by $b\,\gamma$ plot should not be used to characterize albites unless the K-content is known.

K-rich Feldspar: Sources of Data. Cell dimensions of synthetic K-feldspar were measured as follows: (a) Donnay and Donnay (1952): 1 specimen, hydrothermal, 700° C, 1 day; diffractometer; recalculated by Wright and Stewart (1968) for assumed systematic error in calibration,

(b) Orville (1967): 1 specimen, hydrothermal, 800° C, 5 or 7 days; diffractometer,

(c) Wright and Stewart (1968): 1 specimen (labelled Syn San Shaw) made by H. R. Shaw, hydrothermal 700° C, one week; diffractometer,

(d) Kroll (1971b): 6 specimens synthesized hydrothermally at 650 and 700° C for 11 weeks, 800 and 850° C for 5 weeks, 900° C for 3 weeks, 950° C for 11 days; Guinier camera,

(e) Martin (1968): 15 specimens synthesized hydrothermally at 250 to 600° C, 2 to 10 kbars for 2 to 126 days; diffractometer,

(f) Martin (1971): 1 specimen, hydrothermal, 700° C, $3\frac{1}{2}$ days; diffractometer; note also data for boron-substituted specimens.

Cell dimensions of natural K-feldspars have been measured as follows:
(a) Cole *et al.* (1949): Spencer C orthoclase; $\sim Ab_{6.8}An_{2.5}$; single-crystal θ-method; similar diffractometer results quoted in Colville and Ribbe (1968),

(b) Bailey and Taylor (1955): Spencer U intermediate microcline; perthitic with bulk composition $Ab_{12.5}An_{1.4}$, probably K-phase has about Ab_6; single-crystal θ-method; MacKenzie (1954) and Wright and Stewart (1968) gave similar cell dimensions from powder diffractometry; note reorientation of axes of microcline,

(c) MacKenzie (1954): Spencer E intermediate microcline with weak Na-phase, bulk composition $Ab_{14.9}An_{1.8}$; Blue Mountain maximum microcline with weak Na-phase, bulk composition $Ab_{9.2}An_{0.3}$; diffractometer; new data for Blue Mountain specimen quoted by Orville (1967); diffractometer,

(d) Brown and Bailey (1964): Pellotsalo maximum microcline with coarse perthite; K-phase probably contains 5% or so of Ab; single-crystal θ-method,

(e) Finney and Bailey (1964): Pontiskalk maximum microcline, probably with 1% or less of Ab-molecule; single-crystal θ-method,

(f) Orville (1967): Hugo maximum microcline with plagioclase inclusions; K-phase is probably near $An_{0.2}Ab_5Rb$-feldspar$_{2.5}$; data in figs. are for double-exchanged material with $Ab_{0.3}An_{0.2}$; diffractometer,

(g) Wright and Stewart (1968): Spencer B adularia, Ab_{11}; Puye sanidine Or_{42} plus K-exchanged specimen Or_{95}; P 50–90 sanidine Or_{63} plus K-exchanged Or_{98}; Benson orthoclase Or_{95} plus double-exchanged Or_{97}; S 1070 orthoclase Or_{88} plus K-exchanged Or_{96}; P 50–56 F orthoclase plus complete K, Na ion-exchanged series; diffractometer,

(h) various single-crystal film data by Laves (1950, 1952) plus powder data by Goldsmith and Laves (1961); these data were important in outlining the variation of natural feldspars, but have been largely superseded by later data; however, they do indicate the extent of Na-substitution in natural K-feldspars,

(i) Müller (1969): Hagendorf intermediate microcline, perthitic but cell dimensions indicate less than 1% Ab in K-phase; Amazonite A with 2.0% Ab and $2V - 75 \pm 2°$ from Santa Maria, Brazil; Guinier camera; (also partial data for heated and unheated Hugo microcline); see also Bachinski and Müller (1971),

(j) single-crystal film data by Baskin (1956) for authigenic K-feldspars are not sufficiently accurate to warrant detailed consideration; Martin (1971) gives accurate data suggesting boron substitution in certain authigenic K-feldspars,

(k) Gubser and Laves (1967) gave graphical data of a^*, b^*, c^* from Guinier patterns of adularias, both natural and ion-exchanged with KCl; in addition reference data were given for microcline of unstated origin, and of sanidine produced by prolonged heating of the adularias; unfortunately direct cell dimensions could not be calculated because of omission of cell angles; Table 7-2 contains data on a^*, b^* and c^* kindly supplied by R. Gubser,

(l) Kastner (1971): 4 authigenic microclines from carbonate rocks; note that she cautions about problems if detrital feldspar is not carefully separated; diffractometer,

(m) Crosby (1971): 11 natural K-feldspars from charnockitic rocks, Whiteface Mountain, New York; note problem of whether computer refinement with monoclinic symmetry overlooks actual triclinic symmetry; diffractometer,

(n) Scott et al. (1971): 6 natural K-feldspars from ignimbrite, Grant Range, Nevada; note uncertainty resulting from broadening of $\bar{2}01$ peak; diffractometer.

Cell dimensions of heated K-feldspars were measured as follows: (a) Cole et al. (1949): Spencer C orthoclase converted to high sanidine, single-crystal θ-method,

(b) Müller (1969): K-exchanged Itatiaia albite heated for times up to 35 days at 1040° C, 18 days at 1070° C, 9 days at 1100° C and 37 days at 1130° C: Guinier camera.

Cell dimensions of ion-exchanged Na-feldspars were obtained as follows:

(a) Orville (1967): Hugo albite, diffractometer,

(b) Wright and Stewart (1968): 3 synthetic albites, diffractometer,

(c) Müller (1969): 13 albites synthesized by Raase, Guinier camera,

(d) Müller (1969): Itatiaia albite denoted ClB,

(e) Waldbaum and Robie (1971): natural and heated Amelia albite, diffractometer.

K-rich Feldspar: Discussion of Natural and Synthetic Specimens. Figure 7-7 shows the cell dimensions of K-rich feldspars plotted against c, chosen because this parameter shows the greatest range with respect to the experimental error. Table 7-2 contains selected cell dimensions.

Interpretation of Fig. 7-7 is complicated by the presence of several percent of Ab molecule in the natural specimens, as can be seen best from a. The straight line relating a to c is my best estimate of the trend for Na-free feldspars. It is primarily determined by the datum for K-exchanged Hugo microcline with

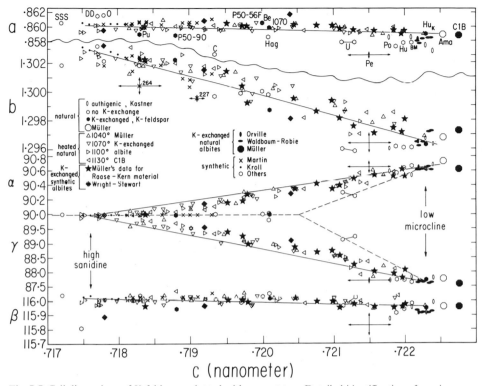

Fig. 7-7. Cell dimensions of K-feldspars plotted with respect to c. Detailed identification of specimens may be obtained from the papers listed in the text together with the key to the symbols given in the center of the diagram. Synthetic sanidines are shown by: SSS Shaw specimen used by Wright and Stewart; DD Donnay and Donnay; O Orville. Other abbreviations are: Pu Puye; Be Benson; Hag Hagendorf; U Spencer U; Pe Pellotsalo; Po Pontiskalk; Hu Hugo; BM Blue Montain; Hu_K K-exchanged Hugo; C1B K-exchanged Itatiaia; Ama Amazonite A. The straight lines join the chosen values for high sanidine and maximum low microcline in Table 7-1. The dashed lines show the estimated trend for the α and γ values of certain natural K-feldspars. Error bars are shown for the Pellotsalo specimen and the synthetic specimens 264 and 227 of Martin. Other errors are not related to the size of the symbols. Typical errors for the powder data are 0.003 in a, 0.0004 in b, 0.0002 in c and 0.03° in the triclinic angles, with a range over a factor of about 5. To these random errors, there may be systematic errors in the cell edges. Note that the natural specimens contain Ab in solid solution which causes deviations from the data for the pure synthetic specimens. The deviations are particularly important for a

only 0.5 % Ab (Orville, 1967) and by the many data for synthetic K-feldspars and heated specimens. Complete substitution of Na for K results in a reduction of 0.045 nm in a, and the a dimensions of the natural K-feldspars indicate (Ab + An) contents up to 9 % for Spencer C and 8 % for Pellotsalo microcline. The former content is consistent with the chemical analysis, while the latter value is slightly higher than the values of 6 and 7 % deduced from the $\bar{2}01$ and 400 spacings of Brown and Bailey (1964) interpreted on Orville's (1967) determinative curves. The cell dimensions of Müller for Amaz A and ClB are anomalous with respect to those of other workers and the c dimension may be wrong.

All the data for the angle β are consistent with a single trend when account is taken of possible experimental error. The data for α and γ, however, clearly demonstrate that there is not a unique relation with c. Almost all natural and synthetic K-feldspars with c below 0.7205 have monoclinic geometry, while those with longer c are mostly triclinic. Even for the natural feldspars there is no unique relation, because the α and γ angles are determined by coarseness of twin texture as well as by the degree of Al, Si ordering (see later). The dashed lines merely show a trend consistent with the untwinned Spencer U microcline.

All the other data for α and γ indicate triclinic geometry except for specimens with c near 0.7175 nm (i.e. high sanidines). The straight continuous lines merely join the chosen points for maximum low microcline and high sanidine. Taking account of the experimental error, these data are consistent with a single curved trend between the dashed and continuous lines. The data are for K-exchanged synthetic albites and for K-exchanged low albite heated by Müller to temperatures between 1040 and 1130° C. The K-exchange of the low albite yielded cell dimensions indistinguishable from those of maximum microcline, and the results of heating should be the same as for a natural maximum microcline. Indeed Goldsmith and Laves (1954a) showed that dry heating of natural microcline at high temperature did yield a complete series of intermediate states to monoclinic K-feldspar, but detailed cell dimensions were not measured. Thorough studies of the effect of dry heating on a variety of natural K-feldspars are desirable to evaluate the effects of Al, Si distribution and domain texture. In the meantime, it will be assumed that Müller's data apply also to natural microcline.

Hence one can distinguish between a one-step trend for dry-heated microcline and for K-exchanged synthetic albites, and a two-step trend for selected natural K-feldspars. From the thermodynamic viewpoint, dry heating at 1040–1130° C need not yield structural states that represent equilibrium at lower temperatures. Natural K-feldspars from igneous rocks tend to follow a two-step trend which is assumed to be the best approach to true equilibrium. Those K-feldspars whose cell dimensions lie between the one- and two-step trends are assumed to have a metastable structural state, or to suffer from the effect of domain strain (see next section).

The distinction between a one-step and a two-step trend is not easy for low values of c, because α and γ are close to 90°. When these angles deviate from 90° by only 0.1–0.2°, each pair of triclinic diffractions overlaps to give a single broadened diffraction whose center is consistent with monoclinic geometry. It might be argued that the synthetic K-feldspars actually have triclinic geometry and thus belong to the one-step trend. However the X-ray patterns are reported to be sharp, and theoretically one would expect the synthetic feldspars to have a disordered Al, Si distribution consistent with an overall monoclinic geometry.

For the b dimension, there is a wide band resulting from a combination of experimental error, effect of Na-substitution, and perhaps a small effect between the one- and two-step trends.

K-rich Feldspar: Problem of Domain Texture. Essentially all natural K-feldspars are either monoclinic or consist of a special intergrowth of Albite and Pericline twins inherited from a monoclinic precursor (see Chapter 18 for

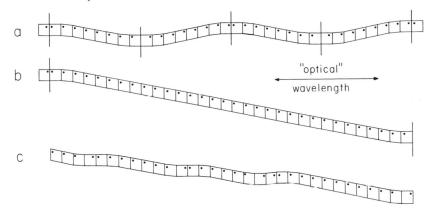

Fig. 7-8. Drawings to illustrate the effect of ordering of T atoms on cell angles and optical properties. Each parallelogram represents a unit cell, while the dot represents an Al atom. The shape of each unit cell is governed by the position of Al atoms in it and in its neighbors. Out-of-step domain boundaries are shown by vertical lines. Diagram a shows small domains each with perfect order, b shows a large domain coarser than the "optical" wavelength, and c shows a single domain with disordered Al atoms. Note that in practice, the optical wavelength would be about 60 times as large as shown here. (From Smith, 1970, Fig. 5)

details of twinning, and Chapter 6 for single-crystal data). Some of these K-feldspars have twins so coarse that the twinning is readily visible as cross-hatching in a polarizing microscope (Chapter 8). In some K-feldspars, it is likely that recrystallization resulted in partial or complete destruction of the twin texture. Some K-feldspars are optically monoclinic even though X-ray patterns show triclinic geometry. For these specimens there is a domain texture of scale finer than the resolution of the microscope such that statistically the triclinic domains act as a monoclinic structure (Fig. 7-8). The resolution of the X-ray technique is about 10^3 higher permitting detection of much finer domains than for optical methods. The problem to be faced here is the meaning of cell dimensions measured for K-feldspars with domain texture. Unfortunately there is no clear answer because there is no reliable theoretical relation between cell dimensions and the atomic and textural properties. Although all workers on K-feldspars would agree that cell dimensions depend on (a) the dimensions and shape of the domains (b) the mutual strain between the domains, and (c) the distribution of Al and Si atoms over the T sites, they would not agree on the relative importance of the effects. Indeed each worker makes his own subjective estimate of the effects and runs the danger of believing that his estimate is better than those of other workers.

Migration of Al into T_1 sites of a monoclinic alkali feldspar, such as sanidine, permits a choice of tetrahedral nodes leading to out-of-step Al, Si distributions (Chapter 3). Statistically, one can envisage a *theoretical low sanidine* in which random occupancy of T_1 sites (and of T_2 sites) avoids the problem of an out-of-step distribution thereby yielding an overall monoclinic symmetry. Actually even for a statistical distribution there must be clusters of T_1 sites that are occupied by Al atoms forming rudimentary domains. When the clusters are small, the continuity of the aluminosilicate framework inhibits the tendency of the clusters to adopt the geometry of microcline. As the clusters get larger, such a tendency increases and one can speak of domains. On single-crystal diffraction photographs (both with X-rays, Chapter 6, and electrons, Chapter 10), the single spot for monoclinic geometry becomes elongated along the minor axis of the domain. As the domains grow in size, the elongated spot breaks up into an individual spot for each domain, but with the spots joined by streaks because of the strained boundary region between the domains. Ultimately the domains break apart such that there is no continuity of the aluminosilicate framework. Only then do the diffraction patterns reveal the geometry appropriate for an isolated homogeneous feldspar.

The development of domain texture is probably governed by many factors both physical and chemical. Once formed, a domain texture is highly metastable because movement of a boundary requires migration of Al and Si atoms.

Figure 7-8 illustrates the problem of interpreting the lattice angles α and γ of K-feldspars as described by Smith (1970). Assume that the Al atom influences the unit cell so that an acute angle occurs at the quadrant occupied by the Al atom. Suppose that the geometry of a unit cell is affected only by the Al position of that unit cell and of its neighbors. In (a) and (b), each domain has perfect order, and distortion occurs only at the out-of-step boundaries. For (b), the boundaries are so far apart that the overall geometry as revealed by diffraction methods would be essentially that of an isolated single domain. For (a), the boundaries are so close that the mean angle measured by X-rays is less than for an isolated domain. Indeed as the domains get smaller the angle becomes effectively 90° since the diffraction pattern consists of single diffuse spots with rectangular geometry. Diagram (c) shows a single domain with some random disorder of the Al atoms chosen to give the same average angle as for the domains in (a). *Mathematically* domains could be visualized in (c), but from the viewpoint of a *correlation coefficient*, the pattern in (c) is best visualized as a single oblique domain with local disorder and not as an assemblage of out-of-step domains.

Obviously this model is too crude for interpretation of feldspars, but it does provide a basis for subjective discussion of the cell dimensions of K-feldspars.

Historically, the problems of interpretation of cell dimensions of domain intergrowths were recognized by Laves (1950, 1952), and the combined effects of domain size and degree of order on the triclinic nature of K-feldspar were discussed thoroughly by Goldsmith and Laves (1954a, b), Laves and Goldsmith (1961), and Smith and MacKenzie (1961).

K-rich Feldspar: Further Interpretation of Natural Specimens. All the maximum microclines described in this section are twinned on such a coarse scale, being visible optically, that the cell dimensions are free of strain.

The Spencer U intermediate microcline was also coarsely twinned, and Bailey and Taylor (1955) made their measurements on an untwinned fragment cut with a razor blade. The cell dimensions for this specimen are clearly distinct from those of the K-exchanged albites. Hence I conclude that untwinned K-feldspars do not have a unique trend between the cell dimensions, irrespective of the various opinions on the effect of domain texture.

All other interpretations are subjective. The Spencer B specimen is an adularia with a domain texture clearly revealed by single-crystal X-ray and electron diffraction techniques. The diffuse streaks on the X-ray photographs, and especially the dark-field electron micrographs, demonstrate the intimacy of the domain texture. It is obvious that there is strong coherence between the domains thereby inhibiting development of triclinic geometry. The peaks on X-ray powder patterns do not show the diffuse streaks, and the cell dimensions must obey monoclinic symmetry. Nevertheless it seems clear to me that this specimen should be regarded locally as triclinic rather than monoclinic.

Wright and Stewart (1968) measured accurate cell dimensions of various sanidines and "orthoclases". They did not give any details of single-crystal X-ray photographs, but it seems probable that none of these specimens show the strong diffuse streaks like those in Spencer B adularia. The Spencer C orthoclase measured by Cole et al. (1949) yields very weak diffuse streaks on single-crystal X-ray photographs exposed for a long time. Probably all the Wright-Stewart specimens show such weak diffractions, by analogy with the observations of MacKenzie and Smith (e.g. Smith and MacKenzie, 1959) on orthoclase perthites, and the earlier data of Laves (1950). However, these diffuse streaks might be interpreted merely as the result of local statistical fluctuations in an Al, Si distribution that essentially obeyed monoclinic symmetry, rather than the result of coherent domains with triclinic distribution of Al and Si atoms. Chapter 9 quotes many of the assertions about the nature of "orthoclase" and "sanidine". It is clear that "orthoclase" covers a variety of K-feldspars as maintained by Laves (e.g. 1960).

Returning to Spencer B, it must be emphasized that this is an adularia that grew metastably at low temperature in an Alpine vein. Many studies have documented the unusual nature of adularias, which probably result from metastable growth either as high sanidine or as an intermediate type followed by metastable change towards maximum microcline. Hence one must be cautious in comparing their cell dimensions with those of the igneous specimens. A detailed survey of the properties of adularia is given in Chapter 36. Gubser and Laves (1967) published values of a^*, b^* and c^* for many unheated and heated adularias, as described later (see Fig. 7-18).

Ion-exchange and Synthesis Series: General. Following the studies of Laves (1951) and Goldsmith and Laves (1961), Orville (1967) measured the cell dimensions of a complete ion-exchange series prepared by heating natural microcline with dry NaCl and KCl. Waldbaum and Robie (1971) prepared a similar series by heating natural microcline with dry NaCl and KCl. The cell dimensions for the low albite are essentially indistinguishable from those of Na-exchanged microcline, and similarly for microcline and K-exchanged albite. However, the cell dimensions for intermediate compositions made by Orville and by Waldbaum and Robie differ by several times the experimental error, and the cause is unknown. Wright and Stewart (1968) prepared another series starting with a natural "orthoclase".

Donnay and Donnay (1952) measured the cell dimensions of a series of synthetic feldspars prepared hydrothermally by Tuttle and Bowen at 700–800° C, and Wright and Stewart refined the data. Orville synthesized hydrothermally a new series of synthetic feldspars also at 700–800° C. Both sets of synthetic specimens belong to the sanidine-high albite series, but the cell dimensions indicate that the structural state is slightly ordered. The above data for the microcline-, orthoclase- and sanidine-series outline the effect of K, Na substitution on the cell dimensions of alkali feldspars, and permitted the development of fundamental interpretations of the distribution of Al, Si atoms in the alkali feldspars.

In detail, the situation is complicated by the evidence of Tuttle and his students that the cell dimensions of alkali feldspars may depend on some factor additional to the K, Na ratio and the Al, Si distribution. Luth and Tuttle (1966) synthesized alkali feldspars from three environments: one with normal feldspar composition, one with excess Al_2O_3 and one with excess alkali. The cell dimensions a and b gave different correlations for the three crystallization conditions.

Ion-exchange and Synthesis Series: Data. Figure 7-9 shows the variation of cell dimensions with chemical composition for the sanidine-, orthoclase- and microcline series (Orville, 1967; Wright and Stewart, 1968; and Waldbaum and Robie, 1971). The data of Donnay and Donnay (1952) are omitted because of a slight systematic error (Smith, 1956). The cell parameter a and the cell volume V are almost independent of structural state, and increase about 6% with complete substitution of Na with K. The b parameter varies inversely with c as the structural state changes for a given chemical composition. For a single series, both b and c vary non-linearly with mol.-% Or. The angle β is almost independent of structural state, and varies only 0.7° with substitution of K for Na.

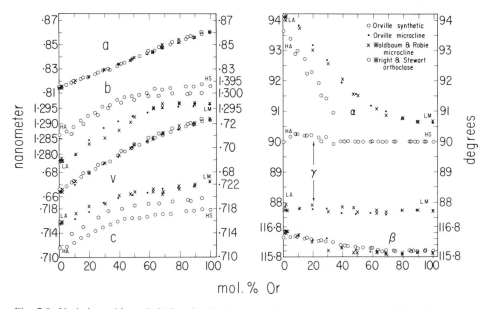

Fig. 7-9. Variation with mol.-% Or of cell dimensions for a synthetic sanidine-high albite series (Orville, 1967); b ion-exchanged Hugo microcline series (Orville, 1967); c ion-exchanged Amelia microcline series (Waldbaum and Robie, 1971) and d ion-exchanged P50–56F orthoclase series (Wright and Stewart, 1968). See Table 7-2 for data and standard errors. The volume is expressed in cubic nanometers

Both the sanidine and orthoclase series are monoclinic from about 40–100 mol.- % Or: for more sodic compositions, γ stays close to 90° but α moves to about 93.5° with little difference between the two structural series. The microcline series has γ near 87.8° for all compositions, but α changes non-linearly from 90.6° for low microcline to 94.0° for low albite.

So much for these general relations which are non-controversial: now for the nasty details. First, there is the problem of the difference between the microcline-low albite series of Orville and of Waldbaum and Robie. The effect is particularly seen in b: whereas the data of Orville follow a parabolic variation with Or, those of Waldbaum and Robie increase linearly from Or_0 to Or_{70} and then stay constant from Or_{70} to Or_{100}. The deviations reach 0.003 nm and are well outside the experimental errors. Smaller deviations occur in c, but the data for a and V are consistent. Orville prepared his specimens from a 100–200 mesh fraction of Hugo microcline $Ab_{11.6}Or_{85.7}An_{0.2}Rb\text{-}F_{2.4}$ by (a) producing low albite $Ab_{98.2}Or_{1.0}An_{0.2}$ by heating with NaCl for 48 h at 900° C, (b) heating some of the low albite with KCl for 48 h at 900° C to produce microcline $Ab_{0.3}Or_{99.5}An_{0.2}$, and (c) homogenizing weighed mixtures of the exchanged albite and microcline at 900° C for 48 h to produce uniform compositions at 10% intervals. He states (pers. comm., 1971) that the specimens were heated in sealed platinum containers, and that no change in the X-ray patterns occurred upon increasing the heating time from 24–48 h. Waldbaum and Robie used a similar procedure, but starting from a 100–400 mesh fraction of Amelia microcline $Ab_{16}Or_{86}An_0Rb\text{-}F_2$. Homogenization was carried out for about 150 h at 935 ± 15° C, with cooling and remixing every 48 h. Electron microprobe analyses showed that most grains were almost homogeneous, but that some of the larger ones were inhomogeneous to ± 10 mol.- % Or. Waldbaum and Robie found that sharpness of an X-ray line such as $\bar{2}01$ is not a sufficient criterion for complete homogeneity. Orville's microcline was perthitic and showed cross-hatched twinning about 0.03–0.3 mm across. Waldbaum and Robie's specimen was an amazonite, but the textural relations were not indicated. The difference between the data of Orville and of Waldbaum and Robie may result from either incomplete homogenization, or some strain effect, or from incorrect refinement of the X-ray data. Fortunately the data for K-rich and Na-rich compositions are almost the same, and the intermediate compositions are thermodynamically unstable and have little relevance to natural feldspars. However it is important for thermochemists that the discrepancy be explained because the same factor that changes the cell dimensions may change heats of solution.

The second problem is minor. Because Orville synthesized his sanidine-high albite series hydrothermally at 700–800° C, some ordering of the Al, Si atoms occurred. A new set of data should be obtained from specimens heated at the solidus. Until then, Orville's data should not be regarded as defining the extreme high structural state. For the low albite-microcline series, there is also uncertainty whether the present data represent the extreme low structural state. The triclinic indicator of Orville's microcline is 0.94 compared to 1 defined by Goldsmith and Laves (1954b) for maximum low microcline.

The third uncertainty involves the orthoclase series prepared by Wright and Stewart (1968) from an orthoclase P 50–56 F whose optics and cell dimensions are indistinguishable from the Spencer C specimen used for structure analysis by Cole *et al.* Gravimetric analysis gave a composition $Or_{87.7}Ab_{10.7}An_{0.4}Cn_{1.2}$ compared to an electron microprobe analysis of $Or_{90.8}Ab_{8.0}An_{0.7}Cn_{0.3}$ others$_{0.2}$ for Spencer C. However flame photometer analyses suggested that the Or + Ab content for P 50–56 F was actually 95.9 %, resulting in an uncertainty of about 2 % Or in the compositions for the orthoclase series. Furthermore, the An and Cn components are not removed during ion-exchange (as is the Rb-F of the microclines). The Cn component probably causes the higher a and V of the orthoclase series (Fig. 7-9), and may also increase b and c.

Ion-exchange and Synthesis Series: Problem of Non-stoichiometry. Luth and Querol-Suñé synthesized 29 feldspars from dehydrated gels held at 500 bars and 800° C in the presence of an aqueous vapor phase, quartz and corundum. Cell dimensions were measured with a Guinier camera, using particular care to reject peaks from overlapping diffractions. The actual chemical compositions of the feldspars are somewhat uncertain. The gels were prepared by the method described

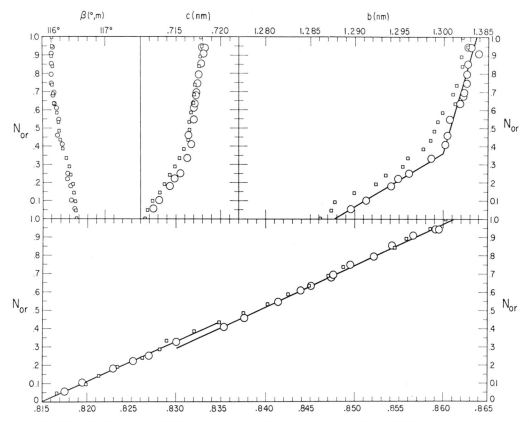

Fig. 7-10. Cell dimensions of feldspars synthesized by Luth and Querol-Suñé (1970) compared with those of Orville (1967). Open squares: Orville; open circles: Luth and Querol-Suñé. The size of the symbols has no significance with respect to errors. The straight lines represent separate regressions for the monoclinic and triclinic members of the Luth and Querol-Suñé data. (From Luth and Querol-Suñé, Fig. 2)

by Luth and Ingamells, and were presumed to be stoichiometric (Na, K)$AlSi_3O_8$. However the synthesis products contained corundum and quartz suggesting that either (a) the original gel compositions were incorrect, (b) the feldspars were non-stoichiometric, or (c) the aqueous phase leached out alkalies. Alternative (c) was dismissed because of the small weight of the aqueous phase and the expected low solubility. Querol-Suñé found by atomic absorption spectrophotometry that the Na + K contents of the crystalline product were equivalent to only 85 – 101 % of feldspar components with a mean of 90.4. Because the products were estimated to contain only 3 – 5 modal % quartz and corundum, the feldspars would seem to deviate from the ideal composition, perhaps by incorporation of $H_3OAlSi_3O_8$ molecule. Infra-red data gave no evidence of protons in the feldspar, and Luth and Querol-Suñé argued that the cell dimensions were too low for incorporation of a large H_3O ion. The situation is obscure, and the interpretation of the cell dimensions in terms of Or content is subject to an unknown error perhaps as large as 5 % of the amount present.

Figure 7-10 shows the comparison by Luth and Querol-Suñé between their data and those of Orville for synthetic feldspars. The two sets of data for a and β agree within the random experimental error, but Orville's values for both b and c are lower than those of Luth and Querol-Suñé. Assuming no systematic experimental errors, these data are puzzling. Change of Al, Si order produces opposite changes in b and c, suggesting that the difference in cell dimensions cannot be explained solely by variation of Al, Si distribution. Assumption of an error in the Or content to explain the deviation in b and c would produce a deviation in a.

Luth and Querol-Suñé conclude "Although the source of these differences may be related to crystalline solution with a hydronium (or oxonium) feldspar "molecule" $H_3OAlSi_3O_8$, a more probable source of these differences is that this feldspar series is less ordered in terms of Al/Si distribution than the sanidine-high albite series". I suggest that this conclusion is unjustified, and that until the real composition of these feldspars is determined the value of their cell dimensions is highly questionable except to show that a problem exists.

Figure 7-11 summarizes the essential data on the cell dimensions of feldspars synthesized in the Tuttle-Luth laboratories. The a and b dimensions are plotted with respect to Orville's data for the sanidine and microcline series. Feldspars synthesized by Luth and Tuttle (1966) from gels of normal feldspar composition yielded data fully consistent with those obtained by Orville, thus removing the possibility of serious systematic bias between the two laboratories. Feldspars crystallized from gels containing excess Al_2O_3 with bulk composition (Na_xK_{1-x}) $AlSi_3O_8 \cdot yAl_2O_3$ yielded a dimensions essentially the same as those for feldspar crystallized from "ideal" gels with the same x, but the b dimensions were larger. Feldspars crystallized from gels containing excess alkali silicate gave the same a dimensions as for the ideal gels, and similar but perhaps slightly smaller b values on average. Gels rich in both Si and Al yielded feldspars with b values unusually high with respect to the a values as described already.

Obviously there is a problem, but the answer is unclear. Comparison of the cell dimensions of the synthetic alkali feldspars with those of the heated natural end-members (see Figs. 7-3 and 7-7) suggests that the former are slightly more

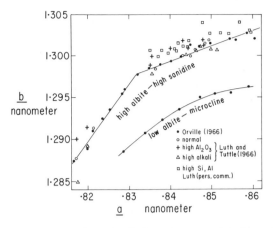

Fig. 7-11. Relation of cell dimensions *a* and *b* determined by Luth and Tuttle (1966) and Luth (personal communication) for synthetic alkali feldspars synthesized in environments of type shown in the key to symbols. The curves for Orville's (1967) data were estimated by eye. The kink for the high albite - high sanidine series corresponds to the triclinic-monoclinic inversion at room temperature

ordered than the latter. This is not surprising because the synthetic alkali feldspars were made hydrothermally at several hundreds of degrees below the solidus. I suspect that the gels used by Luth and co-workers were somewhat off the desired composition. Nevertheless there may be a definite deviation from the $(Na,K)AlSi_3O_8$ composition for feldspars grown at high temperature under conditions of excess alkali or of excess tetrahedral atoms, and this results in small perturbations of the cell dimensions. This assumption is consistent with the preferred explanation for the development of myrmekite (Chapter 20).

For the remainder of this section it will be necessary to ignore these minor complications, and to interpret the variation of cell dimensions in terms of Na, K substitution and Al, Si distribution. In particular, there is no reason to doubt that the synthetic specimens of Donnay-Donnay and Orville are essentially stoichiometric, while the exchanged microcline series should be nearly stoichiometric because of equilibration to a low temperature of the starting materials.

Ion-exchange and Synthesis Series: Regression Equations. Mathematical analysis of the cell dimensions in terms of chemical composition of alkali feldspars is difficult and uncertain because (1) the experimental errors in the cell dimensions are too close to the subtle effects being investigated, (2) the symmetry changes from monoclinic to triclinic in disordered varieties, and (3) the crystal structure may change in a complex manner as the aluminosilicate framework crumples during substitution of Na for K. Nevertheless the regression analyses are valuable, particularly since the excess molar volume determines the pressure effect on the unmixing solvus. Unfortunately in 1973 all cell dimensions for the series of alkali feldspar had been determined at room temperature only, and it is not known whether the excess molar volume is still the same at temperatures of 600–800° C, near the crest of the solvus.

The mathematical basis of regression analysis may be found in Deming (1948). This type of analysis assumes that one parameter (the independent variable) is known with complete accuracy, and that the other parameter (the dependent variable) is subject to a Gaussian error distribution. The regression polynomial results from a minimization of the sum of the squares of deviations of the dependent variable. When both variables are subject to error, the procedure of Hey (1969) is applicable. For cell dimensions of feldspars it is assumed that there is no error in the chemical composition which becomes the independent variable.

Consider a binary composition series such as $(Na,K)AlSi_3O_8$ in which the components are labelled 1 and 2 with mole fractions N_1 and N_2. A physical parameter such as the cell volume V can be expressed by the polynomial

$$V = A + BN_2 + CN_2^2 + DN_2^3 + \cdots .$$

The values of A and B plus the residual error are first calculated for a linear fit using just the first two terms. Then A, B, C and the residual error are calculated for a quadratic fit, and so on. Obviously the more parameters are used, the lower the residual error because n items of data can be fitted perfectly with a polynomial with n parameters. In practice the residual errors are examined and a higher order of polynomial is accepted only if there is a significant drop in the residual. For cell dimensions of feldspars, the experimental error is sufficiently large that a third-order polynomial is always sufficient.

For thermodynamic calculations, the molar volume $\bar{V}$ is best expressed in the form:

$$\bar{V} = \bar{V}_1^0 N_1 + \bar{V}_2^0 N_2 + (\bar{V}_2^* - \bar{V}_2^0)N_1^2 N_2 + (\bar{V}_1^* - \bar{V}_1^0)N_1 N_2^2$$

as shown graphically in Fig. 7-12. It may be seen that V_1^* and V_2^* are obtained from the tangents to the polynomial curve.

An *ideal solution* (see Chapter 21) has a linear relation between mole volume and mole fraction (Fig. 7-12), and pressure has no effect on unmixing. The deviation of the observed volume from that of an ideal solution, $\bar{V}_{ex}$, is obtained from the coefficients of a third-order polynomial as follows:

$$\bar{V}_{ex} = -(C + 2D) N_1 N_2^2 - (C + D) N_2 N_1^2 .$$

For an ideal solution, C and D are zero, of course. A *symmetric regular solution* has C non-zero and D zero. An *asymmetric regular solution* has both C and D non-zero. In practice it is difficult to distinguish between the two types of regular solution because D usually has a high statistical uncertainty for actual data.

For alkali feldspars, there is the serious problem whether the data should be regarded as one or more populations (see Fig. 7-9). Thus Waldbaum and Thompson (1968) considered Orville's data for the sanidine--high albite series as three populations:

(1) monoclinic, (2) monoclinic at the synthesis temperature of 700 or 800° C and triclinic at room temperature, and (3) triclinic at both growth and room temperatures. Figure 7-13 plots the difference between observed and calculated volumes using a quadratic fit for just the monoclinic members. Of the eight data points for the triclinic members, seven are outside the extrapolated error band at the level of one standard deviation. Hence it is reasonable to regard the triclinic

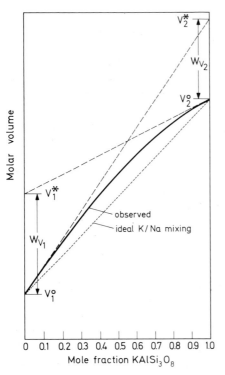

Fig. 7-12. Schematic diagram of molar volume in a solid solution series, as exemplified by alkali feldspar. See text for definition of the terms. (From Waldbaum and Thompson, 1968, Fig. 1)

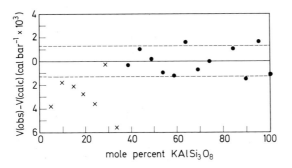

Fig. 7-13. Residuals of molar volumes for sanidine–high albite series of Orville (1967). The calculated values were obtained by a quadratic fit to the monoclinic members (solid dots), and the dashed lines correspond to the standard deviation. The crosses represent the triclinic members. (From Waldbaum and Thompson, 1968, Fig. 5)

members as a separate population from the monoclinic ones. Unfortunately it is quite unclear whether there is any distinction between the theoretical populations of type (1) and (3). The specimens of composition Or_0 and Or_5 should belong to population (3), *if they equilibrated at the synthesis temperature*, but may have crystallized metastably with monoclinic symmetry. Orville (1967) showed that the angular difference between the 131 and $1\bar{3}1$ diffractions of the synthetic albite was similar to that given by MacKenzie (1957) for a specimen equilibrated at

800° C. However there are too few data points in Fig. 7-13 to provide a valid test for the triclinic population, and the question of two populations must remain open until further data are obtained. See Vogel et al. (1973).

The following is a list of regression equations in the literature:

(a) Orville (1967): third-order polynomials for a, b, c, α, β, γ, V and V_{mix} for his sanidine–high albite and microcline–low albite series; note that his Table 4 has been confused by the typesetter and that all the B, C and D coefficients of the angles are in fractions of a degree and not in minutes as shown; the standard error applies to the residual between the observed and calculated cell dimension, not to the individual coefficients,

(b) Waldbaum and Thompson (1968): regression of cell volume and molar volume for sanidine–high albite series of both Donnay and Donnay (1952) and Orville (1967); note that systematic error in the DD data probably gives too high a volume by about 0.2% though the excess molar volume should be unaffected if the systematic error is constant for all compositions; data split into monoclinic and triclinic populations; see Chapter 22 for thermodynamic application of data on molar volumes,

(c) Luth and Querol-Suñé (1970): regression of a, b, c, α, β, γ and V for sanidine–high albite series of Orville and of Luth and Querol-Suñé; the data were treated both as a single population and as separate triclinic and monoclinic populations; LQ ignored Orville's datum for Or_{38} because of incomplete resolution of peaks; standard deviations are given for each coefficient as well as for the residual in the cell dimension: note that the coefficients for the LQ series are probably meaningless because of uncertainty in the chemical composition (see earlier),

(d) Waldbaum and Robie (1971): regression of molar volumes for the two microcline series expressing each as a single population,

(e) Luth (1972): abstract of detailed paper on regression equations for all available series.

7.3.3 Interpretation in Terms of Si, Al Order and K, Na Substitution

The earlier discussion has assumed that the cell dimensions of alkali feldspars depend on the Si, Al order and K, Na substitution. This section presents a quantitative interpretation based essentially on the papers of Orville (1967), Wright and Stewart (1968), Stewart and Ribbe (1969) and Kroll (1971a, b). All other interpretations in the literature are equivalent apart from minor choices of reference data. The section concludes with my own evaluation of the data using diagrams drawn in orientations analogous to a temperature-composition section of the phase diagram. It must be emphasized that no single cell dimension gives a unique measure of any chemical or structural property of a K, Na feldspar: for example, the a dimension depends principally on Na, K substitution but there is an uncertainty of about 4% Ab if the structural state is ignored. Of course, if a specimen is seen optically to be a cross-hatched microcline, the appropriate regression curve can be used without detailed study of the structural state.

General Interpretation. (a) The K, Na substitution can be determined from V, a, or some function dominated by a, with a potential accuracy of 1–2% Or when the structural state is known and impurities are trivial.

(b) Both the K, Na substitution and an estimate of structural state can be obtained from a plot of b vs. c. Substitution of Na causes both b and c to decrease, whereas Si, Al ordering causes b to decrease and c to increase. The cell dimensions of homogeneous feldspars fall inside a parallelogram approximately defined by the extreme series for microcline–low albite and sanidine–high albite (Fig. 7-14). Wright and Stewart (1968) plotted b vs. c for Orville's microcline and sanidine series, Donnay and Donnay's series of synthetic feldspars (using a new

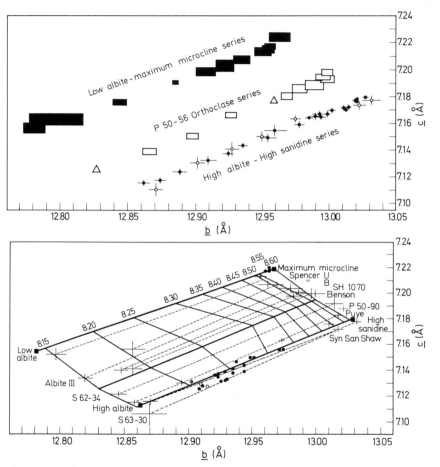

Fig. 7-14. Relation between b and c for alkali feldspars. a Data for two ion-exchange series obtained from a near-maximum microcline (Orville) and the P 50—56 orthoclase (Wright-Stewart) plus data for the synthetic feldspars of Orville (filled circles) and Donnay-Donnay (open circles). The limits of the symbols show one standard error from the least squares refinement. The triangles show interpolated and extrapolated values in the orthoclase series. From Wright and Stewart (1968, Fig. 2a). b Data for specimens ion-exchanged by Wright and Stewart, as given in Table 7-2. The dashed lines connect ion-exchanged specimens, except for P 50—90 which is shown by a dotted cross. Solid lines sloping SW–NE represent the series in (a). Kinked lines sloping NW–SE represent members of the series with equal values of a, as interpolated by Wright and Stewart. The small squares are approximate positions selected for the four extreme feldspars. Small circles represent natural feldspars: solid symbol, unpublished data of T. L. Wright for maximum microclines, and published data of Carmichael and MacKenzie (1964) for anorthoclases; open symbol, published data on anorthoclases by Boudette and Ford (1966); half-solid symbol, unpublished datum of D. B. Stewart on anorthoclase. (From Wright and Stewart, 1968, Fig. 2b)

least-squares refinement) and their own P 50–56 F orthoclase series (Fig. 7-14a). In a second diagram (Fig. 7-14b) they represented the microcline, orthoclase and sanidine series by three bent lines. In addition they plotted the following specimens before and after ion-exchange with molten alkali halide: S 63–30, S 62–34 and Albite III synthetic albites; SynSanShaw synthetic K-feldspar; Puye and P 50–90 sanidines; Benson and SH 1070 orthoclases; Spencer B adularia and Spencer U intermediate microcline. When account is taken of the experimental errors, all the ion-exchange paths are nearly parallel. Data are also shown for natural microclines and anorthoclases.

At first sight, the bc plot provides a unique characterization of structural state, but this is not correct since it does not distinguish between the one- and two-step trends (cf. Fig. 7-2).

In principle, the bc plot provides a check on the estimate of chemical composition from a or V. Figure 7-14b shows contours of a estimated by Wright and Stewart from the data for the synthesis and exchange series. The contours crowd together for K-rich feldspars. Probably some of the kinking results from experimental error, while there are additional problems for the K-rich feldspars.

Figure 7-15 is a plot of b^* vs. c^* whose implications must be the same as those from the bc plot. The diagram is deliberately oriented with albite to the left and the high structural states to the top, as in the conventional TX section of the phase diagram. Here the microcline series of Waldbaum and Robie is plotted and found to deviate seriously from that of Orville. Whereas Orville's series gives a near-linear plot roughly parallel to those of the orthoclase and sanidine series, the Waldbaum-Robie series follows an S-shaped path.

The data points for synthetic albites (Table 7-2c) fall in a single band from low to high albite when account is taken of experimental error. Probably the data of Grundy and Brown (1969) have a systematic bias to lower values of b^* and c^*, because they are displaced from those of the other workers.

The data points for synthetic K-feldspars (Table 7-2d) fall in a band between the K-rich ends of the sanidine and orthoclase series. The horizontal crosses show the data obtained for K-exchanged adularias and microclines (Table 7-2k) by Gubser and Laves (1967) using merely the 060 and 002 lines in a Guinier pattern. (This illustrates the advantage of the b^*c^* plot over the bc plot since it is not necessary to determine all the cell dimensions. For example, using a back-reflexion Weissenberg with a crystal mounted on a, it is possible to measure b^* and c^* from a single photograph). The diagonal crosses show data for adularias "sanidinized" by heating for 200 h at 1100° C. In the inset diagram is a 2-fold enlargement for these data together with the wt.-% Na_2O determined by flame photometry. Taken at face value, these data indicate that for sanidinized K-feldspars, increase of Na content has no significant effect on b^* until the Ab content reaches about 10%. Furthermore, c^* apparently first decreases from Ab_0 to about Ab_{10} before increasing towards the value for pure albite. Detailed diagrams showing the variation of a^*, b^* and c^* with Na-content are given in Gubser and Laves (1967).

Although the general relations of the bc and b^*c^* plots are clear, the details are confusing. Selection of reference values for the extreme end-members depends on one's evaluation of the conflicting data. Stewart and Ribbe (1969) chose the following values: low albite b 1.2784_4, c 0.7157_9; high albite 1.2871_2, 0.7109_9;

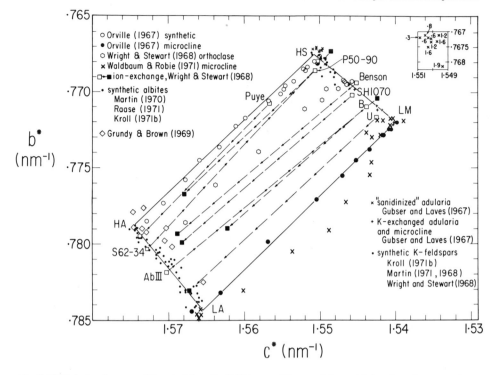

Fig. 7-15. Relation between b^* and c^* for alkali feldspars. The quadrilateral joins the reference values for high sanidine, low microcline, low albite and high albite. The upper left shows the identification of the four reference series, the middle left the key to the synthetic albites and the lower right the key to synthetic and treated natural K-feldspars. The inset diagram is a 2-fold enlargement of the data for "sanidinized" adularias, together with the wt.-% Na_2O. See Table 7-2 for data. Ion-exchange paths are shown for two synthetic albites (S 62—34 and Ab III) and six natural K-feldspars (Wright and Stewart, 1968). Data by Müller (1969) for K-exchanged synthetic albites of Raase (1971) are omitted to avoid overlap: see Table 7-2

maximum microcline 1.2964_3, 0.7221_9; high sanidine 1.3028_9, 0.7176_3 nm. Gubser and Laves (1967) chose the following triplets of a^*, b^* and c^*: sanidine 1.2931, 0.76715, 1.5506; microcline 1.2959, 0.77208, 1.5402 nm^{-1}. I have chosen the following values for the cell dimensions of low microcline (LM), high sanidine (HS), low albite (LA) and high albite (HA):

	LM	HS	LA	HA		LM	HS	LA	HA
a^*	1.2958	1.2934	1.3743	1.3694	a	0.85903	0.86043	0.8138	0.8160
b^*	0.77200	0.76752	0.78436	0.77879	b	1.29659	1.30289	1.2785	1.2873
c^*	1.5400	1.5508	1.5655	1.5746	c	0.72224	0.71763	0.7158	0.7110
α^*	90.42	90	86.40	85.93	α	90.65	90	94.26	93.52
β^*	64.05	63.97	63.49	63.50	β	115.96	116.03	116.60	116.43
γ^*	92.30	90	90.46	87.95	γ	87.65	90	87.68	90.27
					V	0.72262	0.72289	0.66406	0.66711

(angles in degrees, edges in nanometers or nm^{-1}, V in nm^3).

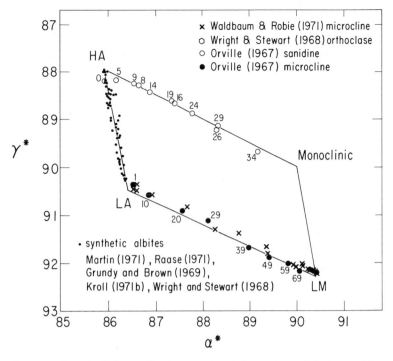

Fig. 7-16. Relation between α^* and γ^* for synthetic, natural and ion-exchanged feldspars. The quadrilateral joins the reference points for monoclinic feldspars, low microcline (*LM*), low albite (*LA*) and high albite (*HA*). See Table 7-2 for data. The numbers show mol.-% Or for the specimens of Orville (1967) and Wright and Stewart (1968)

Comparison of all three sets of data shows agreement within experimental uncertainties.

(c) The relation between α^* and γ^* was introduced by MacKenzie and Smith (1955) to characterize alkali feldspars in perthites (Chapter 19), and Fig. 7-16 shows reference data for synthetic and ion-exchanged feldspars. All members of the sanidine and orthoclase series with more than 40 mol.-% Or are monoclinic and plot at a single point. The data for the more sodic members of this series lie on a straight line between the monoclinic point and high albite, but the distance is not a linear function of mol.-% Or. For the microcline series, all members are triclinic and lie approximately near the straight line between the reference points for low microcline and low albite, with no significant difference between the data of Orville and those of Waldbaum and Robie.

Also shown in Fig. 7-16 are the data for synthetic albites, all of which within experimental error are consistent with the straight line from high albite to low albite. Figure 7-17 shows some data points for natural albites and microcline taken from Table 7-2. The chosen reference points for high albite, low albite and low microcline are consistent with the extreme ranges of synthetic and natural feldspars when account is taken of the experimental error.

Figure 7-17a shows pairs of specimens related by ion-exchange with dry alkali halide. Within experimental error, the ion-exchange paths are nearly parallel to the directions defined by the series in Fig. 7-16. Just as for the $b^* c^*$ plot, it appears that the structural state can be determined uniquely from the $\alpha^* \gamma^*$ plot (except for the monoclinic specimens). However this appearance is misleading as can be seen from Fig. 7-2.

Figure 7-17b shows an $\alpha^* \gamma^*$ plot for 180 individual components of unmixed alkali feldspars from a wide range of perthites measured by MacKenzie and Smith (1962). These and many other data fall into three groups roughly consistent with the microcline, "anorthoclase" and "albite" series of homogeneous feldspars. Although there may be problems concerning the accuracy of these data because of lattice strain, a tentative identification can be made. The microcline group poses no serious problem, but the "anorthoclase" group might result either from the sanidine or "orthoclase" series if only α^* and γ^* are known. The "albite" group also poses a problem since substitution of anorthite for albite molecule causes essentially identical changes as Si, Al disorder in pure albite (Section 7.4). Hence there is a severe ambiguity for this group. Positions are marked for plagioclase in the low structural state with compositions 10, 20 and

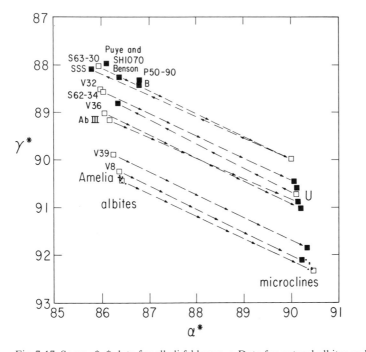

Fig. 7-17. Some $\alpha^* \gamma^*$ data for alkali feldspars. a Data for natural albites and microclines (dots), and data for ion-exchange pairs. Specimens prefixed with a V are synthetic albites measured by Raase (1971) and then K-exchanged by Müller (1969). The other specimens are an Amelia albite (Waldbaum and Robie, 1971) and three synthetic albites (S 63—30, S 62—34, Ab III), one synthetic K-feldspar (SSS) and five natural K-feldspars measured by Wright and Stewart (1968). The specimens Puye, SH 1070, Benson P 50—90 and B were monoclinic originally and ion-exchange paths are omitted. See Table 2 for data. b Data obtained for phases in perthites using the twin method of Smith and MacKenzie (1955). See MacKenzie and Smith (1962) for sources of data. The reference points for the sodic plagioclases in the low structural states are estimated from Fig. 7-41. See Fig. 7-16 for explanation of quadrilateral

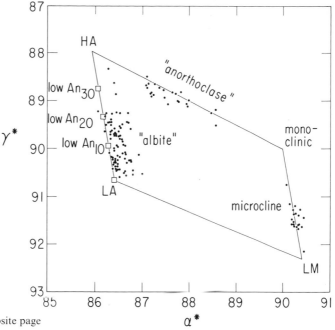

Fig. 7-17b. Legend see opposite page

30 mol. % An. Most of the data points for the "albite" group are displaced towards the positions for K-feldspar, and there is considerable unpublished evidence to indicate that some of this displacement represents genuine solid solution of Or molecule rather than experimental error. It is obvious that before α^* and γ^* are used to characterize sodic feldspars, it is desirable to estimate by some means other than X-ray diffraction methods whether the feldspar contains significant An molecule in solid solution. Full discussion is given in Chapter 19.

(d) Because neither the b^*c^* nor the $\alpha^*\gamma^*$ plot can distinguish between the one- and two-step trends if only one plot is examined, the obvious step is to see if simultaneous study of the two plots can give a complete characterization. Smith (1968) presented orally the results of such a study, but the written paper was rejected for publication on the advice of an anonymous referee that it presented nothing new! Stewart and Ribbe (1969) published a paper using $\alpha^*\gamma^*$ and $b\,c$ plots, the latter being topologically identical to a b^*c^* plot. The present treatment utilizes diagrams from the rejected paper (amended to include new data), and agrees with the general conclusions of the Stewart-Ribbe paper.

Figure 7-18 shows how the b^*c^* and $\alpha^*\gamma^*$ plots are contoured linearly from 0 to 1 to provide indicators of structural state $\Delta(b^*c^*)$ and $\Delta(\alpha^*\gamma^*)$ by reference to the arbitrary reference points given earlier. In addition, the plots are contoured from 0 for Na-feldspar to 1 for K-feldspar to yield the indicators $Or(b^*c^*)$ and $Or(\alpha^*\gamma^*)$ which provide a measure of the Or-content (see later). Figure 7-18 also contains the cell dimensions of alkali feldspars used in X-ray structural analyses.

The use of a quadrilateral does not imply that the extreme feldspar series lie on the quadrilateral boundaries; indeed Luth (1972) argues that the regression equations for the feldspar series (see earlier) do not agree well with these boundaries.

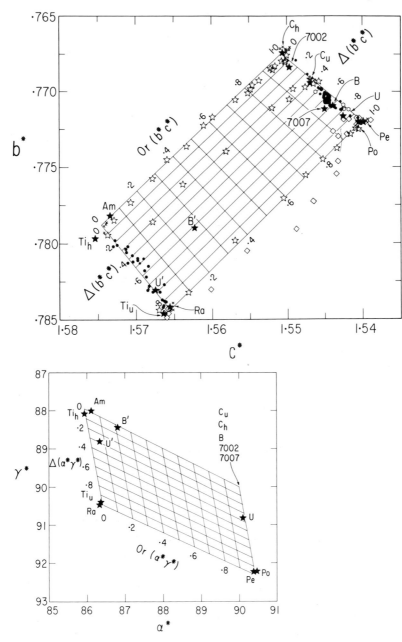

Fig. 7-18. Plots of b^*c^* and $\alpha^*\gamma^*$ in recommended orientations and contoured with the indicators of structural state (Δ) and Or-content. Cell dimensions are plotted of all Na- and K-feldspars for which X-ray structural analyses had been made by 1971 (see Table 7-2a)

The indicators $\Delta(b^*c^*)$ and $\Delta(\alpha^*\gamma^*)$ are plotted against each other in Fig. 7-19. By definition, high albite and high sanidine plot exactly at the extreme lower left and low albite and low microcline at the extreme upper right. This diagram permits distinction between the one- and two-step ordering sequences, a feature

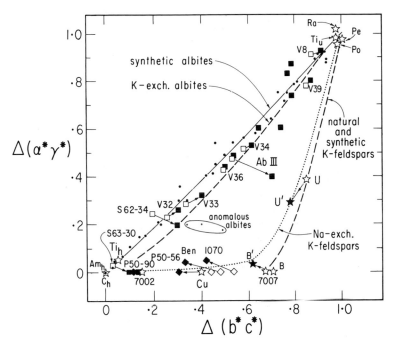

Fig. 7-19. Plot of the indicators of structural state $\Delta(b^*c^*)$ and $\Delta(\alpha^*\gamma^*)$. The open stars show specimens for which X-ray structural analyses have been made (see Table 7-2a). The dots show synthetic albites of Martin (1970) and Kroll (1971b). The open and filled squares, respectively, show synthetic albites before and after K-exchange (Wright and Stewart, 1968; Müller, 1969; Raase, 1971). The adjacent continuous and dashed lines are eye-estimated curves representing synthetic albite and K-exchanged derivatives. Three anomalous albites of Martin (1969) are ringed. Note that the K-exchanged product of Ab III is anomalous. The open and closed diamonds show natural and Na-exchanged K-feldspars (Wright and Stewart, 1968). The filled stars show the effect of K-exchange of U and B specimens. The adjacent dashed and dotted lines, respectively, are eye-estimated curves representing natural K-feldspars and Na-exchanged derivatives

not possessed by the individual b^*c^* and $\alpha^*\gamma^*$ diagrams, though possessed by them jointly, of course. But even the new diagram requires careful examination because K, Na exchange causes displacement on the diagram even when the position of the Si, Al atoms and hence the structural state remains unchanged.

Looking first at the albites, all but three of the synthetic specimens fall within experimental error about a line slightly curved from the diagonal running from bottom left to upper right. The three anomalous specimens are from the suite of Martin (1970) and were produced hydrothermally at low temperature in short runs. It seems reasonable to conclude that, except for such anomalous feldspars, synthetic albites lie on a one-step trend from high to low albite. Some of the synthetic albites were converted into K-feldspars by heating in dry alkali halide (Wright and Stewart, 1968; Müller, 1969). There is considerable scatter of data points, but it seems likely that most of the data are consistent with the dashed line in Fig. 7-19. The specimen Ab III is consistent with other synthetic albites before K-exchange, but the exchange product is anomalous and should be re-investigated.

Turning now to the K-feldspars, the data are consistent with a two-step trend for natural and synthetic specimens both before (dashed line) and after Na-exchange (dotted line). The trend for monoclinic feldspars is well defined, but that for triclinic K-feldspars is poorly determined. Both Spencer B and 7007 specimens are adularias which might be regarded as triclinic because of the strong diffuse streaks in single-crystal diffraction patterns. This and other data imply that the two-step trend should actually be shown by a band rather than by a line. All synthetic K-feldspars are monoclinic with small values of $\Delta(b^*c^*)$, and are omitted from Fig. 7-19 to avoid overlap. The occurrence of out-of-step domain textures with associated lattice strain causes major uncertainties in the interpretation of K-feldspars of intermediate structural state.

Data for heated Na- and K-feldspars are omitted from Fig. 7-19 but the positions can be readily inferred from Fig. 7-5 which is a plot of b^* vs. γ^*. These data show that superheated feldspars give X-ray powder patterns consistent with a one-step continuous transformation.

In general it appears that the $\Delta(b^*c^*)$ vs. $\Delta(\alpha^*\gamma^*)$ plot gives an unequivocal estimate of structural state for those alkali feldspars that are (a) well-crystallized (b) free from lattice distortion, and (c) close to the Ab–Or compositional join. Substitution of An and other molecules can cause problems: in particular, substitution of An molecule in albites leads to higher values of both $\Delta(\alpha^*\gamma^*)$ and $\Delta(b^*c^*)$ causing diagonal displacement towards the top right. The microcline exchange series is controversial; whereas the data of Orville fall close to the top right-hand corner within experimental error, those of Waldbaum and Robie migrate considerably with $\Delta(b^*c^*)$ varying from 0.9–1.2.

(e) Other attempts to estimate structural state from cell dimensions are related to the use of b^*c^* and $\alpha^*\gamma^*$. As emphasized before, the direct cell dimensions give the same implications as the reciprocal cell, thus the use of $b\,c$ by Stewart and Ribbe (1969) is equivalent to the use of b^*c^*. Since b^* and c^* tend to correlate fairly closely for a given Na, K substitution (e.g. Figs. 7-3 and 7-7), the use of the ratio c^*/b^* by Jones (1966) yields similar implications to a b^*c^* plot.

The plot of $\Delta(b^*c^*)$ vs. $\Delta(\alpha^*\gamma^*)$ may be regarded as cumbersome by some readers. An alternative is to plot one of the parameters b, b^*, c and c^* vs. one of the parameters α, α^*, γ and γ^*. Unfortunately there are 16 possible ways and given the cussedness of human nature, one can safely bet that most or all of them will be used!

Figure 7-5 shows the plots by Müller (1969, 1970) of b^* vs. γ^* and c^* vs. γ^* for heated K- and Na-feldspars. Unfortunately these diagrams have K-feldspar on the left and disordered varieties at the bottom. All these feldspars belong to the one-step trend, and are pure end-members. Interpretation of the diagram is simple and unambiguous.

Figure 7-6 shows the plot by Kroll (1971) of γ vs. b which is fortunately in the same orientation as the conventional phase diagram. The data points for the K-feldspars are neatly separated from those of the Na-feldspars, and for each composition the triangle distinguishes the one-step from the two-step trend (or as Kroll nicely expresses in German: Direkt-vs. Umweg). However, it is important to realize that all the data in Fig. 7-6 are given for pure end-member compositions. If the feldspar contained significant K, Na substitution (e.g. Na-exchanged Spencer B with composition near $Or_{11}Ab_{89}$), the cell dimensions were extrapolated by Kroll along an expected ion-exchange path to the pure end-member. If feldspars of intermediate Na, K composition are considered, there would be ambiguity on the $b\gamma$ diagram between the structural state and the Na, K substitution. For example, consider Spencer U intermediate microcline belonging to the two-step trend. Ion-exchange to a composition near Or_{20-30} would give cell dimensions similar to those of a pure K-feldspar on the one-step trend.

Kroll's extrapolation procedure to the nearest end-member is a useful feature, and could be applied profitably to plots of $\Delta(b^*c^*)$ and $\Delta(\alpha^*\gamma^*)$. An alternative procedure (not used so far) would be to use non-linear contouring on the b^*c^* and $\alpha^*\gamma^*$ diagrams so that all members of an ion-exchange series would superimpose to yield a single averaged point on the $\Delta(b^*c^*)$ vs. $\Delta(\alpha^*\gamma^*)$ diagram. As further data are obtained for ion-exchange series, such a procedure should become possible.

Structural Interpretation: b and c. Chapters 2, 3 and 4 cover in detail the properties of the crystal structures of feldspars. The cell dimensions depend on the complex summation of a host of factors. For K, Na feldspars, the principal factors are (a) the crumpling of the framework about the small Na atoms, (b) increase of c and decrease of b as Al transfers into the T_10 site, and (c) effect of strain across domain boundaries on the α and γ angles.

Stewart and Ribbe (1969) quantified and extended earlier suggestions that change in the cell dimensions b and c measured transfer of Al atoms into the T_10 site of low albite and low microcline. Figure 7-20 shows their projections of the crystal structures of high sanidine and low microcline onto the bc plane. Readers will recall from Chapter 2 that there are two topologically distinct tetrahedral sites T_1 and T_2, each of which splits into 0 and m sub-sites in triclinic feldspars. The b repeat consists of the sum of the vectors along the chain of atoms: $O_A2-T_20-O_B0-T_10-O_c0-T_2m-O_A2-O_cm-T_1m-O_Bm-T_2m$, or the chain $O_A2-T_2m-O_D0-T_10-O_c0-T_2m-O_A2-T_20-O_Dm-T_1m-O_cm-T_20$. The vectors are not parallel, but the important feature is that both paths contain one T_10 and T_1m for each pair of T_20 and T_2m. Along c, all paths contain one T_10 and one T_1m but only one T_2 — either a T_20 or T_2m. Since Al-centered tetrahedra are larger than Si-centered tetrahedra, it is obvious that transfer of Al from T_2 to T_1 will increase c and decrease b.

Stewart and Ribbe calculated that for Si–O 0.1605 and Al–O 0.1757 nm, the change from complete disorder of $AlSi_3$ to complete occupancy of T_10 by Al should amount to a decrease of about 0.0076 nm in b and an increase of 0.0038 in c, which values compare well with the differences for the reference values in Table 7-1 for end-members. Indeed Laves (1952) had argued that the near-agreement of differences in cell dimensions between sanidine and microcline, on the one hand, and high and low albite, on the other hand, argued in favor of Al, Si order as the cause of polymorphism.

Actually the vectors are not parallel, and the crumpling of the framework between K-feldspars and albite means that there is no simple relation between bc and Al distribution. To a first approximation, the best assumption is that the transfer of Al from T_2 to T_1 sites is *linearly* related to the change in b and c.

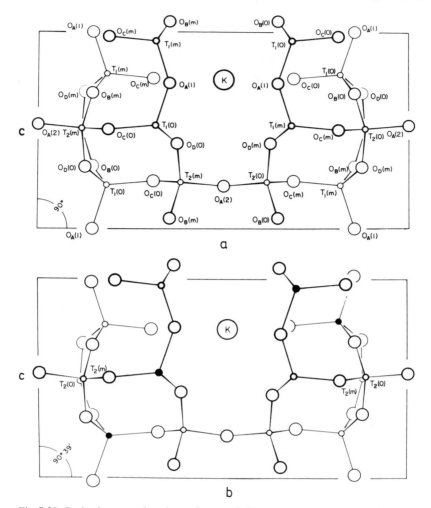

Fig. 7-20. Projection onto bc plane of parts of the crystal structures of (a) high sanidine (b) low microcline. The atom sites are labelled with the Megaw code. Dots show the location of Al atoms in $T_1 0$ sites of microcline. (From Stewart and Ribbe, 1969, Fig. 1)

Stewart and Ribbe plotted the proportional distance $\Delta(bc)$ against the Al-content of T_1 sites deduced from the measured T–O distances of those alkali feldspars subjected to a full structure analysis (Chapter 3). They normalized $\Delta(bc)$ between 0.5 and 1.0 for their choice of reference values for the corners of the quadrilateral in the bc plot. This is because there would be 0.5 Al in the T_1 sites of a fully disordered feldspar of $AlSi_3$ composition, and 1.0 for the fully ordered state. Normalization to 0 and 1.0 as for $\Delta(b^*c^*)$ would merely involve a factor of 2.

Figure 7-21 shows the relation between $\Delta(b^*c^*)$ and estimated Al content of T_1 sites. For K-feldspars (sub-figure a), the data points using Al-contents estimated from T–O distances fall within experimental error close to a single curve. The

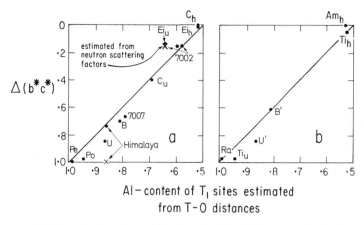

Al−content of T₁ sites estimated
from T−O distances

Fig. 7-21. Relation between $\Delta(b^*c^*)$ and Al-content of T_1 sites for (a) K-feldspars and (b) Na-feldspars. The dots show estimates of Al-content from mean T–O distances, while the crosses show estimates from neutron factors. See Table 3-2 for Al-contents and Tables 7-2 and 7-6 for data on cell dimensions from which $\Delta(b^*c^*)$ was estimated using Fig. 7-18. The specimens may be identified from the abbreviations of source locations

largest deviations are for the Himalaya domain-twinned microcline and an un-heated Eifel sanidine. The two crosses based on neutron-diffraction scattering factors deviate from the corresponding points using T–O distances: the deviation for the 7002 sanidine is close to the experimental error, but that for the Himalaya specimen is larger than the error. The simple model of Stewart and Ribbe implies that the cell dimensions b and c change linearly with the Al-content of the T_1 sites (and correspondingly for b^* and c^*), and a naive conclusion might be that the deviations from a straight line in Fig. 7-21a result from error in the estimates of Al-content from T–O distances and neutron scattering factors. However, the simple model may need modification, especially for specimens with domain twinning such as the Himalaya orthoclase, and no firm conclusions should be made at this time.

Figure 7-21b shows corresponding data for Na-feldspar. Because there are no direct structural data for intermediate albites, data are given for B′ and U′, the Na-exchanged equivalents of two of the K-feldspars shown in Fig. 7-21a. The data show some scatter, but tend to show a similar relation to the data for the K-feldspars.

Because B′ and U′ belong to the two-step trend, they do not represent necessarily albites belonging to the one-step trend. The Stewart-Ribbe theoreti-cal argument implies a strictly linear relation between $\Delta(b\,c)$ and Al-content of T_1 sites, irrespective of whether the feldspar belongs to the one- or two-step trend, but this may be only a first approximation to the truth.

Structural Interpretation: α and γ. For feldspars free of domains, the unit-cell should develop an angular shape appropriate to the Al, Si distribution. Fine-scale domain texture, however, causes the angles to be constrained towards monoclinic values.

In a domain-free feldspar, the angles α and γ are determined by two factors: (a) the crumpling of the framework around the M cation, and (b) the difference

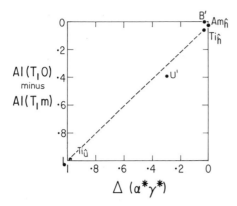

Fig. 7-22. Relation between $\Delta(\alpha^*\gamma^*)$ and the difference of Al-contents in $T_1 0$ and $T_1 m$ deduced from T–O distances of albites and Na-exchanged K-feldspars (B' and U'). The values of $\Delta(\alpha^*\gamma^*)$ were deduced by plotting cell dimensions calculated from Tables 7-2 and 7-6 onto Fig. 7-18b. The Al-contents are given in Table 3-2. The dashed line was drawn arbitrarily between the data points for the four albites

in size of tetrahedra in the 0 and m sub-sites. This may be seen from the diagrams in Fig. 4-5. To a first approximation the effects of the M cation and the distribution of T atoms are additive. Thus on the $\alpha^*\gamma^*$ plot, (Fig. 7-17) the vector from high albite to low albite is similar in length and direction to that between sanidine (the monoclinic point) and low microcline. Comparing reedmergnerite with low albite, the small B atom causes an angular change in the opposite direction to the large Al atom.

Considering only $AlSi_3$ feldspars, the parameter $\Delta(\alpha^*\gamma^*)$ can be interpreted as a measure of the distribution of Al between 0 and m subsites. Since the T–O distances of $T_2 0$ and $T_2 m$ tetrahedra are equal within experimental error for all feldspars, $\Delta(\alpha^*\gamma^*)$ can be used to estimate the difference in Al content of $T_1 0$ and $T_1 m$.

All natural and synthetic albites (except perhaps for chessboard albites, and some synthetic specimens quenched from monalbite) are free of fine-scale domain texture, though many have a fine-scale twinning apparently too coarse for significant distortion of the unit cell. For these normal albites $\Delta(\alpha^*\gamma^*)$ can be used with $\Delta(b^*c^*)$ to give an estimate of the Al distribution of all the sites. From $\Delta(b^*c^*)$ estimate Al in T_1 as in Fig. 7-21b and obtain the amount in T_2 by subtraction from unity. From Fig. 7-22, deduce the difference in Al-contents of $T_1 0$ and $T_1 m$ from $\Delta(\alpha^*\gamma^*)$ or from an equivalent parameter such as the 131 triclinic indicator. Trivial algebraic manipulation gives the individual contents of $T_1 0$ and $T_1 m$. Stewart and Ribbe (1969) showed data (their Table 3) for several intermediate albites [but using $\Delta(bc)$]. Note two errors on their p. 455: correct equations are

$$\Delta Al = Al_{T_1 0} - Al_{T_1 m},$$

$$Al_{T_1 0} = \frac{\Delta(bc) + \Delta(\alpha^*\gamma^*)}{2}.$$

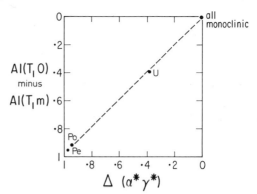

Fig. 7-23. Relation between $\Delta(\alpha^*\gamma^*)$ and the difference in Al content of $T_1 0$ and $T_1 m$ sites deduced from T–O distances of K-rich feldspars. The values of $\Delta(\alpha^*\gamma^*)$ were deduced by plotting cell dimensions calculated from Table 7-2 onto Fig. 7-18b. The Al-contents are given in Table 3-2. The line was drawn arbitrarily

The accuracy of such estimates of Al-content for synthetic Na-feldspars cannot be evaluated objectively. It can be argued that the data are actually consistent with the theoretical one-step trend in which the contents of the $T_1 m$, $T_2 0$ and $T_2 m$ sites are identical, and that the small deviations obtained by Stewart and Ribbe result merely from experimental error in cell dimensions and in the position of the calibration curves.

Turning now to K-feldspars, the interpretation of $\alpha^*\gamma^*$ is difficult. Figure 7-23 shows the relation between $\Delta(\alpha^*\gamma^*)$ and the estimated unbalance of Al in the $T_1 0$ and $T_1 m$ sites as deduced from the structure analyses of three microclines. All the monoclinic feldspars, of course, fall on a single point. Unfortunately this diagram is misleading. Consider the Spencer B and 7007 adularias which fall with the other monoclinic K-feldspars. The structure analyses ignored the strong, diffuse streaks which indicate the occurrence of domains with a triclinic distribution of Al and Si atoms. Thus there was no distinction between the Al-contents of 0 and m sub-sites. The diffuse streaks were not detected on X-ray powder patterns, and cell dimensions automatically show monoclinic geometry. Hence the structure data and cell dimensions are mutually biased to the origin of Fig. 7-23.

Until the domain texture of a particular K-feldspar has been evaluated, the meaning of $\Delta(\alpha^*\gamma^*)$ is ambiguous. Because strain between domains can act only to reduce $\Delta(\alpha^*\gamma^*)$, the actual unbalance of Al-distribution may be greater but not less than that indicated from Fig. 7-23.

The three microclines shown in Fig. 7-23 are either untwinned or so coarsely twinned that their cell dimensions should be unaffected by stress. Hence they can be regarded as defining the limiting relation between $\Delta(\alpha^*\gamma^*)$ and Al distribution.

Analysis by Kroll Using Tr [110] *and* Tr [1$\bar{1}$0]. After completion of the foregoing treatment based largely on the analysis by Wright, Stewart and Ribbe, H. Kroll kindly sent a copy of his Inaugural Dissertation (1971b) of which a small part has been published (1971a), and a further part is in press (1973).

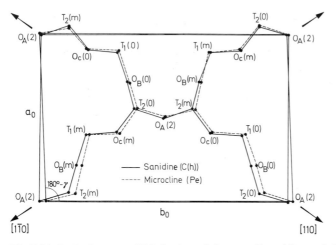

Fig. 7-24. Projection onto (001) for heated Spencer C sanidine and Pellotsalo microcline of T–O chains parallel to [110] and [1̄10]. (From Kroll, 1971 b, Fig. 6)

This treatment is rather elegant, and essentially reworks all the earlier treatments with the benefit of more recent measurements of cell dimensions for heated natural and synthetic feldspars. Unfortunately Kroll prepared his diagrams before the neutron diffraction data cast doubt on estimates of Al contents from the Ribbe-Gibbs linear relation with observed T–O distances, and the diagrams should be revised.

Kroll pointed out that the repeat distances in the [110] and [1̄10] directions were controlled by the distribution of Al atoms between the tetrahedral sites. Figure 7-24 shows his projection on (001) of chains of T and O atoms along [110] and [1̄10] for microcline and sanidine. Along [110], the repeating sequence of tetrahedra is $T_1 0$, $T_2 0$, $T_2 m$, whereas along [1̄10] it is $T_1 m$, $T_2 0$, $T_2 m$. Hence the difference in the repeat distances estimates the transfer of Al from $T_1 m$ to $T_1 0$ sites, while the mean of the distances measures the combined transfer of Al from T_2 to T_1 sites. This assumes, of course, that there is no interaction with the M atom. In practice, there is an effect from the M atom and Kroll prepared separate calibration curves for Na- and for K-feldspar.

The relation to the Wright-Stewart-Ribbe method can be seen as follows: The [110] repeat is related to the cell dimensions by $(Tr_{[110]})^2 = a^2 + b^2 + 2ab$ cosine γ, where $Tr_{[110]}$ follows Kroll's nomenclature. Similarly for [1̄10],

$$(Tr_{[1\bar{1}0]})^2 = a^2 + b^2 - 2ab \text{ cosine } \gamma .$$

To a first approximation for a fixed Na, K ratio the mean of Tr [110] and Tr [1̄10] depends principally on the variation in b since a is nearly constant, whereas the difference depends principally on γ. Hence Kroll's method is related to methods based on bc and $\alpha\gamma$ plots, since b correlates with c and α with γ.

Indeed no matter what choice is made of functions of cell dimensions, one can obtain only two pieces of meaningful information, one of which must depend on b and c, and the other on α and γ. The only essential difference between various methods of going from cell dimensions to Al, Si distributions is in elegance and convenience. There cannot be any fundamental difference between the methods.

Kroll on p. 63 of his dissertation gives 5 reasons why his method is preferable to that of Wright-Stewart-Ribbe, and feldspar workers can judge for themselves. My own opinion is that both methods are theoretically correct, and that the choice of method is unimportant because the answers will be the same.

Figure 7-25a shows Kroll's plot for K-feldspars of $Tr\,[110]$ versus $t_1 0 + t_2 0 + t_2 m$ (the Al-contents of the appropriate tetrahedra) plus a plot of $Tr\,[1\bar{1}0]$ vs. $t_1 m + t_2 0 + t_2 m$. Each triclinic feldspar is represented by two points, the one at the bottom left representing $Tr\,[1\bar{1}0]$ and the one at the upper right, $Tr\,[110]$. Each monoclinic feldspar is represented by only one point because $Tr\,[110] = Tr\,[1\bar{1}0]$ when $\gamma = 90°$. Kroll distinguished between the two-step trend

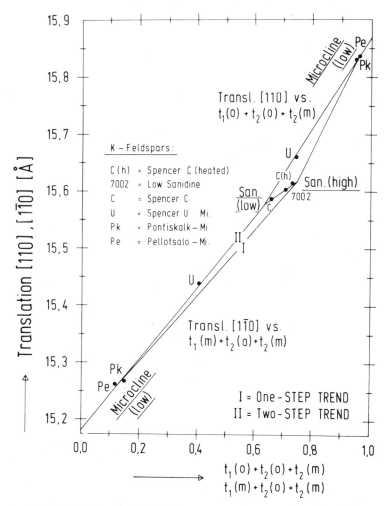

Fig. 7-25a

Fig. 7-25. Calibration by Kroll of $Tr\,[110]$ and $Tr\,[1\bar{1}0]$ with respect to Al-contents determined from T–O distances. a K-feldspar. See text for explanation. b Na-feldspar. Analbite is high albite inverted from monalbite. Modified by Kroll from Figs. 10 and 11 of his 1971 b publication

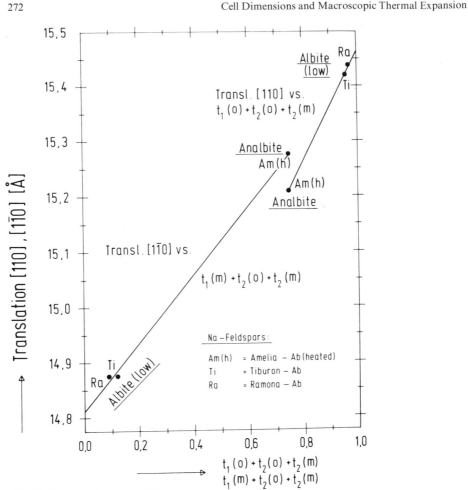

Fig. 7-25b. Legend see page 271

(Umweg of Kroll) that goes from high sanidine to low microcline via (theoretical) low sanidine, and the direct one-step trend (Direktweg of Kroll). Kroll corrected for the assumed Ab-content of U, Pe and Pk feldspars using the $\overline{2}01$ and 400 plots of Orville (1967), and used the chemical estimate for the C and 7002 feldspars.

Figure 7-25b shows Kroll's reference diagram for Na-feldspars. High albite (denoted Analbite) is triclinic resulting in two points in contrast to the single point for high sanidine. Because there is no structure analysis of intermediate albites, Kroll drew straight lines between the data points for the two low albites from Ramona and Tiburon and the heated Amelia albite. These straight lines correspond to the one-step trend (Direktweg).

In order to take account of the Na, K substitution, Kroll developed two diagrams, one each for the one-step and two-step trends. Figure 7-26a for the one-step trend shows contours of constant Or-content (mol.-%) crossing the area defined by Tr [110] and Tr [1$\overline{1}$0] vs. various functions of Al distribution. Plot-

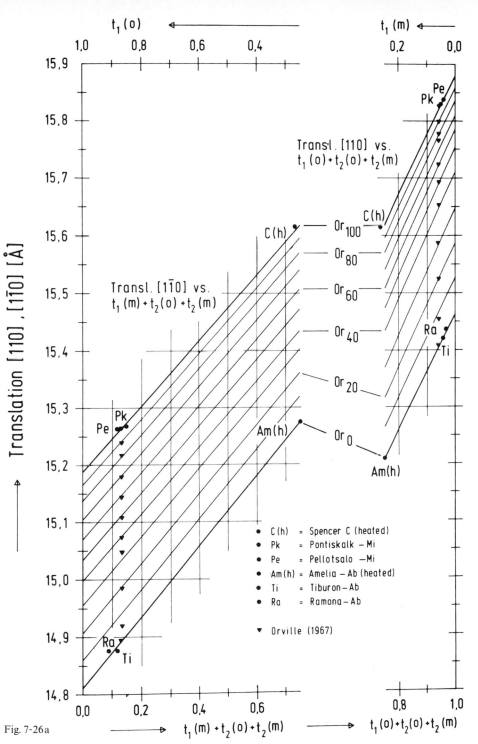

Fig. 7-26. Diagrams by Kroll for determination of Al site occupancy from Tr [110] and Tr [1$\bar{1}$0] for K, Na feldspars. a Diagram for one-step trend. b Diagram for two-step trend. c Diagram for determining difference of Al-content in $T_1 0$ and $T_1 m$ sites for triclinic feldspars. See text for detailed explanation. (From Kroll, 1971 b, Figs. 15, 16 and 17)

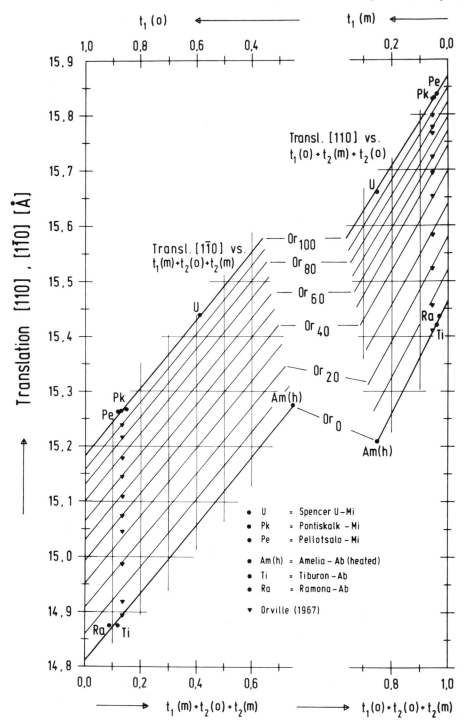

Fig. 7-26b. Legend see page 273

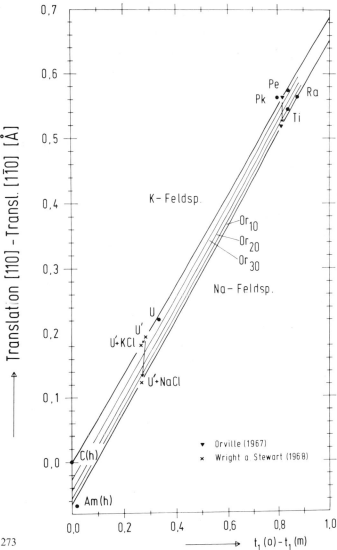

Fig. 7-26c. Legend see page 273

ted on the diagram are data points for various feldspars including Orville's microcline-albite exchange series. To use the diagram, one would measure at least a, b and γ. From a, or some other appropriate measurement, the Or-content would be calculated. From a, b and γ, $Tr\,[110]$ and $Tr\,[1\bar{1}0]$ would be determined. Two points would be plotted on the diagram, and the Al-contents read off either on the bottom, or more simply as $t_1 0$ and $t_1 m$ on the top. Figure 7-26b is a similar plot for the two-step trend. This diagram uses data for the Spencer U intermediate microcline to provide the appropriate reference.

To complete his analysis, Kroll gave a diagram for estimating $t_1 0 - t_1 m$ from $Tr\,[110] - Tr\,[1\bar{1}0]$ as reproduced in Fig. 7-26c. This diagram is also contoured with Or-content to take account of the distortion caused by Na, K substitution. No account is taken in this diagram of the possible effect of strain caused by domain texture.

7.3.4 Cell Dimensions of Perthites and Anomalous Specimens

General. For descriptive purposes, Wright and Stewart (1968) defined an alkali feldspar as having *anomalous* cell dimensions when the quantity [a (observed) — a (estimated from b and c)] exceeds 0.002 nm. The estimate of a is obtained from the contours of Fig. 7-14b.

There are at least four possible contributions towards anomalous cell dimensions:

(a) chemical substituents other than K, Na and Al, Si. The extent of this chemical effect can be estimated from the cell dimensions in Table 7-1 assuming a linear relation. In addition there is the possibility of substitution of silica molecule or of hydroxonium ion. Chapter 14 contains extensive data on the extent of chemical substitution. Different petrologic environments tend to give different chemical substitutions. Thus K-feldspars from pegmatites may contain considerable Rb and Cs, with a corresponding high value of a. Sanidines from volcanic rocks may contain considerable Ba and Fe, again with increase in a.

Martin (1971) showed that certain authigenic K-feldspars from altered rhyolitic tuffs have extremely high a dimensions with respect to b, c, almost certainly explainable by substitution of around 10% Al by B. For example his specimen 123 A has a 0.85973(13), b 1.29758(29), c 0.71716(10), β 115.976(12)°, V 0.71922 (17); standard error in brackets to same decimal level. From Fig. 7-14b, Wright and Stewart would expect a to be 0.835 nm, so this feldspar is anomalous by 12 times the minimum value. Martin synthesized $K(Al,B)Si_3O_8$ feldspars with 0, 5.5, 9.7 and 18.1% B substitution for Al to confirm his supposition of the effect of B but chemical analysis for B in authigenic feldspars is desirable to provide definite proof.

(b) strain between components of a perthite. During segregation of Na and K, the aluminosilicate framework may retain complete or partial continuity with consequent distortion of the cell dimensions of the two components. This effect is greatest in the initial stages of unmixing and disappears for coarse perthites. Details follow in the next section.

(c) the Wright-Stewart reference diagram is implicitly based on one particular variation of Al, Si distribution. Because alkali feldspars actually fall between the extremes of the one-and two-step trends (Fig. 7-2), the implicit assumption of Wright and Stewart that their $b\,c$ plot applies to all structural states need not be correct. Indeed evidence has been given earlier in this Chapter, that anomalous cell dimensions occur in certain synthetic and natural albites. The extent of this possible effect is not known.

(d) inaccurate positioning of contours by Wright and Stewart at the K-rich side of Fig. 7-15c. Luth and Querol-Suñé (1970) found that regression analysis of b as dependent variable vs. Or as independent variable for Orville's cell dimensions of (1967) yielded a maximum value of b, *not* at Or_{100}, but at some composition containing significant amounts of Ab. The details are complex and depend on the assumptions of the regression analysis, but the calculated position lies around 5–15% Ab for the maximum in b. Whatever the details, it is obvious from Fig. 7-9, that b is almost independent of Or content from Or_{80} to Or_{100} for both the sanidine and microcline series. Gubser and Laves (1967, Fig. 3a) showed b^* to be essentially independent of composition from Or_{100} to Or_{80} for their microcline and sanidine series. In this range of Or content, a changes about 0.008 nm: hence there should be a region on the Wright-Stewart plot in which b does not change while a changes 0.008. Actually Fig. 7-14b shows a varying continuously with b and c, though of course the contours are closer for K-rich compositions. Therefore the Wright-Stewart plot is not completely satisfactory, at least in this composition range. They themselves note that "a surprisingly large number of natural alkali feldspars do not, however, fit this simple picture. ... In every such case we find that b, c or both are too *low* relative to a to define a consistent structural state, and as defined earlier, the feldspar is considered to have anomalous cell dimensions".

Figure 7-27a summarizes the data pertinent to definition of an anomalous K-feldspar. From Fig. 7-18a, values of $Or(b^* c^*)$ were determined by use of the linear grid between the assumed extremes for pure K- and Na-feldspars. Each value of $Or(b^* c^*)$ was plotted against a^* in Fig. 7-27. Attention is directed first to the data for Orville's sanidine and microcline series shown by the continuous and dashed lines, respectively. Within the experimental error of about 0.0001–0.0004 nm^{-1} in a^* and about 0.01–0.02 in $Or(b^* c^*)$, the data for these two series are indistinguishable. The data for Wright and Stewart's orthoclase series and Waldbaum and Robie's microcline series show somewhat more scatter but are moderately consistent with Orville's data. The dots show the Gubser and Laves data for adularia, the filled triangles show data for K-exchanged specimens, and the filled diamonds show two K-exchanged microclines. These data are all consistent with those of Orville. The filled squares are for adularias, microclines and a sanidine heated by Gubser and Laves at 1100° C for 200 h. The open squares show data for natural albites K-exchanged by Waldbaum and Robie and by Müller. The two open diamonds show synthetic albites S 62–34 and S 63–30 K-exchanged by Wright and Stewart: the Ab III specimen is not shown because it falls off the diagram. The open ovals show three K-feldspars K-exchanged by Wright and Stewart. All but one of the above specimens tend to lie at values of $Or(b^* c^*)$ higher than those for the Orville series. The open triangles for synthetic K-feldspars fall in a band extending from the region of Orville's data to lower values of $Or(b^* c^*)$.

The spread of these data for supposedly homogeneous K-feldspars seems to be greater than can be accounted for by random experimental error. Possibly there is a systematic bias between the experimental techniques of the various laboratories. Perhaps the reference points for K-feldspars on the $b^* c^*$ plot should be amended. Until this problem is cleared up, one must be cautious in defining an *anomalous* K-feldspar.

The band shown on Fig. 7-27a adequately covers the spread of data in Orville's series, but does not include all the data for the orthoclase series of Wright and Stewart and the microcline series of Waldbaum and Robie. The width of the band corresponds to ± 0.0003 nm, which is 1.5 times the tolerance used

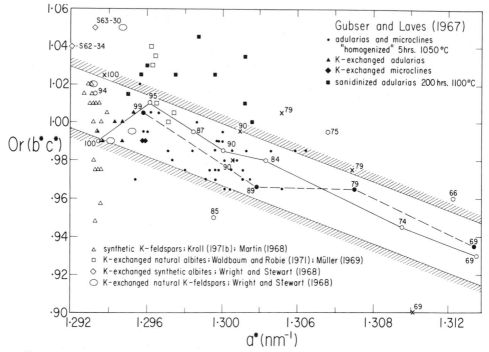

Fig. 7-27 a

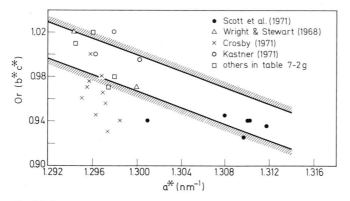

Fig. 7-27 b

Fig. 7-27. Relation between a^* and $Or(b^* c^*)$ for K-rich feldspars. a The open and filled circles, plus the continuous and dashed lines, show the data by Orville (1967) for the sanidine and microcline series. The open hexagons and crosses, respectively, are for the orthoclase series of Wright and Stewart (1968) and the microcline series of Waldbaum and Robie (1971). The numbers show mol.-% Or. The band inside the hatched boundaries corresponds to an error of 0.003 nm in a about the middle of the band assuming no error in $Or(b^* c^*)$. All other specimens are identified in the inset key. The data were obtained from the direct cell dimensions of Table 7-2 after conversion to indirect cell dimensions. b Data for natural K-feldspars are identified in the inset key. All data for $Or(b^* c^*)$ were determined graphically from Fig. 7-18a to the nearest 0.005

by Wright and Stewart for normal K-feldspars. Fig. 7-27b shows some of the available data for natural K-feldspars. The K-rich phases of perthites described by Crosby (1971) mostly fall outside the newly-defined band, while the sanidines of Scott *et al.* (1971) mostly fall inside the band. Of the remaining nine specimens, six fall inside the band.

In spite of the uncertainties described above, at least some K-feldspars with anomalous cell dimensions come from perthites for which there is evidence from single-crystal X-ray diffraction and electron-optical techniques of coherency and strain between the lattices for the K-rich and Na-rich components. The next section describes the phenomenon.

Strain in Perthites. Laves (1952, p. 562), Coombs (1954) and many others found that the $\bar{2}01$ spacings of the two phases of some perthites yielded impossible Or contents from the usual determinative curves, such values being as low as -10% Or and as high as 110%. Laves stated that the aluminosilicate frameworks must be distorted severely, and Smith (1961) proposed a semi-quantitative explanation based on continuity of the aluminosilicate framework across the boundaries.

Chapter 19 describes the detailed structure of perthites. Cryptoperthites (with a sub-optical texture) usually have anomalous cell dimensions while coarse micro- or macro-perthites usually have normal cell dimensions. X-ray and electron-optical data show that the initial stage of unmixing in many crypto-perthites occurs with continuity of the aluminosilicate framework across the boundaries between the K-rich and Na-rich regions. In order to minimize the strain, the regions are anisotropic with the major boundaries nearly parallel to the $(\bar{6}01)$ plane. This results from the *a* repeat showing a greater percentage difference between Na- and K-rich compositions than do *b* and *c*. Single-crystal X-ray photographs contain streaks relating the spots for the two feldspars, whose positions show that the dimensions in the $(\bar{6}01)$ plane are equal.

Smith suggested that to a first approximation the unit-cell volume for the feldspar of each domain is the same as that for an isolated feldspar with the same Na, K ratio. Therefore the direction normal to $(\bar{6}01)$ must undergo an extra expansion in the K-rich feldspar, and an extra contraction in the Na-rich feldspar to compensate for the equal dimensions in the $(\bar{6}01)$ plane. To a first approximation, the *a* axis is normal to $\bar{6}01$, and *b* and *c* lie in it. Smith calculated that the composition gap determined from the $(\bar{2}01)$ spacings would be about 1.64 times too large. Thus cryptoperthites with an apparent composition gap of 120% might really have a composition gap of about 73%. Unfortunately no way has been found to measure directly the composition of individual feldspars of cryptoperthites.

As unmixing proceeds, the perthite coarsens. Electron-optical data (Chapter 10) show that dislocations occur at the boundaries in microperthite. Probably the aluminosilicate framework recrystallizes at the boundaries, perhaps via development and migration of dislocations. Although there is no conclusive experimental evidence, it seems reasonable to suppose that specimens occur with partial coherency across the boundaries. For example one could imagine coherency for (say) one hundred unit cells followed by a dislocation and then coherency again.

A more sophisticated treatment using the stress-strain tensor is given in Chapters 18 and 19.

Recommended Practice for Anomalous Specimens. If cell dimensions are anomalous, the first step is to check that the entire X-ray powder pattern indexes completely, and that the anomalous cell dimensions do not result merely from error in a computer program.

The second step is to make a chemical analysis if possible, paying particular attention to likely substituents. A full wavelength scan with an electron microprobe is particularly useful, though it cannot detect boron accurately.

The third step might consist of preparing a single-crystal X-ray pattern. If the feldspar is part of a perthite, the nature and position of the diffuse streaks should reveal the degree of strain caused by coherency.

If the feldspar has normal composition, and it is not a component of a perthite, it would seem reasonable to suspect something unusual in its Al, Si distribution.

Of course, most feldspars with anomalous cell dimensions will turn out to belong to a perthite with strain distortion. For such feldspars, the K, Na ratio cannot be determined from any single parameter such as the $\bar{2}01$ or 400 spacings. Probably the best estimate of K, Na content is given by the cell volume. It appears that $\Delta(bc)$ or $\Delta(b^*c^*)$ give a reasonable estimate of the structural state (Wright and Stewart, 1968). See Butler (1973) for statistical analysis of data for anomalous cryptoperthites.

7.3.5 Simple Determinative Methods

General. Simple determinative methods using just one or a few peaks in powder patterns are very useful for routine study of a large suite of samples, but at least one sample should be checked completely both for position and intensity of all calculated and observed peaks using the reference data listed in Chapter 6. For perthites, a single-crystal photograph is desirable to check for the presence of features not observable in powder patterns. Having satisfied oneself of the validity of indexing of the peaks, simple methods can be extremely rapid, especially with a diffractometer.

For specimens with normal cell dimensions, the Or-content can be estimated with a reproducibility (*not* accuracy) of 1% from the $\bar{2}01$ peak in a diffractometer pattern or the 400 peak in a Guinier pattern. For specimens with anomalous cell dimensions, the cell volume should be measured by complete indexing of the pattern.

For all specimens the structural state can be measured directly from b^* and c^* using the 060 and 002 peaks in Guinier patterns. In diffractometer patterns, the $\bar{2}04$ peak is more suitable than 002. For general use, the "three-peak" method of Wright (viz. $\bar{2}01$, 060 and $\bar{2}04$) provides a simple technique for simultaneous determination of composition and structural state.

The triclinic angles α^* and γ^* can be estimated from the angular splitting of peaks that would be single for monoclinic symmetry. The 130 and 131 peaks are most convenient.

Table 7-3 lists the calculated d-values for $\bar{2}01$, 400, 060, $\bar{2}04$, $1\bar{3}1$ and 131 given by Orville (1967) for his sanidine and microcline series. The 2θ angles can

Table 7-3. Selected interplanar spacings for K, Na feldspars

(mol.-%) Or	d($\bar{2}$01)	d(400)	d(060)	d($\bar{2}$04)	d(1$\bar{3}$1)	d(131)
	Calculated (nanometer)					

(a) *Microcline-low albite series: Orville* (1967)

0.94	0.40306	0.18188	0.21247	0.17842	0.29614	0.28608
10.27	0.40473	0.18296	0.21280	0.17865	0.29621	0.28780
19.71	0.40695	0.18438	0.21371	0.17909	0.29621	0.29093
29.27	0.40950	0.18545	0.21447	0.17953	0.29600	0.29306
38.96	0.41158	0.18711	0.21490	0.17982	0.29519	0.29671
48.76	0.41345	0.18818	0.21519	0.17997	0.29512	0.29856
58.68	0.41513	0.18913	0.21538	0.18009	0.29492	0.20008
68.71	0.41744	0.19034	0.21565	0.18027	0.29507	0.30140
78.86	0.41910	0.19128	0.21574	0.18032	0.29527	0.30222
89.11	0.42082	0.19204	0.21575	0.18036	0.29532	0.30260
99.48	0.42276	0.19293	0.21587	0.18053	0.29560	0.30320

(b) *Sanidine-high albite series: Orville* (1967)

0.00	0.40345	0.18235	0.21382	0.17750	0.30115	0.28313
4.72	0.40420	0.18260	0.21408	0.17762	0.30111	0.28378
9.47	0.40567	0.18344	0.21441	0.17782	0.30101	0.28503
14.26	0.40632	0.18383	0.21484	0.17809	0.30079	0.28638
19.06	0.40731	0.18436	0.21518	0.17826	0.30026	0.28784
23.90	0.40809	0.18487	0.21542	0.17846	0.29999	0.28939
28.76	0.40943	0.18556	0.21581	0.17865	0.29904	0.29122
33.90	0.40974	0.18618	0.21597	0.17881	0.29717	0.29363
38.58	0.41107	0.18666	0.21628	0.17895	0.29614	0.29614
43.53	0.41228	0.18732	0.21642	0.17908	0.29659	
48.51	0.41348	0.18796	0.21649	0.17910	0.29692	
53.52	0.41464	0.18859	0.21656	0.17908	0.29722	
58.56	0.41565	0.18919	0.21665	0 17915	0.29757	
63.63	0.41666	0.18979	0.21688	0.17923	0.29808	
68.73	0.41761	0.19028	0.21685	0.17925	0.29827	
73.87	0.41876	0.19091	0.21691	0.17926	0.29857	
79.03						
84.22	0.42089	0.19198	0.21701	0.17936	0.29906	
89.45	0.42146	0.19230	0.21699	0.17938	0.29921	
94.71	0.42266	0.19298	0.21712	0.17942	0.29950	
100.00	0.4234	0.19330	0.21702	0.17939	0.29957	

(c) *P 50–56 KF Orthoclase series: Wright* (1968)

100[a]	0.42457[a]		0.21663[a]	0.17990[a]		
94.7	0.42347		0.21665	0.17983		
87.3	0.42231		0.21665	0.17978		
86.5	0.42166		0.21660	0.17988		
77.6	0.41979		0.21665	0.17981		
69.7	0.41824		0.21656	0.17969		
61.9	0.41676		0.21645	0.17969		
53.1	0.41427		0.21633	0.17963		
44.2	0.41217		0.21610	0.17945		
35.4	0.41003		0.21591	0.17934		
27.5	0.40876		0.21535	0.17906		
17.6	0.40697		0.21472	0.17862		
8.8	0.40517		0.21410	0.17825		
0[a]	0.40290[a]		0.21352[a]	0.17788[a]		

[a] extrapolated

be readily determined for any radiation using standard tables such as Fang and Bloss (1966). The table also contains d-values of $\bar{2}01$, 060 and $\bar{2}04$ diffractions for the orthoclase series of Wright and Stewart (1968).

The bulk composition of a perthite can be estimated from the cell dimensions after homogenization. Unfortunately the results have not always proved satisfactory. Probably dry heating even for many days at (say) 1050° C is not always sufficient to give homogenization and inversion even when the $\bar{2}01$ or 400 peaks appear to be sharp. Specimens crystallized at low temperature, such as authigenic feldspars, are particularly resistant to inversion. Whenever possible, feldspars should be homogenized and inverted by hydrothermal treatment in a sealed capsule.

Comparisons of Or contents estimated from cell dimensions with those estimated by direct chemical analysis are given by Koritnig (1961), Carmichael and MacKenzie (1964), Parsons (1965), Kempe (1966) and Jones et al. (1969). There seems to be a tendency for the estimated Or-contents for homogenized perthites to be slightly low when referred to the calibration curve for synthetic feldspars. Orville (1967) homogenized microcline perthites dry at 1000° C for 48 h and hydrothermally at 800° C, 1 kbar for 21 days. The products of the dry treatment yielded $\bar{2}01$ angles mostly lying between his reference curves for the sanidine and microcline series, while the products of hydrothermal treatment tended to lie on the sanidine curve but with a slight bias to the microcline curve. The data suggest that the bulk composition for the hydrothermally-treated specimens can be estimated to an accuracy of 2 or 3% in the Or content.

In natural feldspars of unknown composition, the substitution of Ba, Sr, Rb and Cs in the M site and of Fe in the T site will tend to give a positive bias in Or whereas the substitution of An molecule for Ab will have no effect. Substitution of B for Al will give a negative bias in Or. In general for natural alkali feldspars, at least half the estimates of Or-content of homogeneous or homogenized specimens are probably accurate to within 2 or 3%, but errors up to 5% can be expected for specimens with unusual contents of minor elements. The special problems of "anomalous" specimens and individual members of perthites were discussed in the preceding section.

The accuracy of estimates of structural state from the b, c cell dimensions, or some related parameters, is difficult to judge. Substitution of Fe and B in tetrahedral sites certainly causes some problems, but the effect is probably trivial in most feldspars. Probably strain in perthites has some effect on the estimate of structural state, but the proportional position $\Delta(bc)$ may be valid. The basic problem is that there is no reliable method for checking the structural state of many natural feldspars. Probably for most natural specimens, the cell dimensions b and c yield perhaps ten or twenty steps between the extreme structural states. For albite, the triclinic indicator 131 is extremely sensitive so long as the An-content is zero. However, substitution of An acts like increase in structural disorder causing a severe ambiguity in natural albites unless the An content is measured by some other technique.

Cell volume V. Table 7-2 contains the values determined by Orville (1967) for the sanidine and microcline series. These two series define the two extreme structural states with sufficient accuracy for estimation of Or content. Figure 7-9 shows the relation between V and Or, from which it may be seen that knowledge of the structural state is important only for the extreme compositions. Regression equations with V in terms of Or are given by Orville (1967), Waldbaum and Thompson (1968), Luth and Querol-Suñé (1970) and Waldbaum and Robie (1971). There are subtle differences between the equations depending on the assumptions. To determine Or from V, the equations must be reversed.

Luth and Querol-Suñé gave the following equation for Orville's sanidine series treated as two separate series:

$$N_{Or} = -14.273 + 21.09 \, V \quad \text{for} \quad 100 \quad \text{to} \quad 40\% \, \text{Or}$$
$$= -9.237 + 13.88 \, V \quad \text{for} \quad 40 \quad \text{to} \quad 0\% \, \text{Or}.$$

The volume V is measured in 10^{-27} cubic meters, ranging from 0.72257 for Or_{100} to 0.66611 for Or_0. Similar equations for the microcline-low albite series have not been calculated.

The accuracy of the calibration curve is open to question. Luth and Querol-Suñé quoted standard errors in N_{Or} of 0.017 and 0.008, respectively, for the above equations. Since there is a random error of measurement of V equivalent to 0.01 to 0.02 in N_{Or}, it seems reasonable to estimate a final uncertainty for pure K, Na feldspars of a few percent Or.

$\overline{2}01$ *Spacing.* This peak was selected by Bowen and Tuttle (1950) because it is intense, free of interference from other peaks, and sensitive. Figure 7-28 shows Orville's (1967) calibration curve using $KBrO_3$ as the internal standard. Because the position of $\overline{2}01$ can be measured to 0.01° in 2θ, the Or content can be measured to 1% if the structural state is known, and the calibration curve is free of error.

The continuous lines in Fig. 7-28 show the reference data for synthetic feldspars in the sanidine-high albite series, and were represented by Orville (1963)

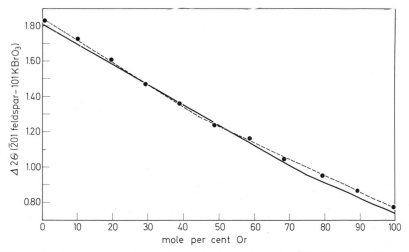

Fig. 7-28. Orville's calibration curve for Or content determined from the $\overline{2}01$ diffraction. The ordinate $\Delta 2\theta$ is the difference between the 2θ angle for the $\overline{2}01$ diffraction and the 101 diffraction of $KBrO_3$ which lies at 20.212°. The microcline–low albite series is represented by solid circles and two dashed lines that meet at 45 mole percent Or. The sanidine–high albite series is shown by the two straight lines whose data points are given in Orville (1963). CuK_{α} radiation. See Table 7-3 for d-values. See Wright (1968, Fig. 4) for a plot of 2θ values vs. *weight* percent Or for microcline, orthoclase and sanidine series. (From Orville, 1967, Fig. 8)

as two straight lines meeting at Or_{75}. These lines for CuK_α radiation have 2θ values of 20.952, 21.172, and 22.022 at compositions of 100, 75 and 0 mol.-% Or, respectively.

The dashed lines in Fig. 7-28 show the reference data for the microcline-low albite series, represented by Orville (1967) as two straight lines meeting at Or_{45} mol.-%. These lines have 2θ values of 20.977, 21.492 and 22.062° at 100, 45 and 0% Or respectively.

Wright (1968) gave the following linear regressions for the sanidine, orthoclase and microcline series, treating each series as a single population and using *weight* percent Or. For $2\theta(\bar{2}01) = m\ Or + b$ with standard error σ in Or, he obtained: sanidine, m -92.18, b 2030.05, σ 1.2; P 50–56 KF orthoclase -87.69, 1930.77, 1.4; microcline -92.19, 2031.77, 2.4. These single linear approximations probably introduce small systematic biases, because other workers suggest that the data are fitted better by two populations.

The choice of an internal standard for calibration of $\bar{2}01$ is rather important because low-angle peaks in a diffractometer pattern are somewhat asymmetric, especially if the instrument is misaligned. Silicon is unsuitable because its first peak occurs at 28.466°. The $KBrO_3$ standard is good because its strong peak at 20.212° 2θ for CuK_α radiation does not overlap with a feldspar peak but is close to $\bar{2}01$. Quartz has a peak near 20.866 which overlaps with the $\bar{2}01$ peak for K-rich feldspar; furthermore natural quartz has a slight variation in cell dimension requiring calibration of each sample against (say) spec-pure silicon. Pure $MgAl_2O_4$ spinel must be calibrated against silicon, but is useful for the entire feldspar pattern because it has several strong peaks with the first near 18.5° 2θ. Christie and Nilssen (1964) recommend lead nitrate.

400 *Spacing*. This peak is commonly used for estimating a^*, and hence the Or content, from Guinier photographs. However it is a relatively weak peak and for some alkali feldspars subject to interference from other diffractions. Thus Luth and Querol-Suñé (1970) reported that in the sanidine series, the $\bar{4}03$ diffraction superimposes at Or_{51} while the 260 diffraction superimposes at Or_{41}. The calculated X-ray patterns of Borg and D. K. Smith (1969) show overlap with the $\bar{3}51$ diffraction for sanidine, but not for microcline. The 400 diffraction in albite is not easy to detect accurately as is shown by the calculated powder patterns of Borg and D. K. Smith (1968). It seems that the 400 diffraction is quite suitable for estimating Or content of microcline, but should be checked carefully in other alkali feldspars.

Table 7-3 lists Orville's calculated d-spacings for 400. His Fig. 9 shows the various determinative curves based on 400. The curves given by Goldsmith and Laves (1961) were based on incomplete data and are obsolete. The reference curves for a^* given by Gubser and Laves (1967, Fig. 2a) agree with those of Orville for Or_{100} but are considerably displaced at Or_{80}. The source of the discrepancy is unclear, and until it is explained, I recommend use of Orville's curve.

Three-peak Method of Wright. The $\bar{2}01$, 060 and $\bar{2}04$ diffractions depend essentially on the Or content and the structural state. The latter two provide the equivalent of the $b\ c$ plot.

Table 7-4 shows the angular positions for K-rich feldspars, anorthoclases and low albites. The calculations of Borg and D. K. Smith (see Chapter 6) show

Table 7-4. Positions of diffractions used in Wright's method for alkali feldspars

hkl	Approximate intensity	Approximate range of 2θ (CuK$_{\alpha_1}$)		
		K-rich phases	Anorthoclases	Albite
$\bar{2}01$	40	20.8–21.2°	21.6–21.9°	21.9–22.1°
002	> 100	27.4–27.8°	27.8–28.0°	27.9–28.1°
$\bar{1}13$	8	38.6–39.0°	not present	not present
060	25	41.6–42.0°	41.7–42.0°	42.2–42.6°
$\bar{2}04$	30	50.5–51.1°	51.1–51.3°	51.2–51.5°

that other diffractions overlap with $\bar{2}04$, but the peak displacement is not worse than 0.01° in 2θ. The $\bar{2}01$ and 060 peaks can be identified unambiguously in all homogeneous alkali feldspars. The $\bar{2}04$ diffraction has a strong, single peak in most alkali feldspars, but in some monoclinic K-feldspars with anomalous cell dimensions, the peak is confused by one or more other diffractions. If all peaks are clearly resolved, the $\bar{2}04$ peak can be identified by measuring the 2θ values of the 002 and $\bar{1}13$ peaks and predicting the $\bar{2}04$ position by the equations:

$$2\theta(\bar{2}04) = 1.1780\,[2\theta(\bar{1}13)] + 5.1048 \quad \text{and}$$
$$= 1.6886\,[2\theta(002)] + 4.1690$$

The actual value should lie within 0.04° 2θ for the first equation and 0.06° for the second.

Figure 7-29 shows the reference plot of $2\theta(060)$ vs. $2\theta(\bar{2}04)$ analogous to the $b\,c$ plot. The three straight lines represent the microcline, orthoclase and sanidine series, while the dashed lines connect ion-exchanged feldspars. Crossing these lines are contours for $2\theta(\bar{2}01)$. Wright considered feldspars to be anomalous if the predicted value of $\bar{2}01$ differed by more than 0.1° from the actual value. For both normal and anomalous feldspars, the structural state can be estimated from the proportional distance between the extreme series. For normal feldspars, the Or content can be estimated from $2\theta(\bar{2}01)$, but for anomalous feldspars it is necessary to determine the cell volume. Wright presented a series of tables to facilitate estimates of cell dimensions from the diffraction angles in order to reduce the chance of incorrect refinement.

The "three-peak" method has been used successfully on many feldspars. Other feldspars show fuzzy $\bar{2}04$ peaks. Some perthites are so complex that assignment of peaks to the individual phases is uncertain. For such feldspars, no powder method is really satisfactory. Indeed lack of success with the "three-peak" method should be taken as a warning that single-crystal methods are desirable as a supplement to the powder method.

130, 131 and 111 Splittings. In monoclinic feldspars, each of these diffractions is represented by a single peak. In triclinic feldspars, each splits into two diffractions useful for giving a measure of the deviation from monoclinic geometry. Let

$$Q = 1/d^2 .$$

Then

$$Q(130) - Q(1\bar{3}0) = 6\,a^*\,b^* \cos\gamma^*$$

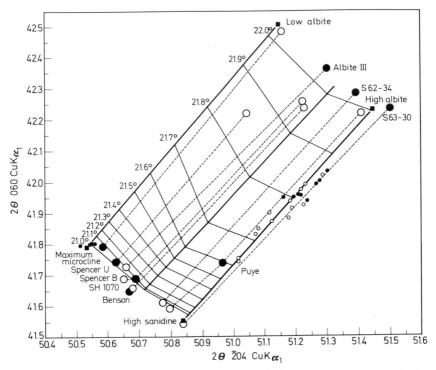

Fig. 7-29. Reference diagram relating $2\theta(060)$ and $2\theta(\overline{2}04)$ in the "three-peak" method of Wright (1968). The four solid squares show reference points for the extreme end-members, and the straight lines represent Orville's microcline and sanidine series and the orthoclase series of Wright and Stewart. The dashed lines show ion-exchange paths. Small circles show data for natural feldspars. The crossing contours show the expected values for $2\theta(\overline{2}01)$. This figure is analogous to Fig. 7-14b, whose legend provides further information. (From Wright, 1968, Fig. 3)

and

$$Q(131) - Q(1\overline{3}1) = 6a^*b^* \cos\gamma^* + 6b^*c^* \cos\alpha^* .$$

Since a^*, b^* and c^* can be readily estimated to an accuracy of 1%, the splitting of the 130 and 131 diffractions permits an easy estimate of α^* and γ^*, which could be plotted on an $\alpha^*\gamma^*$ diagram (Fig. 7-16) if so desired.

Because the cell angles of natural microclines deviate proportionately from 90° within experimental error, there is no need to measure both the 130 and 131 peaks. The same is true for natural anorthoclases but not for the sodic plagioclase component of perthites (Fig. 7-17b).

For microcline, the splitting of the 130 diffraction was used by MacKenzie (1954) while the 131 diffraction was used by Goldsmith and Laves (1954a). The positions and intensities of the 130, 1$\overline{3}$0, 131 and 1$\overline{3}$1 diffractions, plus nearby diffractions for Spencer C orthoclase. (low sanidine) and Pellotsalo maximum microcline are given in Table 6-1. For the maximum microcline the 130 diffraction overlaps with the 200 diffraction and the 1$\overline{3}$1 diffraction with the $\overline{2}$22 diffraction. However the 200 diffraction is only one-sixth as strong as 130, and the 130 peak is essentially unaffected by it. The $\overline{2}$22 diffraction is about 40% as

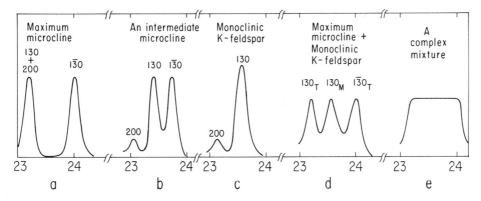

Fig. 7-30. Schematic profiles of diffractometer peaks (or of lines on Guinier films) for the 130 peaks of K-feldspars. The abscissa is 2θ for CuK$_\alpha$ radiation. Note that the peak profile depends on the X-ray technique: the one shown here is typical of commercial diffractometers and Guinier cameras

strong as $1\bar{3}1$ and shifts the peak by $0.01°$ 2θ. Marginally the 130, $1\bar{3}0$ peaks are better than the 131, $1\bar{3}1$ peaks because the overlap with 200 is less effective than with $\bar{2}22$ and because the 130, $1\bar{3}0$ peaks are easier to identify in the presence of peaks from other minerals, including plagioclase.

Goldsmith and Laves (1954) defined the *triclinicity* Δ as 12.5 $[d(131) - d(1\bar{3}1)]$, the value 12.5 being chosen so that Δ reaches unity for maximum microcline. [The spacing d is in Angstrom units]. Several scientists objected to the term triclinicity on the dubious basis that one could not have a degree of triclinic nature: a feldspar was either triclinic or not triclinic! This criticism is invalid because a feldspar may have a different degree of triclinic *geometry* even though the *symmetry* is uniquely triclinic or monoclinic. The term *obliquity* was used, but this suffers from the objection that it is a technical term for the angular misfit in twins, and because it could be applied to the β-angle of the monoclinic cell. Gubser and Laves (1967) suggested that "*triclinicity*" should perhaps be reserved for the more particular concept of the obliquity of triclinic substances, and that the term "*microclinicity*" might then be introduced! For *microcline*, one can define the 130 triclinic indicator as $\Delta(130) = 7.8$ $[d(130) - (1\bar{3}0)]$.

Many natural K-feldspars yield blurred 130 and $1\bar{3}1$ peaks that can be interpreted as the superposition of K-feldspars with different triclinic indicators. MacKenzie (1954), Harker (1954), Goldsmith and Laves (1954a) plus many later workers gave examples. Christie (1962a, b) introduced the concept of random disorder of a multitude of very small volumes each with a different degree of Si/Al order. Figure 7-30 shows possible shapes of diffractometer peaks for the 130 or 131 diffractions. Diagrams (a), (b) and (c) show the progression for homogeneous feldspars from maximum microcline via an intermediate microcline to monoclinic K-feldspar. Very rarely, three sharp peaks occur corresponding to a mixture of maximum microcline and monoclinic K-feldspar (MacKenzie, 1954; Harker, 1954), as shown diagrammatically in (d). If the peaks are somewhat blurred, the assemblage of three peaks would be essentially indistinguishable on powder patterns from a continuous variation of Δ, as in (e). Obviously there are many subtle variants as described by Christie (1962a, b) and Smithson (1962)

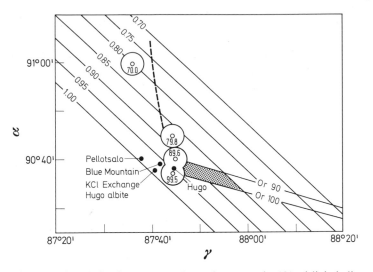

Fig. 7-31. The relation between α and γ angles versus the 131 triclinic indicator (Δ) and Or content of microclines as given by Orville. Contours of Δ range from 1.0—0.7. Open circles show cell dimensions for the microcline–low albite series, and the numbers give the Or content. Solid circles show three maximum microclines and one exchanged albite. The line for Or_{100} projects to the monoclinic point. The stippled area corresponds to the range of Δ-values found to be typical of two-thirds of natural microclines by Dietrich (1962), assuming that their compositions are bounded by Or_{90} and Or_{100}. (From Orville, 1967, Fig. 13)

among others. Laves and Viswanathan (1967) showed that by using only 2 to 3 mgs in a Guinier camera rather than 10 to 15 mgs in a diffractometer the spread of Δ tends to be reduced.

The effect of Ab substitution on the Δ value of microcline is uncertain. Figure 7-31 shows Orville's (1967) interpretation with respect to an $\alpha\gamma$ plot. The contours from 1.00 down to 0.70 show the values of Δ that result mathematically from change in α and γ. The open circles represent three members from his microcline-low albite series with 99.5, 89.6 and 79.8 % Or. The solid circles show cell dimensions obtained by various workers for maximum microclines and K-exchanged Hugo albite. The Or_{100} and Or_{90} lines were obtained by joining the data points for the microcline–low albite series to the monoclinic point at 90°, 90°. If this diagram is correct, substitution of 10% Ab without change of Si, Al distribution reduces Δ by about 0.07. However Laves and co-workers state that the effect of Ab-content on Δ is negligible so long as it does not exceed about 20% (e.g. Laves and Viswanathan, 1967). The data of Goldsmith and Laves (1961) are not as precise as those of Orville, but do not contradict those of Orville when account is taken of errors. Strictly speaking, it appears that Δ should be corrected for Ab substitution by 0.007 for each 1% Ab if Orville's data are accepted.

Albites are treated in detail with the plagioclases, and the 131, $1\bar{3}1$ pair provides a suitable triclinic indicator as used by innumerable workers following MacKenzie (1957). For low albite, the $1\bar{3}1$ peak slightly overlaps other peaks but they are too weak to cause any serious effect. For anorthoclase with a closer approach to monoclinic symmetry than albite, the most suitable peaks for measuring the triclinic geometry are 111 and 1$\bar{1}$1, as used by MacKenzie (1952). With increasing Na-content the 111 peak merges with 1$\bar{3}$0 producing almost a complete overlap for pure high albite. The 130, 1$\bar{3}$0 peaks are not suitable as a general triclinic indicator for Na-rich feldspars because of overlap.

7.3.6 Dimensional Changes Caused by Heating

General. The techniques used to measure the linear dimensions of feldspars may be classified as either macroscopic or submicroscopic. Historically the former came first, while the latter became feasible only with the invention of X-ray diffraction techniques.

Saucier and Saplevitch (1962) reviewed the dilatometric, goniometric and interferometric measurements of thermal expansion and gave preliminary results on the use of crackling varnish to reveal the principal directions of expansion. The macroscopic measurements are complicated by defects caused by chemical impurities and mechanical cracks. During heating and cooling, strains are developed which result in kinks or breaks in the curves relating macroscopic dimension to temperature. This is the simplest explanation of some of the discontinuities seen in the interferometric data of many workers, especially Kôzu *et al.* Other discontinuities represent genuine changes in lattice geometry resulting from atomic interchanges or symmetry changes. Thus heating of a perthite causes homogenization which is displayed macroscopically by an increase in thermal expansion. The transition from triclinic to monoclinic symmetry probably causes a discontinuity or change in slope in the thermal expansion.

The thermal expansion is represented by a second-order tensor which can be displayed graphically by an ellipsoid or hyperboloid with three principal axes each with its principal coefficient. The figure must obey the crystal symmetry. In monoclinic crystals, one axis must be parallel to *b*, but the other axes are free to move in the *ac* plane. In triclinic crystals, there is no symmetry control. Detailed mathematical analysis is given in Nye (1960). The volume expansion is a scalar quantity.

In theory measurement of the expansion in four directions is sufficient to completely define the thermal expansion of monoclinic crystals: viz. *b* and three directions in the *ac* plane. For triclinic crystals, six directions are needed. In practice, the experimental accuracy is such that a least-squares fit for many more directions is desirable.

X-ray diffraction measurements yield the size of the unit cell. The volume thermal expansion is readily obtained by differentiation of the cell volume with temperature. The second-order tensor for thermal expansion can be determined from the temperature variation of the cell edges and angles, as outlined by Willaime *et al.* (1972).

Because of the paucity of crystal structure determinations directly at high temperature, there is no comprehensive explanation of the thermal expansion of feldspars in terms of chemical bonding. For monoclinic K-feldspar the data show that the largest expansion occurs near [301], consistent with flexing of the double-crankshaft. In plagioclase, the orientations are quite different (see next section), and the atomic movements must be more complex. Generally speaking, the cell angles tend to approach monoclinic geometry as the temperature increases, perhaps because the M atoms tend to appear larger because of thermal vibration, and because the framework tends to vibrate in modes of higher symmetry.

All the cell dimensions listed in preceding sections were determined at "room temperature", a value varying from about 18 to 30° C. The cell dimensions depend not only on the temperature of measurement, but also on the previous thermodynamic history. During heating, a feldspar may change structurally in three ways: (a) by change of symmetry between monoclinic and triclinic, (b) by ion-exchange of M atoms, (c) by migration of Si and Al atoms. The effect on the cell dimensions depends on the *relaxation time* for the process.

For migration of Si and Al atoms in alkali feldspars, the relaxation time under dry conditions is so enormous that the process can be ignored for measurements taking up to several days except perhaps just near the melting point. Each individual feldspar has its own metastable curve for thermal expansion, only one point of which can represent equilibrium (the entire curve, of course, can be metastable). The only practical way to determine the equilibrium value of thermal expansion is to prepare an equilibrium feldspar at each of a series of temperatures by prolonged treatment, and then determine the cell dimensions of each feldspar at its equilibrium temperature. Figure 7-32 shows metastable curves of cell volume and an equilibrium curve constructed by joining the equilibrium point from each of the metastable curves.

All direct experimental data on the triclinic-monoclinic inversion are for metastable conditions. The inversion can occur only in those feldspars with an Al, Si distribution that is *topochemically* monoclinic: those with unbalance of Al-content between 0 and m subsites must remain triclinic at all temperatures. For feldspars with monoclinic topochemistry, the inversion proceeds promptly, probably in about a millisecond since it involves merely bending of bonds. Domain twinning results from inversion to triclinic symmetry. At thermodynamic equilibrium, the inversion must involve change of Si, Al distribution, a change that is not thermodynamically *accessible*. A detailed account of inversions is given in Chapter 21. Laves (1960 and elsewhere) distinguished the monoclinic-triclinic

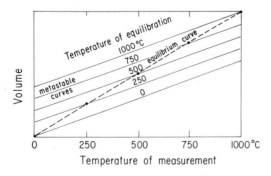

Fig. 7-32. Relation between the equilibrium curve and metastable curves relating cell volume to temperature. The metastable curves are for specimens equilibrated at the temperature specified on the curve. Each solid dot lies at the equilibration temperature on the relevant curve. The equilibrium curve joins the solid dots

inversion as *displacive* or *diffusive*, depending whether bond angles were merely displaced, or whether Si, Al atoms diffused.

The migration of Na, K atoms in heated perthites is described in Chapter 19.

Measurements of cell dimensions at high temperature are not easy. Most high-temperature X-ray equipment has temperature variations of at least several degrees Celsius across the specimen. The specimen holder tends to move slightly causing systematic bias.

More serious is unwitting ion-exchange. Stewart and von Limbach (1967) found that their albites when heated at 1050–1100° C ion-exchanged with K atoms released from the ceramic of the diffractometer heater. Earlier, great confusion was caused by a similar effect in the Zürich laboratory that was not recognized for some years. The literature on "monalbite" is particularly confusing to new readers because the original specimens prepared by Schneider (1957) actually contained potassium produced by alkali exchange of the starting albite as shown by Stewart and von Limbach (1967), Brown (1967), and Hall and Quareni (1967). To avoid further confusion, it should be emphasized that for pure $NaAlSi_3O_8$, monoclinic symmetry can be observed only above 950° C. All specimens *equilibrated* below 980° C have triclinic topochemistry and are triclinic at all temperatures. Substitution of K for Na lowers the temperature permitting monoclinic symmetry at room temperature for specimens of composition Or_{40} with monoclinic topochemistry.

Expansion of K-feldspar and Perthites. Unfortunately the specimens used in the early macroscopic studies are characterized only by general terms such as adularia, sanidine and microcline, resulting in uncertainty about the structural state and the Na, K ratio. Let α_1, α_2 and α_3 be the largest, the median and the least values of the principal thermal expansion coefficients.

Fizeau (1868) found by interferometry of a (monoclinic) adularia from St. Gotthard that from ambient temperature up to 70° C, $\alpha_1 = 19.07$, $\alpha_2 = -1.48$, $\alpha_3 = -2.00$ (all $\times 10^{-6}$ in fractional units per degree Celsius). The smallest expansion α_3 (actually a contraction) was parallel to b, while α_1 was found to lie at 18° 48′ to a in the obtuse angle β. The volume expansion coefficient is 15.59×10^{-6}, considerably smaller than earlier estimates by Kopp (1852) using a dilatometer. The α_1 principal axis lies at 3° to the principal axis for the smallest refractive index. Beckenkamp (1881) from goniometry found for an adularia that α_1 lay at 19° 56′ from a, an angle close to that of Fizeau, while α_3 lay along b. For a sanidine, Offret (1890) found that α_1 was close to a while α_2 was nearly equal to α_3, the latter being parallel to b.

Kôzu and Saiki (1925) studied the expansion of St. Gotthard adularia from 20 to 200° C, from which results Saucier and Saplevitch (1962) found α_2 parallel to b with a positive coefficient 0.95×10^{-6}. Along a, the expansion was 17.8×10^{-6} and along c, 0.22×10^{-6}. These latter two measurements need not give α_1 and α_3. Kôzu and Takane (1929) found by dilatometry that the volume expansion of an orthoclase of composition $Or_{90}Ab_{10}$ was 2.2% at 1000° C, and that increasing Ab content led to greater expansion, such as 3.4% at 24% Ab. These data are probably complicated by homogenization of perthitic albite. Kôzu and Ueda (1928) measured the volume expansion of K-feldspar and other minerals of granite.

Rosenholtz and Smith, D. (1941), by dilatometry of an adularia, found the expansions along [100] [010] and [001] to be 16.63, 0.27, 0.46 × 10⁻⁶ for 0 to 200° C. The expansions for [100] and [001] were essentially linear up to 1000° C, but for [010] the expansion was first positive and then negative. Twelve kinks were observed in the expansion curves, some resulting in permanent expansion. The kink at 900° C is unlikely to correspond to inversion to sanidine because of the short heating time. For a microcline, the corresponding expansions were 16.19, 0.23 and 0.45, again all positive. Twenty kinks were observed. Probably some of the kinks correspond to homogenization of perthite, but most probably result merely from closure of cracks.

Saucier and Saplevitch (1962) determined the position of principal axes by observing the cracks in photo-elastic and crackling varnishes spread over the surface of the feldspar. For an adularia from Göschen, St. Gotthard they found, after cooling from 112° C, regular cracks at -20 to $-22°$ to a on the (010) face compared to Fizeau's value of $-19°$. Using an extensometric gauge they found for the same adularia that $\alpha_1 = 18.7$, $\alpha_2 = 1.3$ and $\alpha_3 = -1.6 \times 10^{-6}$, which values are similar to those of Fizeau except for the change in sign for α_2.

There are no X-ray diffraction data on the thermal expansion of K-feldspars, except for the reconnaissance study of Grundy and Brown (1967) who found no change in the lattice angles of microcline within the experimental error of their precession technique.

Willaime et al. (1972) used this information together with the data of Rosenholtz and Smith to deduce that for microcline the principal expansion is near $[\bar{1}\bar{1}.1.\bar{3}]$, which is close to the direction for sanidine, i.e. near [301]. The lengths and positions of the median and least expansions of microcline and sanidine are quite uncertain.

Saucier and Saplevitch found anomalous increases in volume of perthites, the temperature for the increase being different from one specimen to another. These data have no fundamental value and correspond merely to the accidental kinetics of homogenization plus effects caused by relief of stress.

Expansion of Pure Albite. The thermal expansion of low albite was measured with a dilatometer by Kôzu and Ueda (1933) and by Rosenholtz and Smith (in Yoder and Weir, 1951). The former workers used a polished cube of albite from Alp Rischuna, cut perpendicular to a, (010) and (001), while the latter used an Amelia albite.

X-ray diffraction data were obtained by Stewart and von Limbach (1967) for an Amelia albite ($Or_{1.7}An_{1.3}$) and for an albite synthesized hydrothermally from glass for 3 h at 925° C. The 131 triclinic indicator of the synthetic albite was $1.98 \pm 0.02°$ for CuK_α, somewhat lower than the value for an extreme high albite. Unfortunately heating data were complicated by ion-exchange with K-rich vapor released from the furnace ceramic of the diffractometer. For the Amelia albite, cell dimensions obtained before heating to 1127° C appear to be unaffected by irreversible chemical change, but for the high albite heating to temperatures over 900° C caused irreversible changes. The cell volume indicated Or contents up to 10% Or while X-ray fluorescence analysis showed up to 12%. Table 5A of Stewart and von Limbach shows that only five sets of cell dimensions for the high albite (those at 26, 154, 318, 605, and 931° C) were unaffected by K-substitution. Unfortunately because of the paucity of data, SL used 5 sets of cell dimensions for specimens estimated to have 2 or 3% Or held at 464, 766, 902, 880 and 1026° C. Since (1) 3% Or increases the cell volume by about 1 part in 400 while the total expansion from 25 to 1000° C is about 1 part in 30, and (2) the impure albites were examined mostly at high temperature, the SL data tend to give too high a thermal expansion. The non-linear variation with temperature of the expansion coefficient of high albite in the SL Table 3 and Fig. 5 probably results largely from substitution of Or plus experimental error in the cell dimensions.

Using a similar diffractometer technique, Grundy and Brown (1969) measured the thermal expansion of two natural albites (Schyn-Schluct $Or_{0.5}An_{0.1}$; Amelia $Or_{1.8}An_{0.0}$); synthetic albites equilibrated by MacKenzie (1957) at 500, 600, 700, 750, 800, 850, 900 and 1000° C; heated Schyn-Schluct; and a non-equilibrated albite synthesized hydrothermally from glass at 610° C for only 3 h. The error in the cell dimensions is probably about twice as large as for the SL data, but the GB data show no evidence for K-substitution from the furnace. Analysis of the synthetic specimens showed a uniform K-content corresponding to 0.3% Or, which presumably results from the glass starting material. The inversion in cryolite was found to lie at 565° C compared to a value of 563° C in the literature. The accuracy was believed to be $\pm 10°$ C.

Kayode (1964) measured the cell dimensions of natural and heated albite, but the data are less accurate than those of GB and SL, and are not quoted here.

Figure 7-33 shows data for the non-equilibrium volume expansion of low albite expressed as a percentage increase over the volume at 26° C as given by SL.

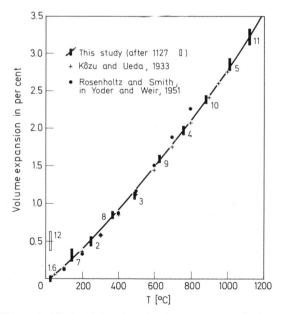

Fig. 7-33. Volume expansion of low albite. The vertical limits of the rectangles show $\pm$ one standard deviation. The numbers show the sequence of measurements by Stewart and von Limbach. The open symbol shows the effect of K-substitution after heating to 1127° C. The curve is a least-squares fit to the SL data. (From Stewart and von Limbach, 1967, Fig. 4)

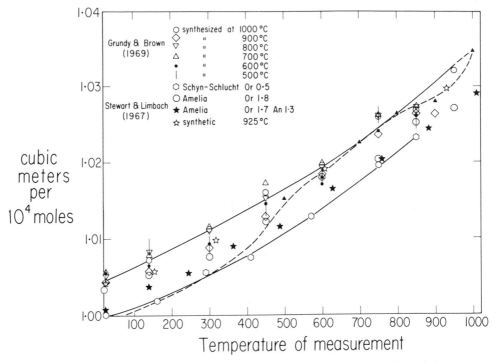

Fig. 7-34. Experimental data on the molar volume of albite. See text for explanation of the curves. Note scale in cubic meters per 10^4 moles rather than original values of cm^3/mol. Data from Grundy and Brown (1969) and Stewart and von Limbach (1967). The size of the symbols has no significance with respect to error, which varies from datum to datum, but tends to be near $\pm$ one part per thousand. Temperature in °C

The agreement between the X-ray data of SL and the dilatometric data of KU and RS is fairly satisfactory when account is taken of the experimental errors. Up to 600° C the X-ray curve tends to lie higher than the dilatometric data. From 600 to 1000° C, the KU and SL data fit excellently but the RS data diverge.

Figure 7-34 shows most of the GB data expressed as molar volume. Unfortunately the experimental errors are too large to permit a reliable interpretation of the equilibrium expansion. The two continuous lines are my estimates for the molar volume of Schyn-Schluct albite and the synthetic albite equilibrated at 1000° C. Curves for the other equilibrated albites are not shown to avoid confusion, but the small solid triangles are my estimates of the molar volume at the temperature of equilibration. The dashed curve is an estimate of the molar volume at equilibrium, (a) beginning for low temperatures slightly below the curve for low albite, (b) crossing it about 300° C, the assumed equilibration temperature of this low albite, and (c) passing by the solid triangles on its way to meet the curve for the 1000° specimen. It is obvious that systematic and random experimental bias might be responsible for some of the bending in this supposed equilibrium curve. Whatever its true position, it must cross from the curve for low albite to the one for high albite.

The data by GB for their two albites, and the SL data for Amelia albite disagree. Since 1 % Or should increase the cell volume by about one part in 800, some of the difference in Fig. 7-34 arises from K-substitution. The remainder presumably arises from systematic experimental error, amounting to about one or two parts in 1000. The thermal expansion obtained by SL is greater than that observed by GB, perhaps because of some systematic bias arising from mechanical design of the diffractometer furnaces.

The SL data for Amelia albite were fitted by least-squares to the curve shown in Fig 7-33 whose equation is

$$V = A T^{-1} + B + C T + D T^2$$

where V is the molar volume in cubic meters, T is in °K, and the coefficients are A -7.8821×10^{-6}, B 9.95300×10^{-5}, C 1.6422×10^{-9}, and D 7.5321×10^{-13}. The standard error is 3.68×10^{-8} cubic meters per mole. The GB data were not fitted to a polynomial. The SL data for high albite were also fitted to a polynomial, but the coefficients are biased and should not be quoted in standard tables.

Until further measurements have been made to clarify the causes of the deviations between the SL and GB data, it would be advisable to be cautious in using the data, though individual measurements of the molar volume should be accurate to about one part in a thousand. Table 7-5 lists some of the experimental data on molar volumes and thermal expansion.

Figure 7-35 compares the variation of cell edges with temperature as found (a) by SL and (b) by GB. For the SL data the solid lines and symbols show data unaffected by K-exchange, whereas the dashed lines show the presumed cooling paths linking specimens that have become more potassic (open symbols). The GB data show the trends for the six equilibrated synthetic specimens plus the F 101 natural albite from Amelia.

Within experimental error, both sets of data show a continuous increase of a with temperature such that the high albites maintain a slightly larger dimension than the low albites. For b, the SL data show a continuous increase with temperature for both high and low albite. The GB data show the same trend for the synthetic albites, but for the F 101 data they show a slight decrease followed by an increase. This reversal may result merely from experimental error. For c, both sets of data are consistent with a small decrease up to several hundreds of degrees Celsius followed by an increase.

Figure 7-36 shows the variation of α^* and γ^* vs. temperature for the equilibrated albites of GB. The dashed lines show my estimates of the change of α^* and γ^* under thermodynamic equilibrium, assuming that monoclinic symmetry is attained at 980° C and that F 101 albite is slightly disordered and that it equilibrated at 300° C. Figure 7-37 shows α^* vs. γ^* and d_{010} vs. d_{001}. These latter two values are the reciprocals of b^* and c^*. The data in Fig. 7-37 show that estimates of structural state from $\Delta(\alpha^* \gamma^*)$ and $\Delta(b^* c^*)$ are essentially unaffected by the temperature of measurement. For a constant structural state, the changes of these cell dimensions are in the same direction as those produced by ion-exchange of Na by K. Indeed one can propose that increased thermal vibration makes the small Na atom act like a larger atom. Roughly speaking, increase of tempera-

Table 7-5. Molar volumes of albite at listed temperature

°C	Specimen label: see footnotes for description									
	a	b	c	d	e	f	g	h	i	j
	Molar volume expressed in 10^{-4} meters^3/mole									
(a) Grundy and Brown (1969)										
25[a]	1.0025	0.9997	1.0038	1.0048	1.0065	1.0064	1.0044	1.0045	1.0047	1.0068
25[b]	1.0048	1.0004	—	1.0055	1.0046	1.0051	1.0058	1.0043	1.0040	1.0054
140	1.0052	—	—	1.0090	1.0065	1.0078	1.0082	1.0057	1.0072	1.0080
150	—	—	1.0082	—	—	—	—	—	—	—
160	—	1.0018	—	—	—	—	—	—	—	—
290	—	1.0055	—	—	—	—	—	—	—	—
300	1.0076	—	1.0103	1.0091	1.0093	1.0115	1.0109	1.0087	1.0112	1.0117
410	—	1.0075	—	—	—	—	—	—	—	—
450	1.0122	—	1.0126	1.0139	1.0145	1.0172	1.0153	1.0128	1.0160	1.0169
600	1.0179	—	1.0177	1.0183	1.0171	1.0197	1.0194	1.0184	1.0195	1.0209
750	1.0203	1.0195	1.0227	1.0262	1.0240	1.0261	1.0260	1.0235	1.0258	1.0257
850	1.0251	1.0231	1.0268	1.0252	1.0260	1.0273	1.0271	1.0263	1.0267	1.0283
900	—	—	—	—	—	—	—	1.0262	—	—
950	1.0271	—	1.0296	—	—	—	—	—	1.0321	—
1000	—	—	—	—	—	—	—	—	—	1.0371

°C	Low[c] albite	High[d] albite
(b) Stewart and v. Limbach (1967)		
0	1.0001	1.0043
26	1.0006	1.0042
100	1.0023	1.0048
200	1.0046	1.0067
300	1.0070	1.0093
400	1.0096	1.0122
500	1.0126	1.0153
600	1.0153	1.0186
700	1.0183	1.0221
800	1.0215	1.0256
900	1.0249	1.0291
1000	1.0283	1.0327
1100	1.0320	1.0364
1200	1.0358	—

[a] Before heating. [b] After heating. [c] Amelia. [d] Hydrothermal, 925° C, 0.25 kbar, 3 h.

a Amelia; b Schyn-Schlucht; c Schyn-Schlucht 32 days 1060° C; d 112 days 500° C; e 73 days 600° C; f 50 days 700° C; g 60 days 800 C; h 41 h 900° C; i 66 h 1000° C; j 3 h 610° C; a, b natural; d–j synthetic, hydrothermal, mostly 1 kbar.

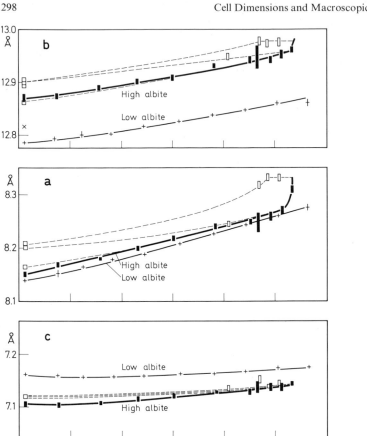

Fig. 7-35 a

Fig. 7-35. Variation of cell edges (Å) of albite with temperature as given by (a) Stewart and von Limbach (1967) and (b) Grundy and Brown (1969). a Reversible changes are shown by the continuous lines and solid symbols. Irreversible changes from K-substitution are shown by dashed lines and open symbols. The height of the symbols.corresponds to $\pm$ one standard error. b The symbol key is: F 101 Amelia natural, solid square; equilibrated synthetic albites, 500° C solid dot, 600° C open upright triangle, 700° C open diamond, 800° C open circle, 900° C reversed triangle, 1000° C horizontal cross. The curves were fitted arbitrarily by GB. The size of the symbols has no significance. (From Stewart and von Limbach, 1967, Fig. 6 and Grundy and Brown, 1969, Fig. 3)

ture from 0° to 1000° C produces the same effects on b^*, c^*, α^* and γ^* as substitution of half of the Na atoms by K atoms. However the effect on a^* (and of course a) is not as large, amounting to the equivalent of substitution of about two-sevenths of the Na atoms.

The change with temperature of the cell angles α^* and γ^* was particularly controversial, but has probably been resolved. It is necessary to distinguish clearly between *equilibrated* and *non-equilibrated* albites, and between structural states that are topochemically either monoclinic or triclinic. The series of albites equilibrated hydrothermally changes from triclinic to monoclinic in pure

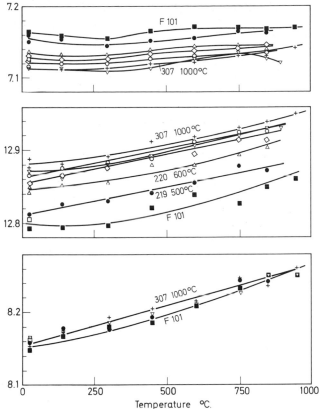

Fig. 7-35b. Legend see opposite page

NaAlSi$_3$O$_8$ at 980° C (Laves, 1960). All specimens equilibrated above 980° C are topochemically monoclinic, and for *rapid* heating the inversion temperature is governed by the interaction of the Na atom with the aluminosilicate framework. All specimens equilibrated under 980° C are topochemically triclinic, and remain triclinic at all temperatures so long as the structural state does not change to one with monoclinic topochemistry.

MacKenzie (1952) first showed that triclinic indicators for synthetic albite varied with the temperature of synthesis. MacKenzie and Smith (1961) placed the inversion to monoclinic albite at about 950° C while Laves (1960, Fig. 9) placed it at 980° C. A natural Amelia albite heated dry for 10 weeks at 1055° C gave an inversion temperature of 960°. The data for sodic plagioclases synthesized dry extrapolated to about 920° C. The hydrothermally-synthesized specimens are now known to contain 0.3% Or, whereas the natural albite probably contains 1 or 2% Or. Probably the estimated temperature is accurate to only 10 to 20° C because of uncertainty in calibration and extrapolation. Taken all together, the value of 980° C given by Laves is consistent for all the data, though there is a possibility of hidden factors perhaps amounting to ~ 50° C.

Laves (1960) distinguished between monalbite which is truly monoclinic and albite which is truly triclinic. Analbite is the triclinic inversion product of mon-

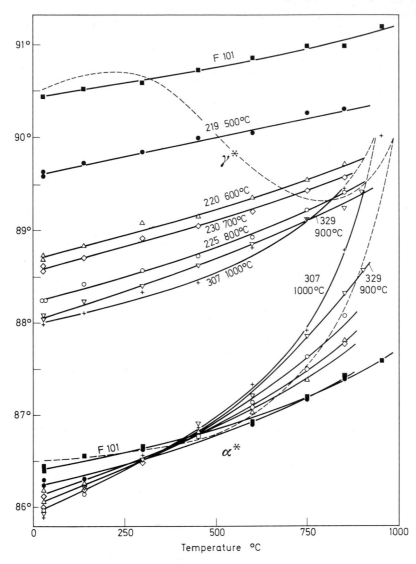

Fig. 7-36. Plot of α^* and γ^* versus temperature for equilibrium albites studied by Grundy and Brown (1969). F 101 is Amelia natural albite. The other labels give the specimen number and temperature of equilibration. Each continuous line represents the data points for a synthetic albite equilibrated at the listed temperature. The dashed lines are my estimates of the change of α^* and γ^* under thermodynamic equilibrium. (From Grundy and Brown, 1969, Fig. 1, with additions)

albite. High albite is also triclinic, but does not invert to monalbite. Thus under equilibrium conditions, albite (low) changes to albite (high) and then to monalbite. Analbite is always metastable. This distinction between high albite and analbite is used in German-speaking countries, but not in English-speaking countries (see Chapter 9).

Stewart and von Limbach (1967) placed the inversion temperature at $1100 \pm 50°$ C, but they did not recognize that their high albite had triclinic topochemistry as a result of hydrothermal synthesis at 925° C.

Grundy et al. (1967) found that a small crystal of Schyn-Schlucht albite, after heating for 32 days at 1060° C in a platinum tube, became monoclinic above about 930° C, as observed by single-crystal precession technique. Grundy and Brown (1969) found that of their equilibrium albites only the one synthesized at 1000° C became monoclinic below the melting point.

Dietz et al. (1970) examined the superheating of cleavelandite ($Or_{0.5}An_{1.0}$) and synthetic high albite (8 weeks dry at 1050° C). They deduced that melting began at $1117 \pm 3°$ C for both and was completed at $1140 \pm 3°$ for the high albite and slightly higher for the low albite. For the high albite, they found that the separation of the 111 and $1\bar{1}1$ peaks extrapolated to zero at about 1150° C. This result is puzzling because MacKenzie (1952) found that feldspars of composition An_{10} and An_5 crystallized dry inverted at 1035 and 960° C, in apparent contradiction to the result of Dietz et al. Synthesis under dry conditions should result in a highly-disordered feldspar with monoclinic topochemistry as implied by the results of MacKenzie (1952). Reinvestigation of dry albite is needed.

Kroll (1971b) found that the 111 triclinic indicator for a series of albites synthesized hydrothermally at 1060, 1000, 950, 900 and 850° C would extrapolate to zero at 980, 980, 1040, 1110 and 1140° C, respectively (Fig. 7-38). Hence the equilibrium inversion was placed at 980° C, exactly consistent with the value estimated by Laves. Because the X-ray peaks stayed diffuse at all temperatures for albites synthesized at 950, 900 and 850° C, Kroll deduced that all three have triclinic topochemistry, and that the extrapolations to 1040, 1110 and 1140° C do not represent real conditions.

The equilibrium temperature for inversion from monoclinic to triclinic symmetry need not correspond exactly with the change from monoclinic to triclinic topochemistry of the T atoms. The latter change may occur at a higher temperature than the former change, because crumpling of the aluminosilicate framework about Na atoms might occur even for monoclinic topochemistry: for example, anorthite is triclinic at all temperatures even though it has monoclinic topochemistry over the entire temperature range.

Monoclinic-triclinic Inversion in Na, K Feldspars. MacKenzie (1952) found that the non-equilibrium inversion from triclinic to monoclinic symmetry dropped in temperature with increasing Or content (Fig. 7-40). For alkali feldspars synthesized hydrothermally at 800° C the inversion curve fell from over 1000° C for pure albite to 0° C near Or_{37} (mol.-%). Natural anorthoclases from volcanic rocks gave similar results when account was taken of substitution of An. Laves (1952) obtained similar results from 4 natural anorthoclases. The symmetry inversion was observed both by X-ray diffractometry and by optical microscopy. Much earlier Forstner (1884) had found the inversion to be reversible and non-quenchable by optical study of natural anorthoclase.

MacKenzie noted that the inversion temperature depended on the synthesis conditions as well as on the chemical composition, as explored thoroughly for albite in the preceding section. The actual situation for the Or, Ab series is extremely complex thermodynamically and has not been resolved experimentally.

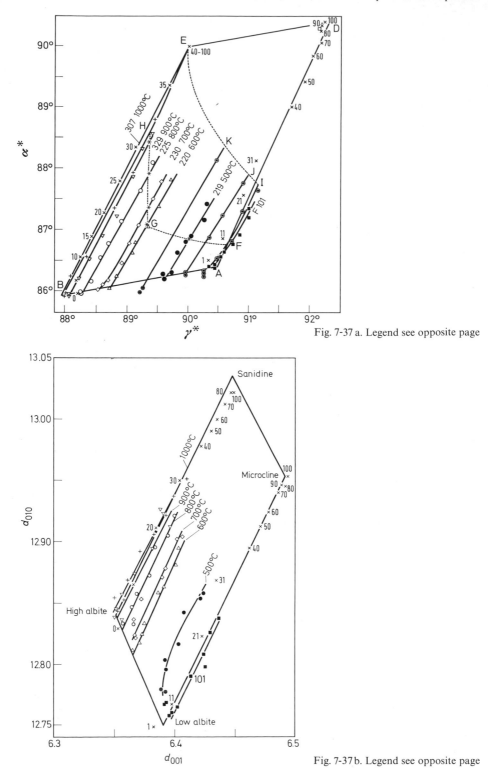

Fig. 7-37 a. Legend see opposite page

Fig. 7-37 b. Legend see opposite page

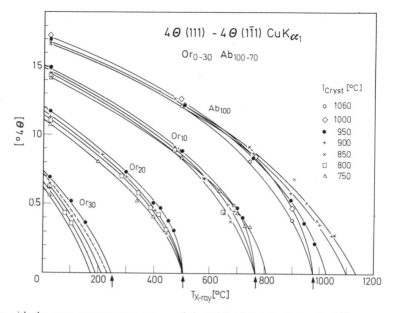

Fig. 7-38. Variation with the measurement temperature of the (111) triclinic indicator for feldspars of bulk composition Ab_{100} to $Or_{30}Ab_{70}$ (mol.-%) crystallized hydrothermally at the temperature specified in the inset key to symbols. The curves were extrapolated subjectively: see statement in text. T_{X-ray} is the temperature at which X-ray measurements were obtained. (From Kroll, 1971b, Fig. 33)

Figure 7-39 shows various possibilities. Diagram (a) shows schematically a possible situation for true thermodynamic equilibrium. There is a discontinuous inversion from monoclinic to triclinic feldspar with an intervening field of two feldspars specified by the binary loops extending to the solvus. Diagram (b) shows a situation for feldspars heated and cooled so rapidly that no movement of Na, K and Al, Si atoms occurs. This particular situation is for feldspars in the high sanidine–high albite series. A non-quenchable inversion occurs at the marked line. All these feldspars are topochemically monoclinic. Diagram (c) shows a similar non-equilibrium situation for the metastable microcline–low albite series. The entire field below the solidus is occupied by triclinic feldspar. Diagram (d) is a common depiction of the stable equilibrium of alkali feldspars

Fig. 7-37. Plot of (a) α^* vs. γ^* and (b) d_{010} vs. d_{001} for equilibrium albites studied by Grundy and Brown (1969). Each synthetic feldspar is represented by a trend line labelled with its synthesis temperature. F 101 is Amelia natural albite. a The points ABDE represent low albite, high albite, maximum microcline and monoclinic feldspars. The crosses show the data for the sanidine and microcline series of Orville (1967) with numbers specifying the Or content. The values near the line AB are for 25° C, with subsequent points at 140, 300, 450, 600, 750, 850, and in some cases at 900 or 950° C. The stars represent the value of α^* and γ^* at the synthesis temperature, and the curve FGHE is the resulting estimate of the equilibrium trend. The open square shows the average value of α^* and γ^* for 25—1000° C obtained for a microcline by Grundy and Brown (1967). The circled dots show data obtained by precession photographs. The dashed line IJKE shows a non-equilibrium disordering path for an albite from Schyn-Schlucht heated at 1050° C. b Symbols as in (a). (From Grundy and Brown, 1959, Figs. 4 and 5)

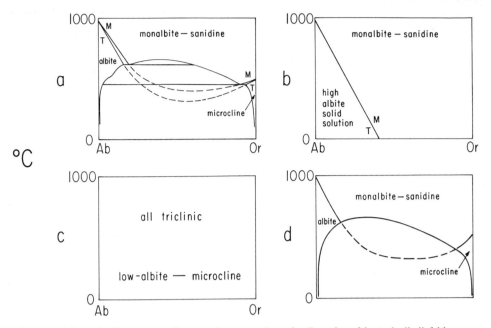

Fig. 7-39. Schematic diagrams to illustrate interpretation of cell angles of heated alkali feldspars. a Possible phase diagram for true thermodynamic equilibrium. The monoclinic feldspars in the monalbite–sanidine series are separated from the triclinic feldspars albite and microcline by a two-phase field. The dashed extension is purely schematic. See Fig. S-1 for more details. b Metastable situation for rapid heating and cooling of monalbite–sanidine series. The diagram is drawn for specimens synthesized hydrothermally at about 1000° C. See Fig. 7-40 for details. c Metastable situation for rapid heating and cooling of low albite-microcline homogenized series. There is no inversion to monoclinic symmetry. d Schematic diagram showing the equilibrium situation assuming that the monoclinic–triclinic transition is continuous without a two-phase field. This diagram is like that of Laves (1960, Fig. 10), but the curves are in slightly different positions

with a single line showing the inversion from monoclinic to triclinic symmetry. Such a single line implies that the inversion is not first-order, with a continuous change of cell angle with temperature. Chapter 21 covers the basic thermodynamic theory, and subsequent chapters discuss the experimental data. This section is concerned merely with the variation of cell angles for heating rates too rapid to permit chemical and structural changes.

The most recent data are by Kroll (1971b) as shown in Fig. 7-38. Feldspars were synthesized hydrothermally with bulk compositions 0, 10, 20 and 30 mol.-% Or. The 111 triclinic indicator was measured with a diffractometer, and the inversion temperature obtained by eye-estimated extrapolation. The data show that the synthetic feldspars have structural states that depend on the synthesis temperature, and that the inversion temperature depends on the structural state. For Or_{30}, it appears that the higher the synthesis temperature, the higher the inversion temperature in contrast to pure albite for which the apparent inversion temperature was higher for those feldspars crystallized below 980° C. Kroll deduced that all these specimens have monoclinic topochemistry.

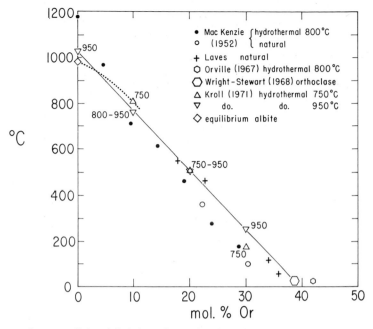

Fig. 7-40. Relation between the monoclinic–triclinic inversion and mol.-% Or. See text for meaning of dotted curve

Figure 7-40 compares the various estimates of the inversion temperature. MacKenzie's (1952) specimens synthesized hydrothermally at 800° C yield temperatures 50–100° C lower than those of Kroll. There is a problem in extrapolating the 111 triclinic indicator to zero, but until further measurements are made, the cause of the bias between the data of Kroll and MacKenzie will remain unknown. MacKenzie measured two natural anorthoclases, $Or_{31.7}An_{1.8}$ and $Or_{23.3}An_{1.3}$ (wt.-%), whose temperatures check well with those of his synthetic specimens. Laves (1952) measured four natural specimens using optical methods but the chemical compositions are known imperfectly. Presumably his data are in weight percent, and I have used compositions $Or_{19}An_{2.2}$, $Or_{23}An_{4.4}$ and Or_{35}, Or_{37} (determined from d_{400}). Orville (1967) estimated the room-temperature inversion to lie at 42 mol.-% Or for his specimens synthesized hydrothermally at 800° C. Wright and Stewart (1968) chose 40 wt.-% Or for the room-temperature inversion in their orthoclase series, and stated that this composition applied to the sanidine series only.

The spread of results in Fig. 7-40 makes it difficult to estimate the equilibrium position of the inversion. In contradiction to Wright and Stewart (1968), I suggest that there is a significant effect from change in structural state.

If the equilibrium inversion is a binary loop as in Fig. 7-38a, the present data do not give its position. However, one might guess that the upper curve of the loop is given by the dotted line in Fig. 7-40. The lower curve of the loop would be inaccessible from the present data.

The X-ray data for microcline are consistent with triclinic symmetry at all temperatures, with little variation of α^* and γ^* with temperature (see Fig. 7-37a).

7.4 Plagioclase Feldspars

7.4.1 General and Historical

All plagioclase feldspars are triclinic, except for monalbite solid solution, and measurement of cell dimensions was very difficult until electronic computers became available. Chao and Taylor (1940) obtained dimensions of moderate accuracy from single-crystal studies. Cole *et al.* (1951) measured cell dimensions of several plagioclases by the accurate single-crystal θ-method. The first systematic study of cell dimensions by Smith (1956) used powder diffractometry permitting delineation of the effects of An-content and structural state for synthetic and natural feldspars up to An_{50}. In detail, interpretation of these early data was slightly uncertain because of imperfections in the chemical analyses. Present knowledge is based on thorough measurements of natural specimens analyzed by the electron microprobe (Bambauer, Eberhard and Viswanathan, 1967), and on carefully synthesized specimens (Eberhard, pers. comm.; Kroll, 1971b).

The complex structural nature of plagioclase feldspars is outlined in the Summary. Some plagioclases (peristerite intergrowth) show two sets of peaks that can be recognized in X-ray patterns. Most plagioclases consist of fine-scale intergrowths, but the X-ray patterns show only one set of peaks because the intergrowths are structurally coherent. From the cell dimensions, one can distinguish two extremes for each chemical composition which define the extreme high and low structural states. Unlike the alkali feldspars, the structural interpretation of these extreme states is unclear. From the cell dimensions or from specific diffractions, an *indicator of structural state* can be measured. Probably there is not a unique relation between an indicator of structural state and the actual crystal structures.

Plagioclase plays an important role in petrogenesis, and rapid methods of estimating An-content and structural state would be valuable. Unfortunately the cell dimensions of plagioclase correlate so closely with each other that separate determination of these two properties is impossible or unreliable for most plagioclases. If the An-content is determined separately, the structural state can be estimated by an appropriate indicator, and vice versa. Unfortunately the cell dimensions are also affected significantly by minor substitutents such as K and Fe, and the details of determinative methods are rather complex.

Early studies of X-ray powder patterns by Claisse (1950) and by Goodyear and Duffin (1954, 1955) were soon extended by comprehensive measurements of *indicators* of *structural state* by Smith, J. R and Yoder (1956) and by Smith, J. V. and Gay (1958). Identification of plagioclase by X-ray powder methods is fully outlined in Chapter 6.

Just as for alkali feldspars, the dimensional changes upon heating depend on the heating rate. The equilibrium situation is governed by migration of Al and Si atoms, and interpretation of existing data is rather uncertain.

The Zürich investigators, following Brown (1960), plotted cell dimensions against the ratio Si/Al rather than An content in the belief that "a nearly linear relation between lattice constants and Si/Al ratios is to be expected". This belief is not justified, and I hope that all workers will plot their data against mol.-% An in order to permit rapid comparison. As far as possible, I have used mol.-%, but some diagrams were copied with other base-lines.

7.4.2 Cell Dimensions of Natural and Synthetic Specimens

Sources of Data Fig. 7-41 plots the cell dimensions vs. mol.-% An of various data selected from the literature as specified in the figure legend. The following is a list of accurate cell dimensions in the literature for room temperature, excluding the values for albite given in Section 7.3:

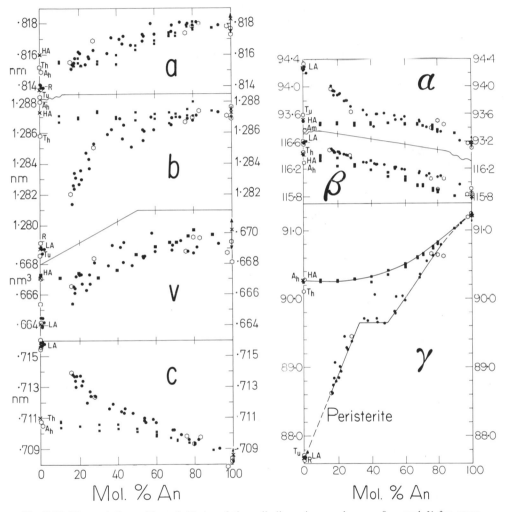

Fig. 7-41. The variation with mol.-% An of the cell dimensions *a*, *b*, *c*, α, β, γ and *V* for some natural and synthetic plagioclases. The circles represent data obtained by Bambauer, Eberhard and Viswanathan (1967) for selected natural plagioclases ascribed to the low structural series. The squares represent data obtained by Kroll (1967) for plagioclase synthesized within 120° C of the solidus. For some compositions, three data points are given for synthesis at 30, 60 and 120° C below the solidus. All syntheses were made for 15 days under dry conditions. The hexagons show the cell dimensions for those specimens used in X-ray structure analysis. The double arrow for pure anorthite shows the range of data for synthetic specimens measured by Stewart (1967), Nager *et al.* (1969) and Kroll (1971b). The data for γ are interpreted on the basis of two limiting series for high and low structural states. See Table 7-6 for data

(a) Cole *et al.* (1951): natural specimens near An_{55} and An_{100} plus partial data for 4 other plagioclases plus heated An_{55}; single-crystal θ-method.

(b) Smith (1956): 8 natural specimens up to An_{48}, 6 of them heated as well; synthetic specimens up to An_{49}; powder diffractometer; see later electron microprobe analyses of Ribbe and Smith (1966) for revised compositions;

(c) Brown (1960): 55 natural specimens from An_0 to An_{100}, some of them heated; α^* γ^* and β^* measured on precession camera; a few data for a^*, b^* and c^*; accuracy of An-content not known;

(d) Nissen *et al.* (1967): two iridescent labradorites $An_{52.5}Or_{2.5}$, $An_{55.5}Or_{2.6}$; Guinier camera; note incorrect dimensions quoted from Cole *et al.*;

(e) Stewart (1967): four anorthites synthesized hydrothermally; diffractometer; also quotes single-crystal data of lower accuracy obtained by Goldsmith and Laves for natural and synthetic anorthites;

(f) Bambauer, Eberhard and Viswanathan (1967): 36 plagioclases assigned to low structural series: An_0 to An_{93}; electron microprobe analyses; Guinier camera;

(g) Eberhard (1967): synthetic plagioclases; cell dimensions sent as private communication to J. V. Smith; Guinier camera;

(h) Doman *et al.* (1965): measurement of γ^* for single grains whose An content was estimated from refractive indices; precession camera;

(i) Wenk (1966): $An_{65-6}Or_{0.6}$; Wenk *et al.* (1968), $An_{84.8}Or_{0.6}$; Wenk (1969), $An_{13.5}Or_{4.1}$; all by diffractometer;

(j) Kroll (1971b): synthetic plagioclases from An_{10} to An_{100}, systematically prepared at temperatures up to $120°$ C below the solidus for various times in order to obtain equilibrium varieties; Guinier camera;

(k) Nager *et al.* (1969): synthetic anorthite, Guinier camera;

(l) Viswanathan (1971b): 17 plagioclases assigned to low structural series; electron microprobe analyses, Guinier camera;

(m) Appleman *et al.* (1971): 15 plagioclases from lunar rocks with compositions estimated either from electron microprobe analyses or optical regression curves; note that most of these plagioclases are chemically zoned and that those from volcanic rocks are non-stoichiometric and contain unusually large amounts of Mg and Fe; diffractometer; Stewart *et al.* (1972): 1 plagioclase from anorthosite;

(n) see Table 7-6(e) for summary of cell dimensions of plagioclases used in X-ray structure analysis; these data were obtained by various techniques and range widely in accuracy (see later for specific comments);

(o) see Table 7-6(f) for axial ratios and interaxial angles obtained from optical goniometry; comparison with cell dimensions from X-ray techniques suggests that the goniometric data are less accurate except perhaps for the anorthites for which it is possible that some of the goniometric data on the angles are more accurate than the X-ray data.

Table 7-6 lists data for many natural plagioclases, plus specimens synthesized close to the solidus temperature.

Correlation with Chemical Composition and Structural State. Many of the above data, plus some unpublished data of I. Borg, are plotted in Nissen (1969) and in Bambauer *et al.* (1967).

Table 7-6. Selected cell dimensions of plagioclase

(a) Synthetic anorthites

Reference	Synthesis conditions	a (nanometer)	b	c	α (degrees)	β	γ	V nm³
Stewart (1967)	An90Qz10 glass; hydrothermal 1300°C	.8182(3)	1.2873(2)	1.4178(3)	93.21(2)	115.83(2)	91.14(2)	1.3403(4)
do.	An glass; hydrothermal 1060°C	.8182(2)	1.2872(2)	1.4181(2)	93.12(2)	115.89(2)	91.25(2)	1.3400(3)
do.	An95Qz5 glass; hydrothermal 750°C	.8174(2)	1.2875(2)	1.4167(3)	93.10(2)	115.84(2)	91.30(2)	1.3381(4)
do.	An glass; hydrothermal 1060°C	.8179(2)	1.2869(2)	1.4174(2)	93.11(2)	115.89(2)	91.23(2)	1.3385(3)
Nager et al.(1969)	solid-state reaction 1500°C	.8181(2)	1.2869(2)	1.4162(3)	93.20(1)	115.78(1)	91.24(1)	1.3387(3)
Kroll (1971b)	An100 glass	.8185	1.2874	1.4176	93.28	115.74	91.11	1.3418
do.	dry mean 5,10,22 mins.	.8182	1.2869	1.4173	93.22	115.75	91.18	1.3404
do.	at mean 45,90,180 mins.	.8182	1.2872	1.4173	93.21	115.77	91.23	1.3404
do.	1430°C mean 6,12,24 hrs. mean 2,4,8,16 days	.8183	1.2873	1.4173	93.19	115.79	91.24	1.3404

(b) Synthetic (Ab,An) plagioclases

mol % An	ΔT (°C)	a (nanometer)	b	c	α (degrees)	β	γ	V nm³
10	30	.8156	1.2871	.7108	93.47	116.33	90.28	.6673
10	30	.8155	1.2871	.7107	93.45	116.37	90.27	.6666
20	60	.8155	1.2867	.7104	93.47	116.40	90.27	.6660
20	120	.8158	1.2870	.7105	93.48	116.25	90.27	.6674
30	30	.8154	1.2869	.7105	93.46	116.37	90.26	.6664
30	120	.8156	1.2871	.7106	93.44	116.25	90.28	.6671
40	30	.8160	1.2874	.7103	93.47	116.27	90.29	.6674
50	120	.8154	1.2869	.7101	93.47	116.19	90.32	.6676
50	30	.8166	1.2873	.7103	93.45	116.32	90.25	.6668
60	120	.8163	1.2868	.7098	93.47	116.15	90.42	.6686
60	60	.8172	1.2872	.7099	93.47	116.09	90.36	.6681
67.5	30	.8169	1.2866	.7097	93.46	116.15	90.50	.6691
67.5	30	.8174	1.2869	.7095	93.44	116.05	90.51	.6687
71	120	.8171	1.2873	.7096	93.46	115.95	90.60	.6694
71	30	.8174	1.2872	.7094	93.43	115.97	90.59	.6695
77	120	.8172	1.2870	.7094	93.43	115.95	90.58	.6694
77	30	.8178	1.2875	.7093	93.40	115.97	90.64	.6692
77	120	.8179	1.2871	.7094	93.43	115.91	90.76	.6698
80	30	.8181	1.2871	.7093	93.43	115.88	90.74	.6702
80	120	.8176	1.2880	.7094	93.35	115.86	90.82	.6702
90	120	.8177	1.2874	.7089	93.32	115.80	91.02	.6699

Kroll (1971b) — all specimens devitrified for 15 days at ΔT below solidus temperature

Table 7-6. (continued)

(c) Natural plagioclase mostly assigned to low structural state.

Reference	Label	mol % An	mol % Or	a	b	c	α	β	γ	V
Bambauer, Eberhard	194	0.0	0.3	.8141	1.2766	.7159	94.25	116.59	87.69	.6645
and Viswanathan	191	0.5	1.2	.8141	1.2785	.7157	94.26	116.59	87.69	.6645
(1967): probe	167	0.7	0.2	.8139	1.2782	.7157	94.29	116.60	87.69	.6639
analyses from	163	1.7	0.6	.8139	1.2785	.7158	94.20	116.61	87.76	.6642
Corlett and	110	11.1	1.4	.8148	1.2798	.7156	94.20	116.57	87.85	.6656
Eberhard (1967);	278	13.0	0.5	.8149	1.2804	.7142	94.07	116.52	88.45	.6651
standard error	84	16.5	0.7	.8151	1.2814	.7138	94.01	116.50	88.63	.6654
usually .0001 for	171	17.2	0.6	.8154	1.2826	.7134	93.94	116.48	88.74	.6665
the edges and 0.1	2	17.6	0.9	.8153	1.2824	.7130	93.95	116.46	88.84	.6661
for the angles	104	17.9	0.5	.8158	1.2831	.7137	93.88	116.45	88.07	.6664
	67	18.5	0.9	.8158	1.2827	.7137	93.94	116.45	88.85	.6672
	162	20.2	3.9	.8162	1.2836	.7131	93.88	116.46	88.85	.6673
	288	21.0	1.2	.8161	1.2836	.7134	93.89	116.45	88.01	.6673
	166	21.5	0.3	.8153	1.2830	.7120	93.90	116.43	88.94	.6667
	114	23.9	1.0	.8154	1.2847	.7127	93.79	116.42	88.94	.6663
	170	25.3	1.0	.8158	1.2843	.7127	93.80	116.41	89.45	.6663
	193	25.6	0.8	.8158	1.2837	.7124	93.80	116.40	89.28	.6673
	101	28.0	0.4	.8163	1.2853	.7124	93.71	116.36	89.26	.6667
	136	35.3	4.2	.8171	1.2859	.7116	93.66	116.42	89.38	.6681
	5	37.4	0.4	.8171	1.2862	.7119	93.59	116.30	89.71	.6679
	94	41.8	0.4	.8170	1.2869	.7114	93.42	116.28	89.68	.6692
	212	43.2	1.3	.8167	1.2856	.7113	93.60	116.27	90.06	.6691
	237	43.7	0.2	.8172	1.2865	.7116	93.61	116.26	89.71	.6681
	91	47.8	0.8	.8166	1.2851	.7113	93.58	116.23	89.66	.6679
	74	53.8	1.0	.8173	1.2855	.7110	93.58	116.22	89.64	.6685
	81	53.7	0.2	.8169	1.2862	.7108	93.52	116.22	89.81	.6684
	48	54.3	1.2	.8172	1.2861	.7107	93.52	116.20	90.03	.6685
	96	58.1	0.2	.8180	1.2870	.7109	93.56	116.20	90.04	.6700
	11	59.8	0.7	.8173	1.2862	.7107	93.56	116.19	89.98	.6688
	45	68.7	0.2	.8175	1.2865	.7102	93.50	116.14	90.31	.6689
	103	69.0	0.6	.8179	1.2870	.7102	93.49	116.16	90.36	.6692
	61	73.1	0.3	.8181	1.2870	.7099	93.41	116.16	90.55	.6695
	36	77.0	0.2	.8180	1.2869	.7096	93.38	116.13	90.63	.6688
	300	80.0	0.2	.8179	1.2868	.7093	93.34	116.08	90.80	.6687
	299	81.9	0.0	.8181	1.2871	.7096	93.34	116.10	90.79	.6691
	166	93.1	0.0	.8179	1.2873	.7090	93.21	115.97	91.11	.6693

Viswanathan (1971b): probe analyses from Corlett and Eberhard (1967); standard error .0002 in edges and .05 in angles

No.	An	Or	a	b	c	α	β	γ	V
3	75	1	.8185	1.2879	.7100	93.39	116.09	90.66	.6705
7	77	0.5	.8185	1.2876	.7101	93.41	116.08	90.57	.6776
24	51.8	2.3	.8179	1.2866	.7109	93.53	116.19	89.94	.6698
31	27.8	3.8	.8163	1.2850	.7125	93.75	116.40	89.37	.6679
34	21.5	1.7	.8168	1.2848	.7133	93.83	116.28	89.10	.6687
37	43.0	2.0	.8175	1.2863	.7120	93.59	116.43	89.63	.6697
40	59.1	2.2	.8181	1.2879	.7107	93.40	116.14	90.39	.6706
53	52.6	2.2	.8175	1.2867	.7118	93.55	116.27	89.68	.6699
54	43.0	2.5	.8176	1.2863	.7112	93.58	116.21	89.78	.6696
83	40.2	3.2	.8187	1.2387	.7138	93.34	116.17	90.23	.6720
86	18.5	5.5	.8166	1.2336	.7136	93.89	116.45	89.89	.6682
87	16.8	3.4	.8160	1.2332	.7161	93.91	116.60	88.80	.6674
98	35.4	5.4	.8143	1.2791	.7124	94.27	116.34	88.99	.6651
105	35.8	2.9	.8170	1.2866	.7121	93.63	116.39	87.69	.6695
158	37.9	0.5	.8160	1.2854	.7119	93.72	116.32	89.62	.6675
173		0.8	.8165	1.2864		93.63		89.49	.6686

peristerites: note problem of intergrowth (0.5–3.0)

No.	An	Or	a	b	c	α	β	γ	V
99	4.6	0.1	.8150	1.2802	.7159	93.63	116.59	89.63	.6661
202	9.6	0.7	.8145	1.2798	.7159	94.24	116.59	87.77	.6655
172	8	0.3	.8151	1.2794	.7157	94.30	116.61	87.87	.6653
203	12.3	1.5	.8151	1.2820	.7150	94.06	116.54	87.75	.6657
135	10.0	0.4	.8150	1.2812	.7151	94.16	116.53	88.39	.6663
129	11	1.6	.8148	1.2816	.7152	94.16	116.54	88.25	.6664
187	12	1.1	.8144	1.2811	.7148	94.17	116.52	88.17	.6657
14	13.2	0.6	.8159	1.2622	.7146	93.98	116.54	88.13	.6675
102	65.6	1.0	.8148	1.2611	.7151	94.16	116.51	88.44	.6661
165	84.8	4.1	.8160	1.2619	.7146	93.95	116.54	88.20	.6672

Wenk (1966)	13.5	0.6	.8186(7)	1.2871(7)	.7109(5)	93.57(4)	116.03(5)	90.37(4)	.671(1)
Wenk et al. (1968)		4.1	.8091(5)	1.2889	1.4206	93.38(5)	115.96	90.97	1.345(2)
Wenk (1969)			.8191(3)	1.2823(3)	.7149(2)	93.91(2)	116.52(2)	88.55(2)	.678(4)

Smith (1956): probe analyses from Ribbe and Smith (1966)

No.	An	Or	a	b	c	α	β	γ	V
	0.2	0.5	.8144	1.2787	.7160	94.26	116.58	87.67	.6649
	16.0	1.9	.8152	1.2821	.7139	93.99	116.46	88.58	.6663
	26.8	3.4	.8171	1.2846	.7129	93.75	116.44	89.25	.6685
	47.6	2.6	.8180	1.2859	.7112	93.52	116.27	89.89	.6693

(d) Heated natural plagioclase

Smith (1956)

No.	An	Or	a	b	c	α	β	γ	V
	0.2	0.5	.8165	1.2872	.7111	93.45	116.43	90.28	.6676
	16.0	1.9	.8169	1.2877	.7112	93.48	116.35	90.20	.6688
	21.1	3.4	.8175	1.2884	.7115	93.40	116.36	90.24	.6699
	26.8	3.4	.8174	1.2880	.7112	93.34	116.30	90.24	.6697
	34.6	1.5	.8169	1.2874	.7109	93.46	116.29	90.23	.6687
	34.8	3.1	.8172	1.2876	.7112	93.44	116.29	90.28	.6693

Table 7-6. (continued)

(e) Plagioclases used in X-ray structural analyses

Reference	Locality	An mol.%	Or	a	b	c	α	β	γ	V
Ferguson et al. (1958)	Ramona, Calif.	0.5	1.0	.8138(6)	1.2789(1)	.7156(2)	94.33(3)	116.57(3)	87.65(3)	.6642
do.	Amelia, Va. heated 1065°C	0.7	1.6	.8149(3)	1.2880(1)	.7106(4)	93.37(3)	116.30(3)	90.28(3)	.6671
Wainwright and Starkey (unpublished)	Tiburon, Calif.	0.0	0.1	.81333	1.27808	.71552	94.272	116.615	87.725	.6631
do.	heated	0.0	0.1	.8152	1.2858	.7108	93.589	116.455	90.115	.6654
Phillips et al. (1971)	Camedo, Switzerland	16	2	.81553(3)	1.28206(5)	.71397(4)	93.965(7)	116.475(3)	88.632(5)	.6659(5)
do.	Mitchell Co., N. Carolina	28	2	.8169(3)	1.2851(4)	.7124(2)	93.63(3)	116.40(2)	89.46(2)	.6684(2)
Wainwright (1971)	Crystal Bay, Minn.	76		.8174	1.2867	1.4197	93.400	116.066	90.670	1.3377
Fleet et al. (1966)	St. Louis Co., Minn.	80?		.8178(3)	1.2870(4)	1.4187(5)	93.50(8)	115.90(8)	90.65(8)	1.3395
Appleman (1971)	Apollo 12038, Moon	83.4	0.4	.8180(3)	1.2874(3)	1.4196(3)	93.45(2)	116.06(2)	90.63(2)	1.3394
Czank et al. (1971)	Vesuvius, Italy	97.5	0.1	.8178	1.2871	1.4157	93.17	115.83	91.20	1.3375
Foit (1971)	Miyake, Japan*	99		.8194(8)	1.2897(8)	1.4190(7)	92.98(5)	115.82(5)	91.15(5)	1.3465
Kempster et al. (1962)	Vesuvius, Italy	100?		.81768	1.28768	1.41690	93.167	115.847	91.222	1.3389
Wainwright (1971)	Val Pesmeda, Austria	100	0?	.8173(1)	1.2869(1)	1.4165(1)	93.116(6)	115.913(6)	91.261(6)	1.3363

*at 400°C

(f) Axial ratios and interaxial angles from optical goniometry.

Reference	Locality	An mol.%	Or	a/b	c/b	α	β	γ	α*	β*	γ*
Melczer (1905)	Nadabula	~0		.6350	.5578	94.10	116.61	87.87	86.375	63.490	90.377
Dreyer et al. (1907)	Greenland	~0		.6367	.5593	94.25	116.62	87.68	86.40	63.58	90.06
Krebs (1921)	Alp Rischuna	0.4	1.9	.6352	.5584	94.243	116.595	87.767			
Cloizeaux (1862)	St. Gotthard	1.0	0.0	.63412	.55738	94.089	116.448	88.112			
Glinka (1889)	Kirebinsk	1.6	3.4	.6330	.5506	94.05	116.48	88.145			
	other localities			to .6397	to .5648	93.93 to 94.49	116.42 to 116.65	87.47 to 88.10			

Reference	Locality			a	b	α	β	γ			
Lewis (1915)	La Fibbia	2?		.6354	.5593	93.96	116.62	87.96	86.60	63.47	90.30
	Alp Rischuna	2.1	0.3	.6335	.5564	93.97	116.35	87.52	86.80*	63.08	90.80

*measured value 86.59° between 010 and 001 faces

Reference	Locality			a	b	α	β	γ			
Rath (1869)	Vesuvius	14.5	16.3	.63206	.55239	93.07	116.37	90.07	86.53	63.58	88.39
Rath (1886)	Arcuentu	33.4	8.5	.63556	.55206	93.38	116.47	89.98	86.23	63.47	88.34
Fels (1903)	St. Christopher	87.4	2.4	.63623	.55024	93.35	115.97	91.17	85.70	63.90	87.06
Kratzert (1921)	Vesuvius	94.6	2.0	.63523	.55048	93.16	115.88	91.27	85.87	64.00	87.05
Beckenkamp (1881)	do.			.63519	.55043	93.135	115.885	91.255	85.87	63.70	86.86
Viola (1899)	do.										
Borgström and Goldschmidt (1906)	do.			.6354	.5500	93.04	116.17	91.47	85.83	63.98	87.02
Zambonini (1910)	do.			.6351	.5504	93.13	115.87	91.23	85.92	64.01	87.11
Schnaase (1936)	do.	97		.63473	.54984	93.145	115.917	91.192			

(g) Plagioclases from lunar rocks.

Reference	Number	An	Or	Ab	Mg-F	a	b	c	α	β	γ	V
Appleman et al. (1971)	10003	85-87	optical			.8192(3)	1.2892(3)	1.4186(4)	93.24(3)	116.03(2)	91.02(2)	1.3426(4)
	12040	88-96	microprobe			.8181(2)	1.2875(2)	1.4180(2)	93.35(2)	115.93(2)*	90.99(2)	1.3394(4)*
See paper for	10050	84.5	0.5	9.4	2.1	.8178(2)	1.2872(2)	1.4184(2)	93.28(2)	115.95(3)	90.95(3)	1.3390(4)
details of	12051	91.4	0.2	7.7	1.7	.8186(2)	1.2877(3)	1.4184(3)	93.31(3)	115.94(2)	90.91(3)	1.3410(4)
analyses: note	10047	84.0	0.5	14.3	1.0	.8187(3)	1.2882(3)	1.4196(2)	93.37(3)	116.05(2)	90.81(3)	1.3414(4)
that zoning is	12021	89-97	microprobe		1.6	.8183(2)	1.2871(2)	1.4180(2)	93.43(2)	115.94(2)	90.79(2)	1.3392(4)
common.	12063	85.0	0.3	10.1		.8185(3)	1.2879(3)	1.4194(4)	93.33(3)	116.01(2)	90.74(3)	1.3412(5)
	12053	70-78	microprobe			.8169(4)	1.2877(3)	1.4186(3)	93.39(3)	115.97(2)	90.65(3)	1.3382(5)
	12038	84.9	0.1	14.8	1.8	.8180(3)	1.2874(3)	1.4194(3)	93.45(2)	116.06(3)	90.63(2)	1.3394(5)
	12052	82	microprobe			.8180(3)	1.2875(5)	1.4190(3)	93.36(3)	116.06(2)	90.59(3)	1.3391(4)
	10020	78-80	microprobe			.8157(3)	1.2861(3)	1.4186(2)	93.46(2)	115.92(2)	90.54(3)	1.3366(6)
	10057	78.0	1.4	17.6	2.6	.8174(3)	1.2876(3)	1.4194(4)	93.34(3)	116.06(2)	90.46(3)	1.3386(4)
	10072	75-76	optical			.8178(2)	1.2871(3)	1.4194(3)	93.39(3)	116.09(2)	90.45(3)	1.3386(4)
	10071	74-75	optical			.8175(3)	1.2860(4)	1.4190(4)	93.25(4)	116.04(3)	90.41(4)	1.3372(6)
	10049	73-74	optical			.8176(2)	1.2864(3)	1.4192(2)	93.40(2)	116.07(2)	90.33(3)	1.3376(4)
Stewart et al. (1972)	15415	97	microprobe	3	0	.8179(1)	1.2879(1)	1.4179(1)	93.18(1)	115.91(1)	91.19(1)	1.3397(2)

*original values in error

The *a* dimension changes less than 1%, and it is impossible to disentangle the contributing factors. Substitution of K should increase the *a* dimension slightly, while Hamilton and Edgar (1969) showed that some structural effect changes the $\bar{2}01$ spacing over about one part in 500 at constant An-content (see Fig. 7-4b). There is a tendency for *a* to increase up to about An_{80} and then stay constant to An_{100}. Feldspars in the high structural state tend to have larger values than those in the low state, but for natural specimens this probably results in part from the generally higher Or content of the high plagioclases.

The *b*, *c*, α and γ dimensions tend to vary in the same way. Probably there are subtle effects resulting from minor chemical substituents, but the major effects derive from the An content and the structural state. The difference between the high and low structural states is greatest at An_0 and falls nearly to zero at

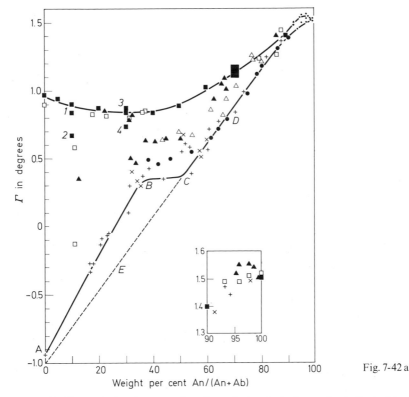

Fig. 7-42 a

Fig. 7-42. The variation for natural and synthetic plagioclases of wt.-% An/(An+Ab) and (a) Gamma $= 2\theta(131) + 2\theta(220) - 4\theta(1\bar{3}1)$ and (b) Beta $= 2\theta(1\bar{1}1) - 2\theta(\bar{2}01)$. CuK$_\alpha$ radiation. The specimens were placed into 6 groups on the basis of petrologic origin and heat treatment: solid square, synthetic; open square, heated natural; solid triangle, volcanic; open triangle, hypabyssal; horizontal cross, plutonic and pegmatitic; inclined cross, metamorphic and charnockitic; solid circle, Skaergaard, Stillwater and Bushveld igneous complexes. In (a), specimens labelled 1 to 4 were synthesized hydrothermally by J. R. Smith and H. S. Yoder. The large rectangle covers six overlapping data. The inset diagram shows an enlargement of the anorthite region. The curves have no statistical significance. In (b), the lower curve represents the synthetic specimens, and the dashed curve the heated natural feldspars; probably they differ because of Or substitution in the latter. (From J. V. Smith and Gay, 1958, Figs. 1 and 2)

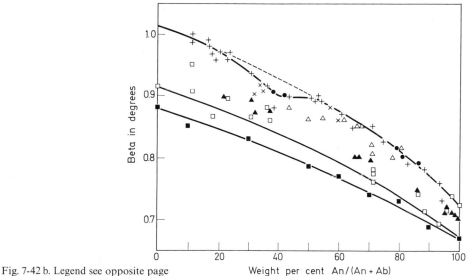

Fig. 7-42 b. Legend see opposite page

An_{100}. For the extreme high state, the data of Kroll (1971b) show that the cell dimensions are almost independent of An content from An_0 to An_{40}, and then change non-linearly to an extreme at or near An_{100}. Smith (1970) suggested that these changes of cell dimension correlated with pronounced increase of local order at An_{50} in a solid solution of high albite type, followed by distant order beginning around An_{85} resulting in the anorthite structure type.

The situation for the low structural series is unclear. Smith and Ribbe (1969) proposed that there is no unique series of low-entropy plagioclase because of idiosyncratic variations of metastable structures with out-of-step domains. Smith and Gay (1958) noted that the envelope curve for the gamma function Γ, a structural indicator mostly dependent on γ^*, did not vary between about An_{35} to An_{55} (Fig. 7-42a). A similar effect can be seen for b, c, α and γ in Fig. 7-41. Doman et al. (1965) gave evidence of definite discontinuities of cell dimension vs. refractive index for single crystals (see Chapter 5). The discontinuities in γ^* were reported to occur near 33, 50, and perhaps 68 and 85 mol.-%. Mossman (1970) from measurements of γ^* and n_α of 4 plagioclases from Greenhills, N. Z. suggested that there is a discontinuity between 90.5 and 93% An which may represent a boundary between transitional and primitive anorthite. Bambauer, Eberhard and Viswanathan (1967) suggested that when cell dimensions were plotted against the Al/Si ratio, the low plagioclases could be represented by straight lines meeting at 33, 50, 76 and perhaps 87 mol.-%. They pointed out that their data for γ^* were inconsistent with those of Doman et al., and concluded that further work was needed to clarify the problem of the nature and significance of discontinuities or kinks in plots of cell dimension versus composition.

Figure 7-43 shows data for the 131 triclinic indicator collected by Nissen (1969). Niggli (1967) proposed theoretical models for Al, Si distribution in plagioclase, as described in Chapter 3. The simplest theoretical models occur every

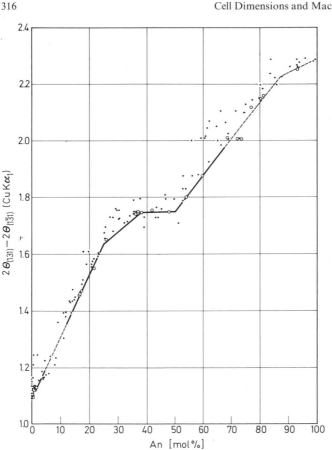

Fig. 7-43. Variation of the 131 triclinic indicator with mol.-% An for specimens in the low structural state selected by Nissen (1969). All specimens have less than 2 mol.-% Or. The open circles show specimens reported by Corlett and Ribbe (1967) to be particularly low in K and homogeneous in An. See text for meaning of the kinked curve. The dashed portions show the bulk compositions for which the peristerite and Huttenlöcher intergrowths occur, and for which the anorthite structure type occurs. (From Nissen, 1969, Fig. 9)

12.5 mol.-% across the Ab, An join, and Nissen interpreted the data of Fig. 7-43 in terms of kinks at 25, 37.5, 50 and 87.5 mol.-%. Readers must make their own judgment of the validity of Nissen's curve. Since the feldspars probably have different structural states, it is impossible to set up statistical tests. In addition, the minor chemical substituents affect the 131 triclinic indicator.

   In detail, Nissen (1969) suggested that (1) there is a kink-point in b near $37.5 \pm 4\%$ An (2) kink-points are not clearly defined for c, but may occur at 25, 50 and between 85 and 90% (3) kink-points occur at 25 and 37.5% for α (4) γ has a similar pattern to γ^* showing linearity between 0 and 25 mol.-% and between 25 and 36–40 mol.-%, while from approximately 40 to 60 mol.-% there is high scatter but a straight line can be drawn from 50 to 87.5 mol.-%.

   I think that looking for kinks presents the same temptation as looking for Magic Numbers. Low-entropy plagioclase may tend to special structural states at particular compositions, but it is absolutely certain that plagioclases at the multiples of 12.5 do not have the fully-ordered structures invented by Niggli.

Whatever one's view of the interpretation of the data, it is possible to obtain an indication of the structural state from b, c, α or γ, or from some readily measured angle in a powder pattern, as described in the Section 7.4.4.

The cell volume tends to vary in the same way as b, c, α and γ, though variation in a, of course, also contributes. It has no determinative value.

Implications from $\beta^*\gamma^*$ Plot. Smith and Gay (1958) discussed the significance of the six cell dimensions for determination of the chemical composition and structural state of plagioclases. They stated: "Unfortunately in sodic plagioclases b^*, c^*, α^* and γ^* vary in a similar manner (but γ^* much more than the others); a^* appears to be unreliable, probably because of solid-solution of potash feldspar, whilst β^*, although showing an independent form of variation, changes so little that it is not of practical value. Hence there is effectively only one useful form of variation, so that either the structural state or An-content must be known before the other can be estimated". Since 1958, the accuracy of determination of cell dimensions has improved, and Fig. 7-44 shows that a plot of β^* and γ^* gives some information on *both* An-content and structural state.

The open and filled rectangles, respectively, show the cell dimensions and standard errors of synthetic plagioclase obtained by Kroll (1967, 1971b) and of natural low plagioclases by Bambauer, Eberhard and Viswanathan (1967). The numbers give mol.-% An. It is obvious that the data for these pure synthetic plagioclases synthesized near the solidus can be represented within the experimental error by a single curve. However, the position of the specimens along the curve is somewhat erratic (for example, the data points for 20 and 30% An overlap), because of the relatively high error in β^*. For anorthite, the melting temperature is 1550° C, and cell dimensions have not been measured for specimens synthesized at this temperature. However the specimens synthesized by Kroll (1971a) at 1430° C should give a fairly good representation of the highest structural state of anorthite. The four open hexagons in Fig. 7-44 show mean values of 16 specimens synthesized from minutes to days (Table 7-6). Although the change in γ^* is slight, it seems that it decreases with increasing time of synthesis. Almost certainly the initial product has significant Si, Al disorder that is reduced by prolonged heating. The position of the curve for the extreme high structural state is not known exactly but should be close to the dashed line in Fig. 7-44.

Turning to the natural plagioclases assigned to the low structural state, most of the data points are consistent with a single curve. The three major exceptions of composition 24, 42 and 73 mol.-% An are displaced towards the curve for synthetic plagioclases, and may actually have an intermediate structural state. The curve for the low structural state is reasonably well determined for sodic plagioclases, except for the possible effect of solid-solution of Or. Reference points for sanidine, "orthoclase" and microcline are shown, and data for natural anorthoclases are given as small diamonds. These data show that substitution of Or should increase both β^* and γ^*. Because natural low plagioclases contain Or in amounts up to 4% or so, some of the displacements in Fig. 7-44 must be ascribed in part to Or content. At the anorthite end, substitution of Or is insignificant.

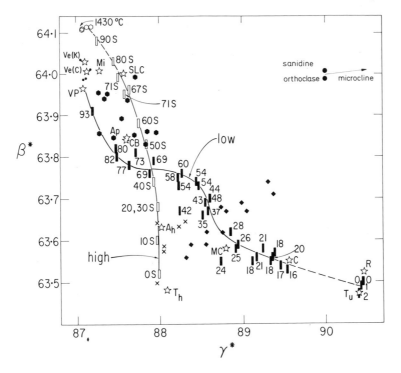

Fig. 7-44. Relation between β^* and γ^* for plagioclase and anorthoclase. The rectangles show the standard error obtained from least-squares refinement of powder data of synthetic (S) plagioclases by Kroll (1967) and of natural plagioclases by Bambauer, Eberhard, and Viswanathan (1967). The number gives the An-content of the specimen rounded-off to the nearest mol. per cent. The diamonds show the data of Carmichael and MacKenzie (1964) for natural anorthoclases. The large filled circles show the data points for orthoclase and sanidinized orthoclase (Spencer C specimen; Cole et al. 1949). The arrow points to the position for a microcline with β^* 64.06, γ^* 92.27° (Hugo microcline; Orville, 1967). The four open hexagons show anorthites synthesized at 1430° C by Kroll (1971a), and the arrow shows the change in cell angles produced by increasing time of synthesis. The small filled circles show anorthite synthesized by Stewart (1967) at temperatures from 1300—750° C. The open stars show cell dimensions for specimens used in X-ray structure analyses, and the source of the data can be identified from the abbreviations using Table 7-6 (e). The filled hexagons show lunar plagioclases (Appleman et al., 1971), and the crosses show heated natural plagioclases (Smith, 1956)

The Val Pesmeda anorthite has probably equilibrated to a lower temperature than the two Vesuvius specimens judging from their petrologic environment, and was chosen as the end-point for the curve representing low plagioclase. The four small dots represent specimens synthesized hydrothermally by Stewart (1967) at 750–1300° C, and their positions suggest intermediate structural states. The two Vesuvius specimens either derive from or are associated with basaltic lava and may well have equilibrated to a temperature in the range of Stewart's specimens. The cell dimensions of the Miyake specimen were obtained at 400° C, but also suggest an intermediate structural state consistent with their origin as crystals hurled out of an exploding volcano.

The solid hexagons show data for lunar plagioclases (Appleman *et al.*, 1971). Some of these contain significant amounts of iron and magnesium plus lattice defects while others appear to be fairly pure members of the An, Ab series. Preliminary data show chemical zoning of some specimens, while diffraction and electron-optical data indicate a range of structural states. The cell angles (not plotted in Fig. 7-44) for the anorthite from the lunar "Genesis" rock, a coarse-grained anorthosite, are almost identical to those of the Val Pesmeda specimen.

The six crosses show heated sodic plagioclases (Smith, 1956).

In general, preliminary indications suggest that the $\beta^* \gamma^*$ plot may permit an estimate of both An-content and structural state, especially if the a^* dimension is checked for unusually high contents of Or. It is obvious that a potassic oligoclase (say $Or_{10}Ab_{70}An_{20}$) in the high structural state will give cell angles γ^* and β^* indicating an intermediate structural state unless a correction is made for the Or-content. Probably the best potential use for the $\beta^* \gamma^*$ plot will be for characterization of anorthites and bytownites for which a plot of γ^* vs. An-content is essentially useless.

Two of the specimens used for X-ray structure analysis fall at unusual positions. The heated Amelia albite and the St. Lawrence County bytownite have β^* values about 0.1° greater than expected, and a check of all the cell dimensions is desirable. Until this is done, the details of the interatomic distances and angles are suspect.

7.4.3 Interpretation in Terms of Crystal Structure

The change in cell dimensions from albite to anorthite (ignoring the doubling of the *c*-repeat) results from complex interaction between (a) expansion of the aluminosilicate framework as Al enters, (b) change from the $AlSi_3$ ordering pattern to the Al_2Si_2 patterns, and (c) increased angular distortion as Ca replaces Na (Fig. 4-6). The interaction is so complex that it is impossible to derive a *simple* method applicable to all plagioclases for estimating Al, Si distribution among lattice sites from the cell dimensions. This contrasts with the situation for alkali feldspars in which a measures the Na, K substitution, and bc and $\alpha\gamma$ measure the Al, Si distribution.

The cell volume tends to increase from albite to anorthite because the effects of the larger Al atoms overcome the effect of other factors.

The effect of structural state on the cell dimensions is greatest for albite (where γ^* varies over 2°) and is least for anorthite (where β^* varies only 0.1°). For pure albite, the change in structural state results from order-disorder of Al and Si atoms with concomitant variation in framework geometry and position of the Na atom. For pure anorthite, the cause of the variation in cell dimensions of specimens examined at room temperature is not certain. There is probably some effect from the nature of the domain texture involving Ca atoms (see Chapter 5), but the effect demonstrated in Fig. 7-44 probably arises from weak disorder of Al and Si atoms. The change of cell dimensions in Kroll's specimens synthesized at 1430° C proceeds over several days, a time consistent with migration of Al and Si atoms, and not consistent with movement of Ca atoms. For intermediate plagioclases, the changes in structural state result from migration of both Al, Si and Na, Ca atoms. The details are extremely complex and imperfectly understood as described in Chapter 5, and cell dimensions may not be a unique measure of any structural variation. Nevertheless several interesting attempts have been made to relate cell dimensions to the crystal structure.

Kroll (1971b) calculated the translations in the [110] and [1$\bar{1}$0] directions as shown in Fig. 7-45. Diagram (a) shows that synthetic plagioclase in the extreme high state has translations that correlate with the An-content as three straight lines meeting near 30–40% and 60–70%. Diagram (b) shows the difference in the [110] and [1$\bar{1}$0] translations for these plagioclases, and for their K-equivalents obtained by ion-exchange with potassium halide. Again, the three regions are displayed. It is particularly important that the difference in the translations is zero for the K-exchanged, low-Ca specimens. Kroll interpreted these data in terms of three structural regions: (a) An_0 to An_{30-40}; high-albite solid-solution with disordered Si,Al (b) An_{60-70} to An_{100}; anorthite solid-solution with avoidance of Al–O–Al contacts (c) An_{30-40} to An_{60-70}; combination of the high-albite and anorthite structures either through domains or by a continuous transition (in German: "gleichen Kristall domänen-artig nebeneinander" or "durch einen allmählichen miteinander verbunden").

The difficulty of structural interpretation may be seen from these diagrams. Both high albite and anorthite have monoclinic topochemistry of the Al, Si atoms, yet anorthite has a large, non-zero $\Delta[110]$ while K-exchanged high-albite has zero Δ. The non-exchanged albite has a small, non-zero Δ. This difference, of course, results from collapse of the framework around the M atoms, which is especially severe for the divalent Ca atoms. Section 7.5.3 mentions the interpretation by Viswanathan (1971b, 1972) of the cell dimensions of plagioclase using both natural and K-exchanged specimens, but the interpretation in my opinion is hindered by problems caused by structural collapse of the framework around the Ca atoms. An interesting approach would be to attempt exchange of Ca by Sr or Ba as well as the exchange of Na by K. Such exchange of divalent cations might be impossible to achieve without destroying the aluminosilicate framework, but if successful should make it possible to evaluate the Al, Si distribution without the complications from the Na and Ca atoms.

Ribbe and co-workers attempted to relate cell dimensions of sodic plagioclase to the distribution of Al and Si atoms. In an abstract, Ribbe et al. (1970) state:

"For isocompositional sodic plagioclase variations of α, α^*, γ, γ^* and related parameters such as $(2\theta_{131} - 2\theta_{1\bar{3}1})$ and σ (for the rhombic section) with Al/Si order $\rightleftarrows$ disorder are directly proportional to ΔAl, the difference in average Al content of the T_10 and T_1m sites. The concomitant change in c cell edge (Δc) is attributed to the total number of Al atoms encountered in tetrahedral chains along z in the ordered structure minus the number encountered in the disordered structure. Thus, $\Delta Al_c = [Al_{T_10} + Al_{T_1m} + Al_{T_20}]_{ord.} - [Al_{T_10} + Al_{T_1m} + Al_{T_20}]_{disord.}$ The change in b cell edge (Δb) is similarly related to ΔAl except that six tetrahedral sites are encountered in chains along y. Based on known changes in cell edges and Al/Si distribution in the low $\rightarrow$ high albite transformation Δb and Δc can be calculated for other sodic plagioclases.

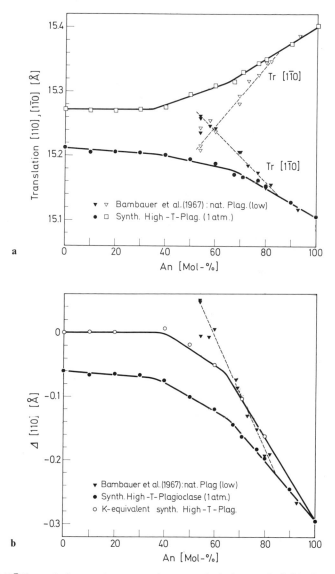

Fig. 7-45. Relation of [110] and [1$\bar{1}$0] translations to An-content for some plagioclases. a Individual values of Tr [110] and Tr [1$\bar{1}$0] for synthetic high-temperature plagioclase (Kroll, 1971b) and for natural low plagioclase (Bambauer et al., 1967). b Values of Tr [110] − Tr [1$\bar{1}$0] for the above plagioclases plus K-exchanged synthetic plagioclases. (From Kroll, 1971b, Figs. 31 and 32)

For high-temperature plagioclases α^*, γ^* and related angular parameters do *not* vary between An_0 and An_{50}: Δ Al is always zero for complete disorder. Since the mean ^{VII}Ca–O bond in An_{100} is 0.16 Å shorter than the mean ^{VII}Na–O bond in high albite and the mean ^{IV}Al–O bond is 0.15 Å longer than the mean ^{IV}Si–O bond, the disordered substitution NaSi $\rightleftarrows$ CaAl is almost exactly compensating in its effect on cell edges, and *b* and *c* are constant between An_0 and An_{50}. Only β^*

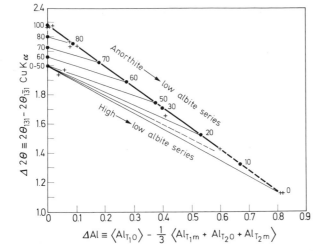

Fig. 7-46. Diagram for estimating Al-distribution in the pseudo-structure of plagioclase from the 131 X-ray indicator. The crosses show data from X-ray structural analyses. The two outer lines represent the extreme high and low structural states, while the linking lines are isopleths of An-content specified by the ringed numbers. (From Ribbe, 1972, Fig. 1)

increases regularly from 63.5–63.7° with An content, although α also shows an apparent slight increase. These account for a small increase in unit cell volume".

Ribbe (1972) provided a diagram for estimating the Al-distribution of any plagioclase from the 131 indicator. He considered only the pseudo-structure averaged for a unit cell with C symmetry and 0.7 nm c-repeat. In this approximation, anorthite appears completely disordered because the regular alternation of Si and Al atoms is averaged out. The Al-content was estimated from the T–O distances as explained in Chapter 3. Figure 7-46 shows the predicted relation between the 131 indicator and the relative concentration of Al in the T sites based on 12 structure determinations. The data are too sparse to test the validity of the linear approximations. Because the T–O distances indicate equal occupancies of the T_1m, T_2O and T_2m sites, this figure provides an estimate of the Al-contents of all sites after trivial arithmetic calculations. See Section 7.5.3 for comments on accuracy of the method.

7.4.4 Simple Determinative Methods

Up to 1971, it was believed that the X-ray powder pattern of plagioclases could not give a unique determination of both An-content and structural state except for low albite. For all other plagioclases, it was necessary to know the An-content (and the Or content) before the structural state could be estimated. Thus typically the An-content would be estimated from chemical analysis or from the refractive indices, and the structural state would be estimated from an X-ray powder pattern using one or more peaks that depend principally on γ^*. There are now two simple ways of estimating both the An-content and structural state from the X-ray powder pattern, but both ways require further study before their assets and liabilities are fully delineated.

The first method utilizes the plot of β^* vs. γ^*, and requires careful indexing and measurement of the peaks followed by least squares fitting of the cell parameters. The value of estimates of An-content and structural state is obvious from Fig. 7-44. For sodic and for calcic plagioclases, both the structural state and An-content can be estimated fairly well but precise estimates of the accuracy cannot be made. For intermediate compositions, the interpretation is very uncertain.

The second method was developed by Viswanathan (1971a) who found that the Na-content of plagioclase could be ion-exchanged with potassium halide producing (K, Ca)-feldspars. The original Ab-content is equated with the Or-content which is estimated from a or some peak such as $\overline{2}01$ which depends significantly on a. Knowing the Ab-content, it is then possible to derive the structural state from peaks that depend on γ^* in the X-ray powder pattern of the original plagioclase. The technique has been demonstrated to work well with natural plagioclases, but some problems have resulted from attempts to ion-exchange synthetic plagioclases produced in granitic bulk compositions (W. S. MacKenzie, pers. comm.). Viswanathan's data are given in Section 7.5.

In spite of the potential value of the two new techniques, the best simple procedure for plagioclases is to estimate the An-content by chemical analysis and then to determine the structural state from the X-ray powder pattern. In many circumstances, the electron microprobe yields the best analysis, permitting measurements of the An, Ab and Or contents to 1% or better, together with measurements of minor elements such as Mg, Fe, Ba and Sr. Furthermore the extent of chemical zoning can be readily determined for plagioclases coarser than 10 μm. The structural state can then be estimated by measurement of peaks in the X-ray powder pattern. Most reference data have been obtained for peaks depending largely on α^* and γ^*: viz. 131, $1\overline{3}1$, $\overline{2}41$, $\overline{2}\overline{4}1$, $\overline{1}32$, 220. Figure 7-42a shows data for the Gamma function $(2\theta(131) + 2\theta(220) - 4\theta(1\overline{3}1))$ used by J. V. Smith and Gay (1958). Smith, J. R. and Yoder (1956) used $2\theta(1\overline{3}1) - 2\theta(131)$ and $2\theta(220) - 2\theta(1\overline{3}1)$, and their data have similar implications. Smith, J. V., and Gay (1958) also used the Beta function $2\theta(1\overline{1}1) - 2\theta(\overline{2}01)$ which appears to give significant variation for calcic feldspars (Fig. 7-42b) whereas the three earlier functions did not. The variation amounts to only about 0.1° in 2θ for CuK$_\alpha$ radiation, and needs further study now that many new plagioclase specimens have become available. Probably the major effect in the Beta function arises from β^*; indeed the data for β in Fig. 7-41 show a similar distribution to those in Fig. 7-42b. In general, for sodic and intermediate plagioclases use some function of γ^* to estimate structural state, while for calcic plagioclases use some function of β^*. Scheidegger (1973) plotted the Beta and Gamma functions of calcic plagioclases against each other and concluded that the structural state can be determined and that the An-content can be estimated to 5%.

The data in Fig. 7-42 suffer somewhat from errors in the chemical composition amounting to several percent of An. New data from Bambauer, Corlett, Eberhard and Viswanathan (1967) have the advantage of accurate electron microprobe analyses. Figure 7-47a shows the 131 structural indicator $(2\theta(131) - 2\theta(1\overline{3}1))$

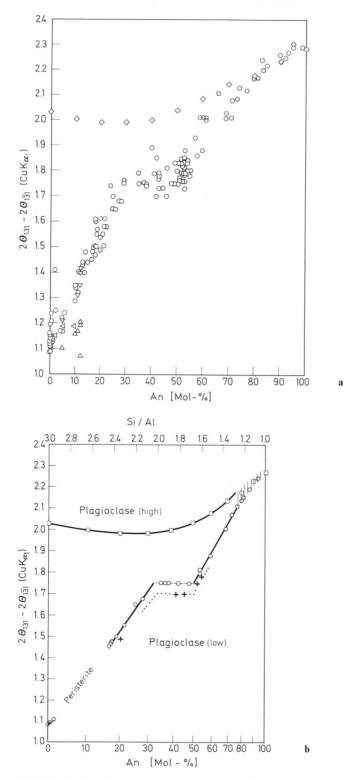

Fig. 7-47. Relation between indicators of structural state and the An content, as given by Bambauer *et al.* (1967). a Data for the 131 indicator. Diamonds represent synthetic plagioclase; circles,

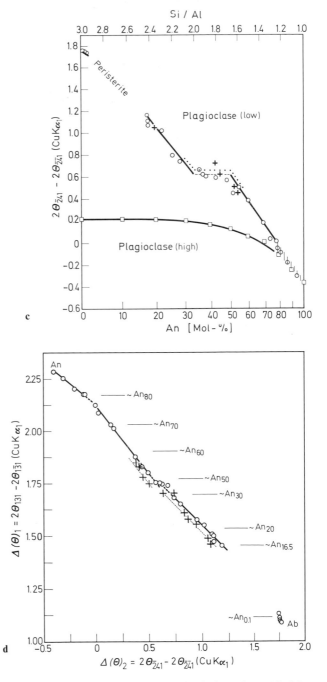

natural homogeneous plagioclase; triangles, peristerites — upward-pointing show Ab-rich component, downward-pointing show An-rich component, and leftward-pointing show data derived from apparently single peaks even when single-crystal X-ray study showed two components. b Selected data for the 131 indicator, and interpretation in terms of high and low series. Squares, synthetic; circles, low plagioclase with Or less than 0.8%; crosses, low plagioclases with Or near 4%. The dotted curve is for the K-rich specimens. Note linear scale for Al/Si ratio and non-linear scale for mol.-% An. c As (b), but for the $\bar{2}41$ indicator. d Relation between the 131 and $\bar{2}41$ indicators for low plagioclase. Note omission of high plagioclase. (From Bambauer *et al.*, 1967, Figs. 4, 5, 6 and 7)

measured with CuK_α radiation for about 190 plagioclases and plotted against mol.-% An. The synthetic plagioclases define a continuous curve, but the natural specimens lie in an irregular band. The peristerite region from An_0 to An_{16} causes problems because specimens may be either homogeneous, or consist of two components near An_0 and An_{25}, or consist of a coherent superstructure (see Chapter 19 for details). Some of the peristerites yielded peaks that could be assigned to a single component as given by the symbol key in the legend to Fig. 7-46. Some specimens in the region An_{67} to An_{83} may consist of two components, but yield single peaks.

Figure 7-47b shows the interpretation by Bambauer, Corlett, Eberhard and Viswanathan. The high plagioclase series is well defined by the synthetic specimens. The low plagioclase series was defined from specimens that satisfied four criteria: (a) contained only one component, (b) were chemically homogeneous, (c) had less than 0.8 mol.-% Or distributed homogeneously as shown by electron microprobe analysis, and (d) had the lowest value of the 131 indicator for any given An content. Bambauer *et al.* plotted their data against a linear scale for Si/Al and drew the two straight lines shown in Fig. 7-46b connected by the horizontal line from An_{33} to An_{50}. The peristerite region was represented by a gap from An_2 to An_{16}. Above An_{70}, the data points for synthetic and natural plagioclase were so close that Bambauer *et al.* stated that a distinction was "perhaps not possible" from the 131 indicator.

The crosses show five plagioclases with about 4% Or, and the dotted curve is a possible representation of the low structural state for these K-rich plagioclases. The 131 structural indicator for maximum microcline is $0.8°$, and for sanidine is 0, so the dotted curve is displaced in the expected direction.

Figure 7-47c shows data on the $\bar{2}41$ structural indicator $(2\theta(\bar{2}41) - 2\theta(\bar{2}\bar{4}1))$ of the same plagioclases. The $\bar{2}41$ and $\bar{2}\bar{4}1$ peaks are weaker than the 131 and $1\bar{3}1$ peaks, and also suffer from interference from other peaks. They also overlap themselves in the bytownite composition range, and some of the data points in Fig. 7-47c must be calculated rather than observed. The $\bar{2}41$ indicator shows similar relations to the 131 indicator, but the effect of K-substitution seems to be lower and more erratic.

Figure 7-47d shows the relation between the 131 and $\bar{2}41$ indicators for the selected plagioclases. The K-rich specimens (2–5% Or) tend to lie to the lower left, but one specimen actually lies to the upper right of the curve representing the K-poor specimens (0–0.8% Or). The cross-marks show the An-content. If one knew that a plagioclase were in the low structural state, this diagram could be used to estimate An-content, and perhaps very crudely the Or-content. However it should be noted that Nissen's interpretation of the relation between the 131 indicator and An-content (Fig. 7-43) is different from that of Bambauer *et al.*, even though many of the specimens are the same.

By analogy with alkali feldspars, one might expect to estimate the Or content from a or V, after suitable correction for An-content and structural state. However, for low plagioclase I have not been able to detect any systematic variation from the available data. It should be noted that the effect seen in Fig. 7-47d may not necessarily arise just from the K atoms. It is known that the Bøggild intergrowth (see Chapter 19) occurs only in K-rich intermediate plagioclases. Hence the effect in Fig. 7-47d might result from some difference in structural state that is indirectly related to K-substitution: for example, K atoms might act merely as a catalyst resulting in different structural states.

Plagioclases from volcanic rocks tend to carry considerable amounts of Or molecule. For alkali feldspars, the substitution of 40% Or molecule into high albite produces monoclinic symmetry. Parsons (1968) showed that for synthetic Ab, Or feldspars the highest values of the 131 indicators for Or_5 and Or_{10} compositions are about 1.9 and 1.8°. Lower values were obtained for specimens annealed at temperatures below 1000° C representing adjustment to a lower structural state. Figure 7-48 shows data for the 131 indicator of sodic plagioclases containing Or in solid solution. The curve for the extreme high structural state of Or-free plagioclases is obtained from Kroll's measurements of synthetic plagioclase. The open squares show six natural plagioclases heated for a long time at 1060° C by Smith (1956), plotted with some revised chemical compositions of Ribbe and Smith (1966). The data are consistent with the specimens being close to the highest structural state with a reduction of the 131 indicator resulting from the Or content. The circles and crosses, respectively, show five plagioclases before and after heating at 1100° C by Carmichael and MacKenzie (1964). Arbitrary contours have been estimated for compositions containing 5 and 10% Or using the data for the heated specimens. The natural specimens of Carmichael and MacKenzie have lower values of the 131 indicator than the heated specimens, implying a structural state that is lower than the extreme state. Harnik (1969, Fig. 16) reached similar conclusions.

There are three possible ways of determining the structural state of sodic plagioclases from volcanic rocks: (a) determine both the An and Or contents by chemical analysis, and make a correction for the Or-content by interpolation on Fig. 7-48, (b) exchange out the Or-content by Viswanathan's method (this ap-

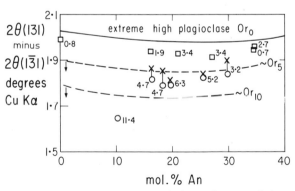

Fig. 7-48. Estimated effect of Or-substitution on the 131 indicator of plagioclase. The open circles and crosses, respectively, show five plagioclases before and after heating at 1100° C by Carmichael and MacKenzie (1964). The open squares show six natural plagioclases heated at 1060° C (Smith, 1956) with some chemical compositions taken from Ribbe and Smith (1966). The numbers give mol.-% Or. The curve for the extreme high state for Or-free plagioclase derives from the data of Kroll (1971 b). The curves for Or_5 and Or_{10} are arbitrary using data for synthetic Ab, Or feldspars of Parsons (1968) to anchor the left-hand sides, and the data for the heated natural specimens to give the variation with An-content. The arrows show the effect of changing the structural state towards the low form

parently requires exchange first to the K-equivalent followed by back-exchange to the pure (Na, Ca)-feldspar) or (c) compare the triclinic indicator for the unheated specimen with that for the specimen heated at 1100° C using sufficient time to attain the highest structural state.

Slemmons (1962) proposed the term "intermediacy index" to characterize the structural state of plagioclase from an appropriate indicator, and he contoured plots of angles vs. An content from 0 for the high to 100 for the low structural state. Bambauer, Corlett, Eberhard, and Viswanathan (1967) stated that "A quantitatively restrictive subdivision into grades of order (e.g. intermediacy index of Slemmons, 1962) is to be avoided (a) because absolutely no quantitative relation between the $\Delta(\theta)$ values and the actual Si, Al distribution is known and (b) because of the difficulties mentioned in the introduction of distinguishing between stable and unstable Al, Si distributions". From the preceding discussion, it seems that Slemmon's intermediacy index is not a simple measure of structural state, but there is no harm in anyone calculating such an index so long as he or others are not fooled by the false illusion of numerical accuracy.

The following papers give examples of the use of simple methods for determining natural plagioclase: Desborough and Cameron (1968), Jackson (1961) and Kleeman and Nesbitt (1967).

In conclusion to this section, it is clear that there is no simple fool-proof method of estimating structural state and An-content of plagioclase just from the X-ray pattern. Now that the electron microprobe and electronic computers for analyzing X-ray powder data are so readily available, the best procedure is to make a full chemical analysis plus determination of all six cell dimensions. Of course, for a systematic study of a rock complex involving hundreds or thousands of plagioclases, the most practical procedure may well involve use of one of the simple indicators such as the 131 indicator after detailed study has shown that it is reliable.

7.4.5 Dimensional Changes Caused by Heating

Just as for alkali feldspars it is necessary to distinguish between the metastable effect of rapid heating that does not change the Si, Al distribution, and the unique effect of true thermodynamic equilibrium.

Macroscopic Thermal Expansion. Saucier and Saplevitch (1962) summarized the early data. Beckenkamp (1881) in a remarkable study measured the dihedral angles for an anorthite crystal from Vesuvius at 20, 80, 140 and 200° C obtaining the following axial elements:

T	20	80	140	200° C
a/b	0.63532	0.63550	0.63569	0.63595
c/b	0.55043	0.55038	0.55042	0.55044
α	93.135	93.133	93.131	93.131
β	115.886	115.867	115.842	115.802
γ	91.255	91.260	91.266	91.290

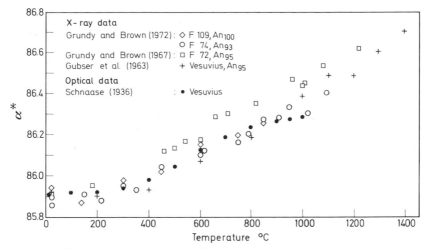

Fig. 7-49. Variation of α* with temperature for anorthites

The accuracy of the data is not known, but they are generally consistent with the later X-ray data. Beckenkamp calculated the thermal expansion from these data, and Saucier and Saplevitch (1962) plotted the principal axes of the thermal expansion ellipsoid. The maximum expansion is in the (010) plane, about 30° to the a-axis, as confirmed by later X-ray data (Willaime et al., 1972). The data indicate considerable angular rotation even for the small temperature rise from 20 to 200° C.

Rinne (1914) measured the angle α* between the {010} and {001} cleavages from −170 to +600° C for plagioclases from albite to anorthite. For anorthite, the angle passed through a weak maximum between 0 and 200° C, later found by X-ray methods to result from a rapid inversion in primitive anorthite.

Schnaase (1936) measured goniometrically the change of axial ratio and interaxial angles up to 1000° C for an anorthite from Vesuvius (Fig. 7-49) obtaining a similar trend to Rinne up to 600° C. Above 800° C, the data diverge from the later X-ray results perhaps because of incorrect temperature measurement.

Offret (1890) observed the thermal expansion of prisms of Bakersville oligoclase prepared parallel to the principal *optic* directions, which data indicated that the principal expansion is near [100].

Kôzu and Ueda (1933) measured the volume expansion of several plagioclases from dilatometry of polished cubes cut perpendicular to a, b^* and c^* (Table 7-7). Figure 7-50 shows that consistently up to 1000° C, the expansion decreases with increasing An-content. This can reasonably be interpreted as the result of the stronger bonding of Ca than of Na atoms to the aluminosilicate framework. The data for albite agree well with those obtained later by X-ray work, but the data for the calcic specimens agree poorly.

X-ray Data on Anorthite. Gubser et al. (1963) measured α* for a Vesuvius anorthite up to 1400° C from precession photographs, and Grundy and Brown (1967) repeated the measurements for the same specimen, $An_{95.4}Or_{1.5}$ (Fig. 7-49). Czank and Schulz (1971) measured all the cell dimensions of a Vesuvius anorthite,

Table 7-7. Volume expansion (%) of plagioclase

°C	Rischuna	Arendal (Norway)	Sotoku (Korea)	Sotoku (Korea)	Mitaki (Japan)	Miyake (Japan)
20	0	0	0	0	0	0
50	0.05	0.03	0.03	0.04	0.04	0.05
100	0.14	0.09	0.09	0.10	0.12	0.12
200	0.36	0.23	0.24	0.24	0.32	0.26
300	0.58	0.41	0.40	0.40	0.46	0.35
400	0.85	0.59	0.56	0.55	0.57	0.45
500	1.13	0.79	0.74	0.73	0.63	0.57
600	1.44	1.00	0.92	0.95	0.78	0.72
700	1.75	1.24	1.11	1.13	0.92	0.89
800	2.07	1.47	1.33	1.32	1.10	1.08
900	2.41	1.71	1.57	1.53	1.27	1.29
950	2.59	1.83	1.67	1.64	1.36	1.41
1000	2.75	1.96	1.80	1.75	1.45	1.53
mol.-% Or	1.0	5.8	—	—	—	—
mol.-% An	0.2	33.7[a]	~38	~44	~95	~94

[a] Incorrectly given as 23 by Kôzu and Ueda. Data from Kôzu and Ueda (1933).

An_{98}, up to 1500° C (Fig. 7-51). Grundy and Brown (1972) determined the cell dimensions of two anorthites, An_{100} and An_{93}, up to 850° C and 950° C, respectively, using an X-ray powder diffractometer. Confirmatory data for the reciprocal cell angles were obtained with a precession camera. Some of the cell dimensions are given in Table 7-8.

Figure 7-49 shows that all the optical and X-ray data on α^* for anorthites show a similar trend, with α^* staying nearly constant up to 300° C followed by an increase with increasing temperature.

An anomalous expansion near 200° C is shown in b and c but not in a. There is another anomaly for b, c and in V between 650 and 1000° C. The anomaly near 200° C is readily identified with the inversion from P- to I-anorthite as ex-

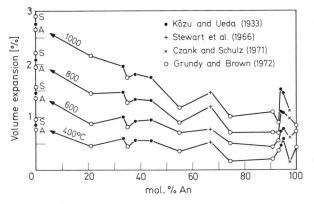

Fig. 7-50. Volume expansion (%) vs. An content (mol.-%) of plagioclase for 1000, 800, 600 and 400° C referred to 20° C. The data of Grundy and Brown (1972) were obtained by interpolation for 400, 600 and 800° C and extrapolation for 1000° C: *A* Amelia; *S* synthetic

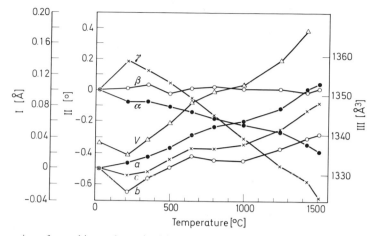

Fig. 7-51. Thermal expansion of anorthite as determined by Czank and Schulz (1971). The data are expressed as the deviation from the value at room temperature, referred to scales I, II and III, respectively, for the edges, angles and volume. The anorthite crystal is from Monte Somma, Vesuvius with composition (wt.-%) An 97.6, Or 0.13, Ab 1.8; Fe 0.076, Ba 0.017. At room temperature the dimensions are a 0.8178, b 1.2871, c 1.4157 nm; α 93° 10', β 115° 50', γ 91° 12'. Note that the scales for the edges and volume are expressed in Å. (From Czank and Schulz, 1971, Fig. 1)

plained in Chapter 5. The anomaly from 650 to 1000° C is not so easily explained, though its validity is supported by the optical anomaly near 800° C observed by Bloss (1964), and by an endothermal peak observed near 800° C in a differential-thermal-analysis study by Köhler and Wieden (1954). The angle γ shows an anomaly at low temperature, but otherwise the angles change steadily.

Figure 7-51 shows that the cell volume decreases from room temperature to 240° C, and then increases steadily up to the highest temperature. The mean expansion coefficient found by Czank and Schulz for 20–1000° C is 11×10^{-6} per °C, which is only about one-third of the value for most inorganic materials. Unfortunately there is considerable variation in the volume expansion for anorthites obtained by the different workers (Fig. 7-50). Kôzu and Ueda obtained much higher values than the other workers, and their data are probably wrong: indeed the expansions would fit with andesine rather than anorthite. The expansions determined at 400 and 600° C by Czank and Schulz for a Vesuvius anorthite are lower than the interpolated values between the data of Grundy and Brown. Careful study of a series of specimens is needed, especially with respect to chemical composition and structural state.

X-ray Data on the Plagioclase Series. Kayode (1964) prepared a Ph. D. thesis on the thermal expansion of both natural and inverted plagioclase covering the entire composition range for the high and low series. Comparison of the data with those of later workers, who restricted their study to fewer specimens, shows that Kayode's data are several times less accurate probably because of erratic movement of the sample holder in the X-ray powder diffractometer. Kayode concluded that:

(a) the volume expansions of high and low plagioclase are almost the same for a given An-content

Table 7-8. Cell dimensions of plagioclase at room temperature and high temperature

Specimen	Composition (mol.-%)			Temperature (°C)	a (nanometer)	b	c	α (degree)	β	γ	V (molar)
	Or	Ab	An								
Grundy and Brown (1972)											
F 101, Amelia pegmatite	1.7	98.3	0.0	25	0.8153	1.2800	0.7164	94.23	116.60	87.74	1.0034
				950	0.8252	1.2862	0.7171	93.29	116.06	87.45	1.0271
307, Synthetic, 66 h 1000° C, 2000 p.s.i.	0	100	0	25	0.8156	1.2882	0.7113	93.59	116.46	90.15	1.0043
				950	0.8261	1.2950	0.7143	90	116.17	90	1.0321
F 36, Mitchell County pegmatite	2.8	76.5	20.7	25	0.8156	1.2824	0.7133	93.85	116.37	88.99	1.0037
				950	0.8240	1.2874	0.7145	92.97	116.09	88.80	1.0231
F 50, Val Maggia pegmatite	0.7	64.4	34.9	25	0.8153	1.2846	0.7121	93.62	116.30	89.69	1.0040
				950	0.8216	1.2890	0.7123	92.89	116.11	89.43	1.0181
F 54, Quebec anorthosite?	2.4	42.6	55.0	25	0.8181	1.2858	0.7108	93.52	116.26	89.85	1.0069
				950	0.8207	1.2891	0.7103	92.95	115.91	89.70	1.0157
do.	—	—	—	25	0.8170	1.2869	0.7100	93.38	116.07	90.38	1.0065
				950	0.8214	1.2885	0.7113	92.64	115.91	90.10	1.0177
F 54 H, 7 days, 1080° C											
F 71, Crystal Bay anorthosite	0.9	24.0	75.1	25	0.8187	1.2872	0.7090	93.39	116.05	90.73	1.0075
				950	0.8221	1.2901	0.7092	92.98	115.89	90.36	1.0165
F 98, Miyake-jima lava	0.2	9.0	90.8	25	0.8181	1.2869	0.7086	93.22	115.77	91.14	1.0083
				950	0.8222	1.2898	0.7088	93.00	115.81	90.69	1.0162
F 74, Grass Valley anorthosite	0.2	6.7	93.1	25	0.8186	1.2874	0.7086	93.20	115.91	91.12	1.0083
				950	0.8224	1.2907	0.7085	92.98	115.75	90.75	1.0173
F 109, Monte Somma lava	0.3	0.2	99.5	25	0.8183	1.2870	0.7085	93.09	115.81	91.28	1.0080
				850	0.8230	1.2892	0.7088	92.94	115.81	90.97	1.0166
Stewart et al. (1966)											
Lake County lava	1.3	31.5	67.2	26	0.8176	1.2865	0.7102	93.45	116.05	90.51	1.0084
				1141	0.8223	1.2927	0.7120	92.81	115.82	90.13	1.0257
Czank and Schulz (1971; pers. comm.)											
Vesuvius lava	0.1	1.8	97.6	20	0.8178	1.2871	0.7078	93.17	115.83	91.20	
				240	0.8187	1.2841	0.7073	93.10	115.84	91.40	
				1430	0.8281	1.2912	0.7116	92.83	115.86	90.61	

Table 7-9. Temperature variation of molar volume of plagioclase

°C	Grundy and Brown (1972)								Stewart et al. (1966)	
	F 36	F 50	F 54	F 54 H	F 71	F 98	F 74	F 109	°C	LCO
25[a]	1.0044	1.0061	1.0078	1.0063	1.0070	1.0087	1.0082	1.0092	26[a]	1.0084(6)[c]
25[b]	1.0030	1.0020	1.0061	1.0064	1.0080	1.0080	1.0085	1.0069	26[b]	1.00876(6)
140	—	—	—	—	—	—	—	1.0091	190	1.01036(6)
150	1.0049	1.0030	1.0061	1.0074	1.0080	1.0087	1.0105	—	330	1.01266(6)
300	1.0057	1.0066	1.0076	1.0083	1.0071	1.0104	1.0109	1.0103	429	1.0141(6)
450	1.0092	1.0095	—	1.0115	1.0102	1.0096	1.0124	1.0136	508	1.0155(7)
600	1.0123	1.0118	1.0135	1.0132	1.0127	1.0141	1.0138	1.0151	654	1.0188(6)
750	1.0166	1.0165	1.0137	1.0150	1.0138	1.0136	1.0152	1.0170	813	1.0206(6)
850	1.0173	1.0176	1.0141	1.0163	1.0155	1.0177	1.0150	1.0166	961	1.0222(8)
950	1.0231	1.0181	1.0157	1.0177	1.0165	1.0162	1.0173	—	1051	1.0233(9)
									1141	1.0257(6)

[a] At beginning.   [b] At end.   [c] Standard error in brackets. Molar volume given in 10^{-4} meters^3/mole.

(b) the volume expansion decreases with increasing An-content such that the value for anorthite is only about half of that for albite

(c) the thermal ellipsoid rotates with temperature, the rotation for a high plagioclase being greater than for a low plagioclase

(d) the position of the rhombic section (see Chapter 18 on twinning) for a given composition and structural state changes by several degrees from 0 to 1000° C.

Details are not given here, because later results of higher accuracy are appearing.

Stewart et al. (1966) determined all the cell dimensions with X-ray powder diffractometry of a calcic labradorite, $An_{67}Or_1$, from Lake County, Oregon. Those for 26 and 1141° C are listed in Table 7-8 while the variation of molar volume is given in Table 7-9. In a plot of molar volume vs. temperature, the point for 654° appears to be anomalous, and Stewart et al. suggested that there is a high-order inversion. However, Grundy and Brown (1967) observed nothing unusual for the lattice angles, and the anomaly requires confirmation before being accepted as genuine.

Grundy and Brown (1967) made a preliminary study of the lattice angles of triclinic feldspars up to 1200° C using X-ray precession photography, following earlier study by Brown (1960). Their figures incorporate data obtained by Stewart et al. (1966) for the calcic labradorite.

Figure 7-52 shows the variation with temperature of α^*, β^* and γ^* for natural plagioclases, all of which are in the low structural state except for the labradorite, An_{67}. Figure 7-52d shows α^* plotted against γ^*. The data points in sequence of increasing α^* are for 26, 200, 400, 600, 800, 1000° C (plus 1200° C as well for anorthite). The symbols are identified in the figure legend, together with the bulk compositions. The An_{67} specimen is from a lava and is probably in an intermediate structural state whose cell dimensions thereby mimic those of the An_{76} specimen.

The reference parallelogram in Fig. 7-52d is outlined by room-temperature data for low and high albite, maximum microcline and monoclinic feldspar. Heating of low albite and anorthite changes α^* and γ^* in the direction of maximum microcline, while the data for intermediate compositions point between microcline and monoclinic feldspar. All these feldspars are triclinic at all temperatures, and the amount of change in α^* and γ^* diminishes with increasing An-content. Roughly speaking, one can state that these angles change with temperature in the same direction as one would expect for substitution of potassium, an effect that might be interpreted as the result of thermal vibration increasing the effective size of the Na and Ca atoms. This effect probably occurs, but the thermal expansion is actually governed by complex structural changes that cannot be specified by any single factor.

Figure 7-52c shows that the variation of β^* is rather small, and that there is a tendency for β^* to be almost independent of An-content at high temperature.

Grundy and Brown (1972) using an X-ray powder diffractometer measured the cell dimensions of the plagioclases described in Table 7-8 at temperatures from 25–950° C. For brevity only the cell dimensions determined at the highest temperature and the mean of those before and after heating are shown in Table 7-8. X-ray precession photographs were used to measure α^*, β^* and γ^*

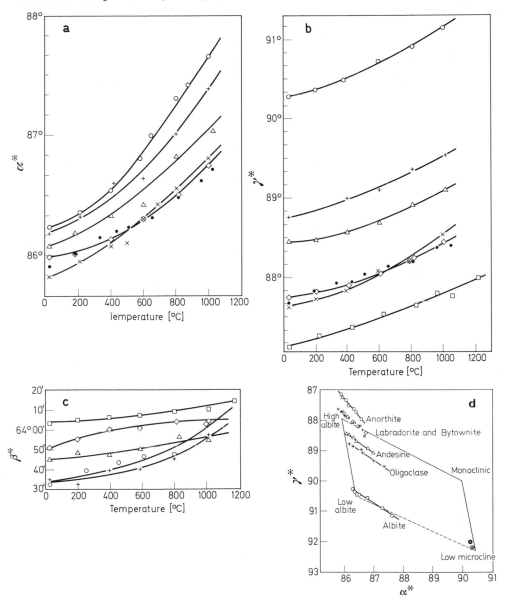

Fig. 7-52. Variation of reciprocal cell angles with temperature for several plagioclases and a micro-cline as measured by Grundy and Brown (1967). For (a), (b) and (c), the symbols represent: open circle, Schyn-Schlucht albite $An_{0.1}Or_{0.6}$; horizontal cross, Bakersville oligoclase $An_{27.2}Or_{2.4}$; triangle, Essex County andesine $An_{47.6}Or_{3.7}$; diamond, Lake County, Oregon labradorite $An_{66.2}Or_{0.9}$; solid dot, Lake County labradorite, powder diffractometer data by Stewart *et al.* (1966); inclined cross, Crystal Bay bytownite $An_{74.7}Or_{0.6}$; square, Vesuvius anorthite, $An_{95.2}Or_{1.4}$ (all mol.-%). See Fig. 7-49 for data on α^* for anorthite. In diagram (d), α^* and γ^* have been plotted against each other to show the effect of temperature in relation to the data for K-feldspars at room temperature. For each plagioclase the points in sequence of increasing α^* are for 26, 200, 400, 600, 800 and 1000° C (plus 1200° C also for anorthite). The open and filled circles, respectively, show a microcline at room temperature and 1020° C. (From Grundy and Brown, 1967, Figs. 1, 2 and 3 plus redrawing of Fig. 5)

(data not shown), as well as to check for subsidiary diffractions. During the heat-treatment, the c diffractions of the F 72 and F 74 anorthites became diffuse. Two crystals of the F 71 bytownite apparently lost their b diffractions which were sharp at room temperature: after cooling, the b diffractions apparently returned in one crystal but not the other. The F 54 labradorite had very diffuse e diffractions which apparently disappeared after mounting at high temperature and cooling. Specimen F 54 H was deliberately heated for 7 days at 1080° C. A specimen of high albite synthesized hydrothermally at 1000° C was also studied.

The data on the molar volumes (Fig. 7-50) are consistent with each other when account is taken of the experimental errors: however, they appear inconsistent with those of other workers. All the dilatometric data of Kôzu and Ueda are higher than those of Grundy and Brown. The X-ray data of Stewart *et al.* also lie higher than the trend of the data of Grundy and Brown. It is obvious that further studies are needed to check these data.

Broadly speaking, the effect of temperature on the cell dimensions of a plagioclase decreases with increasing An-content. For the sodic plagioclases, the effect of temperature is similar to that caused by substitution of Or at room temperature. However the effect on anorthite is different from that produced by substitution of Sr for Ca (see later section).

Willaime *et al.* (1972) calculated the shape and orientation of the thermal expansion figure of plagioclases plus microcline and sanidine. The coefficients of expansion for 300 and 600° C are given in Table 7-10, while the orientations of the principal axes are given in Fig. 7-53. In order to calculate the thermal expansion, graphs were prepared of the variation of cell dimensions with temperature, and smoothed curves were drawn by eye to minimize errors. Calculations of the coefficients of expansion were made for 300 and 600° C because the errors appeared least at these temperatures. For the microcline and sanidine, the cell dimensions of Orville (1967) for room temperature were used together with the linear expansions of Rosenholtz and Smith (1941): the lattice angles were assumed to stay constant.

Table 7-10. Principal coefficients of thermal expansion for feldspars (Willaime *et al.*, 1972)

Specimen	300° C				600° C			
	α_1	α_2	α_3	α_V	α_1	α_2	α_3	α_V
F 109, 99% An	12.8	1.6	− 1.9	12.5	13.0	2.3	− 5.3	10.0
F 71, 75% An	8.9	0.4	− 3.7	5.6	11.5	5.6	− 1.1	16.0
F 50, 35% An	18.8	6.2	− 4.8	20.2	19.4	12.4	− 3.8	28.2
F 36, 21% An	17.3	3.1	− 5.1	15.3	22.4	11.0	− 7.6	25.8
F 101, 0% An	20.5	4.7	− 0.9	24.3	24.8	11.3	− 5.7	30.2
SL[a] low albite	22.7	8.8	− 9.3	22.2	23.3	11.6	− 3.3	36.0
307 high albite	31.4	13.0	−11.9	32.5	44.6	11.8	−23.9	32.5
SL[a] high albite	32.1	10.5	− 13.2	29.4	38.2	14.2	−19.8	32.6
microcline	18.5	0.8	− 0.5	18.8	19.8	2.0	− 0.3	21.5
sanidine	19.6	−0.8	− 1.0	17.8	18.2	0.5	− 0.8	17.9

Given in units of 10^{-6} degree Celsius^{-1}.

[a] Data of Stewart and von Limbach (1967).

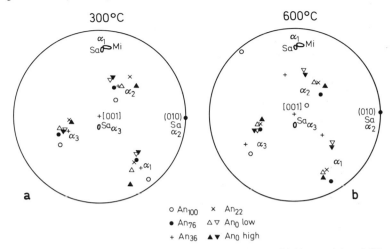

Fig. 7-53. Orientation of the principal axes of the thermal expansion figure of feldspars. (a) and (b) at 300 and 600° C, respectively. See Table 7-10 for identification of samples. An-content given in wt.-%. The normal and inverted triangles, respectively, show the albites of Stewart and von Limbach (1967) and of Grundy and Brown (1969). For microcline only the α_1 axis is shown. All data are plotted in the upper hemisphere with respect to (010) at the extreme right and [001] upwards at the center. (From Willaime et al., 1972, Figs. 1a, b)

None of the thermal expansion figures in Table 7-10 are ellipsoids, because α_3 is always negative. Whereas the figure for the alkali feldspars is almost uniaxial with α_1 near 19×10^{-6} per degree Celsius, those for the plagioclases are significantly biaxial, especially for high and low albite. In the K-feldspars, α_1 lies near [301] with a small deviation from the [010] plane for microcline. The orientation of the ellipsoid is similar in all plagioclases with the exception of monalbite and of anorthite at low temperature, both of which are affected by structural inversions. The orientation is strongly triclinic, and changes only about 20° over the whole series. A check on the accuracy of the data is provided for high albite and low albite. Detailed figures on the variation of the thermal expansion with temperature for albites and anorthite are given by Willaime et al. (1972).

In conclusion, it must be emphasized that subtle structural changes occur upon heating plagioclases (Chapter 5), and that the thermal expansion for equilibrium conditions is not known accurately.

Monoclinic-Triclinic Inversion in High Albite Solid Solution. The preceding data apply mostly to plagioclases in a low or intermediate structural state heated metastably. Pure albite under true thermodynamic equilibrium becomes monoclinic at 980° C, and this monoclinic-triclinic inversion moves to higher temperature with substitution of An, reaching the solidus near An_{10}.

Figure 7-54 shows the data of MacKenzie (1952) and Kroll (1971b). The pioneering results of MacKenzie showed that the lattice angles of heated sodic plagioclase varied with the method of synthesis. The closed squares show the estimated inversion temperatures for specimens of composition 5, 10 and 20 wt.-% An synthesized dry by devitrification just under the solidus. These specimens are poorly crystallized, and both the chemical composition of the crystals and the

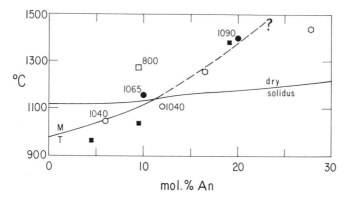

Fig. 7-54. Monoclinic-triclinic inversion in sodic plagioclase. The closed and open squares show data obtained by MacKenzie (1952) for plagioclases synthesized dry and hydrothermally, respectively. The open and closed circles show data obtained by Kroll (1971b) for specimens synthesized hydrothermally and dry at temperatures given by the symbol. The hexagons show data extrapolated from ternary compositions. The curve labelled M/T is similar to Kroll's estimate for the equilibrium inversion. The portion above the solidus is merely a metastable inversion. (Corrected and redrawn from Kroll, 1971b, Fig. 45)

extrapolated temperatures are subject to unknown errors. The open square shows the inversion temperature extrapolated for An_{10} crystallized hydrothermally from glass at 800° C, but the data point may be dubious because of triclinic topochemistry. All measurements were made on the splitting of 111, $1\bar{1}1$ peaks in a diffractometer.

The data of Kroll (1971b) were also obtained by extrapolation of the splitting of the 111, $1\bar{1}1$ peaks in a diffractometer. The open and closed circles show direct measurements of specimens in the Ab,An join, while the hexagons show data extrapolated from compositions in the Ab,An,Or ternary system. The specimens of composition 6 and 12 mol.-% An were prepared at 1040° C, 15 days and 5 bars water pressure (open circles), whereas those of composition 10 and 20 mol.-% An were crystallized dry for 15 days at 1065 and 1090°, respectively (closed circles).

All the data could be mutually consistent if the structural state depends on the crystallization conditions, and if the inversion temperature depends on the Al, Si distribution. The long discussion on the inversion for pure albite (see earlier) suggests that these conditions will be obeyed in sodic plagioclase also. Because the specimens of Kroll invert quite closely to the synthesis temperature, and because they have probably equilibrated at the synthesis temperature, the equilibrium inversion probably lies close to the curve in Fig. 7-53, copied from Kroll's Fig. 45. Specimens equilibrated below this curve invert metastably at a higher temperature, or not at all. Specimens synthesized above this curve may invert metastably at a temperature somewhat below the curve. There are no experimental data on the temperature at which the sodic plagioclases become *topochemically* monoclinic (not *geometrically* monoclinic), but entrance of An should lower the temperature because anorthite is topochemically monoclinic at all temperatures. Theoretically there may be a two-phase field rather than a single line marking the monoclinic-triclinic inversion.

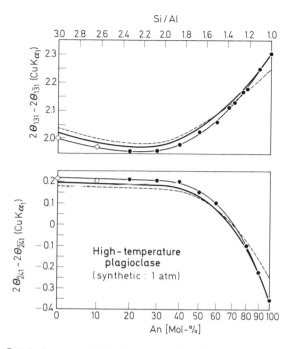

Fig. 7-55. Relation between the 131 and $\bar{2}41$ indicators and the An-content for the initial and equilibrated states of synthetic plagioclase studied by Kroll (1967, 1971 b). The thin curve represents specimens equilibrated at either 60 or 120° C below the solidus (diamonds and dots, respectively). The dashed curve shows the initial value obtained by extrapolation to zero time. The thick line shows the equilibrated value for annealing at the solidus temperature. (Kroll, 1971 b, Fig. 30)

Equilibrium Conditions. Apart from the data for the albite and anorthite ends, the equilibrium variation of cell dimensions with temperature is not known for plagioclase. However, two studies have provided promising indications that useful progress can be made.

Eberhard (1967) measured the 131 indicator for synthetic plagioclase equilibrated for long periods under hydrothermal conditions. Whether true thermodynamic equilibrium was achieved is discussed in Chapter 26.

Kroll (1967, 1971b) made at thorough study of the situation within 120° C of the solidus. Glasses were devitrified at 30, 60 and 120° C below the solidus temperature and held under dry conditions for periods up to 15 days. The 131 and $\bar{2}41$ triclinic indicators changed from the initial value to a value characteristic of the devitrification temperature. Figure 7-55 summarizes the results. The thin line shows the characteristic value for a temperature either 120° C or 60° C below the solidus, as shown respectively by diamonds and dots. The dashed line shows an estimate of the initial value extrapolated to zero time. The thick line shows the equilibrium situation for the solidus temperature. Presumably, the initial product of devitrification has extra disorder that is removed by annealing below the solidus temperature. These results confirm earlier data on anorthite obtained by Goldsmith and Laves (1956). Kroll (1971b) recorded complete cell dimensions for all his annealed specimens, as given in Table 7-6.

7.5 Ternary Feldspars and K-exchanged Plagioclase

7.5.1 General

Under equilibrium conditions, the extent of solid solution between the Or and An end-members is only a few percent (Yoder *et al.*, 1957), while natural K-feldspars and anorthites tend to be even purer. Viswanathan (1971a, b) made the important discovery that the Na atoms of plagioclase could be ion-exchanged with potassium halide at high temperature, leaving the rest of the structure intact. This process is metastable, but the K-exchanged plagioclases are valuable since they provide (1) an X-ray method for estimating the Ab-content of the original plagioclase from the volume expansion of the Or component, and (2) an opportunity to estimate the Al, Si distribution from cell dimensions that are not affected by crumpling around the small Na atoms (of course, crumpling about the Ca atoms still causes problems).

By mixing and homogenizing known amounts of the original and the K-exchanged plagioclase, ternary feldspars can be prepared of known structural state. Ternary feldspars can be synthesized directly, and can be found in rocks crystallized at high temperature. This group of feldspars has a high or nearly high structural state, representing an approach to equilibrium at high temperatures. The K-exchanged plagioclases can cover the entire range of structural state and composition, but are mostly metastable.

7.5.2 K-exchanged Plagioclase

This sub-section covers specimens that have been almost completely exchanged. The choice of exchange conditions is very critical, balancing a tight-rope between lack of reaction and of destruction of the feldspar framework. Viswanathan (1971a, b) used a 30-fold ratio of KCl to feldspar held dry at 850° C for 1.5 h. For calcic plagioclase, it is very important to use the finest powder. Kaliophilite, wollastonite and leucite are typical minor products. X-ray precession photographs of exchanged single crystals show a strong mosaic pattern, making it impossible to measure cell dimensions. Viswanathan was unable to remove original K from natural plagioclase by heating with NaCl, but was able to prepare K-free plagioclase by back-exchange with NaCl after forward exchange with KCl. Direct treatment with NaCl yielded nepheline or sodalite.

The K-exchange of natural plagioclase resulted in no apparent change of Al/Si distribution, no apparent change of mol.-% An, and in preservation of antiperthitic K-feldspar. Double-exchange resulted in essentially the same cell dimensions as for the initial material, though the back-exchange always yielded some sodalite. The temperature of 850° C was chosen for exchange because no change of Al, Si distribution was found at 900° C but change did occur at 1100° C.

The cell dimensions of K-exchanged plagioclase determined by Viswanathan and by Kroll (1971b) were obtained from Guinier photographs. There is a major shift of lines with K/Na ratio and with structural state, though the line intensities are insensitive to composition.

Table 7-11 contains selected cell dimensions from the following studies:

(a) Viswanathan (1971 b): 50 K-exchanged natural plagioclases from the suite assembled by Corlett and Eberhard (1967); the original cell dimensions are given for many specimens in Table 7-6; special attention was paid to ten specimens in the composition range of peristerite; 2 natural plagioclases were heated near the solidus, followed by K-exchange,

(b) Kroll (1971 b): 7 K-exchanged plagioclases synthesized at 60° C below the solidus temperature for 7 or 15 days; 8 natural plagioclases from the suite assembled by Corlett and Eberhard, were K-exchanged and then heated for a long time near the solidus.

Figure 7-56 shows plots of the cell dimensions a, b, c, α, β, γ and V versus mol.-% An for these specimens, which plots may be compared with the trends of cell dimensions for the high and low series of plagioclase outlined in Fig. 7-41.

The cell volume of the K-exchanged plagioclases is almost independent of structural state. Arbitrarily I fitted the data points for the low plagioclases with two straight lines meeting at $V = 0.6924 \times 10^{-27}$ cubic meters for An_{50}, with end-member values of 0.7228 at An_0 and 0.6700 at An_{100}. The data points for the ten peristerites lie above the curves, while those for the heated natural and synthetic specimens lie both above and below the curves with a bias to a lower volume. Such a bias to a greater density would be surprising for disordered material, and may result merely from experimental error. Until further data are obtained, estimation of An-content of K-exchanged plagioclase can be made from these two straight lines irrespective of structural state. A single quadratic curve would give about the same quality of fit as the two lines. Probably the actual variation of volume with composition is complex with weak kinks corresponding to structural changes between various composition ranges.

The cell edge a shows a complex variation with composition. Arbitrarily the data for low plagioclase have been fitted by three straight lines meeting at An_{25} and An_{50} with a 0.8440 and 0.8338 nm, respectively. For the high plagioclase, the situation is rather unclear, especially since the data points for synthetic An_{10} and An_{20} are inconsistent with any straight line passing through the reference point for high sanidine, and since there is no datum between An_{80} and An_{100}. Arbitrarily two straight lines were fitted to meet at An_{25}, a 0.8430, one passing through the reference point for high sanidine, and the other through An_{80}, 0.8234. The line for calcic compositions does not pass through the reference point for anorthite, but this is not surprising since a transition to the I-anorthite structure is expected between An_{80} and An_{90}.

The data for b cannot be expressed in any simple terms. Figure 7-56 shows two straight lines joining the reference point for anorthite to those for low microcline and high sanidine. There is a large scatter for the synthetic and heated natural specimens, with a strong tendency for positive deviations with respect to the reference line from high sanidine. The data for low plagioclase also show considerable scatter. From An_{77} to An_{25}, they tend to fall on the upper straight line, followed by a divergence to the reference point for low microcline. These data

Table 7-11. Cell dimensions of K-exchanged plagioclase

Ref.	Label	An (mol.-%)	Or	a (nanometer)	b	c	α (degrees)	β	γ	V (nm³)
(a) Natural plagioclase: complete exchange										
Viswanathan (1971b) label	3	75	1	0.8258	1.2919	0.7117	93.00	116.08	90.49	0.6806
and probe analyses of	5	37.4–39.0	4.2–3.4	0.8377	1.2973	0.7159	91.85	115.98	89.38	0.6990
original material from Cor-	7	76.1–78.3	0.4–0.6	0.8271	1.2931	0.7120	92.91	116.04	90.33	0.6829
lett and Eberhard (1967);	11	59.8	0.2	0.8307	1.2940	0.7133	92.56	116.02	89.78	0.6882
standard error 0.0002 in	13	73	1.2	0.8273	1.2927	0.7122	92.89	116.05	90.35	0.6830
edges and 0.05 in angles.	14	11	1.4	0.8523	1.2985	0.7204	90.69	115.91	88.29	0.7168
	24	51.8	0.7–2.5	0.8317	1.2944	0.7136	92.47	116.02	89.66	0.6896
	31	27.8	2.3	0.8430	1.2900	0.7174	91.32	115.95	89.04	0.7061
	34	21.5	3.8	0.8456	1.2989	0.7183	91.05	115.92	88.85	0.7094
	36	77.0	0.3	0.8238	1.2909	0.7104	93.10	116.04	90.66	0.6773
	37	43.0	1.7	0.8364	1.2963	0.7153	92.04	116.00	89.34	0.6966
	38	41.3	0.1	0.8366	1.2967	0.7155	92.00	116.01	89.38	0.6971
	40	59.1	2.0	0.8360	1.2945	0.7132	92.55	115.95	90.13	0.6886
	44	60.5	0.6	0.8308	1.2942	0.7130	92.59	115.98	90.12	0.6882
	46	13.7	0.7	0.8515	1.2980	0.7202	90.79	115.90	88.25	0.7517
	50	49.6	2.6	0.8342	1.2956	0.7144	92.26	116.01	89.60	0.6933
	53	52.6	2.2	0.8333	1.2940	0.7137	92.47	115.97	89.55	0.6912
	54	43.0	2.0–2.4	0.8363	1.2966	0.7154	92.05	116.00	89.37	0.6968
	55	52.1	2.1	0.8333	1.2938	0.7137	92.57	116.01	89.64	0.6907
	83	40.2	5.5	0.8371	1.2986	0.7150	91.62	115.93	89.91	0.6987
	84	16.5	0.7	0.8484	1.2983	0.7198	90.99	115.90	88.38	0.7129
	86	18.5	3.2	0.8469	1.2983	0.7187	90.99	115.92	88.75	0.7105
	87	16.8	5.4	0.8491	1.2990	0.7194	90.91	115.91	88.51	0.7135
	88	56.7	2.0	0.8321	1.2949	0.7138	92.42	116.01	89.84	0.6904
	91	47.8	0.2–0.3	0.8345	1.2957	0.7150	92.21	116.00	89.40	0.6943
	98	0.0–1.0	0.5	0.8587	1.2966	0.7223	90.64	115.94	87.63	0.7225
	99	4.9	0.1	0.8567	1.2985	0.7224	90.70	115.94	87.69	0.7220
	101	28.0	0.8	0.8421	1.2983	0.7174	91.44	115.95	89.04	0.7050
	102	12	0.6	0.8522	1.2976	0.7211	90.83	116.00	88.03	0.7163
	105	35.4	2.9	0.8399	1.2982	0.7165	91.68	115.98	89.30	0.7021
	118	1.3	0.3	0.8587	1.2969	0.7219	90.61	115.95	87.71	0.7223
	123	63.9–65.5	1.5–1.7	0.8292	1.2928	0.7123	92.78	116.01	90.26	0.6852
	124	21.5	3.8	0.8467	1.2997	0.7185	91.01	115.91	88.91	0.7111
	126	46.0	4.4	0.8354	1.2957	0.7152	92.20	116.00	89.33	0.6953
	129	10.8	0.5–3.0	0.8537	1.2982	0.7210	90.71	115.93	88.08	0.7182
	135	12.3	0.4	0.8540	1.2985	0.7211	90.69	115.92	88.09	0.7188

Label	An	Or	a	b	c	α	β	γ	V
136	35.3	0.4	0.8395	1.2979	0.7162	91.67	115.94	89.31	0.7014
158	35.8	0.5	0.8393	1.2969	0.7166	91.61	115.97	89.17	0.7010
162	20.2	3.9	0.8468	1.2983	0.7188	91.04	115.92	88.56	0.7105
165	13.2	1.1	0.8514	1.2988	0.7202	90.77	115.94	88.31	0.7159
166	21.5	1.2	0.8468	1.2988	0.7187	91.02	115.93	88.65	0.7107
170	25.3	1.0	0.8445	1.2993	0.7179	91.20	115.95	88.98	0.7081
171	17.2	0.6	0.8487	1.2985	0.7195	90.91	115.91	88.47	0.7130
172	9.6	0.3	0.8552	1.2980	0.7217	90.78	115.98	87.72	0.7196
173	37.9	0.8	0.8378	1.2973	0.7161	91.85	115.98	89.23	0.6993
187	10.0	0.6	0.8525	1.2979	0.7208	90.75	115.91	88.08	0.7169
188	0.5	0.1	0.8589	1.2971	0.7222	90.59	115.97	87.84	0.7229
202	4.6	0.7	0.8557	1.2980	0.7217	90.67	115.89	87.89	0.7207
203	8	1.5	0.8550	1.2987	0.7211	90.66	115.91	88.14	0.7198
262	25.4	1.1	0.8439	1.2992	0.7176	91.25	115.94	88.95	0.7074
T 4	45.5	—	0.8358	1.2964	0.7154	92.07	116.02	89.47	0.6958
T 111	24.2	—	0.8450	1.2983	0.7184	91.18	115.93	88.73	0.7804

Ref.	Days	An	Or	a	b	c	α	β	γ	V
(b) Synthetic plagioclase Kroll (1971b) synthesized 60° C below solidus, dry, for 7 or 15 days.	7	10	0	0.8515	1.3032	0.7166	90	115.90	90	0.7152
	15	20	0	0.8499	1.3036	0.7169	90	115.92	90	0.7144
	15	40	0	0.8375	1.2987	0.7148	91.37	115.90	89.98	0.6991
	15	50	0	0.8334	1.2969	0.7136	92.05	115.91	90.08	0.6932
	15	60	0	0.8300	1.2943	0.7125	92.58	115.91	90.21	0.6876
	15	71	0	0.8261	1.2919	0.7113	92.93	115.87	90.43	0.6817
	7	80	0	0.8234	1.2891	0.7108	93.12	115.79	90.68	0.6778

Ref.	Label	An	Or	a	b	c	α	β	γ	V
(c) Heated natural plagioclase Kroll (1971b)	110	4.1	1.4	0.8570	1.3031	0.7177	90	115.99	90	0.7205
	84	16.5	0.7	0.8483	1.3014	0.7165	90	115.97	90	0.7111
	166	21.5	0.2	0.8458	1.3010	0.7163	90	115.96	90	0.7087
	170	25.3	1.0	0.8430	1.3003	0.7155	90	115.96	90	0.7052
	193	25.6	1.0	0.8429	1.3001	0.7157	90	115.99	90	0.7049
	31	27.8	2.3	0.8414	1.2998	0.7154	90	115.98	90	0.7033
	101	28.0	0.8	0.8418	1.2997	0.7153	90	115.94	90	0.7038
	136	35.3	0.4	0.8400	1.2978	0.7150	90.72	116.10	90.10	0.6999
Viswanathan (1971b)	84	16.5	0.7	0.8482	1.3020	0.7167	90	115.96	90	0.7119
	47	0	—	0.8609	1.3033	0.7179	90	116.04	90	0.7237

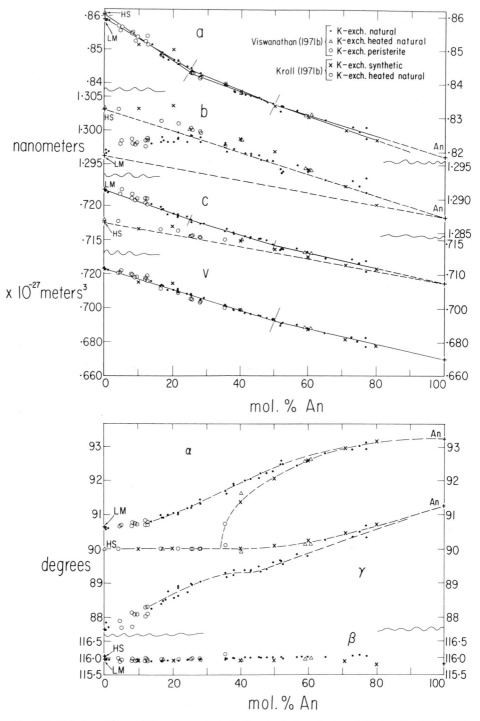

Fig. 7-56. Cell dimensions of K-exchanged plagioclase plotted against mol.-% An. See Table 7-11 for data. See text for meaning of lines, some of which are fitted to the data, and some of which are merely guide-lines joining the reference points for end-member feldspars (Table 7-1)

show a large positive deviation with respect to the straight line joining low microcline to anorthite.

The data for c show a better approach to a linear relation. Those for low plagioclase fit well with three straight lines meeting at An_{25}, 0.7179; An_{50}, 0.7142, and the reference points for low microcline and anorthite. For the high specimens, the data scatter so much that fitting curves is difficult. Viswanathan's data tend to lie about 0.0003 nm higher than those of Kroll, and the reference point for high sanidine. The dashed line in Fig. 7-56 merely joins the reference points for high sanidine and anorthite, to act as a guide for readers to judge the deviations. All the data points lie above this line, and it is obvious that one or more straight lines or a parabola at higher c values would give a better fit.

The data for α and γ show that K-exchange of high plagioclases produces monoclinic feldspars up to about An_{34}. The angle α moves rapidly away from 90° for more calcic compositions, but γ diverges more slowly. For the low plagioclases, there is a sigmoid variation of α and γ with An-content after K-exchange. Possibly there are kinks by analogy with the original low plagioclase. All of the curves were fitted by eye. The angle β changes very little and is of no interest.

The data for the K-exchanged peristerite intergrowths tend to lie closely, but not exactly, between the points for albites and oligoclases of the low series. Viswanathan (1971b) emphasized the problem of interpreting his K-exchanged peristerites as intergrowths of K-exchanged albites and oligoclases because the powder patterns could be indexed in terms of a single geometrical lattice. If peristerite is a mechanical mixture of two low plagioclases of composition An_2 and An_{25}, the powder pattern should consist of two sets of peaks. For example, the a dimensions of An_2 and An_{25} should be near 0.858 and 0.844 nm. The diffraction angles for the $\bar{2}01$ diffractions should differ by about 0.30° in 2θ for CuK_α radiation, about twice the half-width of the normal $\bar{2}01$ diffraction. A full explanation of Viswanathan's data has not been given, but it is likely that his specimens have a complex superstructure with structural continuity. This problem is discussed in Chapter 19.

For determination of An content, the best parameter by far would be the cell volume which is insensitive to structural state. Probably a precision of 1% An is obtainable, while the accuracy may be between 1 and 4% An judging from the data in Fig. 7-56. The a dimension is affected significantly by structural state, but could be used if the structural state were estimated. The $\bar{2}01$ or 400 spacings could then be used to give a quick estimate of An-content. The structural state can be estimated best from parameters that depend on α and γ, such as the 131 or 130 indicators. Appropriate calibrations for $\bar{2}01$, 131 and 130 can be readily calculated from the cell dimensions in the tables. Most workers, of course, will estimate structural state from the original rather than the K-exchanged plagioclase. Furthermore, use of short cuts is risky because the plagioclase may break down partly during K-exchange. Diffractions from the breakdown products may confuse the lines of K-plagioclase. The safest procedure is to (1) check the complete X-ray pattern against standard patterns for all possible breakdown products (2) then determine all the cell dimensions by a least-squares refinement of suitable peaks.

7.5.3 Structural Implication of Cell Dimensions

Section 7.4.3 contains an interpretation of the cell dimensions of plagioclase in terms of the crystal structure. Figure 7-45b shows Kroll's (1971b) interpretation of the cell dimensions of K-exchanged plagioclase on the basis of the translations in the [110] and [1$\bar{1}$0] zone axes. The data for K-exchanged synthetic plagioclase were interpreted in terms of three structure types:

An_0 to An_{30-40}, high albite (Analbite) solid solution,

An_{60-70} to An_{100}, anorthite solid solution,

An_{30-40} to An_{60-70}, Misch oder Übergangstyp.

The first region corresponds to the monoclinic range of K-exchanged synthetic plagioclase, for which Δ[110] is zero. The high content of K atoms allows the aluminosilicate framework to adopt a strictly monoclinic geometry consistent with the topochemical symmetry of the disordered T atoms. Although anorthite has monoclinic topochemistry, crumpling of the framework around the Ca atoms prevents monoclinic symmetry. This crumpling causes serious problems in attempting detailed interpretation of the cell dimensions of K-exchanged plagioclase. Kroll's separation of K-exchanged high plagioclase into three series is subjective and requires checking with objective data from crystal structure analysis.

Viswanathan (1971b, 1972) attempted a structural explanation of the cell dimensions of original and K-exchanged plagioclase in which he emphasized the c dimension. Ribbe (1972) emphasized the 131 indicator which depends on variation in α and γ. Both approaches are interesting and yield estimates of the Al-content of individual tetrahedra from the cell dimension. A detailed study suggests that the approaches are potentially accurate for albite solid solutions but require modification for anorthite solid solutions. Readers should consult the original papers for details.

7.5.4 Ternary Feldspars

K-exchanged Natural and Synthetic Specimens. The cell dimensions of ternary feldspars of any desired structural state and bulk composition can be obtained by ion-exchange with alkali halide, followed by homogenization of weighed mixtures of the ion-exchanged product and starting material.

Viswanathan (1971b) prepared K-exchanged plagioclase from three natural low plagioclases of composition An_{17}, An_{28}, and $An_{44.5}$. Powdered mixtures of plagioclase and K-exchanged equivalent were pressed into tablets and heated to 900° C for 1–3 days. Calcic plagioclases were more resistant to homogenization than sodic ones.

Kroll (1971b) prepared ternary compositions from synthetic plagioclases of composition $An_{16.5}$ and $An_{27.8}$ by homogenizing at 1000° C for $\frac{1}{2}$–14 days.

Table 7-12 contains the cell dimensions listed by Viswanathan and Kroll (note: there were no data for $An_{16.5}$).

Figure 7-57 shows the relation between cell volume and An-content for Viswanathan's and Kroll's data. These data are too sparse to permit precise

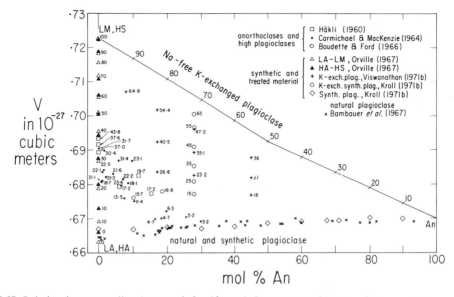

Fig. 7-57. Relation between cell volume and the Ab- and Or-contents of ternary feldspars. Each specimen is plotted with respect to V and An-content, while the Or-content is given by the number next to the symbol. All compositions in mol.-%. See Fig. 7-56 for data justifying the two lines for Na-free, K-exchanged plagioclase. After Viswanathan (1971b, Fig. 6), but with many additional data as specified in the key. Note that two specimens of Häkli are sanidines

positioning of contours of constant Or-content but they suggest a complex relationship between cell volume and chemical composition. Kroll's data for high plagioclase differ somewhat from those of Viswanathan for low plagioclase, but are too sparse to permit definitive evaluation of the effect of structural state.

Anorthoclase and Sodic High Plagioclase. Table 7-12 contains cell dimensions measured by Carmichael and MacKenzie (1964) for 15 natural anorthoclases from various sources; by Boudette and Ford (1966) for 2 anorthoclases from Antarctica; and by Häkli (1960) for 2 sanidines and 4 anorthoclases from Kenya and Tanganyika. Detailed chemical analyses, quoted in these papers, show significant contents of Fe_2O_3 (0.1–0.8 wt.-%), BaO (0.2–0.3), SrO (0.1–0.3) and H_2O^+ (0.1–0.6). Also given are data for five sodic high plagioclases determined by Carmichael and MacKenzie.

Figure 7-57 shows the data on a plot of cell dimensions vs. An-content. Because the anorthoclases and the sodic high plagioclases are in or near the high structural state, they should be compared with the data of Orville (1967) for the high albite-high sanidine series and of Kroll (1971b) for synthetic high plagioclase. When the experimental errors in the cell volume and the chemical composition are taken into account, the data are consistent.

Figure 7-58 provides a further test of the consistency of the data, as given by Carmichael and MacKenzie (1964). The ordinate shows the position of the $\overline{2}01$ peak, and the abscissa the Or-content. The line shows the calibration curve determined by Carmichael and MacKenzie for Orville's synthetic alkali feldspars. The natural specimens show a scatter equivalent to several percent of Or, with a

Table 7-12. Cell dimensions of ternary feldspars

Ref.	An (mol.-%)	Or	a (nanometer)	b	c	α (degrees)	β	γ	V (nm³)
(a) Specimens prepared in the laboratory									
Kroll (1971b) prepared from No. 31	27.8	65	0.8388	1.2993	0.1750	90	116.01	90	0.7004
of Corlett and Eberhard (1967)	27.8	55	0.8364	1.2997	0.7146	90.72	116.10	90.16	0.6965
	27.8	45	0.8316	1.2963	0.7142	91.41	116.14	90.23	0.6909
	27.8	35	0.8277	1.2940	0.7135	92.00	116.17	90.31	0.6853
	27.8	25	0.8246	1.2926	0.7128	92.46	116.21	90.34	0.6807
	27.8	15	0.8222	1.2914	0.7122	92.79	116.24	90.39	0.6771
Viswanathan (1971b)	17.1	26.8	0.8273	1.2893	0.7159	92.89	116.30	88.57	0.6836
Standard error 0.0003 in edges,	17.1	40.5	0.8326	1.2924	0.7174	92.33	116.16	88.46	0.6923
0.05 in angles	17.1	54.4	0.8397	1.2950	0.7185	91.80	116.03	88.46	0.7016
	27.8	23.2	0.8260	1.2903	0.7144	92.90	116.12	89.30	0.6827
	28.0	35.1	0.8304	1.2936	0.7153	92.41	116.14	89.29	0.6893
	27.9	47.2	0.8365	1.2958	0.7164	91.96	116.08	89.20	0.6960
	45.1	17.9	0.8230	1.2896	0.7123	93.22	116.22	89.66	0.6769
	45.1	27.0	0.8260	1.2918	0.1730	92.88	116.12	89.64	0.6820
	45.0	36.2	0.8297	1.2936	0.7143	92.62	116.09	89.56	0.6877
	7.9	64.8	0.8425	1.2964	0.7203	90.95	115.97	88.21	0.7069
(b) Natural specimens (anorthoclase and high plagioclase)									
Carmichael and MacKenzie (1964)	10.3	11.4	0.8203	1.2909	0.7126	92.90	116.39	90.22	0.6749
	7.5	13.5	0.8210	1.2911	0.7128	92.80	116.37	90.21	0.6759
	6.7	17.2	0.8236	1.2912	0.7136	92.56	116.34	90.15	0.6796

8.6	18.1	0.8239	1.2930	0.7133	92.40	116.29	90.27	0.6804
1.1	18.1	0.8239	1.2935	0.7141	92.26	116.38	90.28	0.6810
2.1	21.2	0.8249	1.2944	0.7139	92.19	116.30	90.16	0.6822
0.9	21.1	0.8240	1.2929	0.7139	92.34	116.33	90.14	0.6809
4.3	21.6	0.8263	1.2935	0.7138	92.26	116.33	90.18	0.6830
7.1	22.2	0.8248	1.2934	0.7134	92.42	116.28	90.18	0.6816
1.2	22.1	0.8259	1.2938	0.7147	92.15	116.36	90.15	0.6836
1.5	22.5	0.8260	1.2944	0.7145	91.94	116.31	90.21	0.6842
9.7	23.1	0.8275	1.2949	0.7150	91.79	116.29	90.11	0.6868
1.8	30.4	0.8287	1.2972	0.7156	91.05	116.26	90.15	0.6898
5.9	31.4	0.8279	1.2952	0.7150	91.47	116.32	90.20	0.6869
0.2	31.7	0.8296	1.2975	0.7156	91.03	116.28	90.11	0.6905
29.9	3.2	0.8171	1.2874	0.7114	93.49	116.34	90.05	0.6691
25.5	5.2	0.8177	1.2882	0.7115	93.39	116.31	90.09	0.6704
19.7	6.3	0.8179	1.2886	0.7121	93.36	116.34	90.03	0.6711
18.3	4.7	0.8179	1.2873	0.7119	93.43	116.39	90.00	0.6700
16.4	4.7	0.8170	1.2881	0.7118	93.45	116.33	89.96	0.6699
29.9	3.2	0.8171	1.2874	0.7112	93.39	116.25	90.20	0.6693
18.3	4.7	0.8171	1.2882	0.7111	93.38	116.32	90.14	0.6694
10.1	15.7	0.8211(4)	1.2910(2)	0.7129(2)	92.66(2)	116.36(3)	90.23(3)	0.6761
18.4	16.8	0.8228(3)	1.2915(2)	0.7127(1)	92.59(2)	116.30(2)	90.28(3)	0.6779
0.0	36.8	0.8298	1.2950	0.7160	90.64	116.37	90.04	0.6893
15.3	17.1	0.8219	1.2912	0.7130	92.69	116.39	90.28	0.6773
6.1	23.4	0.8250	1.2930	0.7145	92.05	116.34	90.12	0.6825
11.5	19.7	0.8234	1.2925	0.7138	92.73	116.41	90.10	0.6794
1.0	37.6	0.8308	1.2969	0.7158	90	116.28	90	0.6916
0.0	43.8	0.8322	1.2970	0.7161	90	116.23	90	0.6933

heated 28 days at 1100° C

Boudette and Ford (1966)

Häkli (1960)

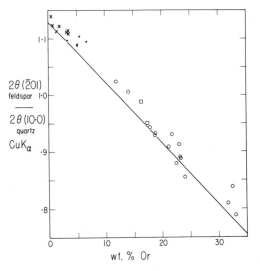

Fig. 7-58. Relation between the $\bar{2}01$ peak position and wt.-% Or for natural anorthoclases and high sanidines. The $10\bar{1}0$ peak of quartz was assumed to lie at 20.876°. The straight line was obtained by Carmichael and MacKenzie (1964) for the synthetic feldspars of Orville (1967), and is drawn from $2\,\theta$ 22.005° for pure albite to 21.631° for 35 wt.-% Or. The open and closed circles, respectively, show anorthoclases and high plagioclases measured by Carmichael and MacKenzie, while the squares show anorthoclases measured by Boudette and Ford (1966). The crosses show seven sodic plagioclases measured by Smith (1956) after heating: these specimens actually contain 0.7—3.5 mol.-% Or with a mean of 1.9% (Smith and Ribbe, 1967). (From Carmichael and MacKenzie, 1964, Fig. 1 plus additions)

tendency to lie above the reference line for Orville's specimens by an amount equivalent to about 1–2% Or. Probably some of the scatter results from uncertainty in the chemical analysis caused partly by chemical zoning. For determination of natural feldspars, it seems best to use Orville's curve to estimate the Or-content and then add about $1\frac{1}{2}$%. Of course, electron microprobe analyses are preferable because they yield data on the minor as well as the major elements.

Carmichael and MacKenzie prepared two diagrams to illustrate the variation of cell parameters with composition for high-temperature sodium-rich feldspars and Boudette and Ford (1966) added further data. Figure 7-59a shows contours for α^* and $2\theta(\bar{2}01)$. The contours for $\bar{2}01$ are parallel to the contours for wt.-% Or, while those for α^* are parallel for Or-poor compositions but change direction

Fig. 7-59. Variation with composition of cell parameters of high feldspars of ternary composition. a Dot-dash lines show contours of $2\,\theta\,(\bar{2}01)$, and continuous lines of α^*. The small filled triangles and circles show, respectively, plagioclases and anorthoclases of Carmichael and MacKenzie (1964), Donnay and Donnay (1952) and Smith (1956). The two larger circles show anorthoclases from Boudette and Ford (1966). The monoclinic-triclinic transition at $Ab_{63}Or_{37}$ is from MacKenzie (1952): see Fig. 7-63 for other data on the transition. From Boudette and Ford (1966, Fig. 5): see also Carmichael and MacKenzie (1964, Fig. 2). b Variation of cell volume of anorthoclase (continuous lines) and of $2\,\theta(131) - 2\,\theta(1\bar{3}1)$ of high plagioclase (dot-dash lines: CuK_{α}). Data from Carmichael and MacKenzie (1964), Donnay and Donnay (1952), Smith (1956) and Häkli (1960). (From Carmichael and MacKenzie, 1964, Fig. 3)

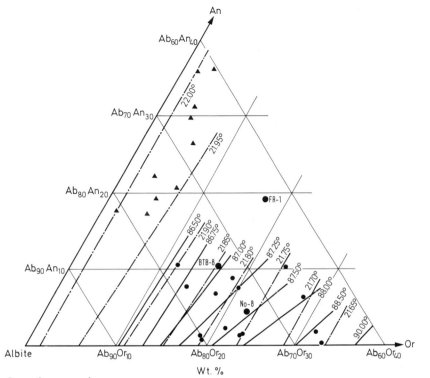

Fig. 7-59 a. Legend see opposite page

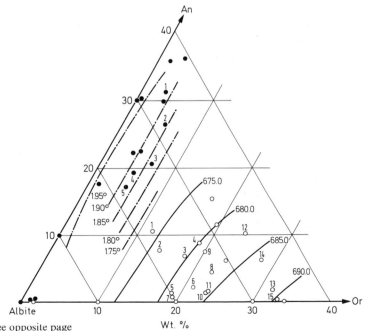

Fig. 7-59 b. Legend see opposite page

for more potassic compositions. The average discrepancy of the observed values of α^* with respect to the contours is $0.1°$. Carmichael and MacKenzie concluded that high feldspars more potassic than about Or_{15} can be determined for their Or and An contents from α^* and $\overline{2}01$ (or related parameters). Less potassic specimens can be determined for their Or content but not for their An content. Figure 7-59b shows two types of contours: the cell volume for anorthoclases, and the 131 indicator for high plagioclase. The contours for the former cross the contours for Or content at a small angle. The 131 indicator drops considerably with Or-substitution.

Monoclinic-triclinic Inversion in High Ternary Feldspar. Whereas ternary feldspars in the low structural state are triclinic at all temperatures, those in the high structural state may become monoclinic depending on their bulk chemical composition and on the detailed nature of the structural state. A full discussion of the complexities for the binary feldspars was given earlier in this chapter.

MacKenzie (1952) determined the inversion temperature for various synthetic feldspars with binary compositions, plus six natural anorthoclases. The splitting of the 111 peak was measured in a counter diffractometer, and the temperature checked optically for two specimens. The data are: Grande Caldeira, $Or_{31.7}An_{1.8}$, $100°$ C; Kenya, $Or_{28.1}An_{10.1}$, $140°$ C; Victoria, $Or_{23.3}An_{1.2}$, $360°$ C; Ropp, $Or_{23.0}An_{7.5}$, $540°$ C (X-ray), 555–580 (optics); Mt. Anakie, $Or_{23.4}An_{8.3}$, $575°$ C (X-ray), 560–590 (optics); Mt. Erebus, $Or_{17.9}An_{18.9}$, $600°$ C. These compositions are given in wt.-%, recalculated to $(Or + Ab + An) = 100\%$. The specimens contain significant amounts of Ba and Sr. See Chapter 19 for data on perthitic inter-

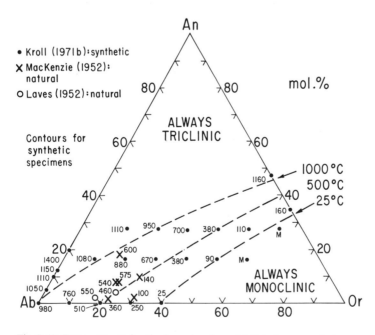

Fig. 7-60. Temperatures for the inversion from triclinic to monoclinic symmetry of feldspars in the Or–Ab–An system. The inversion temperature in °C is given beside the composition. (From Kroll, 1971 b, Fig. 46; redrawn with additions)

growths. Laves (1952) obtained optical data for two specimens: $Or_{17.9}An_{21.2}$, 550° C; $Or_{23.8}An_{4.4}$, 460° C.

Kroll (1971b) prepared ternary feldspars from natural plagioclase by (a) K-exchange followed by (b) heating at 1100° C followed by (c) back-exchange followed by (d) homogenization of weighed mixtures. The inversion temperature was measured from extrapolation of the splitting of the 111 line in a powder diffractometer.

Figure 7-60 shows Kroll's data together with his estimates of contours of composition for 25, 500 and 1000° C. The data for the natural specimens are consistent qualitatively with the synthetic trend, but the temperatures range from 0–300° C lower. Probably the structural state of the natural specimens is different, and certainly there are significant contents of minor elements such as Sr and Ba. The data for the natural specimens are too sparse to permit delineation of contours: probably one can expect that the contours for the synthetic specimens will give a semi-quantitative guide, running about 0 to 300° C too high.

7.6 K, Ba Feldspars

Following exploratory X-ray studies by Vermaas (1953) and Gay (1965), detailed data on the cell dimensions of K, Ba feldspars were reported by Gay and Roy (1968). Other data on X-ray powder patterns are given by Roy (1965, 1967).

The K, Ba feldspars are analogous to the plagioclase feldspars in showing very complex crystal-structural variants (see Chapter 5). Celsian, $BaAl_2Si_2O_8$, has strong or complete Al, Si ordering analogous to that of anorthite but the large size of the Ba atom results in monoclinic symmetry. In the high structural series from celsian to high sanidine, there must be a transition between the two structure types, but the nature and chemical position of the transition is unclear. Natural K, Ba feldspars are either monoclinic, or close to monoclinic geometry, and form a series of structure types. These natural K, Ba feldspars are very rare, and occur mainly in skarns or veins. The K-rich members are not analogous to maximum microcline, and apparently resemble adularia and "orthoclase".

Any deviations from monoclinic geometry are small enough to allow refinement of X-ray powder data in terms of a monoclinic cell. Interpretation of the cell dimensions of natural K, Ba feldspars is complicated by extensive substitution of Ab and An molecules.

Figure 7-61 shows the cell dimensions given in Tables I and II of Gay and Roy (1968). Twenty-eight natural specimens were measured before heating and five after heating for several days at 1200–1400° C. In addition, data are given for specimens synthesized hydrothermally at 2 kbars for 500 and 700° C for 7 days. The quoted accuracy is 0.0006 nm for the edges and 0.08° in β. For convenience, c is referred to the 1.4 nm cell, though many specimens have a 0.7 nm repeat.

The percentage variations in cell edges are small, but generally speaking substitution of BaAl for KSi causes an increase in all three cell edges. Perhaps the clearest change is in β which falls from 116 to 115°.

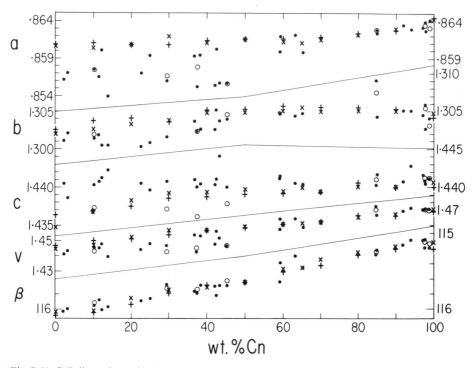

Fig. 7-61. Cell dimensions of K, Ba feldspars plotted against wt.-% of celsian (BaAl$_2$Si$_2$O$_8$). The cell edges and volume are expressed in nanometers, and β in degrees. Note reversed scale for β. Unheated and heated natural specimens are shown by dots and circles, respectively. The diagonal and horizontal crosses show specimens synthesized hydrothermally at 700 and 500° C, respectively. Plotted from Tables I and II of Gay and Roy (1968)

Within experimental error, the data for each cell edge of the synthetic specimens fall on a single curve, which is probably non-linear: thus the data for b appear to go through a maximum near Cn$_{70}$. The data for V and β are consistent with a linear change, and these two parameters probably offer the best determinative methods for synthetic specimens.

The data for the natural specimens are hard to interpret. The cell volumes of the natural specimens are mostly lower than those of the synthetic specimens, resulting principally from substitution of Ab and An molecules rather than increased structural order. Unfortunately Gay and Roy did not obtain complete analyses on all specimens, but many specimens show several weight percent of (Na$_2$O + CaO), which amounts should cause extensive lowering of the cell volume. Heating of the natural specimens caused little change of cell volume, indicating that structural order has an insignificant effect. Somewhat surprising is the observation that the cell volume of six of the seven specimens is reduced by heating, a direction opposite to that expected for disordering. Perhaps the heating causes homogenization of some exsolved Na, Ca feldspar. The data for β lie almost randomly distributed about those for the synthetic feldspars.

Within experimental error, all natural K-rich specimens have a smaller a dimension than for the synthetic specimens, consistent with extensive substitution of Ab and An. At the Ba-rich side, there is no significant difference between a

dimensions of natural and synthetic feldspars, as expected because the natural specimens lie close to the ideal composition trend.

The c dimensions of the natural specimens lie consistently above the trend for the synthetic specimens, suggesting the presence of structural order (see 7.3.3). Heating caused reduction of c to values either on or below the trend for the synthetic specimens. Probably the value of c is augmented by structural order and diminished by substitution of Ab and An molecules. Perhaps the reduction of c during heating gives a valid parameter for estimating the structural order, but it is certain that the position of c for the unheated material does not give a true estimate of structural state. Similar conclusions apply to the data for b, except that b decreases when c increases. Possibly a plot of b vs. c will give valuable information on the structural state of K, Ba feldspars, but no attempt had been made by 1973.

Certain K-rich specimens (i.e. some hyalophanes) are actually triclinic but data on the α and γ angles have not been published. Almost certainly, the situation is very complex with the cell edges and angles resulting from structural differences between barian sanidines from volcanic rocks and K-rich hyalophanes from low-temperature veins.

Gay (1965) found that the 132 peak with spacing near 0.30 nm provided a distinction between members of the K, Ba feldspars, and Roy (1965, 1967) gave further data. The basic features of this plot are quite similar to those for the cell volume (Fig. 7-61), and the interpretation is similar. Because of the chemical complexity of natural K, Ba feldspars, it is recommended that whenever possible the chemical composition be determined by a chemical procedure rather than from the X-ray powder pattern. From the extent of Ab and An substitution, it should then be possible to estimate semi-quantitatively the effect on b and c. Any estimate of structural state from the cell dimensions should be checked by comparison with cell dimensions of the same material after prolonged heat treatment at high temperature.

7.7 Synthetic Analogs

Whereas preceding sections were limited to the major substitutions found in natural feldspars, this section is almost open-ended because of the large number of possible chemical combinations. Since no new principles seem to be involved, the data are treated quite briefly.

Lithium Substitution in Albite. Stewart (1960) and Edgar and Piotrowski (1967) found that the 131 indicator of albites synthesized hydrothermally from 650–830° C for times up to one month mostly at 2 kbars was higher when the bulk composition contained lithium either as $LiAlSiO_4$ or $LiAlSi_2O_6$. However it was not determined whether this effect resulted from a higher structural disorder (of Si, Al atoms), or from entrance of Li into the albite, or from both.

(Ca, Sr) $Al_2Si_2O_8$. Nager et al. (1969) determined the cell dimensions of specimens synthesized by solid-state reaction at 1500° C (Fig. 7-62). All cell edges increase with increasing Sr content, but the variations are strongly non-linear with a positive deviation of volume from an ideal solution. The angle β also varies non-linearly. Increase of Sr-content causes α and γ to approach 90° such

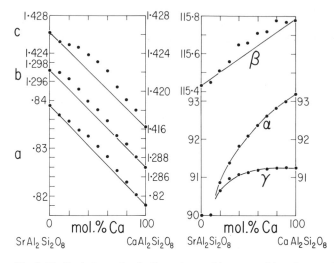

Fig. 7-62. Variation of cell dimensions with composition for synthetic members of the (Sr, Ca) Al$_2$Si$_2$O$_8$ series synthesized at 1500° C. The lines for a, b, c and β merely join the end-members. The curves for α and γ were inserted by eye. Accuracy is 0.002 nm in a and b, 0.0003 in c, and 0.01° in the angles. (Drawn from data table in Nager et al., 1969)

that monoclinic symmetry is achieved at about 91 mol.-% Sr–F. Nager et al. (1970) from high-temperature Guinier photographs showed that the temperature of the symmetry change moved from room temperature for 91 mol.-% Sr–F to 860° C for 70 mol.-% Sr–F. All these observations are generally consistent with the larger ionic radius of Sr than Ca, and with the tendency for increasing thermal vibration to promote monoclinic symmetry.

$NaAlSi_3O_8–BaAl_2Si_2O_8$. Rudert (1970) in an Inaug.-Diss. reported cell dimensions for specimens in the albite-celsian system synthesized hydrothermally at 1 kbar and 850–930° C. This series must undergo a complex structural change from the 0.7 nm cell of albite to the 1.4 nm cell of celsian (cf. Section 7.6). Specimens from 0–10 mol.-% Cn are triclinic, while those from 23 to 100% are monoclinic, again interpretable in terms of the larger ionic radius of Ba than of Na. The details of the cell dimensions await correction of the tabulated data.

$K(Al,B)Si_3O_8$. Martin (1971) synthesized hydrothermally at 700° C and 1 kbar for 3.5 days four specimens from bulk compositions containing 0, 5.5, 9.7 and 18.1 mol.-% boron substitution for Al. The cell dimensions with standard errors in brackets are

	a	b	c	β	V
	(nanometers)			(degrees)	(nm^3)
0	0.86034(10)	1.30234(13)	0.71812(7)	116.009(8)	0.72314(9)
5.5	0.86017(9)	1.30112(15)	0.71711(7)	116.002(9)	0.72134(11)
9.7	0.86002(6)	1.29979(11)	0.71634(6)	116.006(7)	0.71968(8)
18.1	0.85908(9)	1.29827(13)	0.71486(11)	116.009(13)	0.71655(14)

All specimens will have the sanidine structure, but the detailed structural state is unknown. The reduction in the cell edges with increasing boron content is consistent with the ionic radii.

Ga-*Substitutions*. In a personal communication in 1971, Dr. H. Pentinghaus reports preliminary data for the series Ga-albite-Ga-anorthite; albite-Ga-albite; and Ga-albite-Ga-K-feldspar. These series show complex order-disorder and unmixing relations.

Others. Grove and Ito (1973) reported data for high-temperature displacive transformations in synthetic Ca-, Ba-, Sr-, Na-, K-, Rb- and Cs-substituted feldspars.

References

Appleman, D. E. (1971): Crystal structure of a lunar plagioclase of composition An 84. Abstr. H 13 of Program for American Cryst. Assoc. Mtg., Ames, Iowa.

Appleman, D. E., Clark, J. R. (1965): Crystal structure of reedmergnerite, a boron albite, and its relation to feldspar crystal chemistry. AM **50**, 1827–1850.

Appleman, D. E., Nissen, H.-U., Stewart, D. B., Clark, J. R., Dowty, E., Huebner, J. S. (1971): Studies of lunar plagioclases, tridymite and cristobalite. Proc. Second Lunar Science Conf. **1**, 117–133. The M.I.T. Press.

Bachinski, S. W., Müller, G. (1971): Experimental determinations of the microcline-low albite solvus. JP **12**, 329–356.

Bailey, S. W., Taylor, W. H. (1955): The structure of a triclinic potassium felspar. AC **8**, 621—632.

Bambauer, H. U., Eberhard, E., Viswanathan, K. (1967): The lattice constants and related parameters of "plagioclases (low)". Part IV of laboratory investigations on plagioclases. SMPM **47**, 351–364.

Bambauer, H. U., Corlett, M., Eberhard, E., Viswanathan, K. (1967): Diagrams for the determination of plagioclases using X-ray powder methods. (Part III of laboratory investigations on plagioclases). SMPM **47**, 333–350.

Baskin, Y. (1956): A study of authigenic feldspars. JG **64**, 132–155.

Beckenkamp, J. (1881): Über die Ausdehnung monosymmetrischer und asymmetrischer Kristalle durch die Wärme. ZK **5**, 436–466.

Bloss, F. D. (1964): Optical extinction of anorthite at high temperatures. AM **49**, 1125–1131.

Borg, I. Y., Smith, D. K. (1968): Calculated powder patterns: I. Five plagioclases. AM **53**, 1709–1723.

Borg, I. Y., Smith, D. K. (1969): Calculated powder patterns. Part II. Six potassium feldspars and barium feldspar. AM **54**, 163–181.

Borgström, L., Goldschmidt, V. (1906): Kristallberechnung im triklinen System. ZK **41**, 63–91.

Boudette, E. L., Ford, A. B. (1966): Physical properties of anorthoclase from Antarctica. AM **51**, 1374–1387.

Bowen, N. L., Tuttle, O. F. (1950): The system NaAlSi$_3$O$_8$–KAlSi$_3$O$_8$–H$_2$O. JG **58**, 489–511.

Brown, B. E., Bailey, S. W. (1964): The structure of maximum microcline. AC **17**, 1391–1400.

Brown, W. L. (1960): X-ray studies in the plagioclases. Part I. Lattice changes in heat-treated plagioclases — the existence of monalbite at room temperature. Part. 2. The crystallographic and petrologic significance of peristerite unmixing in the acid plagioclases. ZK **113**, 297–344.

Brown, W. L. (1967): A reinterpretation of monalbite. MM **36**, 80–82.

Bruno, E., Facchinelli, A. (1972): Al, Si configurations in lead feldspar. ZK **136**, 296–304.

Bruno, E., Gazzoni, G. (1970a): Feldspati sintetici della serie Sr[Al$_2$Si$_2$O$_8$] – Pb[Al$_2$Si$_2$O$_8$]. Periodico Mineralogia (Roma), **39**, 245–254.

Bruno, E., Gazzoni, G. (1970b): On the system Ba[Al$_2$Si$_2$O$_8$]–Ca[Al$_2$Si$_2$O$_8$]. CMP **25**, 144–152.

Butler, J. C. (1973): Prediction of composition of anomalous cryptoperthites from the Rattlesnake Mountain sill, west Texas, using stepwise multiple linear regression techniques. BGSA **84**, 949–954.

Callegari, E., Pieri, R. de (1967): Crystallographical observations on some chess-board albites. SMPM **47**, 99–110.

Carmichael, I. S. E., MacKenzie, W. S. (1964): The lattice parameters of high-temperature triclinic sodic feldspars. MM **33**, 949–962.

Chao, S. H., Smare, D. L., Taylor, W. H. (1939): An X-ray examination of some potash-soda felspars. MM **25**, 338–350.

Chao, S. H., Taylor, W. H. (1940): Isomorphous replacement and superlattice structures in the plagioclase felspars. Proc. Roy. Soc. London, **176**A, 76—87.

Christie, O. H. J. (1962a): Feldspar structure and the equilibrium between plagioclase and epidote. AJS **260**, 149–153. Reply by R. W. R. Rutland, 153–157.

Christie, O. H. J. (1962b): Observations on natural feldspars: randomly disordered structures and a preliminary suggestion to a plagioclase thermometer. NGT **42**, No. 2, 383–388.

Christie, O. H. J., Nilssen, B. (1964): Lead nitrate, a convenient internal standard for routine X-ray examination of feldspars. AJS **262**, 1230–1233.

Claisse, F. (1950): A roentgenographic method for determining plagioclases. AM **35**, 412–420.

Cloizeaux, A. des (1862): Manuel de minéralogie. Paris.

Cole, W. F., Sörum, H., Kennard, O. (1949): The crystal structures of orthoclase and sanidinized orthoclase. AC **2**, 280–287.

Cole, W. F., Sörum, H., Taylor, W. H. (1951): The structure of the plagioclase felspars I. AC **4**, 20—29.

Colville, A. A., Ribbe, P. H. (1968): The crystal structure of an adularia and a refinement of the structure of orthoclase. AM **53**, 25–37.

Coombs, D. S. (1954): Ferriferous orthoclases from Madagascar. MM **30**, 409–427.

Corlett, M., Eberhard, E. (1967): Das Material für chemische und physikalische Untersuchungen an Plagioklasen. (Teil I der Laboratoriumsuntersuchungen an Plagioklasen). SMPM **47**, 303–316.

Corlett, M., Ribbe, P. H. (1967): Electron probe microanalysis of minor elements in plagioclase feldspars. (Part II of laboratory investigations on plagioclases). SMPM **47**, 317–332.

Crosby, P. (1971): Composition and structural state of alkali feldspars from charnockitic rocks on Whiteface Mountain, New York. AM **56**, 1788–1811.

Czank, M. et al. (1971): Personal communication.

Czank, M., Schulz, H. (1971): Thermal expansion of anorthite. Naturwiss. 58 Jahr, **2**, 94.

Dana, E. D. (1920): The system of mineralogy of James Dwight Dana 1837–1868. Descriptive mineralogy. Sixth Edition entirely rewritten and enlarged. New York: John Wiley and Sons Inc.

Deming, W. E. (1948): Statistical adjustment of data. New York: John Wiley.

Desborough, G. A., Cameron, E. N. (1968): Composition and structural state of plagioclases from the lower part of the eastern Bushveld Complex, South Africa. AM **53**, 116–122.

Dietrich, R. V. (1962): K-feldspar structural states as petrogenetic indicators. NGT **42**, No. 2, 394–414.

Dietz, E. D., Baak, T., Blau, H. H. (1970): The superheating of an albite feldspar. ZK **132**, 340–360.

Doman, R. C., Cinnamon, C. G., Bailey, S. W. (1965): Structural discontinuities in the plagioclase feldspar series. AM **50**, 724–740.

Donnay, G., Donnay, J. D. H. (1952): The symmetry change in the high-temperature alkali feldspar series. AJS Bowen volume, 115–132.

Dreyer, C., Goldschmidt, V., Bøggild, O. B. (1907): Über Albit von Grönland. Meddel. om Grønland, **34**, 1–60. Reprinted NJM **29**, 537–592 (1910).

Eberhard, E. (1967): Zur Synthese der Plagioklase. SMPM **47**, 385–398.

Edgar, A. D., Piotrowski, J. M. (1967): $\Delta 2\theta_{131-1\bar{3}1}$ for albites crystallized in the systems $NaAlSi_3O_8$–β–$LiAlSi_2O_6$–H_2O and $NaAlSi_3O_8$–$LiAlSiO_4$–H_2O. MM **36**, 578–582.

Erd, E. C., White, D. E., Fahey, J. J., Lee, D. E. (1964): Buddingtonite, an ammonium feldspar with zeolitic water. AM **49**, 831–850.

Eugster, H. P., McIver, N. L. (1959): Boron analogues of alkali feldspars and related silicates. BGSA **70**, 1598–1599 (abstr.).

Fang, J. H., Bloss, F. D. (1966): X-ray diffraction tables. Southern Illinois University Press.

Fels, G. (1903): Ein Anorthitauswürfling von der Insel St. Christopher. ZK **37**, 450–460.

Ferguson, R. B., Traill, R. J., Taylor, W. H. (1958): The crystal structures of low-temperature and high-temperature albites. AC **11**, 331–348.

Finney, J. J., Bailey, S. W. (1964): Crystal structure of an authigenic maximum microcline. ZK **119**, 413–436.

Fizeau, H. (1868): Sur la dilatation des corps solides par la chaleur (deuxième Mémoire, seconde partie). Compt. Rend. Acad. Sci. Paris **66**, 1072.

Fleet, S. G., Chandrasekhar, S., Megaw, H. D. (1966): The structure of bytownite ("body-centred an-orthite"). AC **21**, 782–801.

Foit, F. F. (1971): The crystal structure of anorthite at 410 C. Prog. Geol. Soc. Amer. Mtg., Southeastern section, p. 311 (abstract).

Forstner, H. (1884): Über künstliche physikalische Veränderungen der Feldspäthe von Pantelleria. ZK **9**, 333–352.

Gay, P. (1965): An X-ray powder method for the estimation of (K, Ba) feldspars. MM **34** (Tilley Vol.), 204–213.

Gay, P., Roy, N. N. (1968): The mineralogy of the potassium-barium feldspar series. III. Sub-solidus relationships. MM **36**, 914–932.

Gazzoni, G. (1973): Al–Ga and Si–Ge diadochy in synthetic $BaAl_2Si_2O_8$ and $SrAl_2Si_2O_8$. ZK **137**, 24–34.

Ghélis, M., Gasperin, M. (1970): Evolution des paramètres dans le système $KAlSi_3O_8$–$RbAlSi_3O_8$. Compt. Rend. Acad. Sci. Paris, ser. D. 1928–1929.

Glinka, S. von (1889): Russische Albite. Russ. Bergjournal, 1889, No. 4, 5–10. Ref. ZK **22**, 63–70 (1894).

Goldschmidt, V. (1916): Atlas der Krystallformen. Band III. Danalith-Feldspatgruppe. Heidelberg: Carl Winters Universitätsbuchhandlung.

Goldsmith, J. R. (1950): Gallium and germanium substitutions in synthetic feldspars. JG **58**, 518–536.

Goldsmith, J. R., Laves, F. (1954a): The microcline-sanidine stability relations. GCA **5**, 1–19.

Goldsmith, J. R., Laves, F. (1954b): Potassium feldspars structurally intermediate between microcline and sanidine. GCA **6**, 100–118.

Goldsmith, J. R., Laves, F. (1955): Cation order in anorthite ($CaAl_2Si_2O_8$) as revealed by gallium and germanium substitutions. ZK **106**, 213–226.

Goldsmith, J. R., Laves, F. (1956): Crystallization of metastable disordered anorthite at "low tempera-tures". ZK **107**, 396–405.

Goldsmith, J. R., Laves, F. (1961): The sodium content of microclines and the microcline-albite series. CCILM **8**, 81–96.

Goodyear, J., Duffin, W. J. (1954): The identification and determination of plagioclase felspars by the X-ray powder method. MM **30**, 306–326.

Goodyear, J., Duffin, W. J. (1955): The determination of composition and thermal history of plagio-clase by the X-ray powder method. MM **30**, 648–656.

Grove, T. L., Ito, J. (1973): High temperature displacive transformations in synthetic feldspars. Trans. Am. Geophys. Union, **54**, 499 (Abs.)

Grundy, H. D., Brown, W. L. (1967): Preliminary single-crystal study of the lattice angles of triclinic feldspars at temperatures up to 1200 C. SMPM **47**, 21–30.

Grundy, H. D., Brown, W. L. (1969): A high-temperature X-ray study of the equilibrium forms of albite. MM **37**, 156–172.

Grundy, H. D., Brown, W. L. (1972): A high-temperature X-ray study of low and high plagioclase feldspars. Preprint.

Grundy, H. D., Brown, W. L., MacKenzie, W. S. (1967): On the existence of monoclinic $NaAlSi_3O_8$ at elevated temperatures. MM **36**, 83–88.

Gubser, R., Laves, F. (1967): On X-ray properties of "adularia", (K, Na)$AlSi_3O_8$. SMPM **47**, 177–188.

Gubser, R. A., Hoffmann, W., Nissen, H. U. (1963): Röntgenaufnahmen mit der Buergerschen Präzes-sionskamera bei Temperaturen zwischen 1000 C und 2000 C. ZK **119**, 264–272.

Häkli, A. (1960): On high temperature alkali feldspars of some volcanic rocks of Kenya and northern Tanganyika. BCGF **188**, 99–108.

Hall, K. M. et al. (1971): Personal communication.

Hall, K. M., Quareni, S. (1967): A note on monalbite. MM **36**, 78–79.

Hamilton, D. L., Edgar, A. D. (1969): The variation of the $\bar{2}01$ reflection in plagioclase. MM **37**, 16–25.

Harker, R. I. (1954): The occurrence of orthoclase and microcline in the granitic gneisses of the Carn Chuinneag-Inchbae complex, E. Ross-shire. GM **91**, 129–136.

Harlow, G. E., Brown, G. E., Hamilton, W. C. (1973): Neutron diffraction study of Amelia low albite. Trans. Amer. Geophys. Union **54**, 497 (Abs.).

Harnik, A. B. (1969): Strukturelle Zustände in den Anorthoklasen der Rhombenporphyre des Osloge-bietes. Inaug. Diss. Universität Zürich. SMPM **49**, 509–567.

Hey, M. H. (1969): The determinations of multiple correlations between several variables, with especial reference to the correlation of physical properties and chemical composition. MM **37**, 83–89.

Hintze, C. (1897): Handbuch der Mineralogie. II. Silicate und Titanate. Leipzig.

Jackson, E. D. (1961): X-ray determinative curve for some natural plagioclases of composition An_{60-85}. U.S. Geol. Survey Prof. Paper, 424 C, 286–288.

Jones, J. B. (1966): Order in alkali feldspars. N, 210, 1352–1353.

Jones, J. B., Nesbitt, R. W., Slade, P. G. (1969): The determination of the orthoclase content of homogenized alkali feldspars using the $\bar{2}01$ X-ray method. MM 37, 489–496.

Kastner, M. (1971): Authigenic feldspars in carbonate rocks. AM 56, 1403–1442.

Kastner, M., Waldbaum, D. R. (1968): Authigenic albite from Rhodes. AM 53, 1579–1602.

Kayode, A. A. (1964): Thermal expansion and the effect of temperature on the angle of the rhombic section of plagioclase feldspars. Ph. D. thesis, Univ. Chicago, 86 p.

Kempe, D. R. C. (1966): A note on the $\bar{2}01$ spacing of some lime-rich alkali feldspars from Kangerdlugssuaq, East Greenland. MM 35, 704–714.

Kempster, C. J. E., Megaw, H. D., Radoslovich, E. W. (1962): The structure of anorthite, $CaAl_2Si_2O_8$. I. Structure analysis. AC 15, 1005–1017.

Kleeman, J. D., Nesbitt, R. W. (1967): X-ray measurements on some plagioclases from the Mt. Davies intrusion, South Australia. J. Geol. Soc. Australia, 14, 39–42.

Köhler, A., Wieden, P. (1954): Vorläufige Versuche in der Feldspatgruppe mittels der DTA. NJMM 12, 249–252.

Kokscharow, N. v. (1884): Materialien zur Mineralogie Russlands, 9, 1–272. Abstract in German in NJM, 1886, 204–206.

Kopp, H. (1852): Über die Ausdehnung einiger fester Körper durch die Wärme. Ann. Chem. Phys. Poggendorff, 86, 156.

Koritnig, S. (1961): Zur röntgenographischen Bestimmung von Alkalifeldspäten. Naturwiss. 48, 665.

Kôzu, S., Saiki, S. (1925): The thermal expansion of alkali-feldspars. Sci. Repts. Tôhoku Imp. Univ., ser. 3, 2, 203–238.

Kôzu, S., Takane, K. (1929): Expansion of alkali feldspar on heating. J. Petrol. Mineral. and Ore Deposits (Japan) 1, 110–114.

Kôzu, S., Ueda, J. (1928): Change in density of minerals and rocks on heating. J. Geol., Tôhôku Imp. Univ. 35, 399–406.

Kôzu, S., Ueda, J. (1933): Thermal expansion of plagioclase. Proc. Imp. Acad. Japan 9, 262–264.

Kratzert, J. (1921): Die kristallographischen und optischen Konstanten des Anorthits vom Vesuv. ZK 56, 465–488.

Kratzert, J. (1923): Beitrag zur Kenntnis des Andesins von Bodenmais. Sitzber. Heidelbg. Akad. Wiss. math. — nat. Kl, No. 5.

Krebs, B. (1921): Der Albit von Rischuna in morphologischer Bedeutung. ZK 56, 386–407.

Kroll, H. (1967): Untersuchungen an synthetischen Hoch-Temperatur Plagioklasen. Diplomarbeit. Münster: Westfälische Wilhelms-Universität.

Kroll, H. (1971a): Determination of Al, Si distribution in alkali feldspars from X-ray powder data. NJMM, No. 2, 91–94.

Kroll, H. (1971b): Feldspäte im System $K[AlSi_3O_8]$-$Na[AlSi_3O_8]$-$Ca[Al_2Si_2O_8]$: Al, Si-Verteilung und Gitterparameter, Phasen-Transformationen und Chemismus. Inaug.-Diss. der Westfälischen Wilhelms-Universität in Münster.

Kroll, H. (1973): Estimation of the Al, Si distribution of feldspars from the lattice translations $Tr[110]$ and $Tr[1\bar{1}0]$ I. Alkali feldspars. CMP 39, 141–156.

Laves, F. (1950): The lattice and twinning of microcline and other potash feldspars. JG 58, 548–571.

Laves, F. (1951): Artificial preparation of microcline. JG 59, 511–512.

Laves, F. (1952): Phase relations of the alkali feldspars. I. Introductory remarks. II. The stable and pseudo-stable phase relations in the alkali feldspar system. JG 60, 436–450 and 549–574.

Laves, F. (1960): Al/Si-Verteilungen, Phasen-Tranformationen und Namen der Alkalifeldspäte. ZK 113, 265–296.

Laves, F., Goldsmith, J. R. (1961): Polymorphism, order, disorder, diffusion and confusion in the feldspars. CCILM 8, 71–80.

Laves, F., Viswanathan, K. (1967): Relations between optic axial angle and triclinity of potash feldspars, and their significance for the definition of "stable" and "unstable" states of alkali feldspars. SMPM 47, 147–162.

Lewis, W. J. (1915): On crystals of albite from Alp Rischuna, and pericline twins from La Fibbia, Switzerland. MM 17, 178–188.

Long, R. S. (1966): The stability of feldspar structures containing Ga, Fe and Ge under conditions of high pressure. Ph. D. thesis, Univ. Chicago, 113 p.

Luth, W. C. (1972): Experimental data on synthetic alkali feldspars: unit cell parameters and solvus relationships. Abstr. 3.3 in program for Advanced Study Institute on Feldspars, July 1972, Manchester.

Luth, W. C., Querol-Suñé, F. (1970): An alkali feldspar series. CMP **25**, 25–40.

Luth, W. C., Tuttle, O. F. (1966): The alkali feldspar solvus in the system $Na_2O–K_2O–Al_2O_3–SiO_2–H_2O$. AM **51**, 1359–1373.

MacKenzie, W. S. (1952): The effect of temperature on the symmetry of high temperature soda-rich feldspars. AJS, Bowen volume, 319–342.

MacKenzie, W. S. (1954): The orthoclase-microcline inversion. MM **30**, 354–366.

MacKenzie, W. S. (1957): The crystalline modifications of $NaAlSi_3O_8$. AJS **255**, 481–516.

MacKenzie, W. S., Smith, J. V. (1955): The alkali feldspars: I, Orthoclase microperthites. AM **40**, 707–732.

MacKenzie, W. S., Smith, J. V. (1961): Experimental and geological evidence for the stability of alkali feldspars. CCILM **8**, 53–69.

MacKenzie, W. S., Smith, J. V. (1962): Single crystal X-ray studies of crypto- and micro-perthites. NGT **42**, No. 2, 72–103.

Martin, R. F. (1968): Hydrothermal synthesis of low albite, orthoclase, and non-stoichiometric albite. Ph. D. thesis, Stanford University.

Martin, R. F. (1969): The hydrothermal synthesis of low albite. CMP **23**, 323–339.

Martin, R. F. (1970): Cell parameters and infra-red absorption of synthetic high to low albites. CMP **26**, 62–74.

Martin, R. F. (1971): Disordered authigenic feldspars of the series $KAlSi_3O_8–KBSi_3O_8$ from Southern California. AM **56**, 281–291.

Melczer, G. (1905): Daten zur genaueren Kenntnis des Albit. Földtani Közlöny, Budapest **35**, 153. Translation in ZK **40**, 571–587 (1905).

Mossman, D. J. (1970): Transitional-primitive boundary in calcic plagioclase. AM **55**, 1273–1277.

Müller, G. (1969): Die Abhängigkeit der Gitterkonstanten und der Mischkristallbildung der Na- und K-Feldspäte vom Ordnungszustand. Dipl.-Min. Diss. Universität Karlsruhe.

Müller, G. (1970): Der Ordnungs-Unordnungs-Übergang in getemperten Mikroklinen und Albiten. ZK **132**, 212–227.

Nager, H. E., Bambauer, H. U., Hoffmann, W. (1970): Polymorphie in der Mischreihe (Ca,Sr) $[Al_2Si_2O_8]$. Naturwiss. **57**, No. 2, 86–87.

Nager, H. E., Hoffmann, W., Nissen, H.-U. (1969): Die Mischreihe (Ca,Sr) $[Al_2Si_2O_8]$. Naturwiss. **56**, No. 3, 136.

Niggli, A. (1967): Die Ordnungsmöglichkeiten der Si-Al-Verteilung in Plagioklasen. SMPM **47**, 279–287.

Nissen, H.-U. (1969): Lattice changes in the low plagioclase series. SMPM **49**, 491–508.

Nissen, H.-U., Eggmann, H., Laves, F. (1967): Schiller and submicroscopic lamellae of labradorite. A preliminary report. SMPM **47**, 289–302.

Nye, J. F. (1960): Physical properties of crystals. Oxford: University Press.

Offret, A. (1890): De la variation, sous l'influence de la chaleur, des indices de réfraction de quelques espèces minérales, dans l'étendue du spectre visible. BSFM **13**, 405.

Orville, P. M. (1960): Alkali feldspar-alkali chloride hydrothermal ion exchange. ARDGL, Yearbook, 59, 104–108.

Orville, P. M. (1962): Alkali metasomatism and feldspars. NGT **42**, No. 2, 283–316.

Orville, P. M. (1963): Alkali ion exchange between vapor and feldspar phases. AJS **261**, 201–237.

Orville, P. M. (1967): Unit-cell parameters of the microcline-low albite and the sanidine-high albite solid solution series. AM **52**, 55–86. Correction 346–347.

Parsons, I. (1965): The feldspathic syenites of the Loch Ailsh intrusion, Assynt, Scotland. JP **6**, 365–394.

Parsons, I. (1968): An experimental study of ordering in sodium-rich alkali feldspars. MM **36**, 1061–1077.

Pentinghaus, H. (1970): Der Einbau von Al (III), Ga (III), Fe (III) und Si (IV), Ge (IV) in synthetische Alkalifeldspäte. Inaug.-Diss. der Westfälischen Wilhelms-Universität in Münster.

Pentinghaus, H., Bambauer, H. U. (1971a): (Ga, Si) order/disorder in the synthetic feldspar $Na[GaSi_3O_8]$. NJMM, No. 2, 94–96.

Pentinghaus, H., Bambauer, H. U. (1971b): Substitution of Al (III), Ga (III), Fe (III) and Si (IV), Ge (IV) in synthetic alkali feldspars. NJMM 416–418.

Phillips, M. W., Ribbe, P. H. (1971): Personal communication reporting X-ray structure analyses of sanidine 7002 and adularia 7007.

Phillips, M. W., Colville, A. A., Ribbe, P. H. (1971): The crystal structures of two oligoclases: A comparison with low and high albite. ZK **133**, Fritz-Laves-Festband, 43–65.

Raase, P. (1971): Zur Synthese und Stabilität der Albit-Modifikationen. TMPM **16**, 136–155.

Raase, P., Kern, H. (1969): Über die Synthese von Albiten bei Temperaturen von 250 bis 700° C. CMP **21**, 225–237.

Rath, G. vom (1869): Mineralogische Mittheilungen. Fortsetzung *VIII*, No. 35. Über die Zwillingsbildungen des Anorthits vom Vesuv. Ann. Phys. Chem., Poggendorff, **138**, 449–464.

Rath, G. vom (1886): Mineralogische Notizen. 2. Über den Andesin vom Berge Arcuentu, Insel Sardinien. Festschr. Verein Natkde. Cassel, 105–117. (Abstract: ZK **12**, 1887, 538–539).

Ribbe, P. H. (1972): One-parameter characterization of the average Al/Si distribution in plagioclase feldspars. JGR **77**, 5790–5797.

Ribbe, P. H., Smith, J. V. (1966): X-ray emission microanalysis of rock-forming minerals. IV. Plagioclase feldspars. JG **74**, 217–233.

Ribbe, P. H., Stewart, D. B., Phillips, M. W. (1970): Structural explanations for variations in the lattice parameters of sodic plagioclase. Progr. Geol. Soc. Amer. Mtg. Milwaukee, p. 663 (abstr.).

Rinne, F. (1914): Die Kristallwinkelveränderung verwandter Stoffe beim Wechsel der Temperatur. I. Centr. Min. 705–718.

Rosenholtz, J. L., Smith, D. T. (1941): Linear thermal expansion of adularia. AM **26**, 391–394.

Roy, N. N. (1965): Binary system. (KAlSi$_3$O$_8$–BaAl$_2$Si$_2$O$_8$). N, **206**, 501–502.

Roy, N. N. (1967): The mineralogy of the potassium-barium feldspar series. II. Studies on hydrothermally synthesized members. MM **36**, 43–49.

Rudert, V. (1970): Das System Albit-Celsian-H$_2$O. Inaug. Diss. Univ. Köln.

Saucier, H., Saplevitch, A. (1962): La dilatation thermique des feldspaths. NGT **42**, No. 2, 224–243.

Scheel, H. J. (1971): Lead feldspar. ZK **133**, Fritz-Laves-Festband, 264–272.

Scheidegger, K. F. (1973): Determination of structural state of calcic plagioclases by an X-ray powder technique. AM **58**, 134–136.

Schmidt, E. (1915): Die Winkel der kristallographischen Achsen der Plagioklase. Chem. Erde, **1**, 351–406.

Schnaase, H. (1936): Über die Änderung des Achsenverhältnisses und der Lage des rhombischen Schnittes mit der Temperatur beim Anorthit von Vesuv. ZK **93**, 444–463.

Schneider, T. R. (1957): Röntgenographische und optische Untersuchung der Umwandlung Albit-Analbit-Monalbit. ZK **109**, 245–271.

Scott, R. B., Bachinski, S. W., Nesbitt, R. W., Scott, M. R. (1971): Rate of Al–Si ordering in sanidines from an ignimbrite cooling unit. AM **56**, 1208–1221.

Shannon, R. D., Prewitt, C. T. (1969): Effective ionic radii in oxides and fluorides. AC B **25**, 925–946.

Slemmons, D. B. (1962): Observations on order-disorder relations of natural plagioclase. I. A method of evaluating order-disorder. NGT **42**, No. 2, 533–554.

Smith, J. R., Yoder, H. S. (1956): Variations in X-ray powder diffraction patterns of plagioclase feldspars. AM **41**, 632–647.

Smith, J. V. (1956): The powder patterns and lattice parameters of plagioclase felspars. I. The soda-rich plagioclases. MM **31**, 47—68.

Smith, J. V. (1961): Explanation of strain and orientation effects in perthites. AM **46**, 1489–1493.

Smith, J. V. (1970): Physical properties of order-disorder structures with especial reference to feldspar minerals. Lithos, **3**, 145–160.

Smith, J. V., Gay, P. (1958): The powder patterns and lattice parameters of plagioclase felspars. II. MM **31**, 744–762.

Smith, J. V., MacKenzie, W. S. (1955): The alkali feldspars: II, A simple X-ray technique for the study of alkali feldspars. AM **40**, 733–747.

Smith, J. V., MacKenzie, W. S. (1959): The alkali feldspars. V. The nature of orthoclase and microcline perthites, and observations concerning the polymorphism of potassium feldspar. AM **44**, 1169–1186.

Smith, J. V., MacKenzie, W. S. (1961): Atomic, chemical and physical factors that control the stability of alkali feldspars. CCILM **8**, 39–52.

Smith, J. V., Ribbe, P. H. (1969): Atomic movements in plagioclase feldspars: kinetic interpretation. CMP **21**, 157–202.

Smithson, S. B. (1962): Symmetry relations in alkali feldspars of some amphibolite-facies rocks from the Southern Norwegian Precambrian. NGT **42**, No. 2, 586–599.

Stewart, D. B. (1960): Effect of $LiAlSiO_4$ and SiO_2 on the separation of the 131 and $1\bar{3}1$ X-ray diffraction lines of synthetic albite. BGSA **71**, 1985 (abstr.).

Stewart, D. B. (1967): Four phase curve in the system $CaAl_2Si_2O_8$–SiO_2–H_2O between 1 and 10 kilobars. SMPM **47**, 35–59.

Stewart, D. B., Limbach, D. von (1967): Thermal expansion of low and high albite. AM **52**, 389–413.

Stewart, D. B., Ribbe, P. H. (1969): Structural explanation for variations in cell parameters of alkali feldspar with Al/Si ordering. AJS, Schairer Vol. **267**-A, 444–462.

Stewart, D. B., Ross, M., Morgan, B. A., Appleman, D. E., Huebner, J. S., Commeau, R. F. (1972): Mineralogy and petrology of lunar anorthosite 15415. Third Lunar Sci. Conf., Houston, Lunar Science Inst. Contr. No. 88, 726–728.

Stewart, D. B., Walker, G. W., Wright, T. L., Fahey, J. J. (1966): Physical properties of calcic labradorite from Lake County, Oregon. AM **51**, 177–197.

Strüver, J. (1877): Die Mineralien Latiums. ZK **1**, 225–256.

Taylor, W. H., Darbyshire, J. A., Strunz, H. (1934): An X-ray investigation of the felspars. ZK **87**, 464–498.

Vermaas, F. H. S. (1953): A new occurrence of barium-feldspar at Otjosondu, S. W. Africa, and an X-ray method for determining the composition of hyalophane. AM **38**, 845–857.

Viola, C. (1899): Zur Kenntnis des Anorthits von Vesuv. ZK **31**, 484–498.

Viswanathan, K. (1971a): A new X-ray method to determine the anorthite content and structural state of plagioclases. CMP **30**, 332–335.

Viswanathan, K. (1971b): Kationenaustausch an Plagioklasen. Habilitationsschrift der Technischen Universität Hannover.

Viswanathan, K. (1972): Kationenaustausch an Plagioklasen. CMP **37**, 277–290.

Vogel, T. A., Ehrlich, R., Luth, W. C. (1973): Non-linear variation of cell parameters with composition in alkali feldspar series. AM **58**, 905–908.

Wainwright, J. E., Starkey, J. (1968): Crystal structure of a metamorphic low albite. Progr. Geol. Soc. America Mtg., Mexico City, p. 310.

Wainwright, J. E., Starkey, J. (1971): A refinement of the structure of anorthite. ZK **133**, Fritz-Laves-Festband, 75–84.

Waldbaum, D. R. (1966): Calorimetric investigation of the alkali feldspars. Ph. D. thesis, Harvard Univ., 247 p.

Waldbaum, D. R., Robie, R. A. (1971): Calorimetric investigation of Na–K mixing and polymorphism in alkali feldspars. Preprint.

Waldbaum, D. R., Thompson, J. B., Jr. (1968): Mixing properties of sanidine crystalline solutions: II. Calculations based on volume data. AM **53**, 2000–2017.

Weitz, G. (1972): Die Struktur des Sanidins bei verschiedenen Ordnungsgraden. ZK **126**, 418–426.

Wenk, E., Wenk, H.-R., Schwander, H. (1968): Bytownite from Cape Parry, East Greenland. AM **53**, 1759–1764.

Wenk, H.-R. (1966): Labradorite from Surtsey (Iceland). SMPM **46**, 81–84.

Wenk, H.-R. (1969): Annealing of oligoclase at high pressure. AM **54**, 95–100.

Willaime, C., Brown, W. L., Perucaud, M. C. (1972): On the orientation of the thermal expansion ellipsoid in feldspars. Preprint.

Wones, D. R., Appleman, D. E. (1961): X-ray crystallography and optical properties of synthetic monoclinic $KFeSi_3O_8$, iron-sanidine. U.S. Geol. Surv. Prof. Paper **424**C, 309–310.

Wones, D. R., Appleman, D. E. (1963): Properties of synthetic triclinic $KFeSi_3O_8$, iron-microcline, with some observations on the iron-microcline $\rightleftharpoons$ iron sanidine transition. JP **4**, 131–137.

Wright, T. L. (1964): The alkali feldspars of the Tatoosh pluton in Mount Rainier National Park. AM **49**, 715–735.

Wright, T. L. (1968): X-ray and optical study of alkali feldspar. II. An X-ray method for determining the composition and structural state from measurement of 2θ values for three reflections. AM **53**, 88–104.

Wright, T. L., Stewart, D. B. (1968): X-ray and optical study of alkali feldspar. I. Determination of composition and structural state from refined unit-cell parameters and 2V. AM **53**, 38–87.

Wyart,J., Sabatier,G. (1956a): Mobilité des ions alcalins et alcalino-terreaux dans les feldspaths. BSFMC **79**, 444–448.

Wyart,J., Sabatier,G. (1956b): Transformations mutuelles des feldspaths alcalins, reproduction du microcline et de l'albite. BSFMC **79**, 574–581.

Yoder,H.S., Stewart,D.B., Smith,J.R. (1957): Ternary feldspars. ARDGL, Yearbook 56, 206–214.

Yoder,H.S., Weir,C.F. (1951): Change of free energy with pressure of the reaction nepheline + albite = 2 jadeite. AJS **249**, 683–694.

Zambonini,F. (1910): Mineralogia Vesuviana. p. 110–113.

Chapter 8 Light Optics

8.1 General

8.1.1 Historical Survey: Justification of Present Survey: Theory

Light optics are used more than any other physical property for the study of feldspars. Many technical refinements have been developed in the twentieth century, but the basic methods were worked out in the nineteenth century. Early workers naturally concentrated on large clear crystals mostly obtained from pegmatites, veins and coarse-grained rocks. Such crystals tend to occur in a state of low entropy, and it was only in the nineteen-thirties to nineteen-fifties that the effect of structural state on the optics of feldspars was fully established though anomalies had been reported earlier. Because the spatial resolution of light optics is limited to somewhat less than the wavelength of light, many subtle features of feldspar intergrowths are invisible and can be detected only by techniques of higher resolution such as X-ray diffraction. Accordingly light optics serve primarily for reconnaissance work, and have relatively small value for evaluation of subtle structural effects. The optical properties of feldspars vary in response to chemical substitution, especially for the plagioclase series, thereby providing a rapid estimate of composition especially valuable to petrographers. Recently the wide-spread installation of electron microprobes has seriously reduced the use of optical properties for chemical determination, and optical techniques now serve primarily for chemical reconnaissance and for study of morphology, texture and twinning.

There is an enormous literature on the optics of feldspars, and it would be ridiculous to review it completely because (1) the early literature suffers from errors in chemical composition and lack of understanding of the effects of structural state, and (2) there are excellent summaries of the later literature, some of which contain detailed practical instructions on optical measurements of feldspar. I shall deliberately concentrate on those optical data which provide information on the structural variations of feldspars, and shall select only a few of the determinative data.

The following publications should prove useful for various reasons:

(a) Hintze (1893) and Dana (1920) provided detailed accounts of the early literature.

(b) Winchell and Winchell (1951) gave a review of optical data which illustrate the uncertainty of interpretation prior to detailed X-ray study.

(c) Deer et al. (1963) provided a review of the optical properties of feldspars, taking into account the research of the nineteen-fifties: note that the orientation of microcline in Fig. 27a is inconsistent with crystallographic data (see Laves, 1965), and should have the optic directions switched from left to right.

(d) Plas, van der (1966) presented a monograph on the identification of detrital feldspars, which provides practical advice and detailed determinative tables. Account is taken of the effect of structural state.

(e) Burri et al. (1967) prepared a monograph on the optical orientation of plagioclase based on a thorough review of the literature, and on new measurements. All these data were processed by computer methods using Euler angles to specify the angular relation between crystallographic and optical directions. Accurate stereographic projections were given.

(f) Bambauer (1966) reviewed the properties of feldspars as part of a revision of „Optische Bestimmungen der gesteinsbildenden Minerale" by W. E. Tröger, and Bambauer et al. (1971) followed this up with a new set of determinative tables. Probably these tables provide the most concise and accurate summary of data for general optical study of feldspars.

(g) Marfunin (1966, translation of 1962 monograph) emphasized optical properties in a general review of feldspars. Particularly valuable is an account of the author's conclusion on the effect of polymorphism and texture on the optical properties of alkali feldspars.

Unstrained homogeneous feldspars have optical properties definable in terms of an indicatrix (e. g. Nye, 1960) derivable from the electromagnetic field equations (Phemister, 1954). Simple graphical analysis of the indicatrix, as in Bloss (1961), is sufficient for all normal studies. Strained feldspars may show abnormal optical properties (see Chapter 12). There are no substantiated reports of optical activity in feldspars, and all optical data are consistent with a center of symmetry.

Only the purest synthetic and natural feldspars are homogeneous on an atomic scale; nearly all natural feldspars are inhomogeneous on a unit-cell scale or even on a macroscopic scale. The interaction of light with such feldspars depends critically on the scale of the inhomogeneity. Light is propagated as an electromagnetic wave of wavelength $0.4 - 0.7 \mu m$. At any given position in a medium, the interaction of the electric and magnetic vectors with the electric components of the local atoms governs the rate of propagation. The principal interaction is with the deformable electric clouds of the atoms, especially those of oxygen. The electrons in a solid medium move under the influence of a field produced by all other atoms in the medium: however, the influence falls off rapidly with distance and to a first approximation only the nearer neighbors have important effects while distant atoms act as a continuum. The light wave integrates throughout the medium the interactions with all the atoms using an averaging filter governed by its own wavelength: the integration takes into account both amplitude and phase. Small-scale fluctuations in the medium (i.e. less than the wavelength) lead to complex effects including scattering (e.g. as for the color changes caused by scattering of light by the atmosphere) while large-scale fluctuations (i.e. much greater than the wavelength) give the same effect as addition of the individual effects of independent crystals (e.g. as for the effect on light passing through two calcite rhombs in contact on a cleavage face). Rigorous mathematical treatment of inhomogeneous bodies is extremely difficult, especially for fluctuations with dimensions close to the wavelength, and only qualitative suggestions can be made here.

Scattering may be classified into three extreme types: *dependent* scattering when cooperation occurs between the phases of the scattered waves (strictly speaking all materials with atomic disorder, either substitutional or positional, yield scattering, but such scattering may be negligible as for instance in a glassy sanidine; perhaps pulsed laser beams would permit measurements of such scattering); *independent* scattering when particles are far apart, e.g. schiller for hematite flakes in aventurine; *multiple* scattering when the intensity of scattering is so high that the incident light on any scattering center is seriously reduced in intensity by other scatterers encountered earlier (analogous to *extinction* in X-ray diffraction; moonstones probably show multiple scattering). Since scattering can occur for all types of electro-magnetic waves, pertinent literature is scattered over a wide domain including the scattering of radar waves. It is highly desirable that a detailed survey of such literature be made in preparation for a concerted attack on the theory of scattering in feldspars. A casual perusal of the literature suggests that most of the calculations have been based on scattering from interlaminations or from discrete scattering centers of simple geometry (e.g. spherical). Usually the separate media are supposed to be isotropic in contrast to the more complex biaxial optics of a feldspar. Such simple calculations may be found in Born and Wolf (1965), especially Chapter 1.6 for stratified models of isotropic media, and in Hulst, van de (1957), especially Chapter 19.4 on light scattering by small particles in anisotropic media.

8.1.2 Accuracy of Optical Measurements

Several authors suggested that serious errors can arise in measurements of optical properties by conoscopic and orthoscopic methods (especially the latter).

Marfunin (1962) and Munro (1963; this paper includes references to earlier studies) showed that serious errors of a purely technical nature can arise from routine conoscopic and especially orthoscopic measurements. The orthoscopic method is especially inaccurate when $2V$ is small; indeed it is difficult to distinguish a biaxial material with $2V < 20°$ from a uniaxial one. When $2V$ is large, considerable errors can arise from refraction between the different components of a U-stage: Munro compared orthoscopic and conoscopic measurements of topaz ($2V - 65°$) and olivine ($2V - 88°$) with those obtained goniometrically on ground spheres. He found that "many of the universal stage measurements (of $2V$) contain errors due to refraction in the central assembly on the stage. These errors invariably increase when the angle of tilt of the stage and the refractive index of the segments are increased, and they are also greater when very small sub-stage diaphragm apertures are used. They are generally greater for orthoscopic than for conoscopic measurements, and the size of the errors in the former also appears to depend to a marked extent on the refractive index of the center plate of the stage, on the type of objective employed, and on the aperture of the objective diaphragm." For topaz, errors were mostly less than 0.5°, but for olivine, errors reached 5.6° (orthoscopic) and 3.2° (conoscopic) using the smallest aperture of the sub-stage diaphragm and less than 1° using a wide aperture; other effects can be found described in the paper. Marfunin (his Fig. 13) compared his conoscopic measurements on goniometrically oriented sections of the position of c^* relative to the optic symmetry axes X, Y and Z with earlier orthoscopic measurements made by Vardanyants for the same K-feldspars from porphyritic granites of Tyrny-Auz. Whereas Marfunin's measurements fell in a short band about 3° wide, the orthoscopic measurements fell in a band about 10° wide, and about 15° longer. Thus Marfunin concluded that "orthoscopic determinations of the optical orientation of potash feldspars in thin sections may yield unreliable results; measurements by this method of potash feldspars having $2V < 30°$ are, in general, both theoretically and practically condemned to failure". He pointed out that averaging of many measurements need not lead to the correct value because inaccurate measurements of extinction angle of a truly monoclinic material would lead to a non-zero average indicating a triclinic material.

Almost all K-feldspars have been reported to be optically negative, but there are scattered reports of optically positive K-feldspars given the name *iso-orthoclase* or *iso-microcline* — see Barth's (1969) review of data by Duparc (1904), Luczizky (1905), Barth (1933), Tsuboi (1936), Gysin (1948), Kazakov (1956), and others. Neither Marfunin (1962) nor Emerson (1964) were able to find optically positive K-feldspars from rocks similar to those from which earlier workers had reported such properties, and one might choose to attribute all reports of optically positive K-feldspar to erroneous measurement or identification. The most recent reports of iso-orthoclase and iso-microcline are by Pavelescu (1968) and Riederer (1966). W. S. MacKenzie (pers. comm.) asserts that accurate measurements of refractive indices are required to check the validity of such reports based on measurements of $2V$.

Marfunin (1962) reported that Belyankin found that, in younger, normal granites of Caucasian intrusions, K-feldspars exist with small axial angles and triclinic optical orientation, denoted as *K-anorthoclase*. Because Marfunin was not able to observe with conoscopic techniques of oriented sections any deviations from monoclinic symmetry of igneous K-feldspar with $-2V$ less than 40–45° (irrespective of the orientation of the optic axial plane) he concluded that Belyankin's measurements were in error and that the term *K-anorthoclase* should be abolished.

However, it is theoretically possible for triclinic K-feldspars of small $2V$ to actually exist, and indeed there is firm evidence that they do exist in certain adularias formed in veins at low temperatures. In the extreme one-stage ordering trend (Chapter 3), the Al-contents of the (0) and (m) sub-sites of the T_1 sites would become unequal, and triclinic geometry should immediately result upon the beginning of ordering: of course such a change of geometry might not become optically visible because of development of sub-optical twinning. If in igneous rocks, the feldspars follow quite closely the two-stage trend and achieve a state of stranded near-equilibrium, monoclinic symmetry would be found for all igneous K-feldspar with $-2V$ lower than 40–45°. However, it is possible that a non-equilibrium state might be achieved in unusual igneous feldspars, and it seems unwise to dismiss completely such a possibility of triclinic K-feldspars with small optic axial angle. For specimens grown at low temperature, such as adularia, non-equilibrium ordering trends have been deduced from X-ray data.

Marfunin (1966, p. 58, English translation) stated "Using the Fedorov stage, Chaisson (1950) obtained (for) adularias with optic axial angles of 20–60° 'an abnormal optical orientation' with entirely irregular changes. Similarly the measurements of Paraskevopoulos (1953) and Gysin (1957) cannot be considered convincing, although they very rarely contain values or combinations of constants which are 'impossible for potash feldspar'". Because Chaisson (1950) found regions of abnormal optical orientation directly adjacent to regions *in the same crystal* for which the optical orientation was normal, I believe that technical errors of measurement were trivial and that the abnormal optics are genuine. Later careful measurements by Bambauer and Laves (1960), using conoscopic methods on oriented sections, revealed the existence in an adularia from Val Casatscha of unusual optics with non-zero extinction angles for $-2V$ less than 40°. The evidence for abnormal optics in adularia *does* seem to be convincing and will be assumed to be genuine from now on.

Obviously great care must be taken in making measurements and in evaluating optical data in the literature. Whenever possible, both orthoscopic and conoscopic methods should be used, and any discrepancy should be investigated. For alkali feldspars, grains about 0.1–0.5 mm across are convenient for conoscopic study. Those with low birefringence showing rectangular outlines from vertical {010} and {001} cleavages often permit direct observation of the isogyres in U-stage studies. For orthoscopic study of intergrowths or multiple twins, thin sections of less than the usual thickness of 30 µm are useful for examination of the individual components. In order to measure bulk properties, thin sections of greater than the normal thickness are desirable.

8.1.3 Effect of Compositional and Morphological Inhomogeneities

Measurements of the refractive index, birefringence or optic axial angle give a direct measure of the feldspar traversed by the light beam and are unaffected by morphological inhomogeneities. Measurements of the angular orientation of the optic axes with respect to the crystallographic directions depend critically on the validity of the latter. Usually the crystallographic directions are inferred from some morphological feature or from twin components, and both of these may suffer from compositional and morphological inhomogeneities.

Vogel (1964) distinguished between two types of scattering of crystallographic poles with respect to optical poles on a stereographic projection. Lack of equilibrium over a single hand specimen of rock gives rise to *external scatter* in which poles from different crystals are displaced parallel to isopleths of chemical composition or of structural state. Vogel showed that external scatter of plagioclase corresponding to changes of structural state is essentially absent in rocks for which a good approach to a single state of stranded equilibrium is expected (quenched volcanic and regional metamorphic rocks) and is well developed in unquenched igneous rocks. *Internal scatter* was defined by Vogel as "the scatter of the plots (either poles or twin axes) of adjacent (twin) lamellae within a single grain. When adjacent units of a twinned grain are oriented individually and are identified optically, the plots of their poles should coincide. Internal scatter occurs when these plots do not superimpose. By definition then, adjacent lamellae which show internal scatter are not in a true twinned relationship." Earlier Emmons and Gates (1943, p. 288) had claimed that "Adjacent twin lamellae quite commonly differ in composition especially in the more sodic plagioclases, apparently as a result of selective post twinning replacement through deuteric solutions". Nickel (1953) produced supporting optical evidence, and Vogel (1964) produced some inconclusive microprobe evidence.

Tobi (1965) pointed out that whether internal scatter can be demonstrated at all depends on a fundamental choice underlying the procedure of measurement. "This choice is so important that it may serve to distinguish between two different schools of plagioclase determination with the aid of the universal stage. The first school (Reinhard, 1931; Coulson, 1932) assumes that a cleavage plane or a composition plane of a twin (if not obviously irregular) corresponds as a rule closely to its ideal crystallographic orientation. – The second school (Fedorow, 1896; Manolescu, 1934) assumes that adjacent lamellae have the same (chemical) composition and are in true twinned relationship. The pole of the composition plane is not used for measurement of the optical orientation; – Instead, the twinning axis, derived from the indicatrices of adjoining lamellae, – is used as a crystallographic direction of reference."

Vogel's measurements followed the procedures of the first school in which a macroscopic crystallographic parameter was used as a reference. He gave four reasons (Vogel, 1964, p. 628) for internal scatter: (1) "twinning of an individual grain at different structural states" (2) "different degrees of ordering between adjacent units", as suggested earlier by Muir (1955) (3) difference of chemical composition of contiguous lamellae, as suggested earlier by Emmons et al. (1953) (4) "imperfection in the twinning process" – "at the time of formation of the twin or" "from distortion due to deformation and movement along the composition plane of a twinned crystal".

Tobi (1965) distinguished between a "real" and an "ideal" composition plane and claimed that "the optical orientation can be accurately determined with the aid of the twinning axis, whereas the composition plane is of no value". Tobi pointed out qualitative evidence that observed twin composition planes may be irregular and not parallel to the ideal plane of the crystal lattice, and stated that "This origin of internal scatter is not included in the four mechanisms suggested by Vogel". Furthermore he claims that it is actually the most important one. Tobi also pointed to the problems caused by chemical zoning because the light waves on opposite sides of a twin composition plane need not sample the same sequence of zones. Tobi concluded that "the internal scatter reported by Vogel and other authors is due chiefly to composition planes not following the ideal crystallographic directions" and that "if this supposition is correct any revision of determinative charts should be based only on optical orientations determined by construction of twinning axes".

It is obvious that the causes of optical scatter can be resolved only by the combined use of optical, electron microprobe and X-ray diffraction methods on selected single crystals. Study of polished fragments first optically in an apparatus such as Umirg (Fisher, 1960), then in an X-ray diffraction camera, and finally in an electron microprobe would permit tests of (1) the equality or otherwise of the chemical composition across a twin boundary, (2) the parallelism or otherwise of a twin boundary constructed from the lattice axes with that constructed from the indicatrix axes, and (3) comparison of both with the morphological axis. Until this is done, both types of determinative methods are suspect. Obviously the safest procedure in routine optical studies is to determine whether morphological and twin directions agree. If they do, probably the data are meaningful; if not, the morphological and twin directions should be examined for evidence of curvature or irregularity.

Added in Proof. Pringle *et al.* (1973) found by *U*-stage and electron microprobe studies of 7 zoned plagioclase phenocrysts from a tholeiitic diabase that twin-axis optics are reliable whereas twin-boundary optics are anomalous because of vicinal faces.

8.1.4 Effect of Fine-scale Twinning

The importance of the scale of the twin texture to the optical properties was first recognized by Mallard (1876, 1881, 1884), who proposed that orthoclase was merely sub-microscopically twinned microcline. This suggestion is now known to be too simple, and has been superseded by complex ideas involving order disorder of T-atoms and strain across out-of-step boundaries. Nevertheless it has played an important role, partly stimulating and partly stultifying, during the last century.

Marfunin (1962, 1966) attempted to quantify Mallard's ideas. When polysynthetic twinning is sub-optical, and the two orientations have equal volume, the optical indicatrix of the combined intergrowth obeys the symmetry of the twin element added on to the point-group symmetry common to the two individuals. Thus for Albite (and for Pericline) twinning of sub-optically twinned microcline, the 2-fold symmetry of the twin axis is added to the point group symmetry $\bar{1}$ common to each individual. (It is assumed that the optical properties are still represented by a triaxial ellipsoid in the usual way — but this may not be strictly accurate). For Albite twinning, one of the principal optic symmetry axes must be parallel to the twin axis b^*, while for Pericline twinning it would be parallel to b. Marfunin assumed that the other two optic symmetry axes are given by the Biot-Fresnel construction for light travelling down the twin axis. The refractive indices for these three principal directions were obtained directly from the radius vectors of the indicatrix. Table 8-1 shows values for triclinic alkali feldspars calculated from the data for untwinned material.

Figure 8-1a gives the optical relations for a sub-optical, polysynthetic Albite twin referred to a stereographic projection with crystallographic a in the center and b^* to the right. X, Y and Z will be used for the principal symmetry axes of the optical indicatrix, and A and B will be used for the normals to the circular sections. One optic symmetry axis is along b^*, and the other two are in the (010) plane as given by the Biot-Fresnel construction. Pericline twins will give a slightly different orientation for the optical properties of the combined sub-optical twin. In M-twinned feldspars, b^* of the Albite twins is parallel to b of the Pericline twins, and the optical properties of the combined twin should be a mean of those for the Albite and Pericline twins.

Table 8-1. Calculated optical properties of sub-optically twinned feldspars

Feldspar	$n(\gamma)$	$n(\alpha)$	2V	A		B		X		Y		Z	
				λ	φ	λ	φ	λ	φ	λ	φ	λ	φ
Untwinned microcline	1.5260	1.5200	−84°	− 4°	+57°	+13°	−25°	+35°	−72°	−81°	− 8°	+ 7°	+16°
Twinned microcline	1.52542	1.52050	−81	+ 4	+40	+ 4	−40	0	90	−85	0	+ 4	0
Untwinned low albite	1.5392	1.5291	+79	0	+48	+39	−47	−72	+73	−70	+17	−20	+
Twinned low albite	1.53868	1.52911	+87	+20	+43	+20	−43	0	90	−80	0	+20	0
Untwinned high albite	1.5341	1.5272	−50	+ 4	+12	+20	−32	−64	+61	−88	+27	+ 7	0
Twinned high albite	1.53360	1.52740	−32	+10	+16	+10	−16	0	90	−80	0	+10	−10

From Marfunin (1966, Table 21). See Fig. 8-1 for the position of angles λ and φ.

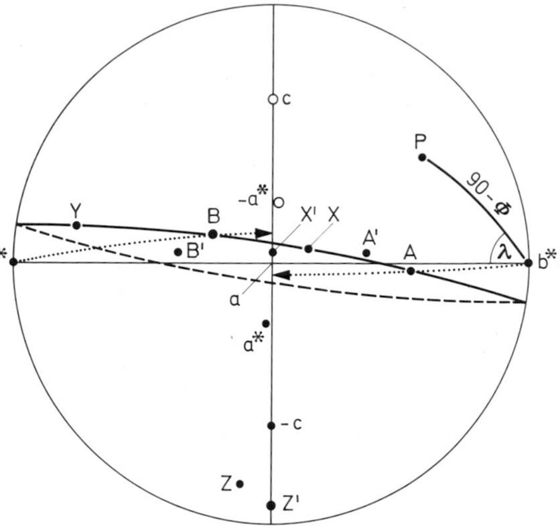

Fig. 8-1 a. Legend see opposite page

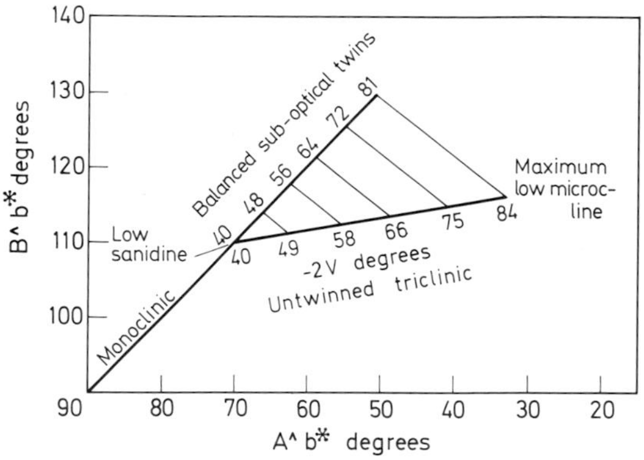

Fig. 8-1 b. Legend see opposite page

Figure 8-1b is a nomogram given by Marfunin for K-feldspars. Untwinned maximum microcline with $2V = -84°$ defines one extreme. All K-feldspars with $-2V$ less than 40° are assumed to be monoclinic. Untwinned microclines with $2V$ from -40 to $-84°$ define the trend with maximum angular deviation from monoclinic geometry. Balanced twins define the other extreme trend with monoclinic optical symmetry. The isopleths show the effect of changing the ratio of the volumes of the twin units, and the numbers at the ends of each line show the optic axial angles for untwinned and pseudo-monoclinic material. If the assumptions implicit in the calculation are correct, this is one of the most important diagrams developed for K-feldspars because it implies that $2V$ would be almost independent of the coarseness of twin intergrowths (e.g. for maximum microcline, sub-optical twinning yields $2V = -81°$, only 3 degrees different from the value of $-84°$ for untwinned material).

However for Na-feldspar there would be a considerable effect of twinning on the optic axial angle. Marfunin calculated that an untwinned high albite with $2V - 50°$ would give rise to a balanced twin with $2V - 32°$. Schneider (1957) measured $-29°$ for a pseudo-monoclinic Analbit (i.e. inverted monalbite), which angle is reasonably consistent with the predicted angle, and quite different from the angle predicted by Schneider (his Fig. 14) from the simple mean of the angular positions of the optic axes for the individual Pericline and Albite twins. For low albite with $2V = -101°$, Marfunin calculated $-93°$ for a balanced twin. He found experimentally that in perthitic albite from a specimen labelled "Taimyr II", $2V$ of individual units was $-101°$ and in areas presumed to be sub-optically twinned $-94°$ and $-92°$. In addition he quoted Barth (1929) who obtained $2V = -92°$ for a pseudo-monoclinic albite with composition An_4. Unfortunately these measurements may be affected by several factors and cannot be taken as proof of Marfunin's model: nevertheless the agreement is sufficiently encouraging to warrant further measurements.

One of the major questions concerning the polymorphism of K-feldspar is whether an optically monoclinic specimen is truly monoclinic or whether it is triclinic and sub-optically twinned.

Figure 8-2 shows data obtained by Marfunin for fairly pure K-feldspars from igneous rocks. The optic axial angle is plotted against the extinction angle $b^*\hat{}Z$ which is zero for monoclinic symmetry. From the distribution of the data, it would appear that all K-feldspars with $-2V$ less than 45° are truly monoclinic, whereas those with $-2V$ greater than 45° are truly triclinic with merely a variation in the twin texture. Note that the maximum value of $-2V$ is about

---

Fig. 8-1. Optical orientation of untwinned and sub-optically Albite-twinned microcline according to Marfunin's model. The great circle to pole P shows the two angles λ and ϕ used by Marfunin to define angular orientation. a Stereographic projection referred to the crystallographic axes a and b^* at the center and extreme right, respectively. For untwinned microcline with $2V = -84°$, the two optic axes are shown by A and B, and the three optic symmetry axes by X, Y and Z: the optical data are from Marfunin (1966, p. 64, average of nos. 44 and 45). The dotted lines show the Biot-Fresnel construction which yields the orientation of the optic symmetry axes X', Y' and Z' for a balanced Albite twin. A' and B' are the corresponding optic axes, with $2V = -81°$. b Nomogram relating the orientation of the optic axes to the optic axial angle for untwinned and sub-optically twinned K-feldspar. (After Marfunin, 1966, Fig. 32)

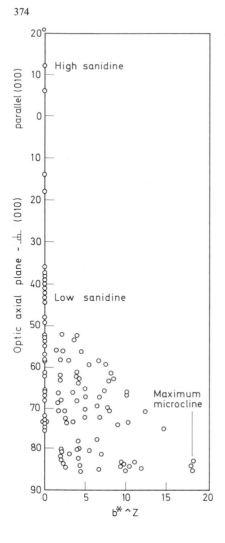

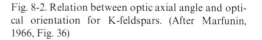

Fig. 8-2. Relation between optic axial angle and optical orientation for K-feldspars. (After Marfunin, 1966, Fig. 36)

85°, irrespective of the extinction angle, and that this is slightly inconsistent with the detailed model of Marfunin in which $-2V$ should fall from $\sim 84°$ to $\sim 81°$ as the extinction angle decreases.

Marfunin's model yields a detailed prediction (Table 8-1) for the variation of birefringence $n(\gamma) - n(\alpha)$ against $-2V$, and Fig. 8-3 plots the few experimental data from Marfunin (1962, 1966), Hewlett (1959) and Spencer (1937) for K-feldspars containing less than 20% Ab in solid solution. Particularly important are data for Spencer C orthoclase, Spencer B adularia, Spencer U intermediate microcline, and the two low microclines from Pontiskalk and Pellotsalo used in X-ray structure determinations (see Chapter 3). Because Spencer C is a typical low sanidine and the three microclines are free of twinning, let us assume that the dashed line represents K-feldspars with "true" optical properties. Marfunin's model yields the dotted line for pseudo-monoclinic sub-optical twins, and the triangular region should encompass all K-feldspars.

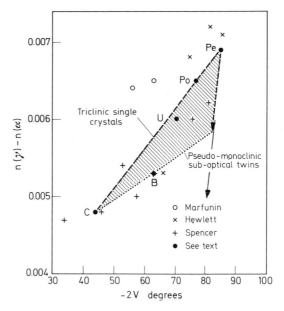

Fig. 8-3. Relation between birefringence and optic axial angle for K-feldspars

Actually the available data scatter quite widely, perhaps because of errors in the measurement of the birefringence. The solid arrow was calculated by Marfunin (see data in Table 8-1), and it appears that he made a poor choice for the birefringence of maximum microcline.

From this analysis of Marfunin's model, it seems necessary to conclude that although the model may be correct in a semi-quantitative sense, it is unlikely to be strictly correct. This would not be surprising because strain and disorder should occur at the twin boundaries thereby violating the assumption of structural homogeneity. Nevertheless Marfunin's model is the only one which attempts to explain in detail the optics of sub-optically twinned feldspars, and provides a target for proof or disproof by experimentalists.

8.1.5 Effect of Fine-scale Intergrowths

Some perthites and most peristerites and the Bøggild and Huttenlocher intergrowths (Chapter 19) contain sub-optical intergrowths of two components with different chemical compositions. Other perthites and a few rare plagioclase intergrowths are optically resolvable into two components. It is generally assumed that the optical properties of the sub-optical intergrowths correlate with the bulk chemical composition, and this assumption seems to be justified from the near-continuity of the plot of refractive indices of low-entropy plagioclase against An-content.

Particularly important is whether optical measurements of a micro-perthite (i.e. a perthite with optically-resolvable components) measure some bulk property. Following Spencer (1937), the optical parameter most used to characterize alkali feldspars has been the optic axial angle, which is generally believed to provide a measure of the ordering of the T atoms. Perhaps the two most extreme views are those of Wright (1964, p. 726) who claims that "Because 2V may be affected by both bulk composition and by parameters which are independent of composition the significance of 2V correlated with bulk composition is ambiguous. For several reasons, then, the method of plotting 2V opposite the bulk composition on a 2V-composition diagram should be abandoned for all perthitic feldspars" and of MacKenzie and J. V. Smith (1955, p. 708-9) who state "To name a particular alkali feldspar using the curves [of Tuttle, 1952], it is not necessary to know whether or not a feldspar is unmixed, the optic axial angle being that of either a homogeneous crystal or the aggregate effect produced by the intergrowth of the separate phases".

The optic axial angle may be measured by two techniques − the orthoscopic method in which extinction angles are measured and the conoscopic method in which isogyres (preferably both) are located. The former is commonly used on thin sections, 30 μm thick, (as by Wright) while the latter is commonly used on grains, 0.1 − 0.4 mm thick, (as by Tuttle and by MacKenzie). Spencer (1937) and Marfunin (1962) used the conoscopic method employing a goniometer and thick slabs of crystals. Crosshatched microcline cannot be measured by the conoscopic method because of confused isogyres. Possibly Wright's (1964) conclusion may differ from that of the other workers because of the differing ratios of the thickness of crystal slab to the perthitic units, and because of the technique employed. Because perthitic units lie roughly perpendicular to the a-axis, which is nearly parallel to the acute bisectrix, light is passing nearly normal to the greatest cross-section of the perthitic units in the conoscopic method (indeed MacKenzie deliberately selected grains lying nearly on the (100) parting with (010) and (001) near-vertical: MacKenzie and Smith, 1956, p. 409). For microperthite, say 10 μm thick, a crystal slab 0.1 mm across would contain 10 perthitic units and one of 0.4 mm about 40; cryptoperthites would yield many more units.

If measurements of 2V really measure the ordering of the T atoms, and are unaffected by the perthitic texture, homogenization of the perthite without movement of the T atoms should result in no change of 2V. Spencer (1937) followed in detail the changes of refractive indices and 2V upon heating microperthites at various temperatures up to 1120° C for one hour followed by rapid cooling. After heating at 400 − 600° C, specimens E, I, M, N, P, Q, U and W showed significant changes of refractive indices attributable to movement of Na and K atoms. However there was little or no change in optic axial angle, consistent with other experimental data that T atoms do not move during such a mild heat treatment. The microcline perthites U and W and the orthoclase perthites E, N and O showed no change of − 2V, and that of orthoclase perthites I and M increased by 2°. The largest increase (5°) occurred for the sanidine perthite P, suggesting caution for this type of perthite. On the whole these data seem to argue that 2V of microperthites does not depend strongly on the distribution of Na and K atoms, and that it can provide some measure of the ordering of T atoms (see Section 8.2.2).

However Wright (1964, p. 726) argued as follows: "One of Spencer's conclusions from short heating runs (1-2 h) at 800° C is that when megascopic exsolution lamellae visible at the start of the experiment were redissolved, there was little or no change in $2V$. This has been interpreted by recent authors to imply the reverse — that is, the $2V$ of an initially homogeneous alkali feldspar does not change with exsolution. Since Spencer's experiments were performed dry and without X-ray confirmation of either homogenization or possible partial conversion to sanidine, the author feels that Spencer's results are inconclusive with respect to the changes in $2V$ resulting from exsolution". Going on from there, Wright advocated the determination of $2V$ of separate phases of microperthites: for his particular microperthites using orthoscopic measurements on individual phases of dimensions ranging from 5–50 μm he was able to obtain a reasonable correlation for the K-phase between the values of $2V$ and the Or-contents estimated by X-ray powder methods. Because a thin section is usually cut about 30 μm thick some of his perthitic units would extend right through the thin section so that the light wave passed only through a single phase.

In conclusion, I support Wright's claim that it is desirable to make orthoscopic measurements of individual components of microperthites, but I believe that measurements of $2V$ obtained by conoscopic methods on grains 0.1–0.5 mm thick provide useful information on the structural nature of the bulk specimen, and can be used for preliminary classification.

8.1.6 Optical Scattering from Iridescent Feldspars

All feldspars with iridescence in the optical or near-optical regions have been found by electron-optical methods to consist of intergrowths of two components on a scale of the wavelength of the scattered radiation. The more regular is the shape and spacing of the components, the more sharply defined is the color and angular distribution of the scattered light. Electron-optical studies (Chapter 10) demonstrated that the texture of the intergrowths varies from elliptical discs embedded in a matrix to regular interlaminations of sheets with near-planar interfaces. The former is typical of moonstone with its milky or bluish iridescence and broad angular distribution, while the latter is typical of plagioclase intergrowths with bright color and sharp angular distribution. Qualitatively the phenomenon of iridescence can be explained by coherent scattering from the boundaries of components with different refractive indices. Unfortunately no complete quantitative theory has been developed, though Bolton et al. (1966) proposed a plausible mathematical model in which infinite sheets of type a and b alternate (Fig. 8-4).

The sheets are assumed to be optically isotropic with refractive indices n_a and n_b, and mean thicknesses d_a and d_b. Let there be $2N$ surfaces between the lamellae. At each surface, the amplitude reflection coefficient for the mth surface is $r_m = (-1)^m r$, where r is assumed to be the same at each surface. The sign change results from the phase change of π between adjacent surfaces. The scattering of light is assumed to be negligibly small at each surface such that the incident beam retains its initial amplitude and such that multiple scattering can be ignored.

Let x_m be the positional coordinate of the mth surface, and θ_a and θ_b the angles of incidence in the a and b layers. Then the path difference between light reflected from the upper and lower reflecting surfaces of a layer is $(x_m - x_{m-1})2$

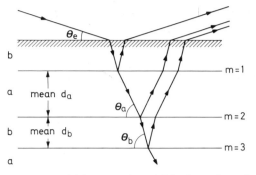

Fig. 8-4. Model for scattering of light from planar intergrowths. Sheets of type *a* and *b* alternate. The difference between θ_a and θ_b is exaggerated greatly. At the external surface, refraction takes place according to Snell's law. (Modified after Bolton *et al.*, 1966, Fig. 7)

$\sin \theta_a$ or $(x_m - x_{m-1}) 2 \sin \theta_b$ depending on whether it is an *a* or *b* type. The total reflected amplitude V is given by

$$V = r\,[1 - \exp i p_a (x_2 - x_1) + \exp i \{p_a(x_2 - x_1) + p_b(x_3 - x_2)\}$$
$$- \exp i \{p_a(x_2 - x_1) + p_b(x_3 - x_2) + p_a(x_4 - x_3)\} \cdots$$
$$- \exp i \{p_a(x_2 - x_1) + \cdots + p_a(x_{2N} - x_{2N-1})\}]$$

where $p_a = \dfrac{2\pi}{\lambda_a}\, 2 \sin \theta_a$ and $p_b = \dfrac{2\pi}{\lambda_b}\, 2 \sin \theta_b$, and λ_a and λ_b are the wavelengths

in the two types of lamellae.

In order to make further progress. Bolton *et al.* assumed that the thickness of each type of sheet obeys a symmetrical probability distribution. The reflecting planes thus have a "progressive disorder". The mathematical problem is analogous to that for X-ray scattering from layer silicates containing interstratified sheets of two types. The further mathematical development is highly technical, and will only be abstracted here. To a good approximation, the maxima of the scattered intensity are given by the Bragg condition $p\lambda = 2(n_a d_a \sin \theta_a + n_b d_b \sin \theta_b)$, where p is an integer. The maxima will not be sharp because of the disorder in the lamellar thicknesses. The proportionate change of wavelength $\delta\lambda/\lambda$ for the wavelength at which the intensity has fallen to half the maximum is approximately proportional to the sum of the variances in the thicknesses of the two types of lamellae. Hence the more irregular the distributions, the greater the angular spread.

For the Bøggild intergrowth. Bolton *et al.* assumed that the refractive indices n_a and n_b of the two types of lamellae are equal at 1.54. Hence $p\lambda = 3.08(d_a + d_b)\sin\theta$, where θ is the *internal* angle of incidence. The external angle of incidence (θ_e) is related to the internal angle by Snell's law. Bolton *et al.* measured the lamellar thickness of two iridescent labradorites. and compared calculated intensity distributions with the observed intensities (Fig. 19-62). The agreement is reasonable if account is taken of the experimental difficulties. Restriction to visible and near-visible regions made it difficult to check the relation between the maxima for first and second order. but the data for the red labradorite at $\theta = 53°$ show moderate agreement.

Although the Bolton *et al.* model provides a good start it needs development to cover (a) the optical anisotropy (b) the dispersion, and perhaps (c) strain and incoherence at the interfaces.

Qualitatively the transition from planar lamellae to ellipsoids embedded in a matrix results in an angular broadening of the scattered light. The degree of broadening depends on the anisotropy of the ellipsoids, and on the extent of scattering coherence. For a triaxial ellipsoid, with one axis much shorter than the other two, the light should appear to be scattered mainly from the major cross-section. If that cross-section is elliptical, the scattered light will be angularly more diffuse in the direction of the shorter axis. As blebs become much smaller than the wavelength of light, and tend to scatter incoherently (i.e. because their distribution is random), the scattering phenomenon should change to that of the Tyndall effect. Obviously there is scope for more detailed theoretical and experimental studies.

8.2 Alkali Feldspars

8.2.1 Introduction

The three principal features of alkali feldspars are the K, Na ratio, the order-disorder of the T atoms, and the nature of intergrowths, if present. In principle the K, Na ratio can be estimated from the mean refractive index, but unfortunately accurate estimation is ruled out by significant effects from minor elements such as Ba and Fe. Intergrowths finer than the resolution limit of a microscope (i.e. about 0.1 μm) cannot be characterized optically. For coarser intergrowths, optical studies provide valuable information on the texture, and sometimes on the nature of the components. In practice, the most useful parameter appears to be the optic axial angle which correlates moderately with the order-disorder of T atoms and the K, Na ratio. For most investigations, X-ray and chemical studies are needed to give detailed characterization of alkali feldspars, and optical studies to provide the basic reconnaissance. Of course, some alkali feldspars such as cross-hatched microcline and low albite can be uniquely identified by optical methods.

8.2.2 Optic Axial Angle: Relation to Order-disorder of T Atoms

Figure 8-5 summarizes the relation between $-2V$ and mole % Or for specimens deliberately selected from the enormous literature. Only those specimens with a range of $2V$ less than 7° are used, thereby eliminating most natural sanidines. Except for a few synthetic and natural specimens for which homogeneity can be assumed, only specimens are used for which the presence or absence of perthite has been proven by X-ray methods (see Chapter 19). Sources of data are: Spencer (1930, 1937, 1938; but with mole % Or taken from electron microprobe analyses of Smith and Ribbe, 1966); Tuttle (1952); Oftedahl (1948); Marfunin (1962); Finney and Bailey (1964); Crawford (1966); Hewlett (1959); J. R. Smith (1958); Raase and Kern (1969).

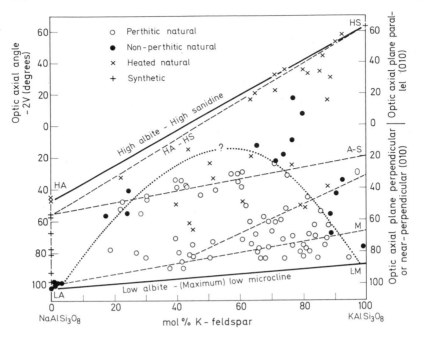

Fig. 8-5. Relation between optic axial angle and composition for alkali feldspars. See text for detailed explanation

The specimens are classified into four groups: perthitic natural specimens, non-perthitic ones, heated ones, and synthetic specimens. Taken together, they occupy a quadrilateral bounded by high albite (upper left), low albite (lower left), high sanidine (upper right) and low microcline (lower right). Note that the optic axial plane for K-feldspars changes from parallel to (010) to perpendicular or near-perpendicular to (010).

There is some doubt about the exact position of the extreme values, and the following chosen values of $-2V$ are somewhat uncertain: HA 47°, LA 102°; HS 63°; LM 88°. The range of measurements is particularly large for high albite, probably because of sub-optical twinning, chemical substitution, and variable structural state. Tuttle and Bowen (1950) obtained 45-55° for heated albite, and about 45° for synthetic albite. Laves and Chaisson (1950) obtained 64 and 40° for heated Amelia albites, and $56 \pm 3°$ for three synthetic albites. Schneider (1957) obtained 50° for a heated vein albite. J. R. Smith (1958) obtained 45 and 47° for heated natural albites. Raase and Kern (1969) found a few small untwinned crystals in their synthetic albites. Most lay on (010) permitting measurement of both optic axes. Within the accuracy of measurement, the values of $2V$ vary linearly with the 131 powder X-ray indicator, and extrapolate to about 48 and 107° for maximum high and low albites, respectively (Fig. 8-7b). The latter value is about 4° higher than the data for natural low albites. For each synthetic albite, Raase and Kern found that $2V$ ranged over about 5-10°. Burri et al. (1967) chose 50° for high albite, and Bambauer et al. (1971) adopted the same value.

For microcline, there is some doubt about the most extreme value. Frequently values of $-2V$ near 84° are listed in the literature. A few surpass 90°, but their validity is highly questionable. Subjectively I have chosen 88° as the extreme value for microcline but it is possible that this value is too large. Neiva (1972) made many measurements of $2V$ and the 130 powder X-ray indicator of microclines from Portugal which are consistent with an extreme value of 88°.

The perthitic specimens occupy a dome-shaped region, and the dotted line roughly separates the perthitic from the non-perthitic specimens. Of course, the dome is an expression of the unmixing solvus in the Ab,Or system. A sharp boundary between perthitic and non-perthitic specimens cannot be expected for various reasons including lack of equilibrium and presence of minor elements (especially Ca). However, it seems certain that any natural alkali feldspar found to occur well within the dome on Fig. 8-5 will be unmixed unless it has undergone metastable homogenization after unmixing occurred. The perthitic nature of the specimens plotted on Fig. 8-5 varies greatly from one specimen to another, as described in Chapter 19.

All specimens to the upper right of a boundary from Or_{100}, $2V-40°$ perpendicular (010) to Or_{40}, $2V\sim0°$ are monoclinic. All those to the lower left (the boundary is only approximate) show X-ray or electron-optical evidence of triclinic symmetry either for the entire specimen (e.g. microcline and low albite) or for part of the specimen (e.g. the albite component of a perthite containing monoclinic K-feldspar). Many of these specimens, however, are optically monoclinic because of sub-optical balanced twinning, or because of fine-scale coherent domain texture. On the whole there is a tendency for triclinic twinning to become optically visible as the specimen plots lower down the diagram. Nevertheless Marfunin (1962, 1966) and others have described optically monoclinic K-rich specimens whose $2V$ places them near the base of the quadrilateral. Furthermore D. B. Stewart (pers. comm.) has shown that there is overlap on the $2V$,Or diagram for K-rich feldspars classified into monoclinic or triclinic varieties on the basis of the X-ray powder pattern.

The possible effect of sub-optical twinning on $2V$ was discussed earlier. If Marfunin's model is correct, sub-optical twinning would result in the following reference values of $-2V$: low microcline, 85°; low albite, 92°; and high albite 29°. Substitution of minor elements may also affect $2V$. Probably the largest effect is from An which tends to favor albite rather than K-feldspar. Substitution of 10% An in low albite should reduce $-2V$ by about 6°, whereas for high albite $-2V$ should increase by about 11°. In general, it seems likely that $2V$ of K-rich specimens is affected little by twinning and chemical substitution of minor elements, but that $2V$ of Na-rich specimens may be affected severely.

Tuttle (1952) examined the distribution of points on a similar diagram to Fig. 8-5, and concluded that alkali feldspars could be classified into four series "(1) microcline-cryptoperthite, (2) orthoclase crypto-perthite, (3) sanidine-anorthoclase cryptoperthite, (4) high sanidine-high albite series", shown on Fig. 8-5 by the dashed lines labelled M, O, A–S and HA–HS, respectively. Later Tuttle and Bowen (1958, p. 104) presented the following summary:

"The optic axial angle of alkali feldspars distinguishes high-temperature modifications from low-temperature forms (Tuttle, 1952) if the chemical composition is known. On the basis of the optic axial angle and position of the optic plane, the alkali feldspars may conveniently be divided into four series: high sanidine–high albite, low sanidine–high albite, orthoclase–low albite, and microcline–low albite. Previous studies indicated that all gradations between the first two and last two series could be expected. The present study suggests that all gradations between the high sanidine–high albite and microcline–low albite series exist, and that the optic axial angle will serve to place an alkali feldspar in or intermediate between these series. The high sanidine–high albite and low sanidine–high albite series are high-temperature modifications since they are found in volcanic and other high-temperature rocks. The other series are representative of low-temperature rocks as they do not occur in the volcanic rocks and they can be changed to the high-temperature series by heating (Spencer, 1937)."

The distribution of points on Fig. 8-5 suggests that distinct series cannot be distinguished except for the extreme high sanidine–high albite and (maximum) low microcline–low albite series. Nevertheless there is a tendency for data to lie in a band centered on Tuttle's line for the anorthoclase-sanidine series (later called the high albite–low sanidine series) and in a triangle whose apices lie at low albite, low sanidine and maximum microcline. This clustering into two regions seems to depend on a tendency for (1) the K-phase of a perthite to order relatively easily from high sanidine to low sanidine followed by a sluggish transition to microcline (2) the Na phase to undergo a sharp transition from an Na-rich sanidine or high albite solid solution to an albite or oligoclase close to the low structural state, and (3) for the transition in the Na-rich phase to occur only after the K-phase has transformed into low sanidine (see Chapter 19). In spite of complexities, there is a qualitative, crude basis for Tuttle's classification. So long as it is realized that an optical classification of alkali feldspars is subject to several uncertainties, there seems no reason why the $2V$,Or diagram should not have some modest qualitative value. The discussion of perthites in Chapter 19 uses an optical classification as a starting point for the complex analysis of the X-ray data.

Is it possible to go further and make a quantitative structural interpretation of the $2V$,Or diagram? Unquestionably there is a strong tendency for the vertical position on the diagram to correlate with Si,Al order-disorder, but it seems that the correlation is somewhat imperfect.

Figure 8-6 provides pertinent information from feldspars ion-exchanged with molten salts in such a manner that the Si,Al distribution did not change (Wright and Stewart, 1968). For the six orthoclases and microclines, the tie-lines joining starting and ion-exchanged material are approximately parallel within experimental error to the reference line for the low albite–low microcline series from Fig. 8-5. Unfortunately the Puye sanidine had a very large range of $2V$ in its natural state [$-50°$ in (010) to $-34°$ perpendicular to (010)], and the effect of ion-exchange on sanidine is unclear. Note that the data for Benson and P 50-56 orthoclases lie only one-third of the way up from the LA–LM series to the HA–HS series, whereas the Na-exchanged equivalents lie over one-half of the way up. Rankin (1967) had great difficulty measuring Orville's ion-exchanged microclines by the orthoscopic method because of fine grid twinning.

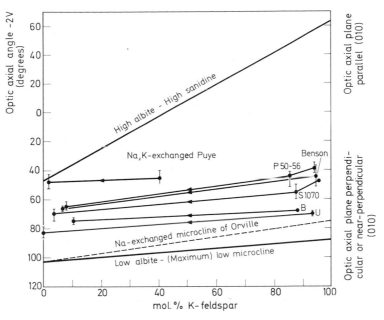

Fig. 8-6. Relation between optic axial angle and composition for natural and ion-exchanged alkali feldspars. The arrow shows the direction of ion-exchange. (Data from Wright and Stewart, 1968 and Rankin, 1967)

From the scattered data, Rankin concluded that $-2V$ varied linearly (dashed line in Fig. 8-6) from 75° for microcline to 103° for low albite.

Figure 8-7a plots $2V$ vs. the Al-contents deduced for the tetrahedral sites in K-feldspars studied by X-ray structural analysis (see Chapter 3). Spencer C orthoclase and the sanidinized form are monoclinic. Spencer B adularia and Himalaya "orthoclase" contain triclinic domains, and the dotted line shows how the pseudo-monoclinic data on Al-contents might be modified to yield a triclinic distribution of Al atoms. Spencer U, Pontiskalk and Pellotsalo microclines are untwinned. Finney and Bailey (1964) and Colville and Ribbe (1968) presented earlier near-equivalents of this diagram.

There are no X-ray structural analyses of intermediate albites, but the 131 X-ray indicator almost certainly yields a good estimate of the degree of order (Chapter 7). Fig. 8-7b shows that there is a linear relation within experimental error between $2V$ and the 131 X-ray indicator for synthetic albites prepared by Raase and Kern (1969). Probably these albites lie on or close to the ideal one-step trend of ordering, and the Al-contents of the tetrahedral sites should be linearly related to the 131 indicator.

Probably the best estimate of Al,Si order from physical properties of alkali feldspar derives from the cell dimensions b and c (see Chapter 7). Fig. 8-8 shows the correlation between $-2V$ and the $b-c$ plot prepared by D. B. Stewart (pers. comm.). The contour lines are his best estimates of $2V$ fitted to data points for natural and ion-exchanged feldspars. Details of the data behind the diagram will be published by D. B. Stewart. Most data points for homo-

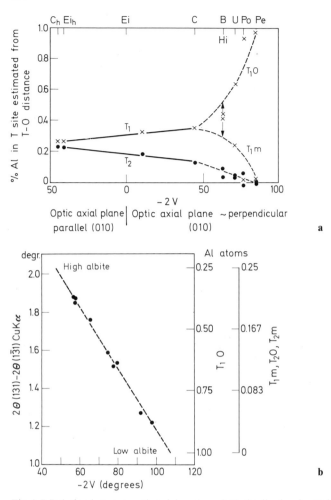

Fig. 8-7. Relation between optic axial angle and Al-distribution for K-feldspar (a) and Na-feldspar (b).
a See Table 3-2 for identification of the structure analyses which yielded the T–O distances from
which the Al-content was estimated. b The data points show the measurements of $2V$ and the
131 powder X-ray indicator obtained by Raase and Kern (1969, Table 1; and pers. comm.) for
synthetic albites. Note that the data in their Fig. 2 are somewhat different. The dashed line
extrapolates to about 48 and 107° in $-2V$ for values of 2.03 and 1.06° in the 131 indicator.
At the right, Al-contents have been estimated assuming a linear relation to the 131 indicator
(see Chapter 7)

geneous feldspars or components of coarse perthites have a value of $-2V$ which
fits within a few degrees with the value predicted from Fig. 8-8 on the basis of
the cell dimensions b and c. Specimens with anomalous cell dimensions
resulting from strain across perthite boundaries (Chapter 7) have normal
values of $2V$. In general there is a good correlation between $2V$ and the cell
dimensions b and c, and the optic axial angle provides a useful estimate of the
degree of Si,Al order. Nevertheless care must be taken with measurement and
interpretation of the optic axial angle of perthites.

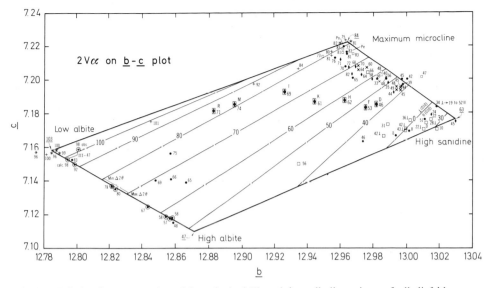

Fig. 8-8. Relation between optic axial angle $(-2V)$ and bc cell dimensions of alkali feldspars. The quadrilateral joins the cell dimensions for low albite, high albite, maximum microcline and high albite whose optic axial angles are underlined. Each natural or ion-exchanged feldspar is plotted at its value of b and c, while the associated number gives the optic axial angle. The linear contours were chosen by D. B. Stewart. Key to symbols: ● sample described in Wright and Stewart (1968); ◆ Spencer (1937) sample with normal cell parameters; ◓ Spencer sample with anomalous cell parameters; + maximum microcline-low albite exchange series measured by Rankin (1967); ☐ miscellaneous samples; × samples described by Fox and Moore (1969); * authigenic feldspars described by Kastner (1971); ⊙ intermediate albites of Raase and Kern (1969); Po Pontiskalk microcline (Finney and Bailey, 1964); Pe Pellotsalo microcline (Brown and Bailey, 1964). (From Stewart, pers. comm., similar to 1972, Fig. 1)

8.2.3 Refractive Indices and Birefringence

Although the refractive indices of alkali feldspar increase with both the Ab-content and Al,Si order (see the thorough experiments of Spencer, 1937), the refractive indices have little determinative value because of the effects of minor elements such as Ca,Ba and Fe (Hewlett, 1959). Figure 8-9 shows data collected by Tuttle (1952, Fig. 2) from Spencer (1937) and his own measurements. For reference, data have been added for the Tiburon albite and Pellotsalo and Pontiskalk microclines used in X-ray structural analysis (Table 8-2). All members of the orthoclase and microcline series lie fairly close to the straight line drawn between the reference albite and microclines, with $n(\alpha)$ and $n(\beta)$ tending to be high, and $n(\gamma)$ tending to be low. Smith and Ribbe (unpublished data based on electron microprobe analyses, 1966) found that after adjusting refractive indices for substitution of Ca, Ba, Sr and Fe using the Gladstone-Dale relation, there was a large reduction of scatter in Fig. 8-9. Increasing Si,Al disorder results in a decrease of the refractive indices, as expected because of the greater volume. Comparison with X-ray data shows that cell dimensions offer much greater accuracy than refractive indices for measurement of the Or content; furthermore

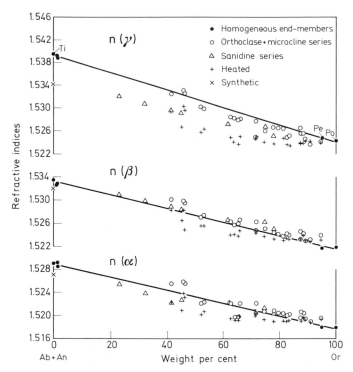

Fig. 8-9. Variation of refractive indices of alkali feldspars with Or content. Data derived from Spencer (1937), Tuttle (1952) and Table 8-2. (Modified from Tuttle, 1952, Fig. 2)

Table 8-2. Optical properties of some feldspars

Type	Source	Ref.	$n(\alpha)$	$n(\beta)$	$n(\gamma)$	$2V$
Microcline	Pellotsalo	Brown and Bailey (1964)	1.5178	1.5217	1.5247	$-82.5°$
Microcline	Pontiskalk	Finney and Bailey (1964)	1.5178	1.5218	1.5243	-77.0
Low albite	Tiburon	Crawford (1966)	1.5290	1.5335	1.5395	$+77$
Low albite	Ramona	J. R. Smith (1958)	1.5286	1.5326	1.5388	$+77.2$
High sanidine	Synthetic	Tuttle (1952)	see Fig. 8-9			-63
High albite	heated Ramona	J. R. Smith (1958)	1.5273	1.5344	1.5357	-46.9
Fe-microcline	Synthetic	Wones and Appleman (1963)	1.585	1.596	1.605	-85
Anorthite	Synthetic	J. R. Smith (1958)	1.5750	1.5834	1.5883	-75.2
Celsian	Natural	Roy (1965)	1.589	1.593	1.599	$+84.1$

the X-ray technique is often easier. Plas, van der (1966) compiled further data on the refractive indices, and reached similar conclusions to those of Tuttle.

Probably the minor elements affect the three principal refractive indices roughly equally (cf. microcline with synthetic Fe-microcline in Table 8-2). Consequently the birefringence can be expected to provide a fairly reliable measurement of the structural state: indeed the birefringence is related to the optic axial angle, and all arguments in the preceding section should apply here.

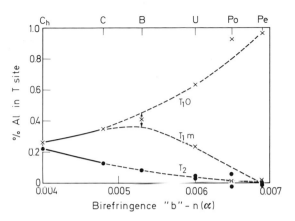

Fig. 8-10. Relation between birefringence "*b*" − *n*(α) and % Al in tetrahedral sites deduced from X-ray structural analysis of K-feldspars (Table 3-2)

Hewlett (1959) proposed to use the birefringence "*b*" − *n*(α) as an optical indicator of structural state, where "*b*" is the principal refractive index nearest to the *b*-axis. To a good approximation, the Hewlett parameter can be measured directly from (001) cleavage fragments because the *X* axis lies near *a* and the other axis lies near *b*. Because the birefringence is more difficult to measure accurately in routine work than the optic axial angle, there has been no comprehensive study of the variation of birefringence with both structural state and Or content. Furthermore, if Marfunin's model for the optics of sub-optical twinning is correct, the birefringence of K-feldspars is affected more seriously than the optic axial angle. Hewlett (1959, Fig. 5a) plotted the birefringence "*b*" − *n*(α) for some of Spencer's specimens, and it is quite clear that the parameter correlates with structural order. Finney and Bailey (1964, Fig. 3) demonstrated a non-linear continuous relation between the birefringence and 2*V* for K-feldspars used in structure determinations. Figure 8-10 shows the relation between birefringence and Al-contents deduced from T–O distances (Chapter 3). Detailed interpretation is similar to that for Fig. 8-7.

8.2.4 Optic Orientation and Extinction Angle

Because the principal cleavages (010) and (001) intersect along the *a*-axis, and because the acute bisectrix is near *a* for all alkali feldspars except low albite, it is most convenient to project stereographic projections of the optic orientation down *a*. Figure 8-11 shows stereographic projections of the optic axes for high sanidine, low sanidine, low microcline, low albite and high albite. Data for many alkali feldspars are given by Marfunin (1962, 1966). For convenience of comparison with plagioclase feldspar, the stereographic projections are actually projected along − *a* with *b*** to the right.

High sanidine has its optic axial plane parallel to (010), and the maximum value of − 2*V* is about 63° (Tuttle, 1952). The acute bisectrix is displaced about 4° from the *a*-axis. Low sanidine has its optic axial plane perpendicular to (010) and − 2*V* ranges up to about 45°. There is a continuous variation between the

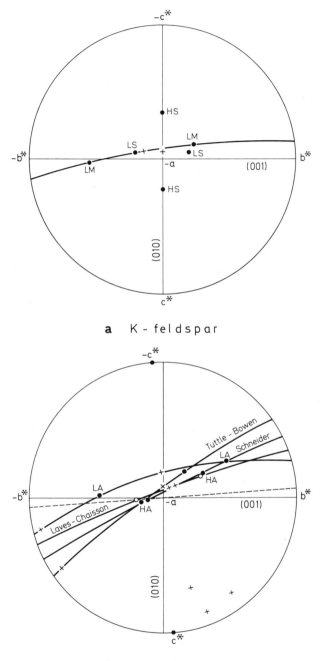

a   K - feldspar

b   Na - feldspar

Fig. 8-11. Stereographic projections of the optical orientation of alkali feldspars. Note that the projection is down $-a$. Traces of the (010) and (001) cleavages are shown. a K-feldspar. HS high sanidine, $-2V\,63°$; LS low sanidine, $-2V\,45°$; LM low microcline, $-2V\,84°$. The dots show the optic axes and the crosses show the acute bisectrix. b Na-feldspar. LA low albite, $-2V\,102°$. For high albite, three orientations are given for the synthetic specimens studied by Tuttle and Bowen (1950) and Laves and Chaisson (1950), and a heated Schmirntal albite by Schneider (1957)

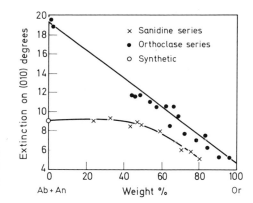

Fig. 8-12. Extinction angle between trace of (001) cleavage and nearest vibration direction on (010) cleavage of alkali feldspars. (From Tuttle, 1952, Fig. 3)

maximum limits of sanidine with $2V$ passing through zero. The dispersion of high sanidines is $r < v$ and for all other K-feldspars it is $r > v$. This change of dispersion provides the fastest optical method of distinguishing a high sanidine from a low sanidine. For untwinned microcline, the optic axial plane tilts away from monoclinic symmetry reaching the position shown in Fig. 8-11a for a microcline with $-2V$ near 84°. Sub-optical twinning gives monoclinic or near-monoclinic optics as described earlier. Adularia gives unusual optics as described in the next chapter.

The optic orientation of low-albite is well-known (e.g. the data by Crawford (1966) for a very pure albite from Tiburon used for X-ray structural analysis). However the optic orientation of high albite is uncertain. Both Tuttle and Bowen (1950) and Laves and Chaisson (1950) had great difficulty measuring hydrothermally-synthesized albite because of polysynthetic twinning. Heated natural albite was also studied by both workers. Tuttle and Bowen observed a range of 45–55° in $-2V$ for heated Amelia albite, and about 45° in synthetic albite. Because 45° checks with the extrapolation of data for plagioclase, Tuttle and Bowen chose this value for high albite. Laves and Chaisson observed a range of about 15° for the optical directions of 11 crystals of synthetic albite, and their data (Fig. 2) for heated Amelia albite gave $-2V$ near 60° suggesting incomplete conversion to high albite. Schneider (1957) measured the orientation of heated Schmirntal albite, obtaining $-2V = 50°$ for untwinned parts. Figure 8-11b shows the optical orientations given by the three workers. Burri et al. (1967) and Bambauer et al. (1971) adopted the orientation of Laves and Chaisson, but one might choose the orientation of Tuttle and Bowen because it fits better with data for high plagioclase. For low albite the dispersion is $r < v$, and for high albite it is $r > v$.

Tuttle (1952) plotted the extinction angle of alkali feldspars versus the Or content (Fig. 8-12) for the cleavage (010). The angle between the trace of the (001) cleavage and the nearest vibration direction tends to fall with increasing Or content and increasing structural disorder.

8.2.5 Polymorphism and Determinative Methods

The polymorphism of both K- and Na-feldspars results from transformation of high sanidine and high albite with disordered Si,Al atoms into low microcline and low albite with Al concentrated into the $T_1 0$ site and Si in the other three sites (Chapter 3). There is an infinite number of ways in which the ordering process can take place ranging between the extremes of the one-step process, in which Al moves from all three T_1m, T_20 and T_2m sites into the T_10 site, and the two-step process, in which Al moves first from the T_2 sites into the T_1 sites followed by movement from T_1m into T_10 sites. It is quite certain that the change of $2V$ depends essentially on the migration of Al atoms from T_2 to T_1 sites, but there is no theoretical calibration. Unbalance in the amount of Al between 0 and m sub-sites yields triclinic optical properties, unless sub-optical twinning gives pseudo-monoclinic properties. All X-ray data for alkali feldspars are consistent within experimental error with equal amounts of Al in T_20 and T_2m sites. Therefore the unbalance in the Al-contents of T_10 and T_1m sites is the factor which affects the triclinic symmetry. For K-feldspar, it is likely that maximum microcline with $-2V=88°$ and extinction angle of about 18° on (001) corresponds to nearly complete segregation of Al into T_10 sites. All smaller values of extinction angle correspond to either less order, or sub-optical twinning, or both. For Na-feldspar, both high and low albite are optically triclinic at room temperature because of twisting of the aluminosilicate framework about the Na atoms. Consequently segregation of Al atoms into T_10 sites causes a rotation of the indicatrix (Fig. 8-11b).

The most serious problem in the interpretation of optical properties is the sub-optical twinning caused by the inversion from monoclinic to triclinic symmetry (see Fig. S-1). Usually the inversion results in combined Albite and Pericline twinning with an intimate intermingling of domains commonly described as cross-hatching. By X-ray and electron-optical methods, the twinning can always be recognized, but by optical methods the twinning can be detected only when it is coarser than the wavelength of light. The coarseness of the twinning appears to depend on trivial factors including the presence of chemical impurities, the rate of the cooling, the presence of shearing stress, etc. Usually cross-hatched twinning in microcline can be distinguished from that in anorthoclase because the boundaries of the former tend to be curved whereas those of the latter tend to be straight (e.g. MacKenzie, 1956). Of course, final identification must be based on the optical orientation.

For determination of alkali feldspar, it is absolutely certain that whenever feasible X-ray methods should be used to give the final characterization. A typical procedure for optical study of alkali feldspar in a rock might go as follows:

(a) Note the morphology, texture and color by eye: note the coexisting minerals. Glassy megacrysts in a volcanic rock obviously imply sanidine or anorthoclase. Milky crystals in a granite are either "orthoclase" or microcline.

(b) In thin section, look for obvious features such as cross-hatched twinning and perthite in grains with refractive indices slightly lower than Lakeside cement or balsam. If cross-hatching is found, microcline can be readily distinguished from anorthoclase by referring the optical properties to the cleavage, and by checking the optic axial angle.

(c) If the alkali feldspar is optically homogeneous in thin section, great care must be taken. Some microclines are untwinned and can be dismissed as "orthoclase" or sanidine by a careless investigator. Search for grains with low birefringence, preferably with two cleavages at right angles. These grains should be oriented with *a* near-vertical and should permit direct measurement of *2V* in many instances. Complete determination of the optical orientation is desirable.

(d) If the alkali feldspar is coarsely perthitic, or coarsely twinned, the optical properties of individual components can be measured by the orthoscopic method. If it is a fine microperthite or is homogeneous, the conoscopic method is best. Grain mounts are particularly useful for approximating the bulk *2V* of microperthites.

(e) Measurement of the refractive indices permits distinction between Na- and K-feldspars, but does not give an accurate estimate of Or-content.

(f) Ideally, the preliminary optical measurements should be supplemented by (1) electron-probe measurement of chemical composition, using broad-beam techniques for microperthites, (2) X-ray powder methods to obtain an estimate of chemical composition, structural state, and degree of unmixing, (3) X-ray single-crystal methods for determination of complex perthites, especially the relative orientation of the components.

(g) Detrital feldspars pose special problems in identification because of the diverse sources. Plas, van der (1966) gave detailed instructions. Preliminary optical study either of thin sections or of grain mounts is mandatory. Probably the best technique involves a further reconnaissance using cathodoluminescence, followed by electron probe analysis of selected grains. After classifying the analyses, selected grains could be studied optically by U-stage methods or examined by the Gandolfi X-ray method.

(h) Optical petrographers should note that thin rims on feldspar grains can easily be overlooked in routine optical studies. Cathodoluminescence usually reveals such rims by a difference in color. Authigenic feldspars commonly nucleate on detrital fragments, from which they can be distinguished by their essential lack of luminescence.

In conclusion to this section on optical properties of alkali feldspars, reference should be made to the ambitious diagram for determination of alkali feldspars just from optical properties (Marfunin, 1961, Fig. 8: see also 1962, 1966). This stereographic projection shows the effect on the optical orientation of chemical composition, Si,Al order-disorder and sub-optical twinning. The important deductions by Marfunin and by other workers on the polymorphism of K-feldspar based on optical and X-ray properties are reviewed in Chapter 9.

8.3 Plagioclase Feldspars

8.3.1 Introduction

Optical properties of plagioclase depend principally on the An-content and the structural state. Marfunin (1962, 1966) and Burri *et al.* (1967) reviewed in detail the historical developments which led to the above conclusion.

By the end of the nineteenth century, establishment of the continuum of optical properties between those of Na- and Ca-feldspar, together with the observed continuum of chemical analyses, specific gravities and crystallographic characters had confirmed Sterry Hunt's (1854, 1855) and Tschermak's (1864) idea of isomorphous mixing, and essentially ruled out the concept of specific chemical compositions with fixed ratios of end-members (Cloiseaux, 1875). (Perhaps it is ironic that for low plagioclase, more and more emphasis is now being placed on specific compositions). The first detailed determinative curve relating an optical property to the An-content was drawn up by Schuster (1880) for measurement of extinction angle on the cleavages (010) and (001). The development of the universal stage by Fedorow (1893, 1894) led to the construction of stereographic projections of optical directions with respect to the principal crystallographic directions, thus extending earlier results from fixed-stage microscopes. Because the optical crystallographers naturally chose the largest, most uniform crystals, and because most of these came from rocks in which there had been an excellent opportunity for annealing, the majority of the data obtained over the next three decades were consistent with a single series of optical properties. A host of techniques was developed and many monographs were written.

Looking backwards, one is surprised to find how few data were actually used in the construction of the stereographic projections: probably the mineralogists and crystallographers had an inherent feeling for the regularity of mineral properties, and hence tended to dismiss deviations as the result merely of experimental error or some chemical substitution. Thus many years passed before explicit recognition of the difference in optics between plagioclase from plutonic and from volcanic rocks by Köhler (1942a, b) and Larsson (1941), though the writing had been on the wall for some years. Kaaden, van der (1951), Marfunin (1962) and Burri et al. (1967) summarized the developments in the fourth decade beginning with the recognition of deviations of optical data for natural plagioclase from the migration curves by Reinhard (1931), and observation of small changes of orientation upon heating by Barth (1931). At first the deviations of data for natural specimens were dismissed as the result of chemical substitutions [such as by K-feldspar, Reinhard (1931)] or by the carnegieite molecule in the anomalous anemousite of Washington and Wright (1910) and of experimental error [such as from referring an optical direction to a vicinal face, Barber (1936b)]. However Ernst and Nieland (1934) showed by new analyses that the famous Linosa feldspars contained little carnegieite molecule though the optical orientations of the Linosa feldspars did differ from those listed in the standard compilations: furthermore Dittler and Köhler (1933) did not find significant substitution of the carnegieite molecule in synthetic feldspars crystallized in the An–Ab–Cg system, and Spaenhauer (1933) found normal optics for calcic plagioclase synthesized in systems containing Or and Cg molecules. Chudoba and Engels (1937a, b) decided that the deviations of optical orientations for certain plagioclases were not caused by substitution of the admixed K-feldspar.

Köhler (1942) and Larsson (1941) independently concluded that the volcanic nature of the host rock was the cause of the deviations of the plagioclase optics which had then been found by several workers (including Homma, 1932, Paliuc, 1932 and Wenk, 1933). Larsson concluded that "it is probable that the rapid fall of temperature from the intratelluric to the effusive state is to be held responsible for the differences (in optics) as against the plagioclases of the rocks crystallized during slow and tolerably continuous cooling". Köhler in a series of papers; (see English summary in 1949) concluded *"The reason seems to be that the optics of volcanic rock-plagioclases (position of the indicatrix) differ fundamentally from those of plutonic rocks.* The high temperature of crystallization of volcanic rocks produces optics which differ measurably from those of plagioclases of the same chemical composition from crystalline schists or plutonic rocks which are crystallized at a lower temperature. As concerns the latter, it can be said without any doubt ··· that the original high-temperature optics changed slowly to the low-temperature optics. ··· It is strange, particularly in the light of our knowledge of the potash feldspars (sanidine-orthoclase-microcline), that the temperature dependency of the optics was not discovered until the sensitive twin optics ··· were used".

Unfortunately the only synthetic feldspars suitable for optical study up to that time were of basic composition, and thus differed only slightly in optical properties with respect to natural plutonic equivalents, while the natural acid plagioclases were only partly converted to the high structural state (Tertsch, 1942a, b, c; Scholler, 1942); thus the large difference in optics between high and low albites was not recognized in the early studies. However Tuttle and Bowen (1950) and Laves and Chaisson (1950) clearly established this difference which was already evident from results for heated alkali feldspars (Spencer, 1937), for natural anorthoclases, and for a synthetic K-bearing albite from a blast furnace (Belyankin, 1934). Köhler (1949) noted that "When one heats plagioclases of plutonic rocks ···, one is struck by the fact that they may be brought to the high-temperature form very easily. Crystals that had once been in the high-temperature state are very easily returned to that state; it seems that 'relic' structures of the high-temperature form initiate and speed up this process. Material that crystallized at low temperature is very difficult to transform to the high form." This difference in conversion rate may explain some of the conflict of experimental data concerning whether or not optical changes were induced by heating (Barber, 1936a).

Since 1950, there have been many attempts to establish reference curves for the optics of high-temperature plagioclase. The existence of transitional optics was envisaged by Köhler (1942a, b) and Scholler (1942), and confirming data for natural plagioclases were provided by many authors including Oftedahl (1944, 1948), Barth and Oftedahl (1947), Nickel (1948), Bradley (1953), and Muir (1955).

In addition to publication of scattered measurements by many authors, several systematic studies of plagioclase optics were made, notably those of Kaaden, van der (1951), Emmons *et al.* (1953), Chayes (1952, 1954), J. R. Smith (1958), Kano (1955), Muir (1955), Schwarzmann (1956), Glauser (1959, 1961), Glauser and Wenk (1957, 1960), Wenk (1960), Slemmons (1962a, b), and Uruno (1963).

In 1961, Burri, Parker and Wenk announced the formation of a study group to review existing data and produce new data. A preliminary report appeared in 1962, a detailed monograph in 1967, and a paper in 1972. Additional papers have appeared as follows: Balconi and Zezza (1968), *2V* vs. An-content;

Bordet (1967), detailed measurements of dispersion; Burri (1968), orientation of a high-temperature labradorite, An_{68}; Glauser (1963, 1964, 1966, 1967, 1968, 1970), optical properties of volcanic plagioclase from Linosa and Iceland; Nieuwenkamp (1966), stereograms for the determination of plagioclase feldspars in random sections; Noble (1965), improvement of U-stage technique by use of larger crystals; Plas, van der (1966), a thorough monograph on the identification of detrital feldspars; Schedler (1971), optical, chemical and structural determinations of volcanic, acid Icelandic plagioclase mostly An_{15-50}; Tsuboi (1968), optical determination of low- and high-temperature plagioclase; E. Wenk et al. (1965), labradorite from Surtsey; E. Wenk and Trommsdorf (1967), optical orientation of synthetic anorthite; E. Wenk et al. (1967), optical orientation of two anorthites from metamorphic rocks; E. Wenk et al. (1968), bytownite from Cape Parry, e. Greenland; H.-R. Wenk (1966), labradorite from Surtsey; H.-R. Wenk (1969), annealing of oligoclase; E. Wenk et al. (1972b), bytownite from Iceland olivine-basalt; Uebel (1973), use of Rittmann zone method when (001) cleavage is absent. The Apollo studies of lunar plagioclase are yielding many optical data, especially of bytownites and anorthites e.g. Agrell et al. (1970). Appleman et al. (1971), Czank et al. (1972), Müller et al. (1972), H.-R. Wenk and Nord (1971), and E. Wenk et al. (1972a). Many of the above papers describe optical properties for volcanic and basic plagioclases for which earlier data were inadequate.

Although the combined set of optical data is very impressive, there are still problems. The effects of chemical substituents, including Or molecule, have not been evaluated in detail. X-ray data have demonstrated the existence of complex intergrowths and structural transformations, and it is probable that these have subtle effects on regression curves between optical and chemical parameters. It is probable that there is not a unique correlation between optical parameters and structural state, if alkali feldspars provide a guide.

The structural state of a plagioclase depends on complex movements of both Al,Si and Ca,Na atoms. At thermodynamic equilibrium, there would be a unique variation of structural state with the pressure, temperature and bulk composition. For a given composition, the temperature probably would have the major control. Early workers referred to "high-temperature" and "low-temperature" optics of plagioclase. Lundegärdh (1941) preferred the terms "supracrustal" and "infracrustal" in reference to the geologic environment. Slemmons (1962a) argued for the terms "volcanic" and "plutonic" optics. Here the simple terms "high" and "low" will be used, recognizing that the implied states of high and low structural disorder cannot be specified in detail from optical properties. Marfunin (1958) drew isopleths to represent the variation of optical properties with chemical composition for a particular degree of ordering. Slemmons (1962a) gave reference data for volcanic and plutonic plagioclases using a universal stage, and invented (1962b) the term "intermediacy index" to express the variation between the two extremes of high and low plagioclase.

Before reviewing the optical properties in detail, it is worth emphasizing that just as for the cell dimensions, the optical properties show the greatest variation with structural state for albite, and that the effect for anorthite is rather small. Furthermore there were few early data for bytownite and anorthite specimens, and only recently has this been rectified. In principle the An-content and structural state can be determined from the refractive indices and optic axial angle. Alternatively both can be estimated from the angular relation between optical and crystallographic axes. In practice, there are uncertainties, especially in measurement of the structural state.

8.3.2 Optic Axial Angle

Figure 8-13 shows some selected data on the relation between optic axial angle $2V$ and mole % An. The open circles and crosses, respectively, show the optic axial angles of chemically-analyzed specimens before and after prolonged heating at high temperature (J. R. Smith, 1958, 1960). The squares show data obtained by Carmichael (1960) for chemically-analyzed phenocrysts from pitch-stones and glassy rocks. The dots show optic axial angles measured by Kano (1955) for plagioclase phenocrysts from volcanic lavas, whose An-contents were estimated from the refractive index $n(\alpha)$ plotted on the regression curve of Chayes (1952). From these data, curves were drawn for the high and low extremes of the structural state.

The low curve shows a sharp bend near An_{20} and a broader one near An_{50}. The high curve is displaced over 50° from the low curve at albite, but rapidly approaches it with increasing An-content, finally crossing over near An_{50} and then running parallel. For anorthites, it is clear that there is little variation in optic axial angle with the structural state determined from X-ray study. Wenk and Trommsdorff (1967) obtained new data for synthetic anorthite which agree with those obtained by J. R. Smith (1958) for an anorthite synthesized at 1500° C.

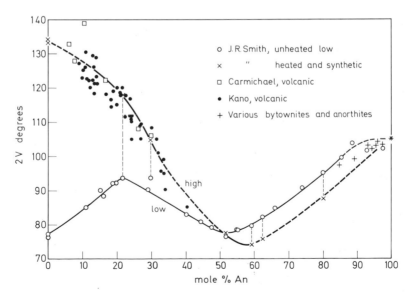

Fig. 8-13. Relation between optic axial angle and mole % An for plagioclase. The curves are estimated for the extreme high and low structural states. (Modified after J. R. Smith, 1958, Fig. 2)

Schwarzmann (1956) collected together many data on plagioclases from volcanic rocks, from a meteorite and from synthetic specimens. She also plotted her own data for plagioclases from inclusions in basalts, but J. R. Smith (1958) thought that her estimates of An-content from measured refractive indices were too high by up to 6% An. On the whole, all these data are roughly consistent with Fig. 8-13 when account is taken of the possible errors and variation in structural state.

Burri et al. (1967, Plate XII) plotted a large number of data from many sources, and although the curves are similar to those given here, there are minor differences, especially for high albite and bytownites.

From Fig. 8-5, the effect on $2V$ of substitution of Or molecule can be estimated by simple interpolation. Because low plagioclase contains little Or the effect on $2V$ is likely to be less than 2°. For high plagioclase, the Or content is trivial for anorthite, but can increase to 20% in the oligoclase range. In these latter specimens, $2V$ might be reduced by several degrees because of the Or content.

Schedler (1971) displayed graphically about 80 measurements of $2V$ for sodic plagioclases from Icelandic volcanic rocks. These data are consistent with the curves of Fig. 8-13 when account is taken of substitution of Or and variation of structural state.

Sodic plagioclases from volcanic rocks are often finely twinned resulting in pseudo-monoclinic optics if the twinning is sub-optical (Oftedahl, 1950).

8.3.3 Refractive Indices

Figure 8-14 summarizes data on refractive indices of plagioclase crystals and glass.

The simplest data are for isotropic glasses prepared synthetically by Schairer et al. (1956) to provide a calibration for Foster's (1955) method in which plagioclase crystals are fused to a glass. The range of refractive indices for the glass is about twice that for crystals, and the refractive index of the isotropic glass is easier to measure than those of the natural feldspars because orientation is not needed. However Emmons et al. (1960) stated that they had "never been successful in producing glass of consistent optical properties from (chemically) analyzed plagioclase. We have chosen to abandon the technique." Some authors noted the formation of bubbles and dark inclusions in the fused feldspar. Iron-bearing impurities might give significant increases in the refractive index of the glass. Dawson and Maxwell (1958) found no significant loss of Na and K during fusion.

In contrast to the optic axial angle, the major variation in refractive indices of plagioclase crystals results from the substitution of An whereas the effect of the structural state is relatively small. Chayes (1950, 1952, 1954) made a detailed statistical study of available data on the refractive indices of plagioclase. On the assumption that the data belonged to a single population, he calculated (1952) determinative curves (Fig. 8-14a) for the An content in relation to the three refractive indices. The paper is rather detailed, but some of the key points are rejection of certain values, inclusion of a few specimens now known not to be in

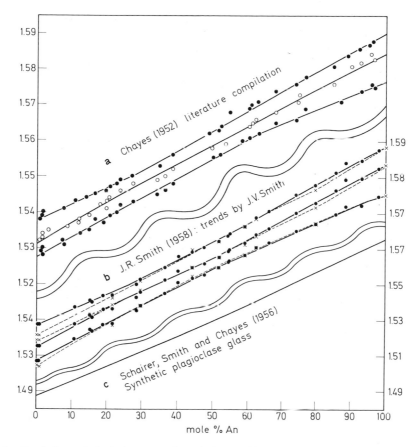

Fig. 8-14. Refractive indices of plagioclase crystals and glass. a Literature compilation by Chayes (1952). All trends are slightly curved because Chayes fitted linear regressions to wt.-% An. b Data of J. R. Smith (1958) for unheated (dots) and heated (crosses) plagioclases. c Data by Schairer et al., (1956) for synthetic glass. Note that the vertical scale is halved over those for (a) and (b)

the low structural state, and fitting of segments for several ranges of composition. Hampered by the scarcity of data, especially for plagioclases of intermediate composition, Chayes arbitrarily ended up by calculating regressions for the regions An_0–An_{30}, An_{30}–An_{70} and An_{70}–An_{100}. He compared his results with the X-ray data of Cole et al. which also indicated changes near An_{30} and An_{70}. Looking back, especially on the basis of the previous discussion of the variation of $2V$ with An for the low plagioclases, one can see that the data used by Chayes were too inaccurate and too sparse to permit significant detection of discontinuities. In 1973, on the basis of detailed X-ray work and on the later optical results, one might suspect that the refractive indices of low plagioclases vary in a complex manner with the An content, and that several discontinuities or kinks in the slope might occur. Obviously it would be quite impracticable to attempt to locate such discontinuities in detail, and for practical purposes simpler determinative curves, such as those of Chayes, are adequate. Chayes

(1954) pointed out a systematic bias in the refractive indices measured by Emmons *et al.* (1953) for their well-known series of plagioclases. Marfunin (1962) showed that the mean refractive index $[n(\alpha) + n(\beta) + n(\gamma)]/3$ varied linearly with An-content.

Perhaps the most accurate data are by J. R. Smith (1958, 1960) for some 20 natural plagioclases in the low structural state, and after prolonged heating. Figure 8-14b shows the data together with regressions estimated by me to fit roughly with the data on the optic axial angle (Fig. 8-13). For the natural plagioclases five lines are drawn between the following points:

	An_0	An_{25}	An_{50}	An_{95}	An_{100}
$n(\gamma)$	1.538_5	1.549_1	1.561_8	1.586_1	1.588_3
$n(\beta)$	1.532_5	1.545_6	1.557_2	1.580_9	1.583_4
$n(\alpha)$	1.528_5	1.546_4	1.554_3	1.573_8	1.575_0

For the heated plagioclase, the following curves are drawn: a parabola for $n(\alpha)$ between An_0 1.527, An_{50} 1.544_5 and An_{100} 1.575_0; for $n(\beta)$, a line from An_0 1.534_4, An_{50} 1.562, followed by a parabola through An_{80} 1.571_5 and An_{100} 1.583_4; for $n(\gamma)$, a line from An_0 1.535_6 to An_{60} 1.562_2, followed by a parabola through An_{80} 1.576_7 and An_{100} 1.588_3. No statistical justification is presented for these data: they just fit nicely with the observations.

From the data it may be seen that $n(\alpha)$ is affected only slightly by the structural state, and that neglect of it should rarely give an error greater than 1 % An. Substitution of Or for Ab in plagioclase should have little effect on the refractive indices judging by the data in Fig. 8-9. The Ba and Sr contents of plagioclase are usually trivial, but the Fe content may rise to 1 wt.-% in some volcanic plagioclases, causing an increase of ~ 0.002 in the refractive indices. This would lead to an error of about 4 % An, and probably represents an upper limit for all natural plagioclases from common rocks. In general, it appears that if account is taken of the structural state, the An-content of most plagioclases can be determined within about 2 % from the determinative curves in Fig. 8-13.

For routine determination of the An-content of plagioclase, Tsuboi's method (1934) has proven easy and quite accurate. Tsuboi noted that the principal optic axis X lies at a similar angle to both of the principal cleavages (010) and (001) and hence that the An-content can be estimated from the lower of the two refractive indices measured for a plagioclase cleavage fragment, irrespective of whether it lies on (010) or (001). The later recognition of high- and low-optics provided a complication but fortunately $n(\alpha)$ and the direction X are affected only slightly by structural state. Plas, van der (1966) described in detail an experimental procedure, which uses wavelength dispersion of the reference oil to permit accurate measurement of the refractive index of the plagioclase. Morse (1968) used the same method, and Fig. 8-15 gives his calibration curve for (001) cleavage fragments based mostly on the low plagioclases of J. R. Smith. From the curves of Burri *et al.* (1967, Plate XVII) it appears that Tsuboi's method is accurate to about 1 % An in the range An_{20} to An_{60}, irrespec-

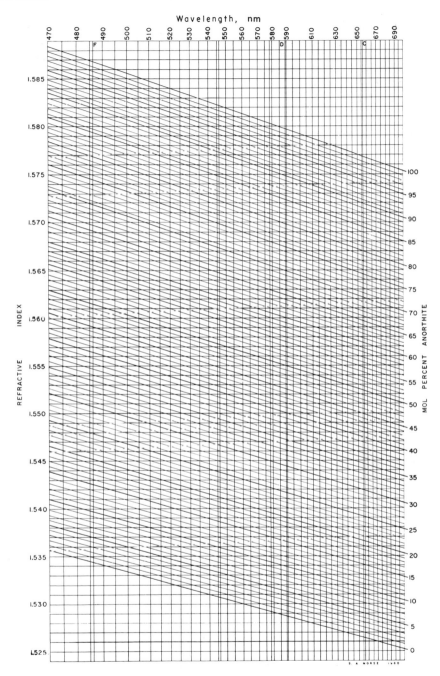

Fig. 8-15. Calibration diagram for Tsuboi's method in which the refractive index of the oil is varied by changing the wavelength of the light. This diagram specifically applies to (001) cleavage fragments of low plagioclase. For (010) cleavage fragments and for the effect of structural state see Burri *et al.*, (1967, Plate XVII). (From Morse, 1968, Fig. 3)

tive of the structural state of the plagioclase, and independent of whether (010) or (001) fragments are used. For albites and bytownites, the structural state and type of cleavage fragment are important and errors up to 3% An can occur if they are neglected. Morse obtained a precision of 0.2% An, but the accuracy of the method depends on many factors including the amount of chemical substituents such as Fe. For low plagioclase of intermediate composition, I believe that an accuracy of about 1% An is obtainable, but that for plagioclase from volcanic rocks errors up to 5% might occur in extreme cases. Bambauer *et al.* (1971, Plate 233-14) utilized Morse's data.

8.3.4 Optic Orientation and Twin Relations

In principle the relation between the optical and crystallographic axes is a simple concept that may be expressed by a stereographic projection. Two suitable orthogonal directions are chosen (e.g. b^* and a) and kept fixed for all plagioclases, while the other directions migrate in response to changing An-content and structural state. Such a diagram is Fig. 8-16 taken from Burri *et al.* (1967), by kind permission of Birkhäuser-Verlag. In this diagram, b^* is at the extreme right and $-a$ is at the middle. Other crystallographic directions change with An-content between the extremes for albite (solid dot) and anorthite (circle). Optic properties of low and high plagioclase are shown respectively by continuous and dotted lines. Curves for the optic symmetry axes are labelled n_α, n_β and n_γ plus the two normals to the circular sections labelled A and B. Each curve has a symbol at every increment of 5% An. In principle, measurement of the optic orientation allows simultaneous determination of An-content and structural state, but in practice there are some difficulties. Readers should note that Burri *et al.* use Z, Y, X for the crystallographic directions c, b^* and the direction perpendicular to both c and b^*; in this treatise Z, Y, X correspond to the optic symmetry axes associated with $n(\gamma)$, $n(\beta)$ and $n(\alpha)$. All crystallographic indices are based on the albite cell.

In Fig. 8-16, each of the optic symmetry angles migrates about a right-angle from Ab to An. The direction of n_α tends to lie near the middle of the diagram passing near the a-axis for oligoclase compositions. No attempt has been made to explain the migrations in terms of changes in the crystal structure. Change of structural state has the largest effect for albite and little effect above An_{70}.

If the optic properties of plagioclase were determined only by the An-content and the structural state, and if U-stage measurements were accurate to $1°$, it would be possible to estimate the An content to about 1% An. Furthermore about 30 steps of ordering might be detected for albite, falling to several steps for labradorite. Unfortunately the scatter of actual data implies that other factors contribute, and it seems necessary to conclude that actual measurements of plagioclases yield much less accurate estimates of An-content and structural state, perhaps by a factor of two to five.

It is instructive to examine in detail the data upon which Burri *et al.* based their curves. Even for plagioclases ascribed to the low series the data scatter over several degrees on each side of the curve (see Burri *et al.*, 1967, Plates I,

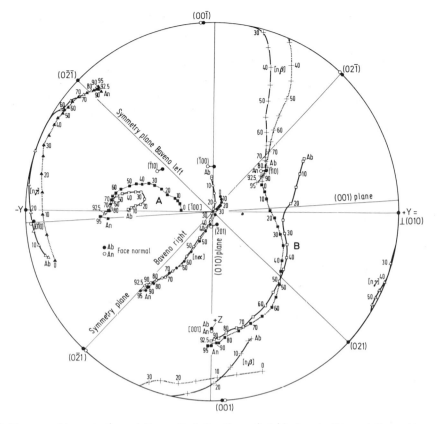

Fig. 8-16. Stereographic projection relating optical directions of plagioclase to the crystallographic axes b^* (extreme right) and $-a$ (center). Other crystallographic directions change slightly from albite (dot) to anorthite (circle). The cleavage and twin plane (010) stays fixed, and the plane (001) is almost fixed. The symmetry planes for the Baveno left and right twins also are almost fixed. Migration curves are given for both high (dotted line) and low (continuous line) plagioclase. The curves A and B give the poles to the circular sections, and $n(\alpha)$, $n(\beta)$ and $n(\gamma)$ give the directions of the optic symmetry axes. (From Burri et al., 1967, Plate VI)

II and III). A similar scatter occurs for specimens ascribed to the high series, but some of the variation may result from variation of structural state because synthetic and heated specimens have been grouped together with volcanic specimens. The chemical compositions were mostly determined by classical chemical analysis, but for some specimens the An-content was estimated from the refractive index of fused glass or from the refractive indices of the plagioclase itself. Probably some of the compositions are wrong by as much as several percent An. The data were collected from over 40 different publications, and it is possible that there are systematic errors between the techniques of the different laboratories. Thus in spite of the thoroughness of Burri et al., it seems likely that their curves may be subject to errors as much as a few degrees and a few percent of An, though for low plagioclase the errors may be only 1° and 1% An. Almost certainly the curve for high plagioclase does not represent the highest structural state. The curves are particularly uncertain for calcic compositions, as shown by many later measurements. Ideally, a completely new set of data should be obtained for specimens checked for chemical homogeneity by electron microprobe analysis, and checked for structural state by X-ray diffraction. Unfortunately it is likely that such a study would produce only small changes in the curves given by Burri *et al.*, thereby providing little incentive for the laborious task. It is quite uncertain what is the effect of Or content on the regression curves, and detailed measurements are desirable.

The optical orientation of plagioclase may be plotted in many ways, and the literature is full of different diagrams all showing essentially the same features, but varying in detail. Although one can quibble about details, the diagrams of Burri *et al.* (1967) are preferred because they are mutually consistent and clearly displayed. The curves show small erratic kinks, especially at the anorthite end, and it is almost certain that these result in part from errors in the chemical analyses and optical data of the reference specimens. In addition, it is likely that the high curve does not represent the state of highest structural disorder especially in the labradorite and bytownite region. Optical measurements of bytownites and anorthites made since 1967 have reduced the uncertainty in this region. Müller *et al.* (1972) showed that there is considerable scatter for both plutonic and volcanic specimens in this composition region with strong overlap of the ranges (Fig. 8-17).

There are several ways in which the optical orientation of plagioclase can be measured and presented on diagrams. The subject is too complex technically to be presented here, and only a general theoretical outline is given.

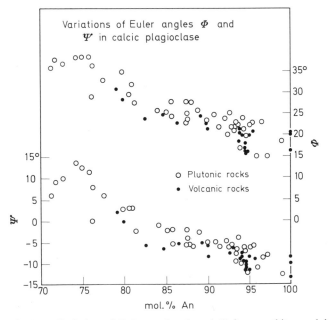

Fig. 8-17. Variation of Euler angles Φ and Ψ for anorthites and bytownites from plutonic and volcanic rocks. Data from various sources. (From Müller *et al.*, 1972, Fig. 1)

Mathematically, the most convenient way to specify the angular orientation is by the three Euler angles which relate two sets of orthogonal axes. For details of the use of Euler angles see the treatment in German by Burri (1956) and Burri *et al.* (1967), in English by Plas, van der (1966) or by Marfunin (1966), and in Russian by Marfunin (1962). For data on Euler angles see Burri *et al.* (1967), Gottardi (1961), Marfunin (1962), and Müller *et al.* (1972).

Ideally the complete orientation should be determined by use of a U-stage (see Plas, van der, 1966, p. 110 for a list of references). In practice there are various methods for routine petrographic study which utilize merely a one-axis petrographic microscope, and measurement of an extinction angle with respect to a morphological or twin direction.

Plagioclase twins can be identified from the optical properties, and once a correct identification has been made, the twin elements can then be used as crystallographic references. Chapter 18 lists information on twin laws. Many plagioclase twins probably obey the twin law strictly and have well-defined twin boundaries. Others may not obey the twin law exactly (synneusis twins and perhaps deformation twins). In any event, care must be taken in checking all the optical and morphological features. Some twin laws at certain compositions are indistinguishable by optical methods (Chapter 18). The whole subject of optical identification of twins is extremely complex, and can be learnt only by extensive practice preferably under the supervision of a skilled worker. Burri *et al.* (1967) and Bambauer *et al.* (1971) give several stereographic projections oriented especially to permit rapid checking of twin orientations.

Köhler (1942b) described the angular relations in twins by plotting the angular separations between the optic symmetry axes associated with the $n(\alpha)$ index against An content for each particular class of twin, together with two more pairs for the Y and the Z axes. Each group of three angles, denoted $\alpha\alpha'$, $\beta\beta'$ and $\gamma\gamma'$ is described collectively as the *Köhler angles*, and the determinative technique which utilizes them is known as the *joined-angle technique*. In addition, the angles between the pairs of optic axes AA' and BB' can be given. The latest data are given by Burri *et al.* (1967) and Bambauer *et al.* (1971). In using the Köhler angles for determinative work, it would seem worth-while to compare morphological directions such as the cleavage traces and twin boundaries with the indicated position of the symmetry element of the twin obtained from averaging between the optical directions. If good agreement were obtained, extra confidence would be obtained in the result.

The simplest method experimentally involves measurement of an extinction angle on a cleavage fragment or against a twin or morphological direction in a thin section. All such methods provide only one measurement, and there is no check that the morphological or twin element has been correctly identified. The extinction angles vary with both structural state and An-content. Probably errors of 5% An are quite common in estimates made from extinction angles, and even larger ones might occur. Reference curves are given by Burri *et al.* (1967) and Bambauer *et al.* (1971).

A. C. Tobi recommends measurement of the extinction angle on sections normal to *a*. Such sections should be recognizable in thin section from traces of the {010} and {001} cleavages lying at 94°. Alternatively, Albite twins might

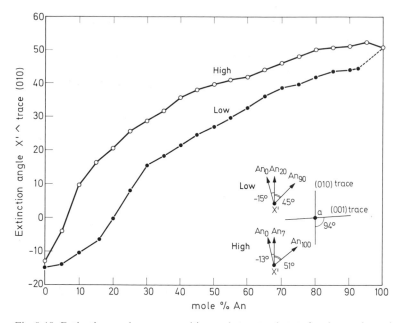

Fig. 8-18. Extinction angle vs. composition and structural state for the *a*-axis section of plagioclase. The curves for the low and high series were estimated graphically by the Biot-Fresnel construction from the data of Burri *et al.* (1967) given in Fig. 8-16. The plotting error should be less than 0.5°. The inset diagram at the lower right shows the angular relations between the crystallographic and optical directions. The traces of the (010) and (001) cleavages lie at 94°. The directions of the fast vibration X′ are shown for various compositions and structural states

be found with the {001} cleavage zig-zagging at + and −94° across the twin boundaries. From Fig. 8-16 it may be seen by eye that the extinction angle for the slow vibration [corresponding nearly to $n(\gamma)$] onto the trace of (001) changes from about −10° for albite to about +50° for anorthite. Figure 8-18 shows extinction angles calculated from Fig. 8-16 using the Biot-Fresnel construction. In order to conform with earlier diagrams in the literature, the angle is given between the fast vibration $X′$ and the trace of (010) using the sign convention shown in the lower left of Fig. 8-18. Structural state has a major effect on the extinction angle. If a high plagioclase were incorrectly measured with the low curve, the resulting estimate of An content would be too high by an amount up to 25% An for intermediate compositions. At pure albite and anorthite, the effect of structural state is trivial, however. Probably plagioclase from plutonic and regionally-metamorphosed rocks can be assigned to the low structural state, and it is likely that the An-content estimated from the extinction angle is accurate within 10% An and perhaps within 2% An. However plagioclase from volcanic and hypabyssal rocks may have a structural state intermediate between the high and low series: consequently the extinction angle may yield compositions uncertain to an amount ranging up to 25% An. The curves in Fig. 8-18 obviously suffer from the same uncertainties as those given by Burri *et al.*, and their position, especially for calcic compositions, may need revision. It seems obvious that extinction angles should be used only for very rough reconnaissance of plagioclase in thin section, and that whenever possible more accurate methods should be used.

For detailed instructions on optical identification of plagioclase feldspars, especially detrital ones, the reader is referred to Plas, van der (1966), who describes many of the available techniques including those developed by A. C. Tobi.

8.3.5 Comparison of Determinative Methods

This section is designed to help the non-specialist decide how the many techniques can be employed most efficiently in assessing the An-content and structural state. The specialist will wish to use electron microprobe (and perhaps ion microprobe) techniques to obtain the chemical composition, both electron-optical and single crystal X-ray methods to determine the structural state, and U-stage optical methods to determine the twin laws. A typical example of such a specialized study is that of Müller et al. (1972).

For routine petrographic study, the An-content can be estimated in favorable cases to about 5% An by extinction angle measurements in thin section or from grains, but larger errors can occur: in any serious study, the preliminary optical observations should be followed by electron microprobe analysis. Chemical zoning should be checked first by optical study of a thin section, and secondly by examination of cathodoluminescence either in a special apparatus or in an electron microprobe. Particular attention should be paid to luminescence at grain margins and around inclusions. Antiperthite is usually detected by a strong color or intensity variation. Apatite, epidote and calcite inclusions usually show luminescence of characteristic color. Careful reference to standards should permit the Ca, Na, K, Al and Si contents to be measured in an electron microprobe to about 1% of the amount present with a detection level of about $0.01 - 0.03$ wt.-%. The minor elements Fe, Mg and Ba can be detected at about the level of $0.01 - 0.02$ wt.-%. If an electron microprobe is not available, the next best estimate of An-content is from the refractive indices. For most purposes, Tsuboi's method seems suitable (e.g. as used by Morse, 1968). Some workers may prefer to use a spindle mount in order to orient the crystal in the best position. The glass bead method of Foster has the disadvantage that the grain is destroyed. If the sample is too fine-grained for Tsuboi's method, probably electron microprobe analysis should be used. Another alternative is a method involving measurement of extinction angles in thin section, but severe difficulties can occur with very small grains because of transmission of light through more than one crystal. Petrographers skilled in U-stage procedure will tend to favor measurements of the optical orientation especially as the structural state may be determinable simultaneously. However even the most skilled operator cannot achieve either the speed or the accuracy of the operator of an electron microprobe.

A real evaluation of the structural state can be obtained only by electron-optical and single-crystal X-ray methods. The former is particularly valuable because dark-field techniques allow evaluation of the domain texture of fine-scale intergrowths; however the technique is rather complex, and there are various subtle features which can be misinterpreted. For many plagioclases, a reasonable idea of the structural state can be obtained from single-crystal X-ray patterns, and the interpretation of the subsidiary diffractions is reasonably clear. Unfortunately the lack of direct information on the texture of intergrowths is a serious failing of the method. X-ray powder methods provide even less information because the subsidiary diffractions cannot be observed at all except in high-quality photographs of anorthites. For reconnaissance work, however, the powder methods are very useful because they permit rapid measurement of accurate cell dimensions. When the An-content is known, the angle γ^* or some simple function such as the 131 indicator allows a rapid estimate of structural state for the region An_0 to An_{70}, though care must be taken to consider the effect of Or substitution especially for ternary feldspars such as potassic oligoclases. For anorthites and bytownites, the effect of structural state on γ^* is small or zero, but the change of β^* although small appears to yield some information especially for pure anorthite. Whenever possible, reconnaissance studies of the structural state of plagioclase should be followed by detailed electron-optical or single-crystal X-ray studies of a few selected samples. Optical methods of estimating the structural state are less sensitive than X-ray powder methods, especially for calcic plagioclase, but are useful for experts in U-stage methods. This technique is particularly valuable when the plagioclase is highly variable as in detrital samples or when it is not easy to obtain an X-ray powder pattern (see Plas, van der, 1966).

   In conclusion, it seems that most petrologists will find that the following procedure will serve as a suitable reconnaissance: (a) preparation of polished thin section followed by routine optical examination for zoning, twinning, etc. (b) electron-microprobe analysis for Na, Ca and K, and perhaps for Fe, Ba and Mg (c) determination of structural state from X-ray powder methods (d) determination of twin-laws from U-stage examination with check of the optical orientation against the previous determinations of An-content and structural state.

8.4 K, Ba Feldspars

The detailed study by Roy (1965) suggests that earlier work (Yosimura, 1939; Segnit, 1946; Vermaas, 1953) contained various errors and should be treated with caution. Figure 8-19a shows the variation of refractive indices and $2V$ against wt.-% Cn molecule (note that Roy incorrectly labeled his diagram with mol.-%). The data are rather erratic, especially for $2V$, and the reason is unknown. Most optical data were obtained with a spindle stage, and each grain was later analyzed for Ba with an electron microprobe. Roy drew two curves which meet about Cn_{45} for each of the refractive indices. All specimens were optically monoclinic, and the potassic ones had Z parallel to b while the Ba-rich ones had Y parallel to b. Figure 8-19b shows extinction angles for $X\hat{a}$ in (010) for the potassic specimens, and $Z\hat{a}$ in (010) for the Ba-rich ones. Figure 8-19c compares $n(\beta)$ for natural and synthetic specimens. The latter show a single continuous variation without the kink displayed by the former.

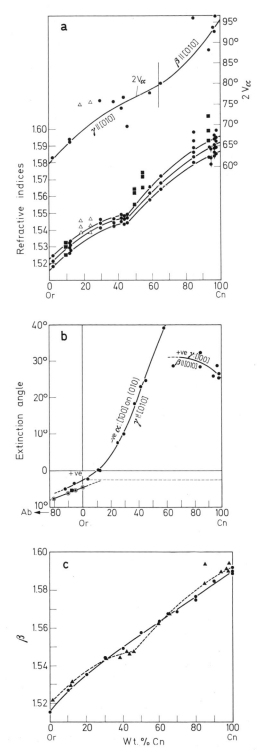

Fig. 8-19. Relation between optical properties and wt.-% Cn for K, Ba feldspars. a Relation for the principal refractive indices and 2V. The solid dots are data for natural specimens from Roy (1965). Squares are from Vermaas (1953); triangles from Yosimura (1939); and the solid dots with a vertical bar from Segnit (1946). b Relation for the extinction angle. Some data are also shown for alkali feldspars in the orthoclase series: dotted circles from Tuttle (1952) and square from Spencer (1937). c Comparison of the relations for the $n(\beta)$ index of natural (triangles) and synthetic (dots) specimens. (From Roy, 1965, Figs. 1, 2 and 6)

Although Roy stated that the extinction angle provided a determinative method for potassic specimens, he cautioned that little is known about the effect of structural state on the optics of K, Ba feldspars.

8.5 Other Feldspars and Related Phases

Winchell and Winchell (1964) collected optical data for all types of feldspars and related phases.

Table 7-1 lists the cell dimensions of many feldspar analogs, but complete optical data have been obtained for only a few.

Buddingtonite (Erd et al., 1964) is monoclinic with $n(\alpha)$ 1.530 $n(\beta)$ 1.531 $n(\gamma)$ 1.534 $\pm$ 0.002, $2V$ not measured, $X \hat{\,} a\, 4°$, $Z = b$, and $Y \hat{\,} c = 19°$.

Reedmergnerite (Milton et al., 1960) is triclinic, $n(\alpha)$ 1.554, $n(\beta)$ 1.565, $n(\gamma)$ 1.573 $\pm$ 0.001, $2V-80°$, optic orientation given in Fig. 5.

Iron-microcline (Wones and Appleman, 1963) is triclinic with $n(\alpha)$ 1.585, $n(\beta)$ 1.596, and $n(\gamma)$ 1.605 $\pm$ 0.002, $2V-85°$ (calculated), $X = b$, $Z \hat{\,} c = 20 \pm 5°$. Iron-sanidine (Wones and Appleman, 1961) is monoclinic with $n(\alpha)$ 1.584, $n(\beta)$ 1.595 and $n(\gamma)$ 1.605 $\pm$ 0.001, $2V \sim -85°$, $Y = b$, $Z \hat{\,} c = 16 \pm 4°$.

Data on paracelsian are given in section 2.4.1.

Hexagonal anorthite (Goldsmith and Ehlers, 1952) is uniaxial positive with refractive indices 1.585 and 1.590. Orthorhombic anorthite (Davis and Tuttle, 1952) has $n(\alpha)$ 1.553, $n(\beta)$ 1.580, $n(\gamma)$ 1.584, $2V-39°$, orientation not measured.

Eskola (1922) reported that the refractive indices of synthetic Sr-feldspar (?) were $n(\alpha)$ 1.574, $n(\beta)$ 1.582 and $n(\gamma)$ 1.586 $\pm$ 0.002. The crystals occurred as untwinned fibers, and the orientation was not determined.

$RbAlSi_3O_8$ (probably with sanidine structure) is monoclinic with $n(\alpha)$ 1.524 and $n(\gamma)$ 1.529 (see Winchell and Winchell, 1964, p. 232).

Goldsmith (1950) determined $n(\alpha)$ and $n(\gamma)$ for various synthetic feldspars containing Ga and Ge (see Winchell and Winchell, p. 232, including a correction supplied by Goldsmith).

References

Agrell, S. O., Scoon, J. H., Muir, I. D., Long, J. V. P., McConnell, J. D. C., Peckett, A. (1970): Observations on the chemistry, mineralogy and petrology of some Apollo 11 lunar samples. Proc. Apollo 11 Lunar Science Conf. 1, 93–128. New York: Pergamon Press.

Appleman, D. E., Nissen, H.-U., Stewart, D. B., Clark, J. R., Dowty, E., Huebner, J. S. (1971): Studies of lunar plagioclases, tridymite and cristobalite. Proc. Second Lunar Science Conf. 1, 117–133. The M.I.T. Press.

Balconi, M., Zezza, U. (1968): Considerazioni sulla determinazione per via ottica dello stato termico dei plagioclasi. Curve % An/2V. PM (Roma) 37, 67–127.

Bambauer, H. U. (1966): Feldspat-Familie $R_x{}^{I}R_{1-x}{}^{II}[Al_{2-x}Si_{2+x}O_8]$, $0 \leq x \leq 1$. In: Tröger, W. E.: Optische Bestimmungen der gesteinsbildenden Minerale Teil 2, Textband, pp. 645–762. Stuttgart: Schweizerbart'sche Verlagsbuchhandlung.

Bambauer, H. U., Laves, F. (1960): Zum Adularproblem. I. Adular vom Val Casatscha: Mimetischer Lamellenbau, Variation von Optik und Gitterkonstanten und ihre genetische Deutung. SMPM 40, 177–205.

Bambauer, H. U., Taborszky, F., Trochim, H. D. (1971): In: Tröger, W. E. (Ed.): Optische Bestimmung der gesteinsbildenden Minerale (nach Teil 1. Bestimmungstabellen. 4. neu bearbeitete Auflage). Stuttgart: Schweizerbart'sche Verlagsbuchhandlung.

Barber, C. T. (1936a): The effects of heat on the optical orientation of plagioclase felspars. MM **24**, 343—352.

Barber, C. T. (1936b): The Tertiary igneous rocks of the Pakokku district and the Salingyi township of the Lower Chindwin district, Burma, with special reference to the determination of the felspars by the Fedoroff method. Mem. Geol. Soc. India **68**, pt. 2, 121—296.

Barth, T. (1929): Über den monoklinen Natronfeldspat. ZK **69**, 476—481.

Barth, T. F. W. (1931): Permanent changes in the optical orientation of feldspars exposed to heat. NGT **12**, 57—72.

Barth, T. F. W. (1933): An occurrence of iso-orthoclase in Virginia. AM **18**, 478—479.

Barth, T. F. W. (1969): Feldspars, 261 pp. New York and London: Wiley, Interscience.

Barth, T. F. W., Oftedahl, C. (1947): High temperature plagioclase in the Oslo igneous rocks. Trans. Amer. Geophys. Union **28**, no. 1.

Belyankin, D. S. (1934): Albite from Druzhnaya Gorka works having a small angle of optic axes. DAN **3**, 651—655. In Russian.

Bloss, F. D. (1961): An introduction to the methods of optical crystallography. New York: Holt, Rinehart and Winston.

Bolton, H. C., Bursill, L. A., McLaren, A. C., Turner, R. G. (1966): On the origin of the colour of labradorite. Phys. stat. sol. **18**, 221—230.

Bordet, P. (1967): Mesure de la dispersion des biréfringences dans les feldspaths plagioclases. BSFMC **90**, 352—355.

Born, M., Wolf, E. (1965): Principles of optics. Third (revised) edition. Oxford: Pergamon Press.

Bradley, O. (1953): An investigation of high-temperature optics in some naturally occurring plagioclases. MM **30**, 227—245.

Brown, B. E., Bailey, S. W. (1964): The structure of maximum microcline. AC **17**, 1391—1400.

Burri, C. (1968): Die optische Orientierung von HT-Labradorit aus Andesite von Khuchiré (Iran), zugleich ein Beitrag zur U-Tischmethodik. SMPM **48**, 781—801.

Burri, C. (1972): Zur Definition und Berechnung der optischen Orientierung von Plagioklasen. SMPM **52**, 497—514.

Burri, C., Parker, R. L., Wenk, E. (1961): Project of a new general catalogue of data for the determination of plagioclases by the universal-stage method. CCILM **8**, 1 (abstr.).

Burri, C., Parker, R. L., Wenk, E. (1962): The optical orientation of the plagioclases. NGT **42**, No. 2, 207—214.

Burri, C., Parker, R. L., Wenk, E. (1967): Die optische Orientierung der Plagioklase – Unterlagen und Diagramme zur Plagioklasbestimmung nach der Drehtische-methode. 334 pp. Basel and Stuttgart: Birkhauser.

Carmichael, I. S. E. (1960): The feldspar phenocrysts of some Tertiary acid glasses. MM **32**, 587—608.

Chaisson, U. (1950): The optics of triclinic adularia. JG **58**, 537—547.

Chayes, F. (1950): On the relation between anorthite content and γ-index of natural plagioclase. JG **58**, 593—595.

Chayes, F. (1952): Relations between composition and indices of refraction in natural plagioclase. AJS, Bowen Vol., 85—105.

Chayes, F. (1954): A test of the revised determinative chart for plagioclases. AJS **252**, 172—180.

Chudoba, K., Engels, A. (1937a): Der Einfluß der Kalifeldspatkomponente auf die Optik der Plagio-klase. II. Chemismus und Optik der eingleider Albit, Anorthit und Microklin. ZM, Abt. A., 103—119.

Chudoba, K., Engels, A. (1937b): Der Einfluß der Kalifeldspatkomponente auf die Optik der Plagioklase. III. Die optische Orientierung kalifeldspathaltiger Plagioklase. ZM, Abt. A, 129—149.

Cloizeaux, A. Des (1875): Memoire sur les propriétés optiques biréfringentes caractéristiques des quatre principaux feldspaths tricliniques, et sur un procédé pour les distinguer immédiatement les uns des autres. Ann. Chim. Phys. IV, 429—444.

Colville, A. A., Ribbe, P. H. (1968): The crystal structure of an adularia and a refinement of the structure of orthoclase. AM **53**, 25—37.

Coulson, A. L. (1932): On the zoning and difference in composition of twinned plagioclase felspars in certain rocks from Sirohi State, Rajputana. Geol. Surv. India Records **65**, 163—172.

Crawford, M. L. (1966): Optical properties of metamorphic albite. AM **51**, 523–524.

Czank, M., Girgis, K., Harnik, A. B., Laves, F., Schmid, R., Schulz, H., Weber, L. (1972): Crystallographic studies of some lunar plagioclases. Third Lunar Sci. Conf., Houston, Lunar Science Inst. Contr. no. 88, 171–173.

Dana, E. D. (1920): The system of mineralogy of James Dwight Dana 1837–1868. Descriptive Mineralogy. Sixth Edition entirely rewritten and enlarged. New York: John Wiley and Sons.

Davis, G. L., Tuttle, O. F. (1952): Two new crystalline phases of the anorthite composition CaO · Al$_2$O$_3$ · 2SiO$_2$. AJS, Bowen Vol. 107–114.

Dawson, K. R., Maxwell, J. A. (1958): Possible loss of sodium and potassium during fusion of plagioclase feldspars. CM **6**, 288–290.

Deer, W. A., Howie, R. A., Zussman, J. (1963): Rock forming minerals, 435 pp. 4. Framework silicates. London: Longmans, Green and Co., Ltd.

Dittler, E., Köhler, A. (1933): Über Mischkristallbildung im ternären System An–Ab–Cg. TMPM **43**, 352–361.

Duparc, L. (1904): Sur une nouvelle variété d'orthose. Compte Rend. Acad. Sci. (Paris) **138**, 714.

Emerson, D. O. (1964): Absence of optically positive potash-feldspar in the Inyo Mountains, California – Nevada. AM **49**, 194–5.

Emmons, R. C., Crump, R. M., Ketner, K. B. (1960). High- and low-temperature plagioclase. BGSA **71**, 1417–20.

Emmons, R. C., Gates, R. M. (1943): Plagioclase twinning. BGSA **54**, 287–304.

Emmons, R. C. (Ed.), Gates, R. M., Clabaugh, S. E., Crump, R. M., Ketner, K. B., Mann, V., Reynolds, C. D., Saunders, D. F., Bradley, C., Lyons, E. J. (1953): Selected petrogenetic relationships of plagioclase. Geol. Soc. Amer., memoir 52, 142 pp.

Erd, R. C., White, D. E., Fahey, J. J., Lee, D. E. (1964): Buddingtonite, an ammonium feldspar with zeolitic water. AM **49**, 831–850.

Ernst, E., Nieland, H. (1934): Plagioklase von Linosa, ein Beitrag zur Anemousitfrage. TMPM **46**, 93–126.

Eskola, P. (1922): The silicates of strontium and barium. AJS, Series 5, **4**, 331–375.

Fedorow, E. (1893): Universal-(Theodolith-) Methode in der Mineralogie und Petrographie. I. Teil. Universalgeometrische Untersuchungen. ZK **21**, 574–714.

Federow, E. (1894): Universal-(Theodolith-) Methode in der Mineralogie und Petrographie. II. Teil. Krystalloptische Untersuchungen. ZK **22**, 229–268.

Federow, E. von (1896): Universalmethode und Feldspatstudien I. Methodische Verfahren. ZK **26**, 225–261.

Finney, J. J., Bailey, S. W. (1964): Crystal structure of an authigenic maximum microcline. ZK **119**, 413–436.

Fisher, D. J. (1960): A new universal-type microscope. ZK **113**, 77–93.

Foster, W. R. (1955): Simple method for the determination of the plagioclase feldspars. AM **40**, 179–185.

Fox, P. E., Moore, J. M. (1969): Feldspars from the Adamant pluton, British Columbia. Canadian Jour. Earth Sci. **6**, 1199–1209.

Glauser, A. (1959): Über die optische Orientierung einiger saurer Plagioklase aus Erguss und Ganggesteinen. SMPM **39**, 301–331.

Glauser, A. (1961): Zur Orientierung der Indikatrix in Plagioklas-Material von R. C. Emmons. SMPM **41**, 443–470.

Glauser, A. (1963): Über die optische Orientierung einiger Plagioklas-Zwillinge aus Linosa. SMPM **43**, 81–90.

Glauser, A. (1964): Zur optischen Orientierung einer komplexen Hochtemperatur-Andesin-Zwillingsgruppe aus Island. SMPM **44**, 429–438.

Glauser, A. (1966): Zur Orientierung der Indikatrix von Hochtemperatur-Plagioklasen in einem andesitischen Gestein aus Island. SMPM **46**, 61–79.

Glauser, A. (1967): Zur optischen Orientierung von Hochtemperatur-Plagioklasen aus einem andesitischen Gestein aus Island. SMPM **47**, 203–212.

Glauser, A. (1968): Zur optischen Orientierung von Hochtemperatur-Plagioklasen eines andesitischen Gesteins aus Island (Fortsetzung II). SMPM **48**, 509–518.

Glauser, A. (1970): Über die optische Orientierung der Hochtemperatur-Plagioklase aus einem Olivin-Dolerit aus Island. SMPM **50**, 245–256.

Glauser, A., Wenk, E. (1957): Über Gesetzmäßigkeiten im Verlaufe der Migrationskurven der Plagioklase (Federow-methode). SMPM **37**, 180–197.

Glauser, A., Wenk, E. (1960): Optische Orientierung und chemische Zusammensetzung einiger Hoch- und Tieftemperatur-Plagioklase. SMPM **40**, 37–53.

Goldsmith, J. R. (1950): Gallium and germanium substitutions in synthetic feldspars. JG **58**, 518–536.

Goldsmith, J. R., Ehlers, E. G. (1952): The stability relations of anorthite and its hexagonal polymorph in the system $CaAl_2Si_2O_8 - H_2O$: JG **60**, 386–397.

Gysin, M. (1948): Les feldspaths potassiques des granites de Gastern et de quelques granites de l'Aar. SMPM **28**, 230–245.

Gysin, M. (1957): Sur l'existence d'«orthoses tricliniques» dans certaines roches de l'Himalaya du Nepal. SMPM **37**, 159–178.

Hewlett, C. G. (1959): Optical properties of potassic feldspars. BGSA, **70**, 511–538.

Hintze, C. (1893): Handbuch der Mineralogie. VII. Silicate und Titanate. Leipzig.

Homma, F. (1932): Über das Ergebnis von Messungen an zonaren Plagioklasen aus Andesiten mit Hilfe des Universaldrehtisches. SMPM **12**, 345–352.

Hulst van de, H. C. (1957): Light scattering by small particles. New York: John Wiley and Sons.

Hunt, T. S. (1854): Illustrations of chemical homology. AJS **18**, 269–271.

Hunt, T. S. (1855): Examinations of some feldspathic rocks. Phil. Mag. **9**, Ser. 4, 354–363.

Kääden, G. van der (1951): Optical studies on natural plagioclase feldspars with high- and low-temperature optics, 105 pp. Dissertation, University Utrecht.

Kano, H. (1955): High temperature optics of natural sodic plagioclases. Miner. Jour. Japan **1**, 255–277.

Kastner, M. (1971): Authigenic feldspars in carbonate rocks. AM **56**, 1403–1442.

Kazakov, A. N. (1956): On the occurrence of positive microclines. Mém. Soc. Russe Min. **85**, 433–434. In Russian.

Köhler, A. (1942a): Die Abhängigkeit der Plagioklasoptik vom vorangegangenen Wärmeverhalten. TMPM **53**, 24–49.

Köhler, A. (1942b): Drehtischmessungen an Plagioklaszwillingen von Tief- und Hochtemperaturoptik. TMPM **53**, 159–179.

Köhler, A. (1949): Recent results of investigations on the feldspars. JG **57**, 592–599.

Larsson, W. (1941): Petrology of interglacial volcanics from the Andes of northern Patagonia. Bull. Geol. Inst. Univ. (Upsala) **28**, 191–405.

Laves, F. (1965): The correlation of optics and lattice geometry of microcline. AM **50**, 509–510.

Laves, F., Chaisson, U. (1950): An X-ray investigation of the "high"-"low" albite relations. JG **58**, 584–592.

Luczizky, W. (1905): Der Granit von Kössein im Fichtelgebirge und seine Einschlüsse. TMPM **24**, 347.

Lundegårdh, P. H. (1941): Bytownit aus Anorthosit von Bönskär im nördlichen Teil der Stockholmer Schären und seine Beziehungen zu verschiedenen Feldspatsbestimmungskurven. Bull. Geol. Inst. Univ. (Upsala) **28**, 415–430.

Mackenzie, W. S. (1956): The orientation of the pericline twin lamellae in triclinic alkali felspars. MM **31**, 41–46.

Mackenzie, W. S., Smith, J. V. (1955): The alkali feldspars: I, Orthoclase microperthites. AM **40**, 707–732.

Mackenzie, W. S., Smith, J. V. (1956): The alkali feldspars. III. An optical and X-ray study of high temperature feldspars. AM **41**, 405–427.

Mallard, F. (1876): Explications des phénomènes optiques anomaux qui présentent un grand nombre de substances cristallisées. Annales des mines, **10**, 187–240. Alternatively, see ZK **1**, 201–237 (1877).

Mallard, F. (1881): Sur l'isomorphisme des feldspaths tricliniques. Bull. Soc. minéral. France **4**, 96–111.

Mallard, F. (1884): Traité de cristallographie II. Paris.

Manolescu, G. (1934): Über die Lage der morphologischen Bezugsrichtungen bei Plagioklasen und ihre Verwendbarkeit zur Bestimmung des Anorthitgehaltes. SMPM **14**, 452–463.

Marfunin, A. S. (1958): A new diagram for the optical orientation of acid and intermediate plagioclases. DAN **118**, 1183–1186. In Russian.

Marfunin, A. S. (1961): The relation between structure and optical orientation in potash-soda feldspars. CCILM **8**, 97–109.

Marfunin, A. S. (1962): Feldspars-phase relations, optical properties, geological distribution. Trans. Inst. Geol. Ore Deposits, Petr., Min., Geochem., No. 78, 275. In Russian.

Marfunin, A. S. (1966): The feldspars: phase relations, optical properties, and geological distribution. (Transl. from the Russian edition, 1962). Jerusalem (Israel Prog. Sci. Translations), 317 pp.

Milton, C., Chao, E. C. T., Axelrod, J. M., Grimaldi, F. S. (1960): Reedmergnerite, $NaBSi_3O_8$. The boron analogue of albite. AM **45**, 188–199.

Morse, S. A. (1968): Revised dispersion method for low plagioclase. AM **53**, 105–115.

Müller, W. F., Wenk, H. R., Thomas, G. (1972): Structural variations in anorthites. CMP **34**, 304–314.

Muir, I. D. (1955): Transitional optics of some andesines and labradorites. MM **30**, 545–568.

Munro, M. (1963): Errors in the measurement of $2V$ with the universal stage. AM **48**, 308–323.

Neiva, A. M. R. (1972): Optic axial angle, obliquity and sodium content of potash feldspars of granites, aplites and pegmatites. Abstr. 6.9 in program for Advanced Study Institute on Feldspars, July 1972, Manchester.

Nickel, E. (1948): Plagioklaseinschlüsse in Sanidineinsprenglingen der Nevadite von den Cerros Alifragas. Heidelberg Beitr. Min. Petr. **1**, 403–406.

Nickel, E. (1953): Zur Perthitbildung durch Plagioklasresorption bei Kalifeldspatblastese. NJMM 246–264.

Nieuwenkamp, W. (1966): Stereograms for the determination of plagioclase feldspars in random sections, 29 pp. Amsterdam: Elsevier.

Noble, D. C. (1965): Determination of composition and structural state of plagioclase with the five-axis universal stage. AM **50**, 367–381.

Nye, J. F. (1960): Physical properties of crystals. Oxford: University Press.

Oftedahl, C. (1944): High temperature optics in plagioclases of the Oslo region. NGT **24**, 75–79.

Oftedahl, C. (1948): Studies on the igneous rock complex of the Oslo region. IX. The feldspars. Norsk Vidensk.-Akad. Oslo, Mat.-Nat. Kl., Skr. No. 3, 71 pp.

Oftedahl, C. (1950): Note on "pseudo-monoclinic" plagioclase. JG **58**, 596–597.

Paliuc, G. (1932): Untersuchungen der Plagioklase einiger tertiärer Ergussgesteine Siebenbürgens (Rumänien) mittelst der Universaldrehtischmethode. SMPM **12**, 423–444.

Paraskevopoulos, G. M. (1953): Beitrag zur Kenntnis der Feldspäte der Tessiner Pegmatite. TMPM **3**, Ser. 3, 191–271.

Pavelescu, L. (1968): Contribution to the study of isortoses in the southern Carpathians. Rev. Roum. Géol. Géophys. Géogr., sér. géol. **12** (1), 37–41.

Phemister, T. C. (1954): Fletcher's indicatrix and the electromagnetic theory of light. AM **39**, 172–192.

Plas, L. van der (1966): The identification of detrital feldspars, 305 pp. Amsterdam: Elsevier.

Pringle, G. J., Trembath, L. T., Pajari, G. E. (1973): Plagioclase feldspar determination in a non-equilibrium system. CM **12**, 87–94.

Raase, P., Kern, H. (1969): Über die Synthese von Albiten bei Temperaturen von 250 bis 700° C. CMP **21**, 225–237.

Rankin, D. W. (1967): Axial angle determinations in Orville's microcline-low albite solid solution series. AM **52**, 414–417.

Reinhard, M. (1931): Universal Drehtischmethoden, 119 p. Basel: B. Wepf et Cie.

Riederer, J. (1966): Rapakivifeldspäte in moldanubischen Graniten. TMPM **11**, 29–40.

Roy, N. N. (1965): The mineralogy of the potassium-barium feldspar series. I. The determination of the optical properties of natural members. MM **35**, 508–518.

Schairer, J. F., Smith, J. R., Chayes, F. (1956): Refractive indices of plagioclase glasses. ARDGL, Yearbook 55, 195–197.

Schedler, R. A. (1971): Optical, chemical, and structural determinations of volcanic, acid Icelandic plagioclase feldspars. SMPM **51**, 463–509.

Schneider, T. R. (1957): Röntgenographische und optische Untersuchung der Umwandlung Albit–Analbit–Monalbit. ZK **109**, 245–271.

Scholler, H. (1942): Versuche zur Temperaturabhängigkeit der Plagioklasoptik. TMPM **53**, 180–221.

Schuster, M. (1880): Über die optische Orientierung der Plagioklase. TMPM **3**, 117–284.

Schwarzmann, S. (1956): Über die Lichtbrechung und die Achsenwinkel von Hochtemperatur-plagioklasen und ihre Entstehungsbedingungen. Heidelberg. Beitr. Min. Petr. **5**, 105–112.

Segnit, E. R. (1946): Barium-felspars from Broken Hill, New South Wales. MM **27**, 166—174.

Slemmons, D. B. (1962a): Determination of volcanic and plutonic plagioclases using a three- or four-axis universal stage. Geol. Soc. Amer. Spec. Paper No. 69, 64 pp.

Slemmons, D. B. (1962b): Observations on order-disorder relations of natural plagioclase. I. A method of evaluating order-disorder. NGT **42**, No. 2, 533–554.

Smith, J. R. (1958): Optical properties of heated plagioclases. AM **43**, 1179–1194.

Smith, J. R. (1960): Optical properties of low-temperature plagioclase. Appendix 3 in Hess, H. H.: Stillwater igneous complex, a quantitative mineralogical study. Geol. Soc. Amer. Memoir **80**, 191–219.

Smith, J. V., Ribbe, P. H. (1966): X-ray-emission microanalysis of rock-forming minerals. III. Alkali feldspars. JG **74**, 197–216.

Spaenhauer, F. (1933): Über das Ergebnis von Messungen an synthetischen Plagioklasen mit Hilfe des Universaldrehtisches. SMPM **13**, 356 – 365.

Spencer, E. (1930): A contribution to the study of moonstone from Ceylon and other areas and of the stability-relations of the alkali-felspars. MM **22**, 291—367.

Spencer, E. (1937): The potash-soda-felspars. I. Thermal stability. MM **24**, 453—494.

Spencer, E. (1938): The potash-soda felspars. II. Some applications to petrogenesis. MM **25**, 87–118.

Stewart, D. B. (1972): Optic axial angle and extinction angles of alkali feldspars related by cell parameters to Al/Si order and composition. In press for proceedings of Advanced Study Institute on Feldspars.

Tertsch, H. (1942a): Die optische Orientierung des Hochtemperatur-Anorthites. TMPM **53**, 50–66.

Tertsch, H. (1942b): Zur Hochtemperaturoptik basischer Plagioklase. TMPM **54**, 193–217.

Tertsch, H. (1942c): Zur Hochtemperatur-Optik der Plagioklase. ZM 137–144.

Tobi, A. C. (1965): On the cause of internal optical scatter in plagioclase, and the occurrence of lamellar Albite-Ala B twinning. AJS **263**, 712–718.

Tschermak, G. (1864): Chemisch-mineralogische Studien. I. Die Feldspathgruppe. SAWW **50**, 566–613.

Tsuboi, S. (1934): A straight-line diagram for determining plagioclases by the dispersion method. Japan Jour. Geol. Geogr. **11**, 325–326.

Tsuboi, S. (1936): Petrological notes (11)–(18). Isoorthoclase. Japan. Jour. Geol. Geogr. **13**, 333–337.

Tsuboi, S. (1968): Optical determination of low- and high-temperature plagioclases. I, II, III. Proc. Japan. Acad. **44**, 151–154, 155–160, 501–506.

Tuttle, O. F. (1952): Optical studies on alkali feldspars. AJS, Bowen Vol., 553–568.

Tuttle, O. F., Bowen, N. L. (1950): High-temperature albite and contiguous feldspars. JG **58**, 572–583.

Tuttle, O. F., Bowen, N. L. (1958): Origin of granite in light of experimental studies in the system NaAlSi$_3$O$_8$-KAlSi$_3$O$_8$ – SiO$_2$ – H$_2$O. Geol. Soc. Amer. Mem. **74**, 153 pp.

Uebel, P.-J. (1972): Ein Verfahren, daß die Anwendung der Zonenmethode nach A. Rittmann auch bei fehlender Spaltbarkeit nach (001) ermöglicht. NJMM 191–192.

Uruno, K. (1963): On the ordering degree of plagioclases. Sci. Repts., Tohoku Imp. Univ. **8**, Ser. A, 171–220.

Vermaas, F. H. S. (1953): A new occurrence of barium-feldspar at Otjosondu, S. W. Africa, and an X-ray method for determining the composition of hyalophane. AM **38**, 845–857.

Vogel, T. A. (1964): Optical-crystallographic scatter in plagioclase. AM **49**, 614–633.

Washington, H. S., Wright, F. E. (1910): A feldspar from Linosa and the existence of soda anorthite (carnegieite). AJS **179**, 52–70.

Wenk, E. (1933): Statistische Drehtischuntersuchungen an Plagioklasen rumänischer Ergußgesteine. SMPM **13**, 205–219.

Wenk, E. (1960): Zur Analyse der Migrationskurven der Hochtemperatur-Plagioklase. SMPM **40**, 313–322.

Wenk, E., Glauser, A., Schwander, H., Trommsdorff, V. (1972a): Optical orientation, composition and twin-laws of plagioclases from rocks 12051, 14053 and 14310. Third Lunar Sci. Conf., Houston. Lunar Science Inst. Contr. No. 88, 794–796.

Wenk, E., Glauser, A., Schwander, H. (1972b): Bytownit aus isländischem Olivinbasalt. SMPM **52**, 515–522.

Wenk, E., Schwander, H., Trommsdorff, V. (1967): Optische Orientierung zweier Anorthite aus metamorphen Gesteinen. SMPM **47**, 219–224.

Wenk, E., Schwander, H., Wenk, H. R. (1965): Labradorit von Surtsey (Island). Acta Naturalia Islandica, II, 5.

Wenk, E., Trommsdorff, V. (1967): The optical orientation of synthetic anorthite. SMPM **47**, 213–218.

Wenk, E., Wenk, H.-R., Schwander, H. (1968): Bytownite from Cape Parry, East Greenland. AM **53**, 1759–1764.

Wenk, H.-R. (1966): Labradorite from Surtsey (Iceland). SMPM **46**, 81–84.

Wenk, H.-R. (1969): Annealing of oligoclase at high pressure. AM **54**, 95–100.

Wenk, H.-R., Nord, G. L. (1971): Lunar bytownite from sample 12032,44. Proc. Second Lunar Science Conf. **1**, 135–150.

Winchell, A. N., Winchell, H. (1951): Elements of optical mineralogy. An introduction to microscopic petrography. Fourth edition. Part II. Descriptions of minerals. New York: John Wiley and Sons.

Winchell, A. N., Winchell, H. (1964): The microscopical characters of artificial inorganic solid substances: Optical properties of artificial minerals. New York: Academic Press.

Wones, D. R., Appleman, D. E. (1961): X-ray crystallography and optical properties of synthetic monoclinic $KFeSi_3O_8$, iron-sanidine. USGS Prof. Paper **424**-C, 309–310.

Wones, D. R., Appleman, D. E. (1963): Properties of synthetic triclinic $KFeSi_3O_8$, iron-microcline, with some observations on the iron-microcline iron-sanidine transition. JP **4**, 131–137.

Wright, T. L. (1964): The alkali feldspars of the Tatoosh pluton in Mount Rainier National Park. AM **49**, 715–735.

Wright, T. L., Stewart, D. B. (1968): X-ray and optical study of alkali feldspar. I. Determination of composition and structural state from refined unit-cell parameters and 2V. AM **53**, 38–87.

Yosimura, T. (1939): Studies on the minerals from the manganese deposit of the Kaso mine, Japan. J. Fac. Sci. Hokkaido Univ. **4**, Ser. 4, 313–451.

Chapter 9 Nomenclature and General Properties of Feldspars

9.1 General

In this chapter, the specific properties of feldspars revealed in other chapters are brought together, and the resulting general properties are used in the naming of this complex family of minerals. A brief survey of the nomenclature is given in the Summary, and Fig. S-4 gives the compositional ranges of various types of feldspars.

This chapter on nomenclature is placed here because measurements must be made before a feldspar can be named. Except for special research studies, most feldspars are named on the basis of optical and X-ray studies. A really satisfactory name can be given only if sufficient measurements of the *right type* have been made. Usually a compromise is made based on the availability of time and equipment. Any scheme of nomenclature should be flexible enough to accommodate the needs of different types of scientists: thus a field petrologist may be content with a simpler characterization than a research mineralogist. In addition, the nomenclature should involve the least dislocation with earlier nomenclatures so that one can go back to earlier results and salvage as many as possible by translation of older nomenclatures.

Most of the names assigned to the feldspars have a long history associated with increasing accuracy of usage. In the nineteenth century, many names were given to specimens now known to be trivial varieties. In the twentieth century, laboratory-oriented mineralogists identified most of the major features of feldspars, but squabbled over fine details. Consequently it is necessary to describe in detail the historical development of the major terms. Abandoned terms from the nineteenth century will be mostly ignored, and readers should refer to the fascinating review by Barth (1969) of old names.

The identifying characteristic of the group of feldspar minerals is the topology of the aluminosilicate framework which specifies the way in which the double-crankshaft chains are linked together. Paracelsian and phillipsite are not feldspars because the chains are hooked together in a different manner. It is customary to distinguish between naturally-occurring feldspars and chemical analogs prepared only in the laboratory.

Surprisingly, the spelling of the name feldspar is still controversial. Most mineral names are transliterated into different languages in response to phonetic needs. The term "feldspat" derives from the Swedish paper of Tilas (1740), probably with the implication of common occurrence in fields (see Barth, 1969, p. 239 for a copy of the original reference. and Zenzén, 1925 for a discussion). Deer *et al.* (1963) listed the different spellings that were used in subsequent years, and accepted the argument of L. J. Spencer that the term felspar should be used. In 1973, most scientists in the world use feldspar, and it would be simplest if the minority joined the majority, irrespective of any etymological or linguistic arguments.

Barth (1969) described the origin of most of the special names applied to feldspar minerals (with the surprising omission of sanidine), together with notes. Other information is contained in Chester (1896). A detailed review of the history of feldspar research is given by Marfunin (1962, 1966).

9.2 Alkali Feldspars

9.2.1 K-feldspars

Of the many names for K-rich feldspars, only the following are worth consideration: sanidine, orthoclase, microcline and adularia.

Orthoclase, named for the perpendicular cleavages (010) and (001) by Breithaupt (1823), was often used as a synonym for K-feldspar, but its meaning has narrowed in recent years. Although the similar term, *orthose*, from Haüy (1801) has priority, and is still used in France, orthoclase is preferred because of its popularity. Before the application of X-ray methods, orthoclase was used in a general sense as a K-feldspar with monoclinic optical properties. Some investigators distinguished *sanidine* as a special type of monoclinic K-feldspar, and others believed that at least some monoclinic K-feldspars were really triclinic with sub-optical twinning.

Sanidine was originally distinguished as a variety of orthoclase on the basis of board-shaped crystals (Nose, 1808). The original crystals of sanidine came from volcanic rocks of the lower Rhine Valley, and had the typical glassy appearance now used for preliminary identification of sanidine. Later, emphasis shifted to the smallness of the optic axial angle (Cloizeaux, des, 1862), and finally to disorder of the T atoms. Optical petrographers distinguish between high sanidine with the optic axial plane parallel to (010) and low sanidine with the optic axial plane crossing (010) – see Fig. 8-5.

Microcline was distinguished from orthoclase by a small deviation from 90° of the angle between the (010) and (001) cleavages (Breithaupt, 1830). Most microcline crystals have monoclinic morphology because of their fine-scale twinning, and the status of microcline was unclear for many years, especially in view of Mallard's model for interpretation of orthoclase as sub-optically twinned microcline (Chapter 8). However the optical goniometric data of Bøggild (1911) and the X-ray data of Laves (1950) clearly established microcline as an independent type of K-feldspar.

Adularia was named by Pini (1783) from the famous St. Gotthard region, erroneously ascribed to the Adula Mountains. All adularias have a distinctive habit (Chapter 17), and are known to occur only by crystallization at low temperature in veins or in some low-grade metamorphic or metasomatic rocks. The low temperature of crystallization results in metastable behavior with a wide range of optical and structural properties.

Perhaps the best idea of the status of the nomenclature of K-feldspar prior to detailed X-ray study of the whole group can be gained from the work of E. Spencer (especially 1937, 1938). From his detailed optical study, he displayed

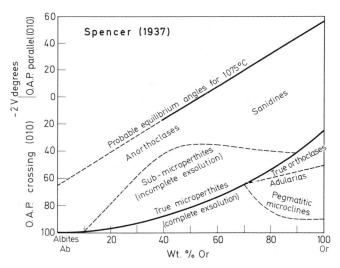

Fig. 9-1. Varieties of alkali feldspars described by Spencer on the basis of optical studies of heated and unheated specimens. Compare with Fig. 8-5, which is based on both X-ray and optical data. (Redrawn from Spencer, 1937, Fig. 19)

alkali feldspars on a diagram of optic axial angle and bulk composition (Fig. 9-1). Although the details are wrong. this diagram is reasonably consistent with modern ideas (e.g. Fig. 8-5). Sanidine and microcline are identified as varieties occurring at high and low temperatures, respectively. The term *true orthoclase* was developed to cover optically monoclinic K-feldspars with $-2V$ near $40°$, so commonly found in granites. Only one adularia was studied in detail, thereby precluding discovery of the wide range of optical properties. The field of perthites should have been extended into the fields of orthoclase and microcline.

Tuttle (1952) extended Spencer's classification (see Fig. 8-5) distinguishing between microcline. orthoclase. low sanidine and high sanidine as end-members of four series of perthites. Spencer (1938. p. 88-89) concluded that his observations "indicate a fundamental difference between orthoclase and microcline, and support Warren's hypothesis of inversion. rather than the (Mallard and Michel-Lévy) hypothesis of pseudo-monoclinic symmetry in orthoclase".

Optical studies cannot reveal textures finer than about 100 unit cells across. thereby precluding complete characterization of K-feldspars by optical means. X-ray diffraction allows characterization at the atomic level. Taylor (1933) determined the topology of the feldspar framework. and the chemical linkages. Barth (1934) proposed that the polymorphism of K-feldspar results from order-disorder of the Al and Si atoms in tetrahedral sites. and a series of X-ray structural analyses in the laboratory of W. H. Taylor verified the proposal. Cole *et al.* (1949) and Bailey and Taylor (1955) provided the key analyses of sanidinized orthoclase and an intermediate microcline, respectively. Chapter 3 lists data for other specimens studied by both X-ray and neutron diffraction. Confirming data were obtained independently by infra-red and nuclear magnetic resonance techniques (Chapter 11), the key studies being those of Hafner and Laves (1957) and Brun *et al.* (1960). The n.m.r. technique was applied only to a few specimens carefully selected for their homogeneity. Running in parallel were X-ray and optical studies of many specimens from a wide range of geological environments. These studies revealed the complexities of K-feldspars, and emphasized the problem of nomenclature.

The pioneering studies of Chao and Taylor (1940) and Chao *et al.* (1939, 1940) began the unveiling of the complexities. but were hampered by the low sensitivity of the X-ray equipment. Laves (1950) made a crucial advance with his characterization of microcline. orthoclase and adularia, and in 1952 (p. 443) summarized his conclusions:

"1. Microcline[3] has $\alpha = 90°39'$; $\gamma = 87°47'$. ([3]Average values $\cdots$ may be somewhat variable depending on Na-content).

2. Adularia (triclinic) [4]has $\alpha = 90° \ 3' - 90° \ 8'$; $\gamma = 89°36' - 89° \ 20'$. ([4]It might not be surprising to find larger and smaller values).

3. Adularia (monoclinic) has $\alpha = 90°$; $\gamma = 90°$.

4. At least three 'types' of *optically monoclinic* feldspar exist: (a) Truly monoclinic feldspars with sharp diffraction spots and $\alpha = \gamma = 90°$. (b) Those which appear optically monoclinic owing to exceedingly fine albite or albite and pericline twinning. In these cases Mallard's view is correct. The tiny triclinic individuals of these crystals have true microcline geometry, as in 1, above. (c) Those which appear optically monoclinic but are actually composed of sub-microscopic triclinic areas twinned predominantly with the albite law. The triclinic areas, unlike microcline. cannot be characterized by definite values of α and γ. These values deviate from 90°. however, in the same direction as do microcline and adularia. The X-ray diffraction spots of this material are both sharp and diffuse $\cdots$.

5. Evaluation of the intensities of the X-ray spots indicated that there is a more or less continuous gradation from the truly monoclinic sanidine structure (which can be precisely characterized by X-ray data) to the truly triclinic microcline structure (which can also be precisely characterized by X-ray data). Intermediate members vary more or less continuously with respect to α, γ, and the degree of diffuseness of the X-ray reflections.

6. Additional preliminary experiments have shown that all 'normal' orthoclases investigated (using Spencer's term for orthoclases which have a 'normal' $2V_\alpha$ of $40° - 60°$ in a plane parallel to the b-axis) show characteristic diffuse reflections... A satisfactory explanation has not yet been given for these diffuse reflections, but they can be considered as an indication that these crystals are not in an equilibrium state". Then he went on to conclude (p. 447–449):

"1. Potash feldspar. $KAlSi_3O_8$. is dimorphic. having two *stable* modifications. These are sanidine, stable above approximately 700° C, and *microcline* stable below this temperature".

[2. and 3. discuss ordering as a continuous process].

"4. It follows that a continuous sequence of potash feldspars, showing variations in order as a function of temperature, may exist under equilibrium conditions somewhat below the transformation temperature.

5. Adularia is formed at temperatures far below the order-disorder transformation temperature. It may thus crystallize as a completely disordered (monoclinic) or highly disordered (somewhat triclinic) form. It may also be possible that under special conditions the highly ordered microcline is formed. From this viewpoint, *adularia* is not a distinct modification of $KAlSi_3O_8$. Aside from its morphology, one of the chief characteristics of adularia is its variability as expressed in optical properties. the variation being induced by environmental differences during and after crystallization. The rate of crystallization might strongly influence the degree of disorder. as might the length of its whole thermal history.

6. In similar fashion *orthoclase*, or rather *common orthoclase* (a name here to be used). is believed to be unstable. Common orthoclase may have formed either above $\sim 700°$ C as a stable disordered monoclinic modification or also as a monoclinic modification below the transformation temperature under non-equilibrium conditions. The large temperature range and variation of environment in which common orthoclase may form probably accounts for the habit variation observed. whereas the limited environmental conditions under which adularia forms probably accounts for its more distinctive morphology. A disordered monoclinic orthoclase, formed either metastably below $\sim 700°$ or stably above this temperature but then cooled below $\sim 700°$ C., tends to go in the direction of the stable microcline. The degree of conversion to microcline is again dependent on environmental conditions. chiefly time and temperature. It is thus not surprising to find in natural crystals a variety of intermediate states expressed by variable optical properties (for example. $2V$) and variable degree of diffuseness in the X-ray diffraction photographs".

On p. 449, Laves explicitly suggested that sanidine could exist either as sanidine (high) with (2Al + 6Si) in each of the T_1 and T_2 sites, or as sanidine (low) with (4Al + 4Si) and 8Si.

Apart from various subtle modifications. this set of conclusions on the polymorphism of K-feldspar was endorsed repeatedly by later research. However the arguments about the subtleties continue onwards and are still unresolved.

In the early nineteen-fifties there was a serious misunderstanding about the uses of the terms orthoclase and sanidine which was not resolved for ten more years. Laves was using *common orthoclase* for a range of K-feldspars thought to be unstable. and *sanidine (low)* for a hypothetical monoclinic ordered K-feldspar. The Cambridge group and Tuttle were using the simple term *orthoclase* to specify feldspars with certain optical properties: perhaps if they had used Spencer's term *true* (or *normal*) orthoclase. confusion would have been less. In addition, the Cambridge X-ray crystallographers were using *orthoclase* in a structural sense to represent the end-product of monoclinic ordering of T atoms; this usage was the same as that proposed by Laves for *sanidine (low)*. Tuttle was using *low sanidine* for the end-member of an optical series.

Two years later Bailey (1954). Goldsmith and Laves (1954a, b) and MacKenzie (1954) established conclusively that K-feldspar shows a continuous gradation from a geometrically monoclinic lattice to a triclinic lattice with angles α 90° 39′ and γ 87° 47′. Following a suggestion from Laves. MacKenzie introduced the term *maximum microcline*. He also stated "The term orthoclase is used throughout the paper to indicate low-temperature monoclinic potash feldspar". Earlier, MacKenzie (1952) had suggested the use of the separation of pairs of peaks in an X-ray diffraction pattern for characterization of K-feldspars, and Goldsmith and Laves (1954a, b) developed this idea into a quantitative tool, the *triclinicity* (called a *triclinic indicator* in this book). Goldsmith and Laves (1954, p. 100) stated "Natural K-feldspars with triclinic geometry (triclinicity) intermediate between that of monoclinic feldspar and microcline (showing maximum triclinicity) are not uncommon. A complete gradation exists between monoclinic material and microcline with maximum triclinicity. This fact necessitates a clarification of the term microcline. It is proposed that the name apply to any of the intermediate K-feldspars that are measurably triclinic, i.e., in which α and γ, and therefore α^* and γ^* deviate measurably from 90°. Triclinic adularia, for example (Laves, 1950, 1952; Chaisson. 1950) is considered as an intermediate microcline with a low Δ-value". In subsequent years many measurements of a triclinic indicator were made, thereby giving a distinction between a monoclinic sanidine and a triclinic microcline.

Most microclines show cross-hatched Albite and Pericline twinning interpreted as the result of inversion from monoclinic symmetry (Laves, 1950). Goldsmith and Laves (1954b. p. 111–113) clearly recognized the problems caused by the varying size of twin domains. and by the strain across the boundaries: e.g. "If the sizes of the (+) and (−) units are sufficiently small, the degree of order cannot be expected to be expressed in the triclinicity". "Optically monoclinic orthoclase characteristically shows diffuseness in certain of the [X-ray] reflections... The diffuseness is somewhat variable from sample to sample... This diffuse scattering. not observed in sanidine, is evidence for the existence of the sub-microscopic regions here discussed." They concluded "A. If the (+) and (−) regions are equal in amount, and are submicroscopic, the material will be optically monoclinic. In principle this is similar to Mallard's hypothesis (Mallard, 1876). X-ray data may show considerable variability in the triclinicity of material of this nature.

B. If the (+) and (−) regions are sufficiently small, even if each region is highly ordered with respect to Al and Si, an apparently monoclinic X-ray pattern can result. The relative rates of nucleation of triclinic material within the original monoclinic material and the rate of "growth" of these nuclei determine the size of the regions.

C. All degrees of AlSi order may exist within the very small (+) and (−) regions. Thus the material may approach true monoclinic symmetry on this basis. [As the degree of order approaches zero (complete disorder), the regions no longer exist. and a true monoclinic material (sanidine) results].

D. K-feldspar that appears monoclinic and that is constituted in one or more of the ways A. B. C described above. is here considered to be what is commonly called orthoclase. The variability in orthoclase, observed both optically and by X-ray diffraction. can be explained by the above model.

E. On the basis of the above reasoning. earlier statements have been made (Laves, 1952; Goldsmith and Laves. 1954a. b) to the effect that 'orthoclase' is a 'group' term and cannot be considered as a unique phase, and that

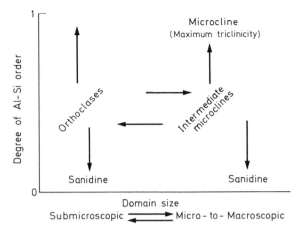

Fig. 9-2. Diagrammatic representation of the relations between K-feldspars in terms of the size of domains and the degree of Al, Si order. (From Goldsmith and Laves, 1954b, Fig. 16)

'orthoclase' as such cannot be assigned a well-defined stability field." Figure 9-2 shows their placement of various types of K-feldspar on a diagram relating degree of Al-Si order to domain size.

Thus Goldsmith and Laves had provided a criterion for selecting out microcline from other K-feldspars on the basis of an indicator measured from an X-ray powder pattern. However this criterion was interpreted to depend on a combination of two properties — Al-Si order and domain size. The experimental problem of sorting out the effects of domain size and extent of ordering had not been solved in detail though it had been recognized. In addition it was not clear whether domains existed under conditions of true equilibrium.

Hafner and Laves (1957) stated "The comparison of the infrared absorption of microcline with that of common orthoclases and adularias indicates that these two minerals are members of a continuous series, structurally between sanidine and microcline. The crystals of this series appear optically monoclinic due to submicroscopic twinning." Thus it is implied that there can be no truly monoclinic orthoclase and adularia. Hafner and Laves pointed out that there is a triply-infinite number of ways in which a K-feldspar can order, in addition to domain effects, and distinguished theoretically between the concepts of "states which are stable under equilibrium conditions and others which are never stable at all."

This new concept of multiple paths of ordering is extremely important. Briefly, there are two extreme ordering paths: the *one-step path* in which high sanidine with complete Al, Si disorder transforms into low microcline with complete ordering of Al into the $T_1 0$ sites by simultaneous migration of Al from the other sites, and the *two-step path* in which Al migrates first from T_2 into T_1 sites, followed by migration from $T_1 m$ into $T_1 0$ sites. A single ordering parameter is no longer sufficient (as in Fig. 9-2), and a more complex description is necessary (see Chapter 3). Particularly important is the theoretical conclusion that the one-step path gives a triclinic pattern of Al, Si atoms immediately ordering commences, whereas the two-step path gives a monoclinic pattern as Al atoms migrate from T_2 to T_1 sites. and only gives a triclinic pattern for the second stage in which Al atoms migrate into $T_1 0$ sites from $T_1 m$ sites. In actual practice, a domain texture may be produced, and the triclinic pattern of the domains may be "averaged-out" to give the appearance of monoclinic symmetry in some experimental techniques. The key factors here are the degree of structural coherence across domain boundaries and the spatial resolution of the experimental equipment. Consequently any attempts to determine the type of K-feldspar must reckon with the experimental technique, and unfortunately the situation is very complex and incompletely understood (Smith, 1970).

Smith and MacKenzie (1959). still using the optic axial angle to characterize K-feldspar, stated "Although the diffuse [X-ray] reflections in orthoclase and low sanidine occupy the same positions as the ... diffuse reflections in intermediate microclines it is thought that they have a different character, and this difference is thought to be important. The diffuse reflections in orthoclase and low-sanidine are much weaker than those in intermediate microclines and a distinction can be made on this basis for most specimens. Further, it appears that the diffuse reflections in orthoclase and low-sanidine have a more uniform drop of intensity and extend a little further than the diffuse reflections in intermediate microcline. However, visual estimation of diffuseness is very difficult, and until quantitative measurements of the streaks have been made, the above conclusion should be treated with some caution. In view of the conflicting views on the nature of orthoclase, such quantitative measurements would appear to be of considerable importance." Such measurements have still not been made, though to me they still seem crucial to the characterization of intermediate K-feldspar. Smith and MacKenzie also re-affirmed the observation by Laves (1950) of diffuse X-ray diffractions in adularia corresponding to $(h + k)$ odd: these diffractions were later explained (Laves and Goldsmith, 1961) by "unti-cell twinning" of "out-of-step domains". Strangely enough, no one has tried to find out whether these diffractions would serve to distinguish between stable and unstable states of K-feldspars: because absence of such X-ray diffractions implies correlation of ordering across the C-face, it might seem that the stronger are these diffractions the more a K-feldspar should deviate from the stable state (normalized. of course, for the overall level of ordering achieved).

Laves (1960a) gave a detailed summary of investigations on the nature of K-feldspar, and proposed a detailed nomenclature of alkali feldspars. The following quotations are translated from the original German:

"A nomenclature of K-feldspars should assign principal names to such states as appear stable at any one temperature (hence called 'stable' states), the names to be consistent as far as possible with those which have already come into use. The following proposal ensues:

Stable Phases. Sanidine = stable. monoclinic. high-temperature form of $KAlSi_3O_8$ with Al/Si distribution shown schematically in Fig. 5 (here reproduced as Fig. 9-3) by a continuous line (in the part above Tc_2 which is assumed to be the critical temperature more or less arbitrarily). Addition of (high), (intermediate) and (low) gives the possibility of quantitative differentiation.

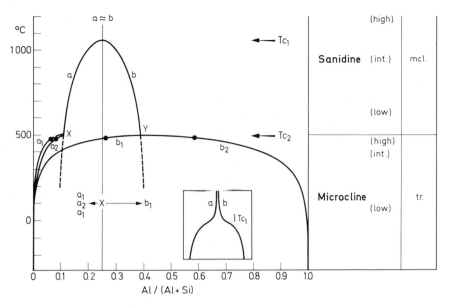

Fig. 9-3. Nomenclature proposed by Laves (1960) for K-feldspars under equilibrium conditions. The left-hand diagram shows the distribution of Al atoms proposed by Laves. The curves a, b, a_1, a_2, b_1 and b_2 represent the probability of occupancy of Al atoms in the tetrahedral sites T_2, T_1, T_20, T_2m, T_1m and T_10. Critical temperatures of ordering are shown at Tc_1 and Tc_2. The inset diagram, according to Laves, should draw attention that at the highest temperature a must be unequal to b. The right-hand diagram gives the proposed nomenclature. (From Laves, 1960a, Fig. 5)

Microcline = stable, triclinic. low-temperature form of $KAlSi_3O_8$ with an Al/Si distribution shown in Fig. 5 (Fig. 9-3) by the continuous lines below Tc_2. (High), (intermediate) and (low) added as for sanidine.

Metastable Phases. Meta-Sanidine. It may be possible that accidentally at temperatures under Tc_2 monoclinic K-feldspars form with Al-contents in the T_1 and T_2 sites which are not stable, as shown by the broken-line extensions in Fig. 5 (Fig. 9-3). To characterize such a hypothetical example the name meta-sanidine is proposed.

Unstable Phases. K-feldspars which have grown as sanidine below Tc_2 (owing to relatively rapid growth – e.g. no doubt most 'adularias': see Laves, 1950 and 1952, also Bambauer and Laves. 1960) and many authigenic feldspars (see Baskin 1956) – or have been brought relatively rapidly to temperature below Tc_2 [without change of the relation $a + b = 0.5$: see legend to Fig. 5 (Fig. 9-3) for meaning of a and b] ought to transform to microcline. Such feldspars should tend to alter so that the point positions T_1 and T_2 split into $T_1(0)$, $T_1(m)$ and $T_2(0)$, $T_2(m)$ with Al-contents whose trends are given by the arrows going out from x in Fig. 5 (Fig. 9-3). Although the states passed through are indeed triclinic they ought not to be called merely 'microcline' because at no temperature are they stable and the above proposal applies only to stable forms. It is proposed to call such states which are more like sanidine or more like microcline 'mikrokliniger pseudo-Sanidin' or 'sanidiniger Mikroklin'. (An English translation might be 'microcline-tending pseudo-sanidine' and 'sanidine-tending microcline'). Although somewhat different Al/Si distributions are possible during the transformation of microcline to sanidine by heat treatment in the laboratory (or likewise in Nature), the states are in principle similar according to this definition.

The names defined above: sanidine. microcline, meta-sanidine, mikrokliniger pseudo-Sanidin and sanidiniger Mikroklin permit characterization of 'phase'-states [by 'phase' Laves means coarse material with essentially no contribution of boundary energy to the free energy]. Often the states which are triclinic occur not in the homogeneous. single-crystal form, but twinned sub-microscopi-cally in Mallard's sense (1876). If the twinning is 'balanced' (Schneider, 1957) the resulting optics are monoclinic yielding 'gewöhnlicher Orthoklas' (English translation is 'common orthoclase'). If it is unbalanced (that such states exist was shown in 1950) the resulting optics are triclinic, and such material can be called 'unbalanced common orthoclase'. If it is possible (e.g. by X-ray methods) to establish that the 'phase' consists of submicrosopic domains this of course can be conveyed as well".

This nomenclature would be quite satisfactory if one could prove whether or not a particular feldspar corresponded to a truly stable state. Distinction of "common orthoclase" from microcline and sanidine would be possible. Un-fortunately almost all K-feldspars found to be triclinic by X-ray methods contain some type of domain texture. At what size of domain does one decide to move a feldspar from the "common orthoclase" to the "microcline" classification?

Going back one year, Barth (1959) described K-feldspar as a ternary system (here shown as Fig. 9-4) in which sanidine with a (25 25 25 25) distribution of Al among the four sites could transform to microcline (0 100 0 0) by an infinite number of trends. Orthoclase was identified as having the extreme (50 50 0 0) distribution. Barth proposed "that the feldspar series from the left corner to the apex are called sanidine-orthoclase. and that feldspars inside the triangle and towards the right corner are called microclines". Later Barth (1965) further expanded his view on the properties and nomenclature of alkali feldspars using the terms (*maximum*) *sanidine*. (*maximum*) *orthoclase* and (*maximum*) *microcline* for the "pure end members" with the extreme possibilities of ordering. In his latest work (1969) he used the terms high sanidine, hypo-orthoclase and max microcline (his Fig. 3-7).

Ansilewski (1961) suggested a detailed terminology of feldspars, but the names are so different from those in current use. that they will not be generally adopted.

The first comprehensive discussions of the nomenclature of K-feldspars took place at the 1960 meeting of the International Mineralogical Association whose proceedings were published (1961) in Cursillos y Conferencias del Instituto "Lucas Mallada". The interplay of ideas in the discussions is delightful. As expected, "orthoclase" played a principal role. In a paper amusingly titled "Polymorphism, order, disorder, diffusion and confusion in the feldspars", Laves and Goldsmith (1961) reviewed their proposals for K-feldspar. They criticized the suggestion by Ferguson *et al.* (1958) that the stability of K-feldspar is governed by charge balance. and argued against a hypothetical model for

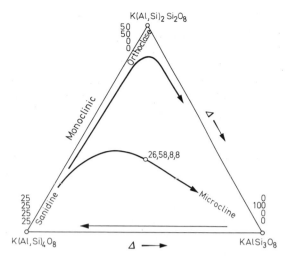

Fig. 9-4. The ternary system of K-feldspar according to Barth (1959). The numbers are the percentages of Al in the T_1m, T_10, T_2m and T_20 sites. Two ordering paths (one passing through the intermediate microcline of Bailey and Taylor) are shown, together with one disordering path. The symbol Δ is a triclinic indicator. (From Barth, 1959, Fig. 2)

orthoclase proposed by Megaw (1959). by analogy with anorthite, in which there is a c-repeat of 1.4 nm with stacking faults. Megaw criticized their suggestion of "domains of unit cell size" to explain the diffuse diffractions of type (h + k) odd in adularia.

Smith and MacKenzie (1961) reviewed the atomic, chemical and physical factors that control the stability of alkali feldspars. In this paper the ideas of local and distant order were first introduced. and met some criticism from Megaw and from Laves. During the subsequent discussion, Smith and Mac-Kenzie stated (p. 52) "... we use orthoclase both for the natural specimens and for the theoretical partly-ordered K-feldspar. The reason is that we believe that the natural specimens have essentially the same Al–Si order as the theoretical feldspar, and because we rely on the context of the term to indicate whether we are talking about the natural specimens or the theoretical structure type. Consequently Laves' theoretical sanidine (low) is the same as our orthoclase used in a theoretical context."

MacKenzie and Smith (1961) discussed experimental and geological evidence for the stability of alkali feldspars. They stated (p. 69) "Studies of feldspars from many granites and metamorphic rocks show that orthoclase, as a constituent of orthoclase-perthites, is a very common mineral. and because of this we think that it has a structure that is either the stable one or very near to the stable one at some intermediate temperature. If not. one would expect to find that orthoclase was a less common mineral. According to our investigation of feldspars from many localities the assemblage orthoclase plus microcline of high obliquity is not common, and may therefore be a consequence of unusual conditions." Laves (p. 66) stated "... I can only express my hope that other readers interested in the subject may be able to understand the reasons why Goldsmith, Hafner and the writer made a distinction between the concepts of 'sanidine' and 'orthoclase'. These distinctions may be rather irrelevant for many *practical purposes* of mineralogists and petrologists. They become relevant, however, if phase relations need to be discussed for a more sophisticated *understanding* of structural states that may exist in nature on theoretical reasoning and which exist in nature, as proved by X-ray work.

The fact that 'orthoclases' are commonly found in nature is not a proof that their structural assemblage is a stable state. The situation can be compared with the fact that most microclines are found finely twinned, but nobody will doubt that a single microcline crystal should be more stable than a finely twinned microcline assemblage."

Marfunin (1961) presented the results of optical and X-ray studies of many alkali feldspars, as developed further in his monograph (1962, 1966). His nomenclature is based on the optic axial angle and a triclinic indicator obtained from optical or X-ray measurements (Fig. 9-5). The optic axial angle was chosen as the prime measure of Si, Al order for reasons given in Chapter 8. Marfunin recognized the effect of domain texture on the triclinic indicator. Particularly important is his statement on p. 134 of the English translation (1966): "Thus in natural K-feldspars there is only one direction of ordering. The state of ordering may be characterized by one value, and not by three (the number of independent concentrations of Al in the four tetrahedral positions), and the concept 'degree of ordering' may correspondingly be expressed not by three number characteristics, but by one value.

It must be stressed that in the present scheme, as distinguished from the schemes of Laves and of Barth, sanidine cannot pass directly into microcline; the following course is necessary: disordered sanidine → ordered sanidine ('orthoclase' of various structural studies) → microcline". Most of the specimens used by Marfunin came from igneous or metamorphic rocks, and he was ignoring the complexities of adularia. Figure 8-2 shows the range of optical data found by Marfunin.

Marfunin did not distinguish in Fig. 9-5 between the methods used to characterize the symmetry. Because a K-feldspar can be monoclinic according to the optical extinction angle and triclinic according to a cell angle, one observer using optical methods could name a feldspar (say) intermediate orthoclase whereas another using X-ray methods could name it intermediate microcline or intermediate triclinic orthoclase. Unless the nature of the technique were also stated, no implication on the coarseness of the twin texture could be obtained from a bare statement of name.

Barth (1965) criticized the term "triclinic orthoclase" used by Marfunin, as follows:

"However, the monoclinic symmetry of sanidine and orthoclase has to most mineralogists become part of the definition; any loosening here necessarily means an innovation on established custom. In my opinion sanidines and orthoclases are monoclinic phases of K-feldspar and should so remain; microclines are the triclinic phases which may be further defined by giving the triclinicity index Δ, or the extinction on (001)."

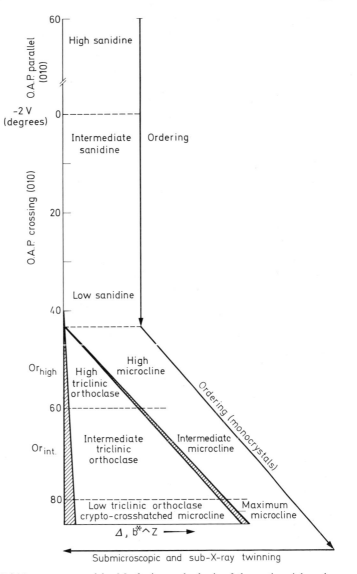

Fig. 9-5. Nomenclature of K-feldspars proposed by Marfunin on the basis of the optic axial angle, and either a triclinic indicator from X-ray patterns (Δ) or an optical extinction angle (b*^Z). (From Marfunin, 1962, Fig. 43)

Laves and Viswanathan (1967) further extended the nomenclature proposed by Laves (1960a). Following Marfunin they used a plot of $2V_\alpha$ versus a triclinic indicator Δ based on cell angles (but *not* on optical extinction angle), here shown as Fig. 9-6. They stated:

"A. The heavy lines represent the $2V/\Delta$ relations, indicated by the results of the present investigation, for stable material undisturbed by submicroscopical twinning.

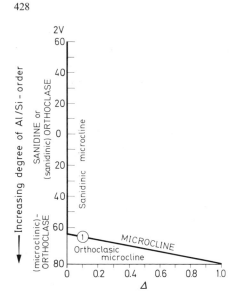

Fig. 9-6. Nomenclature of natural K-feldspars proposed by Laves and Viswanathan on the basis of optic axial angle and a triclinic indicator Δ based on γ^*. (From Laves and Viswanathan, 1967, Fig. 8)

B. Of the branches shown in the diagram the one with $\Delta = 0$ corresponds to (stable) *sanidines* while the one with Δ varying from 0 to 1 applies to (stable) *microclines*.

C. When Δ is different from zero the microcline branch divides the $2V/\Delta$ field into two parts. Material falling into the uppermost of these is to be considered as unstable with regard to its Al/Si distribution. As such material is triclinic (either single crystalline or as a result of unbalanced submicroscopic twinning) but more disordered than stable microcline it might be called 'sanidinic microcline'. Material falling into the lower of the two fields is to be considered as consisting of unbalanced submicroscopical twins with domains having a higher degree of order than indicated by their Δ-value. For such material the term 'orthoclasic microcline' might be appropriate.

D. When $\Delta = 0$ two sub-cases must be distinguished from the point of view of structure.

a) When $2V$ is smaller than about 65° the material *may* be truly monoclinic, i.e. *sanidine*. On the other hand. it *may* show an apparently monoclinic optical behaviour due to a (balanced) submicroscopical twinning of triclinic domains having an unstable Si/Al distribution as in 'sanidine microcline' [presumably a misprint for sanidinic microcline]. In this case (sanidinic) orthoclase would appear to be the proper designation.

b) When $2V$ is greater than about 65° the material *must necessarily* consist of balanced, submicroscopically twinned domains that are more ordered than the sanidine stable at $T_{S/M}$ ($T_{S/M}$ is the temperature at which the phase at the junction of the sanidine and microcline series is truly stable). The name (microclinic) *orthoclase* appears suitable for such material.

There has been much discussion in the literature on the meaning of the word orthoclase. Some authors call all K-feldspars that are optically monoclinic 'orthoclase' and consider sanidine and adularia to be sub-divisions of orthoclase in this sense. Others make a distinction between orthoclase and sanidine using a rather arbitrary value of $2V$ to discriminate between the two. The reasons for such diverging definitions are those given above and (Fig. 9-6) shows that in principle, the arbitrary use of terms can be avoided if *structural* properties are taken into consideration. Of course, the name orthoclase still retains its practical value for the classification of K-feldspars according to *optical* properties and *geological* modes of occurrence.

The name 'adularia' has been avoided in this discussion as its meaning is predominantly a *mineralogical* one based on morphological appearance and geological occurrence. From a *structural* point of view adularia may be sanidine, microcline or orthoclase... As a rule. adularia occurs in states intermediate between those capable of being exactly defined as sanidine, microcline or orthoclase".

Wright and Stewart (1968) on the basis of their detailed measurements of cell dimensions of synthetic and ion-exchanged natural alkali feldspars (Fig. 7-14) proposed the following nomenclature:

"*High sanidine*. Monoclinic. Axial dimensions b and c correspond to those in the high sanidine-high albite series.

Low sanidine. Monoclinic. Axial dimensions b and c fall between those which define the P 50 – 56 F equivalent and the high-sanidine equivalent series [P 50 – 56 F is similar to the Spencer C orthoclase].

Orthoclase. Monoclinic. Axial dimensions b and c fall along the curve for P 50 – 56 F equivalents or between the P 50 – 56 F and maximum microcline equivalent series, if $\alpha = \gamma = 90°$.

Intermediate microcline. Triclinic. α. γ, b and c are distinct from the maximum microcline – low albite series.

Maximum microcline. Triclinic. Unit cell parameters α, γ, b and c correspond to the maximum microcline – low albite series".

Figure 9-7 is a graphical representation of this nomenclature. In this system maximum microcline and high sanidine are very precisely defined, while intermediate microcline and low sanidine are allowed to cover a much wider range than that proposed by Laves, who split up sanidine and microcline each into subdivisions (high), (low) and (intermediate). Orthoclase and intermediate microcline can overlap completely on the b c plot because distinction is based purely on the monoclinic or triclinic nature of the angles α and γ determined from X-ray powder data. Figure 9-7 is actually given in terms of $\Delta(b^*c^*)$ and $\Delta(\alpha^*\gamma^*)$ to permit direct comparison with figures in Chapter 7.

From these quotations from the literature. it is obvious that the use of simple, unqualified names such as sanidine and microcline is insufficient. Confusion can be reduced only by the simultaneous use of adjectives which describe some important property and of adjectives which describe the technique used to established that property. The resulting strings of adjectives are aesthetically displeasing and can be ridiculed as "freight-train" English; the alternative is either continued chaos or a descriptive sentence. Fortunately the context will often permit omission of adjectives.

Because the most important property is the Si,Al order, I shall follow Goldsmith and Laves in using the nouns *sanidine* and *microcline* to correspond respectively to the initial and later stages of ordering. For reasons given earlier, the two forms can only be distinguished exactly on a theoretical basis, while

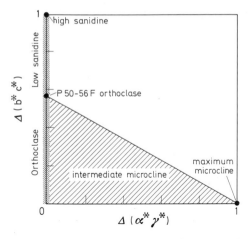

Fig. 9-7. Nomenclature of K-feldspars proposed by Wright and Stewart (1968) on the basis of cell dimensions b, c, α and γ. For convenience, the cell dimensions are expressed by the indicators $\Delta(b^*c^*)$ and $\Delta(\alpha^*\gamma^*)$ as defined in Chapter 7. The P 50 – 56 F orthoclase was used by Wright and Stewart to separate a low sanidine from an orthoclase or microcline

natural feldspars must be distinguished on a somewhat arbitrary basis. The prefixes *high, intermediate* and *low* will be used following Laves (1960a) to indicate ranges, while *maximum* will be applied to both sanidine and microcline to indicate the states of extreme order and disorder. It will be assumed that the *equilibrium* states of feldspars follow the ideal *two-stage* trend: the state of highest disorder with 0.25 Al in each site will be called *theoretical maximum high sanidine*; the state with the highest possible order (mathematically) consistent with equal occupancy of (0) and (m) sub-sites will be called *theoretical maximum low sanidine*; and the state of highest possible order will be called *theoretical maximum low microcline*. Barth and the Cambridge school used the term *orthoclase* in the traditional sense, and there would be no confusion if *theoretical orthoclase* were used in the above sense as an alternative to *theoretical maximum low sanidine*. The boundary between theoretical sanidine and theoretical microcline corresponds to adoption of triclinic symmetry of the Al/Si distribution.

Figure 9-8 illustrates the problems of providing a detailed practical nomenclature. Because optical methods can resolve only those domain textures coarser than the wavelength of light, it is obvious that for routine work one should use X-ray methods to detect triclinic symmetry. The degree of order can be measured either by the optic axial angle or the $b\ c$ cell dimensions. Because there are more data on $2V$ than $b\ c$ at the time of writing, Fig. 9-8 uses $2V$ and γ^* rather than b^*c^* and γ^*. Suppose the ideal two-step trend is as shown. All true single crystals would be strictly monoclinic in the upper part, and triclinic for $-2V = 55$ to $88°$. Specimens with strain between coherent or semi-coherent domains would have a smaller angle of γ^* than true single crystals with the same value of $2V$. Displacement of the Si. Al distribution towards the theoretical one-step trend would have an opposite effect. And therein lies the crux of the problem. Simple measurements of cell dimensions and optical properties do not provide a rigorous way of determining the position of the ideal two-step trend

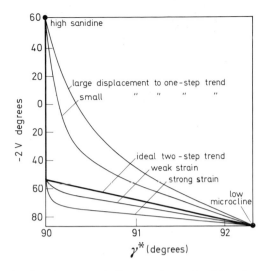

Fig. 9-8. Hypothetical diagram for K-feldspar showing the expected effects on the optic axial angle and γ^* of displacement from the ideal two-step trend caused by either strain across twin domains or deviation to the one-step trend

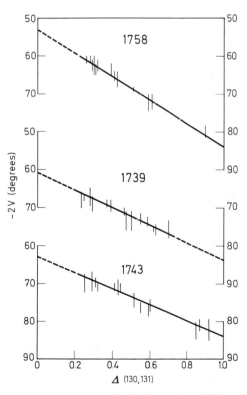

Fig. 9-9. Relation between $-2V$ and $\Delta(130, 131)$ for small fragments of K-feldspars from Ticino, Switzerland. Each sub-diagram includes data for several crystals at each of the three geographic localities identified by the number. (Redrawn from Laves and Viswanathan, 1967, Figs. 3, 4 and 5)

on a diagram such as Fig. 9-8. The opposite effects of domain strain and displacement to the one-step trend cannot be disentangled in detail.

Laves and Viswanathan (1967) carefully studied K-feldspars from quartz-feldspar dikes of pegmatitic appearance in Ticino Canton, Switzerland with the aim of distinguishing between "stable" and "unstable" states of alkali feldspars. Thin-section optical study showed that the K-feldspars were inhomogeneous with $2V$ ranging up to $20°$, and had widely-varying twinning from distinct cross-hatching to apparent absence. Small fragments near $3 \times 3 \times 0.15$ mm were deliberately used to obtain a precise correlation between $2V$ and the 130 and $1\bar{3}1$ triclinic indicators ($\varDelta$) obtained from a Guinier powder pattern of each crushed fragment. Figure 9-9 shows a good correlation between $-2V$ and $\varDelta$ for three specimens studied in detail. For each specimen, the correlation is near-linear extending from a value typical of maximum microcline. However, the projection to monoclinic geometry reaches different values of $-2V$: 53, 61 and $63°$. Laves and Viswanathan chose to use $64°$ for the truly stable form of K-feldspar (see Fig. 9-6).

Figure 9-10 shows other pertinent data collected from many investigations. The triclinic nature of the K-feldspar was determined either from the triclinic

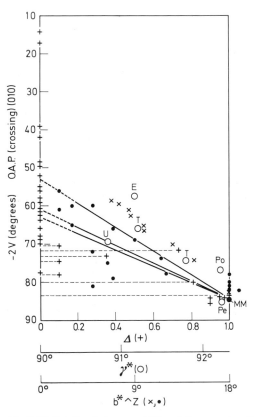

Fig. 9-10. Relation between $-2V$ and X-ray and optical indicators of triclinic symmetry for K-feldspars studied by various investigators. See text for detailed explanation

indicator $\Delta(130, 131)$, or the lattice angle γ^*, or the extinction angle $b^* \char`^ Z$. For all data, the ordinate is $-2V$. Open circles show γ^* measured from X-ray patterns of Spencer E (powder pattern; MacKenzie, 1954), Spencer U (single crystal; Bailey and Taylor, 1955); Pontiskalk (single crystal; Finney and Bailey, 1964); Pellotsalo (single crystal; Brown and Bailey, 1964); Taimyr (two single crystals; Marfunin, 1962). The diagonal crosses are values of the extinction angle $b^* \char`^ Z$ given by Marfunin. Horizontal crosses are values of $\Delta(130, 131)$ obtained from powder patterns by Marfunin (1962): horizontal dashed lines represent broad peaks consistent with a range of values. The small dots show values of $b^* \char`^ Z$ obtained by Harker (1962) for K-feldspars from acid gneisses: X-ray powder data showed that both monoclinic and triclinic K-feldspars occurred in the same powder sample. Figure 8-2 shows optical data from Marfunin (1966, Fig. 36). The three lines in Fig. 9-10 repeat the trends obtained by Laves and Viswanathan (Fig. 9-9). Neiva (1972) reported a similar trend for K-feldspars of granites and associated aplites and pegmatites from northern Portugal. The trend for $-2V$ vs. 131 X-ray powder indicator (Δ) runs from $70°$ for low values of Δ to $88°$ for high values. Measurements of $2V$ were made conoscopically with a 40 times objective and the error was given as $\pm 1°$.

I believe that the ideal two-step trend cannot be identified exactly on the basis of present data, and I have arbitrarily chosen to begin the triclinic portion at $-2V = 55°$ and $\Delta(b^*c^*) = 0.55$ for Or_{10}. It is obvious that other values of $-2V$ from 40 to $65°$ could be proposed. and indeed a change from $55°$ may appear desirable in the future. Figures 9-9 and 9-10 are slightly misleading because they ignore the effect of solid solution of Ab. Figures 9-11 and 9-12 take account of this solid solution, and provide a means of classifying alkali feldspars on the basis of measurements of b^*. c^* or of $2V$ and Or. These diagrams are discussed in detail later, and only the K-rich regions are described here. Note that for "anomalous" feldspars, as defined by Wright and Stewart (Chapter 7), it is necessary to determine the Or content from the cell volume rather than from the b^*c^* plot.

It should be emphasized immediately that the proposed classification does not use the distinction of symmetry: microcline and sanidine are distinguished merely by the value of $\Delta(b^*c^*)$ or of $-2V$. The symmetry can be specified by double adjectives such as *optically monoclinic* and *X-ray triclinic*. Note that a feldspar can be simultaneously optically monoclinic and X-ray triclinic. The extent of the deviation of geometry from the monoclinic condition is better expressed by a number than a name: thus the 131 triclinic indicator or the $b^* \char`^ Z$ extinction angle could be used.

The fields of sanidine and microcline are arbitrarily divided on the b^*c^* plot into sub-fields with prefixes high, intermediate and low, respectively occupying one-quarter, one-half and one-quarter of the major field. Contour lines are drawn for constant $\Delta(b^*c^*)$ to take account of Ab-content. In natural feldspars the fields are terminated by formation of perthite. Although the relation between b^*c^* and $2V$Or is not known precisely (see Fig. 8-8), the fields shown in Fig. 9-12 correspond approximately to those of Fig. 9-11. Further research is required to clarify the relationship. The system of nomenclature takes no account of whether the ordering belongs to a one-step or a two-step trend: it is

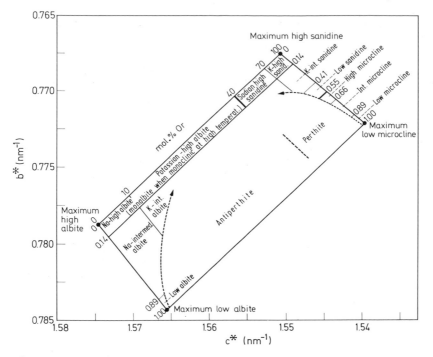

Fig. 9-11. Proposed nomenclature of alkali feldspars based on measurements of b* and c*. The prefixes Na and K denote sodian and potassian, respectively

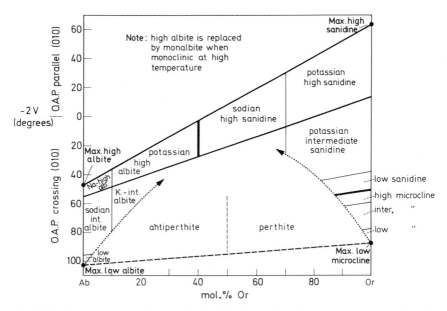

Fig. 9-12. Proposed nomenclature of alkali feldspars based on measurements of optical axial angle and Or-content

simply based on measurements of cell dimensions or of optic axial angle and composition.

How will the scheme work in practice? If identification has been made by the naked eye, the nomenclature must be short and restricted to what has been *seen* not to what has been *guessed*. Thus the simple term K-feldspar with prefixes such as *glassy, chalky,* or *macro-perthitic* is sufficient. Obviously a *glassy* K-feldspar from a rock whose texture indicates a volcanic origin is very likely to be a sanidine, but why risk the danger of an error? It is desirable that both microscopic and X-ray studies be made: preference should be given to the b^*c^* plot in assigning the name. Ideally the feldspar should be characterized by a detailed description showing the cell dimensions and the optical properties $-2V$, extinction angle and texture. Furthermore the bulk composition should be determined either by microprobe, chemical or X-ray methods. Optical methods alone give limited information. If the K-feldspar is homogeneous or if it is part of a coarse perthite it should be possible to measure $-2V$ accurately. If the feldspar is crypto- or micro-perthitic and only $-2V$ of the bulk sample can be measured. there is a problem, and the X-ray methods of Wright and Stewart should be mandatory if a detailed name is desired. Of course there would be no confusion in stating that a feldspar belongs to the low sanidine optical series of Tuttle – indeed such a crude classification may be convenient for simple description.

It would be wildly optimistic to expect all scientists to accept the proposed system, and it thus becomes imperative to see whether other systems can be translated into the present one. Marfunin's system presents no difficulty except that he chooses to divide microcline from sanidine at $-2V = 45°$ rather than $55°$ chosen here: furthermore his modifiers have slightly different meaning (Fig. 9-5). His high-, intermediate- and maximum-orthoclase would be described here as X-ray or optically monoclinic microcline with the prefixes high, intermediate or low. His triclinic orthoclases would be combined with microcline, and an adjective describing the experimental technique would be added. To me the subdivisions orthoclase, triclinic orthoclase and microcline for K-feldspar with the same b^*c^* or $2V$ index is unnecessary. because the triclinic index cannot be related simply to any single important factor.

The nomenclature of Wright and Stewart (Fig. 9-7) can be translated into the one given here if the actual values of b^* and c^* are given. Their orthoclase is combined together from the low sanidine and X-ray monoclinic microclines of the present scheme. The prefixes high. intermediate, low and maximum are used in a different way.

The scheme of Laves and Viswanathan (Fig. 9-6) can be translated satisfactorily if (microclinic) orthoclase is replaced by monoclinic microcline, and if MICROCLINE and orthoclasic microcline are combined together. Their boundary between sanidine and microcline is taken at $-2V \sim 65°$ rather than at $55°$. It should be noted that Laves and Viswanathan used the 131 triclinic indicator and $-2V$ to classify their feldspars.

It is obvious that feldspar workers should present quantitative data for the indexes used to classify the feldspars so that other workers can utilize their data without unnecessary uncertainty.

The above discussion has implicitly assumed that natural K-feldspars follow approximately a two-stage ordering trend with the first part balanced between the (0) and (m) sites, and the second part complicated by textural relations. Fortunately all careful measurements of K-feldspars from igneous and metamorphic rocks appear to be consistent with monoclinic or near-monoclinic symmetry when $-2V$ is less than about 40°. Only some adularias with $-2V$ below 40° appear to give triclinic geometry. For these the prefixes *optically* or *X-ray triclinic sanidine* are suggested in preference to *sanidinic microcline* of Laves and Viswanathan. For their *sanidinic ORTHOCLASE*, in which the Al/Si distribution of the domains is unbalanced, but the domains are so small that the potential triclinic geometry cannot develop, the term *domain-twinned sanidine* is suggested. Fortunately these complications are not likely to bother the petrographer; indeed no definitive proof has been presented for the existence of *domain-twinned sanidine* with unbalanced Al/Si order.

There are many papers in the literature in which *"orthoclase"* has been distinguished from *"microcline"* just on the basis of the 131 triclinic indicator. Actually what has been distinguished is whether there are domains which have attained triclinic geometry. It is doubtful whether this distinction has much significance petrogenetically because of the combined effect of textural factors with Al/Si ordering. The "orthoclase" might just as well be changed to simply *monoclinic K-feldspar* thus avoiding the word "orthoclase" which has become so confused in the literature.

All the physical properties of K-exchanged albites are consistent with the extreme one-step trend (e.g. cell dimensions in Chapter 7), and these K-feldspars are clearly distinguishable from natural K-feldspars belonging to the two-step trend. The term *K-exchanged albite* is preferred to a name such as sanidine or microcline.

9.2.2 Na-feldspars and Ternary Feldspars

The general term *albite* alludes to the white color (Latin: albus) of some specimens commonly found in mineral collections, but albite is inherently transparent. *Pericline* is merely a variety of albite with a special morphology found only in veins. It is somewhat analogous to adularia, but its optical and X-ray properties are less variable than for adularia, typically corresponding to the low structural state. The name was given by Breithaupt (1823) because of the strong inclination between the crystal faces. There is evidence that pericline results from Na-exchange of oligoclase (Chapter 18).

Cleavelandite is another variety of albite with a special morphology. According to Fisher (1968), the name was given by Brooke (1823) to albites from Labrador and from a pegmatite near Chesterfield, Mass. Further study by Fisher of material from the Chesterfield pegmatite led him to conclude: "The term cleavelandite should not be applied to platy crystals of albite which show nearly plane faces parallel (010) and which have additional crystal faces; it should be reserved for near-massive albite occurring in lamellae parallel (010) which are curved and warped and, in general, lack other well-defined crystal faces, and [which] may be twinned on the albite law". Fisher emphasized that the term cleavelandite had been misapplied many times to *platy albite* which often occurs in pegmatites. *Plate albite* occurs as tiny plates in certain microcline perthites and is attributed to exsolution (Chapter 19). Albite also occurs in pegmatites in a *poikilitic* manner (Chapter 19). *Chess-board albite* is yet another type of albite whose distinctive twinning is ascribed to sodium metasomatism of another feldspar (Chapter 18).

Most natural albites from igneous and metamorphic rocks are in the low structural state, and are described most simply as low albite. From X-ray structural analysis, Ferguson *et al.* (1958) showed that low albite has strong Si, Al order, and later X-ray, infra-red and nuclear magnetic resonance studies showed that ordering is nearly complete (Chapters 3 and 11). Disordered albites have been produced in the laboratory by heating natural albites, or by direct synthesis. The physical properties of these products (especially the cell dimensions, Chapter 7) show that they belong to the one-step trend of Al, Si order-disorder. One might expect that a simple nomenclature using the prefixes high-, intermediate- and low- would be sufficient. However, the shape of the framework depends on both the temperature and the Al, Si distribution. Most albites are triclinic at all temperatures but those with high Al, Si disorder become monoclinic just below the melting point. The pre-1965 literature is confusing because of some inaccurate experimental data.

In volcanic rocks, extensive substitution of Or and An molecules precludes the occurrence of pure high albite. Na-rich feldspars from such rocks typically contain over 10% of An and Or molecules, and most show complex physical properties as a result of inversion twinning and exsolution. One of the purest is a high albite $Or_7Ab_{87}An_6$ from a rhyolite at Dundee, Scotland described by Tobi (1972). Many of these feldspars are loosely called *anorthoclase*, while some are classified as *high plagioclase*. A simple nomenclature is impossible.

The difficulties of naming sodium-rich feldspars began with their discovery in volcanic rocks by Brögger (1882) and Förstner (1883, 1884). Rosenbusch (1885) distinguished „Natronorthoklas" (a monoclinic alkali feldspar which would now be called sanidine) from plagioclase (a triclinic feldspar with the principal cleavages (010) and (001) definitely not at right angles), and went on to give the name *anorthoclase* to a series of triclinic K-Na-feldspars whose principal cleavages were either at right angles or very close to 90°. The significance of such anorthoclase could have been derived at that early date because Förstner (1884) had observed the triclinic-monoclinic transition, and because Rosenbusch believed that the close approach to 90° of the angle between (010) and (001) arose from very fine quadrille twinning. Rosenbusch placed anorthoclase in the composition range $Or_{33}Ab_{67}$ to $Or_{18}Ab_{82}$ with from 4–33% of the alkalis substituted by Ca. He noted the variability of the inter-axial angles, and assumed that the triclinic-monoclinic inversion did not occur upon heating of the Ca-rich anorthoclase.

Unfortunately these data were misinterpreted in some later text books, even as recently as 1949. Brögger (1882) had used the name "Natron-mikroklin" – i.e. "soda-microcline" for his Norwegian specimens later placed in the anorthoclase group by Rosenbusch, and objected to the new name because he believed that his material was closely related to microcline.

We now know that the optical resemblance between anorthoclase and microcline arises merely because of the M-type twinning caused by inversion from monoclinic symmetry (Chapter 18); however, this resemblance caused great confusion in the later literature when attempts were made to consider microcline and anorthoclase as members of the same series (e.g. Winchell, 1925). Subsequent experiments showed that anorthoclase crystallized at high temperature with disordered Al, Si atoms whereas microcline has ordered Al and Si atoms and is the stable form of K-feldspar at low temperature. In addition, microcline develops twins by a diffusive transformation whereas anorthoclase twins by a displacive transformation. Furthermore, problems arise because Na-rich feldspars show a wide range of structural states between the extremes of a homogeneous material with disordered M and T atoms and a microcline-albite antiperthite produced by solid-state transformation of the homogeneous variety. The former occurs in volcanic rocks and the latter in plutonic rocks. Much confusion arises if all these specimens are crudely lumped together as anorthoclase.

Winchell (1925) showed that optical and chemical data for anorthoclases described in the literature indicated a solid solution series which would extrapolate to quite different optical properties for $NaAlSi_3O_8$ than those of ordinary albite. He suggested that there might actually be another modification which he called *analbite*. Considerably later than 1925, many workers including Spencer (1937) and Tuttle and Bowen (1950) showed that heated natural albite and synthetic albite indeed had such optical properties predicted by Winchell for analbite and the name *high-temperature albite* was given by Tuttle and Bowen. Laves and Chaisson (1950) characterized the lattice angles of natural and synthetic albites. The synthetic albite forms one end-member of the plagioclase series characterized by "high-temperature" optical properties, and established to exist by Köhler and others in the nineteen-forties (see Köhler, 1949). The word *high-temperature* referred to the formation conditions of the host rock. Later the word "high" was used to refer to the structural state involving high disorder of the Al/Si atoms, while in this treatise it refers to the entropy. Currently the terms *high albite* and *low albite* are commonly used, with simultaneous implications on the crystallization conditions and the structural state. Unfortunately, Winchell and Winchell (1951, 4th ed.) showed a phase diagram in which analbite is the low-temperature form of albite.

Both Alling (1926) and Oftedahl (1948) recognized the complication caused by exsolution of a high-temperature alkali feldspar, but neither came up with a clear statement of the relation of anorthoclase to other feldspars.

The polymorphism of Na-rich K-feldspars was clarified principally by the efforts of Laves and MacKenzie though a reader might not think so when he first encounters the literature! Independently Laves (1952) and MacKenzie (1952) showed by X-ray and optical measurements that natural anorthoclases and synthetic Na-rich feldspars of compositions from around $Or_{37}Ab_{63}$ to Ab_{100} are triclinic at room temperature and become monoclinic reversibly at some higher temperature which increases as the Na content increases (see Fig. 7-40). MacKenzie showed that the inversion temperature of the synthetic feldspars depends somewhat on the conditions of crystallization: in addition he

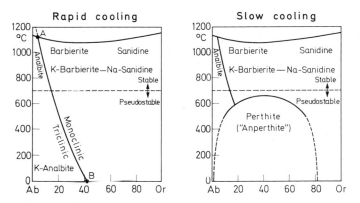

Fig. 9-13. Phase relations of alkali feldspars under conditions of cooling (a) rapid enough to suppress exsolution and ordering of Al and Si atoms and (b) slow enough to permit unmixing of the alkali ions, but rapid enough to suppress ordering of Al and Si atoms. (Redrawn from Laves, 1952, Figs. 8 and 9)

plotted the temperatures on an Or–Ab–An ternary diagram to demonstrate the chemical variation (see Fig. 7-60). Laves interpreted the results in terms of two phase diagrams shown here as Fig. 9-13. Under conditions of cooling rapid enough to suppress exsolution and Al/Si ordering, (Fig. 9-13a), the monoclinic field was split up into *sanidine. Na-sanidine, K-barbierite* and *barbierite* while the triclinic field was split up into *analbite* and *K-analbite*. Under conditions of cooling rapid enough to suppress Al/Si ordering, but slow enough to permit exsolution of the alkali ions (Fig. 9-13b), the lower part was altered by addition of an exsolution dome.

The term *barbierite* had been introduced by Schaller (1910a, b, 1911) for a feldspar originally thought by Barbier and Prost (1908) to be a monoclinic Na-feldspar isomorphous with orthoclase. Later Schneider and Laves (1957) found by X-rays that the "barbierite" is a finely-twinned microcline with exsolved albite. They proposed to discard the name *barbierite*, and to use the name *monalbite* for the monoclinic. high-temperature modification of $NaAlSi_3O_8$. and *K-monalbite* for the K-substituted variety.

Laves (1952) used the name *analbite* in preference to the name *anorthoclase* because of the confusion in the earlier literature about the latter. He stated (p. 567): "No other mineral of importance appears to play such an ambiguous role in mineralogical and petrographic literature as 'anorthoclase'. Numerous attempts have been made to define and characterize this mineral, and virtually every publication and text book considers it in a different way." Readers are recommended to read the subsequent review on pp. 568-570, and also the original paper by Oftedahl (1948) in which considerable progress had been made in characterizing anorthoclase. After defining *barbierite* (later *monalbite*) and *analbite* with respect to the phase diagrams reproduced here as Fig. 9-13, Laves concluded "If one determines a feldspar to be in the composition range defined by Alling ($Or_{70}Ab_{30} - Or_{20}Ab_{80}$) but does not know enough about it or does not care to place it in one of the above-listed eight general categories, it is perhaps best called *anorthoclase*". Laves considered hypothetical phase relations in the Or–Ab–An ternary system. and distinguished monoclinic *Ca-barbierites* and *calcic K-barbierites* from triclinic *anplagioclases* and *potassic anplagioclases*. He concluded "The 'appearance' (symmetry) of the ternary feldspars may be governed largely by the respective values of the transformation temperature and the temperature at which exsolution can take place. Exsolution can take place while the crystal is still monoclinic (before the displacive transformation), and the feldspars therefore appear monoclinic, or it can take place after the transformation. in which case the feldspars appear triclinic".

MacKenzie (1952, p. 339) stated: "The cross-hatched or tartan appearance of the twinning generally seen in anorthoclase crystals on examination in thin sections under a petrographic microscope is often sufficiently characteristic to identify the mineral as anorthoclase. Since the natural crystals investigated here are from lavas or other high temperature environments, it is probable that they crystallized above their inversion temperatures. It is tentatively suggested that the cross-hatched appearance of natural anorthoclase crystals results from the fact that they crystallized with monoclinic symmetry, and, in the process of cooling, become triclinic. From the data presented here, it seems likely that potash-bearing high-temperature albite or oligoclase crystallized with triclinic symmetry with the result that the twinning is clearly defined and the cross-hatched appearance is absent."

Later MacKenzie and Smith (1956) and Smith and MacKenzie (1958) studied systematically a series of feldspars which Tuttle (1952) would have classified in the anorthoclase-low sanidine series. They wrote (1958) "Specimens in the composition range $Or_{60}(Ab + An)_{40}$ to $Or_{25}(Ab + An)_{75}$ were found to be unmixed but could be rendered homogeneous by heating at $700°$ C for a few hours. When homogeneous, specimens more sodium-rich than $Or_{37}(Ab + An)_{63}$ are triclinic, whereas more potassium-rich specimens are monoclinic (note: at room temperature).

Because the high-temperature albite structure can accommodate both potassium and calcium, it is desirable at this stage to make a clear distinction between a high-temperature plagioclase. an anorthoclase and a sanidine. For this purpose the compositional properties of the monoclinic-triclinic inversion may be utilized. Those homogeneous triclinic high-temperature feldspars which invert reversibly to monoclinic symmetry before beginning to melt are called anorthoclases, those which begin to melt before acquiring monoclinic symmetry are plagioclases and those high-temperature feldspars which are monoclinic are called sanidines. The compositional fields of these three types are shown in Fig. 1 (modified slightly from MacKenzie. 1952). Upon heating, the boundary between the triclinic and monoclinic high-temperature sodium-rich feldspars changes and an attempt to delineate the change with temperature has been made in Fig. 1 on the basis of the limited data at present available. Thus all anortho-clases invert at elevated temperatures but high-temperature plagioclases do not. In petrography no confusion in nomenclature should arise since observations are normally made at room temperature." Figure 7-60 contains the data of Fig. 1, together with more recent observations.

Laves (1956) discussed the significance of the barbierite-analbite (displacive) transformation in relation to the optical texture and symmetry of the feldspars in larvikite and rhomb porphyries; in addition he criticized the statement by Muir and Smith (1956) that the feldspars of larvikites showed textural and crystallographic relations that were consistent with the unmixing and inversion from a lime-bearing anorthoclase which had crystallized originally in the high-temperature disordered state. In reply, Smith and Muir (1958) gave X-ray and optical evidence to support an interpretation of the optical texture in relation to the unmixing and the symmetry change; they ended with a statement that "The present assemblages are best described as antiperthites of oligoclase and orthoclase (or microcline)", which were formed by inversion from an Na-rich sanidine and not from an anorthoclase. Harnik (1970) gave detailed chemical data on ternary feldspars from rhomb porphyries (see Chapter 19): these also inverted into antiperthites.

MacKenzie (1957) suggested from measurements of the 131 triclinic indicator of albites synthesized hydrothermally at various temperatures and times "that for each temperature there is a stable crystalline form of $NaAlSi_3O_8$ which is intermediate between high-temperature albite and low-temperature albite, high-temperature albite being stable only above about 1000° C and low-temperature albite only below about 450° C". He decided to define high-temperature, intermediate and low-temperature albite on the basis of the 131 triclinic indicator.

Laves (1960a) presented a detailed survey of the Al/Si distributions, phase transformations and nomenclature of alkali feldspars, of which the portion on K-feldspars has already been quoted. He suggested that the stable scheme of Al/Si ordering in Na-feldspar would be similar to that of K-feldspar (i.e. belonging to the two-step trend) and proposed that the variation with temperature of the Al-contents of the four sites is as given here in Fig. 9-14. He

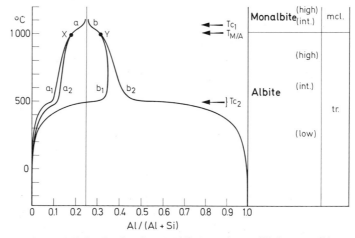

Fig. 9-14. Schematic diagram of the Al/Si distribution for $NaAlSi_3O_8$ under equilibrium conditions as a function of temperature, together with the nomenclature proposed by Laves (1960a). a_1, a_2, b_1, b_2 are the proposed Al-contents of the T_2m, T_20, T_1m and T_10 sites. There are two critical temperatures T_{c_1} and T_{c_2} at which ordering changes rapidly, and a temperature $T_{M/A}$ at which the symmetry changes from monoclinic (M) to triclinic (anorthic A) by a *diffusive* transformation. (From Laves, 1960a, Fig. 7)

suggested that ordering decreased rapidly at a critical temperature Tc_2 assumed to be near 500° C. Above this temperature the topochemical symmetry of the T atoms is close to monoclinic symmetry as shown by near-equality of the Al-contents of the (0) and (m) sub-sites. At $T_{M/A}$, taken to be near 1000° C, the albite becomes truly monoclinic, while at a second critical temperature Tc_1 there is a rapid approach to equality of the Al-contents of the T_1 and T_2 sites. The names *albite* and *monalbite* were used to distinguish the triclinic from the monoclinic members, and the modifiers (low), (intermediate) and (high) were used for the albite, and (intermediate) and (high) for the monalbite. This nomenclature is a theoretical one based on the assumption that the albite has a stable equilibrium distribution of Al/Si atoms which varies continuously with temperature, and that the temperature of the symmetry change is known. Laves noted that the temperature of the monoclinic-triclinic inversion would change across the alkali feldspar system falling to about 500° C for the low sanidine-microcline inversion of $KAlSi_3O_8$.

Laves then clarified the different roles of the sluggish *diffusive* transformation involving interchange of Al/Si atoms, and the *displacive* transformation involving a change of symmetry with temperature for a fixed Al/Si distribution (see Chapter 7). He pointed out that when cooled rapidly enough to preserve the Al/Si distribution, a monalbite with a stable Al/Si pattern would invert to triclinic symmetry at a *lower* temperature than $T_{M/A}$, the temperature for cooling under equilibrium conditions. This conclusion was obtained from the observations of MacKenzie (1952) that the temperature of the symmetry inversion varied with the crystallization temperature: Laves deduced from a plot of MacKenzie's data that the crystallization temperature equalled the temperature of the symmetry inversion at about 980° C and thereby evaluated $T_{M/A}$. Thus under equilibrium conditions albite (high) would invert to monalbite (intermediate) by a diffusive transformation at 980° C. To cover the displacive transition in Na-rich feldspars heated rapidly without change of Al/Si distribution, Laves defined *analbite* as reaching the state of monoclinic symmetry through a displacive transformation. He pointed out that analbite is unstable at all temperatures and develops under non-equilibrium conditions by a displacive inversion during the cooling of monalbite. Laves further classified Na-feldspars by the terms „*albitischer Analbit*", „*analbitischer Albit*" and „*monalbitiger Albit*". The qualifiers were used to express the extent to which Al/Si order occurs during cooling: thus „*albitischer Analbit*" would order slightly upon cooling whereas „*analbitischer Albit*" would order strongly, but *not* the maximum amount, during cooling.

Unfortunately later work has revealed two major revisions in the scheme proposed by Laves. The interpretation by Stewart and Ribbe (1969) of the cell dimensions of albites, together with the data of other workers (see Chapter 7), shows that albite follows the one-step and not the two-step sequence of Al, Si ordering. Although there are no detailed structure analyses of intermediate albites, it is reasonably certain that a_1, a_2 and b are approximately equal at all temperatures, and that there is no critical temperature Tc_2 for which Laves proposed the formation of an albite with b_1 much greater than a_1 and a_2. Syntheses of albites are inconclusive, but there may be a critical temperature between 500 and 700° C (see review by Smith, 1972), but this critical temperature should involve albites following the one-step trend. A second revision in the proposal by Laves involved the suggestion that a monoclinic form of albite occurs much below 980° C (e.g. his Fig. 11). Unfortunately all experimental data for monoclinic symmetry below 980° C in pure albite resulted from erroneous measurements on specimens which had accidentally incorporated K from the furnace (see Chapter 7). The discussion between MacKenzie and Smith (1961) and Laves on the symmetry inversion and nomenclature of albite is obsolete, and the detailed discussion in Chapter 7 should be consulted instead.

Laves (1960a) concluded his paper on the nomenclature of alkali feldspars with a section entitled «On the concept of anorthoclase». It is too long to reproduce here, but the final part is a good summary. The following is translated from the original German. "Practically all mineralogists and petrographers have their own individual concept of 'Anorthoklas'. However all agree that anorthoclase is a relatively Na-rich alkali feldspar, and most permit some indication that it is not strictly monoclinic and that its optical properties are not simply dependent on the chemical composition. From a practical viewpoint, it would cause complications to select one particular set of properties and use this group for the definition of anorthoclase. Then it would be necessary to find a new name for minerals of similar composition but with a different set of properties. Moreover it appears likely that within a few years a new definition would be proposed. From a practical viewpoint of having the fewest bad criteria, anorthoclase in the sense of Alling (1926), can be defined as follows, as already proposed in 1952 (p. 570): 'Anorthoclase may or may not be homogeneous; it may or may not be or appear to be triclinic. An essential compositional range $Or_{70}Ab_{30}$ to $Or_{20}Ab_{80}$ is defined.' If it would be of interest such a definition allows then, of course, the possibility to apply the appropriate prefix to describe the structural properties of special anorthoclases revealed by X-ray examination – viz. homogeneity, inhomogeneity, Al/Si ordering level of separated phases, domain size, twinning etc. One should however not use the name anorthoclase to characterize a structurally definable phase. For this it appears that the already proposed name 'analbite' is well suited, and that the chemical variation from pure $NaAlSi_3O_8$ can be well expressed by the prefixes K–, Ca–, K, Ca–, Ca, K–.

Similarly the chemical variability of the 'monoclinic high-temperature-modification of $NaAlSi_3O_8$', briefly monalbite. can be expressed by the prefixes K–, Ca–, K, Ca–, Ca, K–".

Marfunin (1962; English translation. 1966, pp. 154-5) proposed: "The following varieties are distinguished for Na-feldspars:

Anorthoclase (solid solutions of the composition $Or_{37}Ab_{63} - Or_0Ab_{100}$, on a binary basis). The composition of anorthoclase on a ternary basis is shown in Fig. 30 (K-analbites* of Laves): [this is the diagram given by MacKenzie and Smith, 1955].

Albite
High (analbite of Laves)
Intermediate
Low."

---

* The translation gives K-albite in error.

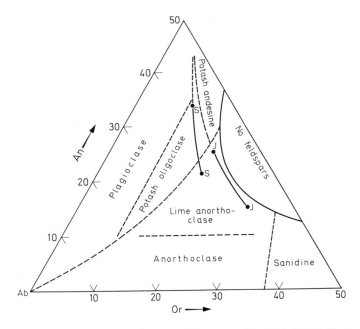

Fig. 9-15. Nomenclature of ternary feldspars used by Muir (1962). The boundary between the fields in which feldspars do and do not crystallize is from Tuttle and Bowen (1958). The boundaries between the fields of sanidine, anorthoclase and plagioclase are from Smith and MacKenzie (1958). The subfields of lime anorthoclase, potash oligoclase and potash andesine were partly but not completely specified by Muir. (Redrawn and simplified from Muir, 1962, Fig. 1)

In Marfunin's proposal, albite (high) should not have been equated with analbite, because Laves deliberately distinguishes between analbite and albite (high); the former is supposed to be unstable and the latter stable.

Muir (1962) presented a review article entitled «The paragenesis and optical properties of some ternary feldspars» in which he subdivided the fields of anorthoclase and plagioclase proposed by MacKenzie and Smith into anorthoclase, lime anorthoclase, plagioclase, potash oligoclase and potash andesine (Fig. 9-15). He wrote:

"Since monoclinic alkali feldspars do not usually contain more than five per cent of the anorthite component, and since normal rock-forming plagioclases rarely contain more than the same amount of the orthoclase component, it is convenient to regard any feldspar containing more than five per cent of the third component as a ternary one. The names most commonly applied to such minerals in present day petrographic nomenclature are anorthoclase, lime anorthoclase, potash oligoclase, and potash andesine. As will be shown, these minerals are common constituents in alkaline lavas especially as groundmass constituents. Their positive identification in the past has been hindered by confusing the influence of the orthoclase content of a plagioclase with that due to the normal high temperature form, and by difficulties unfortunately created by the concept of anemousite.

Although the name anorthoclase is familiar to most petrologists and conjures up ideas of the famous rhomb-shaped feldspars of some of the rocks of the Oslo area, the alkaline lavas of East Africa, and those of Mt. Erebus, Antartica, some of the other names have a long history. The term potash oligoclase was first used by Iddings (1906, p. 322) to include triclinic feldspars (lime-soda microcline or anorthoclase) containing from three to five per cent of lime (15–25% of anorthite). Even more calcic varieties have been described from alkaline Pacific lavas first by Barth (1929), (1931), and later by MacDonald (1942) as potash andesine. The term lime anorthoclase was introduced by Aoki (1959) to cover the feldspar found as microphenocrysts in the alkaline lavas of the Iki Islands and the Higashi-matsuura district of Japan. This mineral has also been found by Muir and Tilley (1961) to be a prominent modal mineral in hawaiites and mugearites. It indicates a mineral lying in the anorthoclase field of (Fig. 9-15) that contains more than ten per cent of the anorthite component".

Thus the petrographer's definitions of high temperature ternary feldspars are tending towards convenient ranges of chemical composition, defined by arbitrary boundaries superimposed on the three basic fields of sanidine, anorthoclase and plagioclase. Because typical specimens are strongly zoned, such as specimens with trends SS and JJ in Fig. 9-15, there seems to be no point in worrying over such niceties as the exact position of boundaries. The petrographer is also not concerned initially whether a high-temperature ternary feldspar is homogeneous or unmixed. Such a distinction could be made by the prefix perthitic or non-perthitic.

Wright and Stewart (1968), on the basis of refined unit cell parameters *measured at room temperature* (Chapter 7), proposed a revised terminology:

"The structural states or ranges of structural states of sodic feldspar from highest to lowest are high albite, intermediate albite and low albite. Albite is arbitrarily restricted to those feldspars containing less than 5% Or component. Anorthoclase is distinguished from albite by its more potassic composition and from high and low sanidines by triclinic symmetry. Definitions are as follows (all triclinic):

High albite. Unit-cell parameters b and c correspond to the sodic end-member of the high sanidine–high albite series.

Intermediate albite. b and c fall between the curves for the two limiting series.

Low albite. Unit-cell parameters b and c correspond to the sodic end-member of the maximum microcline–low albite series.

Anorthoclase. Triclinic with bulk composition containing greater than 5% Or component, but less than 40% Or, the composition of the symmetry change in series containing monoclinic K-feldspar".

No discussion was given by Wright and Stewart of the change of symmetry with temperature, but it is implicit in the above definition that anorthoclase would change to sanidine during heating.

This long review of the literature shows the extreme confusion caused by the differing approaches ranging from those of petrographers requiring a simple definition to those of structural crystallographers searching for a clear definition of atomic properties. Just as for K-feldspars, I shall propose the use of prefixes to clarify the meaning. Because I believe that the attempt by Laves to distinguish "analbite" from "albite" on the basis of whether the Na-feldspar follows an equilibrium or a non-equilibrium path has no practical value, I shall not use the term "analbite". Naturally occurring albites can be characterized from the b^*c^* dimensions *measured at room temperature* by use of the prefixes high, low and intermediate. However I do not like to restrict high and low to just the extreme end-members of the ordering sequence, as has been proposed by Wright and Stewart. Instead I propose to assign a field to each type of albite as shown in Figs. 9-11 and 9-12. Thus high albite corresponds to high sanidine and low albite to low microcline; intermediate albite occupies a much wider field and on the b^* c^* plot would correspond to summation of the fields of inter-mediate- and high-microcline together with the fields of low- and intermediate-sanidine. The prefix maximum is suggested for the states of highest and lowest Al/Si order to give *(maximum) low albite* and *(maximum) high albite*. Of course the prefix will rarely be necessary because of the context.

Low albite is triclinic at all temperatures. Natural specimens contain only a few percent of Or molecule in solid solution, and no special prefix is needed. The composition of a member of the artificial low albite – low microcline series is best specified by giving the Or-content.

Maximum high albite is triclinic at room temperature but becomes monoclinic near the melting point. High albites with some Al, Si order may be triclinic at all temperatures. The monoclinic variety of high albite can be called *monalbite*. Upon cooling, monalbite develops combined Albite and Pericline inversion twinning as it becomes triclinic: the product could be called *inverted monalbite*, corresponding to Analbit in German-speaking countries.

Homogeneous alkali feldspars with strong Al, Si disorder are monoclinic at room temperature from $Or_{100}Ab_0$ to $Or_{40}Ab_{40}$ and triclinic from Or_{40} to Or_0. The simplest nomenclature is to call the first type sanidine and the second type high albite. Upon inversion to monoclinic symmetry, the high albite would be called monalbite. If sub-divisions are desired, I suggest K-sanidine, $Or_{100} - Or_{70}$; Na-sanidine, $Or_{70} - Or_{40}$; K-high albite (or monalbite), $Or_{40} - Or_{10}$; and Na-high albite (or monalbite), $Or_{10} - Or_0$. Some specimens of intermediate composition may be unmixed with preservation of strong Al, Si disorder (Chapter 19), and the addition of perthite is suitable.

Provision must now be made for ternary feldspars. Such a feldspar may derive either from a volcanic rock, in which case it has strong Si, Al disorder, or from a plutonic rock in which case it has undergone ordering and unmixing. Figure 9-16 shows a possible nomenclature for disordered specimens from volcanic rocks, on the assumption that a chemical analysis has been made and the feldspar has been shown to be homogeneous. A curved line outlines the approximate area in which single-phase feldspars are not found in rocks. The region of one feldspar is divided into areas whose boundaries conform with (1) the traditional division of the plagioclase field according to the ranges 0-10, 10-30, 30-50, 50-70, 70-90 and 90-100% An (2) the division of the alkali feldspars according to the ranges 0-10, 10-40, 40-70 and 70-100% Or as just described (3) an arbitrary separation between plagioclase and alkali

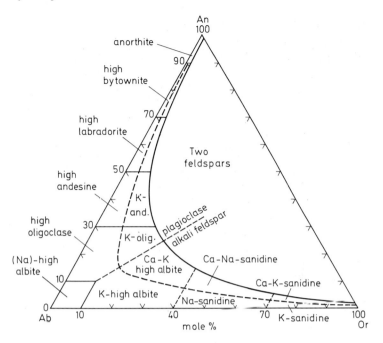

Fig. 9-16. Proposed nomenclature of homogeneous feldspars in a high structural state

feldspar at Or = Ab. All compositions are in mole per cent. Each of the plagioclase sub-fields has been divided into two roughly equal regions, the more potassic of which is indicated by the prefix K. The field of Na-high albite is bounded by the lines Or = 10% and An = 10%. The fields of K-high albite, Na-sanidine and K-sanidine have been subdivided into two regions, the more calcic of which is distinguished by the prefix Ca. With rising temperature, the field of monalbite expands over the field of high albite. The fields of K-oligoclase and Ca–K–high albite are separated arbitrarily by the line Or = An. Although this line corresponds roughly to the boundary between plagioclase and anorthoclase as defined originally by MacKenzie, the boundary is placed strictly with respect to composition. The field of (Na)-high albite is split equally between plagioclase and alkali feldspar.

If chemical data have not been obtained, a petrographer might wish to rely merely on optical data. Thus he might try to distinguish sanidine, anorthoclase and plagioclase from the optical texture; the sanidine would be expected to have sharp extinction consistent with monoclinic symmetry, the anorthoclase would be expected to have patchy extinction and cross-hatched twinning indicative of an inversion from monoclinic symmetry, and the latter would have sharp extinction and sharp twin boundaries indicative of primary growth with triclinic symmetry. Observation of the anorthoclase type of texture should definitely indicate that the feldspar passed through the monoclinic-triclinic inversion; however, observation of monoclinic optical symmetry with sharp extinction is *not* a reliable indication of sanidine because a sub-optical twinned feldspar could appear monoclinic. I recommend that the petrographer consider using the terms *optical-sanidine, optical-anorthoclase* and *optical-plagioclase* if he wishes to be precise about the names implied from his optical observations. Of course, the prefixes can usually be omitted because of the implied context. The optical petrographer will rarely be able to detect perthitic structure in ternary feldspars from high-temperature rocks: by X-ray methods such as those of Wright and Stewart (powder) or of Laves, MacKenzie and Smith (single crystal) he would be able to characterize individual phases. Thus an *optical anorthoclase* might turn out to be an antiperthite of K-high albite and Na-low sanidine. In this system of nomenclature, anorthoclase is an imprecise term corresponding both to a single phase and to an intergrowth of more than one phase. It should be noted that anorthoclase is not coterminous with high albite: whereas all Na-rich feldspars with inversion twinning will fall in the field of high albite if homogeneous, not all high albites will have passed through the monoclinic-triclinic inversion and have the characteristic optical properties of an anorthoclase.

Petrographers may wish to retain the terms *lime anorthoclase, potash oligoclase* and *potash andesine* to sub-divide the anorthoclase and plagioclase fields: however I would like to suggest that they use instead the terms calcian anorthoclase, potassian oligoclase and potassian andesine in accordance with recommendations of the International Mineralogical Association for the use of compositional prefixes.

If it is desired to specify the twin relations of Na-rich feldspar, the prefixes *M-twinned* and *T-twinned* could be used respectively for twinning developed during the symmetry inversion and twinning developed directly in the triclinic state (see Chapter 18). Probably all *M-twinning* in natural sodic feldspars occurs by a displacive inversion; however, a theoretical distinction could be made between twinning arising during displacive and diffusive transformations by using the terms *displacive M-twinning* and *diffusive M-twinning*. The compositional boundaries between an *optical anorthoclase* and an *optical plagioclase* will be imprecise because the temperature of crystallization of such feldspars depends on the bulk chemical composition of the magma, and on the pressure. Because the temperature of crystallization in mugearites and similar rocks can be expected to be near 1000° C, the compositional boundary between M-twinned and T-twinned ternary feldspars is probably close to the arbitrary compositional boundary established between high albite and oligoclase: however, in case of a conflict it is inherent in the present definition that the compositional boundary has priority over a boundary based on the twin properties. It seems doubtful whether this distinction will ever be of practical significance.

Ternary feldspars from hypabyssal and plutonic rocks commonly exsolve into antiperthites with spectacular textures (Chapter 19). Some specimens have the rhomb-shaped morphology typical of the phenocrysts of ternary feldspars in volcanic rocks. If the individual components of the antiperthite have been characterized by X-ray study (or optical study if the texture is sufficiently coarse), a detailed name such as low-sanidine-oligoclase antiperthite might be given. Some specimens have been shown by single-crystal X-ray study to contain both a monoclinic and a triclinic K-feldspar, and it is possible that more than one plagioclase occurs. It is highly desirable that at least one or two crystals be studied by single-crystal X-ray methods before powder X-ray methods are used to give a rapid survey of ternary feldspars from an igneous complex. At an even higher level, electron-optical techniques should be used to reveal the textural features.

9.2.3 General

Most alkali feldspars contain significant amounts of both Or and Ab molecules together with smaller amounts of An, Cn, etc. Only a few of these feldspars remain homogeneous during cooling, and most occur as perthitic intergrowths. During cooling, exsolution may take place in more than one stage in response to changes of symmetry and to the decreasing range of atomic migration. In the initial stage of exsolution, the aluminosilicate framework remains continuous across the domains. If cooling is slow, the domains may break apart. A detailed review is given in Chapter 19 of some of the complexities. It is obvious that the phenomena are so complex and are so idiosyncratic that a comprehensive nomenclature cannot be achieved by the use of just a few terms. Typically a microcline perthite from a pegmatite will show veins of low albite about $0.1 - 1$ mm across in a host of microcline which itself contains films or plates of albite about 0.1 to 10 μm across. The albite and microcline are usually twinned. Some perthites reveal both a monoclinic and a triclinic K-feldspar to single-crystal X-ray study. The structural state and An-content of the exsolved plagioclase may be ambiguous. Chapter 19 should be consulted for information on nomenclature.

Figures 9-11 and 9-12 give a suggested nomenclature of alkali feldspars based on simple X-ray and optical measurements. If an alkali feldspar is homogeneous, and its cell dimensions are not anomalous because of lattice strain or unusual chemical substitutions, its values of b^* and c^* should fall into one of the divisions in Fig. 9-11 outside the regions for perthite and antiperthite. The extreme feldspars fall at the corners of a quadrilateral which is almost rectangular, one dimension of which gives the structural state, and the other the Or content. Whenever possible, the indicated Or-content should be checked by a chemical procedure (e.g. electron microprobe or flame photometry) or by measurement of a^* or the cell volume: because of the relative insensitivity of Or-contents estimated from b^*c^*, an estimate from one of the other techniques is preferred in assigning the nomenclature. For anomalous feldspars, the Or-content should be estimated either chemically or from the cell volume and the point plotted using $\Delta(b^*c^*)$ – see Chapter 7.

Figure 9-12 is a corresponding diagram based on the optic axial angle and Or-content. There are insufficient data to provide a strict comparison between b^*c^* and $2V$, Or, but the boundaries are probably fairly consistent judging from the data in Fig. 8-8.

Figures 9-11 and 9-12 are designed for natural specimens whose cooling history was not complicated by unusual processes. The K-rich feldspars are following a two-step trend, and the Na-rich feldspars probably change discontinuously from a high albite (or monalbite) solid solution to a low plagioclase. Synthetic K-feldspars grown at high temperature probably fit the same two-step trend. Natural and synthetic K-rich specimens grown at low temperature (perhaps below 300° C) are probably anomalous, and require detailed study before a precise name is given. Most synthetic Na-rich feldspars probably follow the one-step trend, and can be named satisfactorily from Fig. 9-11. Ion-exchanged feldspars do not fit the scheme, except for the extreme high and low series. An Na-exchanged low sanidine is *not* structurally equivalent to an intermediate albite, because the former belongs to a two-step trend and the latter to the one-step trend.

The nomenclature used in German-speaking countries is nicely summarized in Table 14 of Bambauer (1966).

9.3 Plagioclase Feldspars

Before 1950, the nomenclature of plagioclase was relatively straightforward, but this was the result mainly of ignorance of the structural complexities. Even in 1973, interpretation of some of the structural features is controversial. The proposed nomenclature is tentative and tied as far as possible to actual observations rather than to interpretations.

At the simplest level, plagioclase can be considered merely in terms of the bulk chemical composition and the "structural state". The former can be precisely measured, but the latter depends on complex atomic movements.

Chemically, plagioclase falls almost entirely into the Or–Ab–An system, and substitution of Fe, Ba and Sr is trivial for the purposes of a primary nomenclature. Deer *et al.* (1963) divided plagioclase into sub-fields by use of boundary lines radiating from Or to the Ab, An side-line. Here (Fig. 9-16), in agreement with Bambauer (1966), the lines are drawn at constant An-content. Although the traditional boundaries between the sub-fields do not correspond to structural changes, it is convenient to retain them.

Historically, there was a long dispute in the nineteenth century whether chemical substitution in the plagioclases was completely continuous or whether discrete compounds occur. Details are given by Marfunin (1966).

The term *plagioclase*, chosen by Breithaupt (1847) on the basis of the oblique angle between the two principal cleavages, came to refer to the entire series of Na, Ca-feldspars. *Oligoclase* was named by Breithaupt (1826) from oligos (little) and klasis (to break) because its cleavage was thought to be less perfect than that of albite. *Andesine* was originally called andesite (now used as a rock name) by Abich (1841) from the Andes mountains. *Labradorite* was named by Werner (1780) from an iridescent specimen from Labrador. *Bytownite* refers to Bytown, Canada from which a greenish-white feldspar was described by Thomson (1835). *Anorthite* was chosen by Rosé (1823) because of the oblique morphology.

Several different substitutional ranges have been used for the above sub-divisions of plagioclase, but modern workers use 0-10, albite; 10-30 oligoclase; 30-50 andesine; 50-70 labradorite; 70-90 bytownite; 90-100 anorthite (all mol.-% An).

The substitution of Or in natural plagioclase falls rapidly with increasing An-content (Chapter 14), maximum values being about 6% at An_{50} and perhaps 1% at An_{100}. Those plagioclases rich in Or may be specified by the prefix potassian (or briefly K) as in Fig. 9-16; however, a precise description such as $Or_4Ab_{50}An_{46}$ is preferable. Chapter 7 describes properties of K-exchanged plagioclases produced by heating plagioclase with molten salts.

The term *structural state* is loosely applied to plagioclase. Unquestionably there is a unique series of high plagioclase whose structure is thermodynamically stable at the solidus (say, for atmospheric pressure). However it is probable that there is not a unique series of low plagioclase, except in theory. Natural specimens assigned to the low series on the basis of optical and powder X-ray data (Chapters 8 and 7) probably do not have a unique set of structural properties (i.e. one cannot predict the atomic distribution merely from knowledge of the An-content and a structural indicator). A heated plagioclase probably does not retrace the sequence of atomic patterns followed by a natural plagioclase cooling in a rock (see summary by Smith and Ribbe, 1969). Nevertheless for routine description of a plagioclase, it is convenient to rely on the An-content and an indicator of structural state, as reviewed in Chapters 7 and 8. Research mineralogists, of course, will wish to use a more complex nomenclature based on detailed X-ray and electron-optical measurements.

A typical recent nomenclature is that of Bambauer (1966), which derived from F. Laves and his students. The following is translated from the original German:

"*Group Names.*

A. Plagioklas-D. Group name for plagioclase with the characteristics of an Al/Si distribution with extensive to maximum disorder (stable or unstable) (D for disordered): comprised of Analbit, Ca-Analbit (to Anplagioklas) and the stable series Plagioklas (hoch) from Albit (hoch) to Anorthit (the earlier description 'Hochtemperatur'-Plagioklas is contained in it).

2. Plagioklas-O. Group name for all plagioclase with the characteristics of an Al/Si distribution with extensive to maximum order (stable or unstable) (O for ordered) comprised of the stable series Plagioklas (tief) from Albit (tief) to Anorthit which is assumed to show in Nature the highest possible Al, Si ordering (coinciding with the earlier description 'Tieftemperatur'-Plagioklas).

Phases

1. Monalbit. Monoclinic Na-feldspar with Al/Si distribution analogous to sanidine. Stable only at high temperatures.

2. Analbit. Triclinic Na-feldspar with unstable Al/Si distribution corresponding to Monalbit. (In the literature also shown as "high albite"). Analogous to Analbit are Ca-Analbit to Anplagioklas.

3. Albit (hoch). Triclinic Na-feldspar with stable Al/Si distribution corresponding to the highest possible disorder consistent with triclinic symmetry. (Not identical with 'high albite').

4. Albit (tief). Triclinic Na-feldspar with an Al/Si distribution of highest order.

5. Anorthit (B): Ca-feldspar with triclinic, body-centered, translation lattice.

6. Anorthit (P): Ca-feldspar with triclinic, primitive, translation lattice.

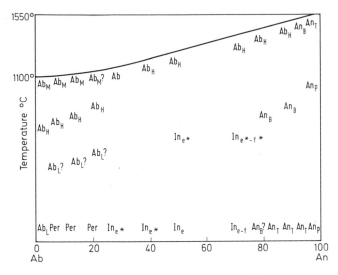

Fig. 9-17. Diagrammatic representation of sub-solidus relations in plagioclase as reviewed by Gay (1962). (Redrawn from Gay, 1962, Figs. 2, 3 and 4)

Pseudomorphs

1. Antiperthit. Regular intergrowth of plagioclase (host) and alkali feldspar (guest).

2. Peristerite. Regular intergrowth of albite and oligoclase".

English-speaking scientists tend to use the terms high- and low- rather than D and O; the prefix intermediate can be used for those between the extreme series. The prefix I is used here rather than B for body-centered anorthite in order to conform with the space-group symbol I$\overline{1}$. Laves (1960b) used the term Disanorthit with sub-divisions (hoch), (int.) and (tief), but did not use it in later papers.

Gay (1962) reviewed information gathered by X-ray studies of plagioclase and gave schematic diagrams summarized in Fig. 9-17. This figure attempts to relate the various structural varieties to the temperature at which they developed. For the albite composition low albite (Ab_L) transforms with rising temperature into high albite (Ab_H) and finally into monalbite (Ab_M). Peristerite (Per) occurs at low temperature in the albite-oligoclase region, and may transform via low albite solid solution into high albite s.s. and ultimately into monalbite s.s. From about An_{25} to An_{70}, intermediate plagioclase (In) occurs, the sodic specimens having diffuse *e* diffractions (*e**), and the more calcic ones having sharp *e* diffractions, and finally both *e* and *f*. Upon heating the *e* diffractions become more diffuse and ultimately disappear giving high albite s.s. Pure anorthite exists with primitive symmetry (An_P) at low temperature and transforms into transitional anorthite (An_T) with diffuse *c* diffractions at the melting point. The body-centered anorthite type (An_B) occurs in a band running from An_{95} at the melting point to An_{80} at lower temperature.

Many studies over the next decade showed that, although several features in Gay's review were correct, others were incorrect or incomplete. Even in 1973, many features were highly controversial, but the review of observations in Fig. S − 2b probably is basically correct. The interpretation of these observations in terms of phase equilibria is highly controversial, and the ideas given in this treatise cannot be expected to survive unscathed. Under these circumstances, it is inevitable that care must be taken in giving names to plagioclases. There is no need to repeat here the review in the summary chapter. For details of the three intergrowths on a micrometer scale, Chapter 19 should be consulted. By 1973, all estimates of the chemical composition of the two components of the intergrowths were indirect: nevertheless it seems certain from cell dimensions and the ratio of the widths of lamellae that *peristerite* consists of a mixture of low albite and an oligoclase near An_{25} with diffuse *e* diffractions. Electron-optical data for the *Bøggild intergrowth* which occurs for bulk compositions from $An_{43} - An_{57}$ suggests that the two components differ in composition by perhaps 10% An. The *Huttenlocher intergrowth* contains a labradorite with sharp *e* diffractions, probably near An_{67}, and a body-centered anorthite of uncertain composition. The scale of the intergrowths varies from about 1 μm down to tens of unit-cell edges, and it is probable that detailed study will lead to a complex nomenclature for the textures.

The structural variation of anorthites is very complex as described in Chapter 5. Although the most obvious feature involves movement of Ca atoms with concomitant bending of the aluminosilicate framework, it is fairly certain that some anorthites show weak disorder of the Al, Si atoms. In addition substitution of Ab molecule causes complications in the distribution of both M and T atoms. Classification of anorthites on the basis of the symmetry (e.g. by the prefixes P and I) is too crude to describe the variations of domain texture and atomic distributions revealed by detailed electron-optical studies (Chapter 10). By 1973 there had been no detailed proposal for the nomenclature of anorthite. Perhaps by analogy with alkali feldspars one might use prefixes high, low and intermediate to refer to the degree of Al, Si disorder. Probably the prefixes P and I, based on the presence or absence of type *c* diffractions, tend to imply correctly the positions of the Ca atoms irrespective of the degree of disorder of the T atoms. However the details of the domain textures must depend on the distributions of both the M and T atoms thus precluding a simple nomenclature. Certainly the safest description uses the type and character of subsidiary diffractions. Thus the descriptions s, d, vd and m might be used to specify that the diffractions are sharp, diffuse or very diffuse, or that they are missing. The original simple concepts of P- and I-anorthites would be expressed as *b*(s)-*c*(s)-anorthite and *b*(s)-*c*(m)-anorthite. The new nomenclature would permit a term such as *b*(d)-*c*(vd) to express an anorthite with diffuse diffractions of type *b* and very diffuse ones of type *c*.

Under equilibrium conditions, the stable form of anorthite at low temperature will have sharp *b* and *c* (and *d*) diffractions, and instead of using the prefix *b*(s)-*c*(s) it is simplest to use P. Disorder of Al, Si atoms will be very slight at the temperature at which the *c* diffractions become very diffuse (probably between 250 and 300° C). At the melting point, the *b* diffractions should be diffuse under equilibrium conditions and the *c* diffractions should be extremely diffuse or missing *when observed at temperature*. For such an anorthite, it seems simplest to use the prefix I. Deliberately in this book, the terms P- and I-anorthite are used whenever no confusion can arise, and a more ponderous nomenclature is used only when strictly needed. The term T-anorthite (or transitional anorthite) is used in a non-precise way to describe anorthites with c diffractions that are seen to be diffuse on X-ray patterns (following Gay, 1962).

Electron-optical methods are more sensitive than X-ray methods in demonstrating diffuseness of diffractions. This arises because the dark-field technique can reveal domain boundaries tens or hundreds of nanometers apart, whereas the resulting broadening of diffraction spots is unmeasurable. Accordingly great care must be taken in evaluating a statement about the diffuseness of diffractions from anorthite. Another complication arises from solid solution. Substitution of Ab must necessarily give Al, Si disorder as well as Na, Ca disorder unless complete exsolution of Ab occurs. From the incomplete electron-optical data of anorthites, it appears that exsolution is rarely complete and that either incipient clustering or formation of fine-scale coherent domains takes place. Most petrographers may wish to ignore these very subtle effects, especially as they probably are affected strongly by trivial factors.

Returning now to plagioclase of intermediate composition, Fig. S-2 summarizes the occurrence of subsidiary diffractions. Specimens crystallized at solidus temperatures have not been investigated in full detail, but it seems likely that those from An_0 to at least An_{80} show only a-diffractions and can be described as *high albite solid solution*. Those from about An_0 to An_{12} become monoclinic upon heating and can be called *monalbite solid solutions* when actually observed to be monoclinic. Pure anorthite probably shows slightly diffuse b and very diffuse or absent c diffractions, and can loosely be described as I-anorthite, though the term T-anorthite might be more appropriate. There is no information on the effect of Ab in solid solution, but presumably the b and c diffractions become more diffuse. Possibly there is a two-phase region between high albite solid solution and anorthite.

In the low series, specimens from about An_{15} to about An_{70} show type e diffractions whose diffuseness decreases as the An-content increases. Those from labradorites also show observable type f diffractions. Often this type of plagioclase has been referred to as *intermediate plagioclase*, but a more direct name would specify the type of diffraction. In this treatise, the term *e-plagioclase* is used. Of course, the prefix f may be used if desired, and the nature of the diffuseness could be specified by s, d and vd. The term *intermediate* is best reserved for the structural state revealed by a simple measure of some X-ray or optical indicator, of which the 131 indicator (or some equivalent such as Γ) seems best for specimens from An_0 to An_{70}. An intermediate-e(d)-plagioclase (An_{56}) could be the name applied to a specimen whose An-content was measured with an electron probe or from a refractive index: the term intermediate could result from X-ray powder measurement of the 131 and $1\bar{3}1$ diffractions, and the term e(d) from X-ray single-crystal observation of diffuseness of the e diffractions.

The nomenclature of plagioclases from An_{70} to An_{100} is uncertain pending clarification of many problems. Some specimens occur as the Huttenlocher intergrowth, but others appear to be fairly homogeneous or at least contain only fine-scale domains. Various diffuse diffractions have been observed including *b*, *c* and *e* types. Chapters 5, 10 and 19 should be consulted. It appears that the complexities result from different degrees of ordering and exsolution under non-equilibrium cooling.

9.4 Other Feldspars

Most Ba-containing feldspars belong fairly closely to the Or – Cn join but substitution of Ab and An occurs. Just as for the plagioclase series there are many structural complexities whose full extent is not completely evaluated. Spencer (1942) gave a thorough review of the occurrence of Ba-feldspars. *Hyalophane*, named for its glassy appearance, was characterized by Sartorius von Waltershausen (1855) in a dolomite at Binnenthal, Switzerland, where it had previously been mistaken for adularia. *Celsian* was discovered by Sjögren (1895) from the manganese mines at Jakobsberg, Sweden and named after the astronomer Anders Celsius. From the chemical analysis (BaO 39.72%), the formula $BaAl_2Si_2O_8$ was deduced correctly, but the symmetry was given incorrectly as triclinic. Strandmark (1903) demonstrated monoclinic symmetry for similar material. *Kasoite* with BaO 25.5% was observed by Yosimura (1936) at the Kaso manganese mine, Japan. Spencer (1942) listed the occurrences of hyalophane and celsian, showing that they mostly occur in association with manganese ores. Probably there is a complete range of chemical compositions between $KAlSi_3O_8$ and $BaAl_2Si_2O_8$. Many K-feldspars contain Ba as a minor constituent, and some sanidines contain up to several percent of Cn.

Gay and Roy (1968) summarized their detailed X-ray studies of K, Ba feldspars in a schematic temperature-composition diagram (Fig. 9-18). K-feldspar is categorized as microcline, orthoclase and sanidine. At solidus temperature, sanidine changes continuously into hyalophane (high) and finally into celsian

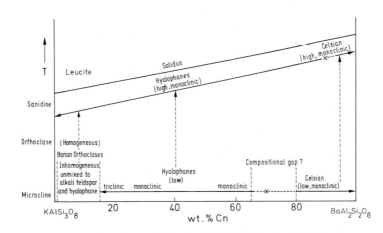

Fig. 9-18. Schematic representation of sub-solidus relations in the $KAlSi_3O_8$–$BaAl_2Si_2O_8$ system. (From Gay and Roy, 1968, Fig. 3)

(high), all with monoclinic symmetry. Synthetic specimens from 70–100 wt.-% Cn show type b diffractions on electron-diffraction photographs. Sanidine certainly has strong Al, Si disorder, but the degree of disorder attainable in celsian at high temperature was not determined. At low temperature, microcline tolerates only a few percent at most of Cn in solid solution. Specimens up to about Cn_{15} (wt.-%) are inhomogeneous and unmixed into K-feldspar and hyalophane: i.e. there is an analogy to peristerite. Hyalophane occurs at low temperature as a homogeneous phase from about Cn_{15} to Cn_{65}, occurring with triclinic symmetry at the more potassic compositions and with monoclinic symmetry from at least Cn_{30} to Cn_{65}. Celsian, with a doubled c-axis characteristic of alternation of Al and Si atoms, occurs from Cn_{100} to about Cn_{80}. No natural specimens have been found from Cn_{65} to Cn_{80}, but this may be fortuitous. Type b diffractions were found for all specimens with more than 80% Cn and for a calcio-celsian with 62% Cn and 20% An molecules: none were found for a specimen with 65% Cn. The cell dimensions of Ba-containing feldspars are given in Chapter 7.

Gay and Roy stated that "common descriptive terms include celsian (usually restricted to members with at least 80–90% Cn) and hyalophane (usually used for the more K-rich specimens though the relationship to celsians is ill-defined), with barium-orthoclase, barium-sanidine, and calcio-celsian applied to particular minerals. It is convenient for the present discussion to use terms which, as far as possible, have a structural significance. Thus 'celsian' is used to describe all homogeneous members with a 14° c-axis; if necessary the nature of the celsian can be specified by the prefix high, low, etc. Any other homogeneous members with more than 15% Cn and a 7 Å c-axis are described as 'hyalophanes'; again prefixes (which may include monoclinic and triclinic) may be added to define the nature of the hyalophane. The lower limit of the hyalophanes has been chosen to take account of those K-rich members of the series that may be homogeneous or unmixed to a greater or lesser degree: for the present it is suggested provisionally that these specimens shall be called "barian orthoclases" to which can be added a perthitic classification if it becomes relevant. It is clear that the nomenclature may need revision particularly with regard to the relations of barian orthoclase and hyalophane in the light of future work...".

Plagioclases typically contain trivial amounts of Ba-feldspar, but those with high Or-contents may contain small amounts of Ba. Spencer (1942) reported that Cloizeaux, des (1877) observed a new barium feldspar from an unknown locality, containing 7.3% BaO, 1.8% CaO, 7.4% Na_2O and 0.83% K_2O: the 3.7% of volatile material is suspicious. Nockolds and Zies (1933) described a barium plagioclase with 5.7% BaO, 14.0% CaO, 2.0% Na_2O and 0.7% K_2O from the Broken Hill district, Australia. These specimens could be described as barian-plagioclase, but further chemical and X-ray studies are desirable.

Reedmergnerite was discovered by Milton et al. (1954) from a brown dolomitic core in an oil well near Duchesne, Utah, and described mineralogically by Milton et al. (1960). The name honors two technicians of the U. S. Geological Survey, F. S. Reed and J. L. Mergner. Reedmergnerite is almost pure $NaBSi_3O_8$, and it has an ordered structure with B in the T_1O site (Chapter 3).

Buddingtonite was found by Erd *et al.* (1964) in the hydrothermal alteration zone of lava flows at the Sulphur Bank quicksilver mine, Lake County, California. It is named after the petrologist A. F. Buddington. Natural buddingtonite is $NH_4AlSi_3O_8 \cdot 0.5 H_2O$. The crystal structure is similar to that of high sanidine, but no water molecules were detected in the X-ray structural analysis (Chapter 3). Synthetic dry buddingtonite was found to absorb water upon exposure to air, and the role of water is unclear (Kimball and Megaw; pers. comm., July 1972).

References

Abich, W. H. (1841): Jahresbericht über die Fortschritte der physischen Wissenschaften. J. J. Berzelius, Tübingen, Vol. XXI, 167. See Chester (1896).

Alling, H. L. (1926): The potash-soda feldspars. JG **34**, 591–611.

Ansilewski, J. (1961): The problem of classification of the alkali feldspars. Arch. Mineral. **23**, 5–59.

Aoki, K. (1959): Petrology of alkali rocks of the Iki Islands and Higashi-matsuura district. Japan. Sci. Rept. Tôhôku Univ., 3rd ser. **6**, 261–310.

Bailey, S. W. (1954): Ph. D. thesis. Cambridge University, England.

Bailey, S. W., Taylor, W. H. (1955): The structure of a triclinic potassium felspar. AC **8**, 621– 632.

Bambauer, H. U. (1966): Feldspat-Familie $R_x{}^I R_{1-x}{}^{II}[Al_{2-x}Si_{2+x}O_8]$, $0 \le x \le 1$. In: Tröger, W. E.: Optische Bestimmungen der gesteinsbildenden Minerale. Teil 2, Textband, p. 645–762. Stuttgart: Schweizerbart'sche Verlagsbuchhandlung.

Bambauer, H. U., Laves, F. (1960): Zum Adularproblem. I. Adular vom Val Casatscha: Mimetischer Lamellenbau, Variation von Optik und Gitterkonstanten und ihre genetische Deutung. SMPM **40**, 177–205.

Barbier, P., Prost, A. (1908): Sur l'existence d'un feldspath sodique monoclinique isomorphe de l'orthose. Bull. Soc. Chim. **3**, 894–899.

Barth, T. (1929): Über den monoklinen Natronfeldspat. ZK **69**, 476–481.

Barth, T. F. W. (1931): Mineralogical petrography of Pacific lavas. Part I. Minerals. AJS **21**, Ser. 5, 377–405.

Barth, T. F. W. (1934): Polymorphic phenomena and crystal structure. AJS **27**, Ser. 5, 273–286.

Barth, T. F. W. (1959): The interrelations of the structural variants of the potash feldspars. ZK **112**, 263–274.

Barth, T. F. W. (1965): Relations between optical orientation and structural state in the system of potassium feldspar. Indian Mineralogist **6**, 40–47.

Barth, T. F. W. (1969): Feldspars, 261 pp. New York and London: Wiley, Interscience.

Baskin, Y. (1956): A study of authigenic feldspars. JG **64**, 132–155.

Bøggild, O. B. (1911): Über die Krystallform des Mikroklins. ZK **48**, 466–472.

Breithaupt, A. (1823): Charakteristik des Mineral-Systems. 2nd edn. Dresden.

Breithaupt, A. (1826): Poggendorff's Ann. Phys. Chem. VIII, 238. See Chester (1896).

Breithaupt, A. (1830): Über die Felsite und einige neue Specien ihres Geschlechts. Schweigger's J. Chem. Phys. **60**, 324.

Breithaupt, A. (1847): Vollständiges Handbuch der Mineralogie. 3 Vols. Dresden und Leipzig.

Brøgger, W. C. (1882): Die silurischen Etagen 2 und 3 im Kristianagebiet und auf Eker. Universitätsprogramm für 2 Sem. 1882, Kristiana, 376 pp.

Brooke, H. J. (1823): A description of the crystalline form of some new minerals. Ann. Phil. (Lond.) **5**, 381–384.

Brown, B. E., Bailey, S. W. (1964): The structure of maximum microcline. AC **17**, 1391–1400.

Brun, E., Hartmann, P., Staub, H. H., Hafner, S., Laves, F. (1960): Magnetische Kernresonanz zur Beobachtung des Al, Si-Ordnungs/Unordnungsgrades in einigen Feldspäten. ZK **113**, 65–76.

Chaisson, U. (1950): The optics of triclinic adularia. JG **58**, 537–547.

Chao, S. H., Hargreaves, A., Taylor, W. H. (1940). The structure of orthoclase. MM **25**, 498–512.

Chao, S. H., Smare, D. L., Taylor, W. H. (1939): An X-ray examination of some potash-soda felspars. MM **25**, 338–350.

Chao, S. H., Taylor, W. H. (1940): The lamellar structure of potash-soda felspars. Proc. Roy. Soc. (Lond.) **174** A, 57—72.

Chester, A. H. (1896): A dictionary of the names of minerals including their history and etymology. New York: John Wiley and Sons.

Cloizeaux, A. des (1862): Manuel de Minéralogie. Paris.

Cloizeaux, A. des (1877): Ein neuer Barytfeldspath. TMPM 99–100. Also (1878): Note sur un nouveau feldspath barytique, Bull. Soc. Min. France **1**, 84–86.

Cole, W. F., Sörum, H., Kennard, O. (1949): The crystal structures of orthoclase and sanidinized orthoclase. AC **2**, 280–287.

Deer, W. A., Howie, R. A., Zussman, J. (1963): Rock forming minerals, 435 pp. 4. Framework silicates. London: Longmans, Green and Co., Ltd.

Erd, R. C., White, D. E., Fahey, J. J., Lee, D. E. (1964): Buddingtonite, an ammonium feldspar with zeolitic water. AM **49**, 831–850.

Ferguson, R. B., Traill, R. J., Taylor, W. H. (1958): The crystal structures of low-temperature and high-temperature albites. AC **11**, 331–348.

Finney, J. J., Bailey, S. W. (1964): Crystal structure of an authigenic maximum microcline. ZK **119**, 413–436.

Fisher, D. J. (1968): Albite, variety cleavelandite, and the signs of its optic directions. AM **53**, 1568–1578.

Forstner, H. (1883): Über die Feldspäthe von Pantelleria. ZK **8**, 513–522.

Forstner, H. (1884): Über künstliche physikalische Veränderungen der Feldspäthe von Pantelleria. ZK **9**, 333–352.

Gay, P. (1962): Sub-solidus relations in the plagioclase feldspars: NGT **42**, No. 2, 37–56.

Gay, P., Roy, N. N. (1968): The mineralogy of the potassium-barium feldspar series. III: Subsolidus relationships. MM **36**, 914–932.

Goldsmith, J. R., Laves, F. (1954a): The microcline-sanidine stability relations. GCA **5**, 1–19.

Goldsmith, J. R., Laves, F. (1954b): Potassium feldspars structurally intermediate between microcline and sanidine. GCA **6**, 100–118.

Hafner, S., Laves, F. (1957): Ordnung/Unordnung und Ultrarotabsorption. II. Variation der Lage und Intensität einiger Absorption von Feldspäten. Zur Struktur von Orthoklas und Adular. ZK **109**, 204–225.

Harker, R. I. (1962): The older ortho-gneisses of Carn Chuinneag and Inchbae. JP **3**, 215–237.

Harnik, A. B. (1970): Strukturelle Zustände in den Anorthoklasen der Rhombenporphyre des Oslogebietes. SMPM **49**, 509–568.

Haüy, R. J. (1801): Traité de minéralogie. 4 Vols., Paris.

Iddings, J. P. (1909): Igneous rocks. New York.

Köhler, A. (1949): Recent results of investigations on the feldspars. JG **57**, 592–599.

Laves, F. (1950): The lattice and twinning of microcline and other potash feldspars. JG **58**, 548–571.

Laves, F. (1952): Phase relations of the alkali feldspars. I. Introductory remarks. II. The stable and pseudo-stable phase relations in the alkali feldspar system. JG **60**, 436–450 and 549–574.

Laves, F. (1956): Über die Bedeutung der Barbierit-Analbit-Umwandlung (displacive transformation) für die Erscheinungsformen der Feldspäte in Larvikiten und Rhombenporphyren. ZK **107**, 196–201.

Laves, F. (1960a): Al/Si-Verteilungen, Phasen-Transformationen und Namen der Alkalifeldspäte. ZK **113**, 265–296.

Laves, F. (1960b): The feldspars, their polysynthetic twinning and their phase relations: Rend. Soc. Mineral. Ital. **16**, 37–68 (in German), 69–100 (in Italian).

Laves, F., Chaisson, U. (1950): An X-ray investigation of the "high"–"low" albite relations. JG **58**, 584–592.

Laves, F., Goldsmith, J. R. (1961): Polymorphism, order, disorder, diffusion and confusion in the feldspars. CCILM **8**, 71–80.

Laves, F., Viswanathan, K. (1967): Relations between optic axial angle and triclinicity of potash feldspars, and their significance for the definition of "stable" and "unstable" states of alkali feldspars. SMPM **47**, 147–162.

MacDonald, G. A. (1942): Potash-oligoclase in Hawaiian lavas. AM **27**, 793–800.

MacKenzie, W. S. (1952): The effect of temperature on the symmetry of high temperature soda-rich feldspars. AJS, Bowen Vol., 319–342.

Mackenzie, W. S. (1954): The orthoclase-microcline inversion. MM **30**, 354–366.

Mackenzie, W. S. (1957): The crystalline modifications of NaAlSi$_3$O$_8$. AJS **255**, 481–516.

Mackenzie, W. S., Smith, J. V. (1955): The alkali feldspars: I, Orthoclase microperthites. AM **40**, 707–732.

Mackenzie, W. S., Smith, J. V. (1956): The alkali feldspars. III. An optical and X-ray study of high temperature feldspars. AM **41**, 405–427.

Mackenzie, W. S., Smith, J. V. (1961): Experimental and geological evidence for the stability of alkali feldspars. CCILM **8**, 53–69.

Mallard, F. (1876): Explications des phénomènes optiques anomaux qui presentent un grand nombre de substances cristallisées. Annales des mines **10**, 187–240. Alternatively, see ZK **1**, 201–237 (1877).

Marfunin, A. S. (1961): The relation between structure and optical orientation in potash-soda feldspars. CCILM **8**, 97–109.

Marfunin, A. S. (1962): Feldspars-phase relations, optical properties, geological distribution. Trans. Inst. Geol. Ore Deposits, Petr., Min., Geochem., No. 78, 275. In Russian.

Marfunin, A. S. (1966): The feldspars: phase relations, optical properties, and geological distribution. (Transl. from the Russian edition, 1962). Jerusalem (Israel Prog. Sci. Translations), 317 pp.

Megaw, H. D. (1959): Order and disorder in the feldspars, I. MM **32**, 226–241.

Milton, C., Axelrod, J. M., Grimaldi, F. S. (1954): New minerals, reedmergnerite (Na$_2$O · B$_2$O$_3$ · 6SiO$_2$) and eitelite (Na$_2$O · MgO · 2CO$_2$), associated with leucosphenite, shortite, searlesite, and crocidolite in the Green River formation, Utah (abstr.). BGSA **65**, 1286–1287.

Milton, C., Chao, E. C. T., Axelrod, J. M., Grimaldi, F. S. (1960): Reedmergnerite, NaBSi$_3$O$_8$, the boron analogue of albite, from the Green River formation, Utah. AM **45**, 188–199.

Muir, I. D. (1962): The paragenesis and optical properties of some ternary feldspars. NGT **42**, No. 2, 477–492.

Muir, I. D., Smith, J. V. (1956): Crystallisation of feldspars in larvikites. ZK **107**, 182–195.

Muir, I. D., Tilley, C. E. (1961): Mugearites and their place in alkali igneous rock series. JG **69**, 186–203.

Neiva, A. M. R. (1972): Optic axial angle, obliquity and sodium content of potash feldspars of granites, aplites and pegmatites. Abstr. 6.9 in program for Advanced Study Institute on Feldspars, July 1972, Manchester.

Nockolds, S. R., Zies, E. G. (1933): On a new barium plagioclase felspar. MM **23**, 448–457.

Nose, K. W. (1808): p. 24 of Mineralogische Studien über die Gebirge am Niederrhein. Ed. J. Nöggerath. Frankfurt.

Oftedahl, C. (1948): Studies on the igneous rock complex of the Oslo region. IX. The feldspars. Norsk Vidensk.-Akad. Oslo, Mat.-Nat. Kl., Skr. No. 3, 71 pp.

Pini, E. (1783): Memorie mineralogico sulla montagne di San Gottardo. Milano.

Rosé, G. (1823): Über den Feldspath, Albit, Labrador und Anorthit. Ann. Phys. Chem. Poggendorf **73**, 173–208. See Chester (1896).

Rosenbusch, H. (1885): Mikroskopische Physiographie der Mineralien und Gesteine. Vol. I. Die petrographisch-wichtigen Mineralien, 2nd ed. Stuttgart: Schweizerbart'sche Verlagsbuchhandlung.

Schaller, W. T. (1910a): La barbierite, un feldspath sodique monoclinique. BSFM **33**, 320–321.

Schaller, W. T. (1910b): Barbierite, a monoclinic soda feldspar. AJS **180**, 358–359.

Schaller, W. T. (1911): Note on barbierite, monoclinic soda feldspar. Jour. Nat. Acad. Sci., Washington **1**, 114.

Schneider, T. R. (1957): Röntgenographische und optische Untersuchung der Umwandlung Albit-Analbit-Monalbit. ZK **109**, 245–271.

Schneider, T. R., Laves, F. (1957): Barbierit oder Monalbit? ZK **109**, 241–4.

Sjögren, H. (1895): Celsian, en anorthiten motsvarande bariumfeldspät från Jakobsberg. Geol. Fören. Förh., (Stockholm) **17**, 578–582.

Smith, J. V. (1970): Physical properties of order-disorder structures with especial reference to feldspar minerals: Lithos **3**, 145–160.

Smith, J. V. (1972): Critical review of synthesis and occurrence of plagioclase feldspars and a possible phase diagram. JG **80**, 505–525.

Smith, J. V., Mackenzie, W. S. (1958): The alkali feldspars. IV. The cooling history of high-temperature sodium-rich feldspars. AM **43**, 872–889.

Smith, J. V., Mackenzie, W. S. (1959): The alkali feldspars. V. The nature of orthoclase and microcline perthites, and observations concerning the polymorphism of potassium feldspar. AM **44**, 1169–1186.

Smith, J. V., Mackenzie, W. S. (1961): Atomic, chemical and physical factors that control the stability of alkali feldspars. CCILM **8**, 39–52.

Smith, J. V., Muir, I. D. (1958): The reaction sequence in larvikite feldspars. ZK **110**, 11–20.

Smith, J. V., Ribbe, P. H. (1969): Atomic movements in plagioclase feldspars: kinetic interpretation CMP **21**, 157–202.

Spencer, E. (1937): The potash-soda-felspars. I. Thermal stability. MM **24**, 453−494.

Spencer, E. (1938): The potash-soda felspars. II. Some applications to petrogenesis. MM **25**, 87−118.

Spencer, L. J. (1942): Barium-felspars (celsian and paracelsian) from Wales. MM **26**, 231−245.

Stewart, D. B., Ribbe, P. H. (1969): Structural explanation for variations in cell parameters of alkali feldspar with Al/Si ordering: AJS, Schairer Vol. **267** A, 444–462.

Strandmark, J. E. (1903): Bidrag till kännedomen om celsian och andra baryt-fältspater. I. Celsian. Geol. Fören. Förh, (Stockholm) **25**, 289–318. See also (1904). II. Baryt-kalifältspater. **26**, 97–133. See Spencer (1942).

Taylor, W. H. (1933): The structure of sanidine and other felspars. ZK **85**, 425–442.

Thomson, T. (1835): [Meeting of Lyceum of Natural History, New York]. Amer. J. Science and Arts **28**, 189.

Tilas, D. (1740): Tanckar om Malmletande, i anledning af löse gråstenar. Vet. Akad. Handl. Stockholm **1**, 198–201.

Tobi, A. C. (1972): A natural high-temperature albite in a rhyolite from the Downtonian shales, Dundee. Abstr. 8.4 in program for Advanced Study Institute on Feldspars, July 1972, Manchester.

Tuttle, O. F. (1952): Optical studies on alkali feldspars. AJS Bowen Vol., 553–568.

Tuttle, O. F., Bowen, N. L. (1950): High-temperature albite and contiguous feldspars. JG **58**, 572–583.

Waltershausen, W. Sartorius von (1855): [Mineralogical notes]. SAWW **14**, 290−292. See Spencer (1942).

Werner, A. G. (1780): Cronstedt's Versuch einer Mineralogie. übersetzt von A. G. Werner. Freiberg. See Chester (1896).

Winchell, A. N. (1925): Studies in the feldspar group. JG **33**, 714–727.

Winchell, A. N., Winchell, H. (1951): Elements of optical mineralogy. An introduction to microscopic petrography. Fourth edition. Part II. Descriptions of minerals. New York: John Wiley and Sons.

Wright, T. L., Stewart, D. B. (1968): X-ray and optical study of alkali feldspar. I. Determination of composition and structural state from refined unit-cell parameters and $2V$. AM **53**, 38–87.

Yosimura, T. (1936): On barium feldspars from the Kaso Mine, Tochiqi Prefecture, Japan. Jour. Geol. Soc. Japan **43**, 877–910. In Japanese.

Zenzén, N. (1925): On the first use of the term feldspat (= feldspar, etc.), by Daniel Tilas in 1740. Geol. För. Förh. (Stockholm) **47**, 390–405.

Chapter 10 Electron-optical Techniques

10.1 General

Bombardment by electrons results in various phenomena of which the following are most useful for the study of feldspars:

(1) emission of X-rays whose wavelength and intensity permit chemical analysis of major and minor elements — see Chapter 13 for technique of electron probe microanalysis which allows chemical analysis of surface areas a few micrometers across,

(2) emission of light (cathodoluminescence) whose wavelength and intensity permits rapid evaluation of chemical zoning and crystallization conditions involving certain trace elements and physical defects — see Chapter 12,

(3) diffraction and absorption of electrons: the techniques of transmission electron diffraction and microscopy (TEM) permit measurement of the texture and atomic arrangements right down to domains a few unit-cells across — this is the main topic of the chapter,

(4) emission of secondary electrons from the surface: the technique of scanning electron microscopy (SEM) allows determination of the topography of the surface. In addition, the technique of photo-emission-electron-microscopy (PEEM) utilizes electrons emitted from a surface irradiated by ultraviolet radiation: focusing of the electrons produces an image of the surface whose intensity depends on the chemical concentration.

All these techniques were developed or improved greatly in the 1960's, and systematic application to feldspars occurred principally after 1965. I am greatly indebted to many workers whose names appear in the text for providing preprints and high-quality photographs.

10.2 Transmission Electron Microscopy

10.2.1 Experimental Details

McLaren (1972) reviewed thoroughly the techniques of transmission electron microscopy in which he enumerated the advantages over other techniques for the study of fine-scale textures, and the pit-falls that can arise in the interpretation. Many photographs covering almost the entire range of feldspar intergrowths were given.

The standard text on electron microscopy of thin crystals is by Hirsch *et al.* (1965). McConnell (1967) reviewed the application of electron microscopy and diffraction to minerals, and Gard (1971) edited a book on the electron microscopy of clay minerals. Heidenreich (1964) described the fundamentals of transmission electron microscopy. Amelinckx (1964) thoroughly reviewed the detection of dislocations by electron-optical methods, and Amelinckx *et al.*, (1970) described diffraction and imaging techniques. McConnell (1971) showed how electron-optical techniques provide crucial information for interpretation of phase transformations.

X-ray, neutron and electron-optical techniques are complementary rather than competitive. Whereas X-rays and neutrons cannot be focused to give a useful microscope, electrons can be focused to give a microscopic resolution below one nanometer in favorable samples. Even the diffraction techniques tend to be complementary because of the greater absorption and scattering coefficients for the latter. With X-rays and neutrons the absorption and scattering coefficients are such that a simple theory based on single scattering with a small correction for extinction is quite adequate for crystals around 0.1 mm across. With electrons, the extinction distance in a feldspar ranges around one micrometer, the value depending greatly on the direction and the electron energy (McLaren, 1972, gives a detailed table for bytownite and electrons accelerated by 100 kV). Furthermore even for specimens thinner than one micrometer, the problem of multiple scattering is so severe that electron diffraction is not used to determine accurate atomic positions of feldspars, a job for which X-rays and neutrons stand supreme. Identification of individual particles smaller than 10 μm is almost impossible by X-ray diffraction, but this size range is preferable for electron diffraction. A typical study is that of Kraeft and Saalfeld (1967) who used electron microscopy and diffraction to identify the inclusions of iron oxide responsible for schiller in aventurine (Section 20.4). X-rays will retain their overwhelming advantage for routine identification of natural feldspars because the equipment is easily handled, and because high-accuracy is obtained in the unit-cell geometry. Electron-optical equipment is more complex, and leads to low accuracy in cell dimensions ($\sim 1\%$) even under the best conditions. Weak subsidiary diffractions, however, are detected with greater sensitivity by electron diffraction. For characterization of defects and fine-scale textures, electron-optical methods stand alone.

Of course, the excellent spatial resolution of electron microscopy is of great value for studying fine-scale textures. However, the two key factors for interpretation of fine-scale textures are *selected-area diffraction* and *diffraction contrast*. In a microscope, a Fraunhofer diffraction pattern of the object is formed in the back focal-plane of the objective lens. The area of the specimen contributing to the diffraction pattern can be chosen by positioning an aperture in the image plane of the objective lens. A perfect image should be obtained of the object if the complete diffraction pattern contributes to it: in practice, technical problems involving lens aberrations permit use of only the central part of the diffraction pattern, allowing a spatial resolution of 0.3 nm for the crystal lattice in favorable conditions. Normally, the transmission electron microscope is used deliberately in a diffraction-contrast mode in which only part of the diffraction pattern is used. The *bright-field image* uses principally the direct beam, and a *dark-field image* uses only one or a few of the diffracted beams.

The simplest interpretation of the image occurs when the specimen is oriented such that only one diffracted beam is strong and has intensity similar to that of the direct beam. For this *two-beam approximation* the relative intensities of the two diffracted beams oscillate during passage through the crystal as energy is transferred between them. In feldspar, a strong diffraction such as 020 would oscillate against the direct beam with a period near 0.5 μm for 100 kV electrons. Even though a crystal has a perfect lattice, its image will show intensity changes merely from variation of thickness, thereby giving *thickness extinction contours*. For 1 MV electrons the extinction distance is larger, and intensity variations are fairly small for most feldspar specimens: however, it is almost impossible to obtain just 2 beams because of the smaller wavelength. If a crystal has constant thickness, but is elastically buckled, only part of the crystal can be in the diffracting condition thereby giving *bend extinction contours*. Because the wavelength of electrons is so small in commercial microscopes (usually operated between 60 and 1,000 kV corresponding to 0.02 and 0.001 nm), a change of lattice orientation of a minute of arc gives a readily detectable change of intensity. Most micrographs in this chapter show extinction contours.

Diffraction contrast at defects depends on the scalar product of the vectors g and R, where g is the normal to the diffracting planes and R is the displacement vector at the defect. When $g \cdot R$ is integral there is no contrast and the defect is invisible. Particularly important is characterization of out-of-step boundaries whose R is the vector relating the two lattices (e.g. Fig. 3-1). By choosing different diffractions to form a microscopic image, it is possible in theory to determine R by looking at the diffraction contrast as a function of the different values of $g \cdot R$.

An inclined boundary between two lattices with different orientation (e.g. a twin boundary), gives a series of fringes, (e.g. Fig. 10-1) whose spacing and intensity depends on the diffraction contrast and the angle of the boundary.

The electron micrographs shown in this chapter contain many confusing features arising merely from some trivial change of thickness or lattice orientation. Such features cause difficulty in unambiguous interpretation of fine-scale intergrowths, but are usually recognizable: the operator of the electron microscope has the advantage of being able to watch the image as the specimen is rotated slowly, thereby receiving a dynamic rather than a static impression. Even so, controversy arises over the interpretation of some features, and strict objectivity is not always possible.

In 1965, most electron-optical studies were made with electrons excited by less than 100 kV passing through the thinner portions of crushed grains. Development of electron microscopes operating up to 1 MV permitted examination of thicker specimens, but application of ion thinning for specimen preparation plus availability of lunar specimens provided the impetus for a great surge of studies. Bombardment of ions allows thinning of specimens in any desired orientation thereby giving greater control. Development of universal stages with provision for heating or cooling provided yet further scope for studies of feldspars.

Electron bombardment of feldspars results in radiation damage and photochemical degradation, requiring care in operation. McConnell (1969b) found that electron bombardment of a perthite produced differential etching at the surface. The etching rate was approximately proportional to the electron flux, was independent of crystallographic orientation and sample thickness, and higher for the albite than the K-feldspar. McConnell ascribed the damage to local ionization

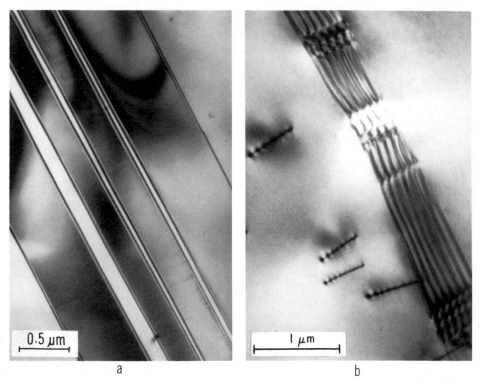

0.5 µm

1 µm

a   b

Fig. 10-1. Twins and dislocations. a TEM showing fine-scale twins in plagioclase from Apollo 10029. Fringes and bend extinction contours are visible. b TEM showing a bent twin boundary and dislocations in a deformed plagioclase from Apollo 12038. The fringes result from interference at the inclined twin boundary, and do not result from a superlattice. (From Radcliffe *et al.*, 1970b, Fig. 15b and Christie *et al.*, 1971, Fig. 17)

whose charge imbalance permits loss of alkali ions by diffusion. Operators of electron microprobes found that serious errors could occur in chemical analysis of feldspars by this effect. Fortunately there is a threshold of electron flux below which no significant damage occurs: it should be noted that both low and high analyses of alkalies can be obtained, the latter arising presumably from formation of alkali-rich materials at the surface. Lally *et al.* (1972) noted that anorthite tended to become amorphous because of electron radiation damage.

10.2.2 Twinning, Dislocations, Deformation

Electron-optical study of these phenomena in feldspars was stimulated by the Apollo program, but by 1973 there were very few data on terrestrial specimens in spite of the tremendous range of phenomena inviting investigations.

Seifert (1965, 1967) located emerging dislocations in plagioclase by electron microscopy of replicas of etched surfaces. He found lines of etch pits along twin boundaries indicating structural misfit. No evidence with implications for crystal growth was reported.

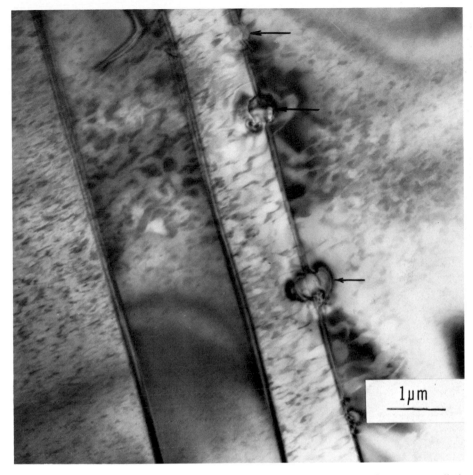

Fig. 10-2. Transmission electron micrograph of anorthite from Apollo 15415. Tiny pyroxenes lie in one of the twin boundaries. Note interference fringes in the twin boundaries. The mottled texture results from *c* domains in weak contrast. Extinction contours are responsible for the broad regions of intensity contrast. (From Lally *et al.*, 1972, Fig. 6c of preprint following abstract)

Plagioclases from lunar basalts commonly show fine-scale twinning, and various investigators reported optical and electron-optical studies (e.g. Radcliffe *et al.*, 1970a, b). Figure 10-1 compares near-planar twins in an undeformed plagioclase with a bent twin boundary and nearby dislocations in a deformed calcic plagioclase. Figure 10-2 from Lally *et al.* (1972) shows twin lamellae in anorthite from the anorthosite 15415 (Genesis Rock). Tiny pyroxene grains lie in one of the twin boundaries, attributed to precipitation during solid-state processes rather than incorporation during growth.

Electron micrographs are particularly useful for revealing mosaic structure and dislocations in deformed grains. Figure 10-3 shows walls of dislocations plus isolated dislocations occurring in a 15415 anorthite. This texture indicates mechanical deformation followed by recovery, perhaps by thermal metamorphism

Fig. 10-3. Transmission electron micrograph of anorthite from Apollo 15415. A twin lamella occurs at the lower left. The thick curved bands are walls of dislocations. Isolated dislocations also occur. 20 μm across. (From Lally *et al.*, 1972, Fig. 6a of preprint following abstract)

in an ejecta blanket. A twin with interference fringes occurs at the lower left. Figure 10-4a shows complex sub-structures in a plagioclase grain from 14321 basalt attributed to strong mechanical deformation with only small regions of recrystallization. Figure 10-4b shows another region in which the sub-structure is "cleaner" corresponding to some recovery from the deformation.

Various statements are given in the Proceedings of the Lunar Science Conferences about the occurrence of twinning and dislocations in lunar and some terrestrial rocks, mostly basalts. Christie *et al.* (1971) reported that the dislocation density of plagioclase was higher in a terrestrial diabase and a Hawaiian andesite, neither of which showed optical evidence of deformation,

▶

Fig. 10-4. Transmission electron micrographs of plagioclases from Apollo 14321 basalt. (a) shows evidence of strong deformation with little recrystallization, while (b) shows some recovery. The rounded areas with different levels of diffraction contrast show regions of recrystallization which have become free of dislocations. (From Lally *et al.*, 1972, Figs. 8c and d of preprint following abstract)

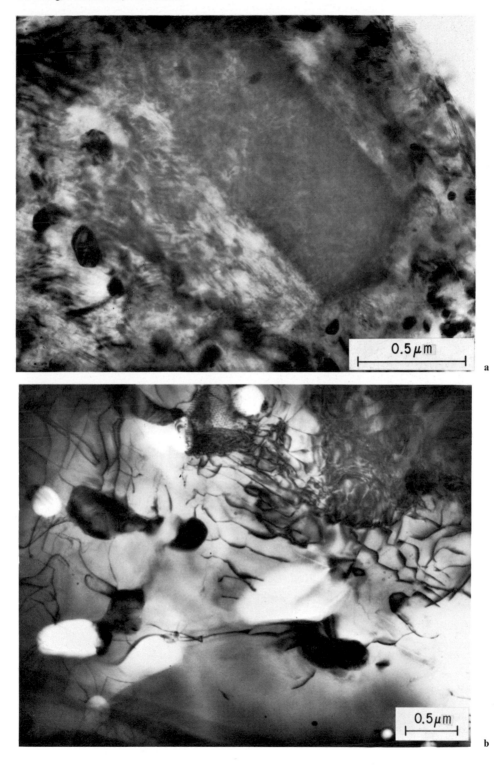

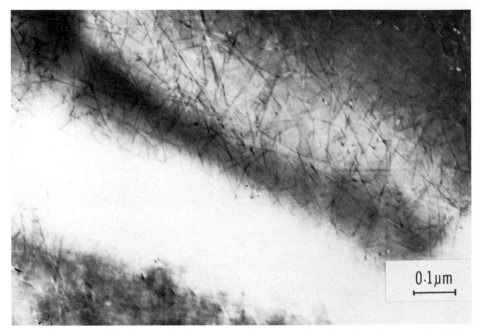

Fig. 10-5. Transmission electron micrograph of radiation tracks in plagioclase from Apollo 14161. Note the strong extinction contours. (From Lally *et al.*, 1972, Fig. 16a of preprint following abstract)

than in Apollo 11 and 12 basalts. It is obvious that in lunar plagioclase recrystallization consequent on mechanical deformation results in complex textures. It is not clear what is the relative role of primary crystallization and mechanical deformation in producing twinning, though present electron-optical data hint at the value of further detailed studies.

Particle tracks can also be seen by transmission electron diffraction. Figure 10-5 shows a density of $6 \times 10^{10} \, \text{cm}^2$ in a plagioclase from Apollo 14161 (Lally *et al.*, 1972). Radcliffe *et al.* (1970a, b) reported evidence of radiation damage revealed as "black spots".

Turkowsky (1969) made an electron-microscopic study of artificially-produced alpha-recoil tracks in Amelia albite. The tracks were revealed by etching. In addition to pits ascribed to alpha-recoil tracks there was a large background of pits of unknown origin, perhaps from lattice defects.

Nord *et al.* (1973) reported electron-optical data for plagioclase in Apollo 15 and 16 rocks.

10.2.3 Alkali Feldspars

Ordering in K-feldspar. Most studies of Si, Al ordering in K-feldspar used optical or X-ray techniques, but exploratory studies by transmission electron microscopy show that much information is to be gained by systematic study with the latter technique.

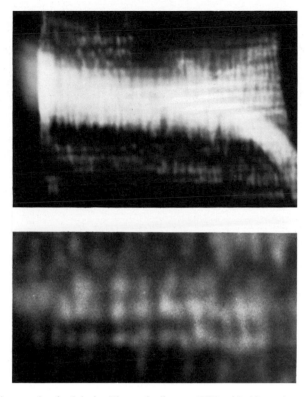

Fig. 10-6. Transmission electron micrograph of adularia. The grain lies on (001) with b^* to the right. Dark-field conditions with $24\bar{1}$. The lower diagram is an enlargement of a region in the lower right of the upper diagram. The upper micrograph is 0.5 μm across. (From McConnell, 1971, Fig. 3. See also McConnell, 1965, Fig. 3)

McConnell (1965, 1971) examined two adularias from St. Gotthard: the well-known Spencer B specimen, and another specimen showing a pale blue iridescence from a cryptoperthite. Both showed the typical diffuse streaks in X-ray diffraction patterns (Chapter 6). Figure 10-6 is a dark-field electron micrograph using $24\bar{1}$ obtained for a flake lying near (001). Superimposed on the extinction bend contours is a fine cross-hatching with a wavelength near 10 nm. One wave-normal is along b^* and one in the $a\,c$ plane at $8°$ to a^* and $18°$ to a. These two directions correspond to the composition planes of Albite and Pericline twins in cross-hatched microcline. Using the criteria of Fig. 5-3, McConnell deduced that the lattice was distorted by two transverse waves as in Fig. 10-7. In this model, the lattice remains coherent, but two simple waves with transverse distortion superimpose to give the double-sigmoid pattern which repeats fairly regularly as shown by Fig. 10-6. Each diamond-shaped unit in Fig. 10-6 corresponds to one double-sigmoid of Fig. 10-7. McConnell interpreted the distortion waves as the result of symmetry degeneration from $C\,2/m$ to $C\bar{1}$ as Si, Al ordering occurred at low temperature in the adularia. He found that the texture was uniform for many crystals, and proposed that it resulted from a state of metastable constrained

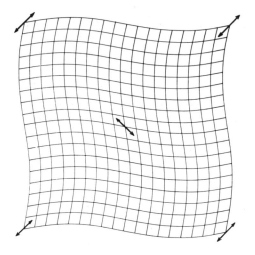

Fig. 10-7. Model of distortion waves in the lattice of adularia. The arrows show the directions of the maximum distortions. (From McConnell, 1965, Fig. 4. See also McConnell, 1971, Fig. 2)

equilibrium in which the reduction of Gibbs free energy from the Si, Al ordering is balanced by local strain energy. He further emphasized that absence of discrete internal phase boundaries precluded a description in terms of simple twinning, though growth of some of the units at the expense of others would lead to the cross-hatched twinning of microcline. For Spencer C orthoclase, he noted that the diffuse streaks were considerably weaker than for the adularias thereby implying a much lower amplitude of the distortion waves. Nissen and Bollmann (1966) also characterized cross-hatching in adularia.

Nissen (1967) examined two "orthoclases" from a granodiorite and a pegmatite in Japan. X-ray powder patterns showed some broadening but no doubling of the 131 and $24\bar{1}$ lines. The $\bar{2}01$ spacing indicated a composition near Ab_{14} for both, while an electron-microprobe analysis gave $Or_{87-88} Ab_{9.2-10} An_{0.1} Cn_{1.5}$ mol-% for the pegmatitic specimen from Ishikawa. Both specimens showed cross-hatching on the scale of 20 nm in transmission electron micrographs. Electron diffraction patterns showed streaking of the spots (cf. streaks occurring as crosses in McConnell, 1965, Fig. 2). Nissen concluded that the cross-hatching resulted from a domain texture of small lamellae twinned after the Albite and Pericline laws, closely resembling the texture of optically monoclinic adularias. Both of the orthoclases were perthitic, and Fig. 3 of Nissen's paper shows a region of cryptoperthite with tiny inclusions of albite lying almost perpendicular to the domain texture of the host K-feldspars.

Although no detailed study has been made by electron-optical methods of "orthoclases", it seems likely from the preliminary electron-optical studies and the many X-ray diffraction studies that a wide range of textures occurs from almost undistorted lattices (as in Spencer C) via lattices with transverse distortion waves (as in adularias) to distinct twin intergrowths. See McLaren (1972) for further data on orthoclase and adularia plus a review of the earlier work.

Akizuki (1972) prepared electron diffraction and dark-field transmission electron micrographs of several microclines. Unfortunately the text is not completely clear because of incomplete translation from Japanese into English, and because it is not clearly stated how the choice of particular diffractions for the dark-field micrographs controls the observed texture. Nevertheless it is certain that a wide range of textures occurs, consistent with the variable X-ray diffraction patterns obtained by earlier workers. I cannot give a reliable summary and therefore quote the author's abstract:

"Fine and coarse twin lamellae of microclines were compared under the polarizing optical microscope and electron microscope. In fine twinned microclines, albite twinning shows a predominant development, whereas pericline twinning is poorly developed and its lamellae are best described in terms of a disordered lattice. Although cross-hatched patterns of polysynthetic albite and pericline twins were observed under the optical microscope, they were not seen under the electron microscope. Microclines with coarse cross-hatching and showing variable extinction angles according to location were composed of wider twinning lamellae in association with finer lamellae, resembling the texture of orthoclase. Microclines with coarse albite twinnings and sharp extinction angles are composed mainly of untwinned microcline with a few finely twinned microcline regions." Further study is desirable using rotation of the specimen in the electron microscope to check for possible lattice misorientation between twin units.

Perthite. The details of electron-optical studies of perthites are more appropriate to Chapter 19. Here a brief historical survey is given together with a few illustrations.

Aberdam and Kern (1962) published the first electron-optical study of a perthite, augmented by further data in Aberdam *et al.* (1964) and Aberdam (1965). Electron micrographs of replicas taken from cleavage faces of perthite etched in HF or bombarded by argon ions showed details of the lamellae, especially rows of etch pits and grooves about 1 μm apart occurring along the lamellar boundaries (Fig. 19-53). Aberdam (1965) attempted to explain the etch pits as the result of dislocations resulting from strain produced by differential thermal contraction of the K-feldspar and albite.

Fleet and Ribbe (1963) took bright- and dark-field electron micrographs of grains of a Ceylon moonstone lying on (001) or (010). Nissen and Bollmann (1966) and Nissen (1967) obtained electron micrographs of moonstones and larvikite feldspars, confirming the conclusions of Fleet and Ribbe that a lamellar structure occurs in the plane of iridescence [near ($\bar{6}$01)]. Figure 10-8 is a dark-field micrograph by Nissen (pers. comm.) of a larvikite feldspar with bluish iridescence. The (001) cleavage fragment shows lamellae of K-feldspar (dark) lying between Na-feldspar with a ladder structure resulting from periodic Albite twinning. The wide variation of thickness and the sinuous boundaries of the lamellae are well displayed, leading to the scattering of many wavelengths and lack of angular sharpness of the iridescence characteristic of moonstones, as explained by Fleet and Ribbe. The mean thickness of the lamellae is proportional to the mean wavelength of the scattered light, being smaller for the blue moonstones than for the white ones. Statistically, the narrower the lamellae of albite, the more

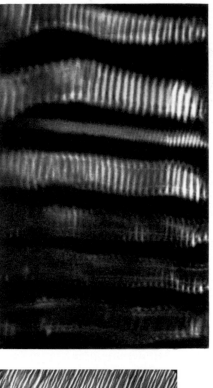

Fig. 10-8. Dark-field electron micrograph of a perthite from larvikite, Stavern, Norway. (001) section with b^* to the right. 0.35 µm across. (From Nissen, pers. comm.)

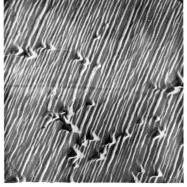

Fig. 10-9. Electron micrograph of replica of (001) cleavage of cryptoperthite from a Norwegian larvikite. The b-axis is parallel to the length of the spindles, and a is perpendicular along the direction of the bulges. (From Rosenqvist, 1965, Plate I, No. 5)

closely spaced the periodic twinning. This has been explained by Willaime and Gandais (1972) and McLaren (1972) in terms of reduction of strain between the albite and K-feldspar (see Chapter 19). The periodic twinning results in a characteristic diffraction pattern as in Fig. 5-1: see McLaren (1972).

Rosenqvist (1965) showed a series of electron micrographs of carbon replicas of perthites etched in HF vapor and shadowed with gold. Cryptoperthite from larvikite with typical blue iridescence revealed strings of laths 1—10 µm long and 0.1 µm wide in (001) section (Fig. 10-9) and 0.1 × 0.3 to 0.5 µm in (010) section. The lamellae frequently bulge along the a-axis. Homogeneous regions occur sporadically. The laths are probably K-feldspar, because larvikite feldspar has a bulk composition rich in albite.

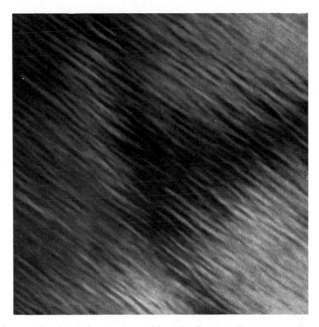

Fig. 10-10. Bright-field electron micrograph of sanidine cryptoperthite. The fine lamellar structure is particularly visible at extinction bend contours. 2 μm across. (From McConnell, 1969a, Fig. 1; and McConnell, 1971, Fig. 4)

In reddish feldspars from a tönsbergite rock, Rosenqvist found homogeneous and non-homogeneous regions. A "moss-like" structure of scale down to 0.1 μm was seen on (010), and interpreted to consist of iron oxide responsible for the red color. Rosenqvist did not find a genetic connection between the perthite and the iron oxide.

McConnell (1969a) observed a very fine-scale intergrowth in a sanidine cryptoperthite, $Or_{36}Ab_{64}$ mol.-%, from a pantellerite lava. X-ray and electron diffraction showed a monoclinic array of Bragg maxima with intense streaks lying normal to b and at $4°$ to $a*$ and $22°$ to a. The intensity distribution corresponded to a longitudinal wave perturbation nearly perpendicular to $a*$ (see Fig. 5-3). A bright-field electron micrograph showed a fine-scale lamellar system of wavelength 10 nm (Fig. 10-10), whose contrast reversed in dark-field. The lamellar structure was ascribed to unmixing into K-rich and Na-rich regions by atomic diffusion controlled by a chemical spinodal. McConnell (1969b) used degradation in the electron beam to show that the chemical variation approximately obeyed a rectangular wave at a resolution of 2 nm. McConnell (1971) discussed the nature of the phase transformation. Down the a-axis, electron micrography revealed cross-hatching similar to that seen in adularia, again consequent upon development of regions of triclinic symmetry in a lattice with overall monoclinic geometry. Owen and McConnell (1971) deliberately homogenized and unmixed the sanidine hydrothermally, and proved that the unmixing occurred by a coherent spinodal mechanism. The chemical amplitude of the perturbation increased with the annealing time at constant temperature, and the wavelength of the perturbation increased with annealing temperature in the

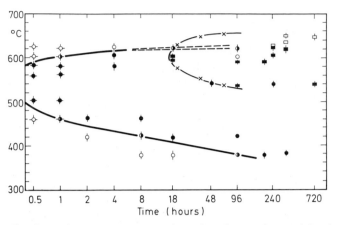

Fig. 10-11. Time-temperature transformation diagram for unmixing in a sanidine $Or_{36}Ab_{64}$. The sanidine was treated hydrothermally and then quenched. Open circle, unmixing not detected; filled circle, unmixing detected but only one lattice (i.e. spinodal decomposition); open square, unmixing detected with two lattices (i.e. nucleation); filled square, unmixing detected with different regions showing either one or two lattices. (From D. C. Owen, pers. comm.)

range 400 to 600° C for times up to 4 days. The development of unmixing was followed by electron diffraction and bright-field microscopy confirming a longitudinal chemical perturbation with wave vector nearly normal to $(\bar{6}01)$. Further experiments (Owen, pers. comm.: Fig. 10-11) showed that nucleation occurred at 550—650° C for hydrothermal treatment longer than one day. Heating at $525 \pm 5°$ C caused some increase of the modulation wavelength from 12—15 nm as the time increased from 2 days to 5 days. With lowered temperature, unmixing was seriously inhibited: at 450° C, it was detected after 2 h treatment but extrapolation suggests that it would not proceed in any reasonable time below 300° C. This thorough study clearly shows the value of electron-optical studies in determining the mechanism of initial unmixing. It should be emphasized that crypto- and micro-perthites with electron-optical (or other) evidence for two separate lattices may have originally unmixed by a spinodal mechanism yielding a single modulated lattice: later annealing might have led to nucleation of separate lattices, or of partial loss of coherency with formation of dislocations.

W. L. Brown and C. Willaime kindly provided details of their unpublished X-ray and transmission electron microscopy of perthites in which they determined the texture and cell dimensions as a test of their models based on lattice strain (see Willaime and Brown, 1972; Brown and Willaime, 1972; Brown et al., 1972; Willaime et al., 1972).

Figure 10-12 is a transmission electron micrograph of an (010) section of a sanidine cryptoperthite from the Isle of Samothrace. The image is rather confused by interference fringes, but it is interpreted as the result of two sets of monoclinic domains with boundaries which cut (001) at $11\dot{7}°$ on average. Rare Pericline twins show as near-horizontal lines cutting the narrower domains. The two sets of domains are structurally continuous, and developed by spinodal decomposition.

Figure 10-13 is a bright-field transmission electron micrograph of an (001) fragment of Spencer P cryptoperthite (see Chapter 19 for chemistry and X-ray

Fig. 10-12. Transmission electron micrograph of sanidine cryptoperthite from Samothrace. The section is parallel to (010) and the trace of (001) lies ESE–WNW. (From Willaime *et al.*, 1972, Fig. 2)

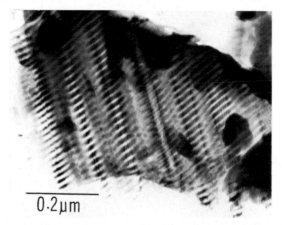

Fig. 10-13. Bright-field transmission micrograph of Spencer P cryptoperthite. The principal grain lies on (010) and the twins lie close to the trace of the (001) cleavage. Smaller grains partly overlap. (From Brown and Willaime, 1972, Fig. 1)

data). The Na-rich lamellae show a grille from the periodic twinning on the Pericline law: the white bars show the composition plane which lies close to the trace of (001). The K-rich host is monoclinic, giving a grayish color. Complex interference phenomena cause the fringes along the Na-rich lamellae. Probably much of the fine structure between the K-rich and Na-rich lamellae results from interference phenomena. The lamellae are fairly straight and lie near $(\bar{6}01)$, the plane of least strain.

Figure 10-14 shows a quite different texture in a perthite L29 with blue iridescence from a syenite at Wausau, Wisconsin. Transmission electron micrographs of (001) cleavage fragments show a zig-zag pattern between Albite-twinned albite (grille texture) and triclinic K-feldspar (white regions). The interfaces are near $\{\bar{6}\bar{6}1\}$.

Fig. 10-14. Bright-field transmission micrograph of L 29 microcline–albite cryptoperthite. The fragment lies on (001). The albite is periodically twinned on the Albite law (grille texture). The microcline occurs with the diagonal association but there is no diffraction contrast resulting in zig-zag white bands. 1 μm across. (From Brown and Willaime, 1972, Fig. 3)

Fig. 10-15. Bright-field transmission micrograph of L 31 microcline–albite cryptoperthite. The fragment lies on (001), and b^* is horizontal. 0.6 μm across. The dark rounded regions result from superimposed fragments. (Similar to Willaime et al., 1972, Fig. 8)

Figure 10-15 shows an even more complex texture in cryptoperthite L 31 composed of albite and microcline. Lamellae a and b are albite twinned periodically on the Albite law giving the familiar grille. The b lamella is sandwiched between the two lamellae c composed of microcline in the diagonal association. Lamellae d are Pericline-twinned albite showing no diffraction contrast in this orientation. Lamellae e are microcline with both Albite- and Pericline-twinning. Note the sinuous boundaries for the cbc sandwich, corresponding to the zig-zag texture of Fig. 10-14. Although Fig. 10-8 is for a perthite with lamellae lying near $\{\overline{6}01\}$, it also has a tendency towards sinuous boundaries.

It is obvious from these examples of transmission electron micrographs of perthites that there is an almost unlimited complexity of textures awaiting detailed study. McLaren (1972) and Willaime et al. (1972) give many examples.

10.2.4 Anorthite and Bytownite

The composition range from about An_{70} to An_{100} involves many complex structural phenomena (see Summary and Chapter 5). The early X-ray investigations revealed the presence of subsidiary b diffractions from alternation of Si and Al atoms, and c diffractions from cooperative displacements of Ca atoms. Later studies by many techniques revealed the Huttenlocher intergrowth of labradorite

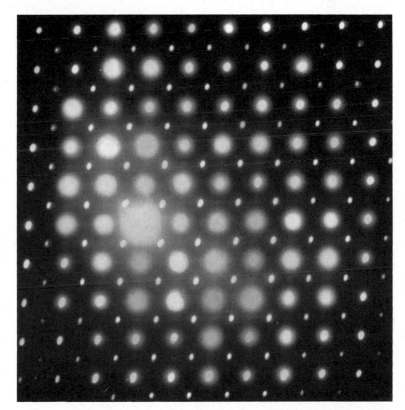

Fig. 10-16. Electron diffraction pattern of a lunar bytownite. The electron beam was parallel to a. The c^* axis lies N–S and b^* E–W. A pseudo-lattice is defined by the strongest set of diffractions: these are of type a with both k and l even in this 0kl section. The weaker set of strong diffractions is of type b with k even and l odd. Faint streaks of type c lie on positions with l even and k odd. Type d diffractions are not visible. (From J. S. Lally, pers. comm. Similar to Christie et al., 1971, Fig. 20.) The streaks were retouched

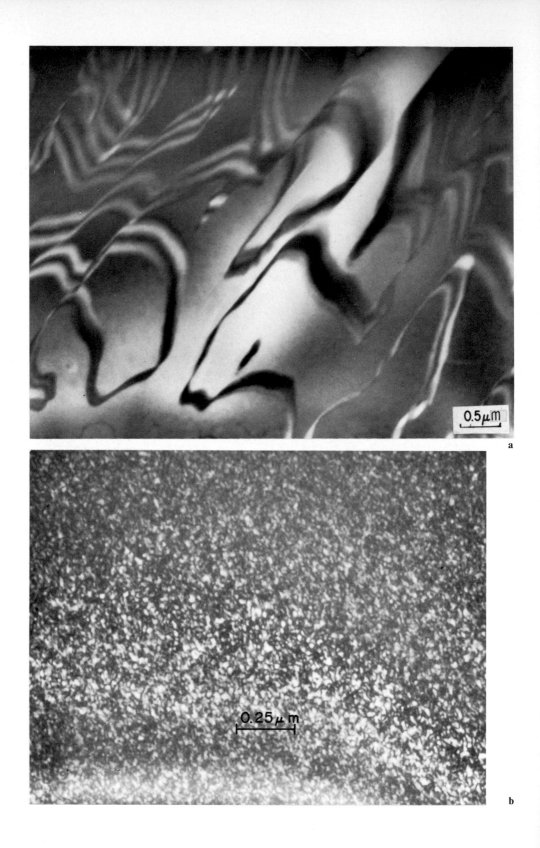

a

b

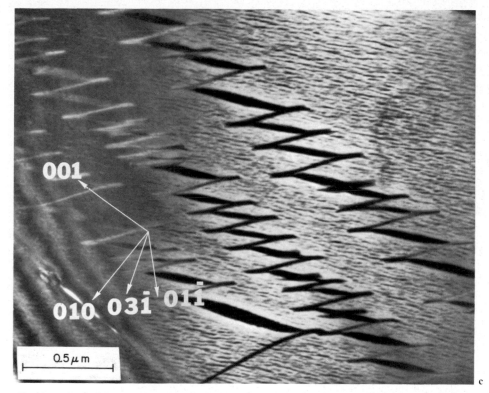

Fig. 10-17. Dark-field electron micrographs imaged with *b* diffractions. a 14310 lunar plagioclase, b 12038 lunar plagioclase, c Stillwater bytownite, An_{82}. In (c), the mottled texture is attributed to exsolution. Note the interference fringes in the domain walls of (a), and the strong bend extinction contours in (a) and (c). (From Lally *et al.*, 1972, Fig. 2a; Heuer *et al.*, 1972, Fig. 2 and Nord *et al.*, 1972, Fig. 1)

and anorthite in some specimens of bulk composition from An_{67} to An_{90} (see Chapter 19). Electron-optical studies have confirmed the X-ray data, but are showing many complex textures previously inaccessible. Figure 10-16 is an electron diffraction pattern of a lunar bytownite taken down the *a*-axis showing an almost undistorted 0kl section (Lally *et al.*, pers. comm.). The strong spots of type *a* outline the pseudo-structure: when indexed on the anorthite cell both k and l are even. In the centers of the pseudo-lattice are the sharp but weaker *b* diffractions with (k + l) even. Finally, there are very weak streaks centered on positions with k even and l odd. In this projection the streaks extend along *b**, but in three dimensions they extend along the normal to the $(2\bar{3}\bar{1})$ planes. In some anorthites, the *c* diffractions are just as sharp as the *b* diffractions, and *d* diffractions also appear.

Type b Diffractions. The most detailed study is by Heuer *et al.* (1972) working mostly with lunar plagioclases — see also Christie *et al.* (1971), Lally *et al.* (1972), Christie *et al.* (1972), Nord *et al.* (1972), and Wenk *et al.* (1972).

Figure 10-17 shows dark-field micrographs using *b* diffractions for plagioclases from (a) lunar basalt 14310 (b) lunar basalt 12038 and (c) Stillwater

Complex (An_{82}). All three show a domain texture which could be imaged only with type b diffractions, and which was interpreted as the result of nucleation of out-of-step domains of anorthite type in an original matrix of albite type. Presumably a solid-solution of high albite type lacking long-range alternation of the Si and Al atoms became ordered upon cooling producing out-of-step domains with phase contrast at the boundaries. Heuer *et al.* proposed that the fault vector is $c/2$, but Müller *et al.* (1973) found by study of diffraction contrast in an anorthite $An_{94.9}$ from Apollo 15459 breccia that the vector is $(a + b)/2$. In I-anorthite these vectors are equivalent, but in P-anorthite they differ: it is not clear when the domains developed and how they were affected by the inversion to P-anorthite. The shape and size of the domains varies: whereas the 12038 plagioclase has a fine, gritty texture, the 14310 plagioclase has widely-spaced curved boundaries. Christie *et al.* (1971, Fig. 19) found zig-zag boundaries for plagioclase from 10029 lunar basalt. The boundaries in the Stillwater plagioclase are also zig-zag, and correlate with the exsolution texture (see later). Plagioclase from the Genesis Rock 15415 showed no domain texture, and presumably crystallized directly with alternation of Al and Si atoms over the entire structure.

Müller *et al.* (1972) correlated X-ray and electron-optical data of four anorthites from (a) lunar basalt 14310, $An_{93.4}Or_{0.2}$, (b) Miyake volcanic tuff, $An_{95.4}Or_{0.02}$, (c) Serra de Magè eucrite, $An_{95.6}Or_{0.05}$, and (d) Val Schiesone metamorphic calcsilicate rock, $An_{97.2}Or_{0.25}$ (mol.-%). Dark-field micrographs with b diffractions revealed domains only in the 14310 basalt; these had curved boundaries like those found by Lally *et al.* (1972).

By 1973, no b-type domains had been found in plagioclase more calcic than An_{95}, and the simplest reason is that all such anorthites crystallize with the anorthite structure type. This does not rule out some disorder of Al and Si atoms: indeed some must occur in all anorthites more sodic than An_{100}. However such disorder must be random without any out-of-step domains. The data on the domain textures are too sparse to permit any correlation of the size and shape of the domains with the An-content and inferred cooling conditions.

Type c Diffractions. Type c diffractions were observed in all electron optical studies of lunar and terrestrial anorthites and bytownites (e.g. Appleman *et al.*, 1971; Christie *et al.*, 1971; Czank *et al.*, 1972; Heuer *et al.*, 1972; Lally *et al.*, 1972; Müller *et al.*, 1972; McLaren, 1972; Nissen, 1972; Nord *et al.*, 1972). The diffractions vary between the extremes of sharp spots for anorthites from the 15415 anorthosite and the Val Schiesone calcsilicate rock to the very diffuse streaks for lunar bytownites (Fig. 10-16). The diffuse streaks are elongated perpendicular to the plane $(2\bar{3}1)$. consistent with the X-ray data of Ribbe and Colville (Chapter 5).

The characteristics and interpretation of dark-field micrographs are controversial in December 1973, though great progress has been made. I am indebted to H. Schulz for supplying the latest ideas and data from E. T. H., Zürich, and to A. H. Heuer and J. S. Lally for electron micrographs with tentative interpretations of studies at Case Western Reserve University, Cleveland using the U. S. Steel microscope at Pittsburgh. It should be noted that the phenomena probably vary in detail from one anorthite to another, and that much work is needed to produce a comprehensive story. In addition it should be noted that anorthite is easily damaged in the electron beam. See also Wenk *et al.* (1972).

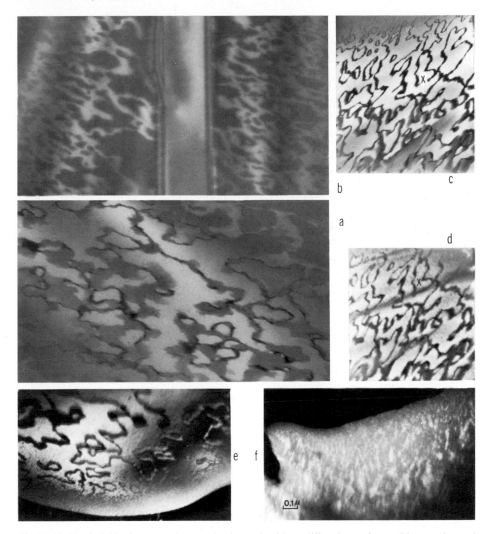

Fig. 10-18. Dark-field electron micrographs imaged with c diffractions of anorthites. a, b, c, d Apollo 15415 anorthite; e, f Vesuvius anorthite. a Natural specimen at room temperature. The dark lines correspond to domain walls along $(23\bar{1})$ nearly perpendicular to the plane of the micrograph. Gray bands correspond to inclined walls. White areas are portions of domains unaffected by effects from the walls. 2 μm across. b Another region showing a Pericline twin flanked by interference fringes. The c domains become coarser near the twin boundary. Several bend extinction contours are visible. c and d. Comparison of domain walls at room temperature before and after heating to 400° C. The electron micrographs were taken under slightly different conditions, and X marks corresponding points. (From A. H. Heuer and J. S. Lally, pers. comm. and Lally et al., 1972, Fig. 6 b). e Specimen showing sharp c diffractions. The diffraction features are consistent with an anti-phase vector $(\boldsymbol{a}+\boldsymbol{b}+\boldsymbol{c})/2$ across each boundary. 1.5 μm across. f Specimen with diffuse c diffractions obtained at elevated temperature. Note the spotty white pattern in a dark background. 1.5 μm across. (From Czank et al., 1973 by courtesy of H. Schulz)

Figure 10-18a is a dark-field micrograph of an untwinned region of the 15415 anorthite (Heuer and Lally, pers. comm.). Domains are separated by walls, vertical ones showing as thin dark lines, and inclined ones as diffuse gray bands.

The domains tend to be elongated parallel to $(2\bar{3}\bar{1})$, which is presumed to be a low-energy surface. Many walls give a zig-zag trace with one direction in $(2\bar{3}\bar{1})$. Micrographs taken with the electron beam inclined to the plane $(2\bar{3}\bar{1})$ do not show sharp walls, and the domains appear to be separated by gray bands as in Fig. 10-18 b (Lally *et al.*, 1972). This micrograph shows coarsening of the domains as a twin boundary is approached. For the 15415 anorthosite, the *d* diffractions gave similar dark-field micrographs to the *c* diffractions, but in the lunar bytownites the *d* diffractions were too weak to be observed. The domain texture was also visible in bright-field micrographs of anorthites.

Figures 10-18 e, f shows dark-field micrographs of Vesuvius anorthite obtained by Czank *et al.* (1973) for specimens with sharp (photo e) and diffuse (photo f) *c* diffractions. The former photograph was taken with the specimen near room temperature, and the latter at elevated temperature. Photograph e shows widely-spaced boundaries and phase effects consistent with an anti-phase vector of $(a + b + c)/2$ across each boundary. The boundaries are irregular, and it appears that they are reasonably similar to those seen by Heuer and Lally for the 15415 anorthite. Photograph f shows an intimate spotty pattern. The phase effects were not inconsistent with the bright spots coming from regions with primitive symmetry, and the dark matrix from regions of body-centered symmetry.

Published micrographs of specimens near room temperature show textures ranging from well-defined domains in the 15415, Vesuvius and Val Schiesone specimens to a fine mottled pattern only a few nanometers across in bytownites. The exact nature of the fine mottled patterns is hard to determine, and it is not clear whether there are anti-phase boundaries or primitive domains in a body-centered matrix, or both. It appears that for slowly-cooled specimens the texture tends to become finer as the Ab-content increases, but systematic data are not available.

Heating of anorthite causes the *c* diffractions to become diffuse such that above a certain temperature they are not easily observed (see Chapter 5 for X-ray data). The mechanism of the phase transformation, and the nature of the atomic movements are controversial. Preliminary data and interpretations by Czank *et al.* (1972) and Christie *et al.* (1972) have been amended.

Czank *et al.* (1972) found that upon heating the Vesuvius anorthite the domain texture became finer, but they obtained no quantitative data. Lally *et al.* (1972) found that upon heating the 15415 anorthite to 400° C the *c* diffractions had lost most of their peak intensity at 400° C but were still visible. A domain texture could not be imaged because of the weakness of the diffractions. Christie *et al.* (1972) found that upon cooling the domains were 100 nm across at 75° C and regained their original size of 500 nm at 25° C: however, the domains changed shape. New data (A. H. Heuer, pers. comm.) show that radiation damage had caused the domains to change shape, and that gentle treatment allowed return of the domains to their original size and shape after heating to 160° C and 400° C. Figure 10-18c compares photographs before and after heating to 400° C, the only difference being a slight speckling ascribed to radiation damage. Heating to 975° C for 12 h led to small domains ~ 5 nm across.

Return of the domains to their original size and shape after heating to *low* temperatures implies the presence of strongly-bonded defects. The best candidates are disordered Al and Si atoms, probably associated with Na and Ca atoms. Local clustering of Na + Si atoms could occur, as well as faults in the alumino-silicate framework.

Czank *et al.* (1973a) briefly reported new results and interpretation, and Czank *et al.* (1973b) gave a detailed description. The pattern for room temperature has the fringes shown in Fig. 10-18e. With rising temperature, the domain walls may move with a slight reduction of domain size. Upon heating above 230° C, the *c* diffractions became weak and diffuse, and the domain walls gradually disappeared leaving a spotty pattern with dark and light patches. The patches were more mobile than the fringe patterns observed at lower temperature. Upon cooling by removing the heat source, the *c* diffractions became sharper, and the domain size increased. However, isolated anti-phase boundaries were not developed unless a cooling holder was used to compensate for beam heating. Czank *et al.*, noting that the spotty pattern is revealed in dark-field micrographs only with *c* diffractions, suggested that the bright patches should have primitive symmetry whereas the dark matrix is either disordered or body-centered.

Müller *et al.* (1973) found by study of diffraction contrast in an anorthite $An_{94.9}$ from Apollo 15459 breccia that the fault vector is $(a + b + c)/2$. Müller and Wenk (1973) found that no change occurred in texture and diffraction contrast of *c* domains for Grass Valley anorthite (An 94.5) heated at 500 and 600° C for one week and then quenched or slowly cooled: however, no *c* domains were observed after heating at 1200° C for one week or 1430° C for a half hour followed by quenching. Anorthites from Schiesone (An 97) and Pesmeda (An 100) when heated directly in the electron microscope to 575° C showed loss of domain boundaries at 200—250° C followed by reappearance at the same positions upon cooling. These data suggested that the domain boundaries are controlled by a pattern of structural disorder formed at much higher temperatures than 200 to 250° C. Structural damage was caused by electron irradiation.

McLaren (1973) found that a Miyake anorthite from Müller *et al.* (1972) showed diffuse *c* diffractions, streaked normal to $(20\bar{1})$ when viewed normal to (010). With $g = (001)$, an image formed from $00\bar{2}, 00\bar{1}, 000, 001$ and 002 showed a perfect set of planes with spacing 0.64 nm. Using $00\bar{1}, 000$ and 001, the planes were resolved only in irregular, elongated patches separated by blank areas. This shows that domains of P-anorthite are interspersed by body-centered regions. Furthermore the domains fall into two sets which are out-of-phase by $\frac{1}{2}d(001)$. There was no out-of-phase relation for $g = (10\bar{1})$, showing that the obvious fault vector is $\frac{1}{2}[11\bar{1}]$. This body-centering vector does not destroy the regular alternation of Si and Al, but does change the direction of displacement of the M atoms. The domains of P-anorthite are elongated normal to the streaks of the *c* diffractions.

Specimens should be exchanged between the various groups to check for the effects of heating and radiation damage in the different instruments. A systematic study should then be made of a range of specimens. The structural problems are discussed in Chapter 5.

Exsolution and e-Diffractions. The electron-optical data on exsolution in the bytownite range are intriguing, but there are many uncertainties. Nissen (1971) and later workers showed that low plagioclases of bulk compositions from about

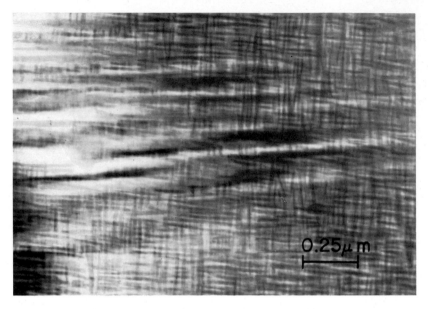

Fig. 10-19. Dark-field micrograph with type *a* diffraction of Stillwater plagioclase, An_{82}. (From Heuer *et al.*, 1972, Fig. 5)

An_{67} to about An_{90} consist of an intergrowth of two plagioclases, one showing *e* and *f* diffractions and the other *b* diffractions. From the electron-optical data of several workers, it is certain that the width of the intergrowth varies from 1 μm down to several unit cells. The bulk of the data on the Huttenlocher intergrowth are given in Chapter 19: here a few electron micrographs are given.

Figure 10-17c shows fine-scale exsolution in a Stillwater plagioclase, An_{82} (Nord *et al.*, 1972). In this dark-field micrograph taken with a *b* diffraction, a spotty texture is visible over the entire field of view except near the domain boundaries. Figure 10-19 shows a dark-field micrograph taken with an *a* diffraction of the Stillwater plagioclase (Heuer *et al.*, 1972). A typical tweed texture is visible, corresponding to exsolution in two directions. Similar textures were found in plagioclase from the lunar 14310 basalt and 14321 breccia (Heuer *et al.*, 1972; Lally *et al.*, 1972), but not in Apollo 11 and 12 basalts. The tweed texture has a scale near 10 to 20 nm, and according to Nord *et al.* (1972) exsolution lamellae lie along $(03\bar{1})$ and $(\bar{1}01)$. The *e* and *f* diffractions occur as curved streaks corresponding to compositions varying from An_{62} to An_{75} on the Bown-Gay plot (see Chapter 5). Another Stillwater plagioclase of composition An_{77-79} showed two sets of exsolution about 80 nm across, and another plagioclase, An_{89}, showed very fine-scale exsolution in the same orientation. Homogenization by dry heating over one week was obtained for a specimen An_{82} when heated above 1225° C. Consequently a solvus between An_{62} and An_{90} passing through An_{82} at 1225° C was proposed for such dry annealing.

McConnell (1971) observed fringes about 5 nm apart in a crystal, An_{70}, using bright-field microscopy with the direct beam and its *f* satellites (Fig. 10-20). This specimen from Wichita Mtns., Oklahoma had been reported earlier by

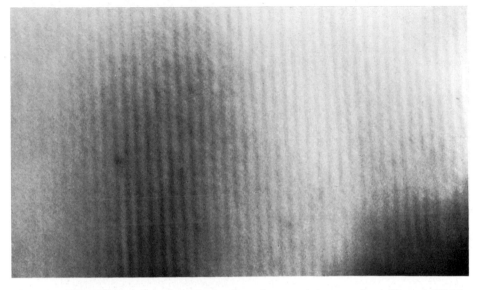

Fig. 10-20. Bright-field micrograph with the direct beam and its two f satellites of Wichita Mountains plagioclase, An_{70}. (From McConnell, 1971, Fig. 5)

Gay to show e and f diffractions but no b and c diffractions. The fringes are very uniform, corresponding to a regular superstructure of the type characteristic of e-plagioclase. McLaren (1972) observed a less regular superlattice in a crystal of composition An_{75} from the Bushveldt Complex (Fig. 10-21). The diffraction photograph (sub-figure a) shows the f satellites straddling the strong a diffractions, and the e satellites symmetrically disposed about the position for b diffractions. The micrograph in sub-figure b, using the direct beam and its f satellites, shows non-parallel fringes of average spacing 8.5 nm corresponding exactly to the splitting of the satellite diffractions. The fringes pinch and swell, as seen especially at the intersection of the arrows: in addition the diffraction contrast changes in response to change of spacing. Very weak b diffractions may occur between the e diffractions, but the fringes cover the whole area of the photograph. However another area gave the micrograph in Fig. 10-22, which shows the fringes terminating in loops leaving narrow strips. These strips may have the anorthite structure and give b diffractions. Exactly the same effects were found by McConnell (1972a) for another specimen from the Bushveldt Complex, $An_{74.7}Or_{1.4}$.

Figure 10-23 shows yet another phenomenon observed by McLaren in the Bushveldt labradorite. This dark-field micrograph using the strong a diffraction, $24\bar{2}$, shows a lamellar pattern about 40 nm across approximately parallel to (010). A weaker pattern crosses almost at right angles. McLaren found that the contrast of the main pattern depended critically on the orientation of the plagioclase, being reduced when the plagioclase was exactly on the Bragg condition. From the rate of loss of contrast as the specimen rotated, McLaren deduced that there was either an angular change of 3.5 min or a fractional change of lattice spacing

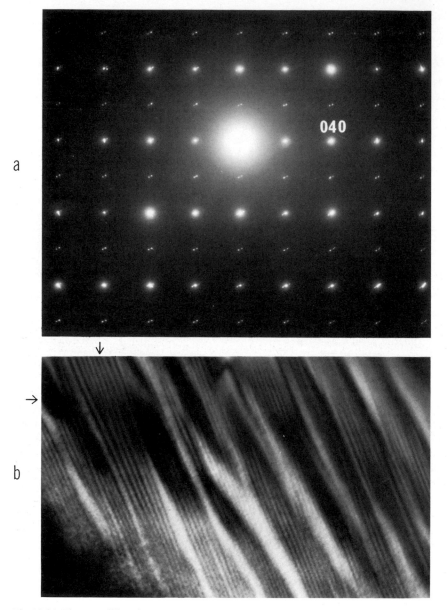

Fig. 10-21. Electron diffraction pattern (a) and micrograph using the direct beam and its f satellites (b) of plagioclase from the Bushveldt Complex, $An_{75.3}Or_{0.9}$ (mol.-%). (From McLaren, 1972, Fig. 3-2)

of 0.1%. The latter was not observed in the diffraction pattern, and McLaren concluded that the contrast arises from a change of lattice orientation. The nature of the lamellar pattern is obscure, but one possibility is a periodic modulation of a coherent lattice associated with incipient unmixing. It is not clear what relation this texture has to the tweed texture observed by Nord *et al.* in the Still-

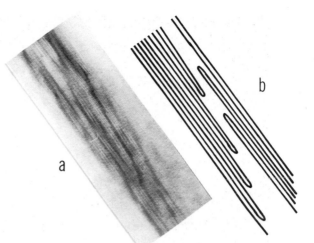

Fig. 10-22. Micrograph using direct beam and its f satellites of same specimen as in Fig. 10-21. The micrograph (a) and the schematic drawing of the fringes (b) are oriented at about 30° to Fig. 10-21. (From McLaren, 1972, Fig. 3-6)

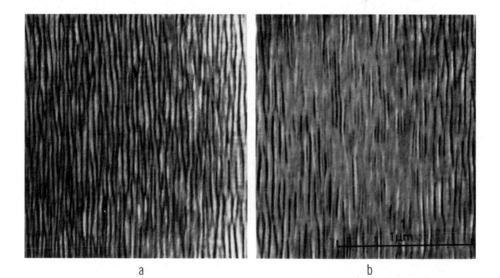

a   b

Fig. 10-23. Quasi-periodic lamellar texture in Bushveldt plagioclase, An_{75}, observed in dark-field using the 242 diffraction. For (a), the specimen is slightly off the Bragg conditions whereas in (b) it is exactly on it. (From McLaren, 1972, Fig. 3-10)

water plagioclase, but the simplest explanation is that both represent some kind of spinodal decomposition.

McConnell (1972a, Fig. 2) observed a similar pattern to that found by McLaren in a Stillwater plagioclase, HC 70413, $An_{75.9}$, showing both b and e diffractions. He interpreted the texture in terms of a finely modulated intergrowth of regions of body-centered anorthite alternating with antiphase regions of e-plagioclase; full details were promised later. Upon hydrothermal treatment at 963° C for 28 days, 1020° for 4 days and 1101° C for 6 days, the e diffractions disappeared, leaving just a and b diffractions. This heating product apparently has the body-centered anorthite structure, but no dark-field micrographs were made to reveal the texture.

10.2.5 Intermediate Plagioclase Compositions

There are three important structural changes in this composition region:

(1) a structural change in a solid solution of albite type: this produces small changes of cell dimension and intensities of type a diffractions which cannot be characterized easily by electron diffraction: X-ray methods (Part 1) suggest that local ordering of T and M atoms occurs,

(2) formation of an intergrowth on a scale of 10 to about 600 nm: this is known as the Bøggild intergrowth, and probably results from exsolution into two compositions with different An-content: electron-diffraction studies are directed to determining the chemical composition of the components, the degree of structural coherency, and the texture and orientation,

(3) development of a superstructure a few unit-cells across characterized by type e diffractions: the nature of the intergrowth is highly uncertain (Chapter 5) but regions related to anorthite and albite may occur in the superstructure: electron-diffraction studies are directed towards characterization of the coherency and texture of the superlattice.

Type e Diffractions. Electron diffraction data are consistent with those obtained by X-ray methods (Chapter 5), and need not be listed in detail. McConnell and Fleet (1963) reported the first electron-diffraction pattern showing e diffractions, using a specimen from Frederiksvärn, $Or_3Ab_{47}An_{50}$ (mol.-%). A dark-field image using a pair of e diffractions showed regular fringes of average separation 3.5 nm. McConnell and Fleet interpreted the fringes as the result of an anti-phase structure. McConnell (1971) observed a similar set of fringes using the direct beam and associated f maxima for a bytownite, An_{70}. Several other workers have observed fringes from e and f diffractions. Figures 10-21 and 10-22 show an electron-diffraction pattern and a dark-field micrograph for a bytownite, An_{75}. Figures 10-24a and b show an electron-diffraction pattern and a corresponding micrograph for an iridescent labradorite, An_{52} (McLaren, 1972) Detailed evaluation is needed to obtain a correct understanding of the structure responsible for the fringes.

McLaren (1972) pointed out errors in earlier interpretations. He showed that a dark-field micrograph of a pair of e diffractions gives the same fringe spacing as a micrograph for an a diffraction plus its pair of associated f diffractions. Unfortunately the X-ray crystallographers had used an *s* vector for the separation in reciprocal space between an e diffraction and the imaginary point midway between a pair of e diffractions. Actually the superlattice responsible for the subsidiary e and f diffractions is based on a reciprocal lattice separation of 2s. Thus for the labradorite of McConnell and Fleet, $|s|$ is near $0.16\,\text{nm}^{-1}$

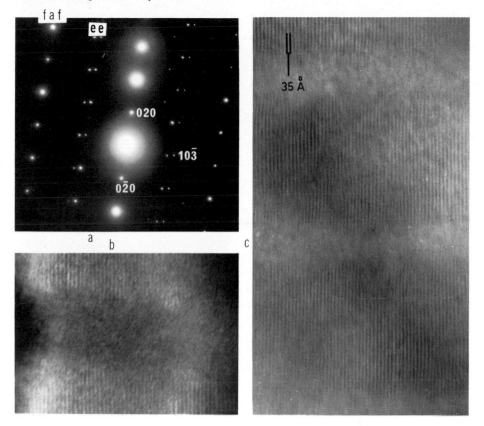

Fig. 10-24. Electron diffraction pattern and dark-field micrographs of a labradorite. The electron beam is nearly normal to (100). (b) is a dark-field micrograph corresponding to the three central *a* diffractions plus *f* diffractions of the diffraction pattern in (a). (c) is a dark-field micrograph of a different area of the same specimen. (From McLaren, 1972, Figs. 3-7 and 3-8 plus pers. comm.)

corresponding to a superlattice of reciprocal spacing $0.32 \, \text{nm}^{-1}$ and a direct spacing of 3 nm (i.e. 30 Å). To avoid further confusion, I shall use t and T for the reciprocal and direct spacings of the superlattice, expressed in nanometers. The parameter t corresponds to the spacing between a pair of e diffractions, or between an a and an f diffraction. The spacing $|T|$ varies from about 2 nm near An_{30} to 5 nm near An_{70}, and the vector t lies near ($10\bar{3}$) for An_{30} and near ($02\bar{1}$) for An_{70} (see Chapter 5).

Figure 10-24a is an electron diffraction pattern for a labradorite $Or_{2.7}An_{52.4}$ (mol.-%) from Labrador, taken by McLaren with the electron beam normal to a (100) section. The 020 and $0\bar{2}0$ diffractions are flanked by weak f diffractions as are the other two rows of a diffractions at the left and right. Two rows of paired e diffractions occur of which the $10\bar{3}$ pair is indexed with the indices for a corresponding b diffraction of I-anorthite. Figure 10-24b shows the dark-field micrograph using the $0\bar{2}0$, 000 and 020 diffractions plus the six f satellites. The (020) planes are not resolved (they would correspond to horizontal fringes with a spacing of 0.6 nm), but the superlattice is resolved as vertical fringes with a spacing of 3.5 nm. The fringes disappear in horizontal bands which correspond to one of the two sets of lamellae responsible for the Bøggild intergrowth. Figure 10-24c shows a dark-field micrograph of another area with somewhat different diffraction contrast because of a very slight angular rotation.

The nature of the superstructure is unknown, and McLaren pointed out the severe technical difficulty of determining the nature of the structural defect at the interface. McConnell used the term anti-phase to describe the intergrowth, and deduced that the out-of-step vector is $c/2$ of the anorthite cell because the e maxima are associated with the b maxima of the anorthite cell. However, it is possible that the superstructure is chemically inhomogeneous with boundary regions of different composition than the centers of the domains. Thus the Megaw model (Chapter 5) consists of regions of anorthite structure separated by boundaries whose T sites are occupied entirely by Si atoms. Megaw used several sets of non-planar stacking faults whose frequency varies with the An-content. Consequently one must distinguish between the out-of-step vector between two regions of anorthite structure, and that between a boundary region and an adjacent domain of anorthite structure.

McLaren emphasized that the stacking fault vectors of the Megaw model are lattice vectors of the albite cell, and would be out-of-contrast for all diffractions other than e and f types. These latter diffractions are rather weak, and their extinction distance is much greater than the thickness of the crystal. Hence inclined stacking faults would not give rise to observable fringes in diffraction contrast; furthermore the situation for edge-on faults is theoretically obscure. At the Study Institute on Feldspars, Hobbs and McLaren reported orally on an attempt to determine the stacking fault vector using direct resolution of lattice planes. The lattice planes 020, 002, 10$\bar{1}$ and 11$\bar{2}$ (indexed on the anorthite cell) were resolved, and the fringes were found to be continuous across the boundaries of the intergrowth. This apparently rules out the following out-of-step vectors (again on the anorthite cell): $a/2$, $b/2$, $c/2$, $(a+b)/2$, $(b+c)/2$ and $(c+a)/2$. The next simplest vector is the body-centering vector $(a+b+c)/2$. Further experimental data plus detailed interpretation are needed, and the situation is uncertain in 1973.

Bøggild Intergrowth. Baier and Pense (1957) observed lamellar discontinuities with a regular period near 0.3 μm in electron micrographs of replicas of a labradorite showing iridescence. They explained the iridescence as the result of coherent diffraction according to Bragg's law, but incorrectly suggested that the lamellae result from polysynthetic twinning.

Laves et al. (1965) and Nissen et al. (1967) correctly interpreted the intergrowth to consist of components of different chemical composition intergrown on one or more irrational planes, parallel to the planes of iridescence measured by Bøggild, and non-parallel to twin planes. Figure 10-25 shows the texture of an etched surface of a labradorite showing red iridescence. Measurements of the average thickness p and q of the two types of lamellae in several labradorites showed that the characteristic wavelength of iridescent light obeys Bragg's law $\lambda = 2(p+q)\sin\theta$ where θ is the angle of incidence. More detailed studies by Bolton et al. are given in Chapter 8.

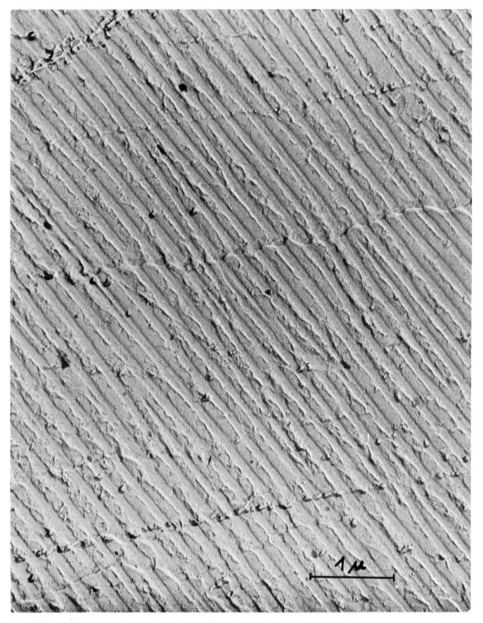

Fig. 10-25. Electron micrograph of etched replica of red-iridescent labradorite from Labrador. (From Nissen *et al.*, 1967, Fig. 4b)

Figure 10-26 shows the etched surface of an area cut by a twin boundary. The lamellae meet at an angle, showing that they do not lie parallel to the twin plane. The boundary between the two orientations of the lamellar intergrowths is erratic, suggesting that some recrystallization has occurred of material near the twin boundary.

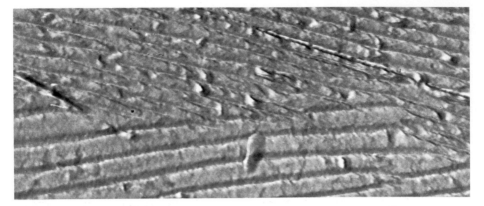

Fig. 10-26. Electron micrograph of etched replica of green-iridescent labradorite from Ylämaa, Finland. A twin boundary passes horizontally throught the middle of the photograph. Note irregularity of twin boundary. (Similar to Nissen *et al.*, 1967, Fig. 4d)

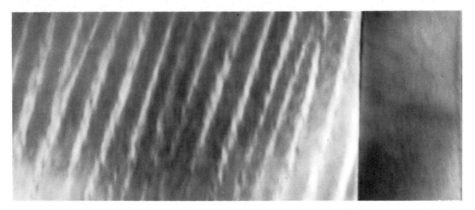

Fig. 10-27. Transmission electron micrograph in bright field using $20\bar{2}$ of a labradorite from Labrador, $Or_{2.1}An_{52.8}$. The lamellae of the Bøggild intergrowth make an angle of about 12° with the (010) twin boundaries of the Albite twin. Note the irregularity of the Bøggild lamellae and the bifurcation at the middle left. The Bøggild intergrowth is out of contrast in the twin lamella at the right. 5 µm across. (Similar to McLaren, 1972, Fig. 3-11)

Figure 10-27 shows a transmission micrograph of a (001) plane of an iridescent labradorite (McLaren, 1972). The lamellae cross the Albite twin boundary at an angle of about 12°, consistent with a plane of iridescence near $(08\bar{1})$.

Figure 10-28 shows an electron micrograph from Nissen *et al.* (1967) of a replica in which lamellar systems occur in different orientations, apparently crossing each other in some areas. This specimen shows iridescence on two planes, each corresponding to one of the orientations on the micrograph. Nissen (unpublished) correlated the orientations of the lamellar systems with the planes of iridescence found by Bøggild. Also observed were several inclusions, probably of K-feldspar.

The key question about the Bøggild intergrowth is the chemical composition of the two components. Probably a detailed answer will come from ion micro-

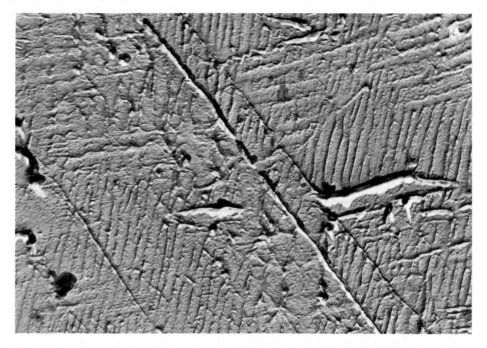

Fig. 10-28. Electron micrograph of replica of etched labradorite with blue iridescence from Madagascar. Note two orientations of the Bøggild intergrowth, with possible inclusions of crypto-antiperthite (ellipsoidal regions of high relief). (From Nissen *et al.*, 1967, Fig. 4c)

probe analysis, but until then the best evidence is indirect. Figure 10-29 shows two dark-field micrographs illustrating the very important conclusion made by McConnell (1972b). McLaren (1972) and Nissen (1972) reported similar data and conclusions. These micrographs were taken with the same conditions as those in Fig. 10-24 by McLaren, but for convenience of printing are rotated by 90°. In Fig. 10-29a the *e* fringes change orientation and spacing as they pass through the boundaries of the Bøggild intergrowth. Because the lattices of the Bøggild components have slightly different orientation, the diffraction contrast is different and it is not possible to get continuous resolution of the *e*-fringes across both Bøggild components. In Fig. 10-29a, the fringes show excellent contrast in one Bøggild component, but are visible only in patches of the second component. Figure 10-30 shows the change of orientation and spacing of the fringes measured by McConnell. The wave corresponds to the spacing of the Bøggild intergrowth (about 200 nm), and tends to be sinusoidal rather than rectilinear. The maximum swings of both angle and spacing correspond to compositions of An_{45} and An_{55} on a plot of X-ray measurements of *e* diffractions vs. An-content (Chapter 5). It must be emphasized that the variation of *e* diffractions with An-content is controversial, and that these compositions are somewhat uncertain. However this implication of dissociation into andesine and labradorite is consistent with all the other properties of the Bøggild intergrowth, and provides a reasonable basis for interpretation of phase relations of plagioclase (see Summary).

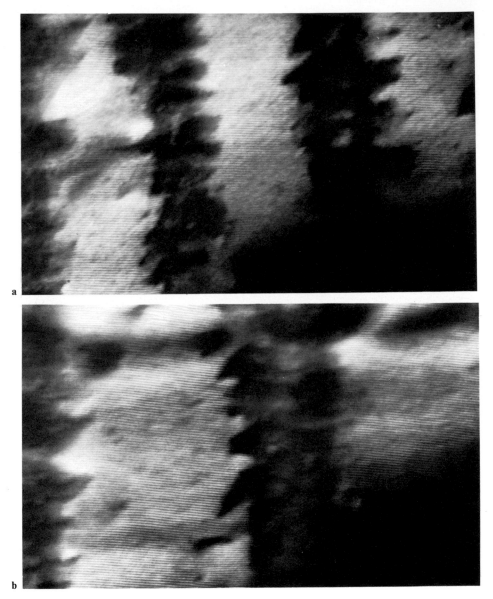

Fig. 10-29. Dark-field electron micrographs of red-iridescent labradorite. The electron beam is nearly parallel to [25, 3, 7] and the micrographs are imaged with the pair of *e* diffractions about the $\bar{1}$61 diffraction of anorthite. The fine horizontal fringes show the *e* superlattice of spacing near 3 nm. The broad vertical bands result from the Bøggild intergrowth, which is coarser in (b) than in (a). (From McConnell, 1972b, Figs. 3a, b)

Now to details. Figure 10-29b is a micrograph obtained for a region in which the Bøggild intergrowth is coarser than for Fig. 10-29a. Here the *e*-fringes change contrast more rapidly. The significance of the serrated boundaries is unclear, and may involve some subtle variation of diffraction contrast.

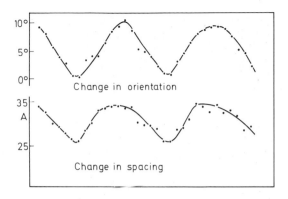

Fig. 10-30. Variation of orientation and spacing of the *e* fringes across the Bøggild intergrowth in the labradorite used in Fig. 10-29. (From McConnell, 1972b, Fig. 4)

Naively one might expect that a change of fringe spacing from 2.6—3.5 nm would involve a dislocation about every third fringe. However *e* diffractions arise from some pattern of ordered atoms on the feldspar pseudolattice. The fringes can change spacing even if the pseudolattice retains complete continuity. Hence distinction must be made between a dislocation in the feldspar lattice and a "dislocation" in the stacking sequence. Two discontinuities of the fringes which look like the cross-section of vertical edge dislocations may be seen in Fig. 10-29b, but detailed study is needed to clarify the real meaning.

McConnell (1972b) reported that the *e* diffractions showed a pear-shaped distortion consistent with overlap of *e* spots of different spacing and orientation. He deduced that the spots corresponded to $|T|$ equal to 3.44 and 2.64 nm with an angle of rotation of 8 to 9°: this is consistent with the measurements from the fringes.

Nissen and Bollmann (1968) reported that electron diffraction patterns of Laue type from iridescent labradorites revealed only one set of spots, but that Kikuchi patterns showed very weak splitting of the lines. Because the lines were doubled in only one direction, the lines were ascribed to two separate lattices sheared slightly on (332).

McLaren (1972) deduced from the change of diffraction contrast with angular rotation that the change of lattice orientation across the Bøggild intergrowth was about 1'. He noted that the interfaces of the Bøggild intergrowth were not sharp, and that this appeared to be associated with a finer sub-structure approximately parallel to (010).

Almost certainly there will be considerable controversy about the relative roles of change of atomic ordering, angular rotation of the crystal lattices, and presence of dislocations, but it is not profitable to pursue this feature on the basis of data available in 1973. Whatever the final outcome, it seems certain that the lattice of the Bøggild intergrowth is strongly coherent: indeed it is possible that for some specimens there is complete coherence with only a slight bending. Furthermore it is likely that the composition varies continuously rather than showing a discontinuous change. Probably the coarser the Bøggild intergrowth, the greater will be the tendency for the lattices to lose coherency.

Added in Proof: McLaren and Marshall (1974) found that 1. phenocrysts An_{77} from Crystal Bay, Minn., contained only domains of $I\bar{1}$ in antiphase relation because of a $C\bar{1} \rightarrow I\bar{1}$ inversion, 2. phenocrysts An_{66} from Lake Co., Ore., contained domains of $C\bar{1}$ and $I\bar{1}$, as revealed by DF images of b diffractions, 3. Phenocrysts An_{50} from Hogarth Range, NSW, yielded only a diffractions, 4. a Bøggild intergrowth An_{52} from Labrador contained coarse A and B lamellae responsible for the iridescence; the e-superlattice occurred only in the A lamellae; and the B lamellae consisted of irregularly-packed small domains of $C\bar{1}$, 5. a non-iridescent andesine An_{32} from Kragero, Norway showed strong e and very weak f diffractions coming from a random distribution of e-domains and $C\bar{1}$ domains. 6. an oligoclase An_{26} from Sweden showed diffuse e diffractions consistent with very small e-domains in a matrix of $C\bar{1}$, 7. direct resolution of the e-superlattice showed that it does not contain a regular array of out-of-step faults and probably consists of a simple sinusoidal distortion consistent with the Toman-Frueh model (Chapter 5).

10.2.6 Sodic Plagioclase

Low plagioclases from An_2 to about An_{16} commonly consist of an intergrowth of two components, one nearly pure albite and the other probably an oligoclase near An_{25}. The intergrowth is known as peristerite, and varies in scale and texture from the near-regular intergrowth giving optical iridescence to finer intergrowths a few unit cells across which can be described as a superstructure. Electron diffraction studies confirmed and extended the earlier X-ray data (see Chapter 19). X-ray data show that e diffractions occur for specimens at least as sodic as An_{15}, but detailed electron diffraction studies of e diffractions in this composition range have not been made. A fine-scale texture was observed in two calcic oligoclases by McLaren (1972) but no structural explanation was given.

Peristerite. Saucier and Saplevitch (1962), using a replica of the (001) face of a peristerite from Villeneuve, reported traces of lamellae parallel to $(0\bar{8}1)$. Fleet and Ribbe (1965), in a comprehensive study of 10 peristerites by electron diffraction and bright-field plus dark-field micrographs, observed lamellae lying parallel to $(0\bar{8}1)$. These lamellae gave two sets of diffraction spots whose geometry was consistent with albite and oligoclase. Twin lamellae on the Albite and Pericline laws were observed, and clearly distinguished from the peristerite lamellae. The albite and oligoclase lamellae tend to be planar over large distances: each type has a range of thickness, and the ratio of the mean thicknesses was found to be approximately consistent with the value expected for unmixing into compositions near An_0 and An_{25}. All specimens with optical iridescence showed lamellae, while some with lamellae showed no iridescence. The characteristic wavelength of the iridescence was comparable to the combined thickness of the lamellae.

McLaren (1972) confirmed these observations, and went on to investigate some details of the peristerite intergrowth. Figure 10-31a shows an electron diffraction pattern for a peristerite from Froland, Norway, $An_{10.0}Or_{1.2}$, with strong white to blue iridescence. The two sets of diffraction spots (diagram b) coalesce down 0k0 but split along the other direction. A weak streak connects

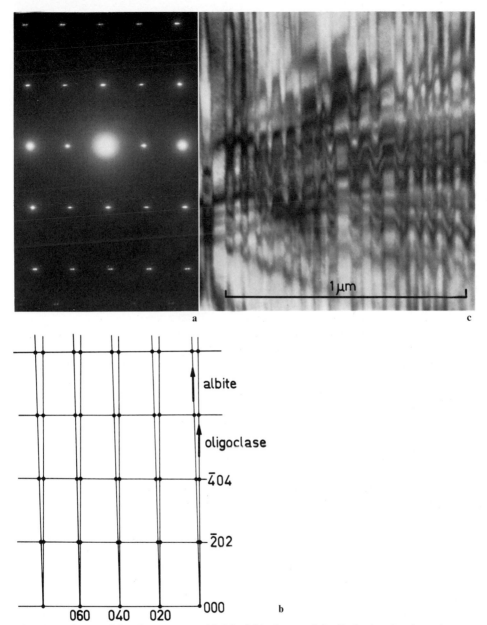

Fig. 10-31. Electron diffraction pattern and bright-field micrograph for Froland peristerite. a electron diffraction pattern and its interpretation b in terms of two lattices. c corresponding bright-field micrograph showing vertical banding of the peristerite intergrowth and various interference and diffraction contrast phenomena. (From McLaren, 1972, Fig. 3-17)

each pair of spots, but is difficult to see in the reproduction. Figure 10-31c shows the corresponding bright-field micrograph which reveals lamellae of different widths averaging about 30 nm. Figure 10-32 shows a bright-field micrograph of a peristerite from Bancroft, Ontario, $An_{7.6}Or_{0.3}$ with the electron beam nearly

Fig. 10-32. Bright-field micrograph of Bancroft peristerite with electron beam nearly normal to (001). The peristerite lamellae pinch-and-swell, but tend to be reasonably planar. The coarser ones are albite, and the thinner ones oligoclase. Diffraction contrast fringes show that the boundaries are inclined to the electron beam. (From McLaren, 1972, Fig. 3-18)

perpendicular to (001). The dominant component is albite, as expected from the sodic composition: note that the more calcic specimen from Froland has a more equal ratio of the two components. Figure 10-32 shows fringes indicating inclined boundaries. By comparing the visibility of the fringes at different orientations of the crystal, and by measuring the position of the cross-sections of the lamellar boundaries, McLaren deduced that the lamellae met near (0$\bar{4}$1). Because the fringes are so sharp in Fig. 10-32, McLaren deduced that the boundary was essentially free of strain.

Several workers, including McLaren and Nissen, found that in some specimens, homogeneous areas coexist with areas showing the peristerite intergrowth. It is not known for certain whether the areas have different chemical composition, but it seems likely from the patchiness of the intergrowths that in at least some specimens the bulk composition is the same for homogeneous areas and intergrowths.

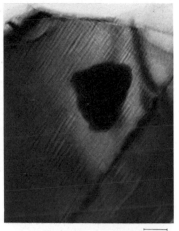

Fig. 10-33. Dark-field micrograph of Sultan Hamud peristerite with electron beam nearly normal to (001). Two
systems of diffraction contrast occur as intersecting lamellae.
The stronger system in the NE–SW orientation corresponds
to the plane (04$\bar{1}$). (From Korekawa et al., 1970, Fig. 8b)

0.1 µ

1 µm

Fig. 10-34. Bright-field micrograph of an albite, $An_{2.6}$ with electron beam normal to (001). The fine
lamellae tend to lie at a few degrees to the boundaries of the Albite twin, but do not cross the
boundary. (From McLaren, 1972, Fig. 3-24)

In some peristerites, the intergrowths are very fine, occurring on the scale
of a few unit cells. Korekawa et al. (1970) found such an intergrowth in an
oligoclase from Sultan Hamud, $An_{16.5}Or_{0.7}$. H.-U. Nissen made transmission
electron micrographs, especially of (001) flakes. Figure 10-33 shows a dark-field
micrograph in which two systems of lamellae cross at about 80°. The lamellae

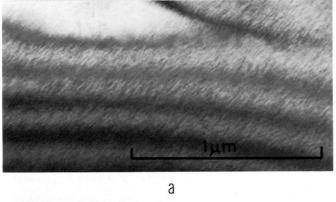

a

b

Fig. 10-35. Dark-field micrographs of (001) flakes of Bakersville oligoclase. a Using the 040 diffraction, showing substructure parallel to the trace of (100). b Using the 20$\bar{2}$ diffraction, showing substructure parallel to the trace of (010). Strong bend extinction contours occur. (From McLaren, 1972, Figs. 3-15 and 3-16)

with the stronger contrast lie about $12°$ to the trace of the (010) cleavage, and presumably lie near (04$\bar{1}$). On average, the lamellae are about 11 nm across, though there is considerable pinching-and-swelling. Electron diffraction patterns showed streaking of high-angle diffractions along the b^* direction. Detailed X-ray data are given in Chapter 19. Nissen (1972) reported data for six peristerites with coherent intergrowths on the scale of 10 nm.

McLaren (1972) found a fine-scale lamellar intergrowth in an albite from Australia, $Or_{0.3}Ab_{2.6}$. A diffraction pattern showed only a diffractions. A bright-field micrograph of an (001) plate (Fig. 10-34) shows Albite twin lamellae crossed by a fine intergrowth of average spacing 25 nm. The lamellae show a complex pattern, but tend to lie at a few degrees to the (010) twin boundary. McLaren pointed out the similarity to those seen in the Sultan Hamud specimen by Korekawa *et al.* Presumably a superstructure is formed between alternate thick slabs of albite and thin slabs of oligoclase giving an average thickness of 25 nm. Further study is needed of the diffraction pattern at high angles.

Calcic Oligoclase. McLaren (1972) found unexplained lamellar systems in two calcic oligoclases from Bakersville, N.C., $Or_{3.3}An_{22.7}$, and Sweden, $Or_{2.2}An_{25.9}$. In dark-field micrographs of (001) plates, a cross-hatched pattern parallel to traces of (010) and (100) was seen on bend contours. Using an 0k0 diffraction, only the substructure parallel to the trace of (100) was seen, while for a h0l diffraction only the other one was seen (Fig. 10-35). No X-ray diffraction data were given, but these specimens probably belong to the low-plagioclase series and show weak diffuse *e* diffractions as well as the *a* diffractions. However the *t* vector should correspond to a spacing below 2 nm, whereas the texture in Fig. 10-35 is on a scale of 10 nm. Is it possible that the texture results from a very fine-scale coherent unmixing of the Or component? Does it relate to either the Bøggild or peristerite intergrowth? Detailed study of further calcic oligoclases, and of andesines is highly desirable.

10.2.7 Chemical Alteration in Feldspar

Guilbert and Sloane (1968) made the first electron-optical study of chemical alteration in feldspars. Plagioclase near An_{50} from the quartz monzonite at Butte, Montana is altered hydrothermally around rock fissures. Plagioclase grains were selected optically to show the different stages of alteration, and polystyrene replicas were shadowed and studied with an electron microscope (Figs. 10-36a-i).

Micrograph (a) shows cleavages and fractured surfaces of plagioclase, unaltered except perhaps for minute spheroids of both positive and negative relief. Micrograph (b) still shows cleavage steps, but they are covered here by sub-spherical units, 0.5 μm across. Guilbert and Sloan called this the *hobnail* texture, and attributed it to development of amorphous material. Electron diffraction patterns of the discoids revealed no spots, and X-ray diffraction patterns showed only a broad band. This product of the first stage of alteration was identified provisionally as allophane. Micrograph (c) shows a more advanced stage in which the discoids tend to merge into clusters of various shapes. Guilbert and Sloan noted a tendency for the discoids to have preferred orientation. Micrograph (d) shows the next stage in which the discoids tend towards polygonal, pseudo-hexagonal outlines, and (e) shows ragged flakes with a tendency towards curling. These were attributed to montmorillonite or perhaps hydrated halloysite. Micrograph (f) shows minute beads and ropy granules, perhaps resulting from montmorillonite grown directly from plagioclase without an amorphous intermediate, or perhaps resulting from rolling-up of the flakes in (e).

Micrograph (g) shows dimples whose negative relief corresponds to the positive relief of the discoids: probably this surface is complementary to one such as in (b), Also shown are irregular wispy ridges of montmorillonite. Micrographs (h) and (i) show massive montmorillonite with a ragged and a compact texture, respectively.

From this series of micrographs selected from 150 plates, Guilbert and Sloan deduced that montmorillonite forms from plagioclase mostly via an amorphous intermediate, but occasionally by direct conversion to wisps or flakes which peel off the surface.

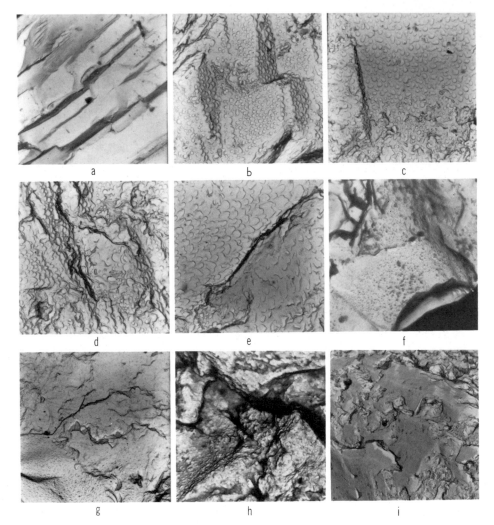

Fig. 10-36. Electron transmission micrographs of replicas of plagioclase altering into montmorillonite. The series a to i shows stages in the conversion as explained in the text. Each micrograph is 16 μm across, except for f which is 8 μm across. (From Guilbert and Sloane, 1968, Figs. 1a, b, d, 2a, c, d, 3a, b, d)

10.3 Scanning Electron Microscopy

Scanning electron microscopy uses secondary electrons of low-energy to modulate the brightness of an oscilloscope screen as it is rastered in synchronization with the electron beam scanning the specimen surface. The yield of secondary electrons depends strongly on the topography of the surface and to a lesser degree on the chemistry of the surface. The scanning beam can be focused to less than 1 nm in special applications, but in routine work insulating surfaces of minerals must be coated with a metallic film cutting down the resolution to

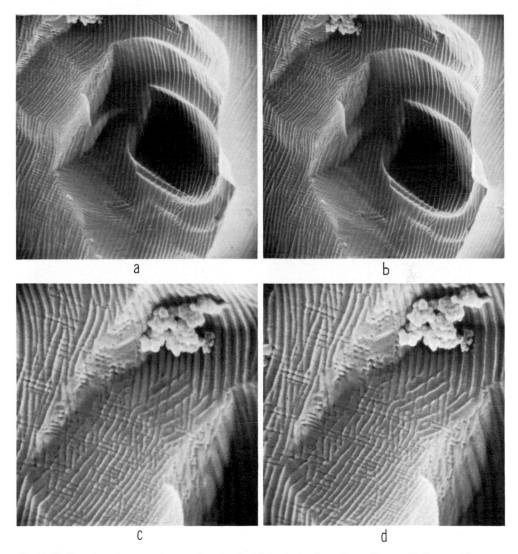

Fig. 10-37. Scanning electron micrographs of etched labradorite from Essex County, N. Y. a and b are stereo pairs, 8 μm across. c and d are enlargements of the upper left. (From Greer, 1970, Figs. 4 and 5)

about 10—20 nm. Probably the greatest advantage is the tremendous depth of field permitting characterization of jagged surfaces: furthermore the surface can be examined directly without making a replica as in conventional transmission microscopy. For study of intergrowths by SEM, it is desirable to etch the surface.

Nissen and Blaschke (1968) studied fracture surfaces of several K-feldspars including ferrian sanidine, adularia, microcline and perthitic orthoclase. Cleavages and conchoidal fractures were nicely illustrated. No evidence of dislocations is visible. The transmission micrograph of a replica of ferrian sanidine shows discs 0.2 μm across lying at steps on the (001) cleavage.

Fig. 10-38. Scanning electron micrograph of etched labradorite (An_{69}) from Narødal, Norway. 70 μm across. (From H.-U. Nissen, pers. comm.)

Grecr (1970) showed an SEM picture of a microcline perthite with fine twin lamellae in the host microcline and deep pits from albite removed by etching. An intimate criss-crossing network was found in a blue-iridescent moonstone with inversion twinning.

Figure 10-37 shows stereo-pairs of an etched labradorite with blue iridescence from the Bøggild intergrowth. There are two intersecting sets of lamellae, and possibly a third set (see enlargements in c, d). The lamellae pinch-and-swell in a complex manner, and in some places the lamellae intersect to give a beaded pattern. The amoeboid area is not related to the Bøggild intergrowth.

Figure 10-38 is a scanning electron micrograph of an etched labradorite, $An_{69.0}Or_{0.6-0.9}$, with the Huttenlocher intergrowth (Nissen, *pers. comm.*). The anorthite lamellae appear as white lines in the gray matrix of labradorite. Although the lamellae tend to be parallel there are numerous bifurcations and apophyses. Polysynthetic Albite twinning also occurs, resulting in a change of orientation of the lamellae at each twin boundary. Probably the twinning is of mechanical origin, and it may prove possible to determine the time sequence of the exsolution and twinning from the textural and chemical relations between the exsolution lamellae near the twin boundary. The bytownite shows red to blue iridescence and is from Narødal, Norway.

10.4 Photo-emission Electron Microscopy

Weber (1972) outlined the application of the technique to feldspars. The general technique is explained by Wegmann (1970). A flat surface of the specimen is bombarded by ultraviolet light. Electrons released from the surface are accelerated and used as the source of an electron microscope. An enlarged image of the surface is thereby obtained with a lateral resolution of about 20 nm and a depth resolution of 10 nm. The contrast of the image arises from variation of chemistry, crystallographic orientation, and topography.

The smallness of the depth resolution allows a useful trick for intergrowths. A ten-fold increase in lateral resolution can be achieved for intergrowths on a scale of 100—200 nm by using a surface at a small angle (say 1—5°) to the plane of the intergrowth.

Weber (1972) described application of the technique to feldspars, especially the peristerite intergrowth, and Laves (1972) described applications to the whole range of feldspar intergrowths. I am indebted to F. Laves for providing a set of photographs of plagioclases taken in association with L. Weber, L. Wegmann and Frl. E. Grauer-Carstensen (Firma Balzers AG).

Figure 10-39 is a PEEM micrograph of a peristerite, $An_{7.2}$, showing the effects of a series of changes. A homogeneous plagioclase crystal dissociated into albite and oligoclase displayed by the dark and light areas. Next, a crack produced a horizontal displacement along the arrows. Finally mechanical deformation

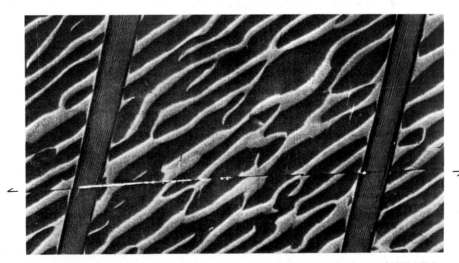

Fig. 10-39. Photo-emission electron micrograph of peristerite. 16 µm across. Dark areas, albite; light areas, oligoclase. (From F. Laves, pers. comm.)

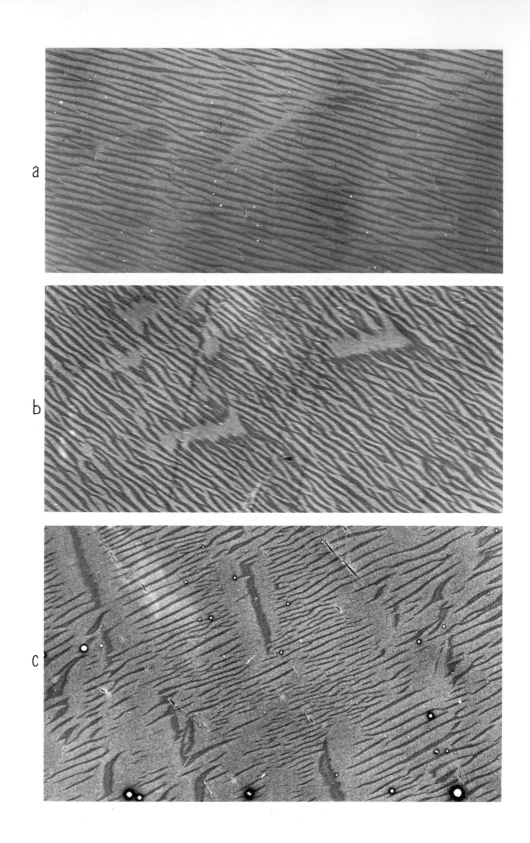

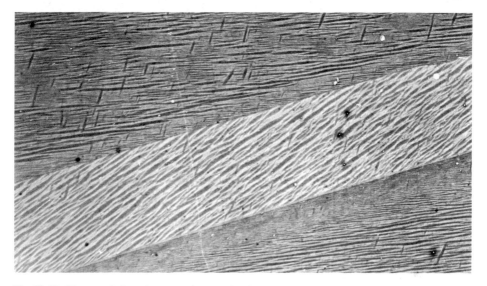

Fig. 10-41. Photo-emission electron micrograph of a bytownite showing the Huttenlocher inter-growth and a mechanical twin lamella. 140 µm across. (From F. Laves, pers. comm., photo EP14)

produced the narrow bands running NNE–SSW, in which recrystallization produced another intergrowth of albite and oligoclase. Just outside the boundaries with the narrow bands, the original oligoclase lamellae appear to have spread out into thin feet. The oligoclase lamellae of the narrow bands appear to avoid the boundary. It is important to emphasize that cutting at a small angle to the boundary of the intergrowth exaggerates the irregularity of the boundary and the width of the lamellae. Presumably the deformation bands are Albite twin lamellae.

Figure 10-40 shows PEEM micrographs of three labradorites, respectively with red, blue and green iridescence. All three show complex textures of the intergrowths. By analogy with the peristerite, the dark areas should be more sodic than the light areas, but this has not been proven. In (a) the lamellae pinch-and-swell but tend to run fairly continuously across the surface. In (b) the texture is highly sinuous, with some areas completely free of the dark component. In (c), the texture is extremely complex with a tendency towards a second orientation. Again it is necessary to emphasize the cutting effect.

Figure 10-41 is a PEEM micrograph of a Huttenlocher intergrowth from Ivrea in which the dark component is labradorite and the light component a bytownite or anorthite. A twin lamella crosses WSW–ENE. Near the twin boundary, the Huttenlocher intergrowth appears finer in the outer units. From this Laves deduced that mechanical twinning plus recrystallization of the Huttenlocher intergrowth took place after the original exsolution. Note that in the unit at the upper left there is a patchy development of the Huttenlocher intergrowth. The blebs lying NNE–SSW are unidentified.

Fig. 10-40. Photo-emission electron micrographs of labradorites a with red iridescence, b blue, and c green. 70 µm across. (From F. Laves, pers. comm.; photos. EN845, EN851, E014)

References

Aberdam, D. (1965): Utilisation de la microscopie électronique pour l'étude des feldspaths. Observations sur des microperthites. Sciences de la Terre **6**, 76 pp.

Aberdam, D., Kern, R. (1962): Observations au microscope électronique de quelques feldspaths perthitiques. Compt. Rend. Acad. Sci. (Paris) **225**, 734 – 736.

Aberdam, D., Kern, R., Leymarie, P., Pierrot, M. (1964): Étude cristallographique détaillée d'une orthose cryptopertitique. Compt. Rend. Acad. Sci. (Paris) **258**, 1268 – 1271.

Akizuki, M. (1972): Electron-microscopic investigation of microcline twinning. AM **57**, 797 – 808.

Amelinckx, S. (1964): The direct observation of dislocations. Solid State Physics, suppl., No. **6**, 487 pp.

Amelinckx, S., Gevers, R., Remaut, G., Landuyt, J. van (1970): Modern diffraction and imaging techniques in material science. Amsterdam: North-Holland.

Appleman, D. E., Nissen, H.-U., Stewart, D. B., Clark, J. R., Dowty, E., Huebner, J. S. (1971): Studies of lunar plagioclase, tridymite and cristobalite. Proc. Second Lunar Science Conf. **1**, 117 – 133. The M. I. T. Press.

Baier, E., Pense, J. (1957): Elektronenmikroskopische Untersuchungen an Labradoren. Naturwiss. **44**, 110 – 111.

Brown, W. L., Willaime, C. (1972): An explanation of exsolution orientations and residual strain in cryptoperthites. Preprint.

Brown, W. L., Willaime, C., Guillemin, C. (1972): Exsolution selon l'association diagonale dans une cryptoperthite: étude par microscopie électronique et diffraction des rayons X. BSFMC **95**, 429 – 436.

Christie, J. M., Heuer, A. H., Lally, J. S., Nord, G. L. (1972): Transmission electron microscopy of calcic plagioclases – Part I. Abstr. 4.6 in program for Advanced Study Institute on Feldspars, July 1972, Manchester.

Christie, J. M., Lally, J. S., Heuer, A. H., Fisher, R. M., Griggs, D. T., Radcliffe, S. V. (1971): Comparative electron petrography of Apollo 11, Apollo 12, and terrestrial rocks. Proc. Second Lunar Science Conf. **1**, 69 – 89. The M. I. T. Press.

Czank, M., Girgis, K., Harnik, A. B., Laves, F., Schmid, R., Schulz, H., Weber, L. (1972): Crystallographic studies of some lunar plagioclases. Third Lunar Sci. Conf., Houston, Lunar Science Inst. Contr. No. 88, 171 – 173.

Czank, M., Landuyt, J. van, Schulz, H., Laves, F., Amelinckx, S. (1972): Temperature dependence of domains in anorthite. Naturwiss. **59**, 646.

Czank, M., Landuyt, J. van, Schulz, H., Laves, F., Amelinckx, S. (1973): Electron microscopic study of the structural changes as a function of temperature in anorthite. ZK **138**, 403 – 418.

Fleet, S. G., Ribbe, P. H. (1963): An electron-microscope investigation of a moonstone. Phil. Mag. (London) **8**, Ser. 8, 1179 – 1187.

Fleet, S. G., Ribbe, P. H. (1965): An electron-microscope study of peristerite plagioclases. MM **35**, 165 – 176.

Gard, J. A. (Ed.) (1971): The electron-optical investigation of clays. Mineralogical Society (of London), monograph No. 3.

Greer, R. T. (1970): Submicron unmixing of phases in the feldspar group of minerals as related to growth and optical properties. Proc. Third Ann. Scanning Electron Microscope Symposium, Chicago, 377 – 384.

Guilbert, J. M., Sloane, R. L. (1968): Electron-optical study of hydrothermal fringe alteration of plagioclase in quartz monzonite, Butte district, Montana. Clays and Clay Minerals **16**, 215 – 221.

Heidenreich, R. D. (1964): Fundamentals of transmission electron microscopy. New York: Interscience.

Heuer, A. H., Lally, J. S., Christie, J. M., Radcliffe, S. V. (1972): Phase transformations and exsolution in lunar and terrestrial calcic plagioclases. Phil. Mag. **26**, 465 – 482.

Hirsch, P. B., Howie, A., Nicholson, R. B., Pashley, D. W., Whelan, M. J. (1965): Electron microscopy of thin crystals. London: Butterworths.

Korekawa, M., Nissen, H.-U., Philipp, D. (1970): X-ray and electron-microscopic studies of a sodium-rich low plagioclase. ZK **131**, 418 – 436.

Kraeft, U., Saalfeld, M. (1967): Über die Aventurin-Oligoklase von Tvedestrand und Bjordam, (Norwegen). SMPM **47**, 247 – 256.

Lally, J. S., Fisher, R. M., Christie, J. M., Griggs, D. T., Heuer, A. H., Nord, G. L., Radcliffe, S. V. (1972): Electron petrography of Apollo 14 and 15 samples. Third Lunar Sci. Conf., Houston, Lunar Science Inst. Contr. No. 88, 469 – 471.

Laves, F. (1972): Unmixing and transformation textures in plagioclase. Abstr. 5.6 in program for Advanced Study Institute on Feldspars, July 1972, Manchester.

Laves, F., Nissen, H.-U., Bollmann, W. (1965): On schiller and submicroscopic lamellae of labradorite (Na, Ca) (Si, Al)$_4$O$_8$. Naturwiss. **52**, No. 14, 427 – 428.

McConnell, J. D. C. (1965): Electron optical study of effects associated with partial inversion in a silicate phase. Philos. Mag. **11**, 1289 – 1301.

McConnell, J. D. C. (1967): Electron microscopy and electron diffraction. In: Zussman, J. (Ed.): Physical methods in determinative mineralogy, Chapter 7. New York: Academic Press.

McConnell, J. D. C. (1969a): Electron-optical study of incipient exsolution and inversion phenomena in the system NaAlSi$_3$O$_8$–KAlSi$_3$O$_8$. Philos. Mag. **19**, 221 – 229.

McConnell, J. D. C. (1969b): Photochemical degradation of a silicate in the beam of the electron microscope. Philos. Mag. **20**, 1195 – 1202.

McConnell, J. D. C. (1971): Electron-optical study of phase transformations. MM **38**, 1 – 20.

McConnell, J. D. C. (1972a): Analysis of the time-temperature-transformation behaviour of the plagioclase feldspars. Preprint for Abstr. 5.1 in program for Advanced Study Institute on Feldspars, July 1972, Manchester.

McConnell, J. D. C. (1972b): Electron-optical study of the fine structure of a schiller labradorite. Preprint for abstr. 4.4 in program for Advanced Study Institute on Feldspars, July 1972, Manchester.

McConnell, J. D. C., Fleet, S. G. (1963): Direct electron-optical resolution of anti-phase domains in a silicate. N **199**, 586.

McLaren, A. C. (1972): Transmission electron microscopy of the feldspars. Preprint of abstr. 4.1 in program for Advanced Study Institute on Feldspars, July 1972, Manchester.

McLaren, A. C. (1973): The domain structure of a transitional anorthite; a study by direct lattice-resolution electron microscopy. CMP **41**, 47 – 52.

McLaren, A. C., Marshall, D. E. (1974). Transmission electron microscope study of the domain structures associated with the b-, c-, d-, e- and f-reflections in plagioclase feldspars. Preprint.

Müller, W. F., Wenk, H. R. (1973): Changes in the domain structure of anorthites induced by heating. NJMM 17 – 26.

Müller, W. F., Wenk, H. R., Bell, W. L., Thomas, G. (1973): Analysis of the displacement vectors of antiphase domain boundaries in anorthites (CaAl$_2$Si$_2$O$_8$). CMP **40**, 63 – 72.

Müller, W. F., Wenk, H. R., Thomas, G. (1972): Structural variations in anorthites. CMP **34**, 304 – 314.

Nissen, H.-U. (1967): Direct electron-microscopic proof of domain texture in orthoclase (KAlSi$_3$O$_8$). CMP **16**, 354 – 360.

Nissen, H.-U. (1971): Exsolution phenomena in bytownite plagioclases. Habilitationsschrift, submitted E. T. H. Zürich, July 30, 1971.

Nissen, H.-U. (1972): Electron microscopy of low plagioclases. Abstr. 4.2 in program for Advanced Study Institute on Feldspars, July 1972, Manchester.

Nissen, H.-U., Blaschke, R. (1968): The fracture surfaces of feldspars in scanning and transmission electron micrographs. Zeit. für Wissen. und Ange. Photog. **104**, 105 – 107.

Nissen, H.-U., Bollmann, W. (1966): Submicroscopic fabrics in feldspars. Electron Microscopy **1**, 591 – 592.

Nissen, H.-U., Bollmann, W. (1968): Doubled Kikuchi lines as a means of distinguishing quasi-identical phases. IVth. Europ. Reg. Conf. Electron Microscopy, Rome.

Nissen, H.-U., Eggmann, H., Laves, F. (1967): Schiller and submicroscopic lamellae of labradorite. A preliminary report. SMPM **47**, 289 – 302.

Nord, G. L., Heuer, A. H., Lally, J. S. (1972): Electron petrography of bytownite substructures. Amer. Geophys. Union Mtg., abstr. V 101 in Transactions, p. 549. Also preprint for Proceedings of Study Institute on Feldspars.

Nord, G. L., Lally, J. S., Christie, J. M., Heuer, A. H., Fisher, R. M., Griggs, D. T., Radcliffe, S. V. (1973): High voltage electron microscopy of igneous rocks from Apollo 15 and 16. Lunar Science IV, 564 – 566. Lunar Science Institute.

Owen, D. C., McConnell, J. D. C. (1971): Spinodal behaviour in an alkali feldspar. N **230**, 118 – 119.

Radcliffe, S. V., Heuer, A. H., Fisher, R. M., Christie, J. M., Griggs, D. T. (1970a): High voltage transmission electron microscopy study of lunar surface material. S **167**, 638 — 640.

Radcliffe, S. V., Heuer, A. H., Fisher, R. M., Christie, J. M., Griggs, D. T. (1970b): High voltage (800 KV) electron petrography of Type B rock from Apollo 11. Proc. Apollo 11 Lunar Science Conf. **1**, 731 — 748. New York: Pergamon Press.

Rosenqvist, I. T. (1965): Electron-microscope investigations of larvikite and tönsbergite feldspars. NGT **45**, 69 — 71.

Saucier, H., Saplevitch, A. (1962): La dilatation thermique des feldspaths. NGT **42**, No. 2, 224 — 243.

Seifert, K. E. (1965): Direct observation of dislocations and plasticity in mineral crystals with special reference to plagioclase. Office of Aerospace Research, U. S. Air Force. Special Reports, **29**, 37 pages.

Seifert, K. E. (1967): Electron microscopy of etched plagioclase feldspar. JACS **50**, 660 — 661.

Turkowsky, C. (1969): Electron-microscopic observation of artificially produced alpha-recoil tracks in albite. EPSL **5**, 492 — 496.

Weber, L. (1972): Das Entmischungsverhalten der Peristerite. Untersuchungen zur chemischen Charakterisierung mittels Photoemissions-Elektronenmikroskop und Sekundärionen-Mikroanalysator. SMPM **52**, 349 — 372.

Wegmann, L. (1970): Photoemissions-Elektronmikroskopie. Mikroskopie **26**, 99 — 110.

Wenk, H.-R., Ulbrich, M., Müller, W. F. (1972): Lunar plagioclase: a mineralogical study. Proc. Third Lunar Sci. Conf. **1**, 569 — 579. The M.I.T. Press.

Willaime, C., Brown, W. L. (1972): Explication de l'orientation des interfaces dans les exsolutions des feldspaths, par un calcul d'énergie élastique. Compt. Rend. Acad. Sci. (Paris) **275**, Ser. D. 627 — 629.

Willaime, C., Brown, W. L., Gandais, M. (1972): An electron microscopic and X-ray study of complex exsolution textures in a cryptoperthitic alkali feldspar. Presented at EMCON, Manchester, September 1972. Submitted to J. Mater. Res.

Willaime, C., Gandais, M. (1972): Study of exsolution in alkali feldspars. Calculations of elastic stresses inducing periodic twins. Phys. stat. sol. (a), **9**, (in press).

Chapter 11 Infra-red Absorption; Nuclear Magnetic Resonance; Electron Spin Resonance; Mössbauer Resonance

11.1 General

These four techniques provide information on the local environment of specific types of atoms. All four depend on the phenomenon of resonance in which electromagnetic radiation of the appropriate frequency is absorbed by some process associated with a specific energy change. Infra-red absorption bands result from vibration or rotation of adjacent atoms. Nuclear magnetic and electric quadrupole resonance (often denoted nmr) results from transitions between quantized energy levels arising from interactions of the magnetic dipole and electric quadrupole of an atomic nucleus with the electrostatic field of the crystal. Electron paramagnetic resonance (epr) arises from interaction of an uncoupled electron spin with the electrostatic field of the crystal. Mössbauer resonance results from absorption of incoming gamma rays whose effective energy is varied by a Doppler displacement of the sample: the absorption spectrum maps out the energy levels which depend on the crystal-chemical environment of the atomic nuclei.

In all four techniques, the observed data result from overlap of signals from all appropriate atoms in the specimen. In a disordered specimen the cumulative resonances for all the atoms result in a broadened signal, although there is a sharp resonance for any individual atom. Only for a spatially-ordered specimen can sharp resonances be observed. Ideally the first three techniques should be applied to single crystals because the signal is anisotropic. In the nmr and epr techniques, frequency shifts arise from the anisotropy of the electrostatic crystal field. Even for a spatially ordered material, a broadened signal is obtained for a powdered sample. The broadening may cause such severe overlap between signals from different lattice sites that a distinction cannot be made between an ordered and a disordered structure using a powder. For infra-red absorption, the anisotropy results in intensity shifts, not in frequency shifts, and powdered specimens can be used for the study of order-disorder. However study of single crystals enables extraction of much more information because the variation of intensity with orientation depends on the direction of the process responsible for the infra-red absorption.

11.2 Infra-red Absorption

General reviews are given by Lecomte (1958) and Houghton and Smith (1966). A brief description is given by Lyon (1967). Interpretation of the infra-red absorption spectrum is complicated by the broadness and serious overlapping of the absorption bands. Consequently the technique is less valuable than X-ray powder diffraction methods for simple identification, especially for feldspar intergrowths. Infra-red patterns have been used to estimate the degree of order-disorder of tetrahedral atoms in feldspars. Because the vibrations depend largely on the bonding between nearest neighbors, the infra-red pattern tends to depend on local rather than distant order. An infra-red powder pattern is easily made, requiring only a few milligrams. Single-crystal study involves difficult preparation of thin, oriented sections. See Chapter 13 for data on OH bands.

11.2.1 Assignment of Absorption Bands

Tarte (1965) interpreted the infra-red spectra of silicates and other multiple oxides in terms of cation coordination, deformation of the coordination poly-hedron, and order-disorder phenomena. Laves and Hafner (1962) gave a quali-tative assignment of the infra-red absorption bands of feldspar. Detailed assign-ments were made by Iiishi *et al.* (1971a) using polarized infra-red spectra for microcline, and were tested by Iiishi *et al.* (1971b) from spectra for many natural and synthetic feldspars plus chemical analogs.

Umegaki and Iiishi (1966) measured polarized infra-red spectra on 15 µm plates of microcline perthite from an Ishikawa pegmatite. The plates were cut on (001), (010), (100), (110) and ($\bar{2}$01): note incorrect interchange of (001) and (100) discovered by Iiishi *et al.* (1971a). To complement the absorption data, Iiishi *et al.* (1971a) prepared reflection spectra with an incident angle of 10°. Figure 11-1

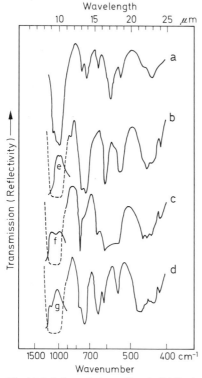

Fig. 11-1. Infra-red absorption (solid line) and reflection (dotted line) spectra of microcline: a powder absorption; b single-crystal absorption in (001) plate with electric vector parallel *b*; c single-crystal absorption (010) *a*; d single-crystal absorption (010) *c*; e single-crystal reflection (001) *b*; f single-crystal reflection (010) *a*; g single-crystal reflection (010) *c*. (From Iiishi *et al.*, 1971a, Fig. 1)

Table 11-1. Polarized infra-red absorption spectra of microcline (Iiishi *et al.*, 1971a)

Observed Frequency cm⁻¹	Calculated Frequency cm⁻¹	Assignments A$_u$	B$_u$	Relative absorption E∥a	E∥b	E∥c
1140	1079		T–O stretching	—	—	st
1111	1104		T–O stretching	st	—	—
1042	1081	T–O stretching		—	sh	—
1000	1053	T–O stretching		—	—	st
1021	1020		coupled T–O and	—	st	—
992	946		T–T stretching	st	—	—
980	1025	coupled T–O and		—	st	—
880	942	T–T stretching		—	m	—
774	784, 788	T–O–T bending	T–T stretching	st	m	m
737	762, 738	T–O–T bending	T–T stretching	w	s	s
650	600		tetrahedron expansion-contraction	m	—	s
610	621, 624	T–T stretching	O–T–O bending	s	s	s
565	570, 527	tetrahedron translation	O–T–O bending	w	m	—
533	514, 529	tetrahedron translation and expansion-contraction	tetrahedron expansion-contraction	m	s	s
465	477, 421	T–T stretching	O–T–O bending	m	m	m
430	423, 401	tetrahedron translation	tetrahedron translation	m	m	m

sh shoulder; st strong; m medium; w weak. Note that additional frequencies occur below 430.

shows typical data which demonstrate the strong pleochroism, while Table 11-1 lists the frequencies and relative absorptions.

Because the infra-red spectra of microcline are quite similar to those of sanidine, Iiishi *et al.* used the simpler crystal structure of the monoclinic feldspar in order to determine the kinds of atomic vibration. In addition to 36 Raman frequencies, there are 16 A$_u$ and 17 B$_u$ infra-red frequencies. Forces from the K ions were neglected, and the force field of microcline was approximated with a modified Urey-Bradley model based on atomic coordinates for sanidine. Ambiguities were resolved from the observed pleochroism, and the force constants were adjusted by trial-and-error. The calculated frequencies agree moderately well with the observed frequencies (Table 11-1) with deviations up to 60 cm⁻¹. At low wave-numbers, observed peaks consist of two unresolved absorptions. In the model, the force constants were assumed to be independent of the type of T atom or of oxygen and the following values were estimated:

T–O	stretching	3.0 md/Å
O–T–O bending		0.5
T–O–T bending		0.05
O–O	repulsion	0.25
T–T	repulsion	0.00
T–O	bond interaction	−0.3
O–T–O angle-interaction		−0.45
T–O–T angle-interaction		0.00

Note: multiply by 100 to convert millidyne per Ångstrom into Newton per meter.

These force constants are consistent with the general concepts used in Chapter 4 to explain the geometry of the feldspar structure: e.g. bending is more difficult at a T atom than an oxygen; the strongest bond is the T–O bond. The lower repulsion between T atoms than between oxygens is explainable by shielding of T atoms by the interposing oxygen. Small splittings of several peaks in the microcline spectrum were explained by ordering of Al atoms into T_1 sites. Detailed drawings of the A_u and B_u vibrational modes are given in Figs. 4 and 5 of Iiishi et al. (1971 a).

Infra-red transmission spectra were determined by Iiishi et al. (1971 b) for many feldspar species using dried powder pressed into a KBr lozenge. Spectra from 400–5000 cm^{-1} were corrected by reference to a polythene standard and were reproducible to ± 2 cm^{-1}. Far infra-red spectra were measured from 60–500 cm^{-1} with a reproducibility of ± 1 cm^{-1} using powder mixed in nujol. Figure 11-2 compares the spectra. Absorption bands for alkali feldspars are listed in Table 11-2 together with band assignments. Fe-microcline, low Ga-albite and high Ge-albite were synthesized hydrothermally. The force constant for Ge–O is less than for Si–O resulting in major reduction of absorption frequencies for the Ge analogs of high sanidine and high albite, except for the 720 cm^{-1} band in high sanidine and the 726 cm^{-1} band in high albite which showed little change: these bands were assumed to be dominated by the Si–Al stretching vibration. The band at 158 cm^{-1} in high sanidine was assigned to a K–O stretching vibration, and the 200 cm^{-1} band in high albite to Na–O stretching. The absorption bands of Fe-microcline correspond closely to those of natural microcline with small reductions of frequency. Similarly the absorption bands of low Ga-albite are similar to but lie at slightly lower frequencies than those of low albite. The ordered feldspars show more fine structure than the disordered ones, as demonstrated first by Laves and Hafner (1956, 1962) and Hafner and Laves (1957).

Absorption bands for $MAl_2Si_2O_8$ feldspars are listed in Table 11-3. There is a strong general similarity between the patterns for the Ca, Sr, Ba and Pb end-members, the pattern for anorthite being most complex because of the triclinic symmetry. A combination of effects from atomic mass and ionic radius was used by Iiishi et al. to explain the band shifts.

Iiishi et al. synthesized plagioclases with 20, 40, 60 and 80% An using gels held at 700° C for 10 days at 1 kbar. Frequencies and band assignments were given in their Table 4.

The spectra for 20, 40, and 60% An are similar to those for high albite with a shift to lower frequency (Fig. 11-2). The spectrum for An_{80} is quite similar to that of anorthite. No X-ray data were given for the structural state of the plagioclase, but it is likely that some ordering, especially for the calcic compositions, occurred during the hydrothermal synthesis. Iiishi et al. assigned seven bands from 237–100 cm^{-1} to Ca–O stretching in anorthite. In high albite only three bands were ascribed to Na–O stretching. These data are consistent with the greater

Fig. 11-2. Infra-red and far infra-red powder absorption spectra for members of the feldspar group plus hexagonal $BaAl_2Si_2O_8$ and $CaAl_2Si_2O_8$. (From Iiishi et al., 1971 b, Figs. 2—7)

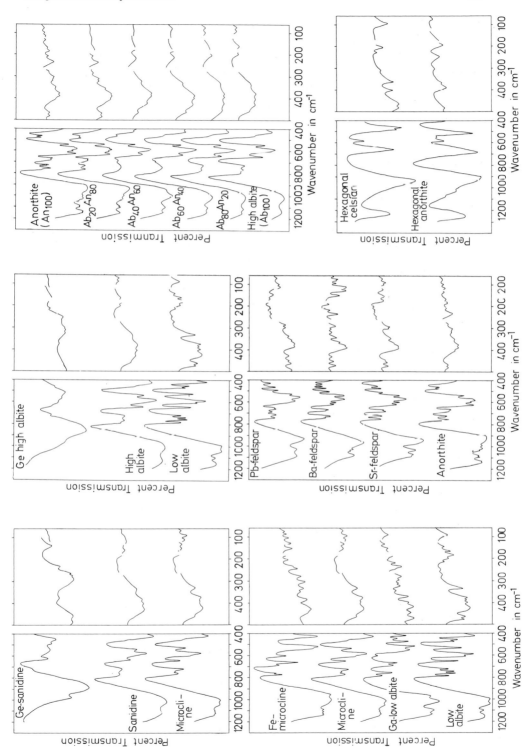

Table 11-2. Infra-red and far infra-red spectra of alkali feldspars (Iiishi *et al.*, 1971b)

	Microcline	Fe-microcline	Sanidine	Low-albite	Low Ga-albite	High albite	High Ge-albite
Synthesis conditions[a]	—	700, 10	700, 10	—	650, 10	700, 10	700, 10
Si–O stretching	1142 vs 1134 vs 1120 vs 1100 vs	1134 vs 1128 vs 1108 vs 1088 vs	1128 vs	1150 vs 1096 vs	1146 vs 1090 vs	1136 vs	960 s
Si(Al)–O stretching	1044 vs 1010 vs	996 vs 952 vs	1020 vs	1032 vs 990 vs	1012 vs 966 s	1017 vs	860 vs
Si–Si stretching	768 s	768, 752 s	770 s	784 vs 758 s	782 s 758 s	792 s 763 s	640 w 610 w
Si–Al(Si) stretching	742 w 728 s	680 w 660 s	720 s	740 s 720 s	690 s 668 s	726 s	720 w
O–Si(Al)–O bending	648 s 602 w 584 s	600 m 532 w	633 s 580 s	648 s 604 w 588 s	606 w 550 s	642 s 587 s	570 w 512 m
Coupling between O–Si–O bending and M–O stretching	535 s 463 w	{518 s 518 s} 445 vw	542 s 464 vw	528 s 476 m 463 m	{519 s 519 s} 474 s 448 m	542 s 460 w	466 w 374 vw
Si–O–Si deformation	428 m 398 m	428 m 384 m	428 m 404 w	425 s 400 m	420 s 399 w	428 w 404 w	324 w 310 w
Si–O–Si (Al) deformation and torsion	378 m 332 m	348 m 332, 302 m	386 w 334 w	388 m 376 m 336 s	374 m 346 w 325, 314 w	380 w 340 w	300 w 252 m
Si–O–Al deformation or torsion		278 m 243, 234 m 203 w		297 vw 252 vw	221 w 202 vw		
M–O stretching	150 w 136 w 115 w 98 w 74 w	154 w 130 w 106 w 90 w 78 w	158 vw	217 w 200 w 165 w 148 w 92 w	221 w 202 vw 158 w 139 w 96 w	200 w 164 w 90 w	213 w

Frequencies in cm^{-1}; intensities: s strong, m medium, w weak, v very.
[a] Hydrothermal lkbar: first number, °C; second, days.

Table 11-3. Infra-red and far infra-red spectra of $MAl_2Si_2O_8$ feldspars (Iiishi *et al.*, 1971b)

	Anorthite	$SrAl_2Si_2O_8$	$BaAl_2Si_2O_8$	$PbAl_2Si_2O_8$
Synthesis conditions[a]	700,10	800,7	700,10	800,7
Si–O stretching	1142, 1132 vs 1092, 1080 vs	1086 vs 1072 vs	1072 vs	1090 vs
Si (Al)–O stretching	1036, 1028. 988 vs 920 vs	1032 vs 948 vs	1040, 1020 vs 960 vs	1028 vs 934 vs
Si–Si stretching	768, 757 s	752 s	737 w	748 s
Si–Al (Si) stretching	730, 726 s	721 s	721 s	712, (688) s
Al (Si)–O stretching	678 s 666 s	698 s 670 s	672 w 664 s	662 m 652 m
O–Si (Al)–O bending	622 s 600 s 580, 568 s	620 s 600 s 572 s	617 s 600 s 572 s	590 s 552 s
Coupling between O–Si–O bending and M–O stretching	536 s 482 m 466 m	540 s 516 m 476 m 458. 448 m	538 s 502 s 472 m 454, 431 m	528 m 497 m 467, 454 m 430 m
Si–O–Si deformation	402 w 386 m	392 m 382 m	392 m 382 m	386 m 376 m
Si–O–Si (Al) deformation and torsion	374 m 348 m 320 w 304 w 280 vw	370 vw 344 m 301 m 294 m 250 vw	366 m 344 m (322), 307 w 293 m 238 m	358 w 340 w 300 m 287 m 238, 232 w
M–O stretching	237 m 208 w 191 w 164 w 136 w 115 w 100 w	226. 220 vw 202 vw 176 m 156 m 124 vw 101 vw 93 w	222 w 195 w 154 m 130 m 116 m (95), 84 w 77 w	213, 209 w 170 vw 151 w 116 w 104 w 76 vw

Frequencies in cm^{-1}: intensities: s strong. m medium, w weak, v very.
[a] Hydrothermal lkbar: first number °C; second, days.

complexity of the anorthite structure with its doubled unit-cell and its anisotropic bonding of Ca atoms.

In general, all the infra-red data for feldspars can be interpreted semi-quantitatively in terms of the known crystal structures. The simplest pattern is for high sanidine with monoclinic symmetry and disordered T atoms. Ordering of the T atoms and distortion of the oxygen arrangement about small M atoms lead to splitting of peaks. As expected from the simplicity of the crystal structure, the infra-red patterns of the hexagonal forms of $CaAl_2Si_2O_8$ and $BaAl_2Si_2O_8$ show few absorptions: again, the greater complexity for the Ca-form can be explained from the distorted arrangement of oxygens about the smaller cation.

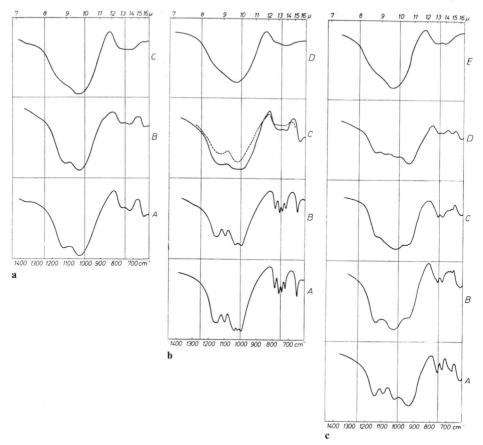

Fig. 11-3. Comparison of infra-red powder absorption spectra of feldspar glasses and crystals. a K-feldspar: A Kaiserstuhl sanidine, B sanidine heated 4 days at 1050° C, C glass. b Na-feldspar: A Gotthard albite, B Amelia albite, C Amelia albite heated 18 weeks at 1050° C, D glass. c Ca-feldspar: A Wadaki anorthite, An_{98-99}, B Vesuvius anorthite, An_{97}, C another Vesuvius specimen, D Vesuvius anorthite heated 5 min near the melting point. E melted Vesuvius anorthite. (From Laves and Hafner, 1956, Figs. 2, 4 and 5)

Dry feldspar glasses give simple infra-red patterns (Fig. 11-3), with a few broad peaks. Broadly speaking each pattern is similar to that of the equivalent crystallized feldspar except for elimination of the fine structure. The patterns for K-feldspar, albite and anorthite glasses (Fig. 11-3), as obtained by Laves and Hafner (1956), are fairly similar, and can be interpreted in terms of tetrahedral bonding of most of the T atoms to oxygen atoms. Perhaps detailed study of infra-red patterns of feldspar glasses prepared hydrothermally at high pressure would elucidate the structural mechanism by which large amounts of H_2O can be dissolved. The infra-red patterns of mechanically-shocked feldspars (Chapter 12) show broadened peaks indicating a transition to the glassy state.

The next sections give details of the changes in the infra-red patterns induced by order-disorder and other phase transformations.

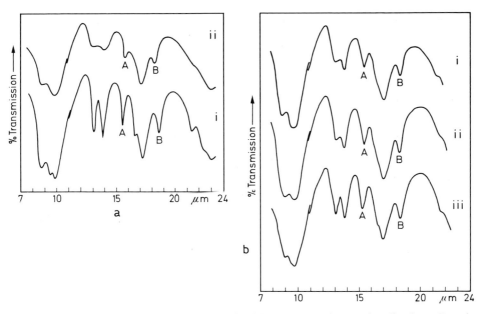

Fig. 11 4. Infra-red powder absorption spectra of K-feldspars. a Maximum microcline from Crystal Peak, Colorado before (i) and after (ii) heating at 1050° C for 30 days. b Optically-monoclinic adularias from (i) Disentis, Switzerland (ii) Piz Blas, Switzerland, core of a crystal (iii) Piz Blas, margin. (From Laves and Hafner, 1962, Figs. 1 and 3)

11.2.2 K-feldspar

Laves and Hafner (1962) measured the pleochroism of 0.1 mm plates parallel to (010) of Pellotsalo microcline and Eifel sanidine, and their Fig. 4 gives data for 5 directions rotated successively by 45°. The sanidine shows little pleochroism while the microcline shows strong pleochroism consistent with the strong Si, Al ordering of the latter. Umegaki and Iiishi (1966) gave extensive data for a microcline perthite as noted earlier.

Laves and Hafner (1956) gave powder spectra for unheated and heated natural microcline, sanidine, adularias and a moonstone. Figure 11-4, taken from Laves and Hafner's summary paper of (1962), compares patterns of adularias with those of natural and heated microcline. A KBr prism was used for 11–24 μm and NaBr for 7–11 μm. The pattern for the heated microcline corresponds to those for heated sanidines and is representative of high sanidine with strong disorder of the T atoms. The patterns for natural adularias fall between those for microcline and high sanidine indicating intermediate states of order. It appears that there is a complete range of states in natural K-feldspars: for example, the margin of an adularia grain from Piz Blas gave a pattern similar to that for microcline, whereas the core gave a pattern about midway between those for microcline and high sanidine (Fig. 11-4b 2 and 3).

Hafner and Laves (1957) made a detailed comparison of natural and synthetic K-feldspars using two well-resolved absorptions at 15.5–15.8 μm and

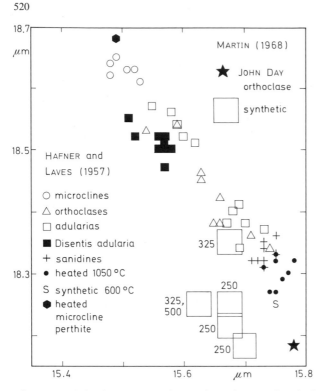

Fig. 11-5. Relation between two chosen absorption wavelengths for K-feldspars. The small symbols represent data from Hafner and Laves (1957, Table 2 and Fig. 2b) as given in the key at lower left. The size of the symbol has no relation to the experimental uncertainty. For the data from Martin (1968), the open squares show ± one standard error for the synthetic specimens

18.3–18.7 μm. Figure 11-5 shows a plot of the data. Six microclines fell in a small cluster near 15.5, 18.63. Perhaps some of the spread results from variation in the Na-content. A Pellotsalo microcline perthite heated for 15 months at 800° C was displaced in the direction of low albite (15.44, 18.82). Heated K-feldspars (including microcline, adularia, orthoclase and sanidine) gave another small cluster centered near 15.75, 18.3. A specimen synthesized hydro-thermally at 600° C fell in the same region, indicating that it crystallized as high sanidine. Natural sanidines from young extrusive rocks, optically clear and monoclinic, fell near 15.73, 18.34, consistent with strong but not complete Al, Si disorder. Orthoclases, defined as optically monoclinic and cloudy, covered over two-thirds of the range between the end-members with one specimen falling with the natural sanidines. Adularias, defined as coming from fissures and having a pseudo-rhombohedral crystal habit, were either clear or cloudy, and either optically monoclinic or pseudo-monoclinic; they covered almost the same range as the orthoclases though no specimen fell in the sanidine region. Hafner and Laves used this evidence to support the concept of Laves (1952) and Goldsmith and Laves (1954a, b) that "orthoclase" and "adularia" consist of submicro-scopically twinned triclinic material whose degree of Al/Si order lies between those of low microcline and high sanidine. Later X-ray and electron-optical data have shown that the properties of K-feldspar are extremely complex, and the exact interpretation of orthoclase and adularia is still controversial.

Hafner and Laves (1957) systematically heated at 1050° C a microcline perthite from Crystal Peak and an adularia from Disentis. X-ray powder patterns of Guinier type showed that the microcline perthite homogenized after one day. The 131 triclinic indicator decreased linearly with time reaching zero after 8 days. During the same period, the infra-red absorption pattern of both specimens changed to that of sanidine. Figure 11-6a shows the change of the two prominent absorptions near 15.6 and 18.4 μm. A rapid near-linear change during the first 10 days was followed by a weak change during the next 60 days. Figure 11-6c shows the variation with time of an intensity ratio measured for absorptions near 12.4 and 13.5 μm. Again there was a rapid change during the first ten days followed by a slower change during the next 60 days. From these results Hafner and Laves concluded that complete disorder of the tetrahedral atoms had not been achieved during heating for 8 days at 1050° C even though the X-ray powder pattern had achieved monoclinic geometry. Further X-ray study is desirable of these samples to determine the variation of cell dimensions a, b and c with time.

Infra-red data on synthetic K-feldspars are sparse. Hafner and Laves (1957) found that a specimen synthesized hydrothermally at 600° C gave an infra-red pattern consistent with those for high sanidine (point s on Fig. 11-5). Martin (1968) gave infra-red patterns for 5 K-feldspars synthesized hydrothermally from gels with excess potassium silicate held at $2 - 10$ kbar, $250 - 500°$ C and 1 week to 4 months. The squares on Fig. 11-5 show one standard error. Only one of the squares falls within the range reported by Hafner and Laves for natural and heated K-feldspars, while 4 have anomalous positions. The cell dimensions of all 5 specimens (Chapter 7) are consistent with sanidine showing strong Al, Si disorder. The infra-red data are closer to those for sanidine than for microcline, but the reason for the anomalous positions is unknown. Also shown on Fig. 11-5 is an orthoclase from the John Day Formation: again the reason for its anomalous position is unknown, but substitution by boron is one possible explanation.

In spite of the uncertainties, it is clear that the major variation in the infra-red pattern of most natural and heated K-feldspars results from Si, Al order-disorder. Further studies are desirable, especially of synthetic material, but careful calibration is needed to eliminate possible systematic errors between different instruments.

11.2.3 Na-feldspar

Hafner and Laves (1957) determined the infra-red absorption for 4 natural albites; 4 specimens synthesized hydrothermally at 600, 850, 1000 and 1000–1020° C for unspecified times; and two low albites heated dry at 1050° C for periods up to 60 days. Martin (1968, 1970) measured infra-red spectra for 2 natural albites and 14 albites synthesized hydrothermally at 1 or 10 kbar and 200–700° C (see Chapter 7 for synthesis conditions and cell dimensions). All these data are consistent generally with a continuous transition from low to high

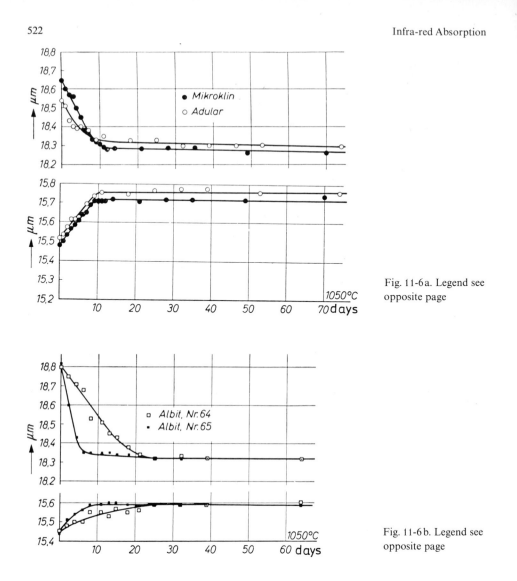

Fig. 11-6a. Legend see opposite page

Fig. 11-6b. Legend see opposite page

albite associated with order-disorder of the tetrahedral atoms. However the details are puzzling.

Figure 11-6c shows the variation of the absorption wavelengths near 15.5 and 18.5 μm with progressive heating of two natural albites at 1050° C. The Schmirntal albite attained the high structural state in about 10 days while the Dorfgastein one took about 20 days. Prolonged heating caused no further detectable changes.

Figure 11-7 gives Martin's summary of the data on albites. His two natural albites from Amelia and Tiburon had a smaller wavelength for the 18.8 μm absorption than the data for the Hafner-Laves specimens, partly explained by a systematic bias between the two techniques. The right-hand part of Fig. 11-7 shows the data for the albites heated by Hafner and Laves: within experimental error they lie near a straight line. The three albites synthesized at 1000, 1000–1020

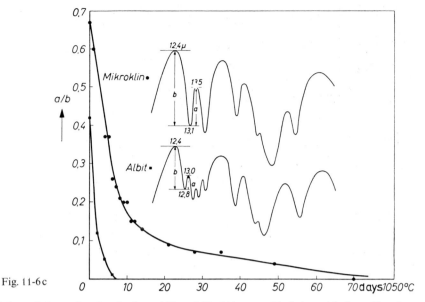

Fig. 11-6c

Fig. 11-6. Infra-red absorption data for heated K- and Na-feldspars. a Variation with time of heating at 1050° C of the wavelength of two absorption peaks for Crystal Peak microcline and Disentis adularia. b Similar data for albites from Dorfgastein (No. 64) and Schmirntal (No. 65). c Variation with time of heating at 1050° C of the intensity ratio for absorptions near 12—13 μm as defined in the inset diagram. (From Hafner and Laves, 1957, Figs. 7, 8 and 11)

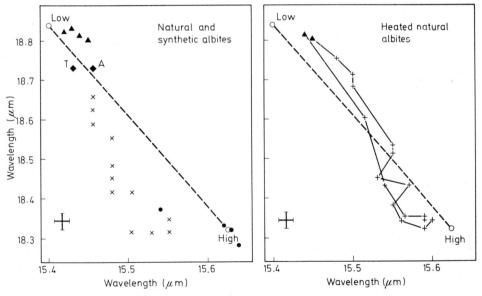

Fig. 11-7. Infra-red absorption data for albites. Relation between absorption wavelengths near 18.5 and 15.5 μm. The dashed line joins reference points for high and low albite (open circles) given by Hafner and Laves (1957). An error bar is given at the lower left. Symbols are: Hafner and Laves (1957); synthetic albites, solid dots; natural albites, solid triangles; two natural albites heated progressively at 1050° C, horizontal crosses: Martin (1968, 1970); synthetic albites, inclined crosses; natural albites from Amelia and Tiburon, solid diamonds.(From Martin, 1968, Figs. 17A and B; also 1970, Figs. 6a, b)

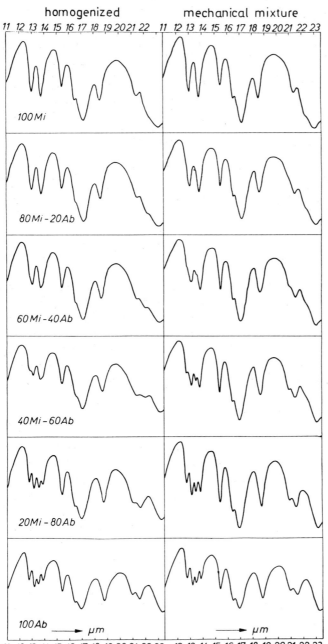

Fig. 11-8. Infra-red absorption patterns in the 11—23 μm region for mechanical mixtures of albite and microcline (right) and specimens homogenized at 1000° C (left). (From Hafner and Laves, 1957, Fig. 3)

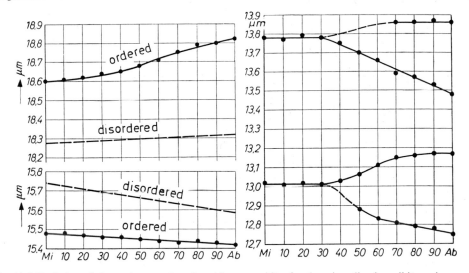

Fig. 11-9. Variation of absorption wavelengths with composition for the microcline-low albite series. The dashed lines join high sanidine and high albite. (From Hafner and Laves, 1957, Figs. 5 and 6)

and 850° C lie close together near the final products of heating the two low albites, and these five specimens yield an estimate of the position for high albite. All the other synthetic albites lie in a curved band between the positions for high and low albite, and are displaced to the left from the band occupied by heated natural albites. Martin concluded from these data that the ordering process may differ from the disordering process. The dashed lines in Fig. 11-7 join the reference points given by Hafner and Laves (1957, Fig. 2c) for high and low albite.

11.2.4 Alkali Feldspar Solid Solutions

There are no systematic infra-red data for the sanidine-high albite series but Hafner and Laves (1957) gave data for the microcline–low albite series. Pontiskalk microcline and Gotthard albite were powdered, mixed, compressed at 10000 atm, and heated to 1000° C for 48 h. Guinier X-ray patterns showed complete homogenization, and further demonstrated that pure microcline and albite were essentially unchanged by the same heat treatment. Figure 11-8 compares infra-red patterns of some of the homogenized samples with those of mechanical mixtures. Each pair of samples with the same bulk composition gives similar infra-red patterns but there are small differences. Figure 11-9 shows that the absorption wavelengths near 18.7 and 15.5 vary continuously with composition (wt.-% Ab) whereas those near 13.0 and 13.8 µm appear to bifurcate near Ab_{30}. See also Liese (1970).

11.2.5 Plagioclase

Laves and Hafner (1956) presented infra-red absorption patterns for various natural plagioclases. In general, the natural plagioclases (Fig. 11-10) show more

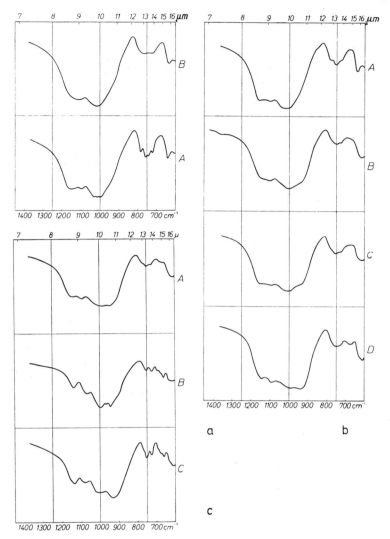

Fig. 11-10. Infra-red powder absorption patterns of plagioclase. a Oligoclase ∼ 15% An: *A* natural; *B* heated 6 weeks at 1000° C. b Intermediate plagioclases: *A* ∼ 23% An; *B* labradorite ∼ 50% An with blue iridescence; *C* mechanical mixture of equal parts of specimens *A* and *D*; *D* ∼ 73% An. c Basic plagioclases: *A* ∼ 66% An; *B* ∼ 78% An; *C* ∼ 96% An. (From Laves and Hafner, 1956, Figs. 8, 9 and 7)

fine structure than synthetic and heated natural specimens (see Fig. 11-2 for patterns of synthetic plagioclase by Iiishi *et al.*, 1971b). This is consistent with greater disorder for the latter two types. Hafner and Laves (1957) stated that with increasing An-content the positions and intensities of the absorption bands change systematically such that absorptions typical of albite disappear as absorptions typical of anorthite appear. Unfortunately the broadness of the absorption bands precludes detailed analysis of the patterns of intermediate plagioclases. However Laves and Hafner concluded that the infra-red pattern of a labradorite

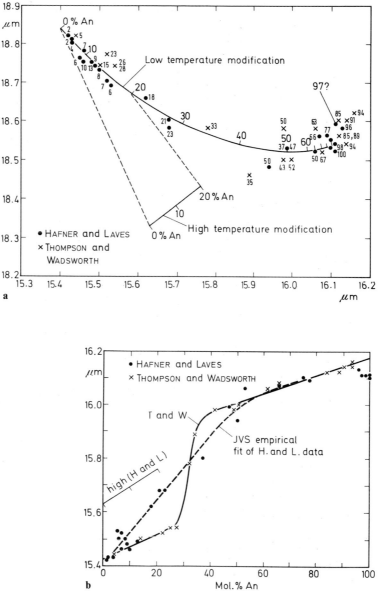

Fig. 11-11. Infra-red absorption data for plagioclases. a Relation between the wavelengths of absorption bands near 18.5 and 15.7 μm for natural plagioclase mostly in the low structural state. The An content (mol.-%) is listed against each datum. The curve for the "low-temperature" modification was given by Hafner and Laves (1957, Fig. 2a) with cross-marks for each 10% An. No data points were given for the "high-temperature" modification. Data were obtained from Hafner and Laves (1957, Table 1: note misprint of 18.39 for An₉₇ specimen) and Thompson and Wadsworth (1957, Table 2). b Relation between the wavelength of the 15—16 μm absorption and the An-content. Thompson and Wadsworth gave the sigmoid curve in their Fig. 2. I have added the dashed line to represent the data of Hafner and Laves in the simplest way. (Redrawn with additions after Hafner and Laves, 1957, Fig. 2a and Thompson and Wadsworth, 1957, Fig. 2)

near 50 % An with blue iridescence was essentially identical with that for a mechanical mixture of an oligoclase near 23 % An and a bytownite near 73 % An. Furthermore they claimed that this is a direct, independent proof of the suggestion of Cole *et al.* (1951) that labradorites are a submicroscopic mixture of phases with compositions near 30 and 70 % An. This suggestion requires careful re-examination in the light of later X-ray and electron-optical results (see Chapter 19). Unfortunately the textural relations are so complex for iridescent labradorites that one cannot make simple qualitative comparisons with mechanical mixtures. At the present time, I think that one can only deduce that (1) natural plagioclases show more order than synthetic plagioclases, and (2) there is a complex variation of the patterns of natural plagioclase with An content that is consistent with transition from the low albite to the anorthite structure type.

Hafner and Laves (1957) made detailed measurements of 26 natural plagioclases, mostly assignable to the low structural state. They found that a plot of the wavelengths for absorptions near 18.5 and 15.7 µm showed a nearly continuous variation with An content (mostly estimated by chemical analysis), but they noted deviations from a smooth curve that were beyond the limits of measurement error (Fig. 11-11a). They suggested that the deviations might arise from (a) analytical errors (b) differences in Al/Si order, and (c) a hitherto undiscovered influence of peristerite unmixing. The actual data points deviate by up to 10 % An at the sodic end and up to 20 % An at the calcic end from the trend given by Hafner and Laves, apparently ruling out these two absorptions as an accurate tool for determining the An-content of plagioclase. Also shown in Fig. 11-11a is a line given by Hafner and Laves for sodic plagioclase in the high structural state. Data obtained independently by Thompson and Wadsworth (1957) scatter rather more than those of Hafner and Laves, and appear to lie at slightly longer wavelengths, probably because of instrumental bias.

Thompson and Wadsworth plotted the wavelength of the 15-16 µm absorption versus the An-content (estimated chemically for some specimens, and optically for others), and their data are combined with those of Hafner and Laves in Fig. 11-11b. Obviously there is a major difference between the two sets of data even though almost all specimens are from "low-temperature" rocks. Whereas Thompson and Wadsworth required a sigmoidal curve to represent their data, I could represent the data of Hafner and Laves by a simple curve.

Angino (1968) measured the far infra-red spectra (500-30 cm^{-1}) of plagioclase feldspars and correlated shifts with the An-content. Estep *et al.* (1971) compared the infra-red spectra of plagioclases from the Apollo 11 and 12 missions with those from terrestrial anorthosites, placing emphasis on the band which shifts from 185 cm^{-1} at An_5 to 235 at An_{95}.

11.2.6 Anorthite

The variation of the crystal structure of anorthite with its thermal history is complex and not completely understood (Chapter 5). Casual studies by several workers demonstrated some variation in the infra-red absorption pattern of anorthites. Aquilano *et al.* (1968) prepared infra-red absorption and emission

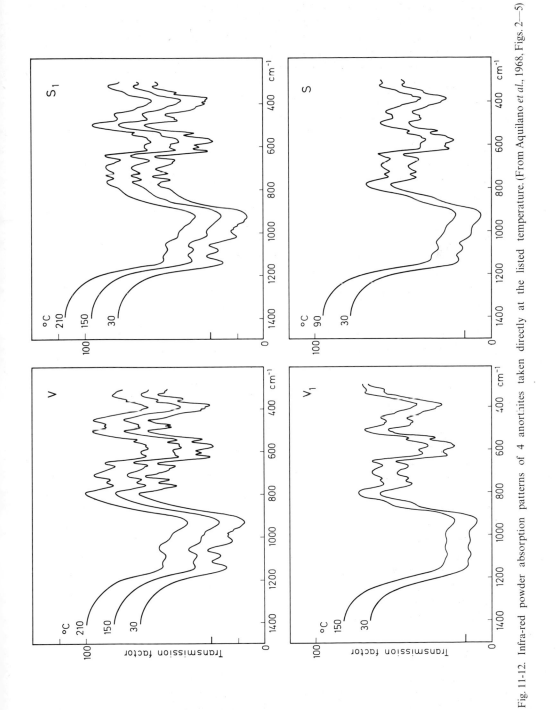

Fig. 11-12. Infra-red powder absorption patterns of 4 anorthites taken directly at the listed temperature. (From Aquilano et al., 1968, Figs. 2—5)

patterns from 1400–300 cm^{-1} directly at temperatures from 30–240° C. Figure 11-12 shows absorption spectra for 4 samples: V, an anorthite from Vesuvius with composition An_{98}; V_1, the result of fusing V and quenching to room temperature in 30 seconds; S, a pure anorthite synthesized by the Verneuil method and cooled over 2 h; S_1, the result of holding S at 1000° C for 200 h and cooling over 12 h. X-ray measurements (probably with a Guinier powder camera) showed that V and S_1 had primitive symmetry, V_1 was body-centered, and S was transitional. Comparison of the spectra at 30° C shows that there is the most fine structure for the two primitive anorthites, and the least for the body-centered anorthite. With increasing temperature, the spectra for the two primitive anorthites blurred out, consistent with the transition to body-centered symmetry found earlier by X-ray methods (Chapter 5). Little change occurred upon heating specimens S and V_1. Differences between the spectra for V and S_1 presumably result at least in part from substitution of some Na-feldspar in the former. Aquilano et al. did not make a detailed analysis of the variations in the spectra, but an attempt should be made to test whether the variations can be explained in terms of both a domain texture involving M cations and an order-disorder relation between the tetrahedral atoms.

11.3 Nuclear Magnetic and Electric Quadrupole Resonance

A detailed description of the general theory and practice is given in Andrews (1958). Laves and Hafner (1962) reviewed applications to feldspars. Only two nuclei (^{27}Al and ^{23}Na) occur with sufficient concentration in natural feldspars to yield measurable signals. In addition a single crystal at least several mms across is needed for detailed interpretation, thereby limiting application of the technique to a few feldspar specimens. The technique gives information on both the degree of order and on the nature of the electrostatic field gradient. Feldspar powders give broad peaks whose interpretation is ambiguous.

In a magnetic field the angular momentum of a nucleus is quantized resulting in equally-spaced energy levels between which transitions may occur (Fig. 11-13). Nuclei with spin number I greater than $\frac{1}{2}$ may possess non-zero electric quadrupole moments which are caused by departure of the nuclear charge distribution from spherical symmetry. The electric quadrupole moment interacts with the electrostatic environment. In a crystal the electrostatic field gradient depends on both the positional coordinates and the angle. When a single crystal is placed in a magnetic field H_0, the nuclear magnetic moment μ adopts one of the quantized angular positions governed by the magnetic quantum number m. As the crystal is rotated, the nuclei stay "locked" in position with respect to the magnetic field, thereby permitting the electric quadrupole moment to "map out" the anisotropy of the electrostatic field gradient. For a first-order perturbation model, the energy levels are

$$E_m = \frac{-m\mu H_0}{I} + \frac{eQ}{4I(2I-1)} [3m^2 - I(I+1)] \frac{\partial^2 E}{\partial^2 z}$$

where I is the nuclear spin number, eQ is the nuclear electric quadrupole moment and $\partial E/\partial z$ is the first derivative of the electrostatic field gradient along the z symmetry axis of the nucleus. The energy levels are measured by observing

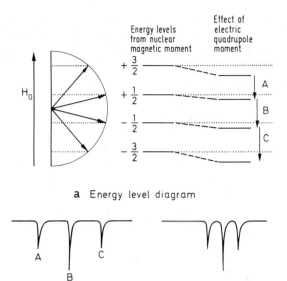

a Energy level diagram

A   C

B

one orientation   another orientation

b Resonance patterns

Fig. 11-13. Schematic energy level diagram for Na^{23} nuclei. The nuclear magnetic moment according to the simple semiclassical picture takes up one of four orientations with respect to the applied magnetic field resulting in four energy levels corresponding to quantum numbers $-3/2$, $-1/2$, $+1/2$ and $3/2$, spaced in units of $2/3\,\mu H_0$. The interaction of the electric quadrupole moment with the electric field gradient gives rise to further energy changes which are greater for the states corresponding to a quantum number $3/2$ than for those corresponding to $1/2$. The three allowed transitions A, B, C give rise to a resonance pattern in which the central peak from B is flanked by two peaks from A and C (bottom left). For a different orientation, the electric quadrupole effect is smaller giving the resonance pattern on the right

absorption of radio-frequency energy transmitted through the specimen as an applied magnetic field is varied.

Nuclear species in crystallographically-distinct sites have distinct resonances for each site. A twinned crystal has two sets of resonances except when the applied magnetic field is symmetrically related to the twin element (e.g. parallel to b^* for an Albite twin). An ordered crystal has only one electrostatic field gradient for each site and the resonances from different sites may be resolved. A disordered crystal has a range of field gradients and the resonances are diffuse. A powdered crystal gives diffuse resonances even if the atoms are fully ordered.

However there are subtle effects. Experiments normally use a frequency near 10 megacycles, and atomic movements more rapid than 10^{-7} sec will be averaged out. Hence any disorder with a relaxation time less than that (including thermal vibrations near 10^{-13} sec) will not be revealed by n.m.r. experiments. Secondly, there are complications arising from the interaction of the nuclear spins, resulting in the broadening of the resonances. If the crystal contains a significant amount of atoms with uncoupled electron spins, the resonances may be weakened or strengthened depending on the relaxation times of the spin states.

The ^{23}Na nucleus has a nuclear spin of 3/2 resulting in an nmr spectrum composed of a central peak flanked by two satellites. The ^{27}Al nucleus has a spin of 5/2 resulting in four satellites. By chance the resonances for ^{23}Na and ^{27}Al partly overlap.

11.3.1 Alkali Feldspar

Brun *et al.* (1960) first described the application of nmr techniques to feldspars, and demonstrated that:

(1) the resonance lines of ^{27}Al and ^{23}Na in single crystals of microcline and low albite are sharp and resolved (Fig. 11-14). The albite crystal from Amelia yielded five sharp peaks for ^{27}Al and three peaks for ^{23}Na, the latter shown by

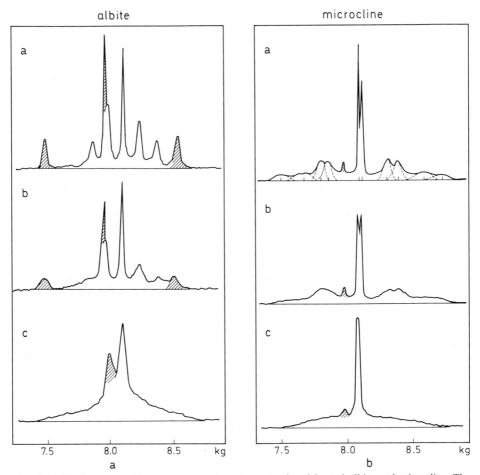

Fig. 11-14. Nuclear magnetic resonance patterns for natural and heated albite and microcline. The abscissa shows the magnetic field in kilogauss. The shaded areas show the resonances for ^{23}Na, and the open areas for ^{27}Al. Amelia albite: a natural; b after heating at 1030° C for 7 days; c 1060° C for 43 days. Microcline perthite from Crystal Peak, Colorado: a unheated-note two sets of peaks corresponding to cross-hatched twinning, and a small shaded peak for ^{23}Na; b after heating at 1050° C for 1 day; c 1050° C for 17 days. (From Brun *et al.*, 1960, Figs. 1 and 3)

shading. The microcline from Crystal Peak, Colorado had a high triclinic index, and contained albite veins from 0.1–0.5 mm across. Because the microcline had cross-hatched twinning, the resonance spectrum consisted of overlapping sets of peaks. In spite of the complications from the albite and the twinning, it was clear that the Al resonances from the microcline were sharp.

(2) the resonances for microcline and low albite heated near 1050° C for several days or weeks were smeared out giving a sharp central signal for ^{27}Al and ^{23}Na centered on a single broad peak.

(3) the resonances for natural sanidine were also smeared out, similar to those for heated microcline (see Fig. 11-17 for spectra of sanidine given by Hafner et al., 1962).

(4) the number of lines in low albite and microcline corresponds to a single point position for Al and one for Na.

(5) the electrostatic field gradients at both the Al and Na sites are strongly anisotropic (see Fig. 11-17 for spectra given by Hafner et al., 1962).

These results furnished strong proof that Al atoms are ordered into a single site in low albite and microcline, and that they are disordered after strong heating. Furthermore these conclusions are fully consistent with the evidence from X-ray structure analysis that Al atoms segregate into $T_1 0$ sites (see Chapter 3).

The sharp resonance lines for ^{23}Na in low albite also imply that the Na atoms do not show positional disorder, apart from that caused by thermal motion about a single site. Around 1960, there was a detailed discussion whether low albite had a domain structure in which the Na atoms occupied two sites about 0.03 nm apart (see Chapter 4). The latest X-ray structure refinement by Wainwright and Starkey (1968) gave no evidence for a domain structure, and the nmr and X-ray data are consistent with anisotropic thermal vibration about a single point position.

The blurred resonances for natural sanidine and for heated albite and microcline result, of course, from atomic disorder which produces different electrostatic field gradients at the crystallographically-related point positions. For albite the blurring results from disorder of the tetrahedral atoms plus associated displacements of the other atoms. In microcline and sanidine, the situation is complicated by substitution of Na and K atoms in the M site.

Following the pioneering studies of Brun et al., measurements were made by Hafner et al. (1962) on adularias and by Hafner and Laves (1963) on moonstones and iron-orthoclases in order to elucidate the structural variations of K-feldspar. A summary of some of the data is given by Laves and Hafner (1962).

Before examining the data, it is necessary to clarify the variation of the nmr spectrum with crystal orientation and twinning (Hafner et al., 1962). Figure 11-15 shows the variation of the satellite resonances for ^{27}Al nuclei in a single crystal of maximum microcline twinned on the Albite law. The crystal was rotated about an axis perpendicular to the applied magnetic field H_0. In diagram I, the rotation axis is a and for the zero angle, H_0 is parallel to b^*. In II, the corresponding directions are b^* and a; in III, they are a direction mutually perpendicular to a and b^*, and one parallel to the a axis. Rotation about b^* results in only one set of four satellites, thereby eliminating any confusion from

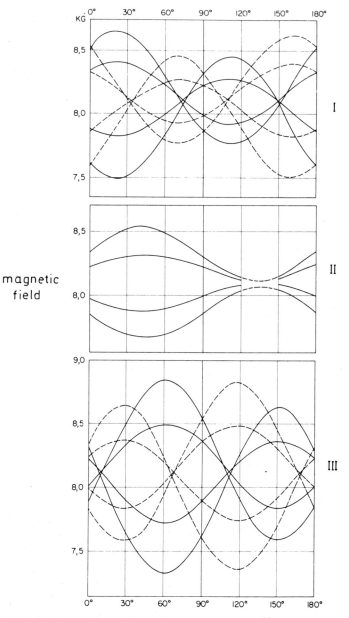

Fig. 11-15. The positions of the satellite resonances for Al^{27} nuclei in a maximum microcline twinned according to the Albite law. The magnetic field is measured in kilogauss (KG). The crystal is rotated about an axis perpendicular to the direction of the applied magnetic field, H_0. In (I) the rotation axis is a and for the angular position $0°$, H_0 is parallel to b^*. In (II) the rotation axis is b^* and at $0°$, a is parallel to H_0. In (III), the rotation axis is the direction mutually perpendicular to a and b^*; at $0°$, a is parallel to H_0. In (II) the signals from the two twin units overlap to yield only four satellites. In (I) and (III), there are two sets of satellites distinguished by the solid and dashed lines. Note that the orientations for the spectra in Fig. 11-14 were for rotation III at $66°$ or $114°$, for which there is particularly good discrimination between the signals because those for one unit almost merge while those from the other twin unit have a large separation. (From Hafner, Hartmann and Laves, 1962, Fig. 1)

Table 11-4. Optical and X-ray properties of K-feldspars studied by n.m.r. methods (Hafner *et al.*, 1962)

Type and locality	Appearance under microscope	Extinction on (001)	α^*	γ^*	%exsolved albite	%albite in solid solution
1. Microcline. (low) Crystal Peak, Colo.	Coarse Albite and Pericline twinning. Domains 2mm across.	18°	90.4°	92.3°		~ 0
2. Microcline (low) Hull, Quebec	Single crystal	19	90.4	92.4	5 – 10	~ 0
3. Microcline (low) Perth	Homogeneous to finely cross-hatched.	~ 0	n.m.	92.3	40	~ 0
4. Microcline (low to intermediate) Snarum, Norway	Homogeneous to finely cross-hatched.	0 – 10	90.25	91.55	25 – 30	~ 0
5. Microcline (high) Tirschheim, Sachsen	Twin domains about .05mm across. Two extinctions observable with diffuse boundaries. $2V = -60$ to $-70°$	1	~90	90.3 to 90.4	15 – 20	8
6. Adularia Disentis, Switzerland	Monoclinic appearance $2V = -69°$, OAP$\perp$(010)	~ 0	0	0	0	10
7. Adularia Piz Blas, Switzerland	Monoclinic appearance $2V = -68°$, OAP$\perp$(010)	~ 0	0	0	0	13
8. Sanidine Laacher See, Germany	Monoclinic $2V = -23$ to $-24°$, OAP$\parallel$(010)	0	0	0	0	11

the Albite twinning. The variation of the electrostatic field gradient is such that the maximum separation is at an angle of about 45° and the minimum near 135°. For rotations I and III, eight satellites are obtained whose separations vary in a complex manner with the angle of rotation.

Hafner *et al.* (1962) compared the nmr spectra of two adularias with those of five microclines and one sanidine in order to clarify the polymorphism of K-feldspar. Table 11-4 summarizes optical and X-ray data, and Fig. 11-16 shows six of the spectra taken in the II, 45° position.

For microclines nos. 1, 3 and 4, peaks for ^{23}Na and ^{27}Al were ascribed to exsolved albite. The remaining five peaks of each spectrum were consistent with ^{27}Al atoms occurring in only one point position. Slight broadening of the peaks for microcline No. 4 was correlated with the optical and X-ray properties, which indicate some deviation from maximum microcline. For microcline No. 5 the peaks for ^{23}Na were partly assigned to exsolved albite and partly to Na substituting for K in the microcline. The satellite peaks for ^{27}Al were so broad that only the inner ones showed distinct maxima. This microcline showed only a small deviation of α^* and γ^* from 90°, while optical study showed only diffuse domains. All these nmr, X-ray and optical data are mutually consistent when account is taken of the resolving power of the techniques: whereas the optical microscope can resolve only those twin domains of ordered microcline coarser

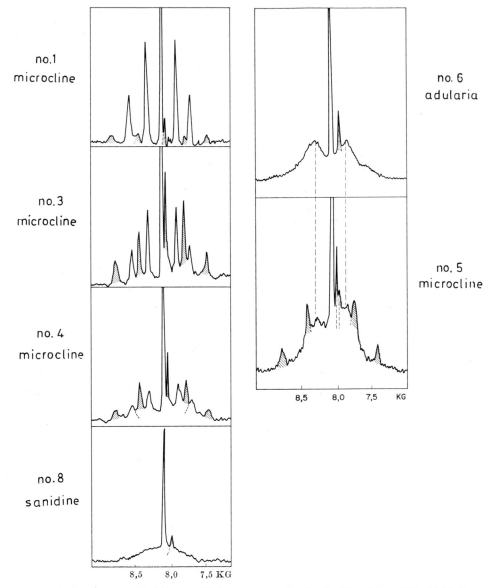

Fig. 11-16. Nmr spectra of K-feldspars. All the spectra are for the II, 45° position of Fig. 11-15. See Table 11-4 for specimen numbers. The dotted and hatched areas show ^{23}Na and ^{27}Al signals for exsolved albite, except for no. 5 microcline which has ^{23}Na signals for albite both exsolved and in solid solution. (From Hafner *et al.*, 1962, Figs. 5 and 6)

than about 0.05 μm, the other two techniques can detect ordering in regions only a few unit cells across.

The two adularias gave identical spectra, essentially the same as that of the No. 5 microcline when account is taken of exsolved albite. Hafner *et al.* concluded that these adularias "consist of very small triclinic but largely ordered domains

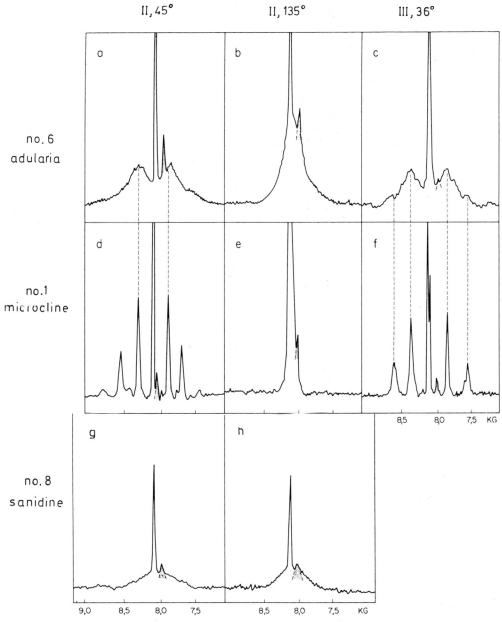

Fig. 11-17. Nmr spectra of K-feldspars. The specimen numbers are those of Table 11-4. The orientation of the sample is specified at the top of the diagram, and may be identified with reference to Fig. 11-15. Dotted areas are for ^{23}Na nuclei. (From Hafner *et al.*, 1962, Figs. 2 and 4)

related to each other by twinning which [is] coherent to X-rays". They thought that "a monoclinic, partially ordered structure" was improbable for the two adularias even though X-ray photographs indicated "a monoclinic lattice (no splitting of hkl and hk̄l reflections)." The evidence is given in Fig. 11-17

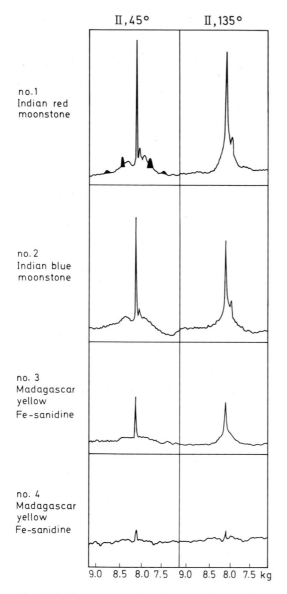

Fig. 11-18. Nmr spectra of "orthoclases". The specimens are described in the text. The orientation of the sample is specified at the top of the diagram, and may be identified with reference to Fig. 11-15. Shaded areas are for exsolved albite. (From Hafner and Laves, 1963, Fig. 1)

which shows spectra for No. 6 adularia compared with No. 1 microcline and No. 8 sanidine. In the II, 45° position, the adularia shows two broad satellites whose peaks correspond in magnetic field to the sharp inner satellites of No. 1 microcline. The No. 8 sanidine shows merely the central signal perched on a broad arch. Furthermore, comparison of spectra in the 45° and 135° positions of orientation II shows a strong anisotropy for the microcline and adularia, but not for the sanidine. Also shown are spectra for the III, 36° positions of the adularia and microcline. No X-ray photographs of the adularias were given in the paper, but it is probable that they showed diffuse diffractions like those of the Spencer B adularia described in Chapter 6. Such diffuse diffractions are consistent with coherent domains whose local Al, Si order attains triclinic symmetry on a local scale but not over the scale of the entire crystal.

In a further study of K-feldspars, Hafner and Laves (1963) studied the nmr patterns of four specimens classified as "orthoclase" (Fig. 11-18). The first two specimens were turbid Indian moonstones with undulose extinction and diffuse indication of cross-hatching. Both had optical axial plane perpendicular to (010). The first gave blue iridescence and $2V = -79°$, and the second red iridescence and $-78°$. X-ray powder and single-crystal patterns showed broadening and "tailing" of lines and spots which would be split for microcline. The nmr spectra for the II, 45 and 135° positions are quite similar to those of the adularia and No. 5 microcline in Fig. 11-16, thereby indicating the occurrence of triclinic domains in twin orientation. The next two specimens were iron-sanidines from Madagascar with the yellow color typical of substitution of ferric iron. Specimen No. 3 had its optic axial plane perpendicular to (010) and $2V = -49°$ while specimen No. 4 had the plane parallel to (010) and $2V = -34°$. The spectra of No. 3 are fairly similar to those of the No. 8 sanidine in Figs. 11-17, but indicate an asymmetry between the 45 and 135° positions not shown by the No. 8 sanidine. Domains with local triclinic symmetry are indicated. The spectra of No. 4 iron-sanidine show only a weak central signal with no detectable satellites, consistent with the high disorder implied by the high-sanidine optics. Probably the weakness of the signals of the Fe-sanidines, especially of No. 4, results from the uncoupled spins of the Fe atoms plus high disorder.

These important qualitative interpretations of Hafner and co-workers might be supplemented by calculations of the spectra to be expected for various models of domains using dimensions measured from electron-optical studies. In the meantime, it is certain that adularias and some microclines have complex domain patterns resulting from Al, Si ordering in a coherent framework, but it is not completely clear what are the separate effects on nmr spectra of domain size and degree of ordering in each domain. The term "orthoclase" encompasses a wide variety of structural states.

11.3.2 Anorthite

Brinkmann and Stähli (1968a) measured the nmr spectra of ^{27}Al in a crystal of anorthite from Tirol. The crystal was rotated about X, Y and Z axes respectively perpendicular to the natural faces ($\bar{1}01$) and (010), and an imaginary face mutually perpendicular to these two. Figure 11-19 shows the great complexity of the spectra, and the high degree of anisotropy. The spectra could be interpreted in terms of eight point positions, each yielding a central signal and four satellites. Arrows in Fig. 11-19 show the change with angle for one set of four satellites. These data are fully consistent with the X-ray structural analysis of primitive

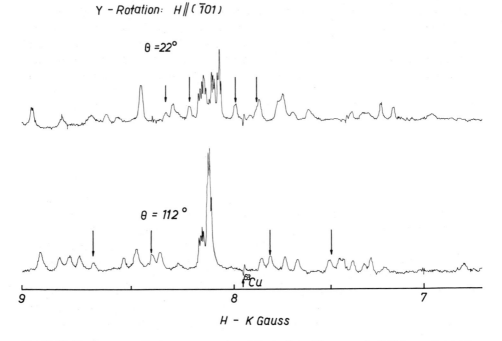

Fig. 11-19. Nuclear magnetic resonance spectra of P-anorthite. The magnetic field is parallel to the face-normal ($\bar{1}01$), and spectra are given for two different angles of rotation. Arrows show the four satellites for one of the point positions occupied by Al. (From Brinkmann and Stähli, 1968a, Fig. 1)

anorthite (Chapters 3 and 4) in which there are eight point positions occupied by Al atoms.

In abstracts, Brinkmann *et al.* (1967) and Brinkmann and Staehli (1968b) reported heating studies on anorthites. A completely reversible phase transition took place between 220 and 250° C, resulting in only 4 point positions for Al. This is consistent with X-ray data which indicate a transition to body-centered symmetry (Chapter 5). Brinkmann and Staehli reported that the Al/Si distribution was ordered between 250 and 400° C. Anorthites heated at temperatures up to 1540° C and quenched to room temperature gave nmr patterns indicating that some Al/Si disorder begins above 1150° C. Unfortunately no details have appeared, and the respective roles of Al/Si order-disorder and Ca-induced domain texture in determining the nmr spectra of heated anorthites are unclear. The effect of the Ca atoms may depend on whether they move more rapidly than the frequency of the electromagnetic field used in the nmr apparatus.

Brinkmann and Stähli (1968a) determined the quadrupole coupling constants, asymmetry parameters and electric field-gradient tensors for the 8 point positions occupied by Al-atoms (their Tables 1 and 2).

Added in Proof. Staehli and Brinkmann (1974a, b) gave full details of their studies of the anorthite $An_{95}Ab_4Or_1$ from s. Tyrol. Italy. The alumino-silicate framework is apparently body-centered above $241 \pm 4°$ C, and the nmr data are consistent with the X-ray data if the Ca atoms jump between the two sites much faster than 6 kHz, the precession frequency of Al nuclei in the local field (see Chapter 5). The 8 spectra for P-anorthite were assigned to the Al sites determined by X-ray methods on the basis of calculated and observed electric field gradient tensors. The quadrupole coupling constant correlated with the distortion of the oxygen tetrahedra, even on a simple point-charge model.

11.3.3 Electric Field Gradient and Oxygen Polarizability

Hafner and Hartmann (1964) made an important advance in understanding the bonding forces of silicates when they interpreted the anisotropy of the nmr spectra of ^{23}Na and ^{27}Al nuclei in albite and of ^{27}Al in microcline in terms of a model incorporating induced electric dipole moments of the oxygen atoms. From the observed variation of the nmr spectra with crystal orientation in the magnetic field, the tensor for the electric field gradient was calculated. Initial calculations of the field gradient using point atoms (i.e. the equivalent of spherical charge distributions) were unsatisfactory, and calculations were then made for polarizable atoms. Because cations are less polarizable than oxygen anions, the former were neglected in calculations of induced dipoles. Distortions of higher order than dipoles were neglected. Because the electric polarizability of oxygen ions has not been established theoretically, calculations were made for a series of values from 0 to 0.5×10^{-24} cm^3. The results gave reasonable agreement with the measured orientations of the principal axes of the electrostatic field gradient tensor (Fig. 11-20) when the polarizability coefficient was taken as 0.24 in the interpretation of the nmr spectra of ^{23}Na in albite, 0.36 for ^{27}Al in albite, and 0.35 for ^{27}Al in microcline. For ^{23}Na in albite, the calculated electrostatic field gradient changed only a little as the coefficient was varied from 0.2–0.4, but for ^{27}Al the change was great. Consequently the best estimate of the polarizability of oxygen is about 0.35×10^{-24} cm^3 for both albite and microcline.

Hafner and Hartmann stated that these estimates of the polarizability were too small for complete ionic bonding, and suggested that there is significant covalent bonding. Calculations of the effect of covalent bonding would be extremely difficult to make, but until they are made it seems that an ionic model with a polarizability coefficient near 0.35×10^{-24} cm^3 should give reasonable results for feldspar. Calculations of the electrostatic field gradient depend critically on the accuracy with which the atomic centers are known from X-ray structural analysis. Strictly speaking, integration is required over an infinite crystal, but Hafner and Hartmann obtained a reasonable approximation for a sphere including about 4000 ions. Although no specific calculations have been made, it seems reasonable to propose that sharp nmr spectra will be obtained only if ordering occurs over regions at least as large as this. Furthermore nmr spectra with broad ill-defined peaks, such as for the adularia and high-microcline in Fig. 11-16, probably result from domains only a few unit cells across.

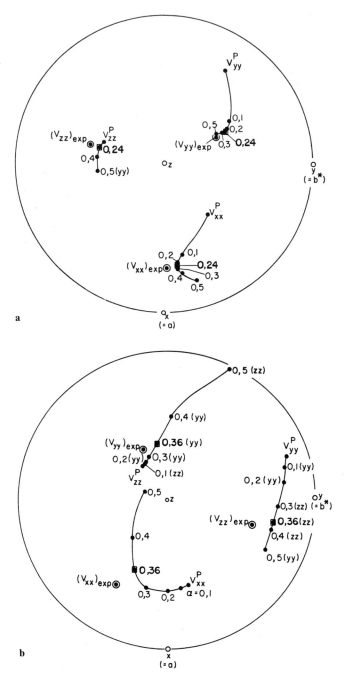

Fig. 11-20. Principal axes (eigen vectors) of the electrostatic field gradients determined by nmr measurements of (a) ^{27}Al in microcline (b) ^{23}Na in albite (c) ^{27}Al in albite; and by epr measurements of (d) Fe^{3+} in microcline. All stereograms are plotted with crystallographic a at extreme bottom and b^* at extreme right. For (a, b, c), the curves show the calculated axes for the dipole model of Hafner and Hartmann in which the polarizability of the oxygen atoms was varied from 0 to 0.5×10^{-24} cm^3.

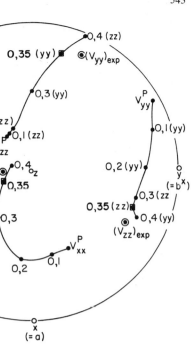

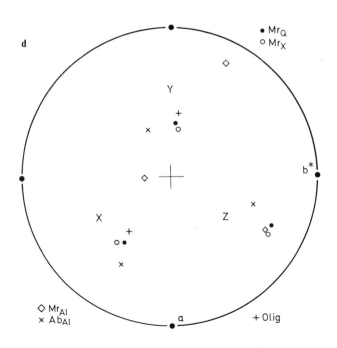

Observed axes are shown by the centered circles. From Hafner and Hartmann (1964, Fig. 1). For (d), Mr_Q and Mr_X refer to the Q and X bands for a microcline (Marfunin *et al.*, 1967); Olig to the Q band of an oligoclase (Marfunin *et al.*, 1967). Mr_{Al} and Ab_{Al} refer to nmr spectra of ^{27}Al in microcline and albite (Hafner and Hartmann, 1964). (From Marfunin *et al.*, 1967, Fig. 4)

11.4 Electron Paramagnetic Resonance

General reviews are given by Ingram (1968), McMillan (1968), Orton (1968) and Wertz (1968). Electron paramagnetic resonance reveals information about the environment of atoms with uncoupled electron spins: so far Fe^{3+}, Mn^{2+}, Ti^{3+} and Pb^+ have been characterized in feldspars. In addition electron-hole centers can be identified: for feldspars, Marfunin and Bershov (1970) ascribed resonances to centers associated with $Al-O^--Al$, $Si\,O^--Si$, O^--Na, O^--Pb and O^--Ag. The epr technique is much more sensitive than nmr, permitting detection of only a few parts per million of the above ions in crystals a few mms across. Although the details are different, the essential features of the experimental method and theoretical interpretation are similar to those for nmr. An applied magnetic field is varied, and a resonance is observed in a radio-frequency detector as an electron jumps between quantized energy levels.

Each point position gives one set of signals whose angular variation for a single crystal rotated in a magnetic field maps out the electrostatic field gradient at the point position. Broadening of the signal results from atomic disorder, mechanical imperfection of the crystal, and spin-spin interactions if the concentration of paramagnetic species is high. Use of a powder results in a pattern averaged over all crystal orientations and magnetic fields for which transitions occur. In all feldspars but iron-sanidines, the concentration of paramagnetic atoms is so low that all broadening can be assigned to atomic disorder or mechanical imperfections. Pioneering studies on feldspars were made by Höchli (1963), Marfunin and Michoulier (1966), and Marfunin et al. (1967). The crystallochemical and petrologic significance of paramagnetic ions in feldspars was discussed by Marfunin and Bershov (1970). The Apollo mission to the Moon stimulated epr studies of feldspars, especially with respect to the oxidation ratio of Fe (e.g. Weeks, 1972).

Usually measurements of epr are made either at 9 or 35 GHz, the latter frequency giving the simplest variation of the spectrum with respect to crystal orientation (e.g. Fig. 3 of Gaite and Michoulier, 1970). Use of two frequencies permits resolution of the components of overlapping spectra. Identification of the electron centers responsible for epr is not easy, especially when the spectra are taken on a powder. Almost certainly spectra from Fe^{3+} have been correctly identified (e.g. Gaite and Michoulier, 1970), but some of the other identifications may be uncertain. Unfortunately the theory and practice of epr is rather complex, and it is quite impossible to reproduce all the pertinent data here.

11.4.1 Fe^{3+} in Alkali Feldspar

Höchli (1963) examined a sample of microcline and interpreted the principal set of resonances to result from Fe^{3+} ions substituting for Al^{3+}. He noted that the lines broadened upon heating to 750° C for several days, and disappeared after heating to 1050° C.

Marfunin et al. (1967) reported epr studies of single crystals of a microcline (using a frequency of 35 GHz in the Q-band and 9.5 in the X band) and an

oligoclase (35 GHz). The spectra were interpreted to result from Fe^{3+} substituting
for Al. Figure 11-20d shows that the orientations of the eigen-vectors X, Y and Z
with respect to the crystallographic axes differ only slightly between microcline
and oligoclase, and vary only slightly with frequency. Furthermore, the Z eigen
vectors are close to those found by Hafner and Hartmann (1964) for the nmr
spectra of ^{27}Al in albite and microcline. Consequently Marfunin et al. interpreted the Fe^{3+} ions to be entering the $T_1 0$ site.

Gaite and Michoulier (1970) determined the epr spectra at 9.6 and 36 GHz
of single crystals (oriented to 0.5° by X-rays) of two albites from Bourg d'Oisans,
France and Schmira, Tyrol; three maximum microclines from the Ukraine
(two specimens) and Arendal, Norway; a microcline microperthite from
Tvedestrand, Norway; an adularia from St.-Gotthard, Switzerland; an iron-
sanidine from Madagascar; and a sanidine from Laacher See, Germany.
Their Fig. 4 gives an orientation for the eigen vectors of microcline which is
inconsistent with that given by Marfunin et al. If Fe^{3+} enters the $T_1 0$ site it
should experience a similar, but not identical, crystal field to that experienced by
Al atoms in the same site. The near-parallelism of the eigen vectors found by
Marfunin et al. and by Hafner and Hartmann suggests that the orientation given

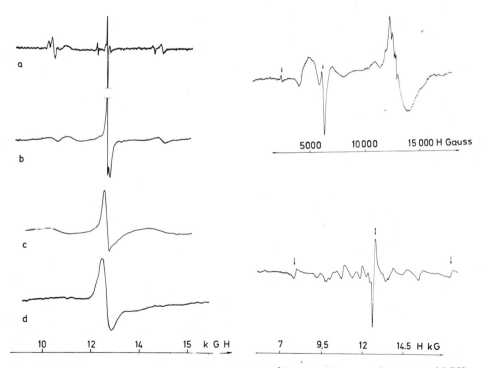

Fig. 11-21. Electron paramagnetic resonance spectra of Fe^{3+} ions in feldspars. All spectra at 35 GHz
with magnetic field (H) parallel to the Z eigen vector and expressed in gauss (G). Left. K-feldspars:
a twinned microcline; b adularia; c Fe-sanidine; d sanidine. Upper right. Bytownite. Lower right.
Anorthite. The arrows show the spectra from the Fe atoms whose Z eigen vector is parallel to the
magnetic field. The other peaks derive from Fe atoms whose Z eigen vector is not parallel to $\mathbf{H}$.
(From Gaite and Michoulier, 1970, Figs. 5, 8 and 9)

by Marfunin *et al.* is probably correct. Possibly Gaite and Michoulier confused the orientations of the twin components of the microcline.

Figure 11-21 compares the spectra of twinned microcline with adularia, Fe-sanidine and sanidine. The adularia spectrum could be interpreted in terms of two overlapping spectra related by symmetry in (010). Compared to microcline, the adularia gave broadened peaks at approximately the same positions. The Fe-sanidine and the sanidine gave even broader peaks. Whereas the sanidine spectrum had the same type of anisotropy as the adularia, the Fe-sanidine spectrum showed hardly any anisotropy, and gave only the central signal. A microcline and a microcline perthite were studied both before and after heating at 1050° C for one day. The spectra developed lower resolution indicating disorder. All these results have implications for the polymorphism of K-feldspar similar to those proposed by Hafner and co-workers using nmr spectra of ^{27}Al nuclei. It is reasonable to assume that Fe^{3+} strongly prefers the $T_1 0$ site in microcline, and that disorder of various kinds increases from microcline to adularia to high sanidine ultimately resulting in Fe^{3+} entering both T_1 and T_2 sites.

The two specimens of low albite gave sharp epr spectra indicating that the Fe^{3+} atoms occupied one site. The eigen-vectors were nearly parallel to those given for microcline. Again it is almost certain that the Fe^{3+} atoms tend to occupy the $T_1 0$ site, but there is a question whether the orientation of the eigen vectors has been confused between twin components.

11.4.2 Fe^{3+}, Ti^{3+} and Mn^{2+} in Plagioclase

Following the work of Marfunin *et al.* (1967) on an oligoclase, Gaite and Michoulier (1970) obtained spectra for three oligoclases; a labradorite (An_{67}) from Lake View, Oregon; a bytownite (An_{73}) from Pigeon Point, Minn.; and two anorthites. Figure 11-21 shows spectra for the bytownite and an anorthite. The spectra for all the intermediate plagioclases were analogous, and the arrows in the spectrum for bytownite show resonances common to all the samples and identified with the $s = -\frac{1}{2} \rightarrow +\frac{1}{2}$ transition in low albite. However a detailed interpretation was not obtained of the spectra, whose complexity is not surprising in view of the other evidence for domain intergrowths. The epr data suggest that the Fe^{3+} ions occur in more than one site, and that there is local ordering.

The two anorthites gave similar patterns whose complexity implied the existence of several point positions occupied by Fe^{3+} ions. The spectrum in Fig. 11-21 was obtained with the magnetic field parallel to the Z eigen vector of one set of Fe^{3+} ions. At least 3 sets of sites were characterized, but a complete interpretation was not obtained. The sharpness of the peaks implied that the anorthites were ordered.

Weeks (1972, 1973, and pers. comm.) measured the epr spectra of powdered plagioclase separates from lunar basalts 14053 and 14321, and of Apollo 16 specimens, using frequencies of 9 and 35 GHz and temperatures of 300 and 130° K. The spectra were interpreted in terms of Fe^{3+}, Ti^{3+} and Mn^{2+}. Assignment of the Fe^{3+} resonances was made on the basis of a measured g-factor of 4.27 which agrees with the theoretical value for the first excited state for a high-spin d^5 configuration. The Fe^{3+} ions occur in various sites of low symmetry, and comparison of the estimated number of Fe^{3+} ions with the total Fe content determined by chemical analysis yielded an oxidation ratio $Fe^{3+}/(Fe^{3+}+Fe^{2+})$ near 0.1. A second set of six resonances with a g-factor of 2.002 and a separation of 80 gauss was assigned to Mn^{2+}. A third set of resonances was ascribed to Ti^{3+} because (1) the resonances changed congruently with temperature, (2) they were characteristic of an electron state with effective spin $\frac{1}{2}$ and non-degenerate eigen-values of the g-tensor when present in a polycrystalline sample, and (3) they had g-values within the range of those for nd^1 ions in octahedral sites such as in rutile. Electron microprobe analyses of lunar plagioclases have revealed concentrations of Fe up to 1 wt.-%, of Ti up to 0.1 wt.-%, and of Mn up to 0.03 wt.-%, thereby strengthening the identifications of the epr resonances.

Weeks also examined a plagioclase separate (probably bytownite) from the Stillwater complex, Montana. Resonances assigned to Fe^{3+} were similar in shape and positions to those of the lunar plagioclases, and their intensity corresponded to a five-fold greater concentration which is consistent with the higher oxidation state of terrestrial rocks. No resonances for Ti^{3+} were detected, probably because all the Ti was in the quadrivalent state. Measurements at 35 GHz revealed the six-peak spectrum of Mn^{2+}.

Hafner et al. (1973) made epr studies at 9.5 GHz of anorthite from Apollo 15415 anorthosite. Lines with g near 2 were ascribed to Mn^{2+}. A second set of lines was assigned to Fe^{3+} in sites 2 and 3 of Gaite and Michoulier. Hafner et al. concluded that 1% of the total iron substituted for Al in at least two non-equivalent T sites. Two unidentified lines behaved similarly to the second set, and may result from Fe^{3+} in different sites, or in sites related by twinning.

11.4.3 Other Ions and Electron Centers

Haskin and Morris (1973) studied the epr spectra of synthetic anorthite doped with Eu^{2+} and Gd^{3+}. Whereas the former ion yielded a fine structure indicating substitution in a regular lattice site (almost certainly replacing Ca), the latter ion yielded a glass-type spectrum.

Marfunin and Bershov (1970) reported briefly on epr spectra of feldspars taken at 9.3 GHz and 78° K. An electron center ascribed to Pb^+ was observed only in amazonites. The spectrum consisted of a central line with two hyperfine-structure lines describable with a spin Hamiltonian with orthorhombic symmetry and g-factors of 1.390, 1.565 and 1.837. When the amazonites were heated to 400–500° C for several hours they lost their green color and Pb^+ spectrum. The epr spectrum ascribed to Fe^{3+} was unchanged by heating. Marfunin and Bershov concluded that the green color of amazonite results from Pb^+ produced by the substitution of Pb^{2+} for K followed by capture of an electron.

Spectra ascribed to Ti^{3+} were observed in orthoclases, microcline and in labradorite. Identification was based on similarity of g-factors with those for Ti^{3+} in quartz.

Resonances attributed to an $Al–O^{-}–Al$ hole center were the most common in feldspars. Identification was made by comparison with the $Si–O^{-}–Al$ center in quartz. The *g*-factors varied somewhat with the An and Or contents of the feldspar, and the factors for albite agreed well with those given earlier by Joffe and Janchevskaya (1966). Upon irradiation with X-rays, almost all feldspars showed this type of center.

Resonances attributed to Si–O⁻–Si hole centers were observed in some slightly-colored amazonites, and ones ascribed to O⁻–Na were observed in some microclines. Spectra attributed to O⁻–Ag hole centers were observed in various orthoclases and microclines from Buzheninov Bor and Teberda which had no Al–O⁻–Al centers.

Interpretation of epr spectra is difficult, and requires checking in as many ways as possible. Hopefully many more data will be obtained in several laboratories to check the present ideas on the epr spectra of feldspars. It is particularly important that some kind of chemical analysis be made to test whether a proposed ion or hole center is possible.

11.5 Mössbauer (Gamma-ray) Resonance

General reviews are given by Goldanskii (1964), Greenwood and Gibb (1971) and Wertheim (1964). Certain nuclei emit gamma rays, of which only one, ^{57}Fe, occurs in sufficient concentration in feldspar to yield measurable resonance. Emission of some of the gamma rays depends on electrostatic interaction of the Fe atom with its surrounding atoms. Bombardment with gamma-rays of varying energy results in resonant absorption at quantized energies which measure this electrostatic interaction. For ^{57}Fe, there are two resonances for each point position, whose energy separation gives the *quadrupole splitting*, and whose mean position with respect to some standard gives the *isomer shift* (or *chemical shift*). Unfortunately the concentration of Fe in most feldspars is so low that the Mössbauer spectra suffer from a large random error. Furthermore, the two peaks are quite wide resulting in serious overlap if more than one type of Fe is involved (e.g. Fig. 11-22). Even after fitting the peaks to a Gaussian shape with least-squares analysis of the spectra, the resulting estimates of the parameters are uncertain. This is a particularly severe problem for many feldspars in which iron may occur as both Fe^{2+} and Fe^{3+}, each of which might occupy more than one point position. Spectra are normally taken at either room temperature or liquid nitrogen temperature. the latter giving somewhat greater resolution. The temperature variation of the spectra aids in the interpretation. Because the energy of the incoming gamma rays is varied by Doppler displacement, the energy of a Mössbauer spectrum is quoted as the Doppler velocity in mm/sec. Interpretation of Mössbauer spectra in terms of charge of the Fe ion and location in the crystal structure is based on qualitative and semi-quantitative comparison of the spectral parameters with those for simple Fe-bearing structures.

11.5.1 Iron Sanidine

Brown and Pritchard (1969) studied iron-sanidines of unspecified origin: one yielded by chemical analysis Al_2O_3 17.69%. Fe_2O_3 1.18%, Na_2O 0.47%,

K_2O 16.68 %. Spectra obtained at 25° C and − 196° C yielded two doublets of intensity ratio 9:1. Referred to sodium nitroprusside standard, the isomer shifts and quadrupole splittings were:

Stronger i.s.	$0.72 + 0.05$ mm/sec	q.s.	0.68 ± 0.05 mm/sec
Weaker	1.5	mm/sec	2.8	mm/sec

The stronger doublet was ascribed to Fe (III) replacing Al in tetrahedral sites, and comparison of the spectral parameters with those of micas suggested that the s electrons are less shielded by covalent interactions than in mica. This proposal was supported by measurements of the optical absorption bands (responsible for the yellow color) which lie at higher wave-numbers than those in phlogopite. The lower shielding in feldspars was ascribed to the framework structure in which all oxygens are bonded to two strongly polarizing cations. The line-width 0.68 ± 0.05 mm/sec is comparable with that for other compounds containing Fe (III) and although large could not be considered as evidence for order-disorder or for a difference between electric field gradients at T_1 and T_2 sites.

The weak doublet is similar to those found in compounds with octahedrally-coordinated high spin Fe (II), and was assumed to arise from ferrous iron.

11.5.2 Plagioclase

Mössbauer studies of plagioclase began with Apollo samples from the Moon, and there are few data for terrestrial plagioclases. Appleman et al. (1971) interpreted the Mössbauer spectrum of a plagioclase separate from 12038 basalt in terms of two overlapping doublets ascribed to Fe^{2+} ions in T and M sites. The most detailed work is by Hafner and his co-workers.

Hafner et al. (1971) measured spectra for plagioclase separates from 10044 and 12021 basalts at both 77 and 295° K, and Schürmann and Hafner (1972: see also Schuermann et al., 1971; Virgo. 1971; Finger et al., 1972) reported data for plagioclases from 14053 and 14310 basalts; 15415 anorthosite; Stillwater and Lake Superior anorthosites; and the Kii lava flow in Hawaii. Figure 11-22 compares spectra obtained for the plagioclase from lunar basalt 10044 and that from the Stillwater anorthosite. The spectrum of the lunar plagioclase was fitted with two doublets, both ascribed to Fe^{2+}, with doublet C for Fe^{2+} in a 7-coordinated Ca^{2+} site, and doublet T for Fe^{2+} in a site of lower coordination. Table 11-5 lists some of the chemical and spectral parameters. The spectra for the terrestrial plagioclases apparently consist of only two peaks, but careful study shows that the peaks have different intensity. Most of the spectrum is interpreted to result from Fe^{2+} substituting in M sites. The asymmetry in peak intensity was ascribed to a small amount of Fe^{3+}, whose 2-peak spectrum with a small quadrupole splitting would not be resolvable from the dominant pair of peaks. For the plagioclase from the Stillwater intrusion (Fig. 11-22b), the proportion of Fe^{3+} was interpreted as about one-quarter, while for those from the Lake Superior anorthosite and Hawaiian lava, the proportion was about one-half. The higher proportion of Fe^{3+} in the terrestrial plagioclases, especially for the

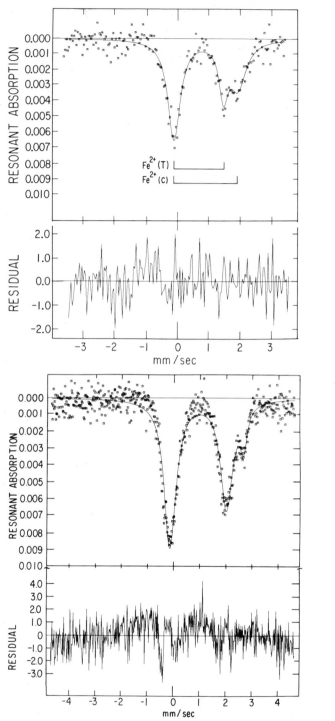

Fig. 11-22a

Fig. 11-22b

Fig. 11-22. Mössbauer spectra of ^{57}Fe in plagioclases. For each spectrum, the resonant absorption is given with respect to the Doppler shift in mm/sec. The curve is the least-squares computer fit, and the residual is shown below. a, b Plagioclase from lunar basalt 10044 at 295 and 77 °K, respectively. (From Hafner et al., 1971, Figs. 1 and 2). c, d Plagioclase from the Stillwater Complex at 295 and 77 °K, respectively. (From Schürmann and Hafner, 1972, Fig. 1)

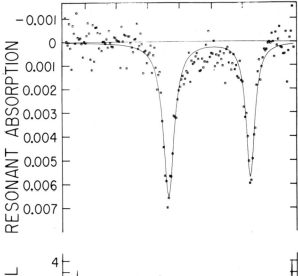
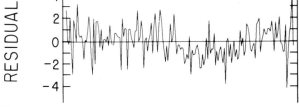

Fig. 11-22c. Legend see opposite page

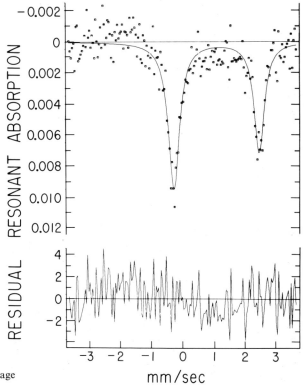

Fig. 11-22d. Legend see opposite page

Table 11-5. Mössbauer spectra of plagioclase

Specimen	Fe-content wt.-%	An-content mol.-%	Heat treatment °C	Temperature °K	Isomer shift mm/sec C	Isomer shift mm/sec T	Quadrupole splitting mm/sec C	Quadrupole splitting mm/sec T	Center of gravity mm/sec	Estimated Fe³/Fe total
10044 basalt	0.31	88–92	Natural	77	1.40	1.10	2.74	2.12	—	—
				295	1.13	0.90	2.01	1.54	1.04(7)	0.10(7)
12021 basalt	0.41	88–90	Natural	295	1.13	0.87	2.03	1.49	1.02(3)	0.12(3)
14053 basalt	~0.5	77–90	Natural	295	—		2.06	1.55	1.05(3)	0.09(3)
			1123	295			2.04	1.58	1.05(3)	0.09(3)
14310 basalt	~0.4	92–93	Natural	295			2.04	1.48	1.03(3)	0.11(3)
15415 an-orthosite	0.08	97–99	Natural	295					1.10(4)	0.04(4)
Stillwater anorthosite	0.41	74	Natural	295	1.14		2.63		0.90(3)	0.25(3)
			Natural	77	1.26		2.78		0.90(2)	0.25(2)
			1000	295	1.13		2.12		0.97(3)	0.18(3)
			1123	295						
Lake Superior anorthosite	0.42	66	Natural	295	—		—		0.76(6)	0.40(6)
Kii lava flow, Hawaii	0.66	56	Natural	295	—		—		0.59(4)	0.57(4)
			Natural	295	—		—			

Data from Hafner et al. (1971), Finger et al. (1972), Schürmann and Hafner (1972) and Hafner (pers. comm.). All data referred to Fe metal.

Lake Superior and Hawaiian specimens. is consistent with the general state of oxidation of the host rocks.

Turning now to details, there is considerable uncertainty about the structural location of the Fe^{2+} atoms responsible for the T doublet. Whereas the C doublet could reasonably be ascribed to Fe^{2+} in an M site (or sites) because of the large isomer shift, the detailed properties of the T doublet did not seem to fit exactly with those expected for simple replacement of Al^{3+}. The large change with temperature of the isomer shift, and the relatively large isomer shift at $77°$ C, compared unfavorably with the shifts expected for strong covalent bonding of Fe^{2+} in a tetrahedral site. Hafner et al. (1971) suggested that doublet T results from Fe^{2+} ions located at non-regular tetrahedral sites "coupled with oxygen vacancies, lattice defects and additional impurities in the immediate environment". Because of the complexity of the crystal structure of calcic plagioclases (see Chapter 5) it is likely that each of the C and T doublets actually results from more than one site: if so, the above interpretation in terms of two doublets must be modified.

Schürmann and Hafner (1972) tentatively interpreted the center of gravity of the total resonance absorption area in terms of the proportion of Fe^{3+}. Measurements of the center of gravity are given in Table 11-5 together with estimates of the Fe^{3+} content.

The width of the resonances provides some measure of the amount of disorder. Two samples of the Stillwater plagioclase were heated in evacuated silica tubes at 1000 and $1123°$ C for 2 days. After such treatment, the resonances had broadened considerably yielding patterns very similar to those for the plagioclases from lunar basalts. Presumably the Fe^{2+} ions in the Stillwater plagioclase were at least partly ordered before heat-treatment, and became disordered upon heating. The lunar plagioclases presumably remained disordered after crystallization under volcanic conditions. Details of the widths and heights of the peaks are given in the original papers.

References

Andrews, E.R. (1958): Nuclear magnetic resonance, 267 pp. Cambridge: University Press.

Angino, E.E. (1968): Far infrared absorption spectra of plagioclase feldspars. Bull. Kansas Geol. Surv. **194**, 9–12.

Appleman, D.E., Nissen, H.-U., Stewart, D.B., Clark, J.R., Dowty, E., Huebner, J.S. (1971): Studies of lunar plagioclases, tridymite and cristobalite. Proc. Second Lunar Science Conf. **1**, 117–133. The M.I.T. Press.

Aquilano, D., Bruno, E., Gazzoni, G. (1968): Assorbimento nell'infrarosso tra 1400 e 300 cm^{-1} di feldspati calcici nell'intervallo di temperatura $30° - 240°$ C. R. C. Soc. Ital. Mineral. Petrol. **24**, 95–109.

Aronson, J.R., Bellotti, L.H., Eckroad, S.W., Emslie, A.G., McConnell, R.K., Thüna, P.C. von (1970): Infrared spectra and radiative thermal conductivity of minerals at high temperatures. JGR **75**, 3443–3456.

Bank, H. (1970): Durchsichtiger blassgelblichter Plagioklas aus den USA. Z. deutschen Gemmologischen Gesell. **19**, 134–136.

Brinkmann, D., Brun, E., Derighetti, B. (1967): Magnetische Kernresonanz im Anorthit. Helvetica Phys. Acta **40**, 381 (abstr.).

Brinkmann, D., Stähli, J. L. (1968a): Magnetische Kernresonanz von ^{27}Al im Anorthit, CaAl$_2$Si$_2$O$_8$. Helvetica Phys. Acta **41**, 274–281.

Brinkmann, D., Staehli, J. L. (1968b). Nuclear magnetic resonance of ^{27}Al in anorthite [CaAl$_2$Si$_2$O$_8$]. Progr. Geol. Soc. Amer., Mtg., Mexico City p. 37.

Brown, F. F., Pritchard, A. M. (1969): The Mössbauer spectrum of iron orthoclase. EPSL **5**, 259 – 260.

Brun, E., Hartmann, P., Staub, H. H., Hafner, S., Laves, F. (1960): Magnetische Kernresonanz zur Beobachtung des Al, Si-Ordnungs/Unordnungsgrades in einigen Feldspäten. ZK **113**, 65–76.

Cole, W. F., Sörum, H., Taylor, W. H. (1951): The structure of the plagioclase felspars I. AC **4**, 20 – 29.

Conn, G. K. T. (1960): Infrared methods: principles and applications. New York: Academic Press.

Estep, P. A., Kovach, J. J., Karr, C. (1971): Infrared vibrational spectroscopic studies of minerals from Apollo 11 and Apollo 12 lunar samples. Proc. Second Lunar Science Conf. **3**, 2137–2151. The M. I. T. Press.

Finger, L. W., Hafner, S. S., Schürmann, K., Virgo, D., Warburton, D. (1972): Distinct cooling histories and reheating of Apollo 14 rocks. Third Lunar Sci. Conf., Houston, Lunar Science Inst. Contr. No. 88, 259–261.

Gaite, J.-M., Michoulier, J. (1970): Application de la résonance paramagnétique électronique de l'ion Fe^{3+} a l'étude de la structure des feldspaths. BSFMC **93**, 341–356.

Goldanskii, V. I. (1964): The Mössbauer effect and its applications to chemistry. New York: Consultants Bureau.

Goldsmith, J. R., Laves, F. (1954a): The microcline-sanidine stability relations. GCA **5**, 1–19.

Goldsmith, J. R., Laves, F. (1954b): Potassium feldspars structurally intermediate between microcline and sanidine. GCA **6**, 100–118.

Greenwood, N. N., Gibb, T. C. (1971): Mössbauer spectroscopy. New York: Harper and Row.

Hafner, S., Hartmann, P. (1964): Elektrische Feldgradienten und Sauerstoff-Polarisierbarkeit in Alkali-Feldspäten (NaAlSi$_3$O$_8$ und KAlSi$_3$O$_8$). Helvetica Phys. Acta **37**, 348–360.

Hafner, S., Hartmann, P., Laves, F. (1962): Magnetische Kernresonanz von Al^{27} in Adular. Zur Deutung der Adularstruktur. SMPM **42**, 277–294.

Hafner, S., Laves, F. (1957): Ordnung/Unordnung und Ultrarotabsorption. II. Variation der Lage und Intensität einiger Absorptionen von Feldspäten. Zur Struktur von Orthoklas und Adular. ZK **109**, 204–225

Hafner, S., Laves, F. (1963): Magnetische Kernresonanz von Al^{27} in einigen Orthoklasen. SMPM **43**, 65–69.

Hafner, S. S., Niebuhr, H. H., Zeira, S. (1973): Ferric iron in plagioclase crystals from anorthosite 15415. Lunar Science IV, 326–328. Lunar Science Institute.

Hafner, S. S., Virgo, D., Warburton, D. (1971): Oxidation state of iron in plagioclase from lunar basalts. EPSL **12**, 159 – 166.

Haskin, L. A., Morris, R. V. (1973): EPR study of Eu^{2+}- and Gd^{3+}-doped synthetic silicates and aluminate minerals. Trans. Am. Geophys. Union **54**, 504 (Abs.).

Höchli, U. (1963): Electron spin resonance of Fe^{3+} in feldspar. Proc. XIIth. Colloque Ampére 191–197.

Houghton, J. T., Smith, S. D. (1966): Infra-red physics. Oxford: Clarendon Press.

Iiishi, K., Tomisaka, T., Kato, T., Umegaki, Y. (1971a): The force field of K-feldspar. ZK **134**, 213–229.

Iiishi, K., Tomisaka, T., Kato, T., Yamuguchi, Umegaki, Y. (1971b): Isomorphous substitution and infrared and far infrared spectra of the feldspar group. NJMA **115**, 98–119.

Ingram, D. J. E. (1968): Electron spin resonance. Handbuch der Physik, **18** (**1**), 94–144. Berlin-Heidelberg-New York: Springer.

Joffe, W. A., Janchevskaya, I. S. (1966): The study of structure defects of feldspars by paramagnetic resonance and thermoluminescence methods. Seventh Inter. Congr. Cryst., abstr. 11.29.

Kolopus, J. L., Kline, D., Chatelain, A., Weeks, R. A. (1971): Magnetic resonance properties of lunar samples: mostly Apollo 12. Proc. Second Lunar Sci. Conf. **3**, 2501–2514. The M. I. T. Press.

Laves, F. (1952): Phase relations of the alkali feldspars. I. Introductory remarks. II. The stable and pseudo-stable phase relations in the alkali feldspar system. JG **60**, 436–450 and 549–574.

Laves, F., Hafner, S. (1956): Ordnung/Unordnung und Ultrarotabsorption I. (Al, Si)-Verteilung in Feldspäten. ZK **108**, 52–63.

Laves, F., Hafner, S. (1962): Infrared absorption effects, nuclear magnetic resonance and structure of feldspars. NGT **42**, No. 2, 57–71.

Lecomte, J. (1958): Spectroscopic dans l'infrarouge. Handbuch der Physik, **26** Light and Matter II, 244–965. Berlin-Göttingen-Heidelberg: Springer.

Liese, H.C. (1970): Supplementary data on the correlation of infra-red absorption spectra and the chemical composition of alkali feldspars. Appl. Spectr. **24**, 609–611.

Lyon, R.J.P. (1967): Infrared absorption spectroscopy. In: Zussman, J. (Ed.): Physical methods in determinative mineralogy, Chapter 8. London: Academic Press.

Marfunin, A.S., Bershov, L.V. (1970): Paramagnetic center(s) in feldspar and their possible crystallo-chemical and petrologic significance. DAN, USSR. Earth Sci. Sect. **193**, 129–131. Transl. from DAN. SSSR **193**, 412–414.

Marfunin, A.S., Bershov, L.V., Meilman, M.L., Michoulier, J. (1967): Paramagnetic resonance of Fe^{3+} in some feldspars. SMPM **47**, 13–20.

Marfunin, A.S., Michoulier, J. (1966): Résonance paramagnétique électronique de l'ion Fe^{3+} dans un monocristal d'oligoclase. Compte Rend. Acad. Sci. Paris **262**, 1543–1546.

Martin, R.F. (1968): Hydrothermal synthesis of low albite, orthoclase, and non-stoichiometric albite: Ph. D. thesis, Stanford University.

Martin, R.F. (1970): Cell parameters and infra-red absorption of synthetic high to low albites. CMP **26**, 62–74.

McMillan, J.A. (1968): Electron paramagnetism. New York: Reinhold Book Corp.

Orton, J.W. (1968): Electron paramagnetic resonance: an introduction to transition group ions in crystals. London: Iliffe.

Schürmann, K., Hafner, S.S. (1972): On the amount of ferric iron in plagioclases from lunar igneous rocks. Proc. Third Lunar Conf. **1**, 615–621. The M.I.T. Press.

Schuermann, K., Warburton, D., Hafner, S.S. (1971): Oxidation state and location of iron in plagioclases from lunar basalts. Progr. Geol. Soc. Am. Mtg. Washington, D. C., p. 697.

Staehli, J.L., Brinkmann, D. (1974a): A nuclear magnetic resonance study of the phase transition in anorthite. ZK preprint.

Staehli, J.L., Brinkmann, D. (1974b): Assignment and structural dependence of electric field gradients in anorthite and simple field gradient calculations in some aluminosilicates. ZK preprint.

Tarte, P. (1965): Etude expérimentale et interprétation du spectre infra-rouge des silicates et des germanates. Application à des problèmes structuraux relatifs a l'état solide. Mem. Acad. Roy. Belgique, Coll. in-8, Cl. Sci. **35**, 260

Thompson, C.S., Wadsworth, M.E. (1957): Determination of the composition of plagioclase feldspars by means of infrared spectroscopy. AM **42**, 334–341.

Umegaki, Y., Iiishi, K. (1966): Infrared absorption in microcline. Journ. Sci., Hiroshima Univ. **5**, ser. C, 157–178.

Virgo, D. (1971): Recent ^{57}Fe Mössbauer spectroscopic studies of some common rock-forming silicates. ARDGL, Year Book 70, 215–221.

Wainwright, J.E., Starkey, J. (1968): Crystal structure of a metamorphic low albite. Progr. Geol. Soc. America Mtg., Mexico City, p. 310.

Weeks, R.A. (1972): Paramagnetic resonance spectra of Ti^{3+}, Fe^{3+} and Mn^{2+} in lunar plagioclases. Amer. Geophys. Union Mtg., abstr. V 112 in Transactions, p. 551. Publ. JGR **78**, 2393–2402.

Weeks, R.A. (1973): Paramagnetic states in Apollo 16 plagioclases: Fe^{3+}, Ti^{3+}, radiation effects. Lunar Science IV, 775–777. Lunar Science Institute.

Wertheim, G.K. (1964): Mössbauer effect: principles and applications. New York: Academic Press.

Wertz, J.E. (1968): Structural information from paramagnetic resonance. Handbuch der Physik, **18 (1)**, 145–264. Berlin-Heidelberg-New York: Springer.

Chapter 12   Miscellaneous Physical Properties

12.1 Color

The color of a feldspar can arise either from an intrinsic property of the crystal structure or from light scattering from discrete impurities: in addition some feldspars show iridescence caused by diffraction effects at internal boundaries (see Chapter 8). Probably only two types of feldspar (iron-sanidine and amazonite) show an intrinsic color which is obvious to the naked eye.

The yellow color of iron-sanidine results from absorptions caused by electronic transitions associated with Fe^{3+} atoms substituting for Al. Faust (1936) showed absorption spectra of iron-orthoclase. Brown and Pritchard (1969) and Faye (1969) independently attributed sharp bands at 26 500, 24 000 and 22 650 cm^{-1} to the $^6A_1 \rightarrow ^4A_1 \, ^4E(G)$, $^6A_1 \rightarrow ^4T_2(G)$ and $^6A_1 \rightarrow 4T_1(G)$ transitions of ferric iron substituting for tetrahedral Al. Faye reported absence of pleochroism in a random section 0.37 cm thick cut from a specimen from Itrongay, Madagascar. The sharp bands were superimposed on an intense broad absorption centered in the ultraviolet which was ascribed to charge transfer between O^{2-} and Fe^{3+}. A sharp weak peak at 20 700 cm^{-1} was unassigned, but was thought to derive possibly from another transition metal, perhaps manganese. Manning (1970) stated that the 26 500 band could not arise from the above assignment and suggested transitions to a field-independent state, probably $^4A_1 \rightarrow ^4E(D)$. In addition, he suggested that either or both of the 22 650 and 24 000 bands represent transitions to the $^4A_1 \, ^4E(G)$ levels.

The characteristic green color of amazonite, the most frequent type of microcline perthite displayed in mineral collections, is believed to be intrinsic, but a definitive interpretation has not yet been made. A review of the early observations on amazonite is given by Rudenko and Vokhmenstev (1969). Although many amazonites are microcline perthites, Čech et al. (1971) found a green, lead-bearing orthoclase (2 V −61°) from a pegmatite at New Broken Hill mine, Australia, and proposed to extend the name to all green K-feldspars from microcline to "orthoclase". Rudenko and Vokhmentsev (1969) found a bluish-green oligoclase (An$_{25}$, optical estimate) from an unknown locality and a greenish-blue oligoclase (An$_{29}$) from the Slyudanka deposit, Mama-Chuya. Both came from granite pegmatites, and were denoted plagioclase-amazonite.

Consider first the green K-feldspars. Although there has been no definitive survey, it appears that such amazonites are rather rare and occur either in pegmatites or in metasomatized rocks.

Oftedal (1957) examined in detail the loss of color upon heating, finding that the rate varied with temperature according to the Arrhenius law. The activation energy of 120 kJoule/mole is in the range of those measured for non-volume diffusion of M cations (Chapter 16). Oftedal deduced from the rapidity of the decolorization process that the color centers were introduced at a temperature below 300° C, and correlated this with field observations that the green color is connected with the formation of cleavelandite veins in the already existing microcline pegmatite. Avdonin (1961) and Dworschak (1962) confirmed that the color of amazonite is lost upon heating, and that it is regained upon subsequent irradiation with X-rays. Sanford and Hedvall (1962) found that the loss of color upon heating to 1200° C was independent of whether the gaseous atmosphere was air, N_2 or H_2. Rudenko and Vokhmentsev (1969) gave spectral reflection curves for two natural amazonites and for one bleached specimen.

Several workers noted that amazonitization occurs during metasomatism (Oftedal, 1957; Taylor et al., 1960; Kuts, 1964; Zhirov and Stishov, 1965), but there is serious disagreement about the specific physical and chemical factors responsible for the green color. Because of the intrinsic coloring properties of Cr, V and Cu ions, Bassett (1956), Sanford and Hedvall (1962) and Taylor et al. (1960), made analyses for these elements. None was found, as might be expected because there are no sites for octahedral coordination. Oftedahl (1957) noted that the principal elements introduced with contemporaneous formation of cleavelandite veins are F, Li, Be and Sn; since F is particularly abundant, he suggested that some O atoms are replaced by F atoms creating an unstable charge distribution. Kapustin (1939) found that the intensity of color was proportional to the Rb-content. Kuts (1964) suggested that both Rb and Pb are responsible for the color, while Zhirov and Stishov (1965) claimed that amazonitization is caused by metasomatism of Pb, Rb and Tl. They noted that an elevated amount of Pb is typical of amazonites and that Pb is $2-3$ times higher in colored than in uncolored parts. The ratio Rb/Tl is the same in colored and uncolored parts whereas the Rb/Pb and Tl/Pb ratios may be similar or smaller in colored parts. The pegmatitic amazonites contained $120-1000$ ppm Pb, $0.15-0.38\%$ Rb and 7–53 ppm Tl (3 samples contained 0.2% Pb). The hydrothermal amazonites contain 50–240 ppm Pb and the same amounts of Rb and Tl as above. Taylor et al. (1960) analyzed for the trace elements Li, Rb, Cs, Tl, Pb, Ca, Sr, Fe, Cr, Mn, Cu, Co, Ni, V, Sn and Fe, and claimed that none was responsible for the color. They suggested that physical defects and strain may cause the color change. Plyusnin (1969) found no correlation between the green color and concentrations of Rb, Cu and Mn. He ruled out Fe^{2+} because the magnetic susceptibility did not change upon heating. Plyusnin concluded that the color resulted from substitution of Pb^{2+} in three stages: (a) $K^+Si^{4+} \rightarrow Pb^{2+}Al^{3+}$, (b) $2K^+ \rightarrow Pb^{2+}$, and (c) $2K^+O^{2-} \rightarrow Pb^{2+}2(OH)^-$. Defect color centers develop in the second stage and are modified in the third stage resulting in a displacement of the absorption band to a shorter wavelength. This model was supported by correlation between measurement of water content and wavelength of the absorption band. Marfunin and Bershov (1970) concluded from epr studies (see Section 11.4.3) that the green color resulted from capture of an electron by Pb^{2+} ions in M sites.

Rudenko and Vokhmentsev (1969) gave optical reflection spectra, both before and after thermal bleaching, for their plagioclase-amazonites. Unlike bleached microcline, the bleached plagioclase-amazonites did not regain their green color upon irradiation with X-rays: in addition bleached plagioclase-amazonite showed strong yellow luminescence when irradiated with ultra-violet rays, whereas bleached microcline showed no luminescence.

The conflicting opinions on the source of the green color require that further measurements be made, but in the interim lead seems to be the best candidate. Chemical analyses must be made of amazonite from a wide variety of geological localities, because previous workers may have been misled by a secondary (rather than a primary) correlation applicable only to one locality.

The color effects caused by discrete impurities are fairly easy to explain. Thus the milky color of many feldspars is the result of alteration to various hydroxyl or hydrous minerals, especially along cracks. The black color of some basic plagioclase is caused principally by a host of minute oxide minerals containing Fe and Ti (Section 20.5).

Oliver and Schultz (1968) made microprobe analyses for Fe in naturally leached and unleached charnockite feldspar from Madras. The white selvage contains less iron than the dark green charnockite, and iron favors the exsolved Na-feldspar and especially the veins of a chloritic (?) material.

wt.-%	Exsolved Na-feldspar	Host K-feldspar	Vein
Dark charnockite	0.121 ± 0.07	0.016 ± 0.011	1.18 ± 0.39
White selvage	0.015 ± 0.015	0.007 ± 0.007	0.29 ± 0.11

Bank (1970) observed a pale yellow bytownite from a pegmatite at Plush, Oregon.

Added in Proof: Černý and Macek (1972) found that Rb-rich K-feldspars from the Tanco pegmatite have dark cores surrounded and penetrated by a white zone which is rimmed by pink feldspar. Increasing equilibration and recrystallization in the stability field of microcline was invoked, in accordance with higher K_2O and Rb_2O, coarser perthite, higher triclinic index, and less distinct twinning in the rim.

Bell and Mao (1973) assigned optical absorption bands in 7 terrestrial anorthites to transitions involving Fe^{2+} and Fe^{3+}. Narrow bands near $0.4\,\mu m$ (also at $0.6\,\mu m$) in oxidized anorthite were ascribed to charge-transfer in Fe^{3+}, and a broad polarized band at $1.2-1.4\,\mu m$ was ascribed to a crystal-field transition in Fe^{2+}. Bell and Mao (1973) suggested that absorption data for lunar anorthite are consistent with both Fe^{2+} and Fe^{3+}.

12.2 Luminescence

A detailed description of luminescence is given in "Luminescence cristalline" by Curie (1960) or the English translation by Garlick (1963). Luminescence is the emission of light not generated simply by atomic vibrations. The initial input of energy may arise from many sources: for feldspars, the most important sources are kinetic energy of electrons and protons giving rise to *cathodoluminescence* and *proton-excited luminescence*, respectively. Stored energy may be released by heating giving rise to *thermoluminescence*.

Of the earlier workers, Haberlandt and Köhler (1940) observed blue fluorescence of feldspars in ultraviolet light and attributed natural thermoluminescence to traces of Eu, Ce and U by analogy with doped synthetic feldspars. Przibram (1956) claimed that green fluorescence is caused partly by Mn but mostly by absorbed water, while blue fluorescence results from Eu. Rothschild (1928) reported phosphorescence in feldspar.

12.2.1 Electron- and Proton-excited Luminescence

Cathodoluminescence provides a simple qualitative tool for characterizing feldspars. Bombardment with electrons of a thin section of a feldspar, either in an electron microprobe or in a special microscope, allows qualitative detection of chemical and textural features. Smith and Stenstrom (1965) showed that different types of feldspar can be distinguished readily in sedimentary rocks such as graywackes on the basis of hue and textural distribution of color. In perthites they observed several textures not obvious by other techniques: (a) albite veins in macroperthites showed intensity zoning of the blue luminescence probably resulting from different stages of growth (b) some microperthites showed broad bands about 0.1 mm across of alternate reddish and bluish luminescence, each band being crossed by microperthite in the Murchison direction displayed by an intensity difference between the Na-rich and K-rich components (c) in a perthite from Tugtutôq, whose X-ray pattern showed that pure albite coexisted with both a monoclinic and a triclinic K-feldspar, luminescence revealed that the K-feldspar veins consisted of irregular beads about $1-2\,\mu m$ across with a bluish luminescence set in a matrix with reddish luminescence. Electron microprobe analysis showed that the beads had compositions near $90-96\%$ Or whereas the matrix was $97-100\%$ Or. The obvious interpretation was that microcline nucleated at the edges of the veins, and that some untransformed monoclinic K-feldspar remained as beads.

Many textural features are readily seen in cathodoluminescence. Twinning is visible without polarizers because the luminescence is emitted anisotropically. Plagioclase phenocrysts from volcanic rocks typically show a thin rim with brighter luminescence that is essentially invisible by ordinary optical methods: the rim is usually about 1 µm wide and consists of a less calcic feldspar. Some inclusions (e.g. apatite with bright yellow luminescence) are readily detectable by luminescence. In aventurine, the tiny flakes of hematite are surrounded by a zone of weaker luminescence indicating chemical reaction.

The Apollo program stimulated detailed studies of luminescence excited by both protons and electrons, and considerable progress was made in deciphering the chemical and physical causes of luminescence in feldspars.

Sippel and Spencer (1970) made detailed spectroscopic measurements of cathodoluminescence from many feldspars including lunar ones using a quartz prism monochromator and a photometer. Uncorrected spectra of four feldspars are shown in Fig. 12-1. Sixteen terrestrial plagioclases with more than 11% An

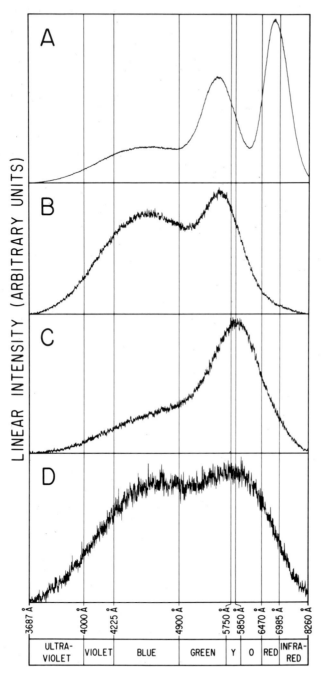

Fig. 12-1. Cathodoluminescence spectra of feldspars and maskelynite using arbitrary intensity scale. See original article for correction function to the intensity. A Terrestrial plagioclase, An_{85}. B Apollo 11 plagioclase, C Shocked plagioclase from Apollo 11 breccia. D Maskelynite from Apollo 11 breccia. (From Sippel and Spencer, 1970, Fig. 3)

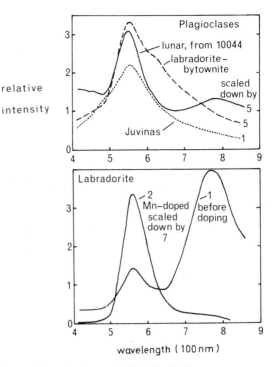

Fig. 12-2. Proton-excited luminescence of feldspars. (From Geake *et al.*, 1971, Figs. 2, 3)

showed three peaks (diagram A), one each in the blue, green and near infra-red regions. Most alkali feldspars showed a broad blue band, a small infra-red peak but no green peak. Three alkali feldspars showed no infra-red peak. Plagioclase from Apollo 11 rocks showed only blue and green peaks (diagram B). As the intensity of shock damage of the lunar plagioclase increased, the cathodo-luminescence became more reddish as the green peak became displaced and broadened (diagram C). Finally the cathodoluminescence of a maskelynite grain is shown in diagram D. Sippel and Spencer presented evidence for blue enhancement for glass produced by shocking plagioclase in both lunar and terrestrial environments. Sippel (1971) added data for Apollo 12 samples.

Geake *et al.* (1971) studied luminescence emission spectra excited by 60 keV protons (Fig. 12-2), and later (1972) used electrons. Diagram a compares spectra of plagioclases from lunar basalt 10044, the Juvinas meteorite, and an unidenti-fied terrestrial labradorite–bytownite.

Because of the absence of the green peak in albites, Sippel and Spencer suggested that it resulted from a divalent activator substituting for Ca^{2+}. Geake *et al.* suggested that Mn is the activator on the basis of spectra for labradorite doped by heating at 1050° C for 30 min. in argon with $MnSO_4$. The addition of about 0.1% Mn resulted in a 16-fold increase in the height of the green peak (Fig. 12-2b). X-ray fluorescence analysis showed that most plagio-clases contain more than 100 ppm Mn, but there was not a simple correlation between intensity of the green peak and Mn content. A detailed crystal-chemical analysis by Geake *et al.* concluded that the green peak had a wavelength consistent with Mn^{2+} substituting for Ca^{2+}.

Sippel and Spencer found that the blue peak varied in shape and position but did not correlate with the chemical composition. Geake *et al.* attributed the peak to lattice defects rather than an impurity activator. This is consistent with enhancement of the blue peak in shocked plagioclase and maskelynite.

The cause of the infra-red peak has not been identified with certainty, though Geake *et al.* (1972) favor Fe^{3+} in Ca^{2+} sites. Whereas Sippel and Spencer observed a strong infra-red peak in all terrestrial plagioclases, Geake *et al.* (1971) observed some specimens with only a weak peak. Geake *et al.* found that lunar samples showed only a weak infra-red peak while plagioclases from chondritic and achondritic meteorites showed no infra-red peak. The wavelength of the infra-red peak ranged from $730-770$ nm. Geake *et al.* (1972) doped terrestrial plagioclase with iron by heating in air to $1200°$ C with ferrous sulfate. All three peaks decreased in intensity, but the infra-red peak decreased the least. No success was obtained by iron doping of synthetic plagioclase. The decay time of the green peak of iron-doped plagioclase was measured as 5 ms whereas that for the infra-red peak was $1-2$ ms. These confusing results were interpreted by Geake *et al.* as circumstantial evidence that the infra-red peak in plagioclase results from Fe^{3+}, and that complexities result from quenching by Fe^{2+} atoms. The weakness or absence of the infra-red peak in lunar and meteoric plagioclase would be consistent with the highly reduced state of the rocks and consequent rarity of Fe^{3+} atoms.

Other observations of proton-induced luminescence in Apollo 11 rocks were made by Blair and Edgington (1970), Dalrymple and Doell (1970), and Nash and Greer (1970).

Added in Proof: Mariano *et al.* (1973) reported briefly on the cathodo-luminescence of synthetic plagioclases doped with various elements. They found the following peaks: Ti^{4+} 460 ± 10 nm; Fe^{2+} 550 ± 5 nm; Fe^{3+} 700 ± 10 nm; Cu^{2+} 420 ± 5 nm; Mn^{2+} 570 ± 5 nm. The rare earths Eu^{2+}, Sm^{3+} and Dy^{3+} gave luminescence typical of REE activators. The blue luminescence of natural feldspars was ascribed to Ti^{4+} because the Eu concentration is too low. The red luminescence comes from Fe^{3+}. The 550 nm band of both lunar and terrestrial plagioclases may come from Mn^{2+} (at 0.0n wt.-% level) or Fe^{2+} (0.n $-$ 1.0 wt.-%), or both.

12.2.2 Thermoluminescence

Absorbed energy is mostly emitted as luminescence with a decay time at room temperature of a few milliseconds. However some energy levels may become occupied which are forbidden to become depopulated by direct transition to a level of lower energy. Such levels can only be depopulated by supply of additional energy permitting transition to a level of higher energy which can radiate energy. If the additional energy is supplied by heating, the intensity of luminescence is governed by the Arrhenius law $A\exp(-E/kT)$, where E is the additional energy and A is the transition efficiency factor. Upon heating at a constant rate, trapping levels of lower energy are emptied first, and typically the temperature-intensity plot consists of several broad peaks. Each trapping level will yield light of a specific wavelength.

Unfortunately thermoluminescence depends on many complex factors (see McDougall, 1968). The thermoluminescence of a feldspar, from a mineral collection or a rock, provides a measure of those trapping levels whose activation energy is too high for significant loss of energy from thermal agitation at ambient conditions. The amount of thermoluminescence depends on the radiation history of the feldspar: of course, unfilled trapping levels may be filled deliberately by irradiation.

Bächtiger (1967) reviewed earlier data on thermoluminescence of feldspars, and examined twenty albites and oligoclases plus one labradorite, both before and after irradiation with X-rays. The data are complex but some trends were apparent. The peaks of the glow curves tended to occur at one or more of three temperatures (~ 290, ~ 350, and $\sim 420°$ C) suggesting three principal types of trapping centers. Glow curves for the natural specimens showed peaks at higher temperatures than those for the irradiated specimens consistent with emptying of trapping levels with low excitation energy during natural cooling. Bächtiger noted tendencies for the glow peaks to correlate with An-content and geographic source of the plagioclases, but the meaning of these tendencies is not known. In addition, he noted that turbid plagioclases showed enhanced thermo-luminescence suggesting a correlation with H_2O or OH.

Panov et al. (1971) examined the thermoluminescence of quartz, plagioclase and K-feldspar from granitoids of northeastern Transbaykalia. They concluded that the intensity of luminescence increased with geological age and could be used to correlate rocks. Plagioclase showed two glow peaks whose relative magnitude changed with age. The peaks for K-feldspar also showed intensity changes which correlated with age. For both feldspars the major luminescence came between 44 and 180° C.

The most detailed study on thermoluminescence of lunar samples is by Garlick et al. (1971) who examined specimens after X-irradiation. Curves of similar shape were obtained for lunar and terrestrial samples indicating related distributions of trapping levels: terrestrial labradorite gave the strongest intensity. Doping with Mn did not change the shape of the thermoluminescence curve but did increase the intensity five-fold. Garlick et al. suggested that the traps result from natural defects in the silicate chains, but gave no definite proof. Measurements of the "drainage" of electrons from relatively deep trapping states indicated the presence of a nonthermal emptying process at low temperature which was especially rapid for terrestrial plagioclases.

Hwang (1970) found that thermoluminescence ages of sanidine phenocrysts from Vesuvian lavas and Pompeiian ash agreed reasonably with the historical ages.

12.3 Electrical Phenomena

G. V. Keller summarized data available up to 1961 in Section 26 of Handbook of Physical Constants, edited by Clark (1966). Electrical properties of rocks and some constituent minerals are reviewed by Parkhomenko (1967). The two chief parameters are the *dielectric constant* which results from electrical polarization caused by an applied electric field, and the *electrical conductivity* which depends on the conduction current. In addition the *dielectric loss* may be measured.

12.3.1 Electrical Conductivity

The most detailed data are by Maury (1968) — see also Maury (1965 a, b; 1967) and Maury and Iiyama (1967). Feldspar powdered to $20 - 40\,\mu m$ was cold-pressed at 6 kbars into a pastille and the electrical conductivity measured at 10 bars for a frequency of 10 kHz. Various tests indicated that the accuracy of the conductivity data is better than 30%.

Table 12-1 summarizes the data obtained from $400 - 900°$ C. Data for feldspars of intermediate compositions are omitted because of uncertainty with regard to presence of intergrowths. For any chosen temperature, the data fall within one order of magnitude such that the highest values occur for albite. All the data for each feldspar agree with an Arrhenius plot, and the values of σ_0 and E are given in Table 12-1. The activation energy ranges from 70 to 80 kJoule/mole.

In the second part of his paper, Maury attempted to identify the structural element responsible for the conductivity. Electron transport and various other processes were ruled out because the electrical conductivity diminished rapidly for a continuous current. Maury favored ionic conductivity, and made the following experiment. When a multi-layered sandwich of pastilles of NaCl, sodic glass, K-feldspar, potassic glass and KCl was placed between nickel electrodes at $500°$ C, a current of $100\,\mu A$ passed in response to a voltage of 110 volts. The K-feldspar changed composition to $Or_{54}Ab_{46}$ while an albite changed to $Or_{17}Ab_{83}$ (the duration of the treatment was not specified).

Theoretically for self-diffusion of alkali ions the resulting electrical conductivity σ is related to the diffusion coefficient D by $D = \sigma k T/Nq^2$, where k is Boltzmann's constant, T is the absolute temperature, N is the number of ions in the cube and q is the ionic charge. This equation assumes that diffusion occurs by random walk of ions through the crystal volume. Maury claimed that his estimates of D fitted well with experimental data for Na diffusion in albite. However Petrovic (1972) showed that Maury's measurements of σ were several orders of magnitude greater for K-feldspar than values of σ calculated from direct measurements of *volume* diffusion of K ions (Chapter 16). The identity of the structural element responsible for electrical conductivity in feldspars is apparently uncertain, and further experiments are needed. Perhaps *non-volume* diffusion of M cations is responsible.

The electrical conductivities of $KFeSi_3O_8$ and $KGaSi_3O_8$ did not obey an Arrhenius relation over the entire temperature range but the structural reason was not identified. Alkali feldspars of intermediate composition also showed a deviation from the Arrhenius relation, perhaps because of unmixing.

Khitarov and Slutskiy (1965; also in French, 1967) measured the electrical conductivity of powdered albite held at pressures of $2800 - 28000\,kg/cm^2$. The albite was dried at $500°$ C and then heated at $120 - 200°$ C per hour until it melted, followed by cooling of the glass. Measurements were made at 10^4 Hz

Table 12-1. Electrical conductivity σ (ohm^{-1} cm^{-1}) of feldspars (Maury, 1968)

Specimen	400° C	500° C	600° C	700° C	800° C	900° C	σ_0	E(kJoule/mole)
Low albite, Grisons: Ab$_{100}$, Ψ 1.07°	8.3 E-9	3.7 E-8	1.5 E-7	5.2 E-7	1.3 E-6	3.0 E-6	1.4 E-2	83
Low albite, Newry: Or$_2$Ab$_{98}$, Ψ 1.15°	2.1 E-8	5.2 E-8	2.0 E-7	7.0 E-7	1.8 E-6	3.9 E-6	1.7 E-2	82
High albite, dry heating: Ab$_{100}$, Ψ 1.80°	5.3 E-8	2.7 E-7	8.0 E-7	2.3 E-6	5.4 E-6	1.0 E-5	1.2 E-2	68
High albite, 600° C, 1kb H$_2$O: Ψ 1.88°	5.0 E-8	1.9 E-7	6.1 E-7	1.8 E-6	3.9 E-6	8.3 E-6	1.1 E-2	70
High albite, 800° C, 1kb H$_2$O: Ψ 1.92°	4.7 E-8	2.5 E-7	7.5 E-7	2.1 E-6	5.2 E-6	9.5 E-6	1.3 E-2	70
Microcline, Arendal: Or$_{94}$Ab$_6$, Ψ 0.75°	7.7 E-9	4.0 E-8	1.6 E-7	5.3 E-7	1.3 E-6	3.1 E-6	1.3 E-2	82
Microcline, K-exchanged: Or$_{100}$, Ψ 0.75°	9.3 E-9	5.0 E-8	1.8 E-7	5.3 E-7	1.3 E-6	2.9 E-6	7.4 E-3	77
Adularia, Grisons: Or$_{84}$Ab$_{16}$	9.3 E-9	5.8 E-8	2.3 E-7	7.7 E-7	2.0 E-6	5.0 E-6	2.4 E-3	83
Adularia, St.-Gotthard: Or$_{95}$Ab$_5$	9.9 E-9	4.8 E-8	1.6 E-7	5.3 E-7	1.4 E-6	3.1 E-6	9.7 E-3	79
KAlSi$_3$O$_8$, 600° C,1 kb H$_2$O	9.3 E-9	3.9 E-8	1.7 E-7	5.3 E-7	1.4 E-6	3.1 E-6	1.4 E-2	82
KFeSi$_3$O$_8$, 600° C, 1 kb H$_2$O	2.6 E-8	3.5 E-8	4.7 E-8	1.4 E-7	4.1 E-7	n. d.	—	—
KGaSi$_3$O$_8$, 600° C, 1 kb H$_2$O	2.2 E-8	4.1 E-8	1.2 E-7	4.0 E-7	1.2 E-6	n. d.	—	—
CaAl$_2$Si$_2$O$_8$, hydrothermal synthesis	n. d.	2.8 E-8	6.4 E-8	1.8 E-7	5.3 E-7	1.2 E-6	6.3 E-3	84
Labradorite, natural: Ab$_{43}$An$_{57}$	5.0 E-9	2.9 E-8	9.5 E-8	2.8 E-7	6.7 E-7	1.6 E-6	3.4 E-3	75

Ψ is $2\theta(131) - 2\theta(1\bar{3}1)$ CuK$_\alpha$. E denotes exponential.

and showed a strictly linear variation between the logarithm of the electrical conductivity and $1/T$ up to the beginning of melting (unfortunately the papers do not give the units of measurement). Across the melting interval, the electrical conductivity changed about two orders of magnitude. Increase of pressure from $2800 - 28000 \, \text{kg/cm}^2$ caused an increase in conductivity of the albite of about an order of magnitude, almost independent of the temperature. The activation energy calculated from Arrhenius plots of data for the unmelted albite ranged from $0.7 - 1.0 \, \text{eV}$ (i.e. $67 - 96 \, \text{kJoule/mole}$), compared to $83 \, \text{kJoule/mole}$ obtained by Maury for low albite.

Parkhomenko (1967, p. 180) found that the conductivity of a microcline cleavage fragment decreased slightly as the pressure was raised to $24000 \, \text{kg/cm}^2$. The conductivity varied from about 10^{-10} at $230°$ C to 10^{-7} at $500°$ C, being slightly greater than the values of Maury for 400 and $500°$ C.

12.3.2 Dielectric Phenomena

G. V. Keller summarized available data up to 1961 in Section 26 of Handbook of Physical Constants, edited by Clark (1966). Detailed measurements were made by Ioffe and Yanchevskaia (1958) of the dielectric permeability (ε) and the loss angle (δ) in four plagioclases (7, 15, 24, and 68% An) and a microcline from $20 - 500 \, °\text{K}$ and 5×10^2 to $5 \times 10^6 \, \text{Hz}$. At very high frequencies, the polarization is caused entirely by the more mobile electrons, at intermediate frequencies the ions contribute, and at low frequencies surface effects may be important. The permeability decreases with frequency and increases with temperature. From the sparse data, it appears that in alkali feldspars the permeability is greater when the field is applied along the b-axis. Chemically, the substitution of Na for K causes little change, but substitution of An molecule causes a progressive increase: this trend can be explained by the stronger bonding of Ca ions to oxygen ions than of Na and K ions.

Ioffe and Yanchevskaia (1958) observed resonance absorption and anomalous permeability dispersion at $5 \times 10^5 \, \text{Hz}$ for all their feldspars, and suggested that it arises from passage of an electron from one oxygen to another in a negatively-charged AlO_4 tetrahedron.

The data on dielectric phenomena are too complex to give here, and the original papers should be consulted. All measurements of permeability fall between 4 and 15.

12.4 Thermal Conductivity

The thermal conductivity is expressed by a second-order tensor which relates the thermal conductivity ellipsoid to the crystallographic axes. Horai (1971) measured the bulk thermal conductivity of 6 K-feldspars, 10 plagioclases and 1 celsian using a needle-probe inserted into a wet powder. The results (Table 12-2) range from $25 - 16 \, \text{mJ/cm sec} \, °\text{C}$ with an erratic tendency for the thermal conductivity to decrease from Or to Ab to An to Cn.

S. P. Clark summarized available data in Section 21 of Handbook of Physical Constants, edited by Clark (1966). Schulz (1924), in a systematic

Table 12-2. Bulk thermal conductivity of feldspars (Horai, 1971)

Feldspar	Source	Conductivity milliJoule/cm sec °C
Microcline	Amelia, Va.	26.0
Microcline	Ontario	24.7
Microcline	Labrador	23.9
Orthoclase	Goodsprings	23.0
Sanidine	Tooele, Utah	16.3
Adularia	Switzerland	20.5
Albite, An_1	Amelia	23.0
Albite, An_4	unknown	23.4
Albite, An_6	Risor, Norway	19.3
Albite, An_8	Sylmar, Pa.	19.7
Oligoclase, An_{11}	Hawk, N.C.	19.7
Labradorite, An_{54}	Nain, Labrador	15.1
Bytownite, An_{73}	Crystal Bay, Minn.	14.7
Bytownite, An_{78}	Minnesota	16.7
Bytownite, An_{80}	Stillwater, Mont.	15.5
Anorthite, An_{96}	Miyakejima, Japan	16.7
Celsian	Broken Hill, Australia	14.2

compilation of the earlier literature on minerals, reported three sets of data on the thermal conductivity of feldspars dating from the nineteenth century. Apart from these, there appears to be only one other set of data on feldspars — that of Eucken and Kuhn (1928) in which they found that the experimental values varied with the particle size of the feldspar. For an "orthoclase" they reported a bulk conductivity coefficient of 42 mJ/cm sec °C, with a distinct anisotropy with ratios of coefficients 0.63:0.90:1.00.

From the data reported by Schulz for studies by Senarmont, Jannettaz and Fizeau for "white feldspar", adularia and "orthoclase" specimens, the major axis of the thermal conductivity ellipsoid is seen to be along b, the mean axis close to c, and the minor axis close to a. From the differing values it seems likely that the mean axis is about 5° from c in the acute angle. The orientation of the thermal conductivity ellipsoid is fairly similar to that of the thermal expansion ellipsoid.

Aronson et al. (1970) in a study of the infrared spectra and radiative thermal conductivity of minerals at high temperature obtained data for an oligoclase from Bakersville, N. C. They used a face cut at 3° to (001), but were unable to obtain accurate data because of cracks. The long-wavelength vibrational bands broadened at high temperature. Upon correction for scattering, the observed radiative conductivity, 0.25 watts/cm °K, changed to 0.42.

12.5 Mechanical Properties

The mechanical properties of minerals depend critically on whether the mineral is deformed elastically or inelastically, and whether the mineral body is homogeneous or inhomogeneous. Section 12.5.1 covers elastic deformation of feldspar mostly at room temperature. It also contains data on photoelasticity, grinding hardness and surface energy. Inelastic deformation results from a combination of mechanisms including fracture, cleavage, and slip with or without twinning and kinking. Experimental data have been obtained at elevated temperature using controlled uniaxial compression and isothermal conditions (Section 12.5.2). Application of shock, either in the laboratory or by meteoritic impact, results in a rapid increase of both temperature and pressure producing spectacular effects (Section 12.5.3).

12.5.1 Elastic Deformation, Photoelasticity, Grinding Hardness, Surface Energy, Cleavage

For elastic homogeneous deformation under isothermal conditions the stress and strain tensors are related by a fourth-order tensor as formalized in Nye (1960). For an isotropic body, *tensile stress* σ results in a *proportional elongation* ε according to Hooke's relation $\varepsilon = s\sigma$, where s is the *elastic compliance constant*. Alternatively, $\sigma = c\varepsilon$, where c is the *elastic stiffness constant* or *Young's modulus*. For anisotropic crystals, the relations in full tensor notation are $\varepsilon_{ij} = s_{ijkl}\,\sigma_{kl}$, or in single suffix notation with factor convention, $\varepsilon_i = s_{ik}\sigma_k$. The *volume compressibility* (K) is $1/s_{iikk}$, and may be expressed as the reciprocal β.

Early determinations of volume compressibility measured the displacement of a piston in a cylinder containing the mineral body suspended in a calibrated liquid (e.g. Adams and Williamson, 1923). Such experiments were isothermal, and results were expressed as $(V_0 - V)/V = aP - bP^2$, where V_0 is the initial volume and V is the volume at pressure P in megabars. Although the data (Table 12-3) are consistent with a general pattern that the compressibility decreases from alkali feldspars to anorthite, the range of data suggests uncertainties of around $5-10\%$ in the coefficient a and an unknown amount in b. Thus Yoder and Weir (1951) found a larger initial compressibility than did Adams and Williamson (1923) for the same specimen of oligoclase. For the specimens of K-feldspar, the extent of Si, Al order and the nature of the perthite probably contribute to the observed variations.

Bridgman (1928) measured the linear compressibility at 30 and 75° C along four directions of an adularia crystal. The temperature effect is trivial. The data indicate that the feldspar is most easily compressible along *a*, and least compressible near *c*, but the data are too sparse to give the tensor components. The volume compressibility coefficient *a* is greater than for the other K-feldspars in Table 12-3.

Added in Proof: Vaidya et al. (1973) measured the compressibility up to 45 kbar of labradorite in a piston-cylinder apparatus. Their data gave $V/V_0 = 10.57 - 1.253\,P + 0.681\,P^2$ where P is in kbars. Towle and Riecker (1968) measured the shear strength for polycrystalline labradorite up to 50 kbar and 900° C.

Alternatively the compressibility is measured from the velocity of sound waves, both of compressional and transverse type. Such velocity measurements are directly applicable to seismic studies, and also yield the stress-strain tensor. Because of the dynamic nature of the technique, the resulting elastic constants are of adiabatic nature and can be compared with elastic constants obtained

Table 12-3. Measurements of density (ϱ) and volume and linear compressibilities (β) from dilatometric experiments. (a) Volume compressibility

Sample	Ref.	ϱ	a (mb^{-1})	b (mb^{-2})	P range (kb)
Microcline perthite; Topsham, Maine; 8 – 10% Ab; perthite in {100}	[1]	2.557 (25° C)	1.923	12.1	2 – 12
Oligoclase; Söndeled, Norway; Ab$_{78}$An$_{22}$ optical estimate	[1]	2.638 (25° C)	1.745[a]	8.3	2 – 8
Labradorite; Nain, Labrador; Ab$_{48}$An$_{52}$ optical estimate; augite and ilmenite inclusions.	[1]	2.695 (25° C)	1.552[a]	10.9	2 – 12
do., same as in Ref. [1]	[2]	2.696 (29.5° C)	1.50	9.8	2 – 12
Labradorite, ?	[3]	—	1.39	3.1	0 – 40
Orthoclase; Madagascar clear	[3]	—	1.78	4.2	0 – 40
Orthoclase; Spain opaque, black inclusions	[3]	—	1.86	7.3	0 – 40
Albite; Varuträsk, Sweden	[4]	2.641 (25.6° C)	2.10[a]	21.6	2 – 10
Oligoclase, same as in Ref. [1]	[4]	—	1.84[a]	13.4	2 – 10

1. Adams and Williamson (1923).
2. Adams and Gibson (1929).
3. Bridgman (1948).
4. Yoder and Weir (1951).
Note: β expressed as $aP-bP^2$.
[a] Recalculated from author's data

Table 12-3 (continued). (b) Linear compressibility (Bridgman, 1928: 0 – 12 kbar)

Sample	Direction	30° C		75° C	
		a (mb^{-1})	b (mb^{-2})	a (mb^{-1})	b(mb^{-2})
Adularia; Fianarantsoa, Madagascar; light green	a	1.013	4.8	1.037	6.2
	b	0.559	4.9	0.549	3.9
	c	0.468	1.3	0.468	1.7
	a^*	1.097	6.9	1.099	6.9
	(volume)	2.123	14.5	2.116	13.9

Note: convert to S. I. units using $1bar = 10^5 N/m^2$.

from static isothermal experiments only after adjustment by a term involving thermal expansion and specific heat coefficients (see Section 7 of Clark, 1966).

Sound-velocity measurements are seriously affected by physical defects such as cleavage cracks and perthite boundaries. Christensen (1966) determined compressional wave velocities at hydrostatic pressures up to 10 kbars for plates of perthite and albite cut parallel to (100), (010), (001), (110), (101) and (011). Simmons (1964) determined velocities up to 10 kbars for three directions in a microcline crystal. Both authors found major increases of velocity (one-fifth to one-half) as the pressure increased to 1 kbar followed by a slower increase to 10 kbar. Probably cracks and cleavages closed up at 1 kbar permitting measurement of the intrinsic wave velocity at higher pressures. Probably the zero-pressure velocities can be estimated from these data using a linear extrapolation from the high-pressure range.

Complete determinations of the stress-strain tensor were reported for various feldspars by Alexandrov and Ryzhova (1962), Ryzhova (1964) and Ryzhova and Alexandrov (1965) using the pulse method at atmospheric pressure. Although a strict comparison is not possible because of chemical differences, the data of Ryzhova and Alexandrov for albite and several perthites agree within ten per cent with those of Christensen extrapolated linearly with pressure from the 1 to 10 kbar region to zero pressure. Furthermore the anisotropy is quantitatively similar between the extrapolated Christensen and the actual Ryzhova-Alexandrov data. Consequently the latter data should give a reasonable estimate of the intrinsic elastic parameters of feldspars.

Monoclinic crystals have 13 elastic constants while triclinic ones have 21. Since their plagioclases and microcline were finely twinned on the Albite and Pericline laws resulting in a pseudo-monoclinic aggregate, Ryzhova and Alexandrov treated them as monoclinic. Slabs were cut parallel to (001), (110), (101), (010), (100) and (011), and measurements made with ultrasonic pulses at 1.7 and 5 megacycles using both compressional and two directions of transverse waves. The 18 velocities (listed in the original papers) were calculated by an error-minimization procedure to yield the 13 elastic constants, but the calculated error was not given.

Table 12-4 contains the elastic constants referred to orthogonal axes $Z = c^*$, $Y = b$ and $X = a$. The first column lists the suffixes using the combined suffix convention. Earlier data of Alexandrov and Ryzhova (1962) are ignored because they were obviously revised.

The plagioclases are increasingly rigid as the An-content increases, consistent with crystal-chemical expectations. When experimental errors are considered, there is no clear-cut change of anisotropy with An-content.

The alkali feldspars show no consistent trends and it is impossible to separate intrinsic from extrinsic factors. Since extrinsic factors lower the stiffness, specimens 75 and 67 may be most affected.

All the elastic data on feldspars are consistent with easiest compliance along the a-axis and least compliance near c. The effects are analogous to the anisotropy of thermal expansion, and can be interpreted in the same structural terms.

Ryzhova (1964) compared graphically her values of elastic constants of plagioclase with those determined by the pulse method. Her data for the volume compressibility are puzzling because they do not equal the sum of the diagonal terms of the stress-strain tensor given in Table 12-2. Furthermore it is not clear whether a correction was made to transform from adiabatic to isothermal conditions.

Ramberg (1961) studied artificial and natural photoelastic effects in quartz and feldspars. In particular he examined orthoclase from charnockite gneisses and granulite facies rocks, for which optical effects were found around various types of less-compressible inclusions. Ramberg noted that the optically disturbed regions of orthoclase appeared to be structurally controlled, giving lighter and darker regions parallel to the cross-hatched twin lamellae of microcline.

Table 12-4. (a) Elastic stiffness constants for feldspar in units of 10^{11} dyne/cm²

	Alkali feldspars[a]							Plagioclase[b]				
	78	75	74	67	65	61	53	9	24	29	53	56
11	6.25	5.72	6.19	5.84	5.96	5.96	6.30	7.49	8.18	8.45	9.70	9.89
22	17.2	14.8	15.8	14.7	15.8	15.7	15.2	13.7	14.5	15.0	16.3	17.2
33	12.4	10.3	10.0	9.88	10.5	11.9	11.8	12.9	13.3	13.2	14.1	14.1
44	1.43	1.37	1.41	1.24	1.39	1.36	1.01	1.72	1.77	1.85	1.96	1.99
55	2.23	1.80	2.03	1.85	2.03	2.26	2.68	3.03	3.12	3.14	3.30	3.41
66	3.74	3.23	3.60	3.43	3.70	3.42	3.56	3.11	3.33	3.43	3.70	3.76
12	4.28	3.28	4.34	3.33	3.62	3.44	3.59	3.63	3.93	4.17	5.07	5.21
13	3.58	3.33	3.68	3.40	3.60	2.80	4.90	3.76	4.07	4.09	4.42	4.41
23	2.41	1.93	2.18	2.16	2.85	2.16	3.61	3.26	3.41	3.30	3.70	3.66
15	-1.54	-1.24	-1.00	-1.07	-1.18	-1.70	-1.29	-0.91	-0.90	-0.87	-0.96	-0.81
25	-1.43	-0.61	-0.18	-0.43	-0.57	-0.59	-0.18	-1.04	-0.79	-0.69	-0.51	-0.51
35	-1.15	-1.12	-1.21	-1.30	-1.29	-1.29	-1.81	-1.91	-1.85	-1.85	-1.50	-1.91
46	-0.28	-0.25	-0.23	-0.30	-0.26	-0.18	-0.26	-0.13	-0.08	-0.11	-0.16	-0.19

(b) Elastic compliance constants for feldspar in units of 10^{-13} cm²/dyne

	78	75	74	67	65	61	53	9	24	29	53	56
11	24.9	26.5	26.0	25.1	25.0	24.4	26.3	17.2	15.9	15.5	13.8	13.4
22	7.05	7.73	7.91	7.84	7.39	7.37	7.74	8.52	8.06	7.79	7.42	6.99
33	9.66	12.2	13.1	13.1	12.4	9.55	13.1	9.83	9.53	9.52	8.63	8.81
44	71.0	73.9	71.6	82.4	73.0	74.0	100.8	58.4	56.5	54.1	51.2	50.5
55	54.5	66.1	55.5	62.8	57.0	57.5	43.4	36.8	35.2	34.8	32.1	31.8
66	27.1	31.3	28.0	29.8	27.4	29.4	28.6	32.3	30.0	29.2	27.1	26.7
12	-4.51	-4.52	-6.03	-4.48	-4.26	-4.35	-4.06	-3.50	-3.33	-3.40	-3.51	-3.34
13	-5.23	-6.36	-7.27	-6.48	-6.28	-3.45	-8.68	-3.91	-3.80	-3.74	-3.19	-3.18
23	0.07	-0.05	0.26	-0.30	-0.64	-0.46	-1.00	-0.94	-0.98	-0.85	-0.88	-0.79
15	11.6	12.8	7.94	8.91	9.36	16.1	6.51	1.50	1.48	1.34	2.02	0.89
25	1.44	-0.52	-2.13	-0.98	-0.81	-1.75	-2.11	-1.28	-0.50	-0.26	-0.27	-0.19
35	1.37	3.16	4.25	5.40	4.00	2.75	4.71	4.70	4.32	4.39	2.86	4.06
46	5.31	5.72	4.57	7.21	5.13	3.90	7.37	2.44	1.36	1.74	2.22	2.55

[a] The number for each alkali feldspar is the Or-content. The first 4 are microcline perthites and the last 3 are monoclinic. See Ryzhova and Alexandrov (1965) for details.

[b] The number for each plagioclase is the An-content (wt. or mol. not specified). Ryzhova (1964).

Holmquist (1914) determined the grinding hardness of feldspars. Mookherjee and Sahu (1960) claimed that the microhardness of plagioclase shows discontinuities at An_{30} and An_{70} but the results are not convincing because of the paucity of samples. Barth (1969) reproduced the original data.

Brace and Walsh (1962) estimated the surface energy of the (001) cleavage of two pegmatitic orthoclases. The measured surface energy of $0.78\,mJ/cm^2$ is much greater than the value of 0.02 estimated from elastic constants. The difference was thought to result from a blocking effect caused by sub-microscopic domains of Na-feldspar, consistent with the splintery surface of the cleavage. Probably detailed study of cleavages by scanning electron microscopy (see Chapter 10) using secondary electrons will prove of great importance in interpreting the mechanism of cleavage.

Although feldspars show several preferred directions of parting or cleavage, none are really well defined as is the basal cleavage of mica. Possibly the ease of cleavage of a particular feldspar depends on a variety of localized properties not always directly correlated with the crystal structure, but giving in total a tendency for a correlation with the crystal structure. Thus the cleavages need not necessarily break T–O bonds, but might result from breaking apart of units already separated by films of impurities. The "murchisonite" parting certainly results from breakage along the surfaces between K- and Na-feldspars in perthites. However, the best-defined cleavages, i.e. the perfect (001) and not so perfect (010) cleavages, break T–O bonds because they are parallel to the major structural unit, the double-crankshaft chains along the a-axis, and because they occur in all types of feldspars. The next most common cleavage, the imperfect (110) cleavage, is parallel to a prominent growth face, and crosses the double-crankshaft chains. Perhaps it and sometimes the (010) and (001) cleavages result from imperfections on growth surfaces. In plagioclases, the ($1\bar{1}0$) cleavage is listed as more easy than (110). Fracture along (100) is fairly common in perthites, probably because coarse perthite lamellae tend to lie along (100).

Passage of high-speed nuclear particles through feldspar and other minerals causes displacement of atoms, and the resultant structural weakening permits the paths to be revealed by etching. Consequently feldspars and other minerals provide a record of the particle flux since the mineral crystallized. Turkowsky (1969) made an electron microscope study of irradiated albite. In addition to studying the recoil tracks of α-particles, he recorded etching effects ascribed to ordinary lattice defects. The studies of Crozaz et al. (1970) and Fleischer et al. (1970) of Apollo 11 rocks illustrate the use of feldspars as recorders of nuclear particles. There are many papers on fossil tracks in feldspars of terrestrial rocks and meteorites. See Price et al. (1973).

12.5.2 Controlled Uniaxial Deformation of Plagioclase

Permanent deformation of plagioclase occurs by four processes (1) shattering (cataclasis) (2) mechanical twinning (3) slip (4) development of deformation lamellae which may also involve slip along as yet unidentified planes or directions.

As described in section 18.5.4, plagioclase whose Si, Al distribution is topologically unchanged by Albite or by Pericline twinning can be mechanically twinned by pressure. Thus disordered plagioclase and pure anorthite can be twinned readily (e.g. by pressing with a needle). Most twin lamellae disappear when the pressure is removed. Plagioclase whose Si, Al distribution would change topologically offers major resistance to mechanical twinning, and it is principally to such material that the work of Borg and collaborators and of Seifert has been directed.

Borg and Heard (1970) summarized the work by Borg and Handin (1966), Borg and Heard (1967, 1969): see also Carter (1971). Plagioclase feldspars were deformed at 25 to $800°$ C and $5-10$ kbar confining pressure.

Cylindrical samples were enclosed in a copper sleeve in a sealed jacket and compressed between hard anvils. Larger samples were confined at 5 kbar and compressed axially such that the length was reduced about 10% by a strain rate of 10^{-4} per second. Smaller samples were held at $8-10$ kbar, and strained at 2×10^{-5}/sec. Most single crystals were oriented to favor Albite or Pericline mechanical twinning such that the compression axis bisected the acute angle between (010) and (001). Orientation of rock cores was random. All specimens initially contained twins and alteration products, especially along cleavages.

Nine natural specimens were examined: An_2, "cleavelandite"; An_6 and An_{13}, peristerites; An_{19}, An_{30}, An_{37}, from pegmatites; An_{44} from anorthosite and An_{55}, both lacking iridescence; An_{59}, volcanic; An_{77} and An_{95} accumulates at top of gabbro sill. Disordered varieties of An_2 and An_{77} were produced by long heating at high temperature.

Up to $700°$ C, compression produced merely faulting and cataclasis, but at $800°$ C mechanical twinning, slip and deformation lamellae became common. Figure 12-3 plots the differential stress (i.e. axial over-pressure) versus the percentage axial strain for constant strain rate. For single crystals An_{30} and An_{55}, the yield strength decreased two-fold in both materials as the temperature increased from $600-800°$ C (diagram a). The failure mode changed from cataclasis at $600°$ C to twin gliding at $800°$ C. The critical resolved shear stress (equal to half the yield stress) is about 1 kbar at $800°$ C for either Albite or Pericline twinning. In diagram b stress-strain curves at $800°$ C are similar for four plagioclases, An_{13}, An_{30}, An_{37} and An_{55}, even though the peristerite failed principally by cataclasis, and the others by twinning. The An_{59} specimen showed strong work-hardening terminating in fracture, probably because of unfavorable orientation of one-half of the crystal with respect to twin gliding. Polycrystalline material is stronger than single crystals at comparable strains (diagrams c and d). Pre-annealing at $900°$ C for $8-20$ days doubles the ultimate strength. Borg and Heard suggested that loss of water caused this, consistent with other evidence for catalytic action by protons.

No mechanical twinning was observed in any plagioclase deformed below $800°$ C. The geometrical nature of the twinning is discussed in section 18.5.4. The atomic structure of the twinned material was not determined by X-ray methods. For the unannealed bytownite, An_{77}, the optic axial angle in 13 new Pericline or Albite twins was $+91.3°$ on average compared to $+96°$ in undeformed areas and $+94°$ in untwinned areas of deformed material. The composition plane of

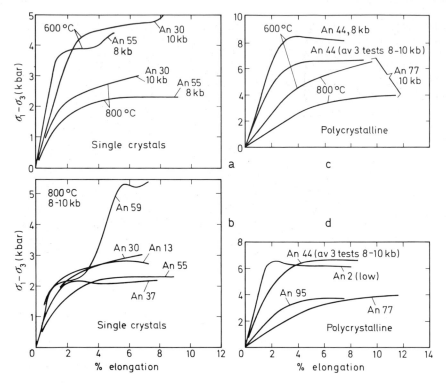

Fig. 12-3. Stress-strain curves for uniaxial compression of plagioclase. The axially-directed over-pressure in kbar is the ordinate and the percentage reduction of length is the abscissa. The chemical composition, temperature and confining pressure are specified in the diagrams. The An_{59} specimen was disordered, but all others were ordered. (From Borg and Heard, 1970, Figs. 1 and 2)

the Pericline twins varied in orientation from $\sigma = 9-15°$ for the narrowest lamellae. These data suggest a change of structural state (see later for evidence by Seifert) but the significance of the rhombic section is ambiguous in this region because of the overlapping effects of temperature and structural state (Section 18.5.1). Intersecting Pericline lamellae were observed only in unannealed bytownite, suggesting no variation in structural state in other specimens.

Albite and Pericline twins appeared to be induced with about equal frequency when the resolved shear stress was comparable. In areas showing both types of twin, there was an occasional tendency to cross-hatching (Fig. 18-24b for An_{30} deformed at 800° C). Non-overlapping areas occur commonly in natural plagioclase (Fig. 18-26a for a labradorite megacryst in a Greenland dike) while overlapping areas (cross-hatched) appear to be rare (Fig. 18-25a for an andesine from the Skaergaard intrusion). The incredible twin texture with fine Pericline lamellae occupying broad Albite lamellae found for a labradorite crystal from Greenland (Fig. 18-26b) has not been duplicated experimentally so far. Vernon (1965) described complex phenomena at the intersections of Pericline and Albite deformation twins occurring in mafic gneisses from Broken Hill, Australia.

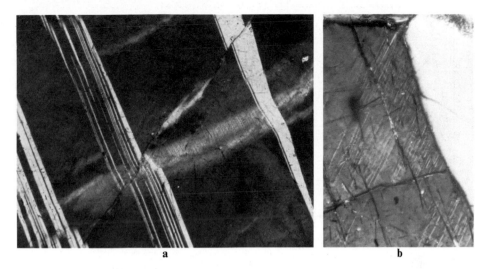

a   b

Fig. 12-4. Slip, kink bands and deformation lamellae in experimentally deformed plagioclase. a Photomicrograph in crossed nicols of low-albite (An_1) deformed at $800°$ C under 10 kbars confining pressure. Pre-existing Albite lamellae slope NW–SE. A broad kink band trends WSW–ENE, and contains very fine (010) slip bands. A fracture runs NNE–SSW. Uniaxial stress approximately NS. 0.1 mm across. b Photomicrograph in crossed nicols of deformation lamellae in An_{44} plagioclase in anorthosite deformed at $800°$ C under 8 kbars confining pressure. The narrow deformation lamellae lie NNE–SSW and traces of the (001) cleavage lie NNW–SSE. 0.3 mm across. (From Borg and Heard, 1969, Fig. 2 d and c)

Slip on {010} was observed in low albite at $800°$ C and 10 kbar, and in peristerite, An_{13}, at 200 and $400°$ C (5 kbar) and at $800°$ C (10 kbar). All crystals were unfavorably oriented for (010) mechanical twinning. Kinking and local rotation up to $7°$ on the slip plane (010) occurred (Fig. 12-4 a), but kink bands and hinges were not marked by sharp boundaries. Probably slip occurs in other plagioclase compositions if (010) is properly oriented with respect to the uniaxial compression. No slip on {001} was observed even though the slip system {001} [010] was favorably oriented.

Seifert (1969) applied uniaxial compression to fine-grained anorthosite from the Ausable quadrangle, Adirondacks. The rock consisted of 90–95% plagioclase and 5–10% mafic minerals. Optical study indicated an average composition near An_{50}, and occurrence of 42 Albite and 9 Pericline twins. The structural state appeared to be low to intermediate. The mafic minerals showed a well-developed foliation, with which the X-axis of the plagioclase tended to be associated. Stress-strain curves were independent of the direction of uniaxial compression with respect to the foliation.

Triaxial compression measurements were made at $400–1000°$ C and 4.4 to 14.8 kbar confining pressure using a constant strain rate of $7.7 \times 10^{-5} sec^{-1}$ (Fig. 12-5). The strength increased with increase of confining pressure and decrease of temperature. The stress-strain curves are strongly non-linear at low temperatures and high strains.

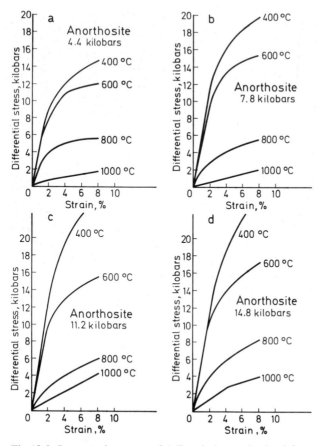

Fig. 12-5. Stress-strain curves of Adirondack anorthosite deformed to 8 percent strain in uniaxial compression at the confining pressure shown on the four sub-diagrams. Seifert (pers. comm. in 1972) stated that new results showed that all the curves are slightly high from the strength of the talc pressure medium. Furthermore the large gap between the curves for 600 and 800° C probably results from a weakening caused by water from hydrous alteration of the plagioclase, and from the talc. (From Seifert, 1969, Figs. 6, 7, 8 and 9)

Thin-section optical study showed that, at lower temperatures and confining pressures, failure occurred along large intergranular shear fractures, whereas at higher temperatures and confining pressures failure occurred by fracture along grain boundaries and by cracking, crushing and rotation of grains. No recrystallization was observed. Although twin gliding might have occurred in some grains at 800 and 1000° C, it could not be distinguished definitely from pre-existing twinning.

Seifert (1971, pers. comm. 1972, 1973) extended these early data, as given in the following summary:

"Two samples of fine-grained recrystallized Adirondack anorthosite, both with low to low transitional plagioclase averaging An_{50} in composition, have been experimentally deformed at a constant strain rate of 10^{-5}/sec over temperatures from $400-1000°$ C and over confining pressures from 5 kb to 17 kb

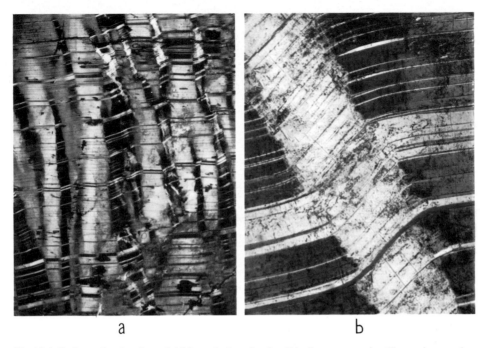

a   b

Fig. 12-6. Deformation bands and Albite twin lamellae in albite from pegmatite. Photomicrographs in crossed polarizers of thin section cut perpendicular to *a*. The albite twin lamellae tend to lie EW and the broad, irregular deformation lamellae tend to lie NS. a Low magnification, 1.1 mm across. b High magnification, 0.08 mm across. (From Seifert, 1965, Figs. 1 and 2)

in a Grigg's type solid confining pressure medium apparatus. At temperatures of 400° C and 600° C, and all confining pressures, the two samples, one heavily altered and the other unaltered, show very similar strengths. However, at 800° C and 1000° C the unaltered sample exhibits considerably greater strength than does the altered sample, and it seems probable that water from dehydration of the sericitic-type alteration is responsible for the weakening of the altered sample. Optical study of thin sections of deformed cores indicates that the original low to low transitional structural states have converted to high transitional structural states in the central portion of cores in both samples at temperatures of 800° C or greater during 30—40 min tests. Cataclastic deformation predominates at all temperatures and pressures at the strain rate of 10^{-5}/sec and total strains of around 15%, but is joined by apparently irrational deformation lamellae at 600° C or greater and albite or pericline twinning at 800° C or greater."

Seifert (1965) described deformation banding in low albite from a pegmatite near Bethel, Maine. Figure 12-6 shows a thin section cut normal to *a*, at low magnification (a) and at high magnification (b). Pre-existing fine Albite lamellae are kinked where they cross the broad deformation lamellae. The latter have irregular wavy boundaries but tend to be bounded by (001) cleavages. The deformation bands average about 1 mm wide and run for about 70 mm. Near the boundaries, the earlier Albite twin lamellae curve smoothly, but retain continuity through the deformation lamellae. Rotation in the deformation bands varies from very slight up to about 45°. Seifert stated that the bands could not be kink bands because the (010) and (001) cleavages are not consistent with well-defined axes of external and internal rotation.

Starkey (1968) discussed the geometry of kink-banding in crystals. For kinking associated with gliding, he suggested that "albite deformation twins may result from 'pericline-type' twin gliding with the rhombic section as glide plane and the b-axis as glide line, while pericline deformation twins could develop by 'albite-type' twin gliding where the slip is on {010} parallel to the trace of b on (010). Hence the twin gliding need not have occurred parallel to the composition plane of the twin." This possibility arises since Albite and Pericline twinning produce the same topologic distribution of atoms, and differ only in the orientation of the whole crystal (Starkey, 1964). Hence rotation of a twinned crystal with introduction of dislocations can turn one twin law into the other. However I. Y. Borg (pers. comm.) reports that Starkey's suggestion is not needed to explain any experimental observations. Kinking occurs with twin gliding, as shown in Fig. 18-24c for An_{55} plagioclase deformed at 800° C, 8 kbar by Borg and Heard (1970). Detailed study, perhaps by electron-optical and microbeam X-ray methods, is needed to clarify the relations between mechanical twinning, gliding and kinking in plagioclase.

Borg and Heard used the general term deformation lamellae for planar features not obeying a twin law. They were produced in specimens An_{37}, An_{44}, and An_{77} at $700-800°$ C and 10 kbar. Figure 12-4b shows fine deformation lamellae crossing (001) cleavage traces in an An_{44} plagioclase deformed at 800° C and a confining pressure of 8 kbar. Clusters of deformation lamellae occur in positions of high resolved shear stress; they are not parallel to any low-index crystallographic planes but tend to be sub-normal to [001] and to lie in the [312] and [$\bar{1}$10] zones of the starting material; they are not strictly parallel, and lack the sharpness of the (001) and (010) cleavages; they do not cross grain boundaries and are restricted to areas without deformation twinning; and they have a typical width near $3-5$ μm, and can show a small change in extinction angle (2°).

Sen (1956) described lamellae in plagioclase from a banded norite near Willow Lake, Oregon. Perhaps some of the lamellae, especially those parallel to ($\bar{1}$01), (150) and (1$\bar{5}$0) are analogous to the deformation lamellae produced synthetically.

In summary, the mechanical strength of plagioclase under uniaxial compression at high confining pressure is remarkably little affected by the chemical composition. Twinning is favored by high temperature. The mode of deformation depends on the angular relation of the uniaxial compression to the crystal lattice. High-temperature annealing leads to greater strength. Presence of water results in decrease of strength.

12.5.3 Shock Deformation

In contrast to the experiments just described, shock deformation involves very rapid deformation with a simultaneous increase of both pressure and temperature along the Hugoniot curve. The passage of a shock wave through a crystal is affected by refraction and reflection at discontinuities. Shock phenomena develop erratically, but the average effect correlates with the shock intensity. In laboratory experiments, the specific volume of the sample is measured as a function of pressure. From observations of rocks collected from meteorite craters, or from the meteorites themselves, detailed textural, optical and chemical data are obtained.

Large reductions of volume take place as the pressure and temperature increase along the Hugoniot curve. From the release adiabats, the equivalent zero-pressure density can be deduced. The data for feldspars indicate rearrangement of the crystal structure to one or more dense phases as the pressure and temperature increase, with inversion to a lower-density phase on cooling. Observations of natural feldspars from rocks showed that as the maximum shock pressure increases, a series of processes results: fracturing; formation of deformation lamellae; formation of shock lamellae with partial or complete vitrification; conversion of whole grains to glass; and formation of glass by mixing the melt from more than one grain. Devitrification features commonly occur. Comparison of the laboratory data with the data for natural rocks permitted establishment of a pressure scale for calibrating natural shock events.

The general study of shock metamorphism was greatly stimulated by unambiguous identification of many meteorite craters on the Earth's surface, and by study of lunar surface material. The book "Shock metamorphism of natural materials" edited by B. M. French and N. M. Short (1968) gives the theoretical and observational background of shock metamorphism, and contains many papers specifically giving data on feldspars (Ahrens and Rosenberg, 1968; Chao, 1968a; Engelhardt and Stöffler, 1968; Dence, 1968; Short, 1968a, b; Bunch, 1968; Robertson et al., 1968; Bunch et al., 1968). Earlier Chao (1967) summarized shock effects in various rock-forming minerals, and Stöffler (1967) gave a detailed account of the shock effects in plagioclase at the Nördlinger Ries crater in Germany. Dworak (1969) described shock metamorphism of anorthosite from Manicouagan crater, Quebec, Canada. The special issues on the Apollo samples from the Moon contain many articles describing shock effects in plagioclase and other minerals. Stöffler (1972) gave a general review of the behavior of minerals under shock compression.

Maskelynite and Diaplectic Plagioclase. DeCarli and Jamieson (1959) and Milton and DeCarli (1963) showed that explosively-shocked plagioclase yielded glass of higher refractive index than glass produced by quenching from a low-pressure melt. Tschermak (1872, 1883) had observed similar high-density glass in meteorites, and named it *maskelynite*. The terms *thetomorphic* or *diaplectic* were introduced as adjectives for such amorphous material by Chao (1967) and Engelhardt and Stöffler (1968), respectively. Binns (1966), Duke and Silver (1967), Duke (1968) and Bunch et al. (1970) described the properties of maskelynite in various meteorites. Maskelynite found in meteorite craters was described by many workers including Bunch et al. (1967) and Stöffler (1967). Maskelynite has refractive indices and density intermediate between those of crystalline plagioclase and the quenched product of low-pressure melted plagioclase (Fig. 12-7).

Tschermak (1872) reported that maskelynite occurred in the Shergotty basaltic achondrite as clear, colorless laths crossed by fine lines. Although it looked like

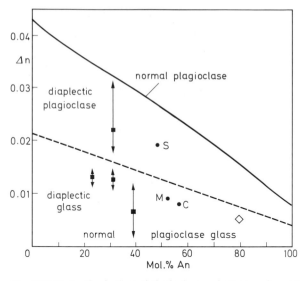

Fig. 12-7. Refractive indices of plagioclase and glasses referred to the refractive index of normal glass produced by quenching melt at low pressure. The ordinate gives the difference of mean refractive index, and the abscissae the mole-% An. Stöffler (1967) plotted the mean and range of refractive index for four specimens from the Nördlinger Ries crater, and separated the field into those for diaplectic plagioclase (anisotropic) and diaplectic glass (isotropic). The three circles are for glass in the Shergotty meteorite (An_{50}), and for glass Clearwater West (An_{58}) and Manicouagan (An_{54}) craters. The diamond represents artificial glass made by Milton and DeCarli (1963)

plagioclase in ordinary light it was completely isotropic in crossed polarizers. Bunch *et al.* (1967) confirmed these observations and noted the presence of cleavages, zoning, and a few patches of low birefringence.

Maskelynite from the meteor crater within the West Clearwater Gabbro, Quebec occurs as single grains or as lamellar intergrowths with plagioclase (see later). In the Manicouagan anorthosite, maskelynite replaces up to 25% of the plagioclase in irregular pods or lenses up to several millimeters wide. Transformation of plagioclase to maskelynite did not disrupt grain boundaries, cleavages or twin composition planes. Strained plagioclase showed changes in the birefringence and optic axial angle.

Figure 12-7 shows the refractive indices measured by Bunch *et al.* for the Shergotty meteorite (S) and the Clearwater (C) and Manicouagan (M) material. Following Stöffler (1967), the refractive indices are plotted with respect to normal glass produced at low pressure. The refractive index for glass produced artificially by shock (Milton and DeCarli, 1963) is also shown. Stöffler divided the region between normal glass and normal plagioclase into two regions: diaplectic plagioclase has birefringence lower than normal plagioclase while diaplectic glass is isotropic. The boundary was estimated by Stöffler from a specimen of composition An_{31} to lie about half-way between the curves for normal glass and normal plagioclase. The mean value for each type of glass coexisting in this specimen is shown by a square. The boundary between the ranges is not clearly definable.

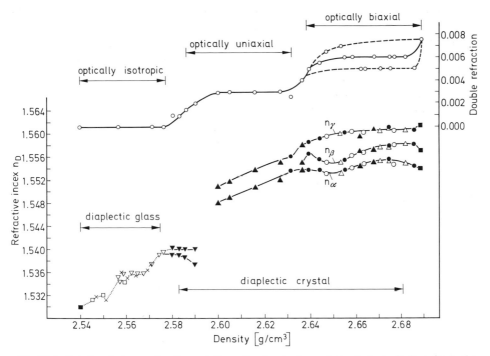

Fig. 12-8. Relation between density and the refractive indices of shocked plagioclase from the Manicouagan crater. The squares are for normal plagioclase, and the various symbols represent different specimens of shocked plagioclase. The variation of double refraction is given in the upper part. (From Dworak, 1969, Fig. 14)

Two other specimens from the Nördlinger Ries crater gave ranges in the region of diaplectic glass. The Shergotty datum lies in the proposed field for diaplectic plagioclase, even though the glass is almost entirely isotropic.

Bunch *et al.* found that Canadian specimens of diaplectic glass showed only a diffuse X-ray diffraction band characteristic of amorphous silicate. Infra-red absorption patterns showed progressive loss of detail in the spectra of ordinary plagioclase referred to maskelynite and to normal glass. The Si–O–Si or Si–O–Al band at $380 \, \text{cm}^{-1}$ shifted to 405 for maskelynite and 480 for normal glass indicating progressive loss of order.

Manicouagan maskelynite transformed to crystalline plagioclase in two hours at $900° \, \text{C}$, but Shergotty maskelynite and normal glass were hardly changed. The Shergotty maskelynite transformed partially in one hour at $1150° \, \text{C}$. Bunch *et al.* suggested that the Shergotty material had been shocked to a higher pressure than the Canadian material, though the data in Fig. 12-7 would suggest otherwise. Perhaps the Shergotty maskelynite contains less water than the Canadian material, thus having fewer proton catalysts.

Dworak (1969) presented detailed data for shocked plagioclase (An_{52-58}) of anorthosite rocks at the Manicouagan crater which confirm and extend the data of Bunch *et al.* Figure 12-8 shows the relations between the refractive indices, and the density (at $22° \, \text{C}$). The specimens of highest density show the normal refractive indices for labradorite. For densities of about $2.60 - 2.63$, the plagioclase was optically uniaxial, and for densities below 2.58, the plagioclase was optically isotropic and was actually maskelynite.

Infra-red absorption spectra (Dworak's Fig. 15) showed a broadening and shift of peak positions as the plagioclase turned into diaplectic glass: however the details are complex and their significance unclear except to indicate increasing structural disorder. X-ray powder diffraction data showed that the angle between the 131 and 1$\bar{3}$1 peaks increased for the diaplectic plagioclase reaching a value of $2.15°$ for $2\,\theta(CuK_\alpha)$. This value is too high for An_{52-58} suggesting that diaplectic plagioclase might disproportion into a more calcic plagioclase and a more sodic glass. Alternatively the X-ray data may be misleading because of diffuseness of the peaks, or because of lattice strain.

The refractive index of feldspar glass increases with static pressure. Chao and Bell (1969) and Bell and Chao (1970) found increases of about 0.03 upon increasing the pressure from $0 - 40$ kbar at which glasses of composition An_{68}, An_{20} and Or_{90} were quenched from a liquid. In addition they showed that annealing was a complex process. At low pressure, higher-density glass annealed more rapidly than lower-density glass. Annealing occurred more rapidly at high temperature than at low temperature. Annealing of An_{68} glass at 10 kbar with steadily rising temperature resulted in no increase of refractive index of quenched glass up to 200° C. A maximum increase occurred at 800° C, followed by a small decrease to 1100°.

Kleeman (1971) experimentally produced diaplectic glass by shock loading orthoclase powder either loosely packed or mixed with copper powder. By utilizing reverberations, pressures up to 345 kbar were obtained with low post-shock temperatures. Diaplectic glass appeared at 240 kbar, and transformation was nearly complete at 320 kbar. The results were independent of pulse times from $1 - 4$ µsec. If singly-shocked in natural events, orthoclase should transform at rather lower pressure because of higher post-shock temperature.

Stöffler and Hornemann (1972) distinguished glass produced by pressure release of high-pressure phase above or below the glass transition temperature.

Hugoniot and Release Adiabatic Curves. Data on Hugoniot and release-adiabat curves are obtained by plotting the specific volume of the sample against the pressure generated by a plane shock wave. Ahrens *et al.* (1969) assembled together their own data on an oligoclase ($An_{19}Or_6Ab_{75}$) and a microcline (unanalyzed) together with data on anorthosite, An_{49}, and albitite, An_{12}, (McQueen *et al.*, 1967), anorthosite (Ahrens and Rosenberg, 1968), anorthosite, albite and labradorite (Ahrens and Gregson, 1964).

Although there are small systematic differences (Fig. 12-9), the data for all the feldspars and feldspar-rich rocks show the same type of curve. The feldspars compress elastically up to $40 - 55$ kbar for oligoclase and $80 - 85$ kbar for microcline. The pressure limit increases slightly with the magnitude of the maximum applied shock pressure. Above the pressure limit, three regimes are apparent. Above 300 kbar for microcline and 400 kbar for oligoclase, conversion to a new high-pressure phase is indicated. From about $140 - 400$ kbar, anomalous compression is indicated. The observed elastic shock velocities compare well with those found by Alexandrov and Ryzhova (1962).

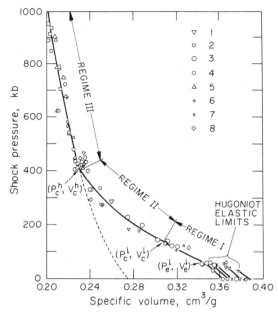

Fig. 12-9. Hugoniot data for various feldspars showing the specific volume in relation to the shock pressure. The data points are identified as follows: *1, 8* oligoclase and microcline (Ahrens *et al.*, 1969); *2, 5* anorthosite and albite (McQueen *et al.*, 1967); *3* anorthosite (Ahrens and Rosenberg, 1968); *4,6,7* anorthosite, albite and labradorite (Ahrens and Gregson, 1964). (From Ahrens *et al.*, 1969, Fig. 6)

Figures 12-10 and 12-11 show the density-pressure relations for the oligoclase and the microcline. Data for the oligoclase were interpreted in terms of an elastic regime, a low-pressure regime, a regime of mixed phases, and a high-pressure regime. The calculated zero-pressure density for the high-pressure phase was 3.69 gm/cm³. For microcline a similar sequence was indicated resulting in a high-pressure phase of density 3.50 gm/cm³.

Interpretation of the release adiabats indicated that for the oligoclase, partial conversion to the high-pressure phase began at about 140 kbar, and that upon pressure release, inversion to maskelynite (or perhaps reversion to plagioclase) occurred.

Robertson (1972, and pers. comm.) shocked microcline up to 417 kbar using discs 0.5 mm thick cut parallel to the (001) cleavage of the perthitic maximum microcline. The optic axial angle increased from 81 to 88° while the refractive indices dropped to n_α 1.490 and n_γ 1.492. In highly-shocked samples some areas were almost isotropic but no maskelynite-type material was seen. The optic axes changed position with respect to the crystallographic axes especially above 200 kbar. Three types of planar elements were formed: (a) *cleavages of unusual orientation* formed above 96 kbar with best development near 300 kbar; common orientations were ($\bar{1}$11) and (11$\bar{1}$) with less frequent (hk0), the latter occurring especially at 96 – 150 kbars; the cleavages occur as fractures inside grains and sometimes contain a material of low birefringence, perhaps glass, (b) "*planar deformation features*" formed above 154 kbar with best development between

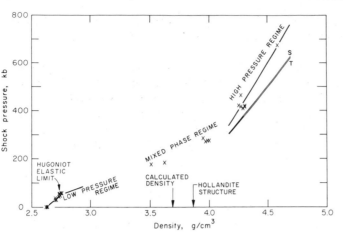

Fig. 12-10. Hugoniot data for oligoclase showing the relation between density and shock pressure. (From Ahrens *et al.*, 1969, Fig. 5)

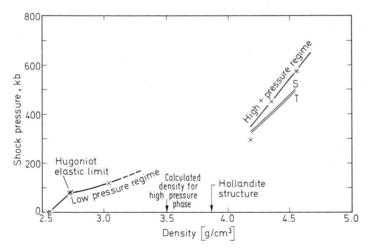

Fig. 12-11. Hugoniot data for microcline showing the relation between density and shock pressure. (From Ahrens *et al.*, 1969, Fig. 7)

190 and 250 kbar; most lie near (11$\bar{1}$) with some near ($\bar{1}$41) and (101), (c) *twin-like features of unusual orientation* formed at 417 kbar; they lay near ($\bar{1}$12) and replaced the unusual cleavages. X-ray powder patterns showed decrease of intensity at 150 kbar, increased prominence of lines from perthitic albite at 167 kbar, and first indication of a new phase at 191 kbar. The new phase did not correspond to any known structure.

Gibbons (1973) produced planar features below 300 kbar and thetomorphic glass above 300 kbar by shocking labradorite in a propellant gun.

Ahrens and Liu (1973) found a compressional velocity by ultrasonic inter-ferometry of 7.53(2) km/sec in polished (001) cleavage plates of iron-sanidine from Madagascar (Or_{89}). A shock-induced phase change began at ~ 115 kbar producing a mixed-phase region which extended to ~ 300 kbar above which a hollandite-type structure was inferred.

The nature of the high-pressure phases is questionable. In static pressure experiments, microcline and germanium-albite (Ringwood et al., 1967a, b) and germanium K-feldspar (Kume et al., 1966) transformed into a hollandite-type structure with zero-pressure density near $3.85 \, gm/cm^3$ (see also Ahrens et al., 1969). This density is higher than the values of $3.5 - 3.7 \, gm/cm^3$ indicated from the shock experiments. Ahrens et al., (1969) suggested that this difference results from incomplete conversion to the high-pressure phase, but I wonder if this is true when partial conversion has been suggested even at 200 kbar. Does the high-pressure shock phase have a different crystal structure than the high-pressure static phase? James (1969) observed strings of jadeite in shocked oligoclase from the Ries crater, but its density ($\sim 3.32 \, gm/cm^3$) is lower than the value of 3.7 estimated for the high-pressure form of oligoclase. Davies and Anderson (1971) suggested disproportionation into stishovite and other phases: in addition they fitted the observed data for shocked feldspars to the Birch-Murnaghan equation obtaining zero-pressure densities of 3.36 (microcline), 3.69 (An_{12}), 3.57 (An_{19}) and 3.57 (An_{49} plus 10% augite). Unfortunately the shock experiments have only yielded maskelynite so far, and until a specimen retains its crystal structure through the release adiabat, the nature of the high-pressure phase will be enigmatic.

Natural Shocked Feldspars. Chao (1968a, b) classified the features found in shocked plagioclase feldspars from the Ries and Lake Bosumtni craters in the following sequence:

normal and fractured;
with deformation lamellae;
with shock lamellae, partly vitrified;
thetomorphic glass;
dense glass;
vesicular glass;
flowed glass;
patchy mixed glass;
mixed impactite glass (containing other mineral components);
vaporized melt (essentially of whole rock composition).

Engelhardt and Stöffler (1968) and Abadian (1972) gave a similar series of changes deduced from their study of the Ries crater, but the detailed nomenclature and groupings are somewhat different. Interpretation of the shock phenomena is subjective, since the debris from explosion craters is extremely mixed up. The following description utilizes material provided in papers by many authors, and may give a false impression of a neat scheme. Data for alkali feldspars are less abundant than for plagioclases, but the general phenomena seem to be similar.

Normal and fractured feldspars apparently result from shock pressures up to a few tens of kilobars, while diffuse fractures with deformation lamellae probably result from higher pressures and temperatures. Bunch (1968) reported two types of fracturing in plagioclase from explosion craters: brittle, tensile-type breaks with no obvious plastic deformation; and diffuse fractures. Crushing and

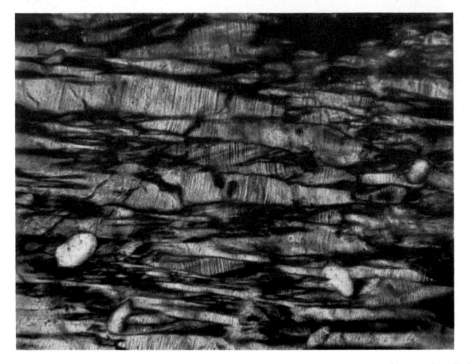

Fig. 12-12. Photomicrograph of deformation bands (EW) crossed by planar features in alkali feldspar from Lac Couture Crater. Crossed polarizers. 1.5 mm across. The small deformation lamellae are on (001) and the twin boundaries are on (010). (From Bunch, 1968, Fig. 13a)

rotation of samples sometimes produced a cataclastic texture. The usual cleavages {001} and {010}, and the rare {110}, are common. Diffuse fractures predominate over brittle features and intermingle with deformation bands. Strained crystals show undulating extinction and variable optic axial angles. Short (1968b) described well-defined cleavages and partings produced in K-feldspar of aplite and in albite grains artificially shocked. Granodiorite shocked to 60 kbar contained fractures which tended to follow the cleavages (Short, 1968a).

Lenticular deformation bands with associated kink bands were well-developed in alkali feldspar grains from a brecciated granite and some polymict breccias (Bunch, 1968). In an example figured by Bunch (Fig. 12-12), the deformation bands are contorted though sub-parallel to (010), with an average width of about 50 μm. The bands are crossed by fine lamellae about 2 μm across and sub-parallel to (001). The optic axial angle appears to vary with the amount of distortion. At a casual glance the texture is similar to that figured by Seifert (1965) for an albite in a pegmatite (Fig. 12-6). However the fine lamellae of Bunch's specimen are not continuous across the deformation lamellae, and the general texture is more erratic.

Deformation bands and kink bands in plagioclase are similar to those of alkali feldspars. Kink bands with slip plane (001) and slip directions [010] were seen in labradorite, with rotation of 24° about *a*.

Deformation twin lamellae on {010} — Albite law — and {001} were recognized by Bunch. Those on {001} were ascribed to the Manebach law, but might actually be on the Pericline law. The photomicrographs for plagioclase in a breccia from Lac Couture show lamellae up to 40 μm across in wavy contact on (010) crossed by fine lamellae on (001) about 2 μm across. The texture is very similar to that of alkali feldspar in Fig. 12-12. Deformation lamellae, not in twin orientation, occur on {010} and {001} causing off-sets in primary Albite twins.

Closely-spaced, multiple planar features produced by shock pressures are not easy to characterize optically because of their narrowness (up to a few micrometers across). Planar features were distinguished into various types (Chao, 1967): (1) fractures or cleavages (2) deformation lamellae as just described; these are seen more clearly under phase contrast than in bright-field illumination as asymmetric features bright on one side and dark on the other (3) planar features which are seen equally well under bright-field or phase-contrast illumination. Commonly this last type consists of alternations of crystalline plagioclase with material of lowered refractive index and lowered or zero birefringence. Microprobe analysis showed that the low-index material has the same chemical composition as the crystalline plagioclase. Stöffler (1967), Engelhardt and Stöffler (1968), and Dworak (1969) divided up the low-index material into diaplectic feldspar and diaplectic glass on the basis of the optical properties (Fig. 12-5), but the exact nature of the distinction is not clear.

The diaplectic material as discussed under the section on maskelynite consists of intermediate levels of structural organization between those of normal crystalline material and normal glass. In thin-section the diaplectic material shows remarkable textures (Fig. 12-13). Lamellae of normal plagioclase alternate with lamellae of lowered refractive index and birefringence (Chao, 1967). Dworak (1969, Fig. 10) showed a scanning electron micrograph in which lamellar inhomogeneities along (010) and (001) were displayed with remarkable clarity at a resolution considerably below 1 μm.

The lamellae tend to lie along rational crystallographic directions, but some appear to be irrational. In the example of Fig. 12-13, three sets of lamellae are consistent with (010), (001), (0$\bar{2}$1). Stöffler (1967) determined the orientation of 124 poles of lamellae with lowered or zero birefringence in 97 andesine crystals from a Ries specimen. The stereographic plot (Fig. 12-14) obtained with respect to the principal optic directions of the plagioclase suggests that many of the lamellae coincide with simple crystallographic planes. However mechanical strain on the plagioclase may modify its optical properties, and care must be taken in interpreting the data. The best-defined clusters appear to be associated with (001), (010) and (100), but other assignments by Stöffler may be equivocal. Dworak (1969, Fig. 11) gave a stereographic projection of 113 measurements of planar features of labradorite from the Manicouagan crater. Definite concentrations occur near the (010) and (001) poles with about half the features lying in other directions.

Chao (1967) pointed out that the tendency for the lamellae to be associated with simple crystallographic planes indicated that the lamellae did not reveal the direction taken by the shock front. Perhaps some existing twin lamellae are transformed into shock lamellae or perhaps act as triggers, but most planar

Fig. 12-13. Photomicrograph of plagioclase from a shocked granitic gneiss from the Ries crater showing several sets of planar features. Phase-contrast illumination. Three sets lie parallel to (010), (001) and (0$\bar{2}$1). Dark material is normal plagioclase of high refractive index while light material has lower refractive index. About 250 μm across. (From Chao, 1967, Fig. 5a)

features seem to be independent of earlier structures. Engelhardt and Stöffler (1968) pointed out that most lamellae are parallel to the shortest vectors of the Bravais lattice and to the greatest density of Si–O bonds. Hence they assumed that they are produced by a peculiar form of shock-induced crystal gliding.

Planar features with diaplectic plagioclase or glass probably form in the range $100-400$ kbar. At even higher pressure, entire grains melt and produce glass of normal or near-normal refractive indices upon release of the shock pressure. For this pressure range (perhaps above 500 kbar) the shock-induced peak temperature should surpass the solidus. The glass shows bubbles and streaks. Some glasses have devitrified (Chao, 1968a, b; Short, 1968a). Ultimately the entire rock melts, with mixing of liquid produced from the individual grains.

Aitken and Gold (1968) studied the structural state of K-feldspar at possible impact sites in Precambrian granitic terranes. The (131) powder diffraction peak varied from site to site and within sites but no clear-cut results were obtained.

James (1969) reported the occurrence of irregular strings of jadeite in thetomorphic glass produced from oligoclase ($Or_6Ab_{72}An_{22}$, mole) by shock metamorphism of amphibolite rock at the Ries crater, Germany. The refractive index of the glass varied from 1.5009 to 1.5123. The jadeite grains were 1 to 5 μm across with refractive index 1.585 ± 0.015. The jadeite was identified from X-ray powder

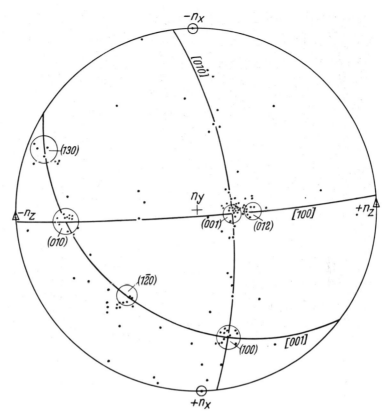

Fig. 12-14. Angle-true stereographic projection of 124 poles of lamellae with lowered or zero birefringence in 97 andesine crystals from a specimen from the Ries crater. The crystallographic poles are referred to the principal optic axes. (From Stöffler, 1967, Fig. 3)

patterns of shocked oligoclase, and from a concentrate produced by HF extraction.

Short (1970a) mentioned fractures and planar features in K-feldspar of quartzite from the Sedan nuclear explosion crater.

The rocks at the surface of the Moon have undergone severe deformation as the result of meteorite impact. Many papers from the Proceedings of the Apollo 11 Lunar Science Conference reported the occurrence of maskelynite and of various shock features in plagioclase. The most detailed contributions are by Chao *et al.* (1970), Dence *et al.* (1970), Engelhardt *et al.* (1970), Quaide and Bunch (1970), Radcliffe *et al.* (1970), Sclar (1970) and Short (1970b).

12.6 Density

Barth (1969) gave a detailed account of the density of feldspars and glasses. Direct measurement of feldspars is complicated by inclusions and defects but theoretical values can be calculated from the cell dimensions (Chapter 7) using atomic

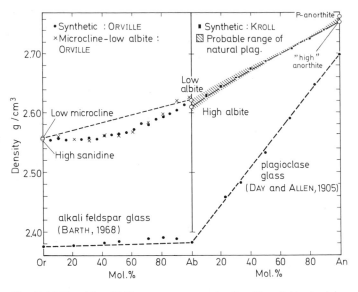

Fig. 12-15. Densities of feldspars on or near the Or–Ab and Ab–An joins

weights referred to H = 1.66043 × 10^{-24} gm. The density of a feldspar can also be estimated from the refractive indices using the Gladstone-Dale relation.

Figure 12-15 shows selected values for the density of feldspars and their glasses. The open circles were calculated from the reference values in Table 7-1: pure celsian has a density of 3.392. Data for synthetic alkali feldspars and the microcline-low albite series were calculated from the cell dimensions measured by Orville (Table 7-2): they show a negative deviation from the straight lines (dashed) joining the end-member values. Densities of synthetic plagioclases measured by Kroll (Table 7-6) show a slight positive deviation from a straight line joining high albite with "high"-anorthite. The hatched area shows the region occupied by natural plagioclases, many of which have lowered densities because of substitution by Or.

Data for plagioclase glasses were measured by Day et al. (1905), and for alkali feldspar glasses were estimated from the refractive indices by Barth (1969). The density difference between crystals and glass is fairly small for anorthite and increases four-fold in the alkali feldspars. There are no data on the density difference at the melting point.

Measurements of densities of natural feldspars are given in Hintze (1893, p. 1343 and 1450), Douglas (1907), Larsen (1909), Merwin (1911), Belyankin (1916), Ahlers (1924), Chudoba (1936), Rottenbach (1936), Poldervaart (1950), Häkli (1960), and Katz and Muravyov (1970).

Bottinga and Weill (1970) estimated the densities of liquid silicates, with special emphasis on whether plagioclase crystals would float in liquid magmas.

Arndt and Häberle (1973) found that for glasses of plagioclase composition the linear thermal expansion coefficient decreased from 7.4 × 10^{-6}/°C for albite composition to 4.9 for a composition near anorthite. The glass transition temperature dropped from $763°$ C for albite composition to $752°$ C for $An_{9.7}$ and then increased linearly to $813°$ C for near-anorthite. A glass made from Madagascar anorthite gave $6.1 \times 10^{-6}/°$ C and $905°$ C.

12.7 Thermogravimetry and Differential Thermal Analysis

The loss of weight consequent upon heating (thermogravimetry) is a valuable tool in the study of materials which decompose. A feldspar with a perfect aluminosilicate framework, whose voids are occupied only by alkali and alkaline-earth metals should not decompose upon heating below the melting point. Nemecz (1959) found weight losses of the order of $0.01-0.20\%$, which were ascribed to loss of H_2O from lattice defects. These weight losses are similar in size to the loss on ignition found in standard gravimetric analysis of feldspars: such loss on ignition is commonly reported as $H_2O^{+110°}$ with the implicit assumption that it consists of H_2O. Nemecz found that both quartz and orthoclase gave different weight loss patterns when derived from magmatic rocks than when derived from "post-magmatic" rocks. Since orthoclase typically contains many impurities, commonly thought to be mica or kaolin, great care must be taken in interpreting thermogravimetric results. Bridgwater and Harry (1968) reported thermogravimetric data for dark and light feldspars from a Greenland rock.

Differential thermal analysis depends on the emission or absorption of heat as a phase change occurs. Such a phase change must be rapid if it is to be recorded in a typical apparatus in which the temperature is changed from $100-500°$ C per hour. Bakken and Rosenqvist (1952), Rosenqvist (1952), and Köhler and Wieden (1954) recorded significant endothermic peaks for albite and various plagioclases in the region $700-900°$ C. Day et al. (1905) found no effect for a natural low albite either on heating or cooling, while Tuttle and Bowen (1950) found no effect for a synthetic high albite. At the present time, a definitive interpretation of the heat effects is not available. For albite there are no known structural changes which could explain the heat effect, and it is possible that some impurity is responsible. For the plagioclase, it might be possible to explain the heat effects in terms of structural changes in the feldspar (Chapter 5). However the peaks are within about $100°$ C of those in albite, and might be explained most easily as the result of the same impurity as in albite.

12.8 Separation and Visual Identification Procedures

Several chemical techniques require the mechanical separation of feldspar from associated minerals. Handpicking under a microscope of crushed fragments is often too time consuming. Section 12.8.1 describes techniques for separation or beneficiation of feldspars. Petrographers commonly desire to know the volume proportions of minerals in a rock. A popular procedure is to determine optically the populations of minerals lying at grid points on a polished surface. Typically such a point-count is made on a thin section in a petrographic microscope. Unfortunately distinction between feldspars is not always obvious (e.g. monoclinic K-feldspar and untwinned plagioclase), nor is distinction between feldspars and other silicates (quartz, cordierite, feldspathoids). Section 12.8.2 describes techniques for color-staining the surfaces of these minerals to permit a reliable and rapid identification. Chapters 6, 7 and 8 cover identification by sophisticated optical and X-ray methods.

Plas, van der (1966) thoroughly covered the special problems of dealing with detrital feldspars, which provide special problems because of the diversity of source material. Perhaps the techniques listed by him could be supplemented profitably by electron microprobe analysis and by cathodoluminescence studies of grain mounts of beneficiated samples. The cathodoluminescence might permit detection of several categories, while microprobe analysis with a scanning beam should permit determination of Ca, K and Na in about one minute per grain. The paper by Douglas et al. (1965) discusses identification of feldspar from the light fraction of soils using gravity separation and staining techniques.

12.8.1 Separation of Feldspars

Concentration by Heavy Liquids. The specific gravity of pure feldspars ranges from about 2.55−2.56 for K-feldspar to 2.61−2.62 for albite to 2.75−2.76 for anorthite. Disorder results in a slightly lowered specific gravity. Actual feldspars contain inclusions and defects that affect the specific gravity somewhat. Substitution of Fe and other elements causes small variations.

The simplest procedure is separation by heavy liquids, such as a mixture of bromoform and decaline, both of which have good wetting properties and fairly low viscosity (Doeglas et al., 1965). For routine separation of K-feldspar and plagioclase from other minerals, fractions from 2.55 to about 2.60 and an appropriate bracket for the plagioclase would be chosen.

The major problem is overlap of specific gravity between oligoclase and quartz (nominally 2.65, but somewhat variable because of impurities). Many chemical analyses of oligoclase show high silica values because of incomplete separation of quartz (e.g. Emmons, 1953). Mixtures of K-feldspar and nepheline (density around 2.6) also provide problems. The next technique of bubble-flotation often provides a solution.

Bubble-flotation. Bubbles of air will attach themselves to certain mineral surfaces when the mineral grains are suspended in water containing certain molecules containing both polar and non-polar groups. Commercial beneficiation of minerals commonly uses the technique. Etching or other treatment of the mineral surface may be needed to obtain reliable flotation.

Buckenham and Rogers (1954) described the flotation of quartz and feldspar by dodecylamine, and there are many industrial processes for beneficiating feldspars by similar procedures. Czygan (1967) described the differential flotation of nepheline and feldspar. The pH was adjusted by addition of HF to the water, and the flotation was achieved by a mixture of sodium hexametaphosphate, laurylamine and amyl alcohol.

Herber (1969) advocated bubble flotation for separation of quartz from oligoclase, obtaining reduction of quartz content from about 20 to about 1 modal % in single runs. The steps for separation of the minerals in a granite involved (a) magnetic separation of ferromagnesian minerals (b) placing remaining sample in water containing HF sufficient to give pH of 2.5 (c) after 5 min, bubble flotation of feldspars with a 1% solution of alamine leaving most of the quartz behind (d) separation of K-feldspar from the oligoclase by use of a heavy liquid containing tetrabromoethane adjusted to a specific gravity of 2.590.

Plas, van der (1966) advocated bubble-flotation for separating feldspars from sediments and gave detailed instructions.

Trondle *et al.* (1969) described flotation of kaolinite and feldspar using amines as collectors.

Magnetic Separation. Usually magnetic separation successfully separates diamagnetic feldspars with other framework silicates from ferromagnesian minerals and opaques, but is of little value for separating the framework silicates from each other. However certain feldspars contain sufficient Fe-rich impurities to permit some separation by this technique, and dark feldspars should always be tested. High-field separators using super-magnets are particularly useful for separation of feldspars.

12.8.2 Rapid Visual Identification

Color Staining. This technique involves surface disintegration by an etching agent followed by reaction with an appropriate selective coloring agent.

Potassium in feldspar is revealed by the yellow color developed by reaction with sodium cobaltinitrite as first developed by Gabriel and Cox (1929). Many minor changes in procedure and equipment have been published. Keith (1939) reported distinction between nepheline and K-feldspar by an HCl etch followed by adsorption of malachite green by the nepheline and by reaction of the K-feldspar with sodium cobaltinitrite. Plagioclase was unaffected. Chayes (1952) gave details of his recommended modification of the Gabriel-Cox method for coloring K-feldspar yellow by sodium cobaltinitrite after an HF etch of the uncovered thin section. He noted problems with cryptoperthite and with Na-rich K-feldspars from volcanic rocks (i.e. sanidines), and recommended times and temperatures. Chayes and Zies (1961) further discussed the problems of staining K-feldspars from volcanic rocks. Rosenblum (1956) and Dawson and Crawley (1963) described various technical improvements of the procedure used by Chayes. Hayes and Klugman (1959) discussed the staining of feldspars in sedimentary rocks. Nold and Erickson (1967) desribed convenient modifications for use in the field. Broch (1961) recommended that the stained thin section be examined using light incident at 15° to the surface, thereby permitting distinction between etched plagioclase (gray-white) from unetched quartz (dark-gray), as well as from the K-feldspar (yellow). See also Lyons (1971) and Sclar and Fahey (1972).

Reeder and McAllister (1957) suggested identification of feldspars from non-aluminous minerals by etching followed by reaction with hemateine which reveals Al by a lilac blue color. Application to sands and soils of staining techniques was discussed. Plas, van der (1966) gave a detailed procedure for staining of grains and of rock slabs and thin sections in two parallel procedures, one with sodium cobaltinitrite to reveal K-feldspar, and one with hemateine to reveal total feldspar.

Bailey and Stevens (1960) invented a method for staining for Ca by (a) etching with HF (b) dipping in BaCl$_2$ to produce ion-exchange of Ba for Ca (c) treatment with potassium rhodizonate to yield the brick-red Ba form. They reported that the stain works for plagioclase more calcic than An$_3$. For albite, they suggested etching followed by ion-exchange with KCl to permit application with sodium cobaltinitrite.

Laniz et al. (1964) described procedures for sequential staining of plagioclase with amaranth and K-feldspar with cobaltinitrite to yield a brillant red and yellow contrast. The amaranth is not specific for plagioclase, but other Ca-minerals can be distinguished by the degree of the stain and by normal optical methods. Sodium-rich plagioclase must be ion-exchanged with CaCl$_2$ after etching. Boone and Wheeler (1968) recommended an additional brief etch between the two staining steps. They also described a method for distinguishing K-rich feldspar from cordierite by staining with cobaltinitrite for the former and trypan blue for the latter. However they did not obtain consistent results in staining plagioclase–cordierite–K-feldspar rocks by amaranth, trypan and cobaltinitrite.

Ford and Boudette (1968) described the problems of staining anorthoclase which can easily be misidentified as plagioclase. They recommended an optical examination using normal techniques followed by careful application of a slightly modified version of the technique of Laniz et al.

Laduron (1966) reviewed staining techniques for thin sections.

Other Techniques. Quantitative analysis of feldspars in mechanical mixtures using X-ray powder methods must be made cautiously. Guinier powder methods and monochromatized diffractometer methods are likely to be best because of high angular resolution. The intensity and position of lines in feldspars varies so much with chemical composition, order-disorder and texture that extreme caution must be used. Calibration with synthetic mixtures should be used: these mixtures should be made from similar minerals to those in the unknown.

Omori (1967) described a technique for semiquantitative determination of the contents of quartz, K-feldspar and oligoclase in acidic rocks using infra-red absorption patterns calibrated with known mixtures.

References

Abadian, M. (1972): Petrographie, Stoßwellenmetamorphose und Entstehung polymikter kristalliner Breccien im Nördlinger Ries. CMP **35**, 245–262.

Adams, L. H., Gibson, R. E. (1929): The elastic properties of certain basic rocks and of their constituent minerals. Proc. Nat. Acad. Sci. (Washington) **15**, 713–724.

Adams, L. H., Williamson, E. D. (1923): The compressibility of minerals and rocks at high pressures. Jour. Franklin Inst. **195**, 475–529.

Ahlers, L. (1924): Über die Dichte von Quarz, Orthoklas, Albit und Anorthit. ZK **59**, 293–334.

Ahrens, T. J., Gregson, V. G., Jr. (1964): Shock compression of crustal rocks: data for quartz, calcite and plagioclase rocks. JGR **69**, 4839–4873.

Ahrens, T. J., Liu, H.-P. (1973): A shock-induced phase change in orthoclase. JGR **78**, 1274–1278.

Ahrens, T. J., Rosenberg, J. T. (1968): Shock metamorphism: experiments on quartz and plagioclase. In: French, B. M., Short, N. M. (Eds.): Shock metamorphism of natural materials, pp. 59–81. Baltimore: Mono Book Corp.

Ahrens, T. J., Petersen, C. F., Rosenberg, J. T. (1969): Shock compression of feldspars. JGR **74**, 2727–2738.

Aitken, F. K., Gold, D. P. (1968): The structural state of potash feldspar: A possible criterion for meteorite impact? In: French, B. M., Short, N. M. (Eds.): Shock metamorphism of natural materials, pp. 509 – 518. Baltimore: Mono Book Corp.

Alexandrov, K. S., Ryzhova, T. V. (1962): Elastic properties of rock-forming minerals, III, feldspars. Bull. Acad. Sci. USSR, Geophys. ser., English trans., No. 2, 129 – 131.

Arndt, J., Häberle, F. (1973): Thermal expansion and glass transition temperatures of synthetic glasses of plagioclase-like compositions. CMP **39**, 175 – 183.

Aronson, J. R., Bellotti, L. H., Eckroad, S. W., Emslie, A. G., McConnell, R. K., Thüna, P. C. von (1970): Infrared spectra and radiative thermal conductivity of minerals at high temperatures. JGR **75**, 3443 – 3456.

Avdonin, V. A. (1961): Amazonite from the Uvil'da alkaline belt in the Urals. Trudy Gorno-Geol. Inst., Akad. Nauk SSSR, No. 56, 77 – 80. In Russian.

Bächtiger, K. (1967): Die Thermolumineszenz einiger skandinavischer und nordamerikanischer Plagioklase. (Teil V der Laboratoriumsuntersuchungen an Plagioklasen). SMPM **47**, 365 – 384.

Bailey, E. H., Stevens, R. E. (1960): Selective staining of K-feldspar and plagioclase on rock slabs and thin sections. AM **45**, 1020 – 1025.

Bakken, R., Rosenqvist, I. T. (1952): Note on different modifications of alkali feldspar. Research **5**, 1 – 3.

Barth, T. F. W. (1969): Feldspars, 261 pp. New York and London: Wiley Interscience.

Bassett, H. (1956): The colouring agent in amazon-stone (amazonite). Records Geol. Surv. Tanganyika **3**, 97 – 99.

Bell, P. M., Chao, E. T. C. (1970): Annealing experiments with naturally and experimentally shocked feldspar glasses. ARDGL, Yearbook 68, 336 – 339.

Bell, P. M., Mao, H. K. (1973): An analytical study of iron in plagioclase from Apollo 16 soils 64501, 64502, 64802, rock 66095, and Apollo 15 rock 15475. Lunar Science IV. 57 – 59. Lunar Science Institute.

Belyankin, D. S. (1916): On the specific gravity and refraction of the potash-soda feldspars. Izvest. Petrograd Polytechnic Inst. **24**, 437 – 452. In Russian.

Binns, R. A. (1966): Stony meteorites bearing maskelynite. N **214**, 1111 – 1112.

Blair, I. M., Edgington, J. A. (1970): Luminescence and thermoluminescence under 159 MeV proton bombardment of the lunar material returned by Apollo 11. Proc. Apollo 11 Lunar Science Conf. **3**, 2001 – 2012. New York: Pergamon Press.

Boone, G. M., Wheeler, E. P. (1968): Staining for cordierite and feldspars in thin section. AM **53**, 327 – 331.

Borg, I. Y., Handin, J. (1966): Experimental deformation of crystalline rocks. Tectonophysics **3**, No. 4, 249 – 368.

Borg, I. Y., Heard, H. C. (1967): Further studies on experimentally deformed plagioclase. In: Heard, H. C. (Ed.). Rock deformation and the deformation mechanisms in torsion tests. Final report: Project Vela-Uniform. Advanced Research Projects Agency.

Borg, I. Y., Heard, H. C. (1969): Mechanical twinning and slip in experimentally deformed plagioclases. CMP **23**, 128 – 135.

Borg, I. Y., Heard, H. C. (1970): Experimental deformation of plagioclases, p. 375 – 403. In: Paulitsch, P. (Ed.): Experimental and natural rock deformation. Berlin-Heidelberg-New York: Springer.

Bottinga, Y., Weill, D. F. (1970): Densities of liquid silicate systems calculated from partial molar volumes of oxide components. AJS **269**, 169 – 182.

Brace, W. F., Walsh, J. B, (1962): Some direct measurements of the surface energy of quartz and orthoclase. AM **47**, 1111 – 1122.

Bridgman, P. W. (1928): The linear compressibility of thirteen natural crystals. AJS **215**, 287 – 296.

Bridgman, P. W. (1948): Rough compressions of 177 substances to 40000 kg/cm^2. Amer. Acad. Arts Sciences Proc. **76**, 71 – 87.

Bridgwater, D., Harry, W. T. (1968): Anorthosite xenoliths and plagioclase megacrysts in Precambrian intrusions of south Greenland. Medd. om Grønland **185**, No. 2, 1 – 243.

Broch, O. A. (1961): Quick identification of potash feldspar, plagioclase, and quartz for quantitative thin section analysis. AM **46**, 752 – 753.

Brown, F. F., Pritchard, A. M. (1969): The Mössbauer spectrum of iron orthoclase. EPSL **5**, 259 – 260.

Buckenham, M. H., Rogers, J. (1954): Flotation of quartz and feldspar by dodecylamine. Trans. Inst. Mining Met. **64**, 11 – 30.

Bunch, T. E. (1968): Some characteristics of selected minerals from craters. In: French, B. M., Short, N. M. (Eds.): Shock metamorphism of natural materials, pp. 413–432. Baltimore: Mono Book Corp.

Bunch, T. E., Cohen, A. J., Dence, M. R. (1967): Natural terrestrial maskelynite. AM **52**, 244–253.

Bunch, T. E., Cohen, A. J., Dence, M. R. (1968): Shock-induced structural disorder in plagioclase and quartz. In: French, B. M., Short, N. M. (Eds.): Shock metamorphism of natural materials, pp. 509–518. Baltimore: Mono Book Corp.

Bunch, T. E., Keil, K., Olsen, E. (1970): Mineralogy and petrology of silicate inclusions in iron meteorites. CMP **25**, 297–340.

Carter, N. L. (1971): Static deformation of silica and silicates. JGR **76**, 5514–5540.

Čech, F., Misař, Z., Povondra, P. (1971): A green lead-containing orthoclase. TMPM **15**, 213–231.

Černý, P., Macek, J. (1972): The Tanco pegmatite at Bernic Lake, Manitoba. V. Coloured potassium feldspars. CM **11**, 679–689.

Chao, E. C. T. (1967): Shock effects in certain rock-forming minerals. S **156**, 192–202.

Chao, E. C. T. (1968a): Pressure and temperature histories of impact metamorphosed rocks — based on petrographic observations. In: French, B. M., Short, N. M. (Eds.): Shock metamorphism of natural materials, pp. 135–158. Baltimore: Mono Book Corp.

Chao, E. C. T. (1968b): Pressure and temperature histories of impact metamorphosed rocks — based on petrographic observations. NJMA **108**, 209–246.

Chao, E. C. T., Bell, P. M. (1969): Annealing characteristics of dense feldspar glass. ARDGL, Yearbook 67, 126–130.

Chao, E. C. T., James, O. B., Minkin, J. A., Boreman, J. A., Jackson, E. D., Raleigh, C. B. (1970): Petrology of unshocked crystalline rocks and evidence of impact metamorphism in Apollo 11 returned lunar sample. Proc. Apollo 11 Lunar Science Conf. **1**, 287–314. New York: Pergamon Press.

Chayes, F. (1952): Notes on the staining of potash feldspar with sodium cobaltinitrite in thin section. AM **37**, 337–340.

Chayes, F., Zies, E. G. (1961): Staining of alkali feldspars from volcanic rocks. ARDGL, Yearbook 60, 172–173.

Christensen, N. I. (1966): Compressional wave velocities in single crystals of alkali feldspar at pressures to 10 kilobars. JGR **71**, 3113–3116.

Chudoba, K. (1936): Dichte und chemische Zusammensetzung der Plagioklase auf ternärer Grundlage. ZM, Abt. A, 1–8.

Clark, S. P. Jr., Ed. (1966): Handbook of physical constants. Geol. Soc. Amer., memoir No. 97, 587 pp.

Crozaz, G., Haack, U., Hair, M., Maurette, M., Walker, R., Woolum, D. (1970): Nuclear track studies of ancient solar radiations and dynamic lunar surface processes. Proc. Apollo 11 Lunar Science Conf. **3**, 2051–2080. New York: Pergamon Press.

Curie, D. (1960): Luminescence cristalline. Paris: Dunod Press.

Czygan, W. (1967): Ein Verfahren zur Trennung von Nephelin und Feldspat mit Hilfe der Flotation. NJMM 84–89.

Dalrymple, G. B., Doell, R. R. (1970): Thermoluminescence of lunar samples from Apollo 11. Proc. Apollo 11 Lunar Science Conf. **3**, 2051–2080. New York: Pergamon Press.

Davies, G. F., Anderson, D. L. (1971): Revised shock-wave equations of state for high-pressure phases of rocks and minerals. JGR **76**, 2617–2627.

Dawson, K. R., Crawley, W. D. (1963): An improved technique for staining potash feldspars. CM **7**, 805–808.

Day, A. L., Allen, E. T., Iddings, J. P. (1905): The isomorphism and thermal properties of the feldspars. Part I Thermal study. Part II Optical study. Carnegie Inst., Washington, Pub. No. 31, 95 pp. (or AJS **169**, 93–142).

DeCarli, P. S., Jamieson, J. C. (1959): Formation of an amorphous form of quartz under shock conditions. J. Chem. Phys. **31**, 1675–1676.

Dence, M. R. (1968): Shock zoning at Canadian craters: petrography and structural implications. In: French, B. M., Short, N. M. (Eds.): Shock metamorphism of natural materials, pp. 169–184. Baltimore: Mono Book Corp.

Dence, M. R., Douglas, J. A. V., Plant, A. G., Traill, R. J. (1970): Petrology, mineralogy and deformation of Apollo 11 samples. Proc. Apollo 11 Lunar Science Conf., **1**, 315–340. New York: Pergamon Press.

Doeglas, D. J., Favejee, J. Ch. L., Nota, D. J. G., Plas, L. van der, (1965): On the identification of feldspars in soils. Mededel. van de landbouwhogeschool Wageningen **65**–9, 1–14.

Douglas, J. A. (1907): On changes of physical constants which take place in certain minerals and igneous rocks, on the passage from the crystalline to the glassy state, with a short note on eutectic mixtures. QJGS **63**, 145 – 161.

Duke, M. B. (1968): The Shergotty meteorite: magmatic and shock metamorphic features. In: French, B. M., Short, N. M. (Eds.): Shock metamorphism of natural materials, pp. 613 – 621. Baltimore: Mono Book Corp.

Duke, M. B., Silver, L. T. (1967): Petrology of eucrites, howardites and mesosiderites. GCA **31**, 1637 – 1665.

Dworak, U. (1969): Stosswellenmetamorphose des Anorthosites von Manicouagan Krater, Québec, Canada. CMP **24**, 306 – 347.

Dworschak, F. (1962): Decoloration measurements on some opaque and optically turbid minerals (fluorite, amazonite, microcline and fibrous salt). SAWW **170**, 1 – 9. In German.

Emmons, R. C. (1953): Selected petrogenic relationships of plagioclase feldspars. Geol. Soc. Amer., memoir No. 52, 142 pp.

Engelhardt, W. von, Arndt, J., Müller, W. F., Stöffler, D. (1970): Shock metamorphism of lunar rocks and origin of the regolith at the Apollo 11 landing site. Proc. Apollo 11 Lunar Science Conf. **1**, 363 – 384. New York: Pergamon Press.

Engelhardt, W. von, Stöffler, D. (1968): Stages of shock metamorphism in crystalline rocks of the Ries Basin, Germany. In: French, B. M., Short, N. M. (Eds.): Shock metamorphism of natural materials, pp. 159 – 168. Baltimore: Mono Book Corp.

Eucken, A., Kuhn, G. (1928): New measurements of the heat conductivity of solid crystalline substances at $0°$ and $-190°$. Zeit. phys. Chemie **134**, 193 – 219. In German.

Faust, G. T. (1936): The fusion relations of iron-orthoclase, with a discussion of the evidence for the existence of an iron-orthoclase molecule in feldspars. AM **21**, 735 – 763.

Faye, G. H. (1969): The optical absorption spectrum of tetrahedrally bonded Fe^{3+} in orthoclase. CM **10**, 112 – 116.

Fleischer, R. L., Haines, E. L., Hart, H. R., Woods, R. T., Comstock, G. M. (1970): The particle track record of the Sea of Tranquillity. Proc. Apollo 11 Lunar Science Conf. **3**, 2103 – 2120. New York: Pergamon Press.

Ford, A. B., Boudette, E. L. (1968): On the staining of anorthoclase. AM **53**, 331 – 334.

French, B. M., Short, N. M. (Eds.) (1968): Shock metamorphism of natural materials. Baltimore: Mono Book Corp.

Gabriel, A., Cox, E. P. (1929): A staining method for quantitative determination of certain rock minerals. AM **14**, 290 – 292.

Garlick, G. F. J. (1963): Luminescence in crystals. New York: John Wiley.

Garlick, G. F. J., Lamb, W. E., Steigmann, G. A. (1971): Thermoluminescence of lunar samples and terrestrial plagioclases. Proc. Second Lunar Science Conf. **3**, 2277 – 2283, The M.I.T. Press.

Geake, J. E., Walker, G., Mills, A. A., Garlick, G. F. J. (1971): Luminescence of Apollo lunar samples. Proc. Second Lunar Science Conf. **3**, 2265 – 2275. The M.I.T. Press.

Geake, J. E., Walker, G., Mills, A. A., Garlick G. F. J. (1972): Luminescence of lunar material excited by protons or electrons. Third Lunar Sci. Conf., Houston, Lunar Science Institute Contr. No. 88, 294 – 296.

Gibbons, R. V. (1973): Experimentally induced shock effects in plagioclase and pyroxene. Trans. Am. Geophys. Union **54**, 351 (Abs.).

Haberlandt, H., Köhler, A. (1940): Investigations on luminescence of feldspars and other rare earth-containing minerals. Chem. Erde **13**, 363 – 386. In German.

Häkli, A. (1960): On high temperature alkali feldspars of some volcanic rocks of Kenya and northern Tanganyika. BCGF **188**, 99 – 108.

Hayes, J. R., Klugman, M. A. (1959): Feldspar staining methods. JSP **29**, 227 – 232.

Herber, L. J. (1969): Separation of feldspar from quartz by flotation. AM **54**, 1212 – 1215.

Hintze, C. (1893): Handbuch der Mineralogie. VII. Silicate und Titanate. Leipzig.

Holmquist, P. J. (1914): Die Schleifhärte der Feldspate. Geol. Fören. Förh. (Stockholm) **36**, 401 – 431.

Horai, K. (1971): Thermal conductivity of rock-forming minerals. JGR **76**, 1278 – 1308.

Hwang, F. S. W. (1970): Thermoluminescence dating applied to volcanic lava. N **227**, 940 – 941.

Ioffe, V. A., Yanchevskaya, I. S. (1958): Dielectric losses in feldspars. Soviet Phys. – Techn. Physics **28**, 1983 – 1991.

James, O. B. (1969): Jadeite: shock-induced formation from oligoclase, Ries crater, Germany. S **165**, 1005 – 1008.

Kapustin, N. P. (1939): Dependence of colour of amazonite on rubidium content of the mineral. Izvest. Akad. Nauk. SSSR., Geol. Ser. **3**, 111 – 115. In Russian.

Katz, M. Ya., Muravyov, V. I. (1970): Density and optical data of low-temperature feldspars and mica. Sedimentology **15**, 123 – 137.

Keith, M. L. (1939): Selective staining to facilitate Rosiwal analysis. AM **24**, 561 – 565.

Khitarov, N. I., Slutskiy, A. B. (1965): The effect of pressure on the melting temperatures of albite and basalt (based on electroconductivity measurements). Geochemistry International **2**, 1034 – 1041. Trans. from Geokhimiya, No. 12, 1395 – 1403.

Khitarov, N. T., Slutsky, A. V. (1967): Influence de la température et de la pression sur la conductibilité électrique de l'albite et du basalt. J. Chim. Phys. **64**, 1085 – 91.

Kleeman, J. D. (1971): Formation of diaplectic glass by experimental shock loading of orthoclase. JGR **76**, 5499 – 5503.

Köhler, A., Wieden, P. (1954): Vorläufige Versuche in der Feldspatgruppe mittels der DTA. NJMM **12**, 249 – 252.

Kume, S., Matsumoto, T., Koizumi, M. (1966): Dense form of germanate orthoclase ($KAlGe_3O_8$). JGR **71**, 4999 – 5000.

Kuts, V. P. (1964): The origin of colour in amazonites. In: Chemical composition and internal structure of minerals. Kiev, Nauk. Dumka, 197 – 201. (Russian with English summary).

Laduron, D. (1966): Sur les procédés de coloration sélective des feldspaths en lamé mince. Soc. Geol. Belgique Ann. **89**, 281 – 294.

Laniz, R. V., Stevens, R. E., Norman, M. B. (1964): Staining of plagioclase feldspar and other minerals with F. D. and C. Red No. 2. USGS., Prof. Paper **501**, B 152 – B 153.

Larsen, E. S. (1909): The relation between the refractive index and the density of some crystallized silicates and their glasses. AJS **28**, Ser. 4, 263 – 274.

Lyons, P. C. (1971): Staining of feldspars on rock-slab surfaces for modal analysis. MM **38**, 518 – 519.

Manning, P. G. (1970): Racah parameters and their relationship to lengths and covalencies of Mn^{2+}- and Fe^{3+}-oxygen bonds in silicates. CM **10**, 677 – 688.

Mao, H. K., Bell, P. M. (1973): Crystal field measurements of iron plagioclase. Trans. Am. Geophys. Union **54**, 503 (Abs.).

Marfunin, A. S., Bershov, L. V. (1970): Paramagnetic center(s) in feldspar and their possible crystallochemical and petrologic significance. DAN, Earth Sci. Sect. **193**, 129 – 131. Trans. from DAN **193**, 412 – 414.

Mariano, A. N., Ito, J., Ring, P. J. (1973): Cathodoluminescence of plagioclase feldspars. Geol. Soc. Am., Abstr. with Programs **5**, 726.

Maury, R. (1965a): Elucidation of the order-disorder transformation in albite by measurement of electrical conductivity. Compt. Rend. Acad. Sci. (Paris) **261**, 3165 – 3168.

Maury, R. (1965b): Mise en évidence de la transformation ordre-désordre de l'albite par la mesure de la conductibilité électrique. Compt. Rend. Acad. Sci. (Paris) **261**, 3165 – 3168.

Maury, R. (1967): Conductibilité électrique des tectosilicates. Doctoral thesis presented to the Faculty of Sciences, Paris.

Maury, R. (1968): Conductibilité électrique des tectosilicates. I. Méthode et résultats experimentaux. II. Discussion des résultats. BSFMC **91**, 267 – 278 and 355 – 366.

Maury, R., Iiyama, J. T. (1967): Conductibilité électrique des feldspaths. SMPM **47**, 1 – 11.

McDougall, D. J. (Ed.) (1968): Thermoluminescence of geological materials. New York: Academic Press.

McQueen, R. G., Marsh, S. P., Fritz, J. N. (1967): Hugoniot equation of state of twelve rocks. JGR **72**, 4999 – 5036.

Merwin, H. E. (1911): The temperature stability ranges, density, chemical composition and optical and crystallographic properties of the alkali feldspars. J. Nat. Acad. Sci. (Washington) **1**, 59 – 60.

Milton, D. J., DeCarli, P. S. (1963): Maskelynite: formation by explosive shock. S **140**, 67 – 68.

Mookherjee, A., Sahu, K. C. (1960): Microhardness of the plagioclase series. AM **45**, 742 – 744.

Nash, D. B., Greer, R. T. (1970): Luminescence properties of Apollo 11 lunar samples and implications for solar-excited lunar luminescence. Proc. Apollo 11 Lunar Science Conf. **3**, 2341 – 2350. New York: Pergamon Press.

Nemecz, E. (1959): A study of the interdependence of crystal lattice defects and mineral genesis by thermogravimetric methods. Acta Geol. Acad. Sci. Hungary **6**, 119 – 151.

Nold, J. L., Erickson, K. P. (1967): Changes in K-feldspar staining methods and adaptations for field use. AM **52**, 1575 – 1576.

References 599

Nye, J. F. (1960): Physical properties of crystals. Oxford: University Press.
Oftedal, I. (1957): Heating experiments on amazonite. MM **31**, 417 – 419.
Oliver, R. L., Schultz, P. K. (1968): Colour in charnockites. MM **36**, 1135 – 1138.
Omori, K. (1967): Infrared study of mechanical mixtures of quartz, orthoclase and oligoclase from 11 to 25 microns. Min. Journ. (Japan) **5**, 169 – 179.
Panov, Ye. N., Sverdlov, Z. M., Alekseyeva, L. N. (1971): Thermoluminescence of quartz, plagioclase and potash feldspar from granitoids of northeastern Transbaykalia. Int. Geol. Rev. **12**, 962 – 970. Trans. from Russian: Geologiya i Geofizika, No. 11, 68 – 77 (1969).
Parkhomenko, E. I. (1967): Electrical properties of rocks. New York: Plenum Press.
Petrović, R. (1972): Alkali ion diffusion in alkali feldspars. Ph. D. thesis, Yale University.
Plas, L. van der (1966): The identification of detrital feldspars, 305 pp. Amsterdam: Elsevier.
Plyusnin, G. S. (1969): Color of amazonites. (in Russian). Zap. Vses. Min. Obschch. **98**, 3 – 17.
Poldervaart, A. (1950): Correlation of physical properties and chemical composition in the plagioclase, olivine and orthopyroxene series. AM **35**, 1067 – 1079.
Price, P. B., Lal, D., Tamhane, A. S., Perelygin, V. P. (1973): Characteristics of tracks of ions of $14 \leq Z \leq 36$ in common rock silicates. EPSL **19**, 377 – 395.
Przibram, K. (1956): Color and luminescence of feldspars-with an addendum: anhydrite fluorescence reversible by tempering. Österr. Akad. Wiss., Math.-naturw. Kl., Sitzber. Abt. II **165**, 281 – 311.
Quaide, W., Bunch, T. (1970): Impact metamorphism of lunar surface materials. Proc. Apollo 11 Lunar Science Conf. **1**, 711 – 729. New York: Pergamon Press.
Radcliffe, S. V., Heuer, A. H., Fisher, R. M., Christie, J. M., Griggs, D. T. (1970): High voltage (800 KV) electron petrography of Type B rock from Apollo 11. Proc. Apollo 11 Lunar Science Conf. **1**, 731 – 748. New York: Pergamon Press.
Ramberg, H. (1961): Artificial and natural photoelastic effects in quartz and feldspars. AM **46**, 934 – 951.
Reeder, S. W., McAllister, A. L. (1957): A staining method for the quantitative determination of feldspars in rocks and sands from soils. Canadian Jour. Soil Sci. **37**, 57 – 59.
Ringwood, A. E., Reid, A. F., Wadsley, A. D. (1967 a): High pressure $KAlSi_3O_8$, an aluminosilicate with sixfold coordination. AC **23**, 1093 – 1095.
Ringwood, A. E., Reid, A. F., Wadsley, A. D. (1967 b): High pressure transformation of alkali aluminosilicates and aluminogermanates. Earth and Planetary Science Letters **3**, 38 – 40.
Robertson, P. B. (1972): Experimental deformation of microcline. Amer. Geophys. Union Mtg., abstr. P 2 in Transactions, p. 427.
Robertson, P. B., Dence, M. R., Vos, M. A. (1968): Deformation in rock-forming minerals from Canadian craters. In: French, B. M., Short, N. M. (Eds.): Shock metamorphism of natural materials, pp. 433 – 452. Baltimore: Mono Book Corp.
Rosenblum, S. (1956): Improved techniques for staining potash feldspars. AM **41**, 662 – 664.
Rosenqvist, I. T. (1952): The metamorphic facies and the feldspar minerals. Univ. Bergen Årbok, Naturvit. rekke, No. 4, 1 – 108.
Rothschild, S. (1928): The phosphorescence of fluorite and orthoclase. Festschrift Victor Goldschmidt (Heidelberg) 243 – 255. Mineralog. Absts. **4**, 210. In German.
Rottenbach, E. (1936): Die Dichte des reinen Kalifeldspatanteils im Mikroklin und dessen allgemeine chemische Zusammensetzung ZM, Abt. A, 231 – 239.
Rudenko, S. A., Vokhmentsev, A. Ya. (1969): Plagioclase-amazonite. DAN **184**, 113 – 115. Trans. from DAN **184**, 422 – 424.
Ryzhova, T. V. (1964): Elastic properties of plagioclase. Izvest. Acad. Nauk, SSSR, Ser. **7**, 633 – 635. (English trans. from Russian 1049 – 1051).
Ryzhova, T. V., Aleksandrov, K. S. (1965): The elastic properties of potassium-sodium feldspars. Izvest. Acad. Nauk, SSSR, Physics of the Solid Earth, No. 1, 98 – 102. (English trans.).
Sanford, F., Hedvall, J. A. (1962): The cause of color of an amazonite preparation. Trans. Chalmers Univ. Technol., Gothenburg, No. **257**, 7 pp.
Schulz, K. (1924): Numerische Angaben über physikalische und chemische Eigenschaften der Mineralien. C. Die Wärmeleitung in Mineralien etc. FMKP **9**, 211 – 411. (Feldspar data on p. 329).
Sclar, C. B. (1970): Shock metamorphism of lunar rocks and fines from Tranquillity Base. Proc. Apollo 11 Lunar Science Conf. **1**, 849 – 864. New York: Pergamon Press.
Sclar, C. B., Fahey, J. J. (1972): The staining mechanism of potassium feldspar and the origin of hieratite. AM **57**, 287 – 291.
Seifert, K. E. (1965): Deformation bands in albite. AM **50**, 1469 – 1472.

Seifert, K. E. (1969): Strength of Adirondack anorthosite at elevated temperatures and pressures. BGSA **80**, 2053 – 2060.

Seifert, K. E. (1971): Triaxial compression tests on Adirondack anorthosite. Trans. Amer. Geophys. Union **52**, 344, abstr. T 14.

Seifert, K. E. (1973): Rapid structural state conversions in intermediate composition plagioclase. CMP **41**, 53 – 56.

Sen, S. K. (1956): Translation gliding in deformed plagioclase from a banded norite near Willow Lake, Oregon. Proc. 20th Intern. Geol. Congr., Mexico City, 263 – 274.

Short, N. M. (1968a): Nuclear-explosion-induced microdeformation of rocks: an aid to the recognition of meteorite impact structures. In: French, B. M., Short, N. M. (Eds.): Shock metamorphism of natural materials, pp. 185 – 210. Baltimore: Mono Book Corp.

Short, N. M. (1968b): Experimental microdeformation of rock materials by shock pressures from laboratory-scale impacts and explosions. In: French, B. M., Short, N. M. (Eds.): Shock metamorphism of natural materials, pp. 219 – 242. Baltimore: Mono Book Corp.

Short, N. M. (1970a): Progressive shock metamorphism of quartzite ejecta from the Sedan nuclear explosion crater. JG **78**, 705 – 732.

Short, N. M. (1970b): Evidence and implications of shock metamorphism in lunar samples. Proc. Apollo 11 Lunar Science Conf. **1**, 865 – 871. New York: Pergamon Press.

Simmons, G. (1964): Velocity of compressional waves in various minerals at pressures to 10 Kilobars. JGR **69**, 1117 – 1121.

Sippel, R. F. (1971): Luminescence petrography of the Apollo 12 rocks and comparative features in terrestrial rocks and meteorites. Proc. Second Lunar Sci. Conf. **1**, 247 – 263. The M.I.T. Press.

Sippel, R. F., Spencer, A. B. (1970): Luminescence petrography and properties of lunar crystalline rocks and breccias. Proc. Apollo 11 Lunar Science Conf. **3**, 2413 – 2426. New York: Pergamon Press.

Smith, J. V., Stenstrom, R. C. (1965): Electron-excited luminescence as a petrologic tool. JG **73**, 627 – 635.

Starkey, J. (1964): Glide twinning in the plagioclase feldspars. Metall. Soc. Conf. **25**, 177 – 191.

Starkey, J. (1968): The geometry of kink bands in crystals. A simple model. CMP **19**, 133 – 141.

Stöffler, D. (1967): Deformation und Umwandlung von Plagioklas durch Stosswellen in den Gesteinen des Nördlinger Ries. CMP **16**, 51 – 83.

Stöffler, D. (1972): Deformation and transformation of rock-forming minerals by natural and experimental shock processes I. Behavior of minerals under shock compression. Fortschr. Miner. **49**, 50 – 113.

Stöffler, D., Hornemann, U. (1972): Quartz and feldspar glasses produced by natural and experimental shock. Meteoritics **7**, 371 – 394.

Taylor, S. R., Heier, K. S., Sverdrup, T. L. (1960): Contributions to the mineralogy of Norway. V. Trace-element variations in three generations of feldspars from the Landsverk I pegmatite, Evje, Southern Norway. NGT **40**, 133 – 156.

Towle, L. C., Riecker, R. E. (1968): The pressure and temperature dependence of the shear strength of minerals. J. Appl. Phys. **39**, 4807 – 4811.

Trondle, H. M. *et al.* (1969): The flotation of kaolinite and feldspar with amines as collectors. Keram. Zeit. **21**, 423 – 427. (In German). Brit. Ceram. Abstr., abstr. 600/70, 1970.

Tschermak, G. (1872): Die Meteoriten von Shergotty und Gopalpur. SAWW **65**, 122 – 146.

Tschermak, G. (1883): Beitrag zur Klassifikation der Meteoriten. SAWW **88**, 347 – 371.

Turkowsky, C. (1969): Electron-microscopic observation of artificially produced alpha-recoil tracks in albite. EPSL **5**, 492 – 496.

Tuttle, O. F., Bowen, N. L. (1950): High-temperature albite and contiguous feldspars: JG **58**, 572 – 583.

Vaidya, S. N., Bailey, S., Pasternack, T., Kennedy, G. C. (1973): Compressibility of fifteen minerals to 45 kilobars. JGR **78**, 6893 – 6898.

Vernon, R. H. (1965): Plagioclase twins in some mafic gneisses from Broken Hill, Australia. MM **35**, 488 – 507.

Yoder, H. S., Weir, C. E. (1951): Change of free energy with pressure of the reaction nepheline + albite = 2 jadeite. AJS **249**, 683 – 694.

Zhirov, K. K., Stishov, S. M. (1965): Geochemistry of amazonitization. Geochemistry International **2**, 16 – 24. Transl. from Geokhimiya, No. 1, 32 – 42.

Subject Index

Ab–An system   5-9
Ab–An–Or–H$_2$O system   9-11
Ab–Or system   2, 9
a diffraction, definition   8
adularia (see also K-feldspar)
   cell dimensions   228, 233, 235, 269
   diffuse diffractions   67, 191, 246-7, 269, 422
   electron optics   469-70
   electron spin resonance   545-6
   general   4, 14
   infra-red absorption   519-22
   light optics   368-9
   nomenclature   416, 418-36
   nuclear magnetic resonance   533-9
   X-ray diffraction   182, 184, 188, 196-7
albite (see also analbite, cleavelandite, high albite,
   low albite, monalbite, pericline)
   anomalous   226-7, 236-7, 263
   atomic coordinates   86
   authigenic   225, 227, 233
   bonding diagram   98
   cation-oxygen distances   91
   cell dimensions   219, 225-41, 258
   compressibility   569-71
   crystal structure, general   36
   deformation   577-8
   Δ indicator   288, 383-4
   electrical conductivity   564-6
   electric spin resonance   545-6
   environment of Na   114, 121
   equilibrium   227, 236, 298-9
   general   2-13
   infra-red absorption   514-25
   lattice   182-3, 199
   light optics   379-89
   Na-exchanged K-feldspar   288, 232, 234,
     240-63
   nomenclature   436-9
   nuclear magnetic resonance   522-33
   optic axial angle   379-86
   optical dispersion   389
   phase relations, general   2-13
   refractive indices   386
   Si, Al order   68-9, 71, 74, 441, 521-5, 532-3
   symmetry inversion   295, 298–301, 337-9
   thermal conductivity   566-7
   thermal expansion   292-301
   thermal motion   122-4

albite (see also analbite, cleavelandite, high albite,
   low albite, monalbite, pericline)
   T–O distances   71, 88, 139
   T–O–T angles   90
   X-ray patterns   200, 202, 207, 211-3
Albite twin (see also twin: casual references
   omitted)
   anorthoclase   440, 447
   chessboard albite   237
   deformation   573-87
   electron optics   469-507
   geometry   182-3
   light optics   371-5
   microcline   390
   plagioclase   403-4
alkali feldspar (see also albite, anorthoclase,
   K-feldspar, perthite)
   cell dimensions   219, 222-305
   compressibility   569-71
   density   590-1
   electron optics   468-77, 503-4
   electron spin resonance   544-6
   general   2-14
   infra-red absorption   511-25
   light optics   379-91
   luminescence   559-63
   nomenclature   11-13, 416-50
   nuclear magnetic resonance   532-9
   optic axial angle   379-85, 404
   optic orientation   387-9
   optical determination   389-91
   phase diagram   2
   refractive indices   385-7
   stress-strain tensor   570-1
   symmetry inversion   301-5
   X-ray diffraction   181-97, 206-10
allophane   501
$\alpha\gamma$ plot, structural interpretation   267-9
$\alpha^*\gamma^*$ plot   259-65, 267-9, 302, 335
aluminum avoidance rule   79
amazonite
   electron spin resonance   547-8
   green color   556-8
ammonium feldspar (see buddingtonite)
analbite (see also albite)
   definition   299-300
   name   438

andesine (see also plagioclase)
  composition range   12, 444, 447
  name   450
anemousite   392
An–Or system   9
anorthite (see also plagioclase)
  atomic coordinates   86, 138
  b diffractions   137-40, 479-80
  β*γ* plot   318
  bonding diagram   99, 110
  Ca-O bonding   109-14
  cation-oxygen distances   91
  c diffractions   140-5, 480-3
  cell dimensions   219, 307-19
  crystal structure, general   36
  dielectric phenomena   566
  d.t.a. effect   150, 331
  domains   140-5, 479-83
  electric conductivity   565
  electron optics   465-7, 477-88
  electron spin resonance   546-7
  Euler angles   402
  general   1, 5-9
  infra-red absorption   514-8, 528-30
  jumping model of Ca   141-3
  lattice   199
  light optics   141, 150, 386, 394-405
  nomenclature   450-3
  nuclear magnetic resonance   539-41
  optic axial angle   395-6
  optical absorption   558
  optical inflexion   141, 150
  phase relations   4-11, 145-50
  refractive indices   386
  Si, Al order   74-8, 137-40, 539-41
  structural types   137-45
  thermal expansion   329-31
  T–O distances   88
  T–O–T angles   90
  X-ray pattern   203, 207-14
anorthoclase (see also high albite)
  α*γ* plot   261
  β*γ* plot   318
  cell dimensions   347-53
  light optics   379-91
  nomenclature   437-48
  symmetry inversion   301-5, 352-3, 437
  twinning   390, 436-43, 446-8
  X-ray pattern   193-4
anplagioclase   440
antiperthite (see also perthite)   12-3, 200-2, 441,
  448
antiphase boundary   53
antiphase vector   51
apatite   405, 559
atomic coordinates
  anorthite   86, 138

atomic coordinates
  other feldspars   86
  sanidine   28
atomic displacements   115-24
authigenic feldspars
  cell dimensions   225-47, 276
  optical identification   391
  structure vs. growth   423
aventurine   14, 559
average structure   78
axial ratios   218, 312-3

b diffractions
  anorthite and bytownite 137-40, 150, 477-80
  definition   8
  plagioclase   146-8, 157, 199, 203
B substitution (see also reedmergnerite)
  cell dimensions   219, 276, 356-7
  infra-red absorption   521
Ba substitution (see also celsian)
  cell dimensions   219, 221, 353-5,
  inversion   357
  light optics   406-8
  nomenclature   455-6
BaAl₂O₄   79
Bambauer nomenclature   450-2
banalsite   44
barbierite   439-40
Barth nomenclature   424-5
Baveno twin   181, 401
bc plot
  data   256-7
  structural interpretation   265-7
  vs. 2V   383-5
b*c* plot   257-65, 302, 434
bγ plot   240
b*γ* plot   238
Be substitution   557
bend-extinction contour   463
Beta function   314-5, 323
β*γ* plot   317-9, 323
Biot-Fresnel construction   404
birefringence (see also refractive indices)
  alkali feldspar   374-5, 385-7
body-centered anorthite (see anorthite)
Bøggild intergrowth
  electron optics   490-6, 503-4
  general   6-8, 13
  heat treatment   146
  infra-red absorption   526-8
  K-content   326
  nomenclature   453
  relation to e-plagioclase   172, 200
  X-ray pattern   199-200, 214
boundary
  anti-phase   134
  out-of-step   51

Bown-Gay X-ray method   180, 198-203
bright-field image   462
bubble flotation   592
buddingtonite
    cell dimensions   219
    crystal structure   36
    light optics   408
    name   457
bytownite (see also Huttenlocher intergrowth,
    plagioclase)
    composition range   12, 447
    name   450

c diffractions
    anorthite and bytownite   140-5, 150, 199,
        480-3
    definition   8
    plagioclase   147, 155, 199
calcite   204, 405
Carlsbad twin   181, 200
carnegieite substitution   392
cataclasis   572-87
cathodoluminescence   391, 558-62, 592
cell dimensions
    alkali feldspars   222-305
    anomalous   276-80
    effect of lattice strain   279-80
    effect of nonstoichiometry   250-2
    effect of Si, Al ordering   245
    end-member feldspars   219, 257-8
    general   217-222
    plagioclase   306-39, 347-53
    regression equations   252-5
    relation to ionic size   220-2
    structural interpretation   265-76, 319-22, 346
celsian (see also Ba substitution)
    atomic coordinates   86
    cation-oxygen distances   91
    cell dimensions   219, 353-5
    crystal structure, general   36
    general   1
    infra-red absorption   514-7
    light optics   386, 406-8
    Si, Al order   74-7
    T–O distances   76
    T–O–T angles   90
    thermal conductivity   566-7
    X-ray pattern   209
center of symmetry, evidence   39
cesium (see Cs)
Chao-Taylor model   157
charge balance   1, 79-80, 95, 100-1, 424
chemical alteration, electron optics   501-2
chemical formula, general   1
chemical spinodal   473
chessboard albite   268, 437

Cinnamon-Bailey, treatment of plagioclase
    170-1
clamping   196
clay minerals   204
cleavage   181, 503, 568, 572, 586
cleavelandite   14, 301, 557
    variety of albite   436-7
close-packing   39-43
clustering   52
coesite   11, 31-3
coherence   127-30
    effect on cell dimensions   223, 279
    electron optics   469-70
    X-ray patterns   193-4
coherent spinodal   3, 6, 8, 52, 473
color   556-8 (see also iridescence, schiller)
common orthoclase   419, 421 (see also ortho-
    clase)
compressibility   568-71
conoscopic optical method   367-9, 376-7
convergent vs. non-convergent order   54
cooperation   55
coordination polyhedron
    data   90-102, 107-15
    general   38
copper (see Cu)
cordierite   594
covalent bonding   24, 104, 541
crankshaft (see double-crankshaft)
critical temperature
    albite   441
    K-feldspar   423
cryptoperthite   3
    electron optics   470-7
    X-ray diffraction   193-5
crystal-chemical theory   23
crystal structure, general   1
Cs substitution   357, 557
Cu substitution   562

d diffractions
    anorthite   140-5
    definition   8
danburite   31, 43, 79
dark-field image   462
Debye model of thermal motion   123
Debye-Scherrer method   204, 206
deformation
    controlled uniaxial   572-8
    electron optics   464-7
    lamella   572-87
    shock   578-91
Δ, triclinic indicator   218, 287
$\Delta(\alpha^*\gamma^*)$
    definition   261-2
    vs. Al content   267-9
    vs. $\Delta(b^*c^*)$ 263-5

$\Delta(bc)$ and $\Delta(b^*c^*)$
  definition   261-2
  vs. Al content   266-7
  vs. $\Delta(\alpha^*\gamma^*)$ 263-5
density   569, 589-91
  vs. shock pressure   583-5
density modulation   130-2
detrital feldspar
  optical identification   391, 406
  separation   592
  X-ray identification   205
diagonal association   182-3
diaplectic   579-88
dielectric phenomena   564, 566
differential thermal analysis   150, 591
diffraction
  contrast   462-3
  from intergrowths   127-37
  from ordered patterns   132-7
  theory   22, 127-37, 164, 166-7
diffractometer   204-6, 280
diffusion   564
diffusive inversion   291, 303-4
dislocation
  effect on diffraction   129
  electron-optical data   464-8, 471, 495, 503
disorder, random   287
dispersion, optical   389
displacive inversion   291, 303-5
distant order   53
district transformation   145
domain
  boundary   52-5
  effect on cell dimensions   244-6, 267-9
  effect on optics   371-91, 421-36
  effect on physical properties   177-8
  twinning   290, 422
  wall energy   170-1
double-crankshaft
  flexing with temperature   289
  general   1, 27-30, 42, 87
  stereoscopic diagram   121

e diffractions
  coordinates   147, 151, 154, 199
  definition   8
  discontinuities   154-5
  e_1 vs. e_2 7, 9, 171-2
  effect of heat treatment   155-67
  electron optics   481-96
  general   8, 150-74, 199-203
  geometry   134
  heat treatment   146-9
  intensities   155, 165
  orientation of t 153
  T wavelength   153
  X-ray diffraction   199-203

elastic deformation   568-72, 582
electric quadrupole resonance
  (see nuclear magnetic resonance)
electrical phenomena   563-6
electron centers   544, 547-8
electron optics
  albite   469-507
  anorthite   465-7, 477-88
  K-feldspar   468-77, 504
  perthite   279, 471-7
  plagioclase   477-507
electron paramagnetic (spin) resonance   59, 511,
    544
electrostatic field gradient   530-1, 541-3
end-members, cell dimensions   218-22
engineering model   87, 94-7
entropy   19
epidote   200, 204, 405
e-plagioclase (see also plagioclase)
  atomic coordinates   173
  diffraction data   151-5
  electron optics   483-96, 501
  general   4-9, 150-74
  heat treatment   147, 155-7, 173-4
  models   157-74
  name   454
  ordering of M atoms   173
  ordering of T atoms   173
  out-of-step feature   172
  Patterson function   167-8
  petrologic occurrence   155-7
  sub-types   171-2
  thermodynamic description   174
  X-ray diffraction   201-2
equilibrium feldspar   227, 290
etching   471, 572
Euler angles   402-3
external scatter   369-71
extinction angle
  alkali feldspar   389
  K, Ba feldspar   406-8
  plagioclase   404-5
extinction contour   463

f diffractions
  definition   8
  electron optics   481-96
  geometry   134
  intensities   155, 165
  occurrence   152
  X-ray diffraction   199-203
fault (= out-of-step) vector   51
F substitution   557
Fe-feldspar (includes Fe substitution)
  cell dimensions   219
  color, yellow   556
  electrical conductivity   564-5

Fe-feldspar (includes Fe substitution)
  electron spin resonance   544-7
  infra-red absorption   514-6
  light optics   386, 408
  luminescence   562
  Mössbauer resonance   548-53
  nuclear magnetic resonance   533, 539
  RbFeSi₃O₈   69
  scanning electron microscopy   503
  Si, Al order   69
  shock deformation'   584-5
Feldspar and felspar, origin of names   415-6
Ferro-displacivity   145
flexible analog   30-1
force constant   513-4
fracture   503, 572-87
framework
  cell dimensions, effect of distortion   223
  concept   26
  contraction around small M   95-100
  distortion, general   38
  engineering model   87, 94-7
  strain   87

gallium substitution (see Ga-feldspar)
Ga-feldspar
  cell dimensions   219, 221, 357
  electrical conductivity   564-5
  infra-red absorption   514-6
  light optics   408
Gamma function   314-5, 323
gamma-ray resonance (see Mössbauer resonance)
Gandolfi X-ray technique   204, 206, 391
germanium substitution (see Ge-feldspar)
Ge-feldspar
  cell dimensions   219, 221
  infra-red absorption   514-6
  hollandite, inversion   585
  light optics   408
gehlenite   79
geometry, pseudo-cubic   40
Gibbs energy function   19, 470
gismondine, topology   27, 31, 44
Gladstone-Dale relation   385
glass
  annealing   582
  cathodoluminescence   560-1
  density   590-1
  infra-red absorption   518, 581-2
  shock-derived   579-89
  thermal expansion   590-1
grinding hardness   568-72
Guinier X-ray technique   204-6

H substitution   563, 581
habit   14
halloysite   501

harmotome, topology   27, 31, 44
heavy-liquid separation   592
hematite   14, 204, 559
hexagonal BaAl₂Si₂O₈   46, 515, 517
hexagonal CaAl₂Si₂O₈   46, 408, 515, 517
high albite (see also albite)
  atomic coordinates   86
  bonding diagram   98
  cell dimensions   219, 225-41, 258
  infra-red absorption   514-6, 518
  M—O distances   91
  monoclinic-triclinic inversion   298, 301, 337-9
  T—O distances   71, 88
  T—O—T angles   90
high sanidine (see sanidine)
historical (lists only sections with special chrono-
    logic sequence)
  cell dimensions   223-4, 306
  framework topology   26-8
  light-optics   365-6, 391-5
  models of e-plagioclase   157-71
  nomenclature   415-57
  ordering   50, 66-70, 74-5
hobnail texture   501
hollandite   11
  crystal structure   44-6
  from shock   15, 585
Hugoniot curve   578-9, 582-5
hurlbutite   43
Huttenlocher intergrowth
  e diffractions   152
  electron optics   483-8, 504-7
  general   6-9, 13
  heat treatment   146-9
  nomenclature   453
  X-ray diffraction   146-9, 199, 214
hyalophane   355 (see also Ba substitution)
  name   455
hydrogen substitution (see H substitution)
hypo-orthoclase   61, 424

I-anorthite (see anorthite)
identification, rapid visual   593-4 (see also
    X-ray, light optics etc.)
infra-red absorption   23, 59, 421, 511-29, 567,
    581-2
intergrowth
  coherent vs. incoherent   129
  diffraction from   127-37
  light optics   375-9
  periodic   130
intermediacy index   328, 394
intermediate plagioclase (see plagioclase)
  name   454
internal energy   19
internal scatter   369-71
inversion   290-1, 303-4

ion-exchange
  cell dimensions of alkali feldspar series
    222-4, 232, 247-55
  in albite and monalbite   291-3, 295
  light optics of alkali feldspar series   382-3
  of plagioclase   320, 340
ionic bonding   23-4, 95, 541
ionic conductivity   564
iridescence
  general   14
  moonstone   471, 539
  optical theory   377-9
  plagioclase   379, 490-6, 507.
iron oxide   473
iron substitution (see Fe-feldspar)
iso-microcline   368
iso-orthoclase   368

jadeite   11, 585, 588
joined-angle technique   403

kaliophilite   340
K-anorthoclase   368
kaolin   591
kasoite   455
K-exchanged albite, cell dimensions   288, 232,
  234, 258, 263
K-exchanged plagioclase, cell dimensions
  340-53
K-feldspar (see also adularia, microcline, orthoclase, sanidine)
  a^* vs. Or$(b^* c^*)$ 277-8
  anomalous   277
  cell dimensions   228-35, 241-8
  crystal structure, general   36
  density   569
  domain texture   244-7, 469-71
  electrical conductivity   564-6
  electron optics   468-77
  electron spin resonance   544-6
  infra-red absorption   532-9
  K-exchanged albite   228, 232, 234
  light optics   372-5
  optic axial angle   379-85
  optic orientation   387-9
  phase relations   2-4
  refractive indices   385-7
  Si, Al order and structural state   66-74, 416-36,
    468-70, 519-21, 532-9, 546
  symmetry inversion   2, 304
  thermal conductivity   566-7
  thermal expansion   291-2, 336-7
  X-ray patterns   181-9, 206-10
Kikuchi pattern   495
kink band   575, 578
Köhler angles   403
Korekawa-Jagodzinski model   161-3
Kroll X-ray procedure   269-76, 320-1, 346

labradorescence   14
labradorite (see also Bøggild intergrowth,
  e-plagioclase, plagioclase)
  composition range   12, 447
  name   450
lattice   19-20
lattice distortion   128-9, 469-70
Laves nomenclatures
  K-feldspar   418-29
  Na-feldspar   441-3
lead substitution (see Pb-feldspar)
leucite   340
light optics (see optics)
lime-anorthoclase   444-5
linear compressibility   568-71
lithium substitution   355, 557
local order   53
Loewenstein rule   79
longitudinal modulation   130-2
long-range order   52
low albite (see also albite)
  atomic coordinates   86
  bonding diagram   98
  cell dimensions   219, 225-41, 258
  electron spin resonance   545-6
  infra-red absorption   514-6, 518
  light optics   379-89
  M–O distances   91
  refractive indices   386
  T–O distances   71, 88
  T–O–T angles   90
low microcline (see microcline)
low sanidine (see orthoclase, sanidine)
luminescence   558-63
lunar feldspars
  cell dimensions   313, 318-9
  electron optics   465-8, 477-83
  electron spin resonance   546-7
  luminescence   559-63
  Mössbauer resonance   549-53
  optical absorption   558
  shock deformation   579, 589

M atoms
  angular environment   113-5
  bonding to oxygen   107-15
  coordination polyhedra   90-115
  M–O distances   91
  ordering in e-plagioclase   173
  symmetry restraint   108
macroperthite   3
magnetic separation   593
Mallard's hypothesis   177, 371, 416-8, 420
Manebach twin   181, 587
Marfunin optical model   371-5
maskelynite   579-89
  cathodoluminescence   560-2

maximum microcline (see also microcline)   420
mechanical properties   567-91
Megaw code   35, 37
Megaw model of plagioclase   157-61, 490
mesoperthite   12-3
metasanidine   424
mica   200, 591
microcline (see also K-feldspar)
  amazonite variety   556-8
  atomic coordinates   86
  authigenic   233
  cell dimensions   219, 228, 232-3, 235, 241-8,
    258
  Δ indicator   287-8
  density   569, 584-5
  dielectric phenomena   566
  electrical conductivity   564-6
  electron optics   470-7, 504
  electron spin resonance   544-6
  general   1-4
  infra-red absorption   512-25
  light optics   372-5, 376
  M–O distances   91
  nomenclature   416-36
  nuclear magnetic resonance   532-9
  optic axial angle   379-85
  refractive indices   386
  thermal conductivity   566-7
  thermal expansion   292
  T–O distances   71, 88
  T–O–T angles   90
  twinning   371-6, 381, 389-90, 418, 420, 428,
    471, 533-5, 586
  X-ray diffraction   182-97, 206-10
microperthite (see also electron optics, X-ray
  diffraction)   3
Mn substitution
  electron spin resonance   546-7
  luminescence   561-2
modulation   127-32
molar volume
  albite   294-7
  alkali feldspar   254
  plagioclase   333
molecular orbital calculation   24-5
monalbite (see also albite)
  general   4, 11
  inversion   298-305, 337-9, 352-3
  ion-exchange   291
  nomenclature   434, 438-48, 454
montmorillonite   501-2
moonstone
  electron optics   471
  name   14
  nuclear magnetic resonance   533, 538-9
  scattering of light   367
morphology   14, 218

Mössbauer resonance   59, 511, 548-53
M-twinning (see also anorthoclase, microcline)
  distortion   185
  effect on optics   371-5, 390, 424, 427-8, 440,
    447-8
  general   11
  geometry and X-ray patterns   182-97
Murchisonite partling   572
myrmekite   15

Na-exchanged K-feldspar
  cell dimensions   228, 232, 234, 240-63
Na-feldspar (see albite)
Natronmikroklin   437
Natronorthoklas   437
nepheline   79, 340, 592
neutron diffraction   59
NH_4 substitution (see buddingtonite)
nomenclature
  general   4, 11-3, 415-6
  K-feldspar   416-36
  labelling of atoms   35
  Na-feldspar and ternary feldspar   436-49
  plagioclase   450-5
non-stoichiometry   250-2
normal orthoclase   419
nuclear magnetic resonance
  albite   123, 522-33
  alkali feldspar   532-9
  anorthite   141, 539-41
  effect of ordering   177-8
  general   23, 59, 511, 530-2
nuclear quadrupole resonance (see nuclear
  magnetic resonance)
nuclear tracks   572

obliquity   266, 287
oligoclase (see also plagioclase)
  composition range   12, 444, 447
  name   450
one-step ordering trend   60-4, 222-4, 262-4,
  271-6, 421-50
optic orientation
  alkali feldspar   387-9
  plagioclase   400-3
optical absorption   558
optical activity   366
optical geometry   218, 312-3
optics, light
  alkali feldspar   379-91
  deformation effects   573-89
  dispersion   389
  fine-scale intergrowths   375-9
  fine-scale twins   371-5, 389
  general   365-79
  K, Ba feldspars   406-8

optics, light
  plagioclase   391-406
  scattering   369-71
optic axial angle
  alkali feldspars   372-7, 379-85, 417, 427-36
  K, Ba feldspars   406-8
  plagioclase   395-6, 573-4
  vs. Al content   383-4
  vs. *b c*   385
  vs. Or   380, 383, 417
Or (α^* γ^*), definition   261-2
Or (*b* c**)
  definition   261-2
  vs. *a**   277-9
Or-content, estimation from cell dimensions
  280-5, 326-7, 350-1
order (see also Si, Al ordering)
  convergent vs. non-convergent   54
  general   1, 50-6
  lattice disorder   50
  local vs. distant order   53, 425
  long- and short-range order   52-3
  matrix description   64-6
  one-step vs. two-step   60-4, 224, 262-4, 271-6,
  430-6, 442-3
  parameters *X, Y, Z*   62
  parity   53
  positional disorder   50
  relation to physical properties   177-8
  substitutional disorder   50
  unit-cell disorder   50
orthoclase (see also K-feldspar, sanidine)
  atomic coordinates   86
  cell dimensions   228-34, 241-7
  compressibility   569
  electron optics   470
  electron spin resonance   547
  general   4, 13
  infra-red absorption   520
  light optics   380-9, 416-36
  nomenclature   416, 418-36
  nuclear magnetic resonance   533-9
  surface energy   572
  T—O distances   71-88
  triclinic   426
  X-ray powder pattern   208
orthorhombic $CaAl_2Si_2O_8$ 47, 408
orthose   416
orthoscopic optical method   367-9, 376-7
Orville series of alkali feldspars
  cell dimensions   231-2, 247-55
  optic axial angle   383
oscillation X-ray method   180, 188-98
O—T—O angles   88-9, 92, 102-6
out-of-step domain boundary   53
out-of-step vector   51

P-anorthite (see anorthite)
paracelsian
  ordering   79
  properties   43-4
  topology   27, 31ʳ
Patterson function   166-8
particle track   468
Pauling's rules   23, 78-9
Pb-feldspar (includes Pb substitution)
  cell dimensions   219
  infra-red absorption   514-7
  substitution in amazonite   557
pericline, variety of albite   14, 436
Pericline twin (see also twin: casual references
  omitted)
  anorthoclase   440, 447
  deformation   573-87
  electron optics   469-70, 474-7, 481
  geometry   182-3
  light optics   371-5
  microcline   390
peristerite (see also plagioclase)
  cell dimensions   307, 311, 341-5
  e-diffractions   151
  electron optics   496-501, 505-7
  general   6-7, 13
  nomenclature   452-3
  X-ray identification   200-2, 207, 214, 326
perthite (casual references omitted)
  α^* γ^* plot   261
  cathodoluminescence   559
  cell dimensions   276-80
  clamping   196
  cryptoperthite   3
  electron optics   471-7
  general   3, 12-4
  light optics   375-7
  macroperthite   3
  microperthite   3
  nomenclature   3, 449
  optic axial angle   379-85
  strain   279
  X-ray patterns   184-97, 207, 210
phase, stable vs. unstable   422-4
phase diagram
  Ab—Or—An—H_2O 9-10
  alkali feldspar   2-4, 304
  plagioclase   5-9, 148-9
phillipsite   31, 44
photoelasticity   568, 570
photo-emission electron microscopy   505-7
π-bonding   24-5, 79-80, 103-4
piezoelectricity   39
plagioclase (see also albite, anorthite,
  e-plagioclase)
  -amazonite   556-8
  An-content, estimation   322-8, 405-6

plagioclase (see also albite, anorthite,
    e-plagioclase)
  b diffractions   140, 164-5, 479-80
  barian   456
  β* γ* plot   317-9
  c diffractions   140, 143, 145-50, 480-3
  cell dimensions   306-39, 347-53
  chemical alteration   501-2
  compressibility   569-71
  deformation   572-89
  density   569, 584-5, 590-1
  determinative methods, comparison   405-6
  discontinuities   7, 9, 154-5, 315, 397-8
  e diffractions   150-74, 488-96
  electron optics   477-507
  electron spin resonance   545-7
  Euler angles   402
  extinction angle   403-4
  general   4-9
  grinding hardness   572
  heat treatment   145-50, 156-7
  high vs. low optics   393-405
  indicators 131 and 2̄41   322-8
  infra-red absorption   514-5, 517-8, 525-8
  intermediate   454
  K-exchanged, cell dimensions   323, 340-53
  light optics   391-406
  luminescence   560-3
  molar volume   333
  monoclinic-triclinic inversion   337-9
  Mössbauer resonance   549-53
  nomenclature   11-3, 450-5
  optic axial angle   395-6
  optic orientation   400-5
  ordering schemes, theoretical   64-6, 315-7
  petrologic occurrence   145-50, 155-7
  phase relations   6-9, 145-50
  refractive indices   396-400
  Si, Al order   74-8, 173, 525-8
  stress-strain tensor   570-1
  structural state, estimation   322-8, 405-6
  thermal conductivity   566-7
  thermal expansion   328-39
  T—O distances   76
  twinning   400-5, 464-7, 481, 490, 492, 504-7,
      573-7, 586-8
  X-ray diffraction   197-203, 207, 210-5
  X-ray methods, simple   322-8
planar elements   583
plate albite   437
platy albite   437
pleochroism, infra-red   512, 519
point group of symmetry   21
polarizability of oxygen   541
polymorphism, K-feldspar   389-90, 417-8, 424
potash andesine   444-5, 448
potash oligoclase   444-5, 448

Powder Diffraction File   204
precession X-ray method   179-87, 197
prehnite   204
primitive anorthite (see anorthite)
proton-excited luminescence   558-62
pseudo-cubic geometry   40
pyroelectricity   39
pyroxene   465

quartz   11, 15, 204, 547, 563, 592

radiation damage   463-4, 468, 572
Raman frequency   513
random disorder   287
rare earths
  electron spin resonance   547
  substitution   81, 562
Rb-feldspar (includes Rb-substitution)
  amazonite, substitution in   557
  atomic coordinates   86
  cell dimensions   219
  color   557-8
  Fe, Si order   69
  inversion   357
  light optics   408
  M—O distances   91
  Si, Al order   69, 71
  T—O distances   71, 88
  T—O—T angles   90
reedmergnerite (includes B substitution)
  atomic coordinates   86
  bonding diagram   98
  cell dimensions   219
  crystal structure, general   36
  light optics   408
  M—O distances   91
  name   456
  polyhedral edges   94
  Si, Al order   69, 71, 80
  T—O distances   71, 88
  T—O—T angles   90
  X-ray pattern   211-3, 215
reference axes   19
refractive indices
  alkali feldspar   385-7
  K, Ba feldspar   406-8
  plagioclase   396-400
  plagioclase glass   396-7
  shocked feldspar   580-3
  various feldspars   408
  various non-feldspars   43, 408
relaxation time   290
release adiabat   579, 582-5
rhombic section   573-4

s vector
  definition   152
  relation to fringes   488-9

sanidine (see also K-feldspar, orthoclase)
  atomic coordinates   28
  bonding diagram   93
  cell dimensions   219, 228-35, 241-7, 258
  electron optics   473-5
  electron spin resonance   545-6
  Fe substitution (see Fe-feldspar)
  general   1-4
  infra-red absorption   514-25
  lattice   182-3
  light optics   379-89
  M—O distances   91
  Mössbauer resonance   548-9
  nomenclature   416, 418-36
  nuclear magnetic resonance   533-9
  optic axial angle   379-85
  optic orientation   387-9
  refractive indices   386
  thermoluminescence age   563
  T—O distances   71, 88
  T—O—T angles   90
  unmixing   473-4
  X-ray patterns   188, 207-10
scanning electron microscopy   502-5
scattering, dependent, independent, multiple   367
schiller, definition   14
selected-area diffraction   462
separation   591-3
shared edges   93-4
shear stress   573
shock deformation   15, 578-89
short-range order   52
Si, Al ordering (references restricted to direct data: see various techniques for many other references)
  Al_2Si_2 vs. $AlSi_3$ 37
  albite   68-9, 71, 74, 441, 521-5, 532-2
  anorthite   74-8, 137-40, 539-41
  celsian   74-7
  charge balance, relation   100
  crystal-chemical explanation   78-81
  e-plagioclase   173
  experimental techniques, general   56-60
  Fe-feldspar   69
  K-feldspar   66-8, 70-4, 468-70, 519-21, 532-9, 546
  mathematical basis   50-6, 60-6
  plagioclase   74-8, 173, 525-8
  Rb-feldspar   69, 71
silver substitution, electron spin resonance   548
σ-bonding   24-5, 104
slip   572-88
Smith-Mackenzie X-ray method   180, 189-91
Smith-Ribbe model for plagioclase   163
Sn substitution   557
sodalite   340

soda-microcline   437
solution types   253-4
sound   velocity   568-70
space group of symmetry   19
Spencer classification of alkali feldspars   417
spinodal decomposition   9, 473-4, 487
Sr-feldspar (includes Sr substitution)
  cell dimensions   219, 221, 355-7
  infra-red absorption   514-7
  inversion in Ca, Sr-feldspar   356-7
  light optics   408
stability   423-4
stable vs. unstable   422-3
staining, color   593-4
strain in perthites   279-80
stress vs. strain curves   573-4
stress-strain tensor   570-1
strontium substitution (see Sr-feldspar)
structural state (see individual feldspar for data)
  characterization   218
  indicator   306
superlattice   55
superstructure
  explanation   55
  mathematical description   157
surface energy   568, 572
symmetry
  change   3, 290
  constraint   55
  general   1, 19-22
  inversion in alkali feldspar   301-5ʼ
  inversion in sodic feldspar   295, 298-301, 352-3
synthesis series, cell dimensions of alkali feldspars   231, 248-55
synthetic feldspars
  albite   207, 225-39, 258-63, 268, 277-8, 292-305, 332, 336, 352-3, 372, 380-9, 438, 520-5, 565
  alkali feldspar   224, 247-55, 281-4, 304-5, 352-3, 380-9
  anorthite   139, 143-5, 201, 203, 219, 308-9, 329, 529-30, 547, 565
  B   219, 356
  Ba   219, 221, 353-6, 514-5, 517
  Cs   357
  Fe   69, 219, 408, 514-6, 562, 564-5
  Ga   219, 221, 357, 408, 514-6, 564-5
  Ge   219, 221, 408, 514-6
  K-feldspar   241-4, 258, 263, 278, 380-9, 519-21
  Mn   561-2
  NH_4 457
  Pb   219, 514-5, 517
  plagioclase   307-27, 336-9, 343, 346-7, 352-3, 392-401
  Rb   69, 71, 86, 88, 90, 91, 219, 357, 408
  REE   562

synthetic feldspars
  Sr   219, 221, 355-7, 514-5, 517
  Ti   562

t vector
  change during heating   174
  definition   152
  orientation   153, 172
  relation to fringes   489
  variation with An   153, 172
T wavelength
  definition   152
  relation to fringes   489
  variation with An   153, 172
TEM (see transmission electron microscopy)
temperature factor B   115
tensile strength   568
ternary feldspars
  cell dimensions   340-53
  nomenclature   436-49
tetrahedral distortion   105-6
theoretical low sanidine   245
thermal conductivity   566-7
thermal expansion
  albite   292-301
  anorthite   329-31
  K-feldspar   291-2, 336-7
  plagioclase   328-39
thermal vibration   101, 115-24
thermodynamic equilibrium   290
thermogravimetry   591
thermoluminescence   559, 562-3
thetomorphic   579
thickness extinction contour   463
Thompson ordering parameters   61-3, 71-2, 76
three-peak method   280, 284-5
Ti substitution
  cathodoluminescence   562
  electron spin resonance   547
Tl, substitution   557
topochemical symmetry   35, 290
topologic symmetry   35
topology   1, 25-35
T—O distances   71, 88, 102-6
T—O—T angles   90, 92, 106-7
Toman-Frueh model of e-plagioclase   163-70
Tr [110] and Tr [1$\bar{1}$0]   269-76, 320-1
transformation
  coherent   3
  diffusive vs. displacive   442
  district   145
  ordering   2
  unmixing   3
transitional anorthite (see anorthite)
transmission electron microscopy
  alkali feldspar   468-77

transmission electron microscopy
  defects   464-7
  experimental details   461-4
  plagioclase   477-501
transverse modulation   127, 130-2
trapping center   562-3
triclinic indicator
  definition   218, 287
  Δ (131) vs. An   315-6, 320-7, 339
  Δ (131) vs. Δ ($\bar{2}$41)   325-6
  Δ ($\bar{2}$41) vs. An   325-6, 339
  Δ (130) and Δ (131) in microcline   287-8
triclinicity, definition   218, 224, 287, 420
true orthoclase   419
Tsuboi optical method   398-400, 405
T-twinning   11, 193-4
Tuttle optical classification of alkali feldspars   381-2, 417, 435
tweed texture   484-6
twin (see also Albite twin, Baveno twin, Carlsbad twin, M-twinning, Pericline twin, T-twinning)
  cathodoluminescence   559
  cross-hatching in deformation twin of plagioclase   574
  deformation   572-88
  domain   290, 422
  electron-optical study   464-7, 471, 474-7, 481, 490, 492, 499, 504-7
  general   14, 578
  microcline   371-6, 381, 389-90, 418, 420, 428, 471, 533-5, 586
  M- vs. T   11, 193
  mechanical   572-88
  Na-rich feldspar   372-3, 381, 390, 436-43, 446-8, 499, 577
  optical anomalies   370-1
  optics of fine-scale   371-5
  periodic   127-8, 186, 192-3, 471-7
  plagioclase   400-5, 464-7, 481, 490, 492, 504-7, 573-7, 586-8
  X-ray diffraction   182-97
two-beam approximation   463
two-step ordering trend   60-4, 222-3, 262-4, 421-36
Tyndall scattering   379

uniaxial compression   572-8
unit cell   19
unmixing, general   3
Urey-Bradley model   513
U-stage optics   367, 392-4

Vickers microhardness   171
volume compressibility   568-9

Waldbaum-Robie series of alkali feldspars, cell dimensions   232, 247-55

Warren inversion idea   417
water
   effect on strength   577-8
   substitution   563
   thermogravimetry   591
Weissenberg X-ray method   180, 188-9
wollastonite   340
work hardening   573
Wright-Stewart diagram   256-7, 276-7
Wright three-peak method   280, 284-5

X-ray diffraction
   adularia   182, 184, 188, 196-7
   albite   200, 202, 207, 211-3
   alkali feldspar   181-97, 206-10
   anorthite   203, 207-14
   anorthoclase   193-4
   celsian   209

X-ray diffraction
   determinative methods   280-9
   e-plagioclase   201-2
   general   56-9
   K-feldspar   181-9, 206-10
   microcline   182-97, 206-10
   orthoclase   208
   perthite   184-97, 207, 210
   plagioclase   197-203, 207, 210-5, 322-8
   powder methods   203-15
   reedmergnerite   211-3, 215
   sanidine   188, 207-10
   single-crystal methods   179-203

Young's modulus   568

zeolite   31, 87
zoning, chemical   11, 405

Name Index

Abadian, M.   585
Aberdam, D.   471
Abich, W. H.   450
Adams, L. H.   568-9
Agrell, S. O.   394
Ahlers, L.   590
Ahrens, T. J.   579, 582-5
Aitken, F. K.   588
Akizuki, M.   471
Alexandrov, K. S.   570-1, 582
Alling, H. L.   438-9, 443
Amelinckx, S.   462
Anderson, D. L.   585
Anderson, J. R.   56
Andrews, E. R.   530
Angino, E. E.   528
Ansilewski, J.   424
Aoki, K.   445
Appleman, D. E.   57, 69, 85-6, 94, 100, 103, 105,
    117-8, 308, 312-3, 318-9, 386, 394, 408, 480,
    549
Aquilano, D.   528-30
Arndt, J.   590
Aronson, J. R.   567
Avdonin, V. A.   557
Azàroff, L. V.   19, 179

Bachinski, S. W.   233, 242
Bächtiger, K.   563
Baier, E.   490
Bailey, E. H.   594
Bailey, S. W.   37-8, 56-8, 67, 80, 85-6, 100, 103,
    117-9, 121, 152, 170-1, 228, 241, 243, 246,
    379, 383, 385-7, 417, 419, 425, 433
Bakakin, V. V.   43
Bakken, R.   591
Balconi, M.   393
Bambauer, H. U.   214, 225, 306-8, 310, 315,
    317-8, 321, 323-6, 328, 347, 366, 369, 380,
    389, 400, 403, 423, 450-1
Bank, H.   558
Barber, C. T.   392-3
Barbier, P.   439
Barth, T. F. W.   37, 50, 61, 224, 368, 373, 392-3,
    415-7, 424-6, 430, 445, 572, 589-90

Baskin, Y.   225, 237, 242, 423
Bassett, H.   557
Baur, W. H.   24
Beckenkamp, J.   40, 218, 291, 313, 328-9
Bell, P. M.   558, 582
Belov, N. V.   43
Belyankin, D. S.   368, 393, 590
Bershov, L. V.   544, 547, 557
Bethe, H.   53
Bhatty, M. S. J.   200
Binns, R. A.   579
Blair, I. M.   562
Blaschke, R.   503
Bloss, F. D.   19, 141, 150, 282, 331, 366
Bøggild, O. B.   416, 490, 492
Bollmann, W.   470-1, 495
Bolton, H. C.   377-9
Boone, G. M.   594
Bordet, P.   394
Borg, I. Y.   206-212, 214, 284, 308, 573-5, 578
Borgström, L.   313
Born, M.   367
Bottinga, J.   590
Boudette, F. L.   256, 347, 349-50, 594
Bowen, N. L.   223, 247, 283, 380-1, 388-9, 393,
    438, 444, 591
Bown, M. G.   140, 145, 147-9, 151-3, 155-6, 180,
    197-8, 200-1, 203, 292
Brace, W. F.   572
Bradley, O.   393
Bragg, W. L.   40
Breithaupt, A.   416, 436, 450
Bridgman, P. W.   568-9
Bridgwater, D.   591
Brinkmann, D.   74, 539, 540
Broch, O. A.   593
Brögger, W. C.   437
Brooke, H. J.   436
Brown, B. E.   67, 85-6, 100, 103, 117, 121, 228,
    241, 243, 385-6, 433
Brown, F. F.   548, 556
Brown, G. E.   24, 57, 68, 80
Brown, W. L.   140, 227, 229, 237, 239, 257-9,
    291-6, 298, 300-1, 303, 306, 308, 329, 330-7,
    474-6
Brun, E.   70, 418, 532-3

Page references are given to the text and figures, but not to the reference lists for the chapters.

Brunner, G. O.   39-43, 113
Bruno, E.   141, 144, 214
Brunton, G. D.   69
Buckenham, M. H.   592
Buddington, A. F.   457
Buerger, M. J.   19, 31, 56
Bunch, T. E.   579-81, 585-7, 589
Burri, C.   40, 366, 380, 389, 391-4, 396, 398-404
Butler, T. C.   280

Callegari, E.   226-7, 237
Cameron, E. N.   328
Campbell Smith, W.   44
Carmichael, I. S. E.   256, 282, 318, 327, 347-8,
    350, 352, 395
Carter, N. L.   573
Čech, F.   556
Celsius, A.   455
Černý, P.   558
Chaisson, U.   186, 369, 380, 388-9, 420, 438
Chandrasekhar, S.   85
Chao, E. C. T.   43, 56, 66, 74, 80, 85, 151, 157,
    162, 223, 306, 418, 579, 582, 585, 587-9
Chayes, F.   393, 395-7, 593
Chester, A. H.   416
Christensen, N. I.   569-70
Christian, J. W.   50
Christie, J. M.   464, 466, 477, 479-80, 482
Christie, O. H. J.   284, 287
Chudoba, K.   392, 590
Cinnamon, C. G.   152, 170-1
Claisse, F.   214, 306
Claringbull, G. F.   40
Clark, J. R.   57, 69, 85-6, 94, 100, 117-8
Clark, S. P.   563, 566, 569
Cloiseaux, A. Des.   312, 392, 416, 456
Cochran, W.   56
Cole, W. F.   28, 37, 66, 85, 151, 223, 225,
    228, 241-2, 247, 250, 306, 308, 318, 397, 417,
    528
Colville, A. A.   67-8, 85, 144, 383, 480
Coombs, D. S.   279
Corlett, M.   214, 310-1, 316, 323, 326, 328,
    341-2, 348
Coulson, A. L.   370
Cowley, J. M.   57
Cox, E. P.   593
Craig, J. R.   43
Crawford, M. L.   379, 386, 389
Crawley, W. D.   593
Crosby, P.   233, 242, 278-9
Crozaz, G.   572
Cruickshank, D. W. J.   24, 80
Curie, D.   558
Czank, M.   75, 137-9, 141-4, 312, 329-32, 394,
    481-3, 480
Czygan, W.   592

Dalrymple, G. B.   562
Dana, E. D.   218, 365
Davies, G. F.   585
Davis, G. L.   47, 408
Dawson, K. R.   396
Day, A. L.   590-1
DeCarli, P. S.   579-80
Deer, W. A.   44, 365, 415
Deganello, S.   101
Deming, W. E.   252
Dence, M. R.   579, 589
Desborough, G. A.   328
DeVore, G. W.   65, 66, 150
Dietrich, R. V.   288
Dietz, E. D.   301
Dittler, E.   392
Doeglas, D. J.   592
Doell, R. R.   562
Dollase, W. A.   79
Doman, R. C.   154-5, 171-2, 308, 315
Donnay, G.   47, 224-5, 240-1, 247-8, 252, 255-6
Donnay, J. D. H.   224-5, 240-1, 247-8, 252, 255-6
Douglas, J. A.   590
Dreyer, C.   312
Duffin, W. J.   214, 306
Duke, M. B.   579
Dunbar, C.   43
Duparc, L.   368
Dworak, U.   579, 581-2, 587
Dworschak, F.   557

Eberhard, E.   214, 225, 306-8, 310-11, 315, 317-8,
    323, 326-8
Edgar, A. D.   226, 236, 314, 355
Edginton, J. A.   562
Ehlers, E. G.   408
Emeleus, C. H.   191-2
Emerson, D. O.   368
Emmons, R. C.   370, 393, 396, 398, 592,
Engelhardt, W. von   579, 585, 587-9
Engels, A.   392
Erd, R. C.   408, 457
Erickson, K. P.   593
Ernst, E.   392
Eskola, P.   408
Estep, P. A.   528
Eucken, A.   567

Fahey, J. J.   593
Fang, J. H.   282
Faust, G. T.   556
Faye, G. H.   556
Fedorow, E.   40, 370, 392
Fels, G.   313
Ferguson, R. B.   68, 79, 100, 122, 225-6, 237,
    239, 312, 424, 437

Finney, J. J.   67, 80, 85, 228, 241, 379, 383, 385-7, 433
Finger, L. W.   549, 552
Fischer, K.   44, 56, 67-8
Fisher, D. J.   370, 436
Fizeau, H.   291-2, 567
Fleet, S. G.   75, 102-4, 152-3, 164, 312, 471, 488, 496
Fleischer, M.   572
Foit, F. F.   137, 139, 141, 150, 156, 180, 312
Ford, A. B.   256, 347, 349-50, 594
Foreman, N.   79
Förstner, H.   301, 437
Foster, W. R.   396, 405
Fox, P. E.   385
French, B. M.   579
Frueh, A. J.   133, 155, 162-71, 173

Gabriel, A.   593
Gait, R. I.   79, 101, 107
Gaite, J.-M.   544-7
Gandais, M.   472
Gard, J. A.   461
Garlick, G. F. J.   558, 563
Gasperin, M.   69, 86, 117
Gates, R. M.   370
Gay, P.   74, 140, 143, 145, 147-158, 180, 197-8, 200-1, 203, 214, 306, 314-15, 317, 323, 353-5, 452, 454-6, 458
Gazzoni, G.   141, 144, 214, 221
Geake, J. E.   561-2
Gibb, T. C.   548
Gibbons, R. V.   584
Gibbs, G. E.   24, 56, 58-9, 64, 69, 70, 80, 103
Gibson, R. E.   569
Glauser, A.   393, 394
Glinka, S.   312
Gold, D. P.   588
Goldanskii, V. I.   548
Goldschmidt, V.   218, 313
Goldsmith, J. R.   50, 74, 78, 100, 139, 143-5, 150-1, 154-5, 171, 184, 191, 197, 218, 220-1, 224, 242, 244, 246-7, 249, 286-8, 308, 339, 408, 419-22, 424, 426, 429, 450
Goodyear, J.   214, 306
Gottardi, G.   403
Grauer-Carstensen, E.   505
Greenwood, N. N.   548
Greer, R. T.   503-4, 562
Gregson, V. G. Jr.   582-3
Grove, T. L.   357
Grundy, H. D.   225, 227, 229, 237, 257-9, 292-6, 298, 300-1, 303, 329-37
Gubser, R.   242, 247, 257-8, 277-8, 284, 287, 329
Guilbert, J. M.   501-2
Gysin, M.   368-9

Haberlandt, H.   559
Häberle, F.   590
Hafner, S.   60, 69-70, 123, 224, 418, 421, 426, 512, 514, 518, 520-8, 530, 533-9, 541-3, 545-7, 549, 551-3
Häkli, A.   347, 349-50, 590
Hall, K. M.   75, 291
Hamilton, D. L.   226, 236, 314
Handin, J.   573
Harker, R. I.   287, 433
Harlow, G. F.   69
Harnik, A. B.   327, 441
Harry, W. T.   591
Hartmann, P.   70, 534, 541-3, 545
Haskin, L. A.   547
Haüy, R. J.   416
Hayes, J. R.   593
Heard, H. C.   573-5, 578
Hedvall, J. A.   557
Heidenreich, R. D.   461
Henry, N. F. M.   19, 179
Herber, L. J.   592
Heuer, A. H.   144, 148, 481-2, 484, 479-80, 482
Hewlett, C. G.   374, 379, 385, 387
Hey, M. H.   253
Hintze, C.   218, 365, 590
Hirsch, P. B.   461
Hobbs, B. E.   490
Höchli, U.   544
Holmquist, P. J.   572
Homma, F.   392
Horai, K.   566-7
Hornemann, U.   582
Houghton, J. T.   511
Hulst, H. C. Van De   367
Hunt, T. S.   392
Hwang, F. S. W.   563

Iddings, J. P.   445
Iiishi, K.   512-4, 516-7, 519, 526
Iiyama, J. T.   564
Ingamells, C. O.   251
Ingram, D. J. E.   544
Ioffe, V. A.   548, 566
Ito, J.   46, 357

Jackson, E. D.   328
Jagodzinski, H.   129, 161-3, 181
James, O. B.   585, 588
Jamieson, J. C.   579
Janchevskaya, I. S. see Yanchevskaia, I. S.
Joffe, W. A. see Ioffe, V. A.
Jones, J. B.   56, 58, 67, 85, 103, 223, 264, 282

Kaaden, G. van der   392-3
Kano, H.   393, 395
Kapustin, N. P.   557

Kastner, M.   225, 227-8, 233, 237, 242-3, 278, 385
Katz, M. Ya.   590
Kayode, A. A.   293, 331
Kazakov, A. M.   368
Keith, M. L.   593
Keller, G. V.   563, 566
Kempe, D. R. C.   282
Kempster, C. J. E.   74, 85, 97, 312
Kern, H.   224, 243, 379-80, 383-5
Kern, R.   471
Khitarov, N. I.   564
Kimball, M.   457
Kleeman, J. D.   328, 582
Klugman, M. A.   593
Köhler, A.   150, 331, 392-3, 403, 438, 559, 591
Kokscharow, N. v.   218
Kopp, H.   291
Korekawa, M.   129-32, 151-3, 161-3, 181, 200, 499, 500
Koritnig, S.   282
Kôzu, S.   289, 291-2, 294, 329-31, 336
Kraeft, U.   462
Kratzert, J.   313
Krebs, B.   40, 312
Krivoglaz, M. A.   22, 50, 57
Kroll, H.   60, 225, 227, 229, 231, 240-1, 243, 255, 258-9, 263-5, 269-73, 275, 278, 301, 303-9, 315, 317-21, 327, 337, 338-41, 343-8, 352-3, 590
Kuhn, G.   567
Kume, S.   46, 585
Kuts, V. P.   557

Laduron, D.   594
Lally, J. S.   148, 464-6, 468, 477, 479, 480-2
Laniz, R. V.   594
Larsen, E. S.   590
Larsson, W.   392
Laves, F.   33-5, 50, 60-1, 69-70, 74-5, 78, 100, 123, 137-9, 141, 143-5, 150-1, 154-5, 171, 184-7, 191, 193, 197, 218, 221, 223-5, 242, 244, 246-7, 249, 257-8, 265, 277-9, 284, 286-8, 290, 299, 301, 304-5, 308, 339, 352-3, 365, 369, 380, 388-9, 393, 416, 418-33, 435-6, 438-43, 446, 448, 451-2, 490, 505-7, 512, 514, 518-28, 530, 533-4, 538-9
Lecomte, J.   511
Liese, H. C.   525
Limbach, D. von   225-6, 291-6, 298. 301, 336-7
Lipson, H.   56
Liu, H.-P.   584
Loewenstein, W.   79
Long, R. S.   44, 47, 220
Lonsdale, K.   19
Louisnathan, J.   79
Luczizky, W.   368
Lundegärdh, P. H.   394
Luth, W. C.   248, 250-2, 255, 261, 276, 283-4

Lyon, R. J. P.   511
Lyons, P. C.   593

Note: Names beginning Mac, Mc, listed in strict alphabetical order.
MacDonald, G. A.   445
Macek, J.   558
Machatschki, F.   26, 43
MacKenzie, W. S.   50, 53, 61, 64, 73-4, 100, 180, 188-96, 209-10, 224-7, 241, 246-7, 254, 256, 259-60, 282, 286-9, 293, 299, 301, 305, 318, 323, 327, 337-8, 347-8, 350, 352, 368, 376, 390, 419-20, 422, 425, 433, 438, 440-4, 447-8
Mallard, F.   177, 371, 416-8, 420, 424
Manning, P. G.   556
Manolescu, G.   370
Mao, H. K.   558
Marfunin, A. S.   366-9, 371-6, 379, 381, 387, 391-2, 394, 398, 403, 416, 426-7, 433, 435, 443-7, 557
Mariano, A. N.   562
Marshall, D. B.   496
Martin, R. F.   224-8, 230, 236-7, 239, 241-3, 258-9, 263, 276, 356, 520-3, 525
Maury, R.   564-6
Maxwell, J. A.   396
McAllister, A. L.   593
McConnell, J. D. C.   6, 9, 55, 70, 130, 146, 148-9, 152-3, 156-7, 171, 461-3, 469-70, 473, 485, 487-8, 490, 493-5
McDougall, D. J.   563
McLaren, A. C.   152-4, 462, 483, 485-90, 492-3, 495-6, 470, 472, 477, 480, 497-501
McMillan, J, A.   544
McQueen, R. G.   582-3
Megaw, H. D.   28, 31-3, 35, 37, 50-1, 53, 64, 66, 69, 74-5, 77, 85-7, 90-1, 93-5, 97, 99, 101-2, 104-5, 108-9, 112-4, 116-7, 122-3, 142, 144-5, 157-60, 162, 172, 425, 457, 490
Melczer, G.   312
Mergner, J. L.   456
Merwin, H. E.   590
Michel-Lévy, A.   417
Michoulier, J.   544-7
Milton, C.   408, 456
Milton, D. J.   579, 580
Mookherjee, A.   572
Moore, J. M.   385
Moore, P. B.   35
Morris, R. V.   547
Morse, S. A.   398-400, 405
Moss, S. C.   57
Mossman, D. J.   315
Muir, I.   370, 393, 441, 444-5
Müller, G.   225-7, 233-4, 237-9, 242-4, 258, 260, 263-4, 277
Müller, W. F.   197, 394, 402-3, 405, 480, 483

Munro, M. 367
Muravyov, V. I. 590

Nager, H. E. 307-9, 355-6
Nash, D. B. 562
Neiva, A. M. R. 381, 383, 433
Nemecz, E. 591
Nesbitt, R. W. 328
Newnham, R. E. 74, 86, 106, 109, 117
Nickel, E. 370, 393
Nieland, H. 392
Nieuwenkamp, W. 394
Niggli, A. 64-6, 150, 315
Niggli, P. 40
Nilssen, B. 284
Nissen, H.-U. 70, 152, 308, 315-16, 470-2, 480, 483, 490-3, 495, 498-9, 503-4
Noble, D. C. 394
Nockolds, S. R. 456
Nold, J. L. 593
Nord, G. L. 146, 148-9, 394, 468, 479-80, 484, 486
Nose, K. W. 416
Nuffield, E. W. 179
Nye, J. F. 289, 366, 568

Offret, A. 291, 329
Oftedahl, C. 379, 393, 396, 438-9
Oliver, R. L. 558
Omori, K. 594
Onorato, E. 85
Orton, J. W. 544
Orville, P. M. 223-6, 230-2, 240-3, 247-59, 264, 272-8, 280-4, 286, 288, 303, 305, 318, 336, 347, 350, 590
Owen, D. C. 473-4

Paliuc, G. 392
Panov, Ye. N. 563
Paraskevopoulos, G. M. 369
Parker, R. L. 393
Parkhomenko, E. I. 563, 566
Parrish, W. 211
Parsons, I. 282, 327
Pauling, L. 23, 79, 93, 101
Pavelescu, L. 368
Peacor, D. R. 79, 137, 139, 141, 150, 156, 180
Pense, J. 490
Pentinghaus, H. 44, 47, 220, 357
Perrotta, A. J. 79
Petrović, R. 564
Phemister, T. C. 366
Philipp, D. 151-3, 162
Phillips, F. C. 19
Phillips, M. W. 68, 75, 91, 102-4, 109, 117, 122, 228, 312
Pieri, R. de 69, 226-7, 237

Pini, E. 416
Piotrowski, J. M. 355
Plas, L. van der 205, 366, 386, 391, 394, 398, 403, 405-6, 592-3
Plyusnin, G. S. 557
Poldervaart, A. 590
Prewitt, C. T. 23, 59, 220
Price, P. B. 572
Prince, E. 68, 228
Pringle, G. J. 371
Pritchard, A. M. 548, 556
Prost, A. 439
Przibam, K. 559

Quaide, W. 589
Quareni, S. 69, 123, 291
Querol-Suñé, F. 250-1, 255, 276, 283-4

Raase, P. 224-5, 227, 229, 243, 258-60, 263, 379-80, 383-5
Radcliffe, S. V. 464-5, 468, 589
Radoslovich, E. W. 97
Ramberg, H. 570
Rankin, D. W. 382-3, 385
Rath, G. vom 313
Reed, F. S. 456
Reeder, S. W. 593
Reid, A. F. 46
Reinhard, M. 370, 392
Ribbe, P. H. 28, 35, 38-9, 56, 58-60, 64, 66-70, 74-5, 77-8, 85-6, 90-1, 101-5, 114-7, 122, 137, 141, 144, 150, 152, 154, 157-8, 160-3, 172-4, 177, 223, 228, 255, 257, 261, 264-71, 308, 311, 315-6, 320, 322, 327, 346, 350, 379, 383, 385, 442, 451, 471, 480, 496
Riederer, J. 368
Riecker, R. E. 568
Rinaldi, F. 27, 29, 31
Ringwood, A. E. 44-6, 585
Rinne, F. 329
Robertson, P. B. 579, 583
Robie, R. A. 255-6, 232-4, 242, 247-9, 255, 257-60, 264, 277-8, 283
Rogers, J. 592
Rose, G. 450
Rosenberg, J. T. 579, 582-3
Rosenblum, S. 593
Rosenbusch, H. 437
Rosenholtz, J. L. 292-4, 336
Rosenqvist, I. T. 472-3, 591
Rothschild, S. 559
Rottenbach, E. 590
Roy, N. N. 353-5, 386, 406-8, 455-6
Rudenko, S. A. 556-7
Rudert, V. 225, 356
Ryzhova, T. V. 570-1, 582

Saalfeld, M.   462
Sabatier, G.   224
Sadanaga, R.   44
Sáenz, I. M. de   187
Sahu, K. C.   572
Saiki, S.   291
Sanford, F.   557
Saplevitch, A.   217, 289, 291-2, 328-9, 496
Saucier, H.   217, 289, 291-2, 328-9, 496
Schairer, J. F.   396-7
Schaller, W. T.   439
Schedler, R. A.   394, 396
Scheidegger, K. F.   323
Schiebold, E.   26
Schmidt, E.   218
Schnaase, H.   218, 313, 329
Schneider, T. R.   291, 373, 380, 388-9, 424, 439
Schuermann, K. see Schürmann, K.
Scholler, H.   393
Schultz, P. K.   558
Schulz, H.   75, 137, 329-32, 480
Schulz, K.   566-7
Schürmann, K.   549-50, 552-3
Schuster, M.   392
Schwarzmann, S.   393, 396
Sclar, C. B.   589, 593
Scott, R. B.   233, 242, 278-9
Segnit, E. R.   406-7
Seifert, K. E.   464, 573-8, 586
Sen, S. K.   578
Shannon, R. D.   23, 220
Short, N. M.   579, 586, 588-9
Silver, L. T.   579
Simmons, G.   569
Sippel, R. F.   559-62
Sjögren, H.   455
Slemmons, D. B.   328, 393-4
Sloane, R. L.   501-2
Slutskiy, A. B.   564
Smirnov, A. A.   50
Smith, D. K.   206-9, 211-2, 214, 284
Smith, D. T.   292-4, 336
Smith, J. R.   214, 306, 314, 323, 379-80, 386,
    393, 395-8
Smith, J. V.   27, 29-31, 34-5, 43, 50, 53, 56-9,
    61, 64, 73-4, 77-9, 90, 95, 100, 137, 139, 141,
    150, 152, 154, 157-8, 160-3, 172-4, 177, 180,
    188-96, 214, 224-6, 245-8, 259-61, 279, 299, 306,
    308, 311, 314-5, 317-9, 323, 327, 350, 376, 379,
    385, 422, 425, 440-4
Smith, S. D.   511
Smithson, S. B.   287
Smyth, J. R.   162
Soldatos, K.   184-7
Sörum, H.   74, 85, 151, 225
Spaenhauer, F.   392
Spencer, A. B.   559-62

Spencer, E.   66, 70, 197, 374-7, 379, 382, 385-6,
    393, 407, 416-7, 419, 438
Spencer, L. J.   43, 415, 455-6
Srinivasan, R.   38-9, 104
Stähli, J. L.   74, 539-40
Starkey, J.   69, 75, 86, 90-1, 102-3, 109-110,
    117-8, 120, 137, 139, 225, 236, 312, 533, 578
Steinfink, H.   44
Stenstrom, R. C.   559
Stevens, R. E.   594
Stewart, D. B.   60, 64, 70, 74, 140, 154, 207, 211,
    214, 223-6, 228-30, 232-4, 240-3, 247-9, 255-61,
    263-71, 275-9, 280-2, 291-6, 298, 301, 305,
    307-9, 313, 318, 330, 332-7, 355, 381-3, 385,
    429-30, 433, 435, 442, 445-6, 448
Stishov, S. M.   557
Stöffler, D.   579-80, 582, 585, 587-9
Strandmark, J. E.   455
Strüver, J.   218
Sueno, S.   124

Takane, K.   291
Takéuchi, Y.   46-7
Tarte, P.   512
Taylor, W. H.   26-8, 33-5, 37, 39, 67, 74, 80, 85,
    95, 103, 123, 143, 150-1, 157, 162, 223, 225, 228,
    241, 246, 306, 417-8, 425, 433, 557
Tertsch, H.   393
Thomson, T.   450
Thompson, C. S.   527-8
Thompson, J. B.   50, 54, 61, 63, 70, 72, 253-5, 283
Tilas, D.   415
Tilley, C. E.   445
Tobi, A. C.   370, 403, 437
Toman, K.   133, 155, 162-71, 173
Towle, L. C.   568
Traill, R. J.   225
Tröger, W. E.   366
Trommsdorf, V.   394-5
Trondle, H. M.   593
Tschermak, G.   392, 579
Tsuboi, S.   368, 394, 398, 405
Turkowsky, C.   468, 572
Tuttle, O. F.   47, 223, 247-8, 251-2, 283, 376,
    379-82, 385-9, 393, 407-8, 417, 419, 435, 438,
    440, 444, 591

Uebel, P.-J.   394
Ueda, J.   291-2, 294, 329-31, 336
Umegaki, T.   512, 519
Uruno, K.   393

Vaidya, S. N.   568
Vardanyants, L. A.   368
Vermaas, F. H. S.   353, 406-7
Vernon, R. H.   574
Viola, C.   313

Virgo, D.   549
Viswanathan, K.   206-7, 210, 214, 225, 288, 306-8, 310-1, 315, 317-8, 320-3, 326-8, 340-8, 427-8, 431-3, 435-6
Vogel, T. A.   225, 369-70
Vokhmentsev, A. Ya.   556-7

Wadsworth, M. E.   527-8
Wainwright, J. E.   69, 75, 86, 90-1, 102-3, 109-10, 117-8, 120-1, 137, 139, 225, 236, 312, 533
Waldbaum, D. R.   225-7, 232-4, 237, 242-3, 247-9, 253-5, 257-60, 264, 277-8, 283
Walsh, J. B.   572
Walterhausen, S. von   455
Waring, J. R. S.   85
Warren, C. H.   417
Weber, L.   505
Weeks, R. A.   544, 546-7
Wegmann, L.   505
Weill, D. F.   590
Weir, C. E.   292-3, 568-9
Weisz, O.   181
Weitz, G.   68, 228
Wells, A. F.   40
Wenk, E.   311, 392-5
Wenk, H.-R.   308, 311, 394, 479-80, 483
Werner, A. G.   450

Wertheim, G. K.   548
Wertz, J. E.   544
Wheeler, E. P.   594
Wieden, P.   150, 331, 591
Willaime, C.   289, 292, 329, 336-7, 472, 474-7
Williams, P. P.   69, 122-3
Williamson, E. D.   568-9
Winchell, A. N.   365, 408, 438
Winchell, H.   365, 408
Wolf, E.   367
Wones, D. R.   386, 408
Wright, F. E.   392
Wright, T. L.   223-6, 228-30, 232, 234, 240-3, 247-9, 255-60, 263, 269-71, 275-86, 305, 376-7, 382-3, 385, 429-30, 433, 435, 445-6, 448

Yanchevskaia, I. S.   548, 566
Yoder, H. S.   214, 292-3, 306, 314, 323, 340, 368-9
Yosimura, T.   406-7, 455

Zambonini, F.   313
Zehme, H.   56, 67-8
Zénzén, N.   415
Zezza, U.   393
Zhirov, K. K.   557
Zies, E. G.   456, 593
Zoltai, T.   31

Locality Index

Arranged mostly under geographic areas, principally countries. Small oceanic islands listed under appropriate ocean. Meteorites listed in Index of Rock Types.

Antarctica   347
 Mt. Erebus   352, 445

Atlantic Ocean
 Azores, Grande Caldeira   193-4, 352
 St. Kitts, St. Christopher   313

Australia   500
 New South Wales
  Broken Hill   76, 456, 574
  Hogarth Range   496
  New Broken Hill mine   556

Austria
 Dorfgastein   207, 522-3
 Schmira   545
 Schmirntal   522
 Val Pesmeda (often listed as Pasmeda)   75-7,
 117, 139, 145, 312, 318-9
 Val Schiesone   480, 482-3

Brazil   225
 Minas Gerais, Itatiaia   225-6, 237-8, 242-3
 Santa Maria   242

Burma
 (Spencer O)   188, 191, 376
 (Spencer Q)   376
 Mogok (Spencer C)   28, 66-7, 71-2, 117, 208,
 228, 241, 243, 247, 250, 262, 267, 272, 273, 286,
 318, 374-5, 383-4
 (Spencer N)   192-3, 376

Canada
 Newfoundland
  Labrador   450, 489, 491-2
  496, 567, 569
  Nain   147
  St. Paul   147
 Manitoba
  Tanco pegmatite   558
 Ontario   567
  Bancroft   497-8
  Blue Mountain   233, 241, 243, 288
  Bytown (old name for Ottawa)   450

 Ontario
  Eganville   225
  Verona   207
 Quebec   332
  Clearwater West Crater   580
  Hull   535
  Lac Couture Crater   586-7
  Manicouagan Crater   579-81, 587
  Villeneuve   496

Ceylon   471
 Ambalangoda (Spencer I and M)   376

Crete   225
 Liopedro   233
 Ravdouka   233

Czechoslovakia
 Nadabula iron mines, Roznava, S.
 Slovakia   312

Finland
 Pellotsalo   67, 71-2, 118, 228, 241, 243, 263,
 267, 269, 272-5, 286, 288, 374-5, 383-4, 386,
 433, 519-20
 Sipoo   147
 Ylämaa   492

France   416
 Bourg d'Oisans   545
 Esterel   147
 Modane   233

Germany
 Eifel (includes Laacher See)   68, 71-2, 207,
 228, 233, 235, 242-3, 267, 384, 519, 535, 539,
 545
 Hagendorf   233, 242-3
 Nördlinger Ries Crater   579-81, 585, 587-9
 Rhine Valley   416
 Tirschheim   535

Greece
 Rhodes   225, 233
 Samothrace   474-5

Greenland   143, 312, 574, 591
  Cape Parry   394
  Skaergaard Intrusion   147, 574
  Tugtutôq   191-2, 559

Iceland   394, 396
  Surtsey   394

India   146, 538-9
  Bihar, Kodarma (Spencer U)   67, 71-3, 117-9,
  208, 226, 228, 243, 246, 257, 262, 267-9, 272,
  274-5, 286, 374-6, 383-4, 433
  Madras   558
  Orissa
    Kalahandi State, Ombadowla (Spencer E)
    241, 376, 433
    Patna State (Spencer W)   376

Ireland
  St. Johns Point   147-8
  Slieve Gullion   191-2, 195

Italy
  Linosa   147, 392, 394
  Monzoni   207
  Sardinia, Arcuentu   313
  South Tyrol   539-40
  Vesuvius   75-6, 137-9, 141, 211, 312-3, 318,
  328-9, 331, 335, 481-2, 530

Japan
  Higashi-matsuura district   445
  Iki island   445
  Ishikawa   470
  Kaso manganese mine   455
  Mitaki   330
  Miyaké   75, 137, 141, 144-5, 150, 312, 218,
  330, 480, 483
  Miyakejima   143, 567

Kenya   347, 352
  Ropp   352
  Sultan Hamud   499, 500

Korea
  Meisen-gun, Kanchin-do (Spencer P)   195, 376
  Sotoku   330

Liberia
  Lake Bosumtni Crater   585

Madagascar   207, 493, 538-9, 545, 585, 591
  Fianarantsoa   569
  Itrongay   556

Moon   308, 312-3, 318-9, 394, 464-6, 468,
  479-81, 483-4, 528, 546-7, 549-50, 552-3, 558,
  560-2, 572, 579, 589

New Zealand
  Greenhills   315

Norway
  Arendal   330, 545, 565
  Bamle   238
  Fredriksvärn (Spencer R)   186, 488
  Froland   496-7
  Krågerö   207, 496
  Narødal   504
  Oslo   445
  Risor   567
  Snarum   535
  Söndeled   569
  Stavern   472
  Tvedestrand   545

Pacific Ocean   445

Portugal   381, 433

Scotland
  Arran   195-6
  Knoydart   147
  Rhum   145
  Skye, Beinn an Dubhaich   195

South Africa
  Bushveldt Complex   314, 485-7
  New Amalfi   147

Spain   569

Sweden   496, 501
  Jakobsberg   455
  Varuträsk   569

Switzerland   228, 567
  Adula Mountains   416
  Alp Rischuna   292, 312-3, 330
  Binnenthal   455
  Camedo   75-6, 117, 312, 318
  Disentis   519-21, 523, 525
  Graubünden   207
  Grisons   565
  La Fibbia   313
  Piz Blas   519, 535
  Piz Miez   225
  Pontiskalk   67, 71-2, 228, 235, 241, 243, 263,
  267, 269, 272-5, 374-5, 383-4, 386, 433, 525
  St. Gotthard (or Gothard)   68, 71-3, 188, 191,
  196, 226, 228, 241, 246-7, 257, 262, 264, 267-9,
  291-2, 312, 374-5, 383, 416, 469, 525, 545, 565
  (includes Spencer B)
  Schmirntal   388-9
  Schyn-Schluct   225, 237, 293-4, 297, 301, 303,
  335

Ticino canton   207, 432
Val Maggia   332

Tanganyika   347

United States of America
California
  Crestmore   147
  Grass Valley   143, 332, 483
  Himalaya mine, Mesa Grande district   68,
  71-3, 228, 267, 383
  Ramona   69, 71, 117, 211, 225, 263, 271,
  273-5, 312, 318, 386
  Sierra Nevada   147
  San Luis Obispo   147
  Spanish Peak   147
  Sulphur Bank quicksilver mine, Lake Co.
  457
  Tiburon   69, 118, 225, 262-3, 267, 271, 273-5,
  312, 318, 386, 389, 523
  Yosemite Valley   146-7, 201, 203
Colorado
  Crystal Peak   519, 521, 523, 532-3, 535
  Kokomo   188
Hawaii   466
  Kii lava flow   549, 552
Maine
  Bethel   577
  Newry   565
  Topsham   569
Massachusetts
  Chesterfield   436
Minnesota
  Beaver Bay   147
  Crystal Bay   75-6, 145, 312, 332, 335, 496,
  567
  Duluth   146-7
  Lake Superior   549, 552
  Pigeon Point   546
  St. Louis Co.   75-6, 145, 312, 318-9
  Split Point   146
Montana
  Butte   501
  Stillwater Complex   86, 146-7, 149, 201,
  203, 314, 479, 484, 486-7, 547, 549-50,
  552-3, 567
Nevada
  Goodsprings   567
  Grant Range   242
New Mexico
  Puye cliff ruins, Jemez Mts.   226, 233-4,
  241, 243, 257, 260, 286, 382-3
  Sedan nuclear explosion crater   489

New York
  Ausable quadrangle, Adirondack Mts.   575-6
  Benson mine, St. Lawrence Co.   226, 233-4,
  241, 243, 257, 260, 263, 286, 382-3
  Essex Co.   75-6, 147, 201, 203, 335, 503
  Glen Falls   233
  North Creek   156
  Peekskill   201, 203
  Whiteface Mt.   242
North Carolina
  Bakersville   147, 329, 335, 500-1, 567
  Hawk mine   147, 567
  Macon Co.   147
  Mitchell Co.   75-6, 118, 147, 312, 318, 332
  Shelby   147
Oklahoma
  Wichita Mts.   484-5
Oregon
  John Day formation, between Mitchell and
  John Day rivers   520
  Lake Co.   332, 335, 496
  Lake View   546
  Plush   558
  Willow Lake   578
Pennsylvania
  Chester Co.   147
  Pleasant Gap, Center Co.   233
  Sylmar   567
South Carolina   147
South Dakota
  Hugo pegmatite, Black Hills   225-6, 232-3,
  238, 241-3, 248-9, 288
Utah
  Clear Lake   147
  Duchesne   456
  Provo   233
  Tooele   567
Virginia
  Amelia Courthouse pegmatite   211, 225-6,
  232-4, 236, 248, 260, 262-3, 267, 271, 273-5,
  292-4, 297-8, 300, 303, 312, 319, 332, 380,
  389, 468, 523, 532, 567
Wisconsin
  Lincoln Co.   147
  Merrill   145
  Wausau   475

USSR
Caucasus region   368
Kirebinsk (Kirensk?, RSFSR)   312
Slyudanka deposit, Mama-Chuya, RSFSR   556
Taimyr National Okrug   433
Transbaykaliya, N. E.   563
Tyrny-Auz, Kabardian ASSR, RSFSR   368
Ukraine region   545

Index of Rock Types

amphibolite 588
andesite 147, 466
anorthosite 78, 146-7, 319, 332, 465, 482, 528, 547, 549, 552, 573, 575-6, 579, 582-3
aplite 433, 586

basalt 147, 318, 466, 480, 484, 549, 552-3
basalt, olivine 394
breccia 480, 483-4, 560, 586

calc-silicate 480
charnockite 242, 558
crystal lapilli 143, 150

dacite 147
diabase 147, 466
dolerite 147
dolomite 455-6

gabbro 147, 167, 573
gneiss, mafic 574
granite 195-6, 368, 433, 586, 588
granodiorite 147, 470, 586
granulite 143

hawaiite 445

ignimbrite 242

larvikite 441, 472

meteorite 143, 562, 572, 579
 eucrite 480
 Juvinas 143, 561
 Serra de Magé 480
 Shergotty 579-81
monzonite 146-7
mugearite 445

norite 143, 578

pantellerite 473
pegmatite 68-9, 75, 78, 147, 332, 432-3, 436, 470, 556-8, 573, 577, 586

quartz monzonite 501

rhomb porphyry 441

schist 147
syenite 475

tönsbergite 473
troctolite 145
tuff 480

Location of Figures

Fig.	Page	Fig.	Page	Fig.	Page	Fig.	Page
S-1	2	5-14	154	7-18	262	8-2	374
2	6	15	155	19	263	3	375
3	10	16	158	20	266	4	378
4	12	17	160	21	267	5	380
1-1	20	18	161	22	268	6	383
2	22	19	163	23	269	7	384
2-1	26	20	165	24	270	8	385
2	27	21	166	25	271	9	386
3	30	22	169	26	273	10	387
4	32	6-1	182	27	278	11	388
5	34	2	183	28	283	12	389
6	37	3	184	29	286	13	395
7	41	4	185	30	287	14	397
8	45	5	186	31	288	15	399
3-1	51	6	187	32	290	16	401
2	52	7	188	33	293	17	402
3	54	8	190	34	294	18	404
4	60	9	102	35	298	19	407
5	63	10	194	36	300	9-1	417
6	64	11	195	37	303	2	421
7	72	12	196	38	303	3	423
8	77	13	197	39	304	4	425
4-1	92	14	199	40	305	5	427
2	92	15	201	41	307	6	428
3	93	16	203	42	314	7	430
4	97	17	207	43	316	8	431
5	99	18	207	44	318	9	431
6	108	19	208	45	321	10	432
7	110	20	211	46	322	11	434
8	114	7-1	220	47	324	12	434
9	120	2	222	48	327	13	439
10	121	3	227	49	329	14	441
11	121	4	236	50	330	15	444
5-1	128	5	238	51	331	16	447
2	129	6	240	52	335	17	452
3	130	7	243	53	337	18	455
4	131	8	245	54	338	10-1	464
5	133	9	248	55	339	2	465
6	134	10	250	56	344	3	466
7	135	11	252	57	347	4	466
8	136	12	254	58	350	5	468
9	143	13	254	59	350	6	469
10	148	14	256	60	352	7	470
11	151	15	258	61	354	8	472
12	153	16	259	62	356	9	472
13	153	17	260	8-1	373	10	473

Fig.	Page	Fig.	Page	Fig.	Page	Fig.	Page
10-11	474	10-28	493	11-4	519	11-21	545
12	475	29	494	5	520	22	550
13	475	30	495	6	523	12-1	560
14	476	31	497	7	523	2	561
15	476	32	498	8	524	3	574
16	477	33	499	9	525	4	575
17	479	34	499	10	526	5	576
18	481	35	500	11	527	6	577
19	484	36	502	12	529	7	580
20	485	37	503	13	531	8	581
21	486	38	504	14	532	9	583
22	487	39	505	15	534	10	584
23	487	40	507	16	536	11	584
24	489	41	507	17	537	12	586
25	491	11-1	512	18	538	13	588
26	492	2	514	19	540	14	589
27	492	3	518	20	542	15	590

List of Tables

2-1 Atomic parameters of sanidinized orthoclase   28
2 General features of feldspar structures   36

3-1 Matrix of adjacent tetrahedral nodes for a cell with $c \sim 0.7$ nm   65
2 Mean T–O distances, indicated Al-distributions, and Thompson coefficients in $AlSi_3$ feldspars   71
3 Mean T–O distances, indicated Al-distributions, and Thompson coefficients in Al-rich feldspars   76

4-1 Atomic parameters in feldspars   86
2 Size of tetrahedra in feldspars   88
3 Intertetrahedral angles at specified oxygen   90
4 Cation-oxygen distances   91
5 Distortion of tetrahedra   105
6 Artificial temperature factors (spherical approximation B)   117
7 Anisotropic displacement ellipsoids for Spencer U intermediate microcline   119
8 Anisotropic displacement ellipsoids of low albite   119

5-1 Atomic coordinates of anorthites at 240 and 1430° C compared with the pseudo-structure of P-anorthite   138
2 Mean T–O distances in anorthite   139
3 Distances between Ca part-atoms   141
4 Root-mean-square atomic displacements in anorthite   142
5 Dry heat-treatment of calcic plagioclase   145
6 Hydrothermal heat-treatment of plagioclase   146
7 Unheated and heated plagioclases   147
8 Amplitude and phase of modulation waves for e satellites in a labradorite   168
9 Displacement of the aluminosilicate chain in the e modulation of a labradorite   169

6-1 Calculated X-ray powder diffractometer patterns of K- and Ba-feldspars   209
2 Calculated X-ray powder diffractometer patterns of plagioclase and reedmergnerite   212

7-1 Cell dimensions of end-member feldspars   219
2 Selected cell dimensions of alkali feldspars   228
3 Selected interplanar spacings for K, Na feldspars   281
4 Positions of diffractions used in Wright's method for alkali feldspars   285
5 Molar volumes of albite at listed temperature   296
6 Selected cell dimensions of plagioclase   309
7 Volume expansion of plagioclase   330
8 Cell dimensions of plagioclase at room temperature and high temperature   332
9 Temperature variation of molar volume of plagioclase   333
10 Principal coefficients of thermal expansion for feldspars   336
11 Cell dimensions of K-exchanged plagioclase   342
12 Cell dimensions of ternary feldspars   348

8-1 Calculated optical properties of sub-optically twinned feldspars   372
2 Optical properties of some feldspars   386

11-1   Polarized infra-red absorption spectra of microcline   513
   2   Infra-red and far infra-red spectra of alkali feldspars   516
   3   Infra-red and far infra-red spectra of $MAl_2Si_2O_8$ feldspars   517
   4   Optical and X-ray properties of K-feldspars studied by n.m.r. methods   535
   5   Mössbauer spectra of plagioclase   552

12-1   Electrical conductivity of feldspars   565
   2   Bulk thermal conductivity of feldspars   567
   3   Measurements of density and volume and linear compressibilities from dilatometric
       experiments   569
   4   Elastic stiffness and compliance constants for feldspars   571

Minerals, Rocks and Inorganic Materials

Monograph Series
of Theoretical and
Experimental Studies

Edited by
W. v. Engelhardt,
Tübingen;
T. Hahn,
Aachen;
R. Roy,
University Park, Pa.;
P. J. Wyllie,
Chicago, Ill.

Springer-Verlag
Berlin
Heidelberg
New York
München Johannesburg
London Madrid New Delhi
Paris Rio de Janeiro
Sydney Tokyo
Utrecht Wien

Vol. 1: W. G. Ernst
Amphiboles

**Crystal Chemistry, Phase Relations
and Occurrence**
With 59 figures. X, 125 pages. 1968
Cloth DM 30,—; US $11.60
ISBN 3-540-04267-9
Subseries: Experimental Mineralogy

Contents: Introduction and acknowledgments. Crystal chemistry of the amphiboles. Compositional variations of the amphiboles. Hydrothermal phase equilibration and natural stability. Experimental phase relations and occurrence of the iron-magnesium amphiboles. Experimental phase relations and occurrence of the calcic amphiboles. Experimental phase relations and occurrence of the sodic amphiboles. Comparison of experimental P-T curves.

Vol. 2: E. Hansen
Strain Facies

With 78 figures, 21 plates. X, 208 pages. 1971
Cloth DM 58,—; US $22.40
ISBN 3-540-05204-6
Distribution rights for U. K., Commonwealth, and the Traditional British Market (excluding Canada): Allen & Unwin, Ltd., London

Contents: Introduction. Twelve properties of mesoscopic folds. Methods of deducing slip-line orientations from the geometry of folds. Geometric types of flow. Trollheimen's rock units. The sahlfold facies. The norfold facies. The discfold facies. The concept of strain facies. References. Index.

Vol. 3: B. R. Doe
Lead Isotopes

With 24 figures. IX, 137 pages. 1970
Cloth DM 36,—; US $13.90
ISBN 3-540-05205-4
Subseries: Isotopes in Geology

This book deals with all aspects of the utilisation of lead isotopes in geology, such as U-Th-Pb dating, common lead interpretation and applications of radioactive lead isotopes.

Vol. 4: O. Braitsch
Salt Deposits —
Their Origin and Composition

Translated from the German edition by P. J. Burek and A. E. M. Nairn in consultation with A. G. Herrmann and R. Evans
With 47 figures. XIV, 297 pages. 1971
Cloth DM 72,—; US $27.80
ISBN 3-540-05206-2

In the study of the stable and metastable equilibria of salt minerals, in the consideration of the physico-chemical conditions affecting the formation of evaporites, and in the mineralogical investigation of salt deposits, German scientists have reigned supreme. The publication of Braitsch's monograph in English comes at a time when evaporites are the subject of an awakening of interest among English-speaking geologists.

Vol. 5: G. Faure, J. L. Powell
Strontium Isotope Geology

With 51 figures. IX, 188 pages. 1972
Cloth DM 48,—; US $18.50
ISBN 3-540-05784-6
Subseries: Isotopes in Geology

The isotope geology of strontium is of interest to every earth scientist in the world. Strontium isotopes are used by geologists to measure the age of rocks from the earth and the moon, and to provide clues regarding the origin and evolution of rocks.

Vol. 6: F. Lippmann
Sedimentary Carbonate
Minerals

With 54 figures. VI, 228 pages. 1973
Cloth DM 58,—; US $22.40
ISBN 3-540-06011-1

Sedimentary carbonate petrology is discussed with reference to crystal chemistry of the rock-forming carbonate minerals and their metastable precursors.

Vol. 7: A. Rittmann
Stable Mineral Assemblages
of Igneous Rocks

A Method of Calculation
With Contributions by V. Gottini, W. Hewers, H. Pichler, R. Stengelin
With 85 figures. XIV, 262 pages. 1973
Cloth DM 76,—; US $29.30
ISBN 3-540-06030-8

A new method is presented for processing chemical analysis of igneous rocks so as to give a norm which shows better agreement with the known mineral composition than the methods in current use (CIPW method and NIGGLI equivalent norm).

Vol. 8: S. K. Saxena
Thermodynamics of Rock-
Forming Crystalline Solutions

With 67 figures. XII, 188 pages. 1973
Cloth DM 48,—; US $18.50
ISBN 3-540-06175-4

This monograph was written for advanced students and research workers in the fields of mineralogy, petrology and physical geochemistry. It introduces the reader to current theories concerning crystalline solutions and the special problems connected with the treatment of heterogeneous and homogeneous phase equilibria.

Vol. 9: J. Hoefs
Stable Isotope Geochemistry

With 37 figures. IX, 140 pages. 1973
Cloth DM 39,—; US $15.10
ISBN 3-540-06176-2

Stable isotopes of chemical elements play an important role in the earth sciences. After a general and technical introduction, the author turns to the fractionation of isotopes of individual elements and finally discusses in detail the ratios in which the various isotopes occur in nature.

Contributions to Mineralogy and Petrology

In Cooperation with the
International Mineralogical Association
(I. M. A.)

Editorial Board (as of January 1974):
I. S. E. Carmichael, Berkeley, Calif.;
C. W. Correns (Managing Editor), Göttingen;
W. v. Engelhardt, Tübingen;
W. S. Fyfe, London/Ontario

The journal publishes contributions in
geochemistry, including isotope geology;
the petrology and genesis of igneous,
metamorphic, and sedimentary rocks;
experimental petrology and mineralogy;
and the distribution as well as the significance of elements and their isotopes
in rocks. In addition to original investigations, review articles are also included.

Languages used: Approximately 80 %
of the articles are in English;
the others, in German and French, are
preceded by an English abstract.

Subscription information, back volumes,
and sample copies upon request.

Springer-Verlag
Berlin · Heidelberg · New York
München Johannesburg London Madrid New Delhi Paris
Rio de Janeiro Sydney Tokyo Utrecht Wien